P H Y S I C S

Volume 1

JAMES S. WALKER

Second Custom Edition for the University of Washington

D1314557

Taken from:
Physics, Fourth Edition
by James S. Walker

Custom Publishing

New York   Boston   San Francisco
London   Toronto   Sydney   Tokyo   Singapore   Madrid
Mexico City   Munich   Paris   Cape Town   Hong Kong   Montreal

Cover Art: Courtesy of Mary Levin

Taken from:

Physics, Fourth Edition
by James S. Walker
Copyright © 2010 by Pearson Education, Inc.
Published by Addison-Wesley
Boston, Massachusetts 02116

This special edition published in cooperation with Pearson Custom Publishing.

Printed in the United States of America

3 4 5 6 7 8 9 10 V092 16 15 14 13 12 11

2009460128

JM

**Pearson
Custom Publishing**
is a division of

www.pearsonhighered.com

ISBN 10: 0-558-38504-4
ISBN 13: 978-0-558-38504-0

About the Author

JAMES S. WALKER

James Walker obtained his Ph.D. in theoretical physics from the University of Washington in 1978. He subsequently served as a post-doc at the University of Pennsylvania, the Massachusetts Institute of Technology, and the University of California at San Diego before joining the physics faculty at Washington State University in 1983. Professor Walker's research interests include statistical mechanics, critical phenomena, and chaos. His many publications on the application of renormalization-group theory to systems ranging from absorbed monolayers to binary-fluid mixtures have appeared in *Physical Review, Physical Review Letters, Physica,* and a host of other publications. He has also participated in observations on the summit of Mauna Kea, looking for evidence of extra-solar planets.

Jim Walker likes to work with students at all levels, from judging elementary school science fairs to writing research papers with graduate students, and has taught introductory physics for many years. His enjoyment of this course and his empathy for students have earned him a reputation as an innovative, enthusiastic, and effective teacher. Jim's educational publications include "Reappearing Phases" (*Scientific American,* May 1987) as well as articles in the *American Journal of Physics* and *The Physics Teacher.* In recognition of his contributions to the teaching of physics at Washington State University, Jim was named the Boeing Distinguished Professor of Science and Mathematics Education for 2001–2003. He currently teaches at Western Washington University.

When he is not writing, conducting research, teaching, or developing new classroom demonstrations and pedagogical materials, Jim enjoys amateur astronomy, eclipse chasing, bird and dragonfly watching, photography, juggling, unicycling, boogie boarding, and kayaking. Jim is also an avid jazz pianist and organist. He has served as ballpark organist for a number of Class A minor league baseball teams, including the Bellingham Mariners, an affiliate of the Seattle Mariners, and the Salem-Keizer Volcanoes, an affiliate of the San Francisco Giants. He can play "Take Me Out to the Ball Game" in his sleep.

About the Cover

The photographs on the cover of this book are a reminder of the wide "spectrum" of physics applications that are a part of our everyday lives.

Wind Turbines and Lightning Bolt: Wind turbines convert the mechanical energy of moving air into electrical energy to power our homes and cities. Electrical energy is also produced by nature, and occasionally unleashed in impressive bolts of lightning.

Scanning Electron Micrograph: Though electrons are usually thought of as "particles," they also have wave-like properties similar to light. The image of a fly's eye was taken with a beam of electrons.

Iceberg in the Errera Channel: A floating iceberg is a visual demonstration that ice has a lower density than liquid water.

Solar Coronal Loops: Magnetic storms often rage on the surface of the Sun. These glowing loops of ionized gas follow the curved lines of the magnetic field.

Surfer in the "Tube" on the North Shore of Oahu: The laws of physics determine the motion of the wave this surfer is riding.

As you study the material in this book, your understanding of physics will deepen, and your appreciation for the world around you will increase as you come to recognize the fundamental physical principles on which all of our lives are based.

Brief Contents

Foundations for Student Success

Walker's *Physics* has always been known for its integrated, coherent approach to teaching students the skills to solve problems successfully.

CONCEPTUAL CHECKPOINTS ➤ help students to master key ideas and relationships in a nonquantitative setting.

The end-of-chapter Conceptual Questions, Conceptual Exercises, and Predict/Explain problems further develop students' conceptual understanding.

CONCEPTUAL CHECKPOINT 15–3 — HOW IS THE SCALE READING AFFECTED?

A flask of water rests on a scale. If you dip your finger into the water, without touching the flask, does the reading on the scale **(a)** increase, **(b)** decrease, or **(c)** stay the same?

REASONING AND DISCUSSION
Your finger experiences an upward buoyant force when it is dipped into the water. By Newton's third law, the water experiences an equal and opposite reaction force acting downward. This downward force is transmitted to the scale, which in turn gives a higher reading.

Another way to look at this result is to note that when you dip your finger into the water, its depth increases. This results in a greater pressure at the bottom of the flask, and hence a greater downward force on the flask. The scale reads this increased downward force.

ANSWER
(a) The reading on the scale increases.

EXERCISES ➤ present brief calculations which illustrate the application of important new relationships.

EXERCISE 7–1

One species of Darwin's finch, *Geospiza magnirostris*, can exert a force of 205 N with its beak as it cracks open a *Tribulus* seed case. If its beak moves through a distance of 0.40 cm during this operation, how much work does the finch do to get the seed?

SOLUTION
$W = Fd = (205 \text{ N})(0.0040 \text{ m}) = 0.82 \text{ J}$

EXAMPLES ➤ model and explain how to solve a particular type of problem.

All Examples use a consistent strategy:

Picture the Problem
Strategy
Solution
Insight

In response to user feedback, selected examples throughout the Fourth Edition are now more challenging.

EXAMPLE 16–6 — WHAT A PANE!

One of the windows in a house has the shape of a square 1.0 m on a side. The glass in the window is 0.50 cm thick. **(a)** How much heat is lost through this window in one day if the temperature in the house is 21 °C and the temperature outside is 0.0 °C? **(b)** Suppose all the dimensions of the window—height, width, thickness—are doubled. If everything else remains the same, by what factor does the heat flow change?

PICTURE THE PROBLEM
The glass from the window is shown in our sketch, along with its relevant dimensions. Heat flows from the 21 °C side of the window to the 0.0 °C side.

STRATEGY

a. The heat flow is given by $Q = kA(\Delta T/L)t$ (Equation 16–16). Note that the area is $A = (1.0 \text{ m})^2$ and that the length over which heat is conducted is, in this case, the thickness of the glass. Thus, $L = 0.0050$ m. The temperature difference is $\Delta T = 21 \text{ C}° = 21$ K, and the thermal conductivity of glass (from Table 16–3) is 0.84 W/(m·K). Also, recall from Section 7–4 that 1 W = 1 J/s.

b. Doubling all dimensions increases the thickness by a factor of 2 and increases the area by a factor of 4; that is, $L \rightarrow 2L$ and $A \rightarrow (2 \times \text{height}) \times (2 \times \text{width}) = 4A$. Use these results in $Q = kA(\Delta T/L)t$.

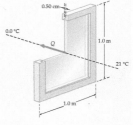

SOLUTION

Part (a)

1. Calculate the heat flow for a given time, t:

$$Q = kA\left(\frac{\Delta T}{L}\right)t$$
$$= [0.84 \text{ W/(m·K)}](1.0 \text{ m})^2\left(\frac{21 \text{ K}}{0.0050 \text{ m}}\right)t = (3500 \text{ W})t$$

2. Substitute the number of seconds in a day, 86,400 s, for the time t in the expression for Q:

$$Q = (3500 \text{ W})t = (3500 \text{ W})(86,400 \text{ s}) = 3.0 \times 10^8 \text{ J}$$

Unique two-column layout helps the students relate the strategy to the math.

Part (b)

3. Replace L with $2L$ and A with $4A$ in Step 1. The result is a doubling of the heat flow, Q:

$$Q = kA\left(\frac{\Delta T}{L}\right)t \rightarrow k(4A)\left[\frac{\Delta T}{(2L)}\right]t \rightarrow 2\left[kA\left(\frac{\Delta T}{L}\right)t\right] = 2Q$$

INSIGHT
Q is a sizable amount of heat, roughly equivalent to the energy released in burning a gallon of gasoline. A considerable reduction in heat loss can be obtained by using a double-paned window, which has an insulating layer of air (actually argon or krypton) sandwiched between the two panes of glass. This is discussed in more detail later in this section, and is explored in Homework Problems 53 and 91.

PRACTICE PROBLEM
Suppose the window is replaced with a plate of solid silver. How thick must this plate be to have the same heat flow in a day as the glass? **[Answer:** The silver must have a thickness of $L = 2.5$ m.**]**

Some related homework problems: Problem 49, Problem 50

Examples end with a related **Practice Problem.**

ACTIVE EXAMPLES ➤ provide a skeleton solution that the student must flesh out, helping to bridge the gap from the Examples to the end-of-chapter problems.

ACTIVE EXAMPLE 15–1 — FIND THE TENSION IN THE STRING

A piece of wood with a density of 706 kg/m³ is tied with a string to the bottom of a water-filled flask. The wood is completely immersed, and has a volume of 8.00×10^{-6} m³. What is the tension in the string?

SOLUTION *(Test your understanding by performing the calculations indicated in each step.)*

1. Apply Newton's second law to the wood: $F_b - T - mg = 0$
2. Solve for the tension, T: $T = F_b - mg$
3. Calculate the weight of the wood: $mg = 0.0554$ N
4. Calculate the buoyant force: $F_b = 0.0785$ N
5. Subtract to obtain the tension: $T = 0.0231$ N

INSIGHT
Since the wood floats in water, its buoyant force when completely immersed is greater than its weight.

YOUR TURN
What is the tension in the string if the piece of wood has a density of 822 kg/m³?

(Answers to Your Turn problems can be found in the back of the book.)

New to the Fourth Edition

PHYSICS IN PERSPECTIVE ➤

Located at key junctures in the book, **Physics in Perspective** two-page spreads focus on the core ideas developed in the preceding several chapters.

Looking back over several chapters, the spreads show unifying perspectives that the students are only now equipped to see.

For instance, the Physics in Perspective spread illustrated here, located after the final thermodynamics chapter, uses the second law to unify and explain ideas that initially had to be presented from a different perspective.

The **Big Picture** feature at the end of each chapter (not shown here) performs a similar function on a chapter level.

Annotated equations help students to see the meaning in the math.

PHYSICS IN PERSPECTIVE

Entropy and Thermo-dynamics

The behavior of heat engines may seem unrelated to the fate of the universe. However, it led physicists to discover a new physical quantity: entropy. The future of the universe is shaped by the fact that the total entropy can only increase. Our fate is sealed.

① Spontaneous processes cannot cause a decrease in entropy

Fundamentally, entropy (S) is randomness or disorder. A process that occurs spontaneously—without a driving input of energy—cannot result in a net increase in order (decrease in entropy).

Irreversible processes: $\Delta S > 0$
An *irreversible* process runs spontaneously in just one direction—for instance, ice melts in warm water; warm water doesn't spontaneously form ice cubes. Irreversible processes always cause a net increase in entropy.

$\Delta S > 0$ Ice melts in warm water

$\Delta S > 0$ Air leaves a popped balloon

$\Delta S > 0$ Cooling embers heat their surroundings

Reversible processes: $\Delta S = 0$
If a process can run spontaneously in either direction—so that a movie of it would look equally realistic run forward or backward—it is *reversible* and causes zero entropy change.

In practice, reversibility is an idealization—real processes are never completely reversible.

The to-and-fro swinging of an ideal frictionless pendulum is a reversible process

$\Delta S = 0$

② Entropy can decrease locally but must increase overall

An input of energy can be used to drive *nonspontaneous* processes that reduce disorder (entropy). That is what your body does with the energy it gains from food.

However, the universe as a whole cannot gain or lose energy, so its total entropy cannot decrease. This means that every process that decreases entropy locally must cause a larger entropy increase elsewhere.

E_{in} Local system E_{out}

Universe

Local system:
Input of energy can drive a decrease in entropy: $\Delta S < 0$.

Universe:
$\Delta E = 0$ (energy is conserved), so
$\Delta S > 0$ (total entropy can only change by increasing)

③ The second law puts entropy in thermodynamic terms

The second law of thermodynamics—that heat moves from hotter to colder objects—actually implies all that we've said about entropy. In fact, the change in entropy ΔS can be defined in terms of the thermodynamic quantities heat Q and temperature T:

Change in system's entropy $\quad \Delta S = \dfrac{Q}{T}$ $\quad$ Heat entering or leaving system (positive if heat enters system)

System's temperature

As the example at right shows, the fact that temperature T is in the denominator means that the transfer of a given amount of heat Q causes a greater magnitude of entropy change for a colder object than for a hotter one.

Therefore, a flow of heat from a hotter to a colder object causes a net increase in entropy—as we would predict from the fact that this process is spontaneous and irreversible.

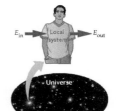

Loss of heat → entropy decrease.
$\Delta S_h = \dfrac{Q}{T_h} = \dfrac{-100\,J}{400\,K} = -0.25\,J/K$

Hot reservoir
$T_h = 400\,K$

$Q = 100\,J$

Cold reservoir
$T_c = 300\,K$

$\Delta S_c = \dfrac{Q}{T_c} = \dfrac{100\,J}{300\,K} = 0.33\,J/K$
Gain of heat → entropy increase.

ANNOTATED FIGURES ➤

Blue explanatory annotations help students to read complex figures and to integrate verbal and visual knowledge.

v
A wave pulse that reflects from a fixed end ...

... has the same shape as before but is inverted.

v

▲ **FIGURE 14–7 A reflected wave pulse: fixed end**
A wave pulse on a string is inverted when it reflects from an end that is tied down.

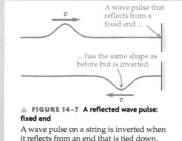

PHYSICS DEMONSTRATION PHOTOS ➤

use high-speed time-lapse photography to illustrate phenomena that illuminate physical principles.

Building on strong pedagogic foundations, the Fourth Edition adds features that help students see beyond the mathematical details to the underlying ideas of physics.

4 A temperature difference can be exploited to do work ...

The tendency of hotter and colder objects to come to the same temperature can be tapped to do work, as in this example:

Initial state: Gases at different temperatures are separated by a locked piston.

Piston unlocked: Pressure difference causes piston to move, doing work on wheel.

Final state: Gases at same temperature; no more work can be done.

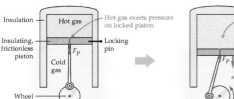

Insulation — Hot gas — Hot gas exerts pressure on locked piston.

Insulating, frictionless piston — F_P — Locking pin

Cold gas

Wheel

Hot gas expands and cools, pushing piston down.

F_P v

Piston does work on wheel and cold gas.

Same temperature; no pressure on piston.

The expansion shown above is a single process, not a cycle, so this piston-cylinder does not constitute a heat engine.

The Physics in Perspective spreads blend words, equations, and pictures into an integrated and highly visual presentation.

5 ... but entropy sets the limit of efficiency for a heat engine

A heat engine is a device that converts part of a heat flow into work. Entropy sets an absolute limit on the efficiency of this process.

To see why, we start with the fact that a heat engine operates on a thermodynamic cycle—it starts in a particular state, goes through a series of proc esses involving heat and work, and returns to its original state. (Think of the cyclic operation of a cylinder in a car engine.)

Because entropy S is a state function, the engine's entropy returns to it s original value at the end of each cycle—so over the course of a cycle, the entropy change ΔS_{engine} of a heat engine is zero. Therefore, the entropy of the engine's *environment*—specifically, of the hot and cold reservoir (S_{h+c})—must increase or stay the same ($\Delta S_{h+c} \geq 0$).

The engine will have the highest efficiency $e = W/Q_h$ when $\Delta S_{h+c} = 0$, because higher values of ΔS_{h+c} entail more waste heat (Q_c) and thus yield less work W. To be more efficient than this, an engine would have to cause a net *decrease* in entropy, which is impossible. Actual engines all have $\Delta S_{h+c} \geq 0$.

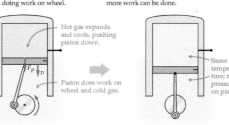

Engine always returns to same state, so state functions (including S) do not change over a cycle.

Thermodynamic cycle

$\Delta S_{engine} = 0$ over cycle.

Hot reservoir T_h

Q_h

Engine

W

Q_c

Cold reservoir T_c

Efficiency e of engine is work W divided by input heat Q_h:

$$e = \frac{W}{Q_h} = \frac{Q_h - Q_c}{Q_h} = 1 - \frac{Q_c}{Q_h}$$

Efficiency is maximal when waste heat Q_c is minimal, which occurs when $\Delta S_{h+c} = 0$:

$$W = Q_h\left(1 - \frac{T_c}{T_h}\right)$$

Maximum possible efficiency

Blue explanatory annotations guide the student through the diagrams.

6 Entropy spells the death of the universe

The night sky shows us a universe of stars and galaxies separated by cold, nearly empty space. Over time, the inexorable growth of entropy will erase these differences, leaving a universe that is uniform in temperature and density—unable ever again to create stars or give rise to life.

Nevertheless, the energy content of the universe will remain the same as at its birth.

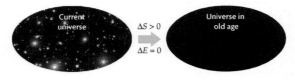

Current universe

$\Delta S > 0$

$\Delta E = 0$

Universe in old age

NEW END-OF-CHAPTER PROBLEM TYPES

PASSAGE PROBLEMS ➤

offer a reading passage followed by a set of multiple-choice questions (the format used by most MCAT questions), testing students' ability to apply what they've learned to a real-world situation.

PREDICT/EXPLAIN PROBLEMS ➤

consist of two linked multiple choice questions — the first asking the student to *predict* the outcome of a situation and the second asking for its physical *explanation*.

PASSAGE PROBLEMS

Navigating in Space: The Gravitational Slingshot
Many spacecraft navigate through space these days by using the "gravitational slingshot" effect, in which a close encounter with a planet results in a significant increase in magnitude and change in direction of the spacecraft's velocity. In fact, a space-

▲ **FIGURE 9–31** Problems 97, 98, 99, and 100

15. • **CE Predict/Explain** A small car collides with a large truck. **(a)** Is the acceleration experienced by the car greater than, less than, or equal to the acceleration experienced by the truck? **(b)** Choose the *best explanation* from among the following:
   I. The truck exerts a larger force on the car, giving it the greater acceleration.
   II. Both vehicles experience the same magnitude of force, therefore the lightweight car experiences the greater acceleration.
   III. The greater force exerted on the truck gives it the greater acceleration.

Applications in the Text

Note: This list includes applied topics that receive significant discussion in the chapter text or a worked Example, as well as topics that are touched on in end-of-chapter Conceptual Questions, Conceptual Exercises, and Problems. Topics of particular relevance to the life sciences or medicine are marked **BIO**. Topics related to Passage Problems are marked **PP**.

ActivPhysics OnLine™ Activities

www.masteringphysics.com

Preface: To the Instructor

Teaching introductory algebra-based physics can be a most challenging—and rewarding—experience. Students enter the course with a wide range of backgrounds, interests, and skills and we, the instructors, strive not only to convey the basic concepts and fundamental laws of physics but also to give students an appreciation of its relevance and appeal.

I wrote this book to help with that task. It incorporates a number of unique and innovative pedagogical features that evolved from years of teaching experience. The materials have been tested extensively in the classroom and in focus groups, and refined based on comments from students and teachers who used the earlier editions of the text. The enthusiastic response I received from users of the first three editions was both flattering and motivating. The fourth edition has been improved in response to this feedback.

Learning Tools in the Text

A key goal of this text is to help students make the connection between a conceptual understanding of physics and the various skills necessary to solve quantitative problems. One of the chief means to that end is the replacement of traditional "textbook" Examples with an integrated system of learning tools: fully worked Examples with Solutions in Two-Column Format, Active Examples, Conceptual Checkpoints, and Exercises. Each of these tools is specialized to meet the needs of students at a particular point in the development of a chapter.

These needs are not always the same. Sometimes students require a detailed explanation of how to tackle a particular problem; at other times, they must be allowed to take an active role and work out the details for themselves. Sometimes it is important for them to perform calculations and concentrate on numerical precision; at other times it is more fruitful for them to explore a key idea in a conceptual context. And sometimes, all that is required is practice using a new equation or definition.

This text attempts to emulate the teaching style of successful instructors by providing the right tool at the right place and the right time.

Perspective Across Chapters

It's easy for students to miss the forest for the trees—to overlook the unifying concepts that are central to physics and that will make the details easier to learn and retain. To address this difficulty, the fourth edition adds two features. At key junctures in the text are six **Physics in Perspective** features, two-page spreads that take a highly visual look at core ideas whose significance students are now prepared to understand. For instance, after working through the energy chapters, do students *really* understand how conservation of energy relates to conservation of mechanical energy, and the role of work done by dissipative and nondissipative forces? And after working through the chapters on electricity and magnetism, do they have a clear view of how electric and magnetic forces relate to each other? These are two of the topics on which the Physics in Perspective pages focus. Each chapter now ends with a **Big Picture box** that links ideas covered in the chapter to related material from earlier and later chapters in the text.

NEW

NEW

WORKED EXAMPLES WITH SOLUTIONS IN TWO-COLUMN FORMAT

Examples model the most complete and detailed method of solving a particular type of problem. The Examples in this text are presented in a format that focuses on the basic strategies and thought processes involved in problem solving. This focus on the intimate relationship between conceptual insights and problem-solving techniques encourages students to view the ability to solve problems as a logical outgrowth of conceptual understanding rather than a kind of parlor trick.

Each Example has the same basic structure:

- **Picture the Problem**   This first step discusses how the physical situation can be represented visually and what such a representation can tell us about how to analyze and solve the problem. At this step, always accompanied by a figure, we set up a coordinate system where appropriate, label important quantities, and indicate which values are known.

- **Strategy**   The Strategy addresses the commonly asked question, "How do I get started?" by providing a clear overview of the problem and helping students to identify the relevant physical principles. It then guides the student in using known relationships to map a step-by-step path to the solution.

- **Solution in Two-Column Format**   In the step-by-step Solution of the problem, each of the steps is presented with a prose statement in the left-hand column and the corresponding mathematical implementation in the right-hand column. Each step clearly translates the idea described in words into the appropriate equations.

- **Insight**   Each Example wraps up with an Insight—a comment regarding the solution just obtained. Some Insights deal with possible alternative solution techniques, others with new ideas suggested by the results.

- **Practice Problem**   Following the Insight is a Practice Problem, which gives the student a chance to practice the type of calculation just presented. The Practice Problems, always accompanied by their answers, provide students with a valuable check on their understanding of the material. Finally, each Example ends with a reference to some related end-of-chapter Problems to allow students to test their skills further.

ACTIVE EXAMPLES

Active Examples serve as a bridge between the fully worked Examples, in which every detail is fully discussed and every step is given, and the homework Problems, where no help is given at all. In an Active Example, students take an active role in solving the problem by thinking through the logic of the steps described on the left and checking their answers on the right. Students often find it useful to practice problem solving by covering one column of an Active Example with a sheet of paper and filling in the covered steps as they refer to the other column. Follow-up questions, called Your Turns, ask students to look at the problem in a slightly different way. Answers to Your Turns are provided at the end of the book.

CONCEPTUAL CHECKPOINTS

Conceptual Checkpoints help students sharpen their insight into key physical principles. A typical Conceptual Checkpoint presents a thought-provoking question that can be answered by logical reasoning based on physical concepts rather than by numerical calculations. The statement of the question is followed by a detailed discussion and analysis in the section titled Reasoning and Discussion, and the Answer is given at the end of the checkpoint for quick and easy reference.

EXERCISES

Exercises present brief calculations designed to illustrate the application of important new relationships, without the expenditure of time and space required by a fully worked Example. Exercises generally give students an opportunity to practice the use of a new equation, become familiar with the units of a new physical quantity, and get a feeling for typical magnitudes.

PROBLEM-SOLVING NOTES

Each chapter includes a number of Problem-Solving Notes in the margin. These practical hints are designed to highlight useful problem-solving methods while helping students avoid common pitfalls and misconceptions.

End-of-Chapter Learning Tools

The end-of-chapter material in this text also includes a number of innovations, along with refinements of more familiar elements.

- Each chapter concludes with a **Chapter Summary** presented in an easy-to-use outline style. Key concepts, equations, and important figures are organized by topic for convenient reference.

- A unique feature of this text is the **Problem-Solving Summary** at the end of the chapter. This summary addresses common sources of misconceptions in problem solving, and gives specific references to Examples and Active Examples illustrating the correct procedures.

- The homework for each chapter begins with a section of **Conceptual Questions**. Answers to the odd-numbered Questions can be found in the back of the book. Answers to even-numbered Conceptual Questions are available in the online Instructor Solutions Manual.

- **Conceptual Exercises (CE)** have been integrated into the homework section at the end of the chapter and consist of multiple-choice and ranking questions. These questions have been carefully selected and written for maximum effectiveness when used with classroom-response systems (clickers). Answers to the odd-numbered Exercises can be found in the back of the book. Answers to even-numbered Conceptual Exercises are available in the online Instructor Solutions Manual.

- **Predict/Explain problems** are new to this edition. These problems ask the student to predict what will happen in a given physical situation and then to choose an explanation for their prediction.   **NEW**

- Also new to this edition, **Passage Problems** are similar to those found on MCAT exams, with associated multiple-choice questions.   **NEW**

- **Interactive Problems** are based on the animations and simulations associated with the Interactive Figures and are found within MasteringPhysics.

- A popular feature within the homework section is the **Integrated Problems (IP).** These problems, labeled with the symbol **IP**, integrate a conceptual question with a numerical problem. Problems of this type, which stress the importance of reasoning from basic principles, show how conceptual insight and numerical calculation go hand in hand in physics.

- In addition, a section titled **General Problems** presents a variety of problems that use material from two or more sections within the chapter, or refer to material covered in earlier chapters.

- **Problems of special biological or medical relevance** are indicated with the symbol **BIO**.

Scope and Organization

TABLE OF CONTENTS

The presentation of physics in this text follows the standard practice for introductory courses, with only a few well-motivated refinements.

- First, note that Chapter 3 is devoted to **vectors and their application to physics.** My experience has been that students benefit greatly from a full discussion of vectors early in the course. Most students have seen vectors and trigonometric functions before, but rarely from the point of view of physics. Thus, including vectors in the text sends a message that this is important material, and it gives students an opportunity to brush up on their math skills.

- Note also that **additional time is given to some of the more fundamental aspects of physics,** such as Newton's laws and energy. Presenting such material in two chapters gives the student a better opportunity to assimilate and master these crucial topics. Sections considered optional are marked with an asterisk.

REAL-WORLD PHYSICS

Since physics applies to everything in nature, it is only reasonable to point out applications of physics that students may encounter in the real world. Each chapter presents a number of discussions focusing on "Real-World Physics." Those of general interest are designated by a globe icon in the margin. Applications that pertain more specifically to biology and medicine are indicated by a green frog icon in the margin.

The Illustration Program

DRAWINGS

Many physics concepts are best conveyed by graphic means. Figures do far more than illustrate a physics text—often, they bear the main burden of the exposition. Accordingly, great attention has been paid to the figures in this book, with the primary emphasis always on the clarity of the analysis. Color has been used consistently throughout the text to reinforce concepts and make the diagrams **NEW** easier for students to understand. New to this edition, helpful **annotations in blue** are included on select figures to help guide students in "reading" graphs and other figures. This technique emulates what instructors do at the chalkboard when explaining figures.

PHOTOGRAPHS

One of the most fundamental ways in which we learn is by comparing and contrasting. Many **companion photos** are presented in groups of two or three that contrast opposing physical principles or illustrate a single concept in a variety of contexts. Grouping carefully chosen photographs in this way helps students to **NEW** see the universality of physics. In this edition, we have added new **demonstration photos** that use high-speed time-lapse photography to dramatically illustrate topics, such as standing waves, static versus kinetic friction, and the motion of center of mass, in a way that reveals physical principles in the world around us.

Resources

The fourth edition is supplemented by an ancillary package developed to address the needs of both students and instructors.

FOR THE INSTRUCTOR

Instructor Solutions Manual by Kenneth L. Menningen (University of Wisconsin–Stevens Point) is available online at the Instructor Resource Center: www.pearsonhighered.com/educator
You will find detailed, worked solutions to every Problem and Conceptual Exercise in the text, all solved using the step-by-step problem-solving strategy of the in-chapter Examples (Picture the Problem, Strategy, two-column Solutions, and Insight). The solutions also contain answers to the even-numbered Conceptual Questions.

Instructor Resource Manual with Notes on ConcepTest Questions
Available at the Instructor Resource Center: www.pearsonhighered.com/educator, this online manual consists of two parts. The first part, prepared by Katherine Whatley and Judith Beck (both of University of North Carolina, Asheville), contains sample syllabi, lecture outlines, notes, demonstration suggestions, readings, and additional references and resources. The second part, prepared by Cornelius Bennhold and Gerald Feldman (both of George Washington University) contains an overview of the development and implementation of ConcepTests, as well as instructor notes for each ConcepTest found in the Instructor Resource Center and available on the Instructor Resource DVD.

Test Bank Available at the Instructor Resource Center:
www.pearsonhighered.com/educator
Written by Delena Bell Gatch (Georgia Southern University), this online, cross-platform test bank contains approximately 3000 multiple-choice, short-answer, and true/false questions, many conceptual in nature. All are referenced to the corresponding text section and ranked by level of difficulty.

Instructor Resource DVD (ISBN 0-321-60193-9)
This cross-platform DVD provides virtually every electronic asset you'll need in and out of the classroom. The DVD is organized by chapter and includes all text illustrations and tables from *Physics*, Fourth Edition, in jpeg and PowerPoint formats. The IRDVD also contains the Interactive Figures, chapter-by-chapter lecture outlines in PowerPoint, ConcepTest "Clicker" Questions in PowerPoint, editable Word files of all numbered equations, the eleven "Physics You Can See" demonstration videos, and pdf files of the *Instructor Resource Manual with Notes on ConcepTest Questions.*

MasteringPhysics™ www.masteringphysics.com
This homework, tutorial, and assessment system is designed to assign, assess, and track each student's progress using a wide diversity of tutorials and extensively pre-tested problems. All the end-of-chapter problems from the text and the Interactive Figures are available in MasteringPhysics. MasteringPhysics provides instructors **NEW** with a fast and effective way to assign uncompromising, wide-ranging online homework assignments of just the right difficulty and duration. The tutorials coach 90% of students to the correct answer with specific wrong-answer feedback. The powerful post-assignment diagnostics allow instructors to assess the progress of their class as a whole or to quickly identify individual student's areas of difficulty.

myeBook is available through MasteringPhysics either automatically when Mastering-Physics is packaged with new books, or available as a purchased upgrade online. **NEW** Allowing students access to the text wherever they have access to the Internet, myeBook comprises the full text, including figures that can be enlarged for better viewing. Within myeBook, students are also able to pop up definitions and terms to help with vocabulary and the reading of the material. Students can also take notes in myeBook using the annotation feature at the top of each page.

ActivPhysics OnLine™ (accessed through the Self Study area within www.masteringphysics.com) provides a comprehensive library of more than 420 tried and tested *ActivPhysics* applets. In addition, it provides a suite of applet-based tutorials developed by education pioneers Alan Van Heuvelen and Paul D'Alessandris. The online exercises are designed to encourage students to confront misconceptions, reason qualitatively about physical processes, experiment quantitatively, and learn to think critically. They cover all topics from mechanics to electricity and magnetism and from optics to modern physics. The *ActivPhysics OnLine* companion workbooks help students work through complex concepts and understand them more clearly.

FOR THE STUDENT
Student Study Guide with Selected Solutions by David Reid (University of Chicago) Volume 1: ISBN 0-321-60200-5; Volume 2: ISBN 0-321-60199-8
The print study guide provides the following for each chapter:

Objectives; Warm-Up Questions from the Just-in-Time Teaching (JiTT) method by Gregor Novak and Andrew Gavrin (Indiana University–Purdue University, Indianapolis); Chapter Review with two-column Examples and integrated quizzes; Reference Tools & Resources (equation summaries, important tips, and tools); Puzzle Questions (also from Novak & Gavrin's JiTT method); Selected Solutions for several end-of-chapter questions and problems.

MasteringPhysics™ (www.masteringphysics.com)
This homework, tutorial, and assessment system is based on years of research into how students work physics problems and precisely where they need help. Studies show that students who use MasteringPhysics significantly increase their final scores compared to hand-written homework. MasteringPhysics achieves this **NEW** improvement by providing students with instantaneous feedback specific to their wrong answers, simpler sub-problems upon request when they get stuck, and partial credit for their method(s) used. This individualized, 24/7 Socratic tutoring is recommended by nine out of ten students to their peers as the most effective and time-efficient way to study.

myeBook is available through MasteringPhysics either automatically when Mastering-**NEW** Physics is packaged with new books, or available as a purchased upgrade online. Allowing students access to the text wherever they have access to the Internet, myeBook comprises the full text, including figures that can be enlarged for better viewing. Within myeBook, students are also able to pop up definitions and terms to help with vocabulary and the reading of the material. Students can also take notes in myeBook using the annotation feature at the top of each page.

ActivPhysics OnLine™ (accessed via www.masteringphysics.com) provides students with a suite of highly regarded applet-based self-study tutorials (see description on previous page). The following workbooks provide a range of tutorial problems designed to use the *ActivPhysics OnLine* simulations, helping students work through complex concepts and understand them more clearly:

- *ActivPhysics OnLine Workbook* Volume 1: Mechanics • Thermal Physics • Oscillations & Waves (ISBN 0-8053-9060-X)

- *ActivPhysics OnLine Workbook* Volume 2: Electricity & Magnetism • Optics • Modern Physics (ISBN 0-8053-9061-8)

Pearson Tutor Services (www.pearsontutorservices.com) Each student's subscription to MasteringPhysics also contains complimentary access to Pearson Tutor Services, powered by Smarthinking, Inc. By logging in with their Mastering-Physics ID and password, they will be connected to highly qualified e-structors™ who provide additional, interactive online tutoring on the major concepts of physics. Some restrictions apply; offer subject to change.

Acknowledgments

I would like to express sincere gratitude to my colleagues at Washington State University and Western Washington University, as well as to many others in the physics community, for their contributions to this project. In particular, I would like to thank Professor Ken Menningen of the University of Wisconsin–Stevens Point for his painstaking attention to detail in producing the Instructor Solutions Manual.

My thanks are due also to the many wonderful and talented people at Addison-Wesley who have been such a pleasure to work with during the development of the fourth edition, and especially to Katie Conley, Michael Gillespie, Margot Otway, and Jim Smith.

In addition, I am grateful for the dedicated efforts of Cindy Johnson, who choreographed a delightfully smooth production process.

Finally, I owe a great debt to all my students over the years. My interactions with them provided the motivation and inspiration that led to this book.

Reviewers

We are grateful to the following instructors for their thoughtful comments on the manuscript of this text.

REVIEWERS OF THE FOURTH EDITION

Raymond Benge
Tarrant County College–NE Campus

Matthew Bigelow
Saint Cloud University

Edward J. Brash
Christopher Newport University

Michaela Burkardt
New Mexico State University

Jennifer Chen
University of Illinois at Chicago

Eugenia Ciocan
Clemson University

Shahida Dar
University of Delaware

Joseph Dodoo
University of Maryland, Eastern Shore

Thomas Dooling
University of Northern Carolina at Pembroke

Hui Fang
Sam Houston State University

Carlos E. Figueroa
Cabrillo College

Lyle Ford
University of Wisconsin, Eau Claire

Darrin Johnson
University of Minnesota, Duluth

Paul Lee
California State University, Northridge

Sheng-Chiang (John) Lee
Mercer University

Nilanga Liyanage
University of Virginia

Michael Ottinger
Missouri Western State University

Melodi Rodrigue
University of Nevada

Claudiu Rusu
Richland College of DCCCD

Mark Sprague
East Carolina University

Richard Szwerc
Montgomery College

Lisa Will
San Diego City College

Guanghua Xu
University of Houston

Bill Yen
University of Georgia

REVIEWERS OF PREVIOUS EDITIONS

Daniel Akerib, *Case Western Reserve University*

Richard Akerib, *Queens College*

Alice M. Hawthorne Allen, *Virginia Tech*

Barbara S. Andereck, *Ohio Wesleyan University*

Eva Andrei, *Rutgers University*

Bradley C. Antanaitis, *Lafayette College*

Michael Arnett, *Kirkwood Community College*

Robert W. Arts, *Pikeville College*

David Balogh, *Fresno City College*

David T. Bannon, *Oregon State University*

Rama Bansil, *Boston University*

Anand Batra, *Howard University*

Paul Beale, *University of Colorado–Boulder*

Mike Berger, *Indiana University*

David Berman, *University of Iowa*

S. M. Bhagat, *University of Maryland*

James D. Borgardt, *Juniata College*

James P. Boyle, *Western Connecticut State University*

David Branning, *Trinity College*

Jeff Braun, *University of Evansville*

Matthew E. Briggs, *University of Wisconsin–Madison*

Jack Brockway, *State University of New York–Oswego*

Neal Cason, *University of Notre Dame*

Thomas B. Cobb, *Bowling Green State University*

Lattie Collins, *Eastern Tennessee State University*

James Cook, *Middle Tennessee State University*

Stephen Cotanch, *North Carolina State University*

David Craig, *LeMoyne College*

David Curott, *University of North Alabama*

William Dabby, *Edison Community College*

Robert Davie, *St. Petersburg Junior College*

Steven Davis, *University of Arkansas–Little Rock*

N. E. Davison, *University of Manitoba*

Duane Deardorff, *University of North Carolina at Chapel Hill*

Edward Derringh, *Wentworth Institute of Technology*

Martha Dickinson, *Maine Maritime Academy*

Anthony DiStefano, *University of Scranton*

David C. Doughty, Jr., *Christopher Newport University*

F. Eugene Dunnam, *University of Florida*

John J. Dykla, *Loyola University–Chicago*

Eldon Eckard, *Bainbridge College*

Donald Elliott, *Carroll College*

David Elmore, *Purdue University*

Robert Endorf, *University of Cincinnati*

Raymond Enzweiler, *Northern Kentucky University*

John Erdei, *University of Dayton*

David Faust, *Mt. Hood Community College*

Frank Ferrone, *Drexel University*

John Flaherty, *Yuba College*

Curt W. Foltz, *Clarion University*

Lewis Ford, *Texas A&M University*

Armin Fuchs, *Florida Atlantic University*

Joseph Gallant, *Kent State University, Trumbull*

Asim Gangopadhyaya, *Loyola University–Chicago*

Thor Garber, *Pensacola Junior College*

David Gerdes, *University of Michigan*

John D. Gieringer, *Alvernia College*

Karen Gipson, *Grand Valley State University*

Barry Gilbert, *Rhode Island College*

Fred Gittes, *Washington State University*

Michael Graf, *Boston College*

William Gregg, *Louisiana State University*

Rainer Grobe, *Illinois State University*

Steven Hagen, *University of Florida*

Mitchell Haeri, *Saddleback College*

Parameswar Hari, *California State University–Fresno*

Xiaochun He, *Georgia State University*

Timothy G. Heil, *University of Georgia*

J. Erik Hendrickson, *University of Wisconsin–Eau Claire*

Scott Holmstrom, *University of Tulsa*

John Hopkins, *The Pennsylvania State University*

Manuel A. Huerta, *University of Miami*

Zafar Ismail, *Daemen College*

Adam Johnston, *Weber State University*

Gordon O. Johnson, *Washington State University*

Nadejda Kaltcheva, *University of Wisconsin–Oshkosh*

William Karstens, *Saint Michael's College*

Sanford Kern, *Colorado State University*

Dana Klinck, *Hillsborough Community College*

Ilkka Koskelo, *San Francisco State University*

Laird Kramer, *Florida International University*

R. Gary Layton, *Northern Arizona University*

Kevin M. Lee, *University of Nebraska–Lincoln*

Michael Lieber, *University of Arkansas*

Ian M. Lindevald, *Truman State University*

Mark Lindsay, *University of Louisville*

Jeff Loats, *Fort Lewis College*

Daniel Ludwigsen, *Kettering University*

Lorin Matthews, *Baylor University*

Hilliard Macomber, *University of Northern Iowa*

Trecia Markes, *University of Nebraska–Kearny*

William McNairy, *Duke University*

Kenneth L. Menningen, *University of Wisconsin–Stevens Point*

Joseph Mills, *University of Houston*

Anatoly Miroshnichenko, *University of Toledo*

Wouter Montfrooij, *University of Missouri*

Gary Morris, *Valparaiso University*

Paul Morris, *Abilene Christian University*

David Moyle, *Clemson University*

Ashok Muthukrishnan, *Texas A&M University*

K. W. Nicholson, *Central Alabama Community College*

Robert Oman, *University of South Florida*

Michael Ottinger, *Missouri Western State College*

Larry Owens, *College of the Sequoias*

A. Ray Penner, *Malaspina University*

Francis Pichanick, *University of Massachusetts, Amherst*

Robert Piserchio, *San Diego State University*

Anthony Pitucco, *Pima Community College*

William Pollard, *Valdosta State University*

Jerry Polson, *Southeastern Oklahoma State University*

Robert Pompi, *Binghamton University*

David Procopio, *Mohawk Valley Community College*

Earl Prohofsky, *Purdue University*

Jia Quan, *Pasadena City College*

David Raffaelle, *Glendale Community College*

Michele Rallis, *Ohio State University*

Michael Ram, *State University of New York–Buffalo*

Prabha Ramakrishnan, *North Carolina State University*

Rex Ramsier, *University of Akron*

John F. Reading, *Texas A&M University*

Lawrence B. Rees, *Brigham Young University*

M. Anthony Reynolds, *Embry Riddle University*

Dennis Rioux, *University of Wisconsin–Oshkosh*

John A. Rochowicz, Jr., *Alvernia College*

Bob Rogers, *San Francisco State University*

Gaylon Ross, *University of Central Arkansas*
Lawrence G. Rowan, *University of North Carolina at Chapel Hill*
Gerald Royce, *Mary Washington College*
Wolfgang Rueckner, *Harvard University*
Misa T. Saros, *Viterbo University*
C. Gregory Seab, *University of New Orleans*
Mats Selen, *University of Illinois*
Bartlett Sheinberg, *Houston Community College*
Peter Shull, *Oklahoma State University*
Christopher Sirola, *Tri-County Technical College*
Daniel Smith, *South Carolina State University*
Leigh M. Smith, *University of Cincinnati*
Soren Sorensen, *University of Tennessee–Knoxville*
Mark W. Sprague, *East Carolina University*
George Strobel, *University of Georgia*
Carey E. Stronach, *Virginia State University*
Irina Struganova, *Barry University*

Daniel Stump, *Michigan State University*
Leo Takahashi, *Penn State University–Beaver*
Harold Taylor, *Richard Stockton College*
Frederick Thomas, *Sinclair Community College*
Jack Tuszynski, *University of Alberta*
Lorin Vant Hull, *University of Houston*
John A. Underwood, *Austin Community College, Rio Grande*
Karl Vogler, *Northern Kentucky University*
Desmond Walsh, *Memorial University of Newfoundland*
Toby Ward, *College of Lake County*
Richard Webb, *Pacific Union College*
Lawrence Weinstein, *Old Dominion University*
Jeremiah Williams, *Illinois Wesleyan University*
Linda Winkler, *Moorhead State University*
Lowell Wood, *University of Houston*
Robert Wood, *University of Georgia*
Jeffrey L. Wragg, *College of Charleston*

STUDENT REVIEWERS

We wish to thank the following students at New Mexico State University and Chemetka Community College for providing helpful feedback during the development of the fourth edition of this text. Their comments offered us valuable insight into the student experience.

Teresa M. Abbott
Rachel Acuna
Sonia Arroyos
Joanna Beeson
Carl Bryce
Jennifer Currier
Juan Farias
Mark Ferra
Bonnie Galloway

Cameron Haider
Gina Hedberg
Kyle Kazsinas
Ty Keeney
Justin Kvenzi
Tannia Lau
Ann MaKarewicz
Jasmine Pando
Jenna Painter

Jonathan Romero
Aaron Ryther
Sarah Salaido
Ashley Slape
Christina Timmons
Christopher Torrez
Charmaine Vega
Elisa Wingerd

We would also like to thank the following students at Boston University, California State University–Chico, the University of Houston, Washington State University, and North Carolina State University for providing helpful feedback via review or focus group for the first three editions of this text:

Ali Ahmed
Joel Amato
Max Aquino
Margaret Baker
Tynisa Bennett
Joshua Carmichael
Sabrina Carrie
Suprna Chandra
Kara Coffee
Tyler Cumby
Rebecca Currell
Philip Dagostino
Andrew D. Fisher
Shadi Miri Ghomizadea

Colleen Hanlon
Jonas Hauptmann
Parker Havron
Jamie Helms
Robert Hubbard
Tamara Jones
Bryce Lewis
Michelle Lim
Candida Mejia
Roderick Minogue
Ryan Morrison
Hang Nguyen
Mary Nguyen
Julie Palakovich

Suraj Parekh
Scott Parsons
Peter Ploewski
Darren B. Robertson
Chris Simons
Tiffany Switzer
Steven Taylor
Monique Thomas
Khang Tran
Michael Vasquez
Jerod Williams
Nathan Witwer
Alexander Wood
Melissa Wright

ATTENDEE: Lynda Klein, *California State University–Chico*

Preface: To the Student

As a student preparing to take an algebra-based physics course, you are probably aware that physics applies to absolutely everything in the natural world, from raindrops and people to galaxies and atoms. Because physics is so wide-ranging and comprehensive, it can sometimes seem a bit overwhelming. This text, which reflects nearly two decades of classroom experience, is designed to help you deal with a large body of information and develop a working understanding of the basic concepts in physics. Now in its fourth edition, it incorporates many refinements that have come directly from interacting with students using the first three editions. As a result of these interactions, I am confident that as you develop a deeper understanding of physics, you will also enrich your experience of the world in which you live.

Now, I must admit that I like physics, and so I may be a bit biased in this respect. Still, the reason I teach and continue to study physics is that I enjoy the insight it gives into the physical world. I can't help but notice—and enjoy—aspects of physics all around me each and every day. As I always tell my students on the first day of class, I would like to share some of this enjoyment and delight in the natural world with you. It is for this reason that I undertook the task of writing this book.

To assist you in the process of studying physics, this text incorporates a number of learning aids, including Two-Column Examples, Active Examples, and Conceptual Checkpoints. These and other elements work together in a unified way to enhance your understanding of physics on both a conceptual and a quantitative level—they have been developed to give you the benefit of what we know about how students learn physics, and to incorporate strategies that have proven successful to students over the years. The pages that follow will introduce these elements to you, describe the purpose of each, and explain how they can help you.

As you progress through the text, you will encounter many interesting and intriguing applications of physics drawn from the world around you. Some of these, such as magnetically levitated trains or the satellite-based Global Positioning System that enables you to determine your position anywhere on Earth to within a few feet, are primarily technological in nature. Others focus on explaining familiar or not-so-familiar phenomena, such as why the Moon has no atmosphere, how sweating cools the body, or why flying saucer shaped clouds often hover over mountain peaks even when the sky is clear. Still others, such as countercurrent heat exchange in animals and humans or the use of sound waves to destroy kidney stones, are of particular relevance to students of biology and the other life sciences.

In many cases, you may find the applications to be a bit surprising. Did you know, for example, that you are shorter at the end of the day than when you first get up in the morning? (This is discussed in Chapter 5.) That an instrument called the ballistocardiograph can detect the presence of a person hiding in a truck, just by registering the minute recoil from the beating of the stowaway's heart? (This is discussed in Chapter 9.) That if you hum next to a spider's web at just the right pitch you can cause a resonance effect that sends the spider into a tizzy? (This is discussed in Chapter 13.) That powerful magnets can exploit the phenomenon of diamagnetism to levitate living creatures? (This is discussed in Chapter 22.)

Writing this textbook was a rewarding experience for me. I hope using it will prove equally rewarding to you, and that it will inspire an interest in and appreciation of physics that will last a lifetime.

James S. Walker

Detailed Contents

PART I   MECHANICS

1 Introduction to Physics

Physics is a quantitative science, based on careful measurements of quantities such as mass, length, and time. In the measurement shown here, a baby elephant is found to have a mass of approximately 425 kilograms, corresponding to a weight of about 935 pounds. Measurements of length and time indicate that the elephant's height is 1.25 meters, and its age is eleven months.

The goal of physics is to gain a deeper understanding of the world in which we live. For example, the laws of physics allow us to predict the behavior of everything from rockets sent to the Moon, to integrated chips in computers, to lasers used to perform eye surgery. In short, everything in nature—from atoms and subatomic particles to solar systems and galaxies—obeys the laws of physics.

As we begin our study of physics, it is useful to consider a range of issues that underlies everything to follow. One of the most fundamental of these is the system of units we use when we measure such things as the mass of an object, its length, and the time between two events. Other equally important issues include methods for handling numerical calculations and basic conventions of mathematical notation. By the end of the chapter we will have developed a common "language" of physics that will be used throughout this book and probably in any science that you study.

1–1 Physics and the Laws of Nature

Physics is the study of the fundamental laws of nature, which, simply put, are the laws that underlie all physical phenomena in the universe. Remarkably, we have found that these laws can be expressed in terms of mathematical equations. As a result, it is possible to make precise, quantitative comparisons between the predictions of theory—derived from the mathematical form of the laws—and the observations of experiments. Physics, then, is a science rooted equally firmly in theory and experiment, and, as physicists make new observations, they constantly test and—if necessary—refine the present theories.

What makes physics particularly fascinating is the fact that it relates to everything in the universe. There is a great beauty in the vision that physics brings to our view of the universe; namely, that all the complexity and variety that we see in the world around us, and in the universe as a whole, are manifestations of a few fundamental laws and principles. That we can discover and apply these basic laws of nature is both astounding and exhilarating.

For those not familiar with the subject, physics may seem to be little more than a confusing mass of formulas. Sometimes, in fact, these formulas can be the trees that block the view of the forest. For a physicist, however, the many formulas of physics are simply different ways of expressing a few fundamental ideas. It is the forest—the basic laws and principles of physical phenomena in nature—that is the focus of this text.

1–2 Units of Length, Mass, and Time

To make quantitative comparisons between the laws of physics and our experience of the natural world, certain basic physical quantities must be measured. The most common of these quantities are **length** (L), **mass** (M), and **time** (T). In fact, in the next several chapters these are the only quantities that arise. Later in the text, additional quantities, such as temperature and electric current, will be introduced as needed.

We begin by defining the units in which each of these quantities is measured. Once the units are defined, the values obtained in specific measurements can be expressed as multiples of them. For example, our unit of length is the **meter** (m). It follows, then, that a person who is 1.94 m tall has a height 1.94 times this unit of length. Similar comments apply to the unit of mass, the **kilogram,** and the unit of time, the **second.**

The detailed system of units used in this book was established in 1960 at the Eleventh General Conference of Weights and Measures in Paris, France, and goes by the name Système International d'Unités, or SI for short. Thus, when we refer to **SI units,** we mean units of meters (m), kilograms (kg), and seconds (s). Taking the first letter from each of these units leads to an alternate name that is often used—the **mks system.**

In the remainder of this section we define each of the SI units.

Length

Early units of length were often associated with the human body. For example, the Egyptians defined the cubit to be the distance from the elbow to the tip of the middle finger. Similarly, the foot was at one time defined to be the length of the royal foot of King Louis XIV. As colorful as these units may be, they are not particularly reproducible—at least not to great precision.

In 1793 the French Academy of Sciences, seeking a more objective and reproducible standard, decided to define a unit of length equal to one ten-millionth the distance from the North Pole to the equator. This new unit was named the metre (from the Greek *metron* for "measure"). The preferred spelling in the United States is *meter*. This definition was widely accepted, and in 1799 a "standard" meter was produced. It consisted of a platinum-iridium alloy rod with two marks on it one meter apart.

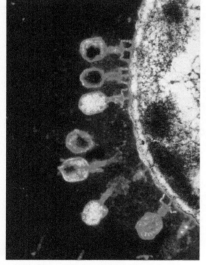

▲ The size of these viruses, seen here attacking a bacterial cell, is about 10^{-7} m.

▲ The diameter of this typical galaxy is about 10^{21} m. (How many viruses would it take to span the galaxy?)

TABLE 1–1 Typical Distances

Distance from Earth to the nearest large galaxy (the Andromeda galaxy, M31)	2×10^{22} m
Diameter of our galaxy (the Milky Way)	8×10^{20} m
Distance from Earth to the nearest star (other than the Sun)	4×10^{16} m
One light-year	9.46×10^{15} m
Average radius of Pluto's orbit	6×10^{12} m
Distance from Earth to the Sun	1.5×10^{11} m
Radius of Earth	6.37×10^{6} m
Length of a football field	10^{2} m
Height of a person	2 m
Diameter of a CD	0.12 m
Diameter of the aorta	0.018 m
Diameter of a period in a sentence	5×10^{-4} m
Diameter of a red blood cell	8×10^{-6} m
Diameter of the hydrogen atom	10^{-10} m
Diameter of a proton	2×10^{-15} m

Since 1983 we have used an even more precise definition of the meter, based on the speed of light in a vacuum. In particular:

> One meter is defined to be the distance traveled by light in a vacuum in 1/299,792,458 of a second.

No matter how its definition is refined, however, a meter is still about 3.28 feet, which is roughly 10 percent longer than a yard. A list of typical lengths is given in Table 1–1.

Mass

In SI units, mass is measured in kilograms. Unlike the meter, the kilogram is not based on any natural physical quantity. By convention, the kilogram has been defined as follows:

> The kilogram, by definition, is the mass of a particular platinum-iridium alloy cylinder at the International Bureau of Weights and Standards in Sèvres, France.

To put the kilogram in everyday terms, a quart of milk has a mass slightly less than 1 kilogram. Additional masses, in kilograms, are given in Table 1–2.

Note that we do not define the kilogram to be the *weight* of the platinum-iridium cylinder. In fact, weight and mass are quite different quantities, even though they are often confused in everyday language. Mass is an intrinsic, unchanging property of an object. Weight, in contrast, is a measure of the gravitational force acting on an object, which can vary depending on the object's location. For example, if you are fortunate enough to travel to Mars someday, you will find that your weight is less than on Earth, though your mass is unchanged. The force of gravity will be discussed in detail in Chapter 12.

Time

Nature has provided us with a fairly accurate timepiece in the revolving Earth. In fact, prior to 1956 the mean solar day was defined to consist of 24 hours, with 60 minutes per hour, and 60 seconds per minute, for a total of $(24)(60)(60) = 84,400$ seconds. Even the rotation of the Earth is not completely regular, however.

Today, the most accurate timekeepers known are "atomic clocks," which are based on characteristic frequencies of radiation emitted by certain atoms. These

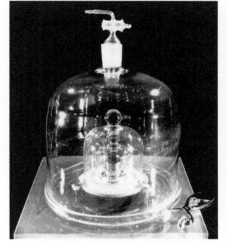

▲ The standard kilogram, a cylinder of platinum and iridium 0.039 m in height and diameter, is kept under carefully controlled conditions in Sèvres, France. Exact replicas are maintained in other laboratories around the world.

TABLE 1–2 Typical Masses

Galaxy (Milky Way)	4×10^{41} kg
Sun	2×10^{30} kg
Earth	5.97×10^{24} kg
Space shuttle	2×10^{6} kg
Elephant	5400 kg
Automobile	1200 kg
Human	70 kg
Baseball	0.15 kg
Honeybee	1.5×10^{-4} kg
Red blood cell	10^{-13} kg
Bacterium	10^{-15} kg
Hydrogen atom	1.67×10^{-27} kg
Electron	9.11×10^{-31} kg

▲ This atomic clock, which keeps time on the basis of radiation from cesium atoms, is accurate to about three millionths of a second per year. (How long would it take for it to gain or lose an hour?)

TABLE 1–3 Typical Times

Age of the universe	5×10^{17} s
Age of the Earth	1.3×10^{17} s
Existence of human species	6×10^{13} s
Human lifetime	2×10^{9} s
One year	3×10^{7} s
One day	8.6×10^{4} s
Time between heartbeats	0.8 s
Human reaction time	0.1 s
One cycle of a high-pitched sound wave	5×10^{-5} s
One cycle of an AM radio wave	10^{-6} s
One cycle of a visible light wave	2×10^{-15} s

"MY GOODNESS, IT'S 12:15:0936420175! TIME FOR LUNCH."

clocks have typical accuracies of about 1 second in 300,000 years. The atomic clock used for defining the second operates with cesium-133 atoms. In particular, the second is defined as follows:

> One second is defined to be the time it takes for radiation from a cesium-133 atom to complete 9,192,631,770 cycles of oscillation.

A range of characteristic time intervals is given in Table 1–3.

The nation's time and frequency standard is determined by a *cesium fountain atomic clock* developed at the National Institute of Standards and Technology (NIST) in Boulder, Colorado. The fountain atomic clock, designated NIST-F1, produces a "fountain" of cesium atoms that are projected upward in a vacuum to a height of about a meter. It takes roughly a second for the atoms to rise and fall through this height (as we shall see in the next chapter), and during this relatively long period of time the frequency of their oscillation can be measured with great precision. In fact, the NIST-F1 will gain or lose no more than one second in every 20 million years of operation.

Atomic clocks are almost commonplace these days. For example, the satellites that participate in the Global Positioning System (GPS) actually carry atomic clocks with them in orbit. This allows them to make the precision time measurements that are needed for an equally precise determination of position and speed. Similarly, the "atomic clocks" that are advertised for use in the home, while not atomic in their operation, nonetheless get their time from radio signals sent out from the atomic clocks at NIST in Boulder. You can access the official U.S. time on your computer by going to http://time.gov on the Web.

Other Systems of Units and Standard Prefixes

Although SI units are used throughout most of this book and are used almost exclusively in scientific research and in industry, we will occasionally refer to other systems that you may encounter from time to time.

For example, a system of units similar to the mks system, though comprised of smaller units, is the **cgs system,** which stands for centimeter (cm), gram (g), and second (s). In addition, the British engineering system is often encountered in everyday usage in the United States. Its basic units are the slug for mass, the foot (ft) for length, and the second (s) for time.

Finally, multiples of the basic units are common no matter which system is used. Standard prefixes are used to designate common multiples in powers of ten. For example, the prefix *kilo* means one thousand, or, equivalently, 10^3. Thus, 1 kilogram is 10^3 grams, and 1 kilometer is 10^3 meters. Similarly, *milli* is the prefix for one thousandth, or 10^{-3}. Thus, a millimeter is 10^{-3} meter, and so on. The most common prefixes are listed in Table 1–4.

EXERCISE 1–1

  a. A minivan sells for 33,200 dollars. Express the price of the minivan in kilodollars and megadollars.
  b. A typical *E. coli* bacterium is about 5 micrometers (or microns) in length. Give this length in millimeters and kilometers.

SOLUTION

  a. 33.2 kilodollars, 0.0332 megadollars
  b. 0.005 mm, 0.000000005 km

1–3 Dimensional Analysis

In physics, when we speak of the **dimension** of a physical quantity, we refer to the *type* of quantity in question, regardless of the units used in the measurement. For example, a distance measured in cubits and another distance measured in light-years both have the same dimension—length. The same is true of compound units such as velocity, which has the dimensions of length per unit time (length/time). A velocity measured in miles per hour has the same dimensions—length/time—as one measured in inches per century.

Now, any valid formula in physics must be **dimensionally consistent;** that is, each term in the equation must have the same dimensions. It simply doesn't make sense to add a distance to a time, for example, any more than it makes sense to add apples and oranges. They are different things.

To check the dimensional consistency of an equation, it is convenient to introduce a special notation for the dimension of a quantity. We will use square brackets, [ ], for this purpose. Thus, if x represents a distance, which has dimensions of length [L], we write this as $x = [L]$. Similarly, a velocity, v, has dimensions of length per time [T]; thus we write $v = [L]/[T]$ to indicate its dimensions. Acceleration, a, which is the change in velocity per time, has the dimensions $a = ([L]/[T])/[T] = [L]/[T^2]$. The dimensions of some common physical quantities are summarized in Table 1–5.

Let's use this notation to check the dimensional consistency of a simple equation. Consider the following formula:

$$x = x_0 + vt$$

In this equation, x and x_0 represent distances, v is a velocity, and t is time. Writing out the dimensions of each term, we have

$$[L] = [L] + \frac{[L]}{[T]}[T]$$

It might seem at first that the last term has different dimensions than the other two. However, dimensions obey the same rules of algebra as other quantities. Thus the dimensions of time cancel in the last term:

$$[L] = [L] + \frac{[L]}{[\cancel{T}]}[\cancel{T}] = [L] + [L]$$

As a result, we see that each term in this formula has the same dimensions. This type of calculation with dimensions is referred to as **dimensional analysis.**

EXERCISE 1–2

Show that $x = x_0 + v_0t + \frac{1}{2}at^2$ is dimensionally consistent. The quantities x and x_0 are distances, v_0 is a velocity, and a is an acceleration.

SOLUTION

Using the dimensions given in Table 1–5, we have

$$[L] = [L] + \frac{[L]}{[\cancel{T}]}[\cancel{T}] + \frac{[L]}{[\cancel{T}]^2}[\cancel{T}^2] = [L] + [L] + [L]$$

Note that $\frac{1}{2}$ is ignored in this analysis because it has no dimensions.

Later in this text you will derive your own formulas from time to time. As you do so, it is helpful to check dimensional consistency at each step of the derivation. If at any time the dimensions don't agree, you will know that a mistake has been made, and you can go back and look for it. If the dimensions check, however, it's not a guarantee the formula is correct—after all, dimensionless factors, like 1/2 or 2, don't show up in a dimensional check.

1–4 Significant Figures

When a mass, a length, or a time is measured in a scientific experiment, the result is known only to within a certain accuracy. The inaccuracy or uncertainty can be caused by a number of factors, ranging from limitations of the measuring device itself to limitations associated with the senses and the skill of the person performing the experiment. In any case, the fact that observed values of experimental

TABLE 1–4 Common Prefixes

Power	Prefix	Abbreviation
10^{15}	peta	P
10^{12}	tera	T
10^9	giga	G
10^6	mega	M
10^3	kilo	k
10^2	hecto	h
10^1	deka	da
10^{-1}	deci	d
10^{-2}	centi	c
10^{-3}	milli	m
10^{-6}	micro	μ
10^{-9}	nano	n
10^{-12}	pico	p
10^{-15}	femto	f

TABLE 1–5 Dimensions of Some Common Physical Quantities

Quantity	Dimension
Distance	$[L]$
Area	$[L^2]$
Volume	$[L^3]$
Velocity	$[L]/[T]$
Acceleration	$[L]/[T^2]$
Energy	$[M][L^2]/[T^2]$

▲ Every measurement has some degree of uncertainty associated with it. How precise would you expect this measurement to be?

quantities have inherent uncertainties should always be kept in mind when performing calculations with those values.

Suppose, for example, that you want to determine the walking speed of your pet tortoise. To do so, you measure the time, t, it takes for the tortoise to walk a distance, d, and then you calculate the quotient, d/t. When you measure the distance with a ruler, which has one tick mark per millimeter, you find that $d = 21.2$ cm, with the precise value of the digit in the second decimal place uncertain. Defining the number of **significant figures** in a physical quantity to be equal to the number of digits in it that are known with certainty, we say that d is known to *three* significant figures.

Similarly, you measure the time with an old pocket watch, and as best you can determine it, $t = 8.5$ s, with the second decimal place uncertain. Note that t is known to only *two* significant figures. If we were to make this measurement with a digital watch, with a readout giving the time to 1/100 of a second, the accuracy of the result would still be limited by the finite reaction time of the experimenter. The reaction time would have to be predetermined in a separate experiment. (See Problem 77 in Chapter 2 for a simple way to determine your reaction time.)

Returning to the problem at hand, we would now like to calculate the speed of the tortoise. Using the above values for d and t and a calculator with eight digits in its display, we find $(21.2 \text{ cm})/(8.5 \text{ s}) = 2.4941176$ cm/s. Clearly, such an accurate value for the speed is unjustified, considering the limitations of our measurements. After all, we can't expect to measure quantities to two and three significant figures and from them obtain results with eight significant figures. In general, the number of significant figures that result when we multiply or divide physical quantities is given by the following rule of thumb:

> The number of significant figures after multiplication or division is equal to the number of significant figures in the *least* accurately known quantity.

In our speed calculation, for example, we know the distance to three significant figures, but the time to only two significant figures. As a result, the speed should be given with just two significant figures, $d/t = (21.2 \text{ cm})/(8.5 \text{ s}) = 2.5$ cm/s. Note that we didn't just keep the first two digits in 2.4941176 cm/s and drop the rest. Instead, we "rounded up"; that is, because the first digit to be dropped (9 in this case) is greater than or equal to 5, we increase the previous digit (4 in this case) by 1. Thus, 2.5 cm/s is our best estimate for the tortoise's speed.

EXAMPLE 1-1   IT'S THE TORTOISE BY A HARE

A tortoise races a rabbit by walking with a constant speed of 2.51 cm/s for 12.23 s. How much distance does the tortoise cover?

PICTURE THE PROBLEM
The race between the rabbit and the tortoise is shown in our sketch. The rabbit pauses to eat a carrot while the tortoise walks with a constant speed.

STRATEGY
The distance covered by the tortoise is the speed of the tortoise multiplied by the time during which it walks.

SOLUTION

1. Multiply the speed by the time to find the distance d:

$$d = (\text{speed})(\text{time})$$
$$= (2.51 \text{ cm/s})(12.23 \text{ s}) = 30.7 \text{ cm}$$

INSIGHT
Notice that if we simply multiply 2.51 cm/s by 12.23 s, we obtain 30.6973 cm. We don't give all of these digits in our answer, however. In particular, because the quantity that is known with the least accuracy (the speed) has only three significant

figures, we give a result with three significant figures. Note, in addition, that the third digit in our answer has been rounded up from 6 to 7.

PRACTICE PROBLEM
How long does it take for the tortoise to walk 17 cm? [**Answer:** $t = (17 \text{ cm})/(2.51 \text{ cm/s}) = 6.8 \text{ s}$]

Some related homework problems: Problem 14, Problem 18

Note that the distance of 17 cm in the Practice Problem has only two significant figures because we don't know the digits to the right of the decimal place. If the distance were given as 17.0 cm, on the other hand, it would have three significant figures.

When physical quantities are added or subtracted, we use a slightly different rule of thumb. In this case, the rule involves the number of decimal places in each of the terms:

> The number of decimal places after addition or subtraction is equal to the smallest number of decimal places in any of the individual terms.

Thus, if you make a time measurement of 16.74 s, and then a subsequent time measurement of 5.1 s, the total time of the two measurements should be given as 21.8 s, rather than 21.84 s.

EXERCISE 1–3

You and a friend pick some raspberries. Your flat weighs 12.7 lb, and your friend's weighs 7.25 lb. What is the combined weight of the raspberries?

SOLUTION
Just adding the two numbers gives 19.95 lb. According to our rule of thumb, however, the final result must have only a single decimal place (corresponding to the term with the smallest number of decimal places). Rounding off to one place, then, gives 20.0 lb as the acceptable result.

▲ The finish of the 100-meter race at the 1996 Atlanta Olympics. This official timing photo shows Donovan Bailey setting a new world record of 9.84 s. (If the timing had been accurate to only tenths of a second—as would probably have been the case before electronic devices came into use—how many runners would have shared the winning time? How many would have shared the second-place and third-place times?)

Scientific Notation

The number of significant figures in a given quantity may be ambiguous due to the presence of zeros at the beginning or end of the number. For example, if a distance is stated to be 2500 m, the two zeros could be significant figures, or they could be zeros that simply show where the decimal point is located. If the two zeros are significant figures, the uncertainty in the distance is roughly a meter; if they are not significant figures, however, the uncertainty is about 100 m.

To remove this type of ambiguity, we can write the distance in **scientific notation**—that is, as a number of order unity times an appropriate power of ten. Thus, in this example, we would express the distance as 2.5×10^3 m if there are only two significant figures, or as 2.500×10^3 m to indicate four significant figures. Likewise, a time given as 0.000036 s has only two significant figures—the preceding zeros only serve to fix the decimal point. If this quantity were known to three significant figures, we would write it as 3.60×10^{-5} s to remove any ambiguity. See Appendix A for a more detailed discussion of scientific notation.

EXERCISE 1–4

How many significant figures are there in **(a)** 21.00, **(b)** 21, **(c)** 2.1×10^{-2}, **(d)** 2.10×10^{-3}?

SOLUTION
(a) 4, **(b)** 2, **(c)** 2, **(d)** 3

Round-Off Error

Finally, even if you perform all your calculations to the same number of significant figures as in the text, you may occasionally obtain an answer that differs in its last digit from that given in the book. In most cases this is not an issue as far as understanding the physics is concerned—usually it is due to **round-off error.**

Round-off error occurs when numerical results are rounded off at different times during a calculation. To see how this works, let's consider a simple example. Suppose you are shopping for knickknacks, and you buy one item for $2.21, plus 8 percent sales tax. The total price is $2.3868, or, rounded off to the nearest penny, $2.39. Later, you buy another item for $1.35. With tax this becomes $1.458 or, again to the nearest penny, $1.46. The total expenditure for these two items is $2.39 + $1.46 = $3.85.

Now, let's do the rounding off in a different way. Suppose you buy both items at the same time for a total before-tax price of $2.21 + $1.35 = $3.56. Adding in the 8% tax gives $3.8448, which rounds off to $3.84, one penny different from the previous amount. This same type of discrepancy can occur in physics problems. In general, it's a good idea to keep one extra digit throughout your calculations whenever possible, rounding off only the final result. But while this practice can help to reduce the likelihood of round-off error, there is no way to avoid it in every situation.

1–5 Converting Units

It is often convenient to convert from one set of units to another. For example, suppose you would like to convert 316 ft to its equivalent in meters. Looking at the conversion factors on the inside front cover of the text, we see that

$$1 \text{ m} = 3.281 \text{ ft} \qquad \text{1–1}$$

Equivalently,

$$\frac{1 \text{ m}}{3.281 \text{ ft}} = 1 \qquad \text{1–2}$$

Now, to make the conversion, we simply multiply 316 ft by this expression, which is equivalent to multiplying by 1:

$$(316 \text{ ft})\left(\frac{1 \text{ m}}{3.281 \text{ ft}}\right) = 96.3 \text{ m}$$

Note that the conversion factor is written in this particular way, as 1 m divided by 3.281 ft, so that the units of feet cancel out, leaving the final result in the desired units of meters.

Of course, we can just as easily convert from meters to feet if we use the reciprocal of this conversion factor—which is also equal to 1:

$$1 = \frac{3.281 \text{ ft}}{1 \text{ m}}$$

For example, a distance of 26.4 m is converted to feet by canceling out the units of meters, as follows:

$$(26.4 \text{ m})\left(\frac{3.281 \text{ ft}}{1 \text{ m}}\right) = 86.6 \text{ ft}$$

Thus, we see that converting units is as easy as multiplying by 1—because that's really what you're doing.

WAIMEA   3 mi
              5 km

HANAPEPE   9 mi
             14 km

LIHUE   26 mi
             42 km

▲ From this sign, you can calculate factors for converting miles to kilometers and vice versa. (Why do you think the conversion factors seem to vary for different destinations?)

EXAMPLE 1–2 A HIGH-VOLUME WAREHOUSE

A warehouse is 20.0 yards long, 10.0 yards wide, and 15.0 ft high. What is its volume in SI units?

PICTURE THE PROBLEM
In our sketch we picture the warehouse, and indicate the relevant lengths for each of its dimensions.

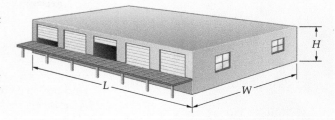

STRATEGY
We begin by converting the length, width, and height of the warehouse to meters. Once this is done, the volume in SI units is simply the product of the three dimensions.

SOLUTION

1. Convert the length of the warehouse to meters:

$$L = (20.0 \text{ yard})\left(\frac{3 \text{ ft}}{1 \text{ yard}}\right)\left(\frac{1 \text{ m}}{3.281 \text{ ft}}\right) = 18.3 \text{ m}$$

2. Convert the width to meters:

$$W = (10.0 \text{ yard})\left(\frac{3 \text{ ft}}{1 \text{ yard}}\right)\left(\frac{1 \text{ m}}{3.281 \text{ ft}}\right) = 9.14 \text{ m}$$

3. Convert the height to meters:

$$H = (15.0 \text{ ft})\left(\frac{1 \text{ m}}{3.281 \text{ ft}}\right) = 4.57 \text{ m}$$

4. Calculate the volume of the warehouse:

$$V = L \times W \times H = (18.3 \text{ m})(9.14 \text{ m})(4.57 \text{ m}) = 764 \text{ m}^3$$

INSIGHT
We would say, then, that the warehouse has a volume of 764 cubic meters—the same as 764 cubical boxes that are 1 m on a side.

PRACTICE PROBLEM
What is the volume of the warehouse if its length is one-hundredth of a mile, and the other dimensions are unchanged?
[**Answer:** $V = 672 \text{ m}^3$]

Some related homework problems: Problem 20, Problem 21

Finally, the same procedure can be applied to conversions involving any number of units. For instance, if you walk at 3.00 mi/h, how fast is that in m/s? In this case we need the following additional conversion factors:

$$1 \text{ mi} = 5280 \text{ ft} \qquad 1 \text{ h} = 3600 \text{ s}$$

With these factors at hand, we carry out the conversion as follows:

$$(3.00 \text{ mi/h})\left(\frac{5280 \text{ ft}}{1 \text{ mi}}\right)\left(\frac{1 \text{ m}}{3.281 \text{ ft}}\right)\left(\frac{1 \text{ h}}{3600 \text{ s}}\right) = 1.34 \text{ m/s}$$

Note that in each conversion factor the numerator is equal to the denominator. In addition, each conversion factor is written in such a way that the unwanted units cancel, leaving just meters per second in our final result.

ACTIVE EXAMPLE 1–1 FIND THE SPEED OF BLOOD

Blood in the human aorta can attain speeds of 35.0 cm/s. How fast is this in **(a)** ft/s and **(b)** mi/h?

SOLUTION
(Test your understanding by performing the calculations indicated in each step.)

Part (a)

1. Convert centimeters to meters and then to feet: 1.15 ft/s

CONTINUED ON NEXT PAGE

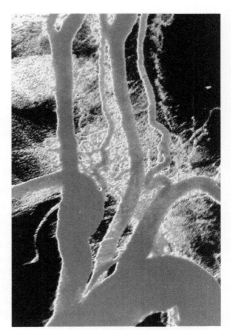

▲ Major blood vessels branch from the aorta (bottom), the artery that receives blood directly from the heart.

▲ Enrico Fermi (1901–1954) was renowned for his ability to pose and solve interesting order-of-magnitude problems. A winner of the 1938 Nobel Prize in physics, Fermi would ask his classes to obtain order-of-magnitude estimates for questions such as "How many piano tuners are there in Chicago?" or "How much is a tire worn down during one revolution?" Estimation questions like these are known to physicists today as "Fermi Problems."

CONTINUED FROM PREVIOUS PAGE

Part (b)

2. First, convert centimeters to miles: $2.17 \times 10^{-4} \, \text{mi/s}$

3. Next, convert seconds to hours: $0.783 \, \text{mi/h}$

INSIGHT

Of course, the conversions in part (b) can be carried out in a single calculation if desired.

YOUR TURN

Find the speed of blood in units of km/h.   (*Answers to* **Your Turn** *problems are given in the back of the book.*)

1–6 Order-of-Magnitude Calculations

An **order-of-magnitude** calculation is a rough "ballpark" estimate designed to be accurate to within a factor of about 10. One purpose of such a calculation is to give a quick idea of what order of magnitude should be expected from a complete, detailed calculation. If an order-of-magnitude calculation indicates that a distance should be on the order of 10^4 m, for example, and your calculator gives an answer on the order of 10^7 m, then there is an error somewhere that needs to be resolved.

For example, suppose you would like to estimate the speed of a cliff diver on entering the water. First, the cliff may be 20 or 30 feet high; thus in SI units we would say that the order of magnitude of the cliff's height is 10 m—certainly not 1 m or 10^2 m. Next, the diver hits the water something like a second later—certainly not 0.1 s later nor 10 s later. Thus, a reasonable order-of-magnitude estimate of the diver's speed is 10 m/1 s = 10 m/s, or roughly 20 mi/h. If you do a detailed calculation and your answer is on the order of 10^4 m/s, you probably entered one of your numbers incorrectly.

Another reason for doing an order-of-magnitude calculation is to get a feeling for what size numbers we are talking about in situations where a precise count is not possible. This is illustrated in the following Example.

EXAMPLE 1–3 ESTIMATION: HOW MANY RAINDROPS IN A STORM

A thunderstorm drops half an inch (~0.01 m) of rain on Washington D.C., which covers an area of about 70 square miles (~10^8 m²). Estimate the number of raindrops that fell during the storm.

PICTURE THE PROBLEM

Our sketch shows an area $A = 10^8 \, \text{m}^2$ covered to a depth $d = 0.01$ m by rainwater from the storm. Each drop of rain is approximated by a small sphere with a diameter of 4 mm.

STRATEGY

To find the number of raindrops, we first calculate the volume of water required to cover $10^8 \, \text{m}^2$ to a depth of 0.01 m. Next, we calculate the volume of an individual drop of rain, recalling that the volume of a sphere of radius r is $4\pi r^3/3$. We estimate the diameter of a raindrop to be about 4 mm. Finally, dividing the volume of a drop into the volume of water that fell during the storm gives the number of drops.

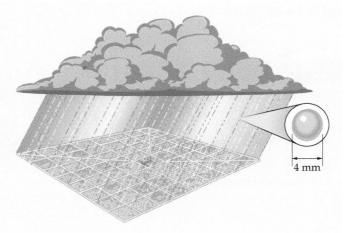

SOLUTION

1. Calculate the order of magnitude of the volume of water, V_{water}, that fell during the storm:

$$V_{water} = Ad = (10^8 \text{ m}^2)(0.01 \text{ m}) \approx 10^6 \text{ m}^3$$

2. Calculate the order of magnitude of the volume of a drop of rain, V_{drop}. Note that if the diameter of a drop is 4 mm, its radius is $r = 2$ mm $= 0.002$ m:

$$V_{drop} = \frac{4}{3}\pi r^3 \approx \frac{4}{3}\pi(0.002 \text{ m})^3 \approx 10^{-8} \text{ m}^3$$

3. Divide V_{drop} into V_{water} to find the order of magnitude of the number of drops that fell during the storm:

$$number\ of\ raindrops \approx \frac{V_{water}}{V_{drop}} \approx \frac{10^6 \text{ m}^3}{10^{-8} \text{ m}^3} = 10^{14}$$

INSIGHT

Thus the number of raindrops in this one small storm is roughly 100,000 times greater than the current population of the Earth.

PRACTICE PROBLEM

If a storm pelts Washington D.C. with 10^{15} raindrops, how many inches of rain fall on the city?   [**Answer:** About 5 inches]

Some related homework problems: Problem 36, Problem 38

Appendix B provides a number of interesting "typical values" for length, mass, speed, acceleration, and many other quantities. You may find these to be of use in making your own order-of-magnitude estimates.

1–7 Scalars and Vectors

Physical quantities are sometimes defined solely in terms of a number and the corresponding unit, like the volume of a room or the temperature of the air it contains. Other quantities require both a numerical value *and* a direction. For example, suppose a car is traveling at a rate of 25 m/s in a direction that is due north. Both pieces of information—the rate of travel (25 m/s) and the direction (north)—are required to fully specify the motion of the car. The rate of travel is given the name **speed;** the rate of travel combined with the direction is referred to as the **velocity.**

In general, quantities that are specified by a numerical value only are referred to as **scalars;** quantities that require both a numerical value and a direction are called **vectors:**

- A scalar is a numerical value, expressed in terms of appropriate units. An example would be the temperature of a room or the speed of a car.
- A vector is a mathematical quantity with both a numerical value and a direction. An example would be the velocity of a car.

All the physical quantities discussed in this text are either vectors or scalars. The properties of numbers (scalars) are well known, but the properties of vectors are sometimes less well known—though no less important. For this reason, you will find that Chapter 3 is devoted entirely to a discussion of vectors in two and three dimensions and, more specifically, to how they are used in physics.

The rather straightforward special case of vectors in one dimension is discussed in Chapter 2. There, we see that the direction of a velocity vector, for example, can only be to the left or to the right, up or down, and so on. That is, only two choices are available for the direction of a vector in one dimension. This is illustrated in **Figure 1–1**, where we see two cars, each traveling with a speed of 25 m/s. We also see that the cars are traveling in opposite directions, with car 1 moving to the right and car 2 moving to the left. We indicate the direction of travel with a plus sign for motion to the right, and a negative sign for motion to the left. Thus, the velocity of car 1 is written $v_1 = +25$ m/s, and the velocity of car 2 is $v_2 = -25$ m/s. The speed of each car is the absolute value, or **magnitude,** of the velocity; that is, speed $= |v_1| = |v_2| = 25$ m/s.

Whenever we deal with one-dimensional vectors, we shall indicate their direction with the appropriate sign. Many examples are found in Chapter 2 and, again, in later chapters where the simplicity of one dimension can again be applied.

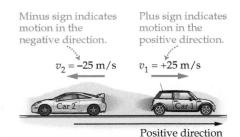

Minus sign indicates motion in the negative direction.

Plus sign indicates motion in the positive direction.

$v_2 = -25$ m/s $v_1 = +25$ m/s

Positive direction

▲ **FIGURE 1–1 Velocity vectors in one dimension**

The two cars shown in this figure have equal speeds of 25 m/s, but are traveling in opposite directions. To indicate the direction of travel, we first choose a positive direction (to the right in this case), and then give appropriate signs to the velocity of each car. For example, car 1 moves to the right, and hence its velocity is positive, $v_1 = +25$ m/s; the velocity of car 2 is negative, $v_2 = -25$ m/s, because it moves to the left.

1–8 Problem Solving in Physics

Physics is a lot like swimming—you have to learn by doing. You could read a book on swimming and memorize every word in it, but when you jump into a pool the first time you are going to have problems. Similarly, you could read this book carefully, memorizing every formula in it, but when you finish, you still haven't learned physics. To learn physics, you have to go beyond passive reading; you have to interact with physics and experience it by doing problems.

In this section we present a general overview of problem solving in physics. The suggestions given below, which apply to problems in all areas of physics, should help to develop a systematic approach.

We should emphasize at the outset that there is no recipe for solving problems in physics—it is a creative activity. In fact, the opportunity to be creative is one of the attractions of physics. The following suggestions, then, are not intended as a rigid set of steps that must be followed like the steps in a computer program. Rather, they provide a general guideline that experienced problem solvers find to be effective.

- **Read the problem carefully** Before you can solve a problem, you need to know exactly what information it gives and what it asks you to determine. Some information is given explicitly, as when a problem states that a person has a mass of 70 kg. Other information is implicit; for example, saying that a ball is dropped from rest means that its initial speed is zero. Clearly, a *careful* reading is the essential first step in problem solving.

- **Sketch the system** This may seem like a step you can skip—but don't. A sketch helps you to acquire a physical feeling for the system. It also provides an opportunity to label those quantities that are known and those that are to be determined. All Examples in this text begin with a sketch of the system, accompanied by a brief description in a section labeled "Picture the Problem."

- **Visualize the physical process** Try to visualize what is happening in the system as if you were watching it in a movie. Your sketch should help. This step ties in closely with the next step.

- **Strategize** This may be the most difficult, but at the same time the most creative, part of the problem-solving process. From your sketch and visualization, try to identify the physical processes at work in the system. Ask yourself what concepts or principles are involved in this situation. Then, develop a strategy—a game plan—for solving the problem. All Examples in this book have a "Strategy" spelled out before the solution begins.

- **Identify appropriate equations** Once a strategy has been developed, find the specific equations that are needed to carry it out.

- **Solve the equations** Use basic algebra to solve the equations identified in the previous step. Work with symbols such as x or y for the most part, substituting numerical values near the end of the calculations. Working with symbols will make it easier to go back over a problem to locate and identify mistakes, if there are any, and to explore limits and special cases.

- **Check your answer** Once you have an answer, check to see if it makes sense: (i) Does it have the correct dimensions? (ii) Is the numerical value reasonable?

- **Explore limits/special cases** Getting the correct answer is nice, but it's not all there is to physics. You can learn a great deal about physics and about the connection between physics and mathematics by checking various limits of your answer. For example, if you have two masses in your system, m_1 and m_2, what happens in the special case that $m_1 = 0$ or $m_1 = m_2$? Check to see whether your answer and your physical intuition agree.

The **Examples** in this text are designed to deepen your understanding of physics and at the same time develop your problem-solving skills. They all have the same basic structure: Problem Statement; Picture the Problem; Strategy; Solution, presenting the flow of ideas and the mathematics side-by-side in a two-column format; Insight; and a Practice Problem related to the one just solved. As you work through the Examples in the chapters to come, notice how the basic problem-solving guidelines outlined above are implemented in a consistent way.

In addition to the Examples, this text contains a new and innovative type of worked-out problem called the **Active Example,** the first one of which appears on page 9. The purpose of Active Examples is to encourage active participation in the solution of a problem and, in so doing, to act as a "bridge" between Examples—where each and every detail is worked out—and homework problems—where you are completely on your own. An analogy would be to think of Examples as like a tricycle, with no balancing required; homework problems as like a bicycle, where balancing is initially difficult to master; and Active Examples as like a bicycle with training wheels that give just enough help to prevent a fall. When you work through an Active Example, keep in mind that the work you are doing as you progress step-by-step through the problem is just the kind of work you'll be doing later in your homework assignments.

Finally, it is tempting to look for shortcuts when doing a problem—to look for a formula that seems to fit and some numbers to plug into it. It may seem harder to think ahead, to be systematic as you solve the problem, and then to think back over what you have done at the end of the problem. The extra effort is worth it, however, because by doing these things you will develop powerful problem-solving skills that can be applied to unexpected problems you may encounter on exams—and in life in general.

THE BIG PICTURE PUTTING PHYSICS IN CONTEXT

LOOKING BACK

The three physical dimensions introduced in this chapter—mass, length, time—are the only ones we'll use until Chapter 19, when we introduce electric charge. Other quantities found in the next several chapters, like force, momentum, and energy, are combinations of these three basic dimensions.

In this chapter we discussed the idea of a vector in one spatial dimension and showed how the direction of the vector can be indicated by its sign. These concepts are developed in more detail in Chapter 2.

LOOKING AHEAD

Dimensional analysis is used frequently in the coming chapters to verify that each term in an equation has the correct dimensions. See, for example, the discussion following Equation 2–7, where we show that each term has the dimensions of velocity. We also use dimensional analysis to help derive some results, such as the speed of waves on a string in Section 14–2.

Vectors are extended to two and three spatial dimensions in Chapter 3. After that, they are a standard tool throughout mechanics, and they appear again in electricity and magnetism.

CHAPTER SUMMARY

1–1 PHYSICS AND THE LAWS OF NATURE

Physics is based on a small number of fundamental laws and principles.

1–2 UNITS OF LENGTH, MASS, AND TIME

Length
One meter is defined as the distance traveled by light in a vacuum in 1/299,792,458 second.

Mass
One kilogram is the mass of a metal cylinder kept at the International Bureau of Weights and Standards.

Time
One second is the time required for a particular type of radiation from cesium-133 to undergo 9,192,631,770 oscillations.

1–3 DIMENSIONAL ANALYSIS

Dimension
The dimension of a quantity is the type of quantity it is, for example, length [L], mass [M], or time [T].

Dimensional Consistency
An equation is dimensionally consistent if each term in it has the same dimensions. All valid physical equations are dimensionally consistent.

Dimensional Analysis
A calculation based on the dimensional consistency of an equation.

1–4 SIGNIFICANT FIGURES

Significant Figures
The number of digits reliably known, excluding digits that simply indicate the decimal place. For example, 3.45 and 0.0000345 both have three significant figures.

Round-off Error
Discrepancies caused by rounding off numbers in intermediate results.

1–5 CONVERTING UNITS

Multiply by the ratio of two units to convert from one to another. As an example, to convert 3.5 m to feet, you multiply by the factor (1 ft/0.3048 m).

1–6 ORDER-OF-MAGNITUDE CALCULATIONS

A ballpark estimate designed to be accurate to within the nearest power of ten.

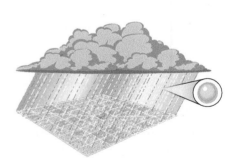

1–7 SCALARS AND VECTORS

A physical quantity that can be represented by a numerical value only is called a scalar. Quantities that require a direction in addition to the numerical value are called vectors.

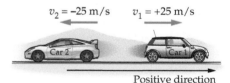

$v_2 = -25$ m/s $\quad$ $v_1 = +25$ m/s

Positive direction

1–8 PROBLEM SOLVING IN PHYSICS

A good general approach to problem solving is as follows: read; sketch; visualize; strategize; identify equations; solve; check; explore limits.

CONCEPTUAL QUESTIONS

For instructor-assigned homework, go to www.masteringphysics.com

(Answers to odd-numbered Conceptual Questions can be found in the back of the book.)

1. Can dimensional analysis determine whether the area of a circle is πr^2 or $2\pi r^2$? Explain.

2. If a distance d has units of meters, and a time T has units of seconds, does the quantity $T + d$ make sense physically? What about the quantity d/T? Explain in both cases.

3. Is it possible for two quantities to **(a)** have the same units but different dimensions or **(b)** have the same dimensions but different units? Explain.

4. Give an order-of-magnitude estimate for the time in seconds of the following: **(a)** a year; **(b)** a baseball game; **(c)** a heartbeat; **(d)** the age of the Earth; **(e)** the age of a person.

5. Give an order-of-magnitude estimate for the length in meters of the following: **(a)** a person; **(b)** a fly; **(c)** a car; **(d)** a 747 airplane; **(e)** an interstate freeway stretching coast-to-coast.

PROBLEMS AND CONCEPTUAL EXERCISES

Note: Answers to odd-numbered Problems and Conceptual Exercises can be found in the back of the book. **IP** *denotes an integrated problem, with both conceptual and numerical parts;* **BIO** *identifies problems of biological or medical interest;* **CE** *indicates a conceptual exercise. On all problems, red bullets (•, ••, •••) are used to indicate the level of difficulty.*

SECTION 1–2 UNITS OF LENGTH, MASS, AND TIME

1. • **Spiderman** The movie *Spiderman* brought in $114,000,000 in its opening weekend. Express this amount in **(a)** gigadollars and **(b)** teradollars.

2. • **BIO The Thickness of Hair** A human hair has a thickness of about 70 μm. What is this in **(a)** meters and **(b)** kilometers?

3. • The speed of light in a vacuum is approximately 0.3 Gm/s. Express the speed of light in meters per second.

4. • **A Fast Computer** IBM has a computer it calls the Blue Gene/L that can do 136.8 teracalculations per second. How many calculations can it do in a microsecond?

SECTION 1–3 DIMENSIONAL ANALYSIS

5. • **CE** Which of the following equations are dimensionally consistent? **(a)** $x = vt$, **(b)** $x = \frac{1}{2}at^2$, **(c)** $t = (2x/a)^{1/2}$.

6. • **CE** Which of the following quantities have the dimensions of a distance? **(a)** vt, **(b)** $\frac{1}{2}at^2$, **(c)** $2at$, **(d)** v^2/a.

7. • **CE** Which of the following quantities have the dimensions of a speed? **(a)** $\frac{1}{2}at^2$, **(b)** at, **(c)** $(2x/a)^{1/2}$, **(d)** $(2ax)^{1/2}$.

8. • Velocity is related to acceleration and distance by the following expression: $v^2 = 2ax^p$. Find the power p that makes this equation dimensionally consistent.

9. • Acceleration is related to distance and time by the following expression: $a = 2xt^p$. Find the power p that makes this equation dimensionally consistent.

10. • Show that the equation $v = v_0 + at$ is dimensionally consistent. Note that v and v_0 are velocities and that a is an acceleration.

11. •• Newton's second law (to be discussed in Chapter 5) states that acceleration is proportional to the force acting on an object and is inversely proportional to the object's mass. What are the dimensions of force?

12. •• The time T required for one complete oscillation of a mass m on a spring of force constant k is

$$T = 2\pi\sqrt{\frac{m}{k}}$$

Find the dimensions k must have for this equation to be dimensionally correct.

SECTION 1–4 SIGNIFICANT FIGURES

13. • The first several digits of π are known to be $\pi = 3.14159265358979\ldots$. What is π to **(a)** three significant figures, **(b)** five significant figures, and **(c)** seven significant figures?

14. • The speed of light to five significant figures is 2.9979×10^8 m/s. What is the speed of light to three significant figures?

15. • A parking lot is 144.3 m long and 47.66 m wide. What is the perimeter of the lot?

16. • On a fishing trip you catch a 2.35-lb bass, a 12.1-lb rock cod, and a 12.13-lb salmon. What is the total weight of your catch?

17. •• How many significant figures are there in **(a)** 0.000054 and **(b)** 3.001×10^5?

18. •• What is the area of a circle of radius **(a)** 14.37 m and **(b)** 3.8 m?

SECTION 1–5 CONVERTING UNITS

19. • **BIO Mantis Shrimp** Peacock mantis shrimps (*Odontodactylus scyllarus*) feed largely on snails. They shatter the shells of their prey by delivering a sharp blow with their front legs, which have been observed to reach peak speeds of 23 m/s. What is this speed in **(a)** feet per second and **(b)** miles per hour?

20. • **(a)** The largest building in the world by volume is the Boeing 747 plant in Everett, Washington. It measures approximately 631 m long, 707 yards wide, and 110 ft high. What is its volume in cubic feet? **(b)** Convert your result from part (a) to cubic meters.

21. • The Ark of the Covenant is described as a chest of acacia wood 2.5 cubits in length and 1.5 cubits in width and height. Given that a cubit is equivalent to 17.7 in., find the volume of the ark in cubic feet.

22. • How long does it take for radiation from a cesium-133 atom to complete 1.5 million cycles?

23. • **Angel Falls** Water going over Angel Falls, in Venezuela, the world's highest waterfall, drops through a distance of 3212 ft. What is this distance in km?

24. • An electronic advertising sign repeats a message every 7 seconds, day and night, for a week. How many times did the message appear on the sign?

25. • **BIO Blue Whales** The blue whale (*Balaenoptera musculus*) is thought to be the largest animal ever to inhabit the Earth. The longest recorded blue whale had a length of 108 ft. What is this length in meters?

26. • **The Star of Africa** The Star of Africa, a diamond in the royal scepter of the British crown jewels, has a mass of 530.2 carats, where 1 carat = 0.20 g. Given that 1 kg has an approximate weight of 2.21 lb, what is the weight of this diamond in pounds?

27. • **IP** Many highways have a speed limit of 55 mi/h. **(a)** Is this speed greater than, less than, or equal to 55 km/h? Explain. **(b)** Find the speed limit in km/h that corresponds to 55 mi/h.

28. • What is the speed in miles per hour of a beam of light traveling at 3.00×10^8 m/s?

29. • **BIO Woodpecker Impact** When red-headed woodpeckers (*Melanerpes erythrocephalus*) strike the trunk of a tree, they can experience an acceleration ten times greater than the acceleration of gravity, or about 98.1 m/s². What is this acceleration in ft/s²?

30. •• **A Jiffy** The American physical chemist Gilbert Newton Lewis (1875–1946) proposed a unit of time called the "jiffy." According to Lewis, 1 jiffy = the time it takes light to travel one centimeter. **(a)** If you perform a task in a jiffy, how long has it taken in seconds? **(b)** How many jiffys are in one minute? (Use the fact that the speed of light is approximately 2.9979×10^8 m/s.)

31. •• **The Mutchkin and the Noggin** **(a)** A mutchkin is a Scottish unit of liquid measure equal to 0.42 L. How many mutchkins are required to fill a container that measures one foot on a side? **(b)** A noggin is a volume equal to 0.28 mutchkin. What is the conversion factor between noggins and gallons?

32. •• Suppose 1.0 cubic meter of oil is spilled into the ocean. Find the area of the resulting slick, assuming that it is one molecule thick, and that each molecule occupies a cube 0.50 μm on a side.

33. •• **IP** **(a)** A standard sheet of paper measures 8 1/2 by 11 inches. Find the area of one such sheet of paper in m². **(b)** A second sheet of paper is half as long and half as wide as the one described in part (a). By what factor is its area less than the area found in part (a)?

34. •• **BIO Squid Nerve Impulses** Nerve impulses in giant axons of the squid can travel with a speed of 20.0 m/s. How fast is this in **(a)** ft/s and **(b)** mi/h?

35. •• The acceleration of gravity is approximately 9.81 m/s² (depending on your location). What is the acceleration of gravity in feet per second squared?

SECTION 1–6 ORDER-OF-MAGNITUDE CALCULATIONS

36. • Give a ballpark estimate of the number of seats in a typical major league ballpark.

Shea Stadium, in New York. How many fans can it hold?
(Problem 36)

37. • Milk is often sold by the gallon in plastic containers. **(a)** Estimate the number of gallons of milk that are purchased in the United States each year. **(b)** What approximate weight of plastic does this represent?

38. •• New York is roughly 3000 miles from Seattle. When it is 10:00 A.M. in Seattle, it is 1:00 P.M. in New York. Using this information, estimate **(a)** the rotational speed of the surface of Earth, **(b)** the circumference of Earth, and **(c)** the radius of Earth.

39. •• You've just won the $12 million cash lottery, and you go to pick up the prize. What is the approximate weight of the cash if you request payment in **(a)** quarters or **(b)** dollar bills?

GENERAL PROBLEMS

40. • **CE** Which of the following equations are dimensionally consistent? **(a)** $v = at$, **(b)** $v = \frac{1}{2}at^2$, **(c)** $t = a/v$, **(d)** $v^2 = 2ax$.

41. • **CE** Which of the following quantities have the dimensions of an acceleration? **(a)** xt^2, **(b)** v^2/x, **(c)** x/t^2, **(d)** v/t.

42. • **BIO Photosynthesis** The light that plants absorb to perform photosynthesis has a wavelength that peaks near 675 nm. Express this distance in **(a)** millimeters and **(b)** inches.

43. • **Glacial Speed** On June 9, 1983, the lower part of the Variegated Glacier in Alaska was observed to be moving at a rate of 210 feet per day. What is this speed in meters per second?

Alaska's Variegated Glacier
(Problem 43)

44. •• **BIO Mosquito Courtship** Male mosquitoes in the mood for mating find female mosquitoes of their own species by listening for the characteristic "buzzing" frequency of the female's wing beats. This frequency is about 605 wing beats per second. **(a)** How many wing beats occur in one minute? **(b)** How many cycles of oscillation does the radiation from a cesium-133 atom complete during one mosquito wing beat?

45. •• **Ten and Ten** When Coast Guard pararescue jumpers leap from a helicopter to save a person in the water, they like to jump when the helicopter is flying "ten and ten," which means it is 10 feet above the water and moving forward with a speed of 10 knots. What is "ten and ten" in SI units? (A knot is one nautical mile per hour, where a nautical mile is 1.852 km.)

46. •• **IP** A Porsche sports car can accelerate at 14 m/s². **(a)** Is this acceleration greater than, less than, or equal to 14 ft/s²? Explain. **(b)** Determine the acceleration of a Porsche in ft/s². **(c)** Determine its acceleration in km/h².

47. •• **BIO Human Nerve Fibers** Type A nerve fibers in humans can conduct nerve impulses at speeds up to 140 m/s. **(a)** How fast are the nerve impulses in miles per hour? **(b)** How far (in meters) can the impulses travel in 5.0 ms?

The impulses in these nerve axons, which carry commands to the skeletal muscle fibers in the background, travel at speeds of up to 140 m/s. (Problem 47)

48. •• **BIO Brain Growth** The mass of a newborn baby's brain has been found to increase by about 1.6 mg per minute. **(a)** How much does the brain's mass increase in one day? **(b)** How long does it take for the brain's mass to increase by 0.0075 kg?

49. •• **The Huygens Probe** NASA's Cassini mission to Saturn released a probe on December 25, 2004, that landed on the Saturnian moon Titan on January 14, 2005. The probe, which was named Huygens, was released with a gentle relative speed of 31 cm/s. As Huygens moved away from the main spacecraft, it rotated at a rate of seven revolutions per minute. **(a)** How many revolutions had Huygens completed when it was 150 yards from the mother ship? **(b)** How far did Huygens move away from the mother ship during each revolution? Give your answer in feet.

50. ••• Acceleration is related to velocity and time by the following expression: $a = v^p t^q$. Find the powers p and q that make this equation dimensionally consistent.

51. ••• The period T of a simple pendulum is the amount of time required for it to undergo one complete oscillation. If the length of the pendulum is L and the acceleration of gravity is g, then T is given by

$$T = 2\pi L^p g^q$$

Find the powers p and q required for dimensional consistency.

52. ••• Driving along a crowded freeway, you notice that it takes a time t to go from one mile marker to the next. When you increase your speed by 7.9 mi/h, the time to go one mile decreases by 13 s. What was your original speed?

PASSAGE PROBLEMS

BIO Using a Cricket as a Thermometer

All chemical reactions, whether organic or inorganic, proceed at a rate that depends on temperature—the higher the temperature, the higher the rate of reaction. This can be understood in terms of molecules moving with increased energy as the temperature is increased, and colliding with other molecules more frequently. In the case of organic reactions, the result is that metabolic processes speed up with increasing temperature.

An increased or decreased metabolic rate can manifest itself in a number of ways. For example, a cricket trying to attract a mate chirps at a rate that depends on its overall rate of metabolism. As a result, the chirping rate of crickets depends directly on temperature. In fact, some people even use a pet cricket as a thermometer.

The cricket that is most accurate as a thermometer is the snowy tree cricket (*Oecanthus fultoni* Walker). Its rate of chirping is described by the following formula:

$$N = \text{number of chirps per 13.0 seconds}$$
$$= T - 40.0$$

In this expression, T is the temperature in degrees Fahrenheit.

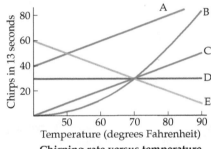

Chirping rate versus temperature

▲ **FIGURE 1–2** Problem 53

53. • Which plot in **Figure 1–2** represents the chirping rate of the snowy tree cricket?

A   B   C   D   E

54. • If the temperature is 43 degrees Fahrenheit, how long does it take for the cricket to chirp 12 times?

A. 12 s   **B.** 24 s   **C.** 43 s   **D.** 52 s

55. •• Your pet cricket chirps 112 times in one minute (60.0 s). What is the temperature in degrees Fahrenheit?

A. 41.9   **B.** 47.0   **C.** 64.3   **D.** 74.7

56. •• Suppose a snowy cricket is chirping when the temperature is 65.0 degrees Fahrenheit. How many oscillations does the radiation from a cesium-133 atom complete between successive chirps?

A. 7.98×10^7 **B.** 3.68×10^8

C. 4.78×10^9 **D.** 9.58×10^9

2 One-Dimensional Kinematics

These sprinters, crossing the finish line of the 100-m dash, illustrate one-dimensional motion. At the moment shown in the photograph the runners are moving with constant velocity at a speed of approximately 10 m/s.

We begin our study of physics with **mechanics,** the area of physics perhaps most apparent to us in our everyday lives. Every time you raise an arm, stand up or sit down, throw a ball, or open a door, your actions are governed by the laws of mechanics. Basically, mechanics is the study of how objects move, how they respond to external forces, and how other factors, such as size, mass, and mass distribution, affect their motion. This is a lot to cover, and we certainly won't try to tackle it all in one chapter.

Furthermore, in this chapter we treat all physical objects as *point particles;* that is, we consider all the mass of the object to be concentrated at a single point. This is a common practice in physics. For example, if you are interested in calculating the time it takes the Earth to complete a revolution about the Sun, it is reasonable to consider the Earth and the Sun as simple particles. In later chapters, we extend our studies to increasingly realistic situations, involving motion in more than one dimension and physical objects with shape and size.

2–1 Position, Distance, and Displacement

The first step in describing the motion of a particle is to set up a **coordinate system** that defines its position. An example of a coordinate system in one dimension is shown in **Figure 2–1**. This is simply an x axis, with an origin (where $x = 0$) and an arrow indicating the positive direction—the direction in which x increases. In setting up a coordinate system, we are free to choose the origin and the positive direction as we like, but once we make a choice we must be consistent with it throughout any calculations that follow.

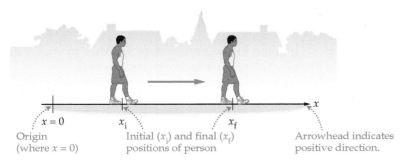

$x = 0$
Origin
(where $x = 0$)

x_i
Initial (x_i) and final (x_f)
positions of person

x_f

x
Arrowhead indicates
positive direction.

◀ **FIGURE 2–1 A one-dimensional coordinate system**

You are free to choose the origin and positive direction as you like, but once your choice is made, stick with it.

The particle in Figure 2–1 is a person who has moved to the right from an initial position, x_i, to a final position, x_f. Because the positive direction is to the right, it follows that x_f is greater than x_i; that is, $x_f > x_i$.

Now that we've seen how to set up a coordinate system, let's use one to investigate the situation sketched in **Figure 2–2**. Suppose that you leave your house, drive to the grocery store, and then return home. The **distance** you've covered in your trip is 8.6 mi. In general, distance is defined as follows:

Definition: Distance

distance = total length of travel

SI unit: meter, m

Using SI units, the distance in this case is

$$8.6 \text{ mi} = (8.6 \text{ mi})\left(\frac{1609 \text{ m}}{1 \text{ mi}}\right) = 1.4 \times 10^4 \text{ m}$$

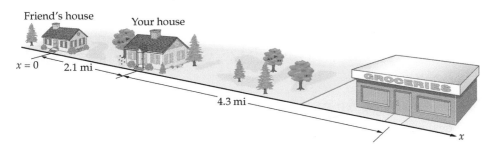

Friend's house

Your house

$x = 0$ 2.1 mi

4.3 mi

GROCERIES

x

◀ **FIGURE 2–2 One-dimensional coordinates**

The locations of your house, your friend's house, and the grocery store in terms of a one-dimensional coordinate system.

In a car, the distance traveled is indicated by the odometer. Note that distance is always positive and, because it has no direction associated with it, it is a scalar, as discussed in Chapter 1.

Another useful way to characterize a particle's motion is in terms of the **displacement**, Δx, which is simply the change in position.

Definition: Displacement, Δx

displacement = change in position = final position − initial position

displacement = $\Delta x = x_f - x_i$ 2–1

SI unit: meter, m

Notice that we use the delta notation, Δx, as a convenient shorthand for the quantity $x_f - x_i$. (See Appendix A for a complete discussion of delta notation.) Also, note that Δx can be positive (if the final position is to the right of the initial position, $x_f > x_i$), negative (if the final position is to the left of the initial position, $x_f < x_i$), or zero (if the final and initial positions are the same, $x_f = x_i$). In fact, the displacement is a one-dimensional vector, as defined in Chapter 1, and its direction (right or left) is given by its sign (positive or negative, respectively).

The SI units of displacement are meters—the same as for distance—but displacement and distance are really quite different. For example, in the round trip from your house to the grocery store and back the distance traveled is 8.6 mi, whereas the displacement is zero because $x_f = 2.1$ mi $= x_i$. Suppose, instead, that you go from your house to the grocery store and then to your friend's house. On this trip the distance is 10.7 mi, but the displacement is

$$\Delta x = x_f - x_i = (0) - (2.1 \text{ mi}) = -2.1 \text{ mi}$$

As mentioned in the previous paragraph, the minus sign means your displacement is in the negative direction, that is, to the left.

ACTIVE EXAMPLE 2–1   FIND THE DISTANCE AND DISPLACEMENT

Calculate **(a)** the distance and **(b)** the displacement for a trip from your friend's house to the grocery store and then to your house.

SOLUTION *(Test your understanding by performing the calculations indicated in each step.)*

Part (a)

1. Add the distances for the various parts of the total trip: $2.1 \text{ mi} + 4.3 \text{ mi} + 4.3 \text{ mi} = 10.7 \text{ mi}$

Part (b)

2. Determine the initial position for the trip, using Figure 2–2: $x_i = 0$
3. Determine the final position for the trip, using Figure 2–2: $x_f = 2.1 \text{ mi}$
4. Subtract x_i from x_f to find the displacement: $\Delta x = 2.1 \text{ mi}$

YOUR TURN

Suppose we choose the origin in Figure 2–2 to be at your house, rather than at your friend's house. In this case, find **(a)** the distance and **(b)** the displacement for the trip from your friend's house to the grocery store and then to your house. *(Answers to **Your Turn** problems are given in the back of the book.)*

2–2 Average Speed and Velocity

The next step in describing motion is to consider how rapidly an object moves. For example, how long does it take for a Randy Johnson fastball to reach home plate? How far does an orbiting space shuttle travel in one hour? How fast do your eyelids move when you blink? These are examples of some of the most basic questions regarding motion, and in this section we learn how to answer them.

The simplest way to characterize the rate of motion is with the **average speed:**

$$\text{average speed} = \frac{\text{distance}}{\text{elapsed time}} \qquad \text{2–2}$$

The dimensions of average speed are distance per time or, in SI units, meters per second, m/s. Both distance and elapsed time are positive; thus average speed is always positive.

EXAMPLE 2–1 THE KINGFISHER TAKES A PLUNGE

A kingfisher is a bird that catches fish by plunging into water from a height of several meters. If a kingfisher dives from a height of 7.0 m with an average speed of 4.00 m/s, how long does it take for it to reach the water?

PICTURE THE PROBLEM
As shown in the sketch, the kingfisher moves in a straight line through a vertical distance of 7.0 m. The average speed of the bird is 4.00 m/s.

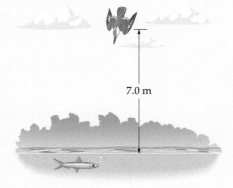

7.0 m

STRATEGY
By rearranging Equation 2–2 we can solve for the elapsed time.

SOLUTION

1. Rearrange Equation 2–2 to solve for elapsed time:

$$\text{elapsed time} = \frac{\text{distance}}{\text{average speed}}$$

2. Substitute numerical values to find the time:

$$\text{elapsed time} = \frac{7.0 \ \text{m}}{4.00 \ \text{m/s}} = \frac{7.0}{4.00} \text{s} = 1.8 \ \text{s}$$

INSIGHT
Note that Equation 2–2 is not just a formula for calculating the average speed. It relates speed, time, and distance. Given any two of these quantities, Equation 2–2 can be used to find the third.

PRACTICE PROBLEM
A kingfisher dives with an average speed of 4.6 m/s for 1.4 s. What was the height of the dive?
[**Answer:** distance = (average speed) (elapsed time) = (4.6 m/s) (1.4 s) = 6.4 m]

Some related homework problems: Problem 13, Problem 15

Next, we calculate the average speed for a trip consisting of two parts of equal length, each traveled with a different speed.

CONCEPTUAL CHECKPOINT 2–1 AVERAGE SPEED

You drive 4.00 mi at 30.0 mi/h and then another 4.00 mi at 50.0 mi/h. Is your average speed for the 8.00-mi trip **(a)** greater than 40.0 mi/h, **(b)** equal to 40.0 mi/h, or **(c)** less than 40.0 mi/h?

REASONING AND DISCUSSION
At first glance it might seem that the average speed is definitely 40.0 mi/h. On further reflection, however, it is clear that it takes more time to travel 4.00 mi at 30.0 mi/h than it does to travel 4.00 mi at 50.0 mi/h. Therefore, you will be traveling at the lower speed for a greater period of time, and hence your average speed will be *less* than 40.0 mi/h—that is, closer to 30.0 mi/h than to 50.0 mi/h.

ANSWER
(c) The average speed is less than 40.0 mi/h.

To confirm the conclusion of the Conceptual Checkpoint, we simply apply the definition of average speed to find its value for this trip. We already know that the distance traveled is 8.00 mi; what we need now is the elapsed time. On the first 4.00 mi the time is

$$t_1 = \frac{4.00 \text{ mi}}{30.0 \text{ mi/h}} = (4.00/30.0) \text{ h}$$

The time required to cover the second 4.00 mi is

$$t_2 = \frac{4.00 \text{ mi}}{50.0 \text{ mi/h}} = (4.00/50.0) \text{ h}$$

Therefore, the elapsed time for the entire trip is

$$t_1 + t_2 = (4.00/30.0) \text{ h} + (4.00/50.0) \text{ h} = 0.213 \text{ h}$$

This gives the following average speed:

$$\text{average speed} = \frac{8.00 \text{ mi}}{0.213 \text{ h}} = 37.6 \text{ mi/h} < 40.0 \text{ mi/h}$$

Note that a "guess" will never give a detailed result like 37.6 mi/h; a systematic, step-by-step calculation is required.

In many situations, there is a quantity that is even more useful than the average speed. It is the **average velocity,** v_{av}, and it is defined as displacement per time:

Definition: Average velocity, v_{av}

$$\text{average velocity} = \frac{\text{displacement}}{\text{elapsed time}}$$

$$v_{av} = \frac{\Delta x}{\Delta t} = \frac{x_f - x_i}{t_f - t_i} \qquad \qquad 2\text{--}3$$

SI unit: meter per second, m/s

Not only does the average velocity tell us, on average, how fast something is moving, it also tells us the *direction* the object is moving. For example, if an object moves in the positive direction, then $x_f > x_i$, and $v_{av} > 0$. On the other hand, if an object moves in the negative direction, it follows that $x_f < x_i$, and $v_{av} < 0$. As with displacement, the average velocity is a one-dimensional vector, and its direction is given by its sign. Average velocity gives more information than average speed; hence it is used more frequently in physics.

In the next Example, pay close attention to the positive and negative signs.

EXAMPLE 2–2   SPRINT TRAINING

An athlete sprints 50.0 m in 8.00 s, stops, and then walks slowly back to the starting line in 40.0 s. If the "sprint direction" is taken to be positive, what are **(a)** the average sprint velocity, **(b)** the average walking velocity, and **(c)** the average velocity for the complete round trip?

PICTURE THE PROBLEM

In our sketch we set up a coordinate system with the sprint going in the positive x direction, as described in the problem. For convenience, we choose the origin to be at the starting line. The finish line, then, is at $x = 50.0$ m.

STRATEGY

In each part of the problem we are asked for the average velocity and we are given information for times and distances. All that is needed, then, is to determine $\Delta x = x_f - x_i$ and $\Delta t = t_f - t_i$ in each case and apply Equation 2–3.

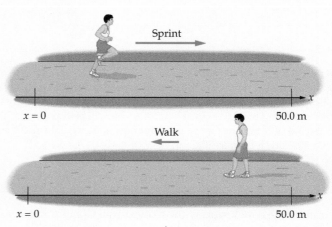

SOLUTION

Part (a)

1. Apply Equation 2–3 to the sprint, with $x_f = 50.0$ m, $x_i = 0$, $t_f = 8.00$ s, and $t_i = 0$:

$$v_{av} = \frac{\Delta x}{\Delta t} = \frac{x_f - x_i}{t_f - t_i} = \frac{50.0 \text{ m} - 0}{8.00 \text{ s} - 0} = \frac{50.0}{8.00} \text{ m/s} = 6.25 \text{ m/s}$$

Part (b)

2. Apply Equation 2–3 to the walk. In this case, $x_f = 0$, $x_i = 50.0$ m, $t_f = 48.0$ s, and $t_i = 8.00$ s:

$$v_{av} = \frac{x_f - x_i}{t_f - t_i} = \frac{0 - 50.0 \text{ m}}{48.0 \text{ s} - 8.00 \text{ s}} = -\frac{50.0}{40.0} \text{ m/s} = -1.25 \text{ m/s}$$

Part (c)

3. For the round trip, $x_f = x_i = 0$; thus $\Delta x = 0$:

$$v_{av} = \frac{\Delta x}{\Delta t} = \frac{0}{48.0 \text{ s}} = 0$$

INSIGHT

Note that the sign of the velocities in parts (a) and (b) indicates the direction of motion; positive for motion to the right, negative for motion to the left. Also, notice that the average *speed* for the entire 100.0-m trip (100.0 m/48.0 s = 2.08 m/s) is nonzero, even though the average velocity vanishes.

PRACTICE PROBLEM

If the average velocity during the walk is −1.50 m/s, how long does it take the athlete to walk back to the starting line?
[**Answer:** $\Delta t = \Delta x/v_{av} = (-50.0 \text{ m})/(-1.50 \text{ m/s}) = 33.3$ s]

Some related homework problems: Problem 9, Problem 17, Problem 18

Graphical Interpretation of Average Velocity

It is often useful to "visualize" a particle's motion by sketching its position as a function of time. For example, consider a particle moving back and forth along the x axis, as shown in **Figure 2–3 (a)**. In this plot, we have indicated the position of a particle at a variety of times.

This way of keeping track of a particle's position and the corresponding time is a bit messy, though, so let's replot the same information with a different type of graph. In **Figure 2–3 (b)** we again plot the motion shown in Figure 2–3 (a), but this time with the vertical axis representing the position, x, and the horizontal axis representing time, t. An **x-versus-t graph** like this makes it considerably easier to visualize a particle's motion.

An x-versus-t plot also leads to a particularly useful interpretation of average velocity. To see how, suppose you would like to know the average velocity of the particle in Figures 2–3 (a) and 2–3 (b) from $t = 0$ to $t = 3$ s. From our definition of average velocity in Equation 2–3, we know that $v_{av} = \Delta x/\Delta t = (2 \text{ m} - 1 \text{ m})/(3 \text{ s} - 0) = +0.3$ m/s. To relate this to the

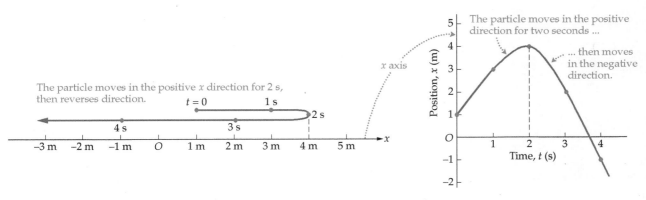

(a) The particle's path shown on a coordinate axis

The particle moves in the positive x direction for 2 s, then reverses direction.

(b) The same path as a graph of position x versus time t

▲ **FIGURE 2–3 Two ways to visualize one-dimensional motion**
Although the path in (a) is shown as a "U" for clarity, the particle actually moves straight back and forth along the x axis.

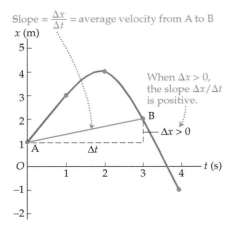

Slope $= \dfrac{\Delta x}{\Delta t}$ = average velocity from A to B

When $\Delta x > 0$, the slope $\Delta x / \Delta t$ is positive.

(a) Average velocity between $t = 0$ and $t = 3$ s

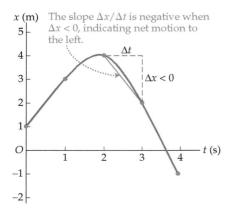

The slope $\Delta x / \Delta t$ is negative when $\Delta x < 0$, indicating net motion to the left.

(b) Average velocity between $t = 2$ s and $t = 3$ s

▲ **FIGURE 2–4 Average velocity on an x-versus-t graph**
The slope of a straight line between any two points on an x-versus-t graph equals the average velocity between those points. Positive slopes indicate net motion to the right; negative slopes indicate net motion to the left.

▲ A speedometer indicates the instantaneous speed of a car. Note that the speedometer gives no information about the *direction* of motion. Thus, the speedometer is truly a "speed meter," not a velocity meter.

x-versus-t plot, draw a straight line connecting the position at $t = 0$ (call this point A) and the position at $t = 3$ s (point B). The result is shown in **Figure 2–4 (a)**.

The slope of the straight line from A to B is equal to the rise over the run, which in this case is $\Delta x / \Delta t$. But $\Delta x / \Delta t$ is the average velocity. Thus we see that:

- The slope of a line connecting two points on an x-versus-t plot is equal to the average velocity during that time interval.

As an additional example, let's calculate the average velocity between times $t = 2$ s and $t = 3$ s in Figure 2–3 (b). A line connecting the corresponding points is shown in **Figure 2–4 (b)**.

The first thing we notice about this line is that it has a negative slope; thus $v_{av} < 0$ and the particle is moving to the left. We also note that it is inclined more steeply than the line in Figure 2–4 (a), hence the magnitude of its slope is greater. In fact, if we calculate the slope of this line we find that $v_{av} = -2$ m/s for this time interval.

Thus, connecting points on an x-versus-t plot gives an immediate "feeling" for the average velocity over a given time interval. This type of graphical analysis will be particularly useful in the next section.

2–3 Instantaneous Velocity

Though average velocity is a useful way to characterize motion, it can miss a lot. For example, suppose you travel by car on a long, straight highway, covering 92 mi in 2.0 hours. Your average velocity is 46 mi/h. Even so, there may have been only a few times during the trip when you were actually driving at 46 mi/h. You may have sped along at 65 mi/h during most of the time, except when you stopped to have a bite to eat at a roadside diner, during which time your average velocity was zero.

To have a more accurate representation of your trip, you should average your velocity over shorter periods of time. If you calculate your average velocity every 15 minutes, you have a better picture of what the trip was like. An even better, more realistic picture of the trip is obtained if you calculate the average velocity every minute or every second. Ideally, when dealing with the motion of any particle, it is desirable to know the velocity of the particle at each instant of time.

This idea of a velocity corresponding to an instant of time is just what is meant by the **instantaneous velocity.** Mathematically, we define the instantaneous velocity as follows:

Definition: Instantaneous Velocity, v

$$v = \lim_{\Delta t \to 0} \frac{\Delta x}{\Delta t} \qquad 2\text{–}4$$

SI unit: meter per second, m/s

In this expression the notation $\lim_{\Delta t \to 0}$ means "evaluate the average velocity, $\Delta x / \Delta t$, over shorter and shorter time intervals, approaching zero in the limit." Note that the instantaneous velocity can be positive, negative, or zero, just like the average velocity—and just like the average velocity, the instantaneous velocity is a one-dimensional vector. The magnitude of the instantaneous velocity is called the **instantaneous speed.** In a car, the speedometer gives a reading of the vehicle's instantaneous speed.

As Δt becomes smaller, Δx becomes smaller as well, but the ratio $\Delta x / \Delta t$ approaches a constant value. To see how this works, consider first the simple case of a particle moving with a constant velocity of $+1$ m/s. If the particle starts at $x = 0$ at $t = 0$, then its position at $t = 1$ s is $x = 1$ m, its position at $t = 2$ s is $x = 2$ m, and so on. Plotting this motion in an x-versus-t plot gives a straight line, as shown in **Figure 2–5**.

Now, suppose we want to find the instantaneous velocity at $t = 3$ s. To do so, we calculate the average velocity over small intervals of time centered at 3 s, and let the time intervals become arbitrarily small, as shown in the Figure. Since x-versus-t is a straight line, it is clear that $\Delta x / \Delta t = \Delta x_1 / \Delta t_1$, no matter how small the time interval Δt. As Δt becomes smaller, so does Δx, but the ratio $\Delta x/\Delta t$ is simply the slope of the line, 1 m/s. Thus, the instantaneous velocity at $t = 3$ s is 1 m/s.

Of course, in this example the instantaneous velocity is 1 m/s for any instant of time, not just $t = 3$ s. Therefore:

- When velocity is constant, the average velocity over any time interval is equal to the instantaneous velocity at any time.

In general, a particle's velocity varies with time, and the x-versus-t plot is not a straight line. An example is shown in **Figure 2–6**, with the corresponding numerical values of x and t given in Table 2–1.

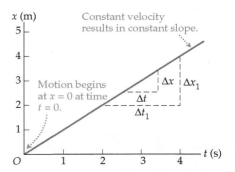

▲ **FIGURE 2–5 Constant velocity corresponds to constant slope on an x-versus-t graph**
The slope $\Delta x_1/\Delta t_1$ is equal to $(4\,\text{m} - 2\,\text{m})/(4\,\text{s} - 2\,\text{s}) = (2\,\text{m})/(2\,\text{s}) = 1\,\text{m/s}$. Because x-versus-t is a straight line, the slope $\Delta x/\Delta t$ is also equal to 1 m/s for any value of Δt.

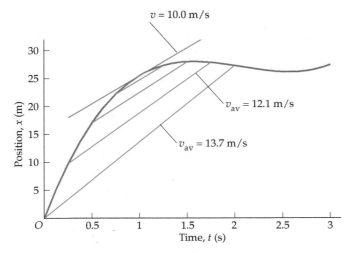

▲ **FIGURE 2–6 Instantaneous velocity**
An x-versus-t plot for motion with variable velocity. The instantaneous velocity at $t = 1$ s is equal to the slope of the tangent line at that time. The average velocity for a small time interval centered on $t = 1$ s approaches the instantaneous velocity at $t = 1$ s as the time interval goes to zero.

In this case, what is the instantaneous velocity at, say, $t = 1.00$ s? As a first approximation, let's calculate the average velocity for the time interval from $t_i = 0$ to $t_f = 2.00$ s. Note that this time interval is centered at $t = 1.00$ s. From Table 2–1 we see that $x_i = 0$ and $x_f = 27.4$ m, thus $v_{av} = 13.7$ m/s. The corresponding straight line connecting these two points is the lowest straight line in Figure 2–6.

The next three lines, in upward progression, refer to time intervals from 0.250 s to 1.75 s, 0.500 s to 1.50 s, and 0.750 s to 1.25 s, respectively. The corresponding average velocities, given in Table 2–2, are 12.1 m/s, 10.9 m/s, and 10.2 m/s. Table 2–2 also gives results for even smaller time intervals. In particular, for the interval from 0.900 s to 1.10 s the average velocity is 10.0 m/s. Smaller intervals also give 10.0 m/s. Thus, we can conclude that the instantaneous velocity at $t = 1.00$ s is $v = 10.0$ m/s.

The uppermost straight line in Figure 2–6 is the tangent line to the x-versus-t curve at the time $t = 1.00$ s; that is, it is the line that touches the curve at just a single point. Its slope is 10.0 m/s. Clearly, the average-velocity lines have slopes that

TABLE 2–1
x-versus-t Values for Figure 2–6

t (s)	x (m)
0	0
0.25	9.85
0.50	17.2
0.75	22.3
1.00	25.6
1.25	27.4
1.50	28.1
1.75	28.0
2.00	27.4

TABLE 2–2 Calculating the Instantaneous Velocity at $t = 1$ s

t_i (s)	t_f (s)	Δt (s)	x_i (m)	x_f (m)	Δx (m)	$v_{av} = \Delta x/\Delta t$ (m/s)
0	2.00	2.00	0	27.4	27.4	13.7
0.250	1.75	1.50	9.85	28.0	18.2	12.1
0.500	1.50	1.00	17.2	28.1	10.9	10.9
0.750	1.25	0.50	22.3	27.4	5.10	10.2
0.900	1.10	0.20	24.5	26.5	2.00	10.0
0.950	1.05	0.10	25.1	26.1	1.00	10.0

approach the slope of the tangent line as the time intervals become smaller. This is an example of the following general result:

- The instantaneous velocity at a given time is equal to the slope of the tangent line at that point on an *x*-versus-*t* graph.

Thus, a visual inspection of an *x*-versus-*t* graph gives information not only about the location of a particle, but also about its velocity.

CONCEPTUAL CHECKPOINT 2–2   INSTANTANEOUS VELOCITY

Referring to Figure 2–6, is the instantaneous velocity at *t* = 0.500 s **(a)** greater than, **(b)** less than, or **(c)** the same as the instantaneous velocity at *t* = 1.00 s?

REASONING AND DISCUSSION
From the *x*-versus-*t* graph in Figure 2–6 it is clear that the slope of a tangent line drawn at *t* = 0.500 s is greater than the slope of the tangent line at *t* = 1.00 s. It follows that the particle's velocity at 0.500 s is greater than its velocity at 1.00 s.

ANSWER
(a) The instantaneous velocity is greater at *t* = 0.500 s.

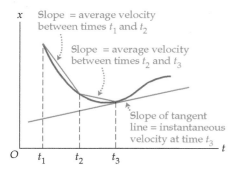

▲ **FIGURE 2–7 Graphical interpretation of average and instantaneous velocity**
Average velocities correspond to the slope of straight-line segments connecting different points on an *x*-versus-*t* graph. Instantaneous velocities are given by the slope of the tangent line at a given time.

▲ The space shuttle *Discovery* accelerates upward on the initial phase of its journey into orbit. During this time the astronauts on board the shuttle experience an approximately linear acceleration that may be as great as 20 m/s².

In the remainder of the book, when we say velocity it is to be understood that we mean *instantaneous* velocity. If we want to refer to the average velocity, we will specifically say average velocity.

Graphical Interpretation of Average and Instantaneous Velocity

Let's summarize the graphical interpretations of average and instantaneous velocity on an *x*-versus-*t* graph:

- Average velocity is the slope of the straight line connecting two points corresponding to a given time interval.
- Instantaneous velocity is the slope of the tangent line at a given instant of time.

These relations are illustrated in **Figure 2–7**.

2–4 Acceleration

Just as velocity is the rate of change of *displacement* with time, **acceleration** is the rate of change of *velocity* with time. Thus, an object accelerates whenever its velocity *changes*, no matter what the change—it accelerates when its velocity increases, it accelerates when its velocity decreases. Of all the concepts discussed in this chapter, perhaps none is more central to physics than acceleration. Galileo, for example, showed that falling bodies move with constant acceleration. Newton showed that acceleration and force are directly related, as we shall see in Chapter 5. Thus, it is particularly important to have a clear, complete understanding of acceleration before leaving this chapter.

We begin, then, with the definition of **average acceleration:**

Definition: Average Acceleration, a_{av}

$$a_{av} = \frac{\Delta v}{\Delta t} = \frac{v_f - v_i}{t_f - t_i}$$

2–5

SI unit: meter per second per second, m/s²

Note that the dimensions of average acceleration are the dimensions of velocity per time, or (meters per second) per second:

$$\frac{\text{meters per second}}{\text{second}} = \frac{\text{m/s}}{\text{s}} = \frac{\text{m}}{\text{s}^2}$$

This is generally expressed as meters per second squared. For example, the acceleration of gravity on the Earth's surface is approximately 9.81 m/s², which means that the velocity of a falling object changes by 9.81 meters per second (m/s) every second (s). In addition, we see that the average acceleration can be positive, negative, or zero. In fact, it is a one-dimensional vector, just like displacement, average velocity, and instantaneous velocity. Typical magnitudes of acceleration are given in Table 2–3.

EXERCISE 2–1

a. Saab advertises a car that goes from 0 to 60.0 mi/h in 6.2 s. What is the average acceleration of this car?

b. An airplane has an average acceleration of 5.6 m/s² during takeoff. How long does it take for the plane to reach a speed of 150 mi/h?

SOLUTION

a. average acceleration $= a_{av} = (60.0\ \text{mi/h})/(6.2\ \text{s})$

$$= (26.8\ \text{m/s})/(6.2\ \text{s}) = 4.3\ \text{m/s}^2$$

b. $\Delta t = \Delta v/a_{av} = (150\ \text{mi/h})/(5.6\ \text{m/s}^2) = (67.0\ \text{m/s})/(5.6\ \text{m/s}^2) = 12\ \text{s}$

TABLE 2–3 Typical Accelerations (m/s²)

Ultracentrifuge	3×10^6
Bullet fired from a rifle	4.4×10^5
Batted baseball	3×10^4
Click beetle righting itself	400
Acceleration required to deploy airbags	60
Bungee jump	30
High jump	15
Acceleration of gravity on Earth	9.81
Emergency stop in a car	8
Airplane during takeoff	5
An elevator	3
Acceleration of gravity on the Moon	1.62

Next, just as we considered the limit of smaller and smaller time intervals to find an instantaneous velocity, we can do the same to define an **instantaneous acceleration:**

Definition: Instantaneous Acceleration, *a*

$$a = \lim_{\Delta t \to 0} \frac{\Delta v}{\Delta t} \qquad\qquad 2\text{–}6$$

SI unit: meter per second per second, m/s²

As you might expect, the instantaneous acceleration is a one-dimensional vector, just like the average acceleration, and its direction is given by its sign. For simplicity, when we say acceleration in the future we are referring to the instantaneous acceleration.

One final note before we go on to some examples. If the acceleration is constant, it has the same value at all times. Therefore:

- When acceleration is constant, the instantaneous and average accelerations are the same.

We shall make use of this fact when we return to the special case of constant acceleration in the next section.

Graphical Interpretation of Acceleration

To see how acceleration can be interpreted graphically, suppose that a particle has a constant acceleration of −0.50 m/s². This means that the velocity of the particle *decreases* by 0.50 m/s each second. Thus, if its velocity is 1.0 m/s at *t* = 0, then at *t* = 1 s its velocity is 0.50 m/s, at *t* = 2 s its velocity is 0, at *t* = 3 s its velocity is −0.50 m/s, and so on. This is illustrated by curve I in **Figure 2–8**, where we see that a plot of *v*-versus-*t* results in a straight line with a negative slope. Curve II in Figure 2–8 has a positive slope, corresponding to a constant acceleration of +0.25 m/s². Thus, in terms of a *v*-versus-*t* plot, a constant acceleration results in a straight line with a slope equal to the acceleration.

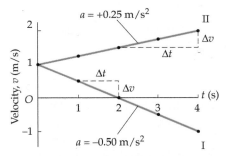

▲ **FIGURE 2–8** *v-versus-t* plots for motion with constant acceleration

Curve I represents the movement of a particle with constant acceleration $a = -0.50$ m/s². Curve II represents the motion of a particle with constant acceleration $a = +0.25$ m/s².

CONCEPTUAL CHECKPOINT 2–3 SPEED AS A FUNCTION OF TIME

The speed of a particle with the *v*-versus-*t* graph shown by curve II in Figure 2–8 increases steadily with time. Consider, instead, a particle whose *v*-versus-*t* graph is given by curve I in Figure 2–8. As a function of time, does the speed of this particle **(a)** increase, **(b)** decrease, or **(c)** decrease and then increase?

REASONING AND DISCUSSION

Recall that speed is the *magnitude* of velocity. In curve I of Figure 2–8 the speed starts out at 1.0 m/s, then *decreases* to 0 at *t* = 2 s. After *t* = 2 s the speed *increases* again. For example, at *t* = 3 s the speed is 0.50 m/s, and at *t* = 4 s the speed is 1 m/s.

CONTINUED ON NEXT PAGE

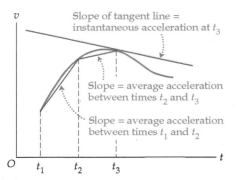

▲ FIGURE 2–9 Graphical interpretation of average and instantaneous acceleration
Average accelerations correspond to the slope of straight-line segments connecting different points on a *v*-versus-*t* graph. Instantaneous accelerations are given by the slope of the tangent line at a given time.

CONTINUED FROM PREVIOUS PAGE

Did you realize that the particle represented by curve I in Figure 2–8 changes direction at $t = 2\,\text{s}$? It certainly does. Before $t = 2\,\text{s}$ the particle moves in the positive direction; after $t = 2\,\text{s}$ it moves in the negative direction. At precisely $t = 2\,\text{s}$ the particle is momentarily at rest. However, regardless of whether the particle is moving in the positive direction, moving in the negative direction, or instantaneously at rest, it still has the same constant acceleration. Acceleration has to do only with the way the velocity is *changing* at a given moment.

ANSWER
(c) The speed decreases and then increases.

The graphical interpretations for velocity presented in Figure 2–7 apply equally well to acceleration, with just one small change: Instead of an *x*-versus-*t* graph, we use a *v*-versus-*t* graph, as in **Figure 2–9**. Thus, the average acceleration in a *v*-versus-*t* plot is the slope of a straight line connecting points corresponding to two different times. Similarly, the instantaneous acceleration is the slope of the tangent line at a particular time.

EXAMPLE 2–3   AN ACCELERATING TRAIN

A train moving in a straight line with an initial velocity of 0.50 m/s accelerates at 2.0 m/s^2 for 2.0 seconds, coasts with zero acceleration for 3.0 seconds, and then accelerates at −1.5 m/s^2 for 1.0 second. **(a)** What is the final velocity of the train? **(b)** What is the average acceleration of the train?

PICTURE THE PROBLEM
We begin by sketching a *v*-versus-*t* plot for the train. The basic idea is that each interval of constant acceleration is represented by a straight line of the appropriate slope. Therefore, we draw a straight line with the slope 2.0 m/s^2 from $t = 0$ to $t = 2.0\,\text{s}$, a line with zero slope from $t = 2.0\,\text{s}$ to $t = 5.0\,\text{s}$, and a line with the slope −1.5 m/s^2 from $t = 5.0\,\text{s}$ to $t = 6.0\,\text{s}$. The line connecting the initial and final points determines the average acceleration.

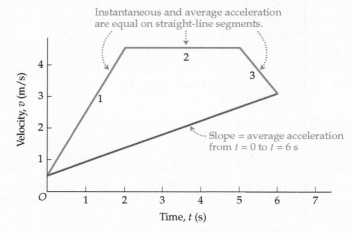

STRATEGY
During each period of constant acceleration the change in velocity is $\Delta v = a_{av}\Delta t = a\Delta t$.

a. Adding the individual changes in velocity gives the total change, $\Delta v = v_f - v_i$. Since v_i is known, this expression can be solved for the final velocity, v_f.

b. The average acceleration can be calculated using Equation 2–5, $a_{av} = \Delta v/\Delta t$. Note that Δv has been obtained in part (a), and that the total time interval is $\Delta t = 6.0\,\text{s}$, as is clear from the graph.

SOLUTION

Part (a)

1. Find the change in velocity during each of the three periods of constant acceleration:

$$\Delta v_1 = a_1\Delta t_1 = (2.0\,\text{m/s}^2)(2.0\,\text{s}) = 4.0\,\text{m/s}$$
$$\Delta v_2 = a_2\Delta t_2 = (0)(3.0\,\text{s}) = 0$$
$$\Delta v_3 = a_3\Delta t_3 = (-1.5\,\text{m/s}^2)(1.0\,\text{s}) = -1.5\,\text{m/s}$$

2. Sum the change in velocity for each period to obtain the total Δv:

$$\Delta v = \Delta v_1 + \Delta v_2 + \Delta v_3$$
$$= 4.0\,\text{m/s} + 0 - 1.5\,\text{m/s} = 2.5\,\text{m/s}$$

3. Use Δv to find v_f, recalling that $v_i = 0.50\,\text{m/s}$:

$$\Delta v = v_f - v_i$$
$$v_f = \Delta v + v_i = 2.5\,\text{m/s} + 0.50\,\text{m/s} = 3.0\,\text{m/s}$$

Part (b)

4. The average acceleration is $\Delta v / \Delta t$:

$$a_{av} = \frac{\Delta v}{\Delta t} = \frac{2.5 \text{ m/s}}{6.0 \text{ s}} = 0.42 \text{ m/s}^2$$

INSIGHT

Note that the average acceleration for these six seconds is not simply the average of the individual accelerations, 2.0 m/s^2, 0 m/s^2, and -1.5 m/s^2. The reason is that different amounts of time are spent with each acceleration. In addition, the average acceleration can be found graphically, as indicated in the v-versus-t sketch on the previous page. Specifically, the graph shows that Δv is 2.5 m/s for the time interval from $t = 0$ to $t = 6.0 \text{ s}$.

PRACTICE PROBLEM

What is the average acceleration of the train between $t = 2.0 \text{ s}$ and $t = 6.0 \text{ s}$?
[**Answer:** $a_{av} = \Delta v / \Delta t = (3.0 \text{ m/s} - 4.5 \text{ m/s}) / (6.0 \text{ s} - 2.0 \text{ s}) = -0.38 \text{ m/s}^2$]

Some related homework problems: Problem 36, Problem 38

In one dimension, nonzero velocities and accelerations are either positive or negative, depending on whether they point in the positive or negative direction of the coordinate system chosen. Thus, the velocity and acceleration of an object may have the same or opposite signs. (Of course, in two or three dimensions the relationship between velocity and acceleration can be much more varied, as we shall see in the next several chapters.) This leads to the following two possibilities:

- When the velocity and acceleration of an object have the same sign, the speed of the object increases. In this case, the velocity and acceleration point in the same direction.
- When the velocity and acceleration of an object have opposite signs, the speed of the object decreases. In this case, the velocity and acceleration point in opposite directions.

These two possibilities are illustrated in **Figure 2–10**. Notice that when a particle's speed increases, it means either that its velocity becomes more positive, as in **Figure 2–10 (a)**, or more negative, as in **Figure 2–10 (d)**. In either case, it is the magnitude of the velocity—the speed—that increases.

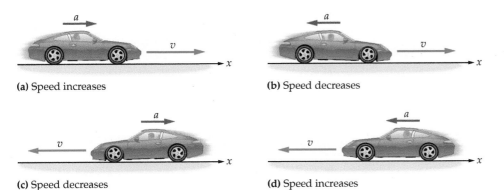

(a) Speed increases

(b) Speed decreases

(c) Speed decreases

(d) Speed increases

◀ **FIGURE 2–10 Cars accelerating or decelerating**
A car's speed increases when its velocity and acceleration point in the same direction, as in cases **(a)** and **(d)**. When the velocity and acceleration point in opposite directions, as in cases **(b)** and **(c)**, the car's speed decreases.

◀ The winner of this race was traveling at a speed of 313.91 mi/h at the end of the quarter-mile course. Since the winning time was just 4.607 s, the *average* acceleration during this race was approximately three times the acceleration of gravity (Section 2–7).

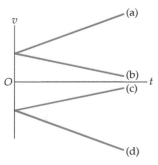

▲ **FIGURE 2–11** *v-versus-t* **plots with constant acceleration**

Four plots of v versus t corresponding to the four situations shown in Figure 2–10. Note that the speed increases in cases **(a)** and **(d)**, but decreases in cases **(b)** and **(c)**.

When a particle's speed decreases, it is often said to be *decelerating*. A common misconception is that deceleration implies a negative acceleration. This is not true. Deceleration can be caused by a positive or a negative acceleration, depending on the direction of the initial velocity. For example, the car in **Figure 2–10 (b)** has a positive velocity and a negative acceleration, while the car in **Figure 2–10 (c)** has a negative velocity and a positive acceleration. In both cases, the speed of the car decreases. Again, all that is required for deceleration in one dimension is that the velocity and acceleration have *opposite signs*; that is, they must point in *opposite directions*, as in parts (b) and (c) of Figure 2–10.

Velocity-versus-time plots for the four situations shown in Figure 2–10 are presented in **Figure 2–11**. In each of the four plots in Figure 2–11 we assume constant acceleration. Be sure to understand clearly the connection between the *v*-versus-*t* plots in Figure 2–11 and the corresponding physical motions indicated in Figure 2–10.

EXAMPLE 2–4   THE FERRY DOCKS

A ferry makes a short run between two docks; one in Anacortes, Washington, the other on Guemes Island. As the ferry approaches Guemes Island (traveling in the positive x direction), its speed is 7.4 m/s. **(a)** If the ferry slows to a stop in 12.3 s, what is its average acceleration? **(b)** As the ferry returns to the Anacortes dock, its speed is 7.3 m/s. If it comes to rest in 13.1 s, what is its average acceleration?

PICTURE THE PROBLEM
Our sketch shows the locations of the two docks and the positive direction indicated in the problem. Note that the distance between docks is not given, nor is it needed.

STRATEGY
We are given the initial and final velocities (the ferry comes to a stop in each case, so its final speed is zero) and the relevant times. Therefore, we can find the average acceleration using $a_{av} = \Delta v / \Delta t$, being careful to get the signs right.

SOLUTION

Part (a)

1. Calculate the average acceleration, noting that $v_i = 7.4$ m/s and $v_f = 0$:

$$a_{av} = \frac{\Delta v}{\Delta t} = \frac{v_f - v_i}{\Delta t} = \frac{0 - 7.4 \text{ m/s}}{12.3 \text{ s}} = -0.60 \text{ m/s}^2$$

Part (b)

2. In this case, $v_i = -7.3$ m/s and $v_f = 0$:

$$a_{av} = \frac{\Delta v}{\Delta t} = \frac{v_f - v_i}{\Delta t} = \frac{0 - (-7.3 \text{ m/s})}{13.1 \text{ s}} = 0.56 \text{ m/s}^2$$

INSIGHT
In each case, the acceleration of the ferry is opposite in sign to its velocity; therefore the ferry decelerates.

PRACTICE PROBLEM
When the ferry leaves Guemes Island, its speed increases from 0 to 5.8 m/s in 9.25 s. What is its average acceleration?
[**Answer:** $a_{av} = -0.63$ m/s^2]

Some related homework problems: Problem 34, Problem 35

2–5 Motion with Constant Acceleration

In this section, we derive equations describing the motion of particles moving with **constant acceleration.** These "equations of motion" can be used to describe a wide range of everyday phenomena. For example, in an idealized world with no air resistance, falling bodies have constant acceleration.

As mentioned in the previous section, if a particle has constant acceleration— that is, the same acceleration at every instant of time—then its instantaneous acceleration, a, is equal to its average acceleration, a_{av}. Recalling the definition of average acceleration, Equation 2–5, we have

$$a_{av} = \frac{v_f - v_i}{t_f - t_i} = a$$

where the initial and final times may be chosen arbitrarily. For example, let $t_i = 0$ for the initial time, and let $v_i = v_0$ denote the velocity at time zero. For the final time and velocity we drop the subscripts to simplify notation; thus we let $t_f = t$ and $v_f = v$. With these identifications we have

$$a_{av} = \frac{v - v_0}{t - 0} = a$$

Therefore,

$$v - v_0 = a(t - 0) = at$$

or

Constant-Acceleration Equation of Motion: Velocity as a Function of Time

$v = v_0 + at$ 2–7

Note that Equation 2–7 describes a straight line on a v-versus-t plot. The line crosses the velocity axis at the value v_0 and has a slope a, in agreement with the graphical interpretations discussed in the previous section. For example, in curve I of Figure 2–8, the equation of motion is $v = v_0 + at = (1 \text{ m/s}) + (-0.5 \text{ m/s}^2)t$. Also, note that $(-0.5 \text{ m/s}^2)t$ has the units $(\text{m/s}^2)(\text{s}) = \text{m/s}$; thus each term in Equation 2–7 has the same dimensions (as it must to be a valid physical equation).

EXERCISE 2–2

A ball is thrown straight upward with an initial velocity of $+8.2$ m/s. If the acceleration of the ball is -9.81 m/s^2, what is its velocity after

    a. 0.50 s, and   **b.** 1.0 s?

SOLUTION

   a. Substituting $t = 0.50$ s in Equation 2–7 yields
$$v = 8.2 \text{ m/s} + (-9.81 \text{ m/s}^2)(0.50 \text{ s}) = 3.3 \text{ m/s}$$
   b. Similarly, using $t = 1.0$ s in Equation 2–7 gives
$$v = 8.2 \text{ m/s} + (-9.81 \text{ m/s}^2)(1.0 \text{ s}) = -1.6 \text{ m/s}$$

Next, how far does a particle move in a given time if its acceleration is constant? To answer this question, recall the definition of average velocity:

$$v_{av} = \frac{\Delta x}{\Delta t} = \frac{x_f - x_i}{t_f - t_i}$$

Using the same identifications given previously for initial and final times, and letting $x_i = x_0$ and $x_f = x$, we have

$$v_{av} = \frac{x - x_0}{t - 0}$$

Thus,

$$x - x_0 = v_{av}(t - 0) = v_{av}t$$

or

$$x = x_0 + v_{av}t$$ 2–8

Now, Equation 2–8 is fine as it is. In fact, it applies whether the acceleration is constant or not. A more useful expression, for the case of constant acceleration, is obtained by writing v_{av} in terms of the initial and final velocities. This can be done by referring to **Figure 2–12 (a)**. Here the velocity changes linearly (since a is

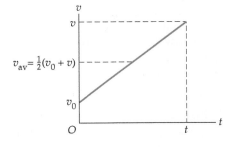

(a)

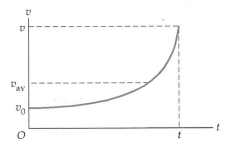

(b)

▲ **FIGURE 2–12 The average velocity**
(a) When acceleration is constant, the velocity varies linearly with time. As a result, the average velocity, v_{av}, is simply the average of the initial velocity, v_0, and the final velocity, v. **(b)** The velocity curve for nonconstant acceleration is nonlinear. In this case, the average velocity is no longer midway between the initial and final velocities.

constant) from v_0 at $t = 0$ to v at some later time t. The average velocity during this period of time is simply the average of the initial and final velocities; that is, the sum of the two velocities divided by two:

Constant-Acceleration Equation of Motion: Average Velocity

$$v_{av} = \tfrac{1}{2}(v_0 + v) \qquad\qquad 2\text{–}9$$

The average velocity is indicated in the figure. Note that if the acceleration is not constant, as in **Figure 2–12 (b)**, this simple averaging of initial and final velocities is no longer valid.

Substituting the expression for v_{av} from Equation 2–9 into Equation 2–8 yields

Constant-Acceleration Equation of Motion: Position as a Function of Time

$$x = x_0 + \tfrac{1}{2}(v_0 + v)t \qquad\qquad 2\text{–}10$$

This equation, like Equation 2–7, is valid *only* for constant acceleration. The utility of Equations 2–7 and 2–10 is illustrated in the next Example.

PROBLEM-SOLVING NOTE

"Coordinate" the Problem

The first step in solving a physics problem is to produce a simple sketch of the system. Your sketch should include a coordinate system, along with an origin and a positive direction. Next, you should identify quantities that are given in the problem, such as initial position, initial velocity, acceleration, and so on. These preliminaries will help in producing a mathematical representation of the problem.

EXAMPLE 2–5 FULL SPEED AHEAD

A boat moves slowly inside a marina (so as not to leave a wake) with a constant speed of 1.50 m/s. As soon as it passes the breakwater, leaving the marina, it throttles up and accelerates at 2.40 m/s². **(a)** How fast is the boat moving after accelerating for 5.00 s? **(b)** How far has the boat traveled in this time?

PICTURE THE PROBLEM
In our sketch we choose the origin to be at the breakwater, and the positive x direction to be the direction of motion. With this choice the initial position is $x_0 = 0$, and the initial velocity is $v_0 = 1.50$ m/s.

STRATEGY
The acceleration is constant, so we can use Equations 2–7 to 2–10. In part (a) we want to relate velocity to time, so we use Equation 2–7, $v = v_0 + at$. In part (b) our knowledge of the initial and final velocities allows us to relate position to time using Equation 2–10, $x = x_0 + \tfrac{1}{2}(v_0 + v)t$.

SOLUTION

Part (a)
1. Use Equation 2–7 with $v_0 = 1.50$ m/s and $a = 2.40$ m/s²:

$$v = v_0 + at = 1.50 \text{ m/s} + (2.40 \text{ m/s}^2)(5.00 \text{ s})$$
$$= 1.50 \text{ m/s} + 12.0 \text{ m/s} = 13.5 \text{ m/s}$$

Part (b)
2. Apply Equation 2–10, using the result for v obtained in part (a):

$$x = x_0 + \tfrac{1}{2}(v_0 + v)t$$
$$= 0 + \tfrac{1}{2}(1.50 \text{ m/s} + 13.5 \text{ m/s})(5.00 \text{ s})$$
$$= (7.50 \text{ m/s})(5.00 \text{ s}) = 37.5 \text{ m}$$

INSIGHT
Since the boat has a constant acceleration between $t = 0$ and $t = 5.00$ s, its velocity-versus-time curve is linear during this time interval. As a result, the average velocity for these 5.00 seconds is the average of the initial and final velocities, $v_{av} = \tfrac{1}{2}(1.50 \text{ m/s} + 13.5 \text{ m/s}) = 7.50$ m/s. Multiplying the average velocity by the time, 5.00 s, gives the distance traveled—which is exactly what Equation 2–10 does in Step 2.

PRACTICE PROBLEM
At what time is the boat's speed equal to 10.0 m/s? [**Answer:** $t = 3.54$ s]

Some related homework problems: Problem 47, Problem 48

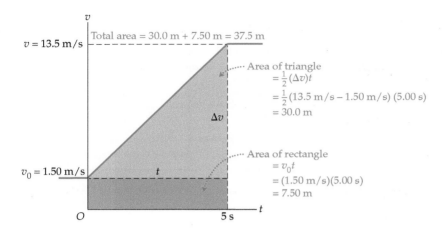

The distance traveled by the boat between $t = 0$ and $t = 5.00$ s is equal to the corresponding area under the velocity curve.

The velocity of the boat in Example 2–5 is plotted as a function of time in **Figure 2–13**, with the acceleration starting at time $t = 0$ and ending at $t = 5.00$ s. We will now show that the *distance* traveled by the boat from $t = 0$ to $t = 5.00$ s *is equal to the corresponding area under the velocity-versus-time curve*. This is a general result, valid for any velocity curve and any time interval:

- The distance traveled by an object from a time t_1 to a time t_2 is equal to the area under the velocity curve between those two times.

In this case, the area is the sum of the areas of a rectangle and a triangle. The rectangle has a base of 5.00 s and a height of 1.50 m/s, which gives an area of $(5.00 \text{ s})(1.50 \text{ m/s}) = 7.50$ m. Similarly, the triangle has a base of 5.00 s and a height of $(13.5 \text{ m/s} - 1.50 \text{ m/s}) = 12.0$ m/s, for an area of $\frac{1}{2}(5.00 \text{ s})(12.0 \text{ m/s}) = 30.0$ m. Clearly, the total area is 37.5 m, just as found in Example 2–5.

Staying with Example 2–5 for a moment, let's repeat the calculation of part (b), only this time for the general case. First, we use the final velocity from part (a), calculated with $v = v_0 + at$, in the expression for the average velocity, $v_{av} = \frac{1}{2}(v_0 + v)$. Symbolically, this gives the following:

$$\tfrac{1}{2}(v_0 + v) = \tfrac{1}{2}[v_0 + (v_0 + at)] = v_0 + \tfrac{1}{2}at \qquad \textit{(constant acceleration)}$$

Next, we substitute this result into Equation 2–10, which yields

$$x = x_0 + \tfrac{1}{2}(v_0 + v)t = x_0 + \left(v_0 + \tfrac{1}{2}at\right)t$$

Multiplying through by t gives the following result:

Constant-Acceleration Equation of Motion: Position as a Function of Time

$$x = x_0 + v_0 t + \tfrac{1}{2}at^2 \qquad\qquad\qquad 2\text{–}11$$

Here we have an expression for position versus time that is explicitly in terms of the acceleration, a.

Note that each term in Equation 2–11 has the same dimensions, as they must. For example, the velocity term, $v_0 t$, has the units $(\text{m/s})(\text{s}) = \text{m}$. Similarly, the acceleration term, $\frac{1}{2}at^2$, has the units $(\text{m/s}^2)(\text{s}^2) = \text{m}$.

EXERCISE 2–3

Repeat part (b) of Example 2–5 using Equation 2–11.

SOLUTION

$$x = x_0 + v_0 t + \tfrac{1}{2}at^2 = 0 + (1.50 \text{ m/s})(5.00 \text{ s}) + \tfrac{1}{2}(2.40 \text{ m/s}^2)(5.00 \text{ s})^2 = 37.5 \text{ m}$$

The next Example gives further insight into the physical meaning of Equation 2–11.

EXAMPLE 2–6　PUT THE PEDAL TO THE METAL

A drag racer starts from rest and accelerates at 7.40 m/s². How far has it traveled in **(a)** 1.00 s, **(b)** 2.00 s, **(c)** 3.00 s?

PICTURE THE PROBLEM
We set up a coordinate system in which the drag racer starts at the origin and accelerates in the positive x direction. With this choice, it follows that $x_0 = 0$ and $a = +7.40$ m/s². Also, since the racer starts from rest, its initial velocity is zero, $v_0 = 0$. Incidentally, the positions of the racer in the sketch have been drawn to scale.

$t = 0.00$　$t = 1.00$ s　　　$t = 2.00$ s　　　　　$t = 3.00$ s

O ⊢―――――――――――――――――→ x

STRATEGY
Since this problem gives the acceleration, which is constant, and asks for a relationship between position and time, we use Equation 2–11.

SOLUTION

Part (a)
1. Evaluate Equation 2–11 with $a = 7.40$ m/s² and $t = 1.00$ s:

$$x = x_0 + v_0 t + \tfrac{1}{2}at^2 = 0 + 0 + \tfrac{1}{2}at^2 = \tfrac{1}{2}at^2$$

$$x = \tfrac{1}{2}(7.40 \text{ m/s}^2)(1.00 \text{ s})^2 = 3.70 \text{ m}$$

Part (b)
2. From the calculation in part (a), Equation 2–11 reduces to $x = \tfrac{1}{2}at^2$ in this situation. Evaluate $x = \tfrac{1}{2}at^2$ at $t = 2.00$ s:

$$x = \tfrac{1}{2}at^2$$

$$= \tfrac{1}{2}(7.40 \text{ m/s}^2)(2.00 \text{ s})^2 = 14.8 \text{ m} = 4(3.70 \text{ m})$$

Part (c)
3. Repeat with $t = 3.00$ s:

$$x = \tfrac{1}{2}at^2$$

$$= \tfrac{1}{2}(7.40 \text{ m/s}^2)(3.00 \text{ s})^2 = 33.3 \text{ m} = 9(3.70 \text{ m})$$

INSIGHT
This Example illustrates one of the key features of accelerated motion—position does not change uniformly with time when an object accelerates. In this case, the distance traveled in the first two seconds is 4 times the distance traveled in the first second, and the distance traveled in the first three seconds is 9 times the distance traveled in the first second. This kind of behavior is a direct result of the fact that x depends on t^2 when the acceleration is nonzero.

PRACTICE PROBLEM
In one second the racer travels 3.70 m. How long does it take for the racer to travel $2(3.70 \text{ m}) = 7.40$ m?
[Answer: $t = \sqrt{2}$ s $= 1.41$ s]

Some related homework problems: Problem 49, Problem 64

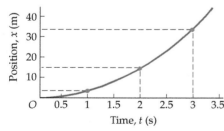

▲ **FIGURE 2–14　Position versus time for Example 2–6**
The upward-curving, parabolic shape of this x-versus-t plot indicates a positive, constant acceleration. The dots on the curve show the position of the drag racer in Example 2–6 at the times 1.00 s, 2.00 s, and 3.00 s.

Figure 2–14 shows a graph of x-versus-t for Example 2–6. Notice the parabolic shape of the x-versus-t curve, which is due to the $\tfrac{1}{2}at^2$ term, and is characteristic of constant acceleration. In particular, if acceleration is positive ($a > 0$), then a plot of x-versus-t curves upward; if acceleration is negative ($a < 0$), a plot of x-versus-t curves downward. The greater the magnitude of a, the greater the curvature. In contrast, if a particle moves with constant velocity ($a = 0$) the t^2 dependence vanishes, and the x-versus-t plot is a straight line.

Our final equation of motion with constant acceleration relates velocity to position. We start by solving for the time, t, in Equation 2–7:

$$v = v_0 + at \quad \text{or} \quad t = \frac{v - v_0}{a}$$

Next, we substitute this result into Equation 2–10, thus eliminating t:

$$x = x_0 + \tfrac{1}{2}(v_0 + v)t = x_0 + \tfrac{1}{2}(v_0 + v)\left(\frac{v - v_0}{a}\right)$$

Noting that $(v_0 + v)(v - v_0) = v_0 v - v_0^2 + v^2 - vv_0 = v^2 - v_0^2$, we have

$$x = x_0 + \frac{v^2 - v_0^2}{2a}$$

Finally, a straightforward rearrangement of terms yields

Constant-Acceleration Equation of Motion: Velocity in Terms of Displacement

$$v^2 = v_0^2 + 2a(x - x_0) = v_0^2 + 2a\Delta x \qquad\qquad 2\text{–}12$$

This equation allows us to relate the velocity at one position to the velocity at another position, without knowing how much time is involved. The next Example shows how Equation 2–12 can be used.

EXAMPLE 2–7   TAKEOFF DISTANCE FOR AN AIRLINER

REAL-WORLD PHYSICS Jets at JFK International Airport accelerate from rest at one end of a runway, and must attain takeoff speed before reaching the other end of the runway. **(a)** Plane A has acceleration a and takeoff speed v_{to}. What is the minimum length of runway, Δx_A, required for this plane? Give a symbolic answer. **(b)** Plane B has the same acceleration as plane A, but requires twice the takeoff speed. Find Δx_B and compare with Δx_A. **(c)** Find the minimum runway length for plane A if $a = 2.20 \text{ m/s}^2$ and $v_{to} = 95.0 \text{ m/s}$. (These values are typical for a 747 jetliner.)

PICTURE THE PROBLEM
In our sketch, we choose the positive x direction to be the direction of motion. With this choice, it follows that the acceleration of the plane is positive, $a = +2.20 \text{ m/s}^2$. Similarly, the takeoff velocity is positive as well, $v_{to} = +95.0 \text{ m/s}$.

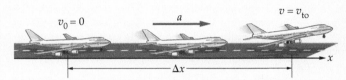

STRATEGY
From the sketch it is clear that we want to express Δx, the distance the plane travels in attaining takeoff speed, in terms of the acceleration, a, and the takeoff speed, v_{to}. Equation 2–12, which relates distance to velocity, allows us to do this.

SOLUTION

Part (a)

1. Solve Equation 2–12 for Δx. To find Δx_A, set $v_0 = 0$ and $v = v_{to}$:

$$\Delta x = \frac{v^2 - v_0^2}{2a} \qquad \Delta x_A = \frac{v_{to}^2}{2a}$$

Part (b)

2. To find Δx_B, simply change v_{to} to $2v_{to}$ in part (a):

$$\Delta x_B = \frac{(2v_{to})^2}{2a} = \frac{4v_{to}^2}{2a} = 4\Delta x_A$$

Part (c)

3. Substitute numerical values into the result found in part (a):

$$\Delta x_A = \frac{v_{to}^2}{2a} = \frac{(95.0 \text{ m/s})^2}{2(2.20 \text{ m/s}^2)} = 2050 \text{ m}$$

INSIGHT
For purposes of comparison, the shortest runway at JFK International Airport is 04R/22L, which has a length of 2560 m.

This Example illustrates the fact that there are many advantages to obtaining symbolic results before substituting numerical values. In this case, we find that the takeoff distance is proportional to v^2; hence, we conclude immediately that doubling v results in a fourfold increase of Δx.

PRACTICE PROBLEM
Find the minimum acceleration needed for a takeoff speed of $v_{to} = (95.0 \text{ m/s})/2 = 47.5 \text{ m/s}$ on a runway of length $\Delta x = (2050 \text{ m})/4 = 513 \text{ m}$.   [**Answer:** $a = v_{to}^2/2\Delta x = 2.20 \text{ m/s}^2$]

Some related homework problems: Problem 55, Problem 57

Finally, all of our constant-acceleration equations of motion are collected for easy reference in Table 2–4.

TABLE 2–4 Constant-Acceleration Equations of Motion

Variables Related	Equation	Number
velocity, time, acceleration	$v = v_0 + at$	2–7
initial, final, and average velocity	$v_{av} = \frac{1}{2}(v_0 + v)$	2–9
position, time, velocity	$x = x_0 + \frac{1}{2}(v_0 + v)t$	2–10
position, time, acceleration	$x = x_0 + v_0 t + \frac{1}{2}at^2$	2–11
velocity, position, acceleration	$v^2 = v_0^2 + 2a(x - x_0) = v_0^2 + 2a\Delta x$	2–12

2–6 Applications of the Equations of Motion

We devote this section to a variety of examples further illustrating the use of the constant-acceleration equations of motion. In our first Example, we consider the distance and time needed to brake a vehicle to a complete stop.

EXAMPLE 2–8   HIT THE BRAKES!

A park ranger driving on a back country road suddenly sees a deer "frozen" in the headlights. The ranger, who is driving at 11.4 m/s, immediately applies the brakes and slows with an acceleration of 3.80 m/s². **(a)** If the deer is 20.0 m from the ranger's vehicle when the brakes are applied, how close does the ranger come to hitting the deer? **(b)** How much time is needed for the ranger's vehicle to stop?

PICTURE THE PROBLEM

We choose the positive x direction to be the direction of motion. With this choice it follows that $v_0 = +11.4$ m/s. In addition, the fact that the ranger's vehicle is slowing down means its acceleration points in the *opposite* direction to that of the velocity [see Figure 2–10 (b) and (c)]. Therefore, the vehicle's acceleration is $a = -3.80$ m/s². Finally, when the vehicle comes to rest its velocity is zero, $v = 0$.

STRATEGY

The acceleration is constant, so we can use the equations listed in Table 2–4. In part (a) we want to find a distance when we know the velocity and acceleration, so we use a rearranged version of Equation 2–12. In part (b) we want to find a time when we know the velocity and acceleration, so we use a rearranged version of Equation 2–7.

SOLUTION

Part (a)

1. Solve Equation 2–12 for Δx:

$$\Delta x = \frac{v^2 - v_0^2}{2a}$$

2. Set $v = 0$, and substitute numerical values:

$$\Delta x = -\frac{v_0^2}{2a} = -\frac{(11.4 \text{ m/s})^2}{2(-3.80 \text{ m/s}^2)} = 17.1 \text{ m}$$

3. Subtract Δx from 20.0 m to find the distance between the stopped vehicle and the deer:

$$20.0 \text{ m} - 17.1 \text{ m} = 2.9 \text{ m}$$

Part (b)

4. Set $v = 0$ in Equation 2–7 and solve for t:

$$v = v_0 + at = 0$$
$$t = -\frac{v_0}{a} = -\frac{11.4 \text{ m/s}}{(-3.80 \text{ m/s}^2)} = 3.00 \text{ s}$$

INSIGHT

Note the difference in the way t and Δx depend on the initial speed. If the initial speed is doubled, for example, the time needed to stop also doubles, but the distance needed to stop increases by a factor of four. This is one reason why speed on the highway has such a great influence on safety.

PRACTICE PROBLEM

Show that using $t = 3.00$ s in Equation 2–11 results in the same distance needed to stop.
[**Answer:** $x = x_0 + v_0 t + \frac{1}{2}at^2 = 0 + (11.4 \text{ m/s})(3.00 \text{ s}) + \frac{1}{2}(-3.80 \text{ m/s}^2)(3.00 \text{ s})^2 = 17.1$ m, as expected.]

Some related homework problems: Problem 57, Problem 58

In Example 2–8, we calculated the distance necessary for a vehicle to come to a complete stop. But how does v vary with distance as the vehicle slows down? The next Conceptual Checkpoint deals with this topic.

CONCEPTUAL CHECKPOINT 2-4   STOPPING DISTANCE

The ranger in Example 2–8 brakes for 17.1 m. After braking for only half that distance, $\frac{1}{2}(17.1\text{ m}) = 8.55$ m, is the ranger's speed **(a)** equal to $\frac{1}{2}v_0$, **(b)** greater than $\frac{1}{2}v_0$, or **(c)** less than $\frac{1}{2}v_0$?

REASONING AND DISCUSSION

As pointed out in the Insight for Example 2–8, the fact that the stopping distance, Δx, depends on v_0^2 means that this distance increases by a factor of four when the speed is doubled. For example, the stopping distance with an initial speed of v_0 is four times the stopping distance when the initial speed is $v_0/2$.

To apply this observation to the ranger, suppose that the stopping distance with an initial speed of v_0 is Δx. It follows that the stopping distance for an initial speed of $v_0/2$ is $\Delta x/4$. This means that as the ranger slows from v_0 to 0, it takes a distance $\Delta x/4$ to slow from $v_0/2$ to 0, and the remaining distance, $3\Delta x/4$, to slow from v_0 to $v_0/2$. Thus, at the halfway point the ranger has not yet slowed to half of the initial velocity—the speed at this point is greater than $v_0/2$.

ANSWER

(b) The ranger's speed is greater than $\frac{1}{2}v_0$.

Clearly, v does not decrease uniformly with distance. A plot showing v as a function of x for Example 2–8 is shown in **Figure 2–15**. As we can see from the graph, v changes more in the second half of the braking distance than in the first half.

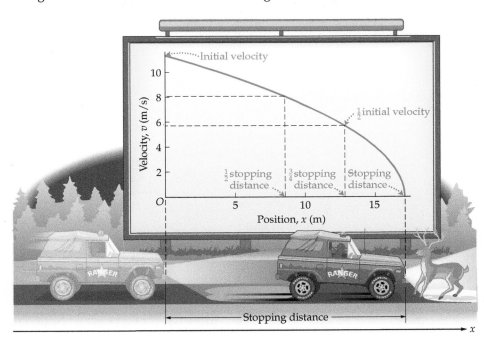

◄ **FIGURE 2–15 Velocity as a function of position for the ranger in Example 2–8**

The ranger's vehicle in Example 2–8 comes to rest with constant acceleration, which means that its velocity decreases uniformly with time. The velocity *does not* decrease uniformly with distance, however. In particular, note how rapidly the velocity decreases in the final one-quarter of the stopping distance.

We close this section with a familiar, everyday example: a police car accelerating to overtake a speeder. This is the first time that we use two equations of motion for two different objects to solve a problem—but it won't be the last. Problems of this type are often more interesting than problems involving only a single object, and they relate to many types of situations in everyday life.

PROBLEM-SOLVING NOTE

Strategize

Before attempting to solve a problem, it is a good idea to have some sort of plan, or "strategy," for how to proceed. It may be as simple as saying, "The problem asks me to relate velocity and time, therefore I will use Equation 2–7." In other cases the strategy is a bit more involved. Producing effective strategies is one of the most challenging—and creative—aspects of problem solving.

EXAMPLE 2-9   CATCHING A SPEEDER

A speeder doing 40.0 mi/h (about 17.9 m/s) in a 25 mi/h zone approaches a parked police car. The instant the speeder passes the police car, the police begin their pursuit. If the speeder maintains a constant velocity, and the police car accelerates with a constant acceleration of 4.51 m/s², **(a)** how long does it take for the police car to catch the speeder, **(b)** how far have the two cars traveled in this time, and **(c)** what is the velocity of the police car when it catches the speeder?

PICTURE THE PROBLEM

Our sketch shows the two cars at the moment the speeder passes the resting police car. At this instant, which we take to be $t = 0$, both the speeder and the police car are at the origin, $x = 0$. In addition, we choose the positive x direction to be the direction of motion; therefore, the speeder's initial velocity is given by $v_s = +17.9$ m/s, and the police car's initial velocity is zero. The speeder's acceleration is zero, but the police car has an acceleration given by $a = +4.51$ m/s². Finally, our plot shows the linear x-versus-t plot for the speeder, and the parabolic x-versus-t plot for the police car.

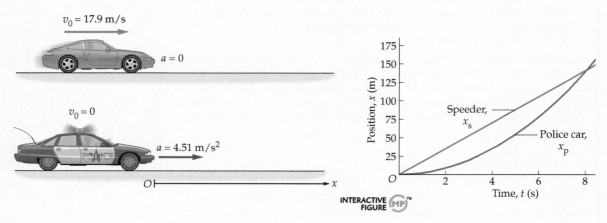

STRATEGY

To solve this problem, first write down a position-versus-time equation for the police car, x_p, and a separate equation for the speeder, x_s. Next, we find the time it takes the police car to catch the speeder by setting $x_p = x_s$ and solving the resulting equation for t. Once the catch time is determined, it is straightforward to calculate the distance traveled and the velocity of the police car.

SOLUTION

Part (a)

1. Write equations of motion for the two vehicles. For the police car, $v_0 = 0$ and $a = 4.51$ m/s². For the speeder, $v_0 = 17.9$ m/s $= v_s$ and $a = 0$:

$$x_p = \tfrac{1}{2}at^2$$
$$x_s = v_st$$

2. Set $x_p = x_s$ and solve for the time:

$$\tfrac{1}{2}at^2 = v_st \text{ or } (\tfrac{1}{2}at - v_s)t = 0$$

two solutions: $t = 0$ or $t = \dfrac{2v_s}{a}$

3. Clearly, $t = 0$ corresponds to the initial conditions, because both vehicles started at $x = 0$ at that time. The time of interest is obtained by substituting numerical values into the other solution:

$$t = \frac{2v_s}{a} = \frac{2(17.9 \text{ m/s})}{4.51 \text{ m/s}^2} = 7.94 \text{ s}$$

Part (b)

4. Substitute $t = 7.94$ s into the equations of motion for x_p and x_s. Note that $x_p = x_s$, as expected:

$$x_p = \tfrac{1}{2}at^2 = \tfrac{1}{2}(4.51 \text{ m/s}^2)(7.94 \text{ s})^2 = 142$$
$$x_s = v_st = (17.9 \text{ m/s})(7.94 \text{ s}) = 142 \text{ m}$$

Part (c)

5. To find the velocity of the police car use Equation 2–7, which relates velocity to time:

$$v_p = v_0 + at = 0 + (4.51 \text{ m/s}^2)(7.94 \text{ s}) = 35.8 \text{ m/s}$$

INSIGHT

When the police car catches up with the speeder, its velocity is 35.8 m/s, which is exactly twice the velocity of the speeder. A coincidence? Not at all. When the police car catches the speeder, both have traveled the same distance (142 m) in the same time (7.94 s), therefore they have the same average velocity. Of course, the average velocity of the speeder is simply v_s. The average velocity of the police car is $\tfrac{1}{2}(v_0 + v)$, since its acceleration is constant, and thus $\tfrac{1}{2}(v_0 + v) = v_s$. Since $v_0 = 0$ for the police car, it follows that $v = 2v_s$. Notice that this result is independent of the acceleration of the police car, as we show in the following Practice Problem.

PRACTICE PROBLEM

Repeat this Example for the case where the acceleration of the police car is $a = 3.25$ m/s². [**Answer:** (a) $t = 11.0$ s, (b) $x_p = x_s = 197$ m, (c) $v_p = 35.8$ m/s]

Some related homework problems: Problem 54, Problem 65

2–7 Freely Falling Objects

The most famous example of motion with constant acceleration is **free fall**—the motion of an object falling freely under the influence of gravity. It was Galileo (1564–1642) who first showed, with his own experiments, that falling bodies move with constant acceleration. His conclusions were based on experiments done by rolling balls down inclines of various steepness. By using an incline, Galileo was able to reduce the acceleration of the balls, thus producing motion slow enough to be timed with the rather crude instruments available.

Galileo also pointed out that objects of different weight fall with the *same* constant acceleration—provided air resistance is small enough to be ignored. Whether he dropped objects from the Leaning Tower of Pisa to demonstrate this fact, as legend has it, will probably never be known for certain, but we do know that he performed extensive experiments to support his claim.

Today it is easy to verify Galileo's assertion by dropping objects in a vacuum chamber, where the effects of air resistance are essentially removed. In a standard classroom demonstration, a feather and a coin are dropped in a vacuum, and both fall at the same rate. In 1971, a novel version of this experiment was carried out on the Moon by astronaut David Scott. In the near-perfect vacuum on the Moon's surface he dropped a feather and a hammer and showed a worldwide television audience that they fell to the ground in the same time.

To illustrate the effect of air resistance in everyday terms, consider dropping a sheet of paper and a rubber ball (**Figure 2–16**). The paper drifts slowly to the ground, taking much longer to fall than the ball. Now, wad the sheet of paper into a tight ball and repeat the experiment. This time the ball of paper and the rubber ball reach the ground in nearly the same time. What was different in the two experiments? Clearly, when the sheet of paper was wadded into a ball, the effect of air resistance on it was greatly reduced, so that both objects fell almost as they would in a vacuum.

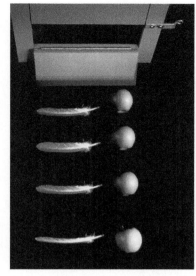

▲ In the absence of air resistance, all bodies fall with the same acceleration, regardless of their mass.

◄ **FIGURE 2–16 Free fall and air resistance**

(a) Dropping a sheet of paper and a rubber ball

(b) Dropping a wadded-up sheet of paper and a rubber ball

Before considering a few examples, let's first discuss exactly what is meant by "free fall." To begin, the word *free* in free fall means free from any effects other than gravity. For example, in free fall we assume that an object's motion is not influenced by any form of friction or air resistance.

- Free fall is the motion of an object subject *only* to the influence of gravity.

Though free fall is an idealization—which does not apply to many real-world situations—it is still a useful approximation in many other cases. In the following examples we assume that the motion may be considered as free fall.

Next, it should be realized that the word *fall* in free fall does not mean the object is necessarily moving downward. By free fall, we mean *any* motion under the influence of gravity alone. If you drop a ball, it is in free fall. If you throw a ball upward or downward, it is in free fall as soon as it leaves your hand.

- An object is in free fall as soon as it is released, whether it is dropped from rest, thrown downward, or thrown upward.

Finally, the acceleration produced by gravity on the Earth's surface (sometimes called the gravitational strength) is denoted with the symbol g. As a shorthand

▲ Whether she is on the way up, at the peak of her flight, or on the way down, this girl is in free fall, accelerating downward with the acceleration of gravity. Only when she is in contact with the blanket does her acceleration change.

TABLE 2–5 Values of g at Different Locations on Earth (m/s^2)

Location	Latitude	g
North Pole	90° N	9.832
Oslo, Norway	60° N	9.819
Hong Kong	30° N	9.793
Quito, Ecuador	0°	9.780

name, we will frequently refer to g simply as "the acceleration due to gravity." In fact, as we shall see in Chapter 12, the value of g varies according to one's location on the surface of the Earth, as well as one's altitude above it. Table 2–5 shows how g varies with latitude.

In all the calculations that follow in this book, we shall use $g = 9.81 \text{ m/s}^2$ for the acceleration due to gravity. Note, in particular, that g always stands for $+9.81 \text{ m/s}^2$, never -9.81 m/s^2. For example, if we choose a coordinate system with the positive direction upward, the acceleration in free fall is $a = -g$. If the positive direction is downward, then free-fall acceleration is $a = g$.

With these comments, we are ready to explore a variety of free-fall examples.

EXAMPLE 2–10   DO THE CANNONBALL!

A person steps off the end of a 3.00-m-high diving board and drops to the water below. **(a)** How long does it take for the person to reach the water? **(b)** What is the person's speed on entering the water?

PICTURE THE PROBLEM
In our sketch we choose the origin to be at the height of the diving board, and we let the positive direction be downward. With these choices, $x_0 = 0$, $a = g$, and the water is at $x = 3.00$ m. Of course, $v_0 = 0$ since the person simply steps off the board.

STRATEGY
We can neglect air resistance in this case and model the motion as free fall. This means we can assume a constant acceleration equal to g and use the equations of motion in Table 2–4. For part (a) we want to find the time of fall when we know the distance and acceleration, so we use Equation 2–11. For part (b) we can relate velocity to time by using Equation 2–7, or we can relate velocity to position by using Equation 2–12. We will implement both approaches and show that the results are the same.

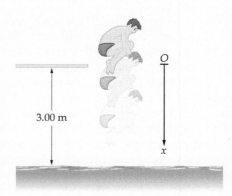

3.00 m

SOLUTION

Part (a)

1. Write Equation 2–11 with $x_0 = 0$, $v_0 = 0$, and $a = g$:

$$x = x_0 + v_0 t + \tfrac{1}{2}at^2 = 0 + 0 + \tfrac{1}{2}gt^2 = \tfrac{1}{2}gt^2$$

2. Solve for the time, t, and set $x = 3.00$ m:

$$t = \sqrt{\frac{2x}{g}} = \sqrt{\frac{2(3.00 \text{ m})}{9.81 \text{ m/s}^2}} = 0.782 \text{ s}$$

Part (b)

3. Use the time found in part (a) in Equation 2–7:

$$v = v_0 + gt = 0 + (9.81 \text{ m/s}^2)(0.782 \text{ s}) = 7.67 \text{ m/s}$$

4. We can also find the velocity without knowing the time by using Equation 2–12 with $\Delta x = 3.00$ m:

$$v^2 = v_0{}^2 + 2a\Delta x = 0 + 2g\Delta x$$

$$v = \sqrt{2g\Delta x} = \sqrt{2(9.81 \text{ m/s}^2)(3.00 \text{ m})} = 7.67 \text{ m/s}$$

INSIGHT
Let's put these results in more common, everyday units. If you step off a diving board 9.84 ft (3.00 m) above the water, you enter the water with a speed of 17.2 mi/h (7.67 m/s).

PRACTICE PROBLEM
What is your speed on entering the water if you step off a 10.0-m diving tower?   [**Answer:** $v = \sqrt{2(9.81 \text{ m/s}^2)(10.0 \text{ m})} = 14.0 \text{ m/s} = 31.4 \text{ mi/h}$]

Some related homework problems: Problem 71, Problem 83

The special case of free fall from rest occurs so frequently, and in so many different contexts, that it deserves special attention. If we take x_0 to be zero, and positive to be downward, then position as a function of time is $x = x_0 + v_0 t + \tfrac{1}{2}gt^2 = 0 + 0 + \tfrac{1}{2}gt^2$, or

$$x = \tfrac{1}{2}gt^2 \qquad\qquad 2\text{–}13$$

Similarly, velocity as a function of time is

$$v = gt \qquad\qquad 2\text{–}14$$

and velocity as a function of position is

$$v = \sqrt{2gx}$$ 2–15

The behavior of these functions is illustrated in **Figure 2–17**. Note that position increases with time squared, whereas velocity increases linearly with time.

Next we consider two objects dropped from rest, one after the other, and discuss how their separation varies with time.

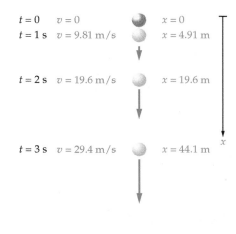

$t = 0$	$v = 0$		$x = 0$
$t = 1\,\text{s}$	$v = 9.81\,\text{m/s}$		$x = 4.91\,\text{m}$
$t = 2\,\text{s}$	$v = 19.6\,\text{m/s}$		$x = 19.6\,\text{m}$
$t = 3\,\text{s}$	$v = 29.4\,\text{m/s}$		$x = 44.1\,\text{m}$
$t = 4\,\text{s}$	$v = 39.2\,\text{m/s}$		$x = 78.5\,\text{m}$

CONCEPTUAL CHECKPOINT 2–5

FREE-FALL SEPARATION

You drop a rock from a bridge to the river below. When the rock has fallen 4 m, you drop a second rock. As the rocks continue their free fall, does their separation **(a)** increase, **(b)** decrease, or **(c)** stay the same?

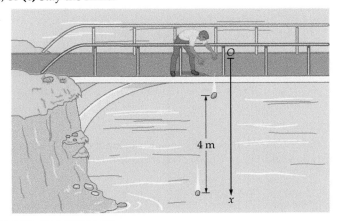

4 m

▲ FIGURE 2–17 Free fall from rest
Position and velocity are shown as functions of time. It is apparent that velocity depends linearly on t, whereas position depends on t^2.

REASONING AND DISCUSSION
It might seem that since both rocks are in free fall, their separation remains the same. This is not so. The rock that has a head start always has a greater velocity than the later one; thus it covers a greater distance in any interval of time. As a result, the separation between the rocks increases.

ANSWER
(a) The separation between the rocks increases.

An erupting volcano shooting out fountains of lava is an impressive sight. In the next Example we show how a simple timing experiment can determine the initial velocity of the erupting lava.

PROBLEM-SOLVING NOTE

Check Your Solution

Once you have a solution to a problem, check to see whether it makes sense. First, make sure the units are correct; m/s for speed, m/s² for acceleration, and so on. Second, check the numerical value of your answer. If you are solving for the speed of a diver dropping from a 3.0-m diving board and you get an unreasonable value like 200 m/s ($\approx$450 mi/h), chances are good that you've made a mistake.

EXAMPLE 2–11   BOMBS AWAY: CALCULATING THE SPEED OF A LAVA BOMB

REAL-WORLD PHYSICS
A volcano shoots out blobs of molten lava, called lava bombs, from its summit. A geologist observing the eruption uses a stopwatch to time the flight of a particular lava bomb that is projected straight upward. If the time for it to rise and fall back to its launch height is 4.75 s, and its acceleration is 9.81 m/s² downward, what is its initial speed?

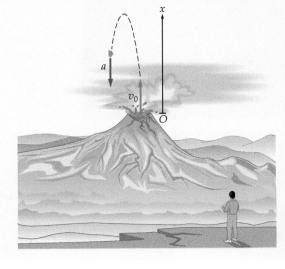

PICTURE THE PROBLEM
Our sketch shows a coordinate system with upward as the positive x direction. For clarity, we offset the upward and downward trajectories slightly. In addition, we choose $t = 0$ to be the time at which the lava bomb is launched. With these choices it follows that $x_0 = 0$ and the acceleration is $a = -g = -9.81\,\text{m/s}^2$. The initial speed to be determined is v_0.

CONTINUED ON NEXT PAGE

CONTINUED FROM PREVIOUS PAGE

STRATEGY

Once again, we can neglect air resistance and model the motion of the lava bomb as free fall—this time with an initial upward velocity. We know that the lava bomb starts at $x = 0$ at the time $t = 0$ and returns to $x = 0$ at the time $t = 4.75$ s. This means that we know the bomb's position, time, and acceleration ($a = -g$), from which we would like to determine the initial velocity. A reasonable approach is to use Equation 2–11 and solve it for the one unknown it contains, v_0.

SOLUTION

1. Write out $x = x_0 + v_0t + \frac{1}{2}at^2$ with $x_0 = 0$ and $a = -g$. Factor out a time, t, from the two remaining terms:

$$x = x_0 + v_0t + \tfrac{1}{2}at^2 = v_0t - \tfrac{1}{2}gt^2 = \left(v_0 - \tfrac{1}{2}gt\right)t$$

2. Set x equal to zero, since this is the position of the lava bomb at $t = 0$ and $t = 4.75$ s:

$$x = \left(v_0 - \tfrac{1}{2}gt\right)t = 0 \text{ two solutions:}$$
$$\text{(i) } t = 0$$
$$\text{(ii) } v_0 - \tfrac{1}{2}gt = 0$$

3. The first solution is simply the initial condition; that is, $x = 0$ at $t = 0$. Solve the second solution for the initial speed:

$$v_0 - \tfrac{1}{2}gt = 0 \quad \text{or} \quad v_0 = \tfrac{1}{2}gt$$

4. Substitute numerical values for g and the time the lava bomb lands:

$$v_0 = \tfrac{1}{2}gt = \tfrac{1}{2}(9.81 \text{ m/s}^2)(4.75 \text{ s}) = 23.3 \text{ m/s}$$

INSIGHT

A geologist can determine a lava bomb's initial speed by simply observing its flight time. Knowing the lava bomb's initial speed can help geologists determine how severe a volcanic eruption will be, and how dangerous it might be to people in the surrounding area.

PRACTICE PROBLEM

A second lava bomb is projected straight upward with an initial speed of 25 m/s. How long is it in the air?   [**Answer:** $t = 5.1$ s]

Some related homework problems: Problem 73, Problem 86

▲ In the absence of air resistance, these lava bombs from the Kilauea volcano on the big island of Hawaii would strike the water with the same speed they had when they were blasted into the air.

What is the speed of a lava bomb when it returns to Earth; that is, when it returns to the same level from which it was launched? Physical intuition might suggest that, in the absence of air resistance, it should be the same as the initial speed. To show that this hypothesis is indeed correct, write out Equation 2–7 for this case:

$$v = v_0 - gt$$

Substituting numerical values, we find

$$v = v_0 - gt = 23.3 \text{ m/s} - (9.81 \text{ m/s}^2)(4.75 \text{ s}) = -23.3 \text{ m/s}$$

Thus, the velocity of the lava when it lands is just the negative of the velocity it had when launched upward. Or put another way, when the lava lands, it has the same speed as when it was launched; it's just traveling in the opposite direction.

It is instructive to verify this result symbolically. Recall from Example 2–11 that $v_0 = \frac{1}{2}gt$, where t is the time the bomb lands. Substituting this result into Equation 2–7 we find

$$v = \tfrac{1}{2}gt - gt = -\tfrac{1}{2}gt = -v_0$$

The advantage of the symbolic solution lies in showing that the result is not a fluke—no matter what the initial velocity, no matter what the acceleration, the bomb lands with the velocity $-v_0$.

These results hint at a symmetry relating the motion on the way up to the motion on the way down. To make this symmetry more apparent, we first solve for the time when the lava bomb lands. Using the result $v_0 = \frac{1}{2}gt$ from Example 2–11, we find

$$t = \frac{2v_0}{g} \qquad \text{(time of landing)}$$

Next, we find the time when the velocity of the lava is zero, which is at its highest point. Setting $v = 0$ in Equation 2–7, we have $v = v_0 - gt = 0$, or

$$t = \frac{v_0}{g} \qquad \text{(time when } v = 0\text{)}$$

Note that this is exactly half the time required for the lava to make the round trip. Thus, the velocity of the lava is zero and the height of the lava is greatest exactly halfway between launch and landing.

This symmetry is illustrated in **Figure 2–18**. In this case we consider a lava bomb that is in the air for 6.00 s, moving without air resistance. Note that at $t = 3.00$ s the lava is at its highest point and its velocity is zero. At times equally spaced before and after $t = 3.00$ s, the lava is at the same height, has the same speed, but is moving in opposite directions. As a result of this symmetry, a movie of the lava bomb's flight would look the same whether run forward or in reverse.

Figure 2–19 shows the time dependence of position, velocity, and acceleration for an object in free fall without air resistance after being thrown upward. As soon as the object is released, it begins to accelerate downward—as indicated by the negative slope of the velocity-versus-time plot—though it isn't necessarily moving downward. For example, if you throw a ball *upward* it begins to accelerate *downward* the moment it leaves your hand. It continues moving upward, however, until its speed diminishes to zero. Since gravity is causing the downward acceleration, and gravity doesn't turn off just because the ball's velocity goes through zero, the ball continues to accelerate downward even when it is momentarily at rest.

Similarly, in the next Example we consider a sandbag that falls from an ascending hot-air balloon. This means that before the bag is in free fall it was moving upward—just like a ball thrown upward. And just like the ball, the sandbag continues moving upward for a brief time before momentarily stopping and then moving downward.

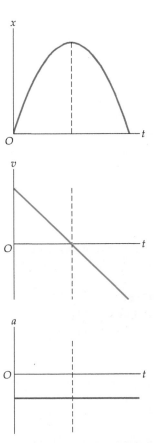

▲ **FIGURE 2–19 Position, velocity, and acceleration of a lava bomb as functions of time**

The fact that x versus t is curved indicates an acceleration; the downward curvature shows that the acceleration is negative. This is also clear from v versus t, which has a negative slope. The constant slope of the straight line in the v-versus-t plot indicates a constant acceleration, as shown in the a-versus-t plot.

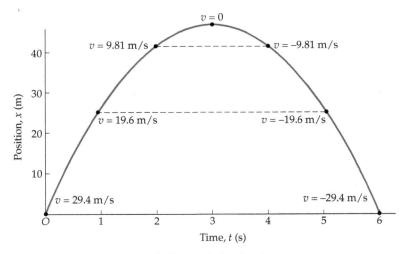

▲ **FIGURE 2–18 Position and velocity of a lava bomb**

This lava bomb is in the air for 6 seconds. Note the symmetry about the midpoint of the bomb's flight.

EXAMPLE 2–12 LOOK OUT BELOW! A SANDBAG IN FREE FALL

A hot-air balloon is rising straight upward with a constant speed of 6.5 m/s. When the basket of the balloon is 20.0 m above the ground, a bag of sand tied to the basket comes loose. **(a)** How long is the bag of sand in the air before it hits the ground? **(b)** What is the greatest height of the bag of sand during its fall to the ground?

PICTURE THE PROBLEM

We choose the origin to be at ground level and positive to be upward. This means that, for the bag, we have $x_0 = 20.0$ m, $v_0 = 6.5$ m/s, and $a = -g$. Our sketch also shows snapshots of the balloon and bag of sand at three different times, starting at $t = 0$ when the bag comes loose. Note that the bag is moving upward with the balloon at the time it comes loose. It therefore continues to move upward for a short time after it separates from the basket, exactly as if it had been thrown upward.

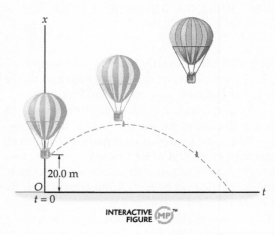

STRATEGY

The effects of air resistance on the sandbag can be ignored. As a result, we can use the equations in Table 2–4 with a constant acceleration $a = -g$.

In part (a) we want to relate position and time—knowing the initial position and initial velocity—so we use Equation 2–11. To find the time the bag hits the ground, we set $x = 0$ and solve for t.

For part (b) we have no expression that gives the maximum height of a particle—so we will have to come up with something on our own. We can start with the fact that $v = 0$ at the greatest height, since it is there the bag momentarily stops as it changes direction. Therefore, we can find the time t when $v = 0$ by using Equation 2–7, and then substitute t into Equation 2–11 to find x_{max}.

SOLUTION

Part (a)

1. Apply Equation 2–11 to the bag of sand, where x_0 and v_0 have the values given. Set $x = 0$:

$$x = x_0 + v_0 t - \tfrac{1}{2}gt^2 = 0$$

2. Note that we have a quadratic equation for t in the form $v_f = v_i$ where $A = -\tfrac{1}{2}g$, $B = v_0$, and $C = x_0$. Solve this equation for t. The positive solution, 2.78 s, applies to this problem: (Quadratic equations and their solutions are discussed in Appendix A. In general, one can expect two solutions to a quadratic equation.)

$$t = \frac{-v_0 \pm \sqrt{v_0{}^2 - 4\left(-\tfrac{1}{2}g\right)(x_0)}}{2\left(-\tfrac{1}{2}g\right)}$$

$$= \frac{-(6.5 \text{ m/s}) \pm \sqrt{(6.5 \text{ m/s})^2 + 2(9.81 \text{ m/s}^2)(20.0 \text{ m})}}{(-9.81 \text{ m/s}^2)}$$

$$= \frac{-(6.5 \text{ m/s}) \pm 20.8 \text{ m/s}}{(-9.81 \text{ m/s}^2)} = 2.78 \text{ s}, -1.46 \text{ s}$$

Part (b)

3. Apply Equation 2–7 to the bag of sand, then find the time when the velocity equals zero:

$$v = v_0 + at = v_0 - gt$$

$$v_0 - gt = 0 \quad \text{or} \quad t = \frac{v_0}{g} = \frac{6.5 \text{ m/s}}{9.81 \text{ m/s}^2} = 0.66 \text{ s}$$

4. Use $t = 0.66$ s in Equation 2–11 to find the maximum height:

$$x_{max} = 20.0 \text{ m} + (6.5 \text{ m/s})(0.66 \text{ s}) - \tfrac{1}{2}(9.81 \text{ m/s}^2)(0.66 \text{ s})^2$$
$$= 22 \text{ m}$$

INSIGHT

The positive solution to the quadratic equation is certainly the one that applies here, but the negative solution is not completely without meaning. What physical meaning might it have? Well, if the balloon had been *descending* with a speed of 6.5 m/s, instead of rising, then the time for the bag to reach the ground would have been 1.46 s. Try it! Let $v_0 = -6.5$ m/s and repeat the calculation given in part (a).

PRACTICE PROBLEM

What is the velocity of the bag of sand just before it hits the ground? [**Answer:** $v = v_0 - gt = (6.5 \text{ m/s}) - (9.81 \text{ m/s}^2)(2.78 \text{ s}) = -20.8$ m/s; the minus sign indicates the bag is moving downward.]

Some related homework problems: Problem 90, Problem 107

THE BIG PICTURE   PUTTING PHYSICS IN CONTEXT

LOOKING BACK

In this chapter we have made extensive use of the sign conventions for one-dimensional vectors—positive for one direction, negative for the opposite direction—as introduced in Chapter 1. See, for example, the positive and negative velocities in Figure 2–18.

We have been careful to check the dimensional consistency of our equations in this chapter. For example, the discussion following Equation 2–11 shows that all the terms in that equation have the dimensions of length.

LOOKING AHEAD

The distinctions developed in this chapter between velocity and acceleration will play a key role in our understanding of Newton's laws of motion in Chapters 5 and 6, and everywhere else that Newton's laws are used throughout the text.

The equations developed for motion with constant acceleration in this chapter (Equations 2–7, 2–10, 2–11, and 2–12) will be used again with slightly different symbols when we study rotational motion in Chapter 10. See, in particular, Equations 10–8, 10–9, 10–10, and 10–11.

CHAPTER SUMMARY

2–1   POSITION, DISTANCE, AND DISPLACEMENT

Distance

Total length of travel, from beginning to end. The distance is always positive.

Displacement

Displacement, Δx, is the change in position:

$$\Delta x = x_f - x_i \qquad \qquad 2\text{–}1$$

When calculating displacement, it is important to remember that it is always *final* position minus *initial* position—never the other way. Displacement can be positive, negative, or zero.

Positive and Negative Displacement

The *sign* of the displacement indicates the *direction* of motion. For example, suppose we choose the positive direction to be to the right. Then $\Delta x > 0$ means motion to the right, and $\Delta x < 0$ means motion to the left.

Units

The SI unit of distance and displacement is the meter, m.

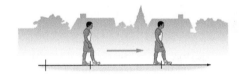

2–2   AVERAGE SPEED AND VELOCITY

Average Speed

Average speed is *distance* divided by elapsed time:

$$\text{average speed} = \text{distance/time} \qquad \qquad 2\text{–}2$$

Average speed is never negative.

Average Velocity

Average velocity, v_{av}, is *displacement* divided by time:

$$v_{av} = \frac{\Delta x}{\Delta t} = \frac{x_f - x_i}{t_f - t_i} \qquad \qquad 2\text{–}3$$

Average velocity is positive if motion is in the positive direction, and negative if motion is in the negative direction.

Graphical Interpretation of Velocity

In an *x*-versus-*t* plot, the average velocity is the slope of a line connecting two points.

Units

The SI unit of speed and velocity is meters per second, m/s.

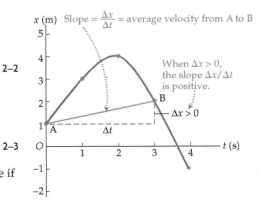

2–3 INSTANTANEOUS VELOCITY

The velocity at an instant of time is the limit of the average velocity over shorter and shorter time intervals:

$$v = \lim_{\Delta t \to 0} \frac{\Delta x}{\Delta t} \qquad 2\text{–}4$$

Instantaneous velocity can be positive, negative, or zero, with the sign indicating the direction of motion.

Constant Velocity
When velocity is constant, the instantaneous velocity is equal to the average velocity.

Graphical Interpretation
In an x-versus-t plot, the instantaneous velocity at a given time is equal to the slope of the tangent line at that time.

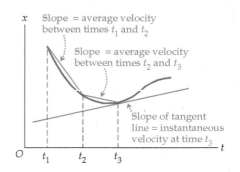

2–4 ACCELERATION

Average Acceleration
Average acceleration is the change in velocity divided by the change in time:

$$a_{av} = \frac{\Delta v}{\Delta t} = \frac{v_f - v_i}{t_f - t_i} \qquad 2\text{–}5$$

Average acceleration is positive if $v_f > v_i$, is negative if $v_f < v_i$, and is zero if $v_f = v_i$.

Instantaneous Acceleration
Instantaneous acceleration is the limit of the average acceleration as the time interval goes to zero:

$$a = \lim_{\Delta t \to 0} \frac{\Delta v}{\Delta t} \qquad 2\text{–}6$$

Instantaneous acceleration can be positive, negative, or zero, depending on whether the velocity is becoming more positive, more negative, or is staying the same. Knowing the sign of the acceleration *does not* tell you whether an object is speeding up or slowing down, and it *does not* give the direction of motion.

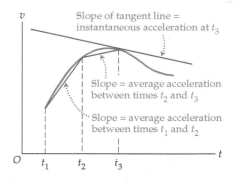

Constant Acceleration
When acceleration is constant, the instantaneous acceleration is equal to the average acceleration.

Deceleration
An object whose speed is decreasing is said to be decelerating. Deceleration occurs whenever the velocity and acceleration have opposite signs.

Graphical Interpretation
In a v-versus-t plot, the instantaneous acceleration is equal to the slope of the tangent line at a given time.

Units
The SI unit of acceleration is meters per second per second, or m/s^2.

2–5 MOTION WITH CONSTANT ACCELERATION

Several different "equations of motion" describe particles moving with constant acceleration. Each equation relates a different set of variables:

Velocity as a Function of Time

$$v = v_0 + at \qquad 2\text{–}7$$

Initial, Final, and Average Velocity

$$v_{av} = \tfrac{1}{2}(v_0 + v) \qquad 2\text{–}9$$

Position as a Function of Time and Velocity

$$x = x_0 + \tfrac{1}{2}(v_0 + v)t \qquad 2\text{–}10$$

Position as a Function of Time and Acceleration

$$x = x_0 + v_0 t + \tfrac{1}{2}at^2 \qquad 2\text{–}11$$

Velocity as a Function of Position

$$v^2 = v_0^2 + 2a(x - x_0) = v_0^2 + 2a\Delta x \qquad 2\text{–}12$$

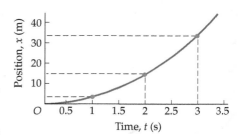

2–7 FREELY FALLING OBJECTS

Objects in free fall move under the influence of gravity alone. An object is in free fall as soon as it is released, whether it is thrown upward, thrown downward, or released from rest.

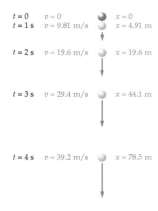

$t = 0$	$v = 0$		$x = 0$
$t = 1\,\text{s}$	$v = 9.81\ \text{m/s}$		$x = 4.91\ \text{m}$
$t = 2\,\text{s}$	$v = 19.6\ \text{m/s}$		$x = 19.6\ \text{m}$
$t = 3\,\text{s}$	$v = 29.4\ \text{m/s}$		$x = 44.1\ \text{m}$
$t = 4\,\text{s}$	$v = 39.2\ \text{m/s}$		$x = 78.5\ \text{m}$

Acceleration Due to Gravity

The acceleration due to gravity on the Earth's surface varies slightly from place to place. In this book we shall define the acceleration of gravity to have the following magnitude:

$$g = 9.81\ \text{m/s}^2$$

Note that g is always a positive quantity. If we choose the positive direction of our coordinate system to be downward (in the direction of the acceleration of gravity), it follows that the acceleration of an object in free fall is $a = +g$. On the other hand, if we choose our positive direction to be upward, the acceleration of a freely falling object is in the negative direction; hence $a = -g$.

PROBLEM-SOLVING SUMMARY

Type of Calculation	Relevant Physical Concepts	Related Examples
Relate velocity to time.	In motion with uniform acceleration a, the velocity changes with time as $v = v_0 + at$ (Equation 2–7).	Examples 2–5, 2–8, 2–9, 2–10, 2–11, 2–12
Relate velocity to position.	If an object with an initial velocity v_0 accelerates with a uniform acceleration a for a distance Δx, the final velocity, v, is given by $v^2 = v_0{}^2 + 2a\Delta x$ (Equation 2–12).	Examples 2–7, 2–8, 2–10
Relate position to time.	The position of an object moving with constant acceleration a varies with time as follows: $x = x_0 + \frac{1}{2}(v_0 + v)t$ (Equation 2–10) or equivalently $x = x_0 + v_0t + \frac{1}{2}at^2$ (Equation 2–11).	Examples 2–5, 2–6, 2–9, 2–10, 2–11, 2–12

CONCEPTUAL QUESTIONS

For instructor-assigned homework, go to www.masteringphysics.com

(Answers to odd-numbered Conceptual Questions can be found in the back of the book.)
(The effects of air resistance are to be ignored in this chapter.)

1. You and your dog go for a walk to a nearby park. On the way, your dog takes many short side trips to chase squirrels, examine fire hydrants, and so on. When you arrive at the park, do you and your dog have the same displacement? Have you traveled the same distance? Explain.

2. Does an odometer in a car measure distance or displacement? Explain.

3. Can you drive your car in such a way that the distance it covers is **(a)** greater than, **(b)** equal to, or **(c)** less than the magnitude of its displacement? In each case, give an example if your answer is yes, explain why not if your answer is no.

4. An astronaut orbits Earth in the space shuttle. In one complete orbit, is the magnitude of the displacement the same as the distance traveled? Explain.

5. After a tennis match the players dash to the net to congratulate one another. If they both run with a speed of 3 m/s, are their velocities equal? Explain.

6. Does a speedometer measure speed or velocity? Explain.

7. Is it possible for a car to circle a race track with constant velocity? Can it do so with constant speed? Explain.

8. Friends tell you that on a recent trip their average velocity was +20 m/s. Is it possible that their instantaneous velocity was negative at any time during the trip? Explain.

9. For what kind of motion are the instantaneous and average velocities equal?

10. If the position of an object is zero, does its speed have to be zero? Explain.

11. Assume that the brakes in your car create a constant deceleration, regardless of how fast you are going. If you double your driving speed, how does this affect **(a)** the time required to come to a stop, and **(b)** the distance needed to stop?

12. The velocity of an object is zero at a given instant of time. **(a)** Is it possible for the object's acceleration to be zero at this time? Explain. **(b)** Is it possible for the object's acceleration to be nonzero at this time? Explain.

13. If the velocity of an object is nonzero, can its acceleration be zero? Give an example if your answer is yes, explain why not if your answer is no.

14. Is it possible for an object to have zero average velocity over a given interval of time, yet still be accelerating during the interval? Give an example if your answer is yes, explain why not if your answer is no.

15. A batter hits a pop fly straight up. **(a)** Is the acceleration of the ball on the way up different from its acceleration on the way down? **(b)** Is the acceleration of the ball at the top of its flight different from its acceleration just before it lands?

16. A person on a trampoline bounces straight upward with an initial speed of 4.5 m/s. What is the person's speed when she returns to her initial height?

17. After winning a baseball game, one player drops a glove, while another tosses a glove into the air. How do the accelerations of the two gloves compare?

18. A volcano shoots a lava bomb straight upward. Does the displacement of the lava bomb depend on **(a)** your choice of origin for your coordinate system, or **(b)** your choice of a positive direction? Explain in each case.

PROBLEMS AND CONCEPTUAL EXERCISES

Note: Answers to odd-numbered Problems and Conceptual Exercises can be found in the back of the book. **IP** *denotes an integrated problem, with both conceptual and numerical parts;* **BIO** *identifies problems of biological or medical interest;* **CE** *indicates a conceptual exercise.* Predict/Explain *problems ask for two responses:* **(a)** *your prediction of a physical outcome, and* **(b)** *the best explanation among three provided. On all problems, red bullets* (•, ••, •••) *are used to indicate the level of difficulty.*

(The effects of air resistance are to be ignored in this chapter.)

SECTION 2-1 POSITION, DISTANCE, AND DISPLACEMENT

1. • Referring to Figure 2–20, you walk from your home to the library, then to the park. **(a)** What is the distance traveled? **(b)** What is your displacement?

▲ **FIGURE 2–20** Problems 1 and 4

2. • The two tennis players shown in Figure 2–21 walk to the net to congratulate one another. **(a)** Find the distance traveled and the displacement of player A. **(b)** Repeat for player B.

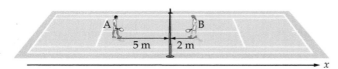

▲ **FIGURE 2–21** Problem 2

3. • The golfer in Figure 2–22 sinks the ball in two putts, as shown. What are **(a)** the distance traveled by the ball, and **(b)** the displacement of the ball?

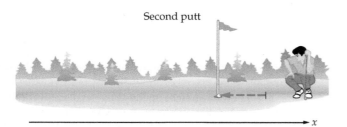

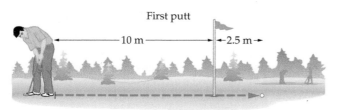

▲ **FIGURE 2–22** Problem 3

4. • In Figure 2–20, you walk from the park to your friend's house, then back to your house. What is your **(a)** distance traveled, and **(b)** displacement?

5. • A jogger runs on the track shown in Figure 2–23. Neglecting the curvature of the corners, **(a)** what is the distance traveled and the displacement in running from point A to point B? **(b)** Find the distance and displacement for a complete circuit of the track.

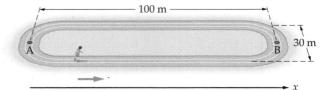

▲ **FIGURE 2–23** Problem 5

6. •• **IP** A child rides a pony on a circular track whose radius is 4.5 m. **(a)** Find the distance traveled and the displacement after the child has gone halfway around the track. **(b)** Does the distance traveled increase, decrease, or stay the same when the child completes one circuit of the track? Explain. **(c)** Does the displacement increase, decrease, or stay the same when the child completes one circuit of the track? Explain. **(d)** Find the distance and displacement after a complete circuit of the track.

SECTION 2-2 AVERAGE SPEED AND VELOCITY

7. • **CE Predict/Explain** You drive your car in a straight line at 15 m/s for 10 kilometers, then at 25 m/s for another 10 kilometers. **(a)** Is your average speed for the entire trip more than, less than, or equal to 20 m/s? **(b)** Choose the *best* explanation from among the following:
  I. More time is spent at 15 m/s than at 25 m/s.
  II. The average of 15 m/s and 25 m/s is 20 m/s.
  III. Less time is spent at 15 m/s than at 25 m/s.

8. • **CE Predict/Explain** You drive your car in a straight line at 15 m/s for 10 minutes, then at 25 m/s for another 10 minutes. **(a)** Is your average speed for the entire trip more than, less than, or equal to 20 m/s? **(b)** Choose the *best* explanation from among the following:
  I. More time is required to drive at 15 m/s than at 25 m/s.
  II. Less distance is covered at 25 m/s than at 15 m/s.
  III. Equal time is spent at 15 m/s and 25 m/s.

9. • Joseph DeLoach of the United States set an Olympic record in 1988 for the 200-meter dash with a time of 19.75 seconds. What was his average speed? Give your answer in meters per second and miles per hour.

10. • In 1992 Zhuang Yong of China set a women's Olympic record in the 100-meter freestyle swim with a time of 54.64 seconds. What was her average speed in m/s and mi/h?

11. • **BIO** Kangaroos have been clocked at speeds of 65 km/h. **(a)** How far can a kangaroo hop in 3.2 minutes at this speed? **(b)** How long will it take a kangaroo to hop 0.25 km at this speed?

12. • **Rubber Ducks** A severe storm on January 10, 1992, caused a cargo ship near the Aleutian Islands to spill 29,000 rubber ducks and other bath toys into the ocean. Ten months later hundreds of rubber ducks began to appear along the shoreline near Sitka, Alaska, roughly 1600 miles away. What was the approximate average speed of the ocean current that carried the ducks to shore in **(a)** m/s and **(b)** mi/h? (Rubber ducks from the same spill began to appear on the coast of Maine in July 2003.)

13. • Radio waves travel at the speed of light, approximately 186,000 miles per second. How long does it take for a radio message to travel from Earth to the Moon and back? (See the inside back cover for the necessary data.)

14. • It was a dark and stormy night, when suddenly you saw a flash of lightning. Three-and-a-half seconds later you heard the thunder. Given that the speed of sound in air is about 340 m/s, how far away was the lightning bolt?

15. • **BIO Nerve Impulses** The human nervous system can propagate nerve impulses at about 10^2 m/s. Estimate the time it takes for a nerve impulse generated when your finger touches a hot object to travel to your brain.

16. • Estimate how fast your hair grows in miles per hour.

17. •• A finch rides on the back of a Galapagos tortoise, which walks at the stately pace of 0.060 m/s. After 1.2 minutes the finch tires of the tortoise's slow pace, and takes flight in the same direction for another 1.2 minutes at 12 m/s. What was the average speed of the finch for this 2.4-minute interval?

18. •• You jog at 9.5 km/h for 8.0 km, then you jump into a car and drive an additional 16 km. With what average speed must you drive your car if your average speed for the entire 24 km is to be 22 km/h?

19. •• A dog runs back and forth between its two owners, who are walking toward one another (**Figure 2–24**). The dog starts running when the owners are 10.0 m apart. If the dog runs with a speed of 3.0 m/s, and the owners each walk with a speed of 1.3 m/s, how far has the dog traveled when the owners meet?

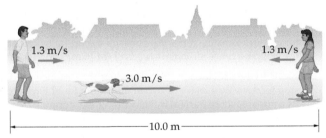

1.3 m/s   1.3 m/s

3.0 m/s

————————10.0 m————————

▲ **FIGURE 2–24** Problem 19

20. •• **IP** You drive in a straight line at 20.0 m/s for 10.0 minutes, then at 30.0 m/s for another 10.0 minutes. **(a)** Is your average speed 25.0 m/s, more than 25.0 m/s, or less than 25.0 m/s? Explain. **(b)** Verify your answer to part (a) by calculating the average speed.

21. •• In heavy rush-hour traffic you drive in a straight line at 12 m/s for 1.5 minutes, then you have to stop for 3.5 minutes, and finally you drive at 15 m/s for another 2.5 minutes. **(a)** Plot a position-versus-time graph for this motion. Your plot should extend from $t = 0$ to $t = 7.5$ minutes. **(b)** Use your plot from part (a) to calculate the average velocity between $t = 0$ and $t = 7.5$ minutes.

22. •• **IP** You drive in a straight line at 20.0 m/s for 10.0 miles, then at 30.0 m/s for another 10.0 miles. **(a)** Is your average speed 25.0 m/s, more than 25.0 m/s, or less than 25.0 m/s? Explain. **(b)** Verify your answer to part (a) by calculating the average speed.

23. •• **IP** An expectant father paces back and forth, producing the position-versus-time graph shown in **Figure 2–25**. Without performing a calculation, indicate whether the father's velocity is positive, negative, or zero on each of the following segments of the graph: **(a)** A, **(b)** B, **(c)** C, and **(d)** D. Calculate the numerical value of the father's velocity for the segments **(e)** A, **(f)** B, **(g)** C, and **(h)** D, and show that your results verify your answers to parts (a)–(d).

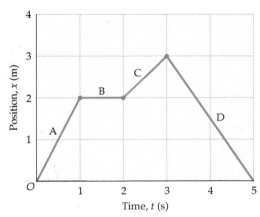

▲ **FIGURE 2–25** Problem 23

24. •• The position of a particle as a function of time is given by $x = (-5 \text{ m/s})t + (3 \text{ m/s}^2)t^2$. **(a)** Plot x versus t for $t = 0$ to $t = 2$ s. **(b)** Find the average velocity of the particle from $t = 0$ to $t = 1$ s. **(c)** Find the average speed from $t = 0$ to $t = 1$ s.

25. •• The position of a particle as a function of time is given by $x = (6 \text{ m/s})t + (-2 \text{ m/s}^2)t^2$. **(a)** Plot x versus t for $t = 0$ to $t = 2$ s. **(b)** Find the average velocity of the particle from $t = 0$ to $t = 1$ s. **(c)** Find the average speed from $t = 0$ to $t = 1$ s.

26. •• **IP** A tennis player moves back and forth along the baseline while waiting for her opponent to serve, producing the position-versus-time graph shown in **Figure 2–26**. **(a)** Without performing a calculation, indicate on which of the segments of the graph, A, B, or C, the player has the greatest speed. Calculate the player's speed for **(b)** segment A, **(c)** segment B, and **(d)** segment C, and show that your results verify your answers to part (a).

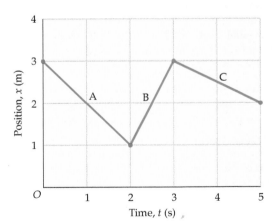

▲ **FIGURE 2–26** Problem 26

27. ••• On your wedding day you leave for the church 30.0 minutes before the ceremony is to begin, which should be plenty of time since the church is only 10.0 miles away. On the way, however, you have to make an unanticipated stop for construction work on the road. As a result, your average speed for the first 15 minutes is only 5.0 mi/h. What average speed do you need for the rest of the trip to get you to the church on time?

SECTION 2-3 INSTANTANEOUS VELOCITY

28. • **CE** The position-versus-time plot of a boat positioning itself next to a dock is shown in **Figure 2–27**. Rank the six points indicated in the plot in order of increasing value of the velocity v, starting with the most negative. Indicate a tie with an equal sign.

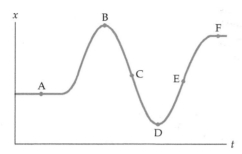

▲ **FIGURE 2–27** Problem 28

29. •• The position of a particle as a function of time is given by $x = (2.0 \text{ m/s})t + (-3.0 \text{ m/s}^3)t^3$. **(a)** Plot x versus t for time from $t = 0$ to $t = 1.0$ s. **(b)** Find the average velocity of the particle from $t = 0.35$ s to $t = 0.45$ s. **(c)** Find the average velocity from $t = 0.39$ s to $t = 0.41$ s. **(d)** Do you expect the instantaneous velocity at $t = 0.40$ s to be closer to 0.54 m/s, 0.56 m/s, or 0.58 m/s? Explain.

30. •• The position of a particle as a function of time is given by $x = (-2.00 \text{ m/s})t + (3.00 \text{ m/s}^3)t^3$. **(a)** Plot x versus t for time from $t = 0$ to $t = 1.00$ s. **(b)** Find the average velocity of the particle from $t = 0.150$ s to $t = 0.250$ s. **(c)** Find the average velocity from $t = 0.190$ s to $t = 0.210$ s. **(d)** Do you expect the instantaneous velocity at $t = 0.200$ s to be closer to −1.62 m/s, or −1.66 m/s? Explain.

SECTION 2-4 ACCELERATION

31. • **CE Predict/Explain** Two bows shoot identical arrows with the same launch speed. To accomplish this, the string in bow 1 must be pulled back farther when shooting its arrow than the string in bow 2. **(a)** Is the acceleration of the arrow shot by bow 1 greater than, less than, or equal to the acceleration of the arrow shot by bow 2? **(b)** Choose the *best explanation* from among the following:
    I. The arrow in bow 2 accelerates for a greater time.
    II. Both arrows start from rest.
    III. The arrow in bow 1 accelerates for a greater time.

32. • A 747 airliner reaches its takeoff speed of 173 mi/h in 35.2 s. What is the magnitude of its average acceleration?

33. • At the starting gun, a runner accelerates at 1.9 m/s² for 5.2 s. The runner's acceleration is zero for the rest of the race. What is the speed of the runner **(a)** at $t = 2.0$ s, and **(b)** at the end of the race?

34. • A jet makes a landing traveling due east with a speed of 115 m/s. If the jet comes to rest in 13.0 s, what are the magnitude and direction of its average acceleration?

35. • A car is traveling due north at 18.1 m/s. Find the velocity of the car after 7.50 s if its acceleration is **(a)** 1.30 m/s² due north, or **(b)** 1.15 m/s² due south.

36. •• A motorcycle moves according to the velocity-versus-time graph shown in **Figure 2–28**. Find the average acceleration of the motorcycle during each of the following segments of the motion: **(a)** A, **(b)** B, and **(c)** C.

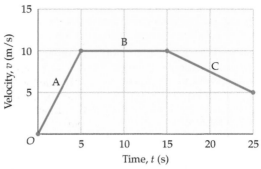

▲ **FIGURE 2–28** Problem 36

37. •• A person on horseback moves according to the velocity-versus-time graph shown in **Figure 2–29**. Find the displacement of the person for each of the following segments of the motion: **(a)** A, **(b)** B, and **(c)** C.

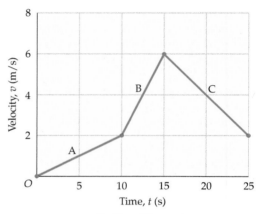

▲ **FIGURE 2–29** Problem 37

38. •• Running with an initial velocity of +11 m/s, a horse has an average acceleration of −1.81 m/s². How long does it take for the horse to decrease its velocity to +6.5 m/s?

39. •• **IP** Assume that the brakes in your car create a constant deceleration of 4.2 m/s² regardless of how fast you are driving. If you double your driving speed from 16 m/s to 32 m/s, **(a)** does the time required to come to a stop increase by a factor of two or a factor of four? Explain. Verify your answer to part (a) by calculating the stopping times for initial speeds of **(b)** 16 m/s and **(c)** 32 m/s.

40. •• **IP** In the previous problem, **(a)** does the distance needed to stop increase by a factor of two or a factor of four? Explain. Verify your answer to part (a) by calculating the stopping distances for initial speeds of **(b)** 16 m/s and **(c)** 32 m/s.

41. •• As a train accelerates away from a station, it reaches a speed of 4.7 m/s in 5.0 s. If the train's acceleration remains constant, what is its speed after an additional 6.0 s has elapsed?

42. •• A particle has an acceleration of +6.24 m/s² for 0.300 s. At the end of this time the particle's velocity is +9.31 m/s. What was the particle's initial velocity?

SECTION 2-5 MOTION WITH CONSTANT ACCELERATION

43. • Landing with a speed of 81.9 m/s, and traveling due south, a jet comes to rest in 949 m. Assuming the jet slows with constant acceleration, find the magnitude and direction of its acceleration.

44. • When you see a traffic light turn red, you apply the brakes until you come to a stop. If your initial speed was 12 m/s, and

you were heading due west, what was your average velocity during braking? Assume constant deceleration.

45. CE •• A ball is released at the point $x = 2$ m on an inclined plane with a nonzero initial velocity. After being released, the ball moves with constant acceleration. The acceleration and initial velocity of the ball are described by one of the following four cases: case 1, $a > 0$, $v_0 > 0$; case 2, $a > 0$, $v_0 < 0$; case 3, $a < 0$, $v_0 > 0$; case 4, $a < 0$, $v_0 < 0$. **(a)** In which of these cases will the ball definitely pass $x = 0$ at some later time? **(b)** In which of these cases is more information needed to determine whether the ball will cross $x = 0$? **(c)** In which of these cases will the ball come to rest momentarily at some time during its motion?

46. •• Suppose the car in Problem 44 comes to rest in 35 m. How much time does this take?

47. •• Starting from rest, a boat increases its speed to 4.12 m/s with constant acceleration. **(a)** What is the boat's average speed? **(b)** If it takes the boat 4.77 s to reach this speed, how far has it traveled?

48. •• **IP BIO** A cheetah can accelerate from rest to 25.0 m/s in 6.22 s. Assuming constant acceleration, **(a)** how far has the cheetah run in this time? **(b)** After sprinting for just 3.11 s, is the cheetah's speed 12.5 m/s, more than 12.5 m/s, or less than 12.5 m/s? Explain. **(c)** What is the cheetah's average speed for the first 3.11 s of its sprint? For the second 3.11 s of its sprint? **(d)** Calculate the distance covered by the cheetah in the first 3.11 s and the second 3.11 s.

SECTION 2–6 APPLICATIONS OF THE EQUATIONS OF MOTION

49. • A child slides down a hill on a toboggan with an acceleration of 1.8 m/s². If she starts at rest, how far has she traveled in **(a)** 1.0 s, **(b)** 2.0 s, and **(c)** 3.0 s?

50. • **The Detonator** On a ride called the Detonator at Worlds of Fun in Kansas City, passengers accelerate straight downward from rest to 45 mi/h in 2.2 seconds. What is the average acceleration of the passengers on this ride?

The Detonator (Problem 50)

51. • **Air Bags** Air bags are designed to deploy in 10 ms. Estimate the acceleration of the front surface of the bag as it expands. Express your answer in terms of the acceleration of gravity g.

52. • **Jules Verne** In his novel *From the Earth to the Moon* (1866), Jules Verne describes a spaceship that is blasted out of a cannon, called the *Columbiad*, with a speed of 12,000 yards/s. The *Columbiad* is 900 ft long, but part of it is packed with powder, so the spaceship accelerates over a distance of only 700 ft. Estimate the acceleration experienced by the occupants of the spaceship during launch. Give your answer in m/s². (Verne realized that

the "travelers would . . . encounter a violent recoil," but he probably didn't know that people generally lose consciousness if they experience accelerations greater than about $7g \sim 70$ m/s².)

53. •• **BIO Bacterial Motion** Approximately 0.1% of the bacteria in an adult human's intestines are *Escherichia coli*. These bacteria have been observed to move with speeds up to 15 μm/s and maximum accelerations of 166 μm/s². Suppose an *E. coli* bacterium in your intestines starts at rest and accelerates at 156 μm/s². How much **(a)** time and **(b)** distance are required for the bacterium to reach a speed of 12 μm/s?

54. •• Two cars drive on a straight highway. At time $t = 0$, car 1 passes mile marker 0 traveling due east with a speed of 20.0 m/s. At the same time, car 2 is 0.10 km east of mile marker 0 traveling at 30.0 m/s due west. Car 1 is speeding up with an acceleration of magnitude 2.5 m/s², and car 2 is slowing down with an acceleration of magnitude 3.2 m/s². **(a)** Write x-versus-t equations of motion for both cars, taking east as the positive direction. **(b)** At what time do the cars pass next to one another?

55. •• **A Meteorite Strikes** On October 9, 1992, a 27-pound meteorite struck a car in Peekskill, NY, leaving a dent 22 cm deep in the trunk. If the meteorite struck the car with a speed of 130 m/s, what was the magnitude of its deceleration, assuming it to be constant?

56. •• A rocket blasts off and moves straight upward from the launch pad with constant acceleration. After 3.0 s the rocket is at a height of 77 m. **(a)** What are the magnitude and direction of the rocket's acceleration? **(b)** What is its speed at this time?

57. •• **IP** You are driving through town at 12.0 m/s when suddenly a ball rolls out in front of you. You apply the brakes and begin decelerating at 3.5 m/s². **(a)** How far do you travel before stopping? **(b)** When you have traveled only half the distance in part (a), is your speed 6.0 m/s, greater than 6.0 m/s, or less than 6.0 m/s? Support your answer with a calculation.

58. •• **IP** You are driving through town at 16 m/s when suddenly a car backs out of a driveway in front of you. You apply the brakes and begin decelerating at 3.2 m/s². **(a)** How much time does it take to stop? **(b)** After braking half the time found in part (a), is your speed 8.0 m/s, greater than 8.0 m/s, or less than 8.0 m/s? Support your answer with a calculation. **(c)** If the car backing out was initially 55 m in front of you, what is the maximum reaction time you can have before hitting the brakes and still avoid hitting the car?

59. •• **IP BIO A Tongue's Acceleration** When a chameleon captures an insect, its tongue can extend 16 cm in 0.10 s. **(a)** Find the magnitude of the tongue's acceleration, assuming it to be constant. **(b)** In the first 0.050 s, does the tongue extend 8.0 cm, more than 8.0 cm, or less than 8.0 cm? Support your conclusion with a calculation.

It's not polite to reach! (Problem 59)

60. •• **IP** Coasting due west on your bicycle at 8.4 m/s, you encounter a sandy patch of road 7.2 m across. When you leave the sandy patch your speed has been reduced by 2.0 m/s to 6.4 m/s. **(a)** Assuming the sand causes a constant acceleration, what was the bicycle's acceleration in the sandy patch? Give both magnitude and direction. **(b)** How long did it take to cross the sandy patch? **(c)** Suppose you enter the sandy patch with a speed of only 5.4 m/s. Is your final speed in this case 3.4 m/s, more than 3.4 m/s, or less than 3.4 m/s? Explain.

61. •• **BIO Surviving a Large Deceleration** On July 13, 1977, while on a test drive at Britain's Silverstone racetrack, the throttle on David Purley's car stuck wide open. The resulting crash subjected Purley to the greatest "*g*-force" ever survived by a human—he decelerated from 173 km/h to zero in a distance of only about 0.66 m. Calculate the magnitude of the acceleration experienced by Purley (assuming it to be constant), and express your answer in units of the acceleration of gravity, $g = 9.81$ m/s^2.

62. •• **IP** A boat is cruising in a straight line at a constant speed of 2.6 m/s when it is shifted into neutral. After coasting 12 m the engine is engaged again, and the boat resumes cruising at the reduced constant speed of 1.6 m/s. Assuming constant acceleration while coasting, **(a)** how long did it take for the boat to coast the 12 m? **(b)** What was the boat's acceleration while it was coasting? **(c)** When the boat had coasted for 6.0 m, was its speed 2.1 m/s, more than 2.1 m/s, or less than 2.1 m/s? Explain.

63. •• A model rocket rises with constant acceleration to a height of 3.2 m, at which point its speed is 26.0 m/s. **(a)** How much time does it take for the rocket to reach this height? **(b)** What was the magnitude of the rocket's acceleration? **(c)** Find the height and speed of the rocket 0.10 s after launch.

64. •• The infamous chicken is dashing toward home plate with a speed of 5.8 m/s when he decides to hit the dirt. The chicken slides for 1.1 s, just reaching the plate as he stops (safe, of course). **(a)** What are the magnitude and direction of the chicken's acceleration? **(b)** How far did the chicken slide?

65. •• A bicyclist is finishing his repair of a flat tire when a friend rides by with a constant speed of 3.5 m/s. Two seconds later the bicyclist hops on his bike and accelerates at 2.4 m/s^2 until he catches his friend. **(a)** How much time does it take until he catches his friend? **(b)** How far has he traveled in this time? **(c)** What is his speed when he catches up?

66. •• A car in stop-and-go traffic starts at rest, moves forward 13 m in 8.0 s, then comes to rest again. The velocity-versus-time plot for this car is given in **Figure 2–30**. What distance does the car cover in **(a)** the first 4.0 seconds of its motion and **(b)** the last 2.0 seconds of its motion? **(c)** What is the constant speed *V* that characterizes the middle portion of its motion?

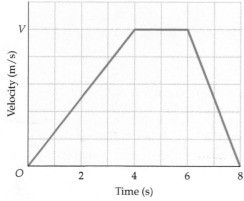

▲ **FIGURE 2–30** Problem 66

67. ••• A car and a truck are heading directly toward one another on a straight and narrow street, but they avoid a head-on collision by simultaneously applying their brakes at $t = 0$. The resulting velocity-versus-time graphs are shown in **Figure 2–31**. What is the separation between the car and the truck when they have come to rest, given that at $t = 0$ the car is at $x = 15$ m and the truck is at $x = -35$ m? (Note that this information determines which line in the graph corresponds to which vehicle.)

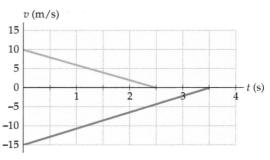

▲ **FIGURE 2–31** Problem 67

68. ••• In a physics lab, students measure the time it takes a small cart to slide a distance of 1.00 m on a smooth track inclined at an angle θ above the horizontal. Their results are given in the following table.

θ	10.0°	20.0°	30.0°
time, s	1.08	0.770	0.640

(a) Find the magnitude of the cart's acceleration for each angle. **(b)** Show that your results for part (a) are in close agreement with the formula, $a = g \sin \theta$. (We will derive this formula in Chapter 5.)

SECTION 2–7 FREELY FALLING OBJECTS

"IT GOES FROM ZERO TO SIXTY IN ABOUT THREE SECONDS."

(Problems 71 and 72)

69. • **CE** At the edge of a roof you throw ball 1 upward with an initial speed v_0; a moment later you throw ball 2 downward with the same initial speed. The balls land at the same time. Which of the following statements is true for the instant just before the balls hit the ground? **A.** The speed of ball 1 is greater than the speed of ball 2; **B.** The speed of ball 1 is equal to the speed of ball 2; **C.** The speed of ball 1 is less than the speed of ball 2.

70. • Legend has it that Isaac Newton was hit on the head by a falling apple, thus triggering his thoughts on gravity. Assuming the story to be true, estimate the speed of the apple when it struck Newton.

71. • The cartoon shows a car in free fall. Is the statement made in the cartoon accurate? Justify your answer.

72. • Referring to the cartoon in Problem 71, how long would it take for the car to go from 0 to 30 mi/h?

73. • **Jordan's Jump** Michael Jordan's vertical leap is reported to be 48 inches. What is his takeoff speed? Give your answer in meters per second.

74. • **BIO** Gulls are often observed dropping clams and other shellfish from a height to the rocks below, as a means of opening the shells. If a seagull drops a shell from rest at a height of 14 m, how fast is the shell moving when it hits the rocks?

75. • A volcano launches a lava bomb straight upward with an initial speed of 28 m/s. Taking upward to be the positive direction, find the speed and direction of motion of the lava bomb **(a)** 2.0 seconds and **(b)** 3.0 seconds after it is launched.

76. • **An Extraterrestrial Volcano** The first active volcano observed outside the Earth was discovered in 1979 on Io, one of the moons of Jupiter. The volcano was observed to be ejecting material to a height of about 2.00×10^5 m. Given that the acceleration of gravity on Io is 1.80 m/s^2, find the initial velocity of the ejected material.

77. • **BIO Measure Your Reaction Time** Here's something you *can* try at home—an experiment to measure your reaction time. Have a friend hold a ruler by one end, letting the other end hang down vertically. At the lower end, hold your thumb and index finger on either side of the ruler, ready to grip it. Have your friend release the ruler without warning. Catch it as quickly as you can. If you catch the ruler 5.2 cm from the lower end, what is your reaction time?

How fast are your reactions? (Problem 77)

78. •• **CE Predict/Explain** A carpenter on the roof of a building accidentally drops her hammer. As the hammer falls it passes two windows of equal height, as shown in **Figure 2–32. (a)** Is the *increase* in speed of the hammer as it drops past window 1 greater than, less than, or equal to the *increase* in speed as it drops past window 2? **(b)** Choose the *best explanation* from among the following:
  I. The greater speed at window 2 results in a greater increase in speed.
  II. Constant acceleration means the hammer speeds up the same amount for each window.
  III. The hammer spends more time dropping past window 1.

▲ **FIGURE 2–32** Problem 78

79. •• **CE Predict/Explain Figure 2–33** shows a v-versus-t plot for the hammer dropped by the carpenter in Problem 78. Notice that the times when the hammer passes the two windows are indicated by shaded areas. **(a)** Is the area of the shaded region corresponding to window 1 greater than, less than, or equal to the area of the shaded region corresponding to window 2? **(b)** Choose the *best explanation* from among the following:
  I. The shaded area for window 2 is higher than the shaded area for window 1.
  II. The windows are equally tall.
  III. The shaded area for window 1 is wider than the shaded area for window 2.

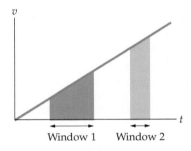

▲ **FIGURE 2–33** Problem 79

80. •• **CE** A ball is thrown straight upward with an initial speed v_0. When it reaches the top of its flight at height h, a second ball is thrown straight upward with the same initial speed. Do the balls cross paths at height $\frac{1}{2}h$, above $\frac{1}{2}h$, or below $\frac{1}{2}h$?

81. •• Bill steps off a 3.0-m-high diving board and drops to the water below. At the same time, Ted jumps upward with a speed of 4.2 m/s from a 1.0-m-high diving board. Choosing the origin to be at the water's surface, and upward to be the positive x direction, write x-versus-t equations of motion for both Bill and Ted.

82. •• Repeat the previous problem, this time with the origin 3.0 m above the water, and with downward as the positive *x* direction.

83. •• On a hot summer day in the state of Washington while kayaking, I saw several swimmers jump from a railroad bridge into the Snohomish River below. The swimmers stepped off the bridge, and I estimated that they hit the water 1.5 s later. **(a)** How high was the bridge? **(b)** How fast were the swimmers moving when they hit the water? **(c)** What would the swimmers' drop time be if the bridge were twice as high?

84. •• **Highest Water Fountain** The world's highest fountain of water is located, appropriately enough, in Fountain Hills, Arizona. The fountain rises to a height of 560 ft (5 feet higher than the Washington Monument). **(a)** What is the initial speed of the water? **(b)** How long does it take for water to reach the top of the fountain?

85. •• Wrongly called for a foul, an angry basketball player throws the ball straight down to the floor. If the ball bounces straight up and returns to the floor 2.8 s after first striking it, what was the ball's greatest height above the floor?

86. •• To celebrate a victory, a pitcher throws her glove straight upward with an initial speed of 6.0 m/s. **(a)** How long does it take for the glove to return to the pitcher? **(b)** How long does it take for the glove to reach its maximum height?

87. •• **IP** Standing at the edge of a cliff 32.5 m high, you drop a ball. Later, you throw a second ball downward with an initial speed of 11.0 m/s. **(a)** Which ball has the greater *increase* in speed when it reaches the base of the cliff, or do both balls speed up by the same amount? **(b)** Verify your answer to part (a) with a calculation.

88. •• You shoot an arrow into the air. Two seconds later (2.00 s) the arrow has gone straight upward to a height of 30.0 m above its launch point. **(a)** What was the arrow's initial speed? **(b)** How long did it take for the arrow to first reach a height of 15.0 m above its launch point?

89. •• While riding on an elevator descending with a constant speed of 3.0 m/s, you accidentally drop a book from under your arm. **(a)** How long does it take for the book to reach the elevator floor, 1.2 m below your arm? **(b)** What is the book's speed relative to you when it hits the elevator floor?

90. •• A hot-air balloon is descending at a rate of 2.0 m/s when a passenger drops a camera. If the camera is 45 m above the ground when it is dropped, **(a)** how long does it take for the camera to reach the ground, and **(b)** what is its velocity just before it lands? Let upward be the positive direction for this problem.

91. •• **IP** Standing side by side, you and a friend step off a bridge at different times and fall for 1.6 s to the water below. Your friend goes first, and you follow after she has dropped a distance of 2.0 m. **(a)** When your friend hits the water, is the separation between the two of you 2.0 m, less than 2.0 m, or more than 2.0 m? **(b)** Verify your answer to part (a) with a calculation.

92. •• A model rocket blasts off and moves upward with an acceleration of 12 m/s² until it reaches a height of 26 m, at which point its engine shuts off and it continues its flight in free fall. **(a)** What is the maximum height attained by the rocket? **(b)** What is the speed of the rocket just before it hits the ground? **(c)** What is the total duration of the rocket's flight?

93. ••• **Hitting the "High Striker"** A young woman at a carnival steps up to the "high striker," a popular test of strength where the contestant hits one end of a lever with a mallet, propelling a small metal plug upward toward a bell. She gives the mallet a mighty swing and sends the plug to the top of the striker, where it rings the bell. **Figure 2–34** shows the corresponding position-versus-time plot for the plug. Using the in-

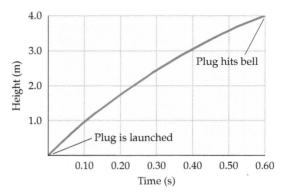

▲ **FIGURE 2–34** Problem 93

formation given in the plot, answer the following questions: **(a)** What is the average speed of the plug during its upward journey? **(b)** By how much does the speed of the plug decrease during its upward journey? **(c)** What is the initial speed of the plug? (Assume the plug to be in free fall during its upward motion, with no effects of air resistance or friction.)

94. ••• While sitting on a tree branch 10.0 m above the ground, you drop a chestnut. When the chestnut has fallen 2.5 m, you throw a second chestnut straight down. What initial speed must you give the second chestnut if they are both to reach the ground at the same time?

GENERAL PROBLEMS

95. • In a well-known Jules Verne novel, Phileas Fogg travels around the world in 80 days. What was Mr. Fogg's approximate average speed during his adventure?

96. • An astronaut on the Moon drops a rock straight downward from a height of 1.25 m. If the acceleration of gravity on the Moon is 1.62 m/s², what is the speed of the rock just before it lands?

97. • You jump from the top of a boulder to the ground 1.5 m below. Estimate your deceleration on landing.

98. • **A Supersonic Waterfall** Geologists have learned of periods in the past when the Strait of Gibraltar closed off, and the Mediterranean Sea dried out and become a desert. Later, when the strait reopened, a massive saltwater waterfall was created. According to geologists, the water in this waterfall was supersonic; that is, it fell with speeds in excess of the speed of sound. Ignoring air resistance, what is the minimum height necessary to create a supersonic waterfall? (The speed of sound may be taken to be 340 m/s.)

99. •• **CE** At the edge of a roof you drop ball A from rest, and then throw ball B downward with an initial velocity of v_0. Is the increase in speed just before the balls land more for ball A, more for ball B, or the same for each ball?

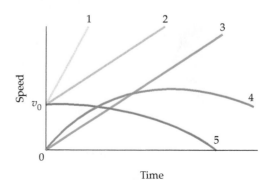

▲ **FIGURE 2–35** Problem 100

100. •• **CE** Suppose the two balls described in Problem 99 are released at the same time, with ball A dropped from rest and ball B thrown downward with an initial speed v_0. Identify which of the five plots shown in **Figure 2–35** corresponds to **(a)** ball A and **(b)** ball B.

101. •• Astronauts on a distant planet throw a rock straight upward and record its motion with a video camera. After digitizing their video, they are able to produce the graph of height, y, versus time, t, shown in **Figure 2–36**. **(a)** What is the acceleration of gravity on this planet? **(b)** What was the initial speed of the rock?

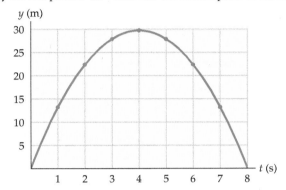

▲ **FIGURE 2–36** Problem 101

102. •• **Drop Tower** NASA operates a 2.2-second drop tower at the Glenn Research Center in Cleveland, Ohio. At this facility, experimental packages are dropped from the top of the tower, on the 8th floor of the building. During their 2.2 seconds of free fall, experiments experience a microgravity environment similar to that of a spacecraft in orbit. **(a)** What is the drop distance of a 2.2-s tower? **(b)** How fast are the experiments traveling when they hit the air bags at the bottom of the tower? **(c)** If the experimental package comes to rest over a distance of 0.75 m upon hitting the air bags, what is the average stopping acceleration?

103. •• **IP** A youngster bounces straight up and down on a trampoline. Suppose she doubles her initial speed from 2.0 m/s to 4.0 m/s. **(a)** By what factor does her time in the air increase? **(b)** By what factor does her maximum height increase? **(c)** Verify your answers to parts (a) and (b) with an explicit calculation.

104. •• At the 18th green of the U.S. Open you need to make a 20.5-ft putt to win the tournament. When you hit the ball, giving it an initial speed of 1.57 m/s, it stops 6.00 ft short of the hole. **(a)** Assuming the deceleration caused by the grass is constant, what should the initial speed have been to just make the putt? **(b)** What initial speed do you need to make the remaining 6.00-ft putt?

105. •• **IP** A popular entertainment at some carnivals is the blanket toss (see photo, p. 39). **(a)** If a person is thrown to a maximum height of 28.0 ft above the blanket, how long does she spend in the air? **(b)** Is the amount of time the person is above a height of 14.0 ft more than, less than, or equal to the amount of time the person is below a height of 14.0 ft? Explain. **(c)** Verify your answer to part (b) with a calculation.

106. •• Referring to Conceptual Checkpoint 2–5, find the separation between the rocks at **(a)** $t = 1.0$ s, **(b)** $t = 2.0$ s, and **(c)** $t = 3.0$ s, where time is measured from the instant the second rock is dropped. **(d)** Verify that the separation increases linearly with time.

107. •• **IP** A glaucous-winged gull, ascending straight upward at 5.20 m/s, drops a shell when it is 12.5 m above the ground. **(a)** What are the magnitude and direction of the shell's acceleration just after it is released? **(b)** Find the maximum height above the ground reached by the shell. **(c)** How long does it take for the shell to reach the ground? **(d)** What is the speed of the shell at this time?

108. •• A doctor, preparing to give a patient an injection, squirts a small amount of liquid straight upward from a syringe. If the liquid emerges with a speed of 1.5 m/s, **(a)** how long does it take for it to return to the level of the syringe? **(b)** What is the maximum height of the liquid above the syringe?

109. •• A hot-air balloon has just lifted off and is rising at the constant rate of 2.0 m/s. Suddenly one of the passengers realizes she has left her camera on the ground. A friend picks it up and tosses it straight upward with an initial speed of 13 m/s. If the passenger is 2.5 m above her friend when the camera is tossed, how high is she when the camera reaches her?

110. ••• In the previous problem, what is the minimum initial speed of the camera if it is to just reach the passenger? (*Hint:* When the camera is thrown with its minimum speed, its speed on reaching the passenger is the same as the speed of the passenger.)

111. ••• **Old Faithful** Watching Old Faithful erupt, you notice that it takes a time t for water to emerge from the base of the geyser and reach its maximum height. **(a)** What is the height of the geyser, and **(b)** what is the initial speed of the water? Evaluate your expressions for **(c)** the height and **(d)** the initial speed for a measured time of 1.65 s.

112. ••• **IP** A ball is thrown upward with an initial speed v_0. When it reaches the top of its flight, at a height h, a second ball is thrown upward with the same initial velocity. **(a)** Sketch an x-versus-t plot for each ball. **(b)** From your graph, decide whether the balls cross paths at $h/2$, above $h/2$, or below $h/2$. **(c)** Find the height where the paths cross.

113. ••• Weights are tied to each end of a 20.0-cm string. You hold one weight in your hand and let the other hang vertically a height h above the floor. When you release the weight in your hand, the two weights strike the ground one after the other with audible thuds. Find the value of h for which the time between release and the first thud is equal to the time between the first thud and the second thud.

114. ••• A ball, dropped from rest, covers three-quarters of the distance to the ground in the last second of its fall. **(a)** From what height was the ball dropped? **(b)** What was the total time of fall?

115. ••• A stalactite on the roof of a cave drips water at a steady rate to a pool 4.0 m below. As one drop of water hits the pool, a second drop is in the air, and a third is just detaching from the stalactite. **(a)** What are the position and velocity of the second drop when the first drop hits the pool? **(b)** How many drops per minute fall into the pool?

116. ••• You drop a ski glove from a height h onto fresh snow, and it sinks to a depth d before coming to rest. **(a)** In terms of g and h, what is the speed of the glove when it reaches the snow? **(b)** What are the magnitude and direction of the glove's acceleration as it moves through the snow, assuming it to be constant? Give your answer in terms of g, h, and d.

117. ••• To find the height of an overhead power line, you throw a ball straight upward. The ball passes the line on the way up after 0.75 s, and passes it again on the way down 1.5 s after it was tossed. What are the height of the power line and the initial speed of the ball?

118. ••• Suppose the first rock in Conceptual Checkpoint 2–5 drops through a height h before the second rock is released from rest. Show that the separation between the rocks, S, is given by the following expression:

$$S = h + (\sqrt{2gh})t$$

In this result, the time t is measured from the time the second rock is dropped.

119. ••• An arrow is fired with a speed of 20.0 m/s at a block of Styrofoam resting on a smooth surface. The arrow penetrates a certain distance into the block before coming to rest relative to it. During this process the arrow's deceleration has a magnitude of 1550 m/s^2 and the block's acceleration has a magnitude of 450 m/s^2. **(a)** How long does it take for the arrow to stop moving with respect to the block? **(b)** What is the common speed of the arrow and block when this happens? **(c)** How far into the block does the arrow penetrate?

120. ••• Sitting in a second-story apartment, a physicist notices a ball moving straight upward just outside her window. The ball is visible for 0.25 s as it moves a distance of 1.05 m from the bottom to the top of the window. **(a)** How long does it take before the ball reappears? **(b)** What is the greatest height of the ball above the top of the window?

121. ••• **The Quadratic Formula from Kinematics** In this problem we show how the kinematic equations of motion can be used to derive the quadratic formula. First, consider an object with an initial position x_0, an initial velocity v_0, and an acceleration a. To find the time when this object reaches the position $x = 0$ we can use the quadratic formula, or apply the following two-step procedure: **(a)** Use Equation 2–12 to show that the velocity of the object when it reaches $x = 0$ is given by $v = \pm\sqrt{v_0{}^2 - 2ax_0}$. **(b)** Use Equation 2–7 to show that the time corresponding to the velocity found in part (a) is $t = \dfrac{-v_0 \pm \sqrt{v_0{}^2 - 2ax_0}}{a}$. **(c)** To complete our derivation, show that the result of part (b) is the same as applying the quadratic formula to $x = x_0 + v_0 t + \frac{1}{2}at^2 = 0$.

PASSAGE PROBLEMS

Bam!—*Apollo 15* Lands on the Moon

The first word spoken on the surface of the Moon after *Apollo 15* landed on July 30, 1971, was "Bam!" This was James Irwin's involuntary reaction to their rather bone-jarring touchdown. "We did hit harder than any of the other flights!" says Irwin. "And I was startled, obviously, when I said, 'Bam!'"

The reason for the "firm touchdown" of *Apollo 15,* as pilot David Scott later characterized it, was that the rocket engine was shut off a bit earlier than planned, when the lander was still 4.30 ft above the lunar surface and moving downward with a speed of 0.500 ft/s. From that point on the lander descended in lunar free fall, with an acceleration of 1.62 m/s^2. As a result, the landing speed of *Apollo 15* was by far the largest of any of the *Apollo* missions. In comparison, Neil Armstrong's landing speed on *Apollo 11* was the lowest at 1.7 ft/s—he didn't shut off the engine until the footpads were actually on the surface. *Apollos 12, 14,* and *17* all landed with speeds between 3.0 and 3.5 ft/s.

To better understand the descent of *Apollo 15,* we show its trajectory during the final stages of landing in **Figure 2–37 (a)**. In **Figure 2–37 (b)** we show a variety of speed-versus-time plots.

122. • How long did it take for the lander to drop the final 4.30 ft to the Moon's surface?

A. 1.18 s   **B.** 1.37 s

C. 1.78 s   **D.** 2.36 s

123. •• What was the impact speed of the lander when it touched down? Give your answer in feet per second (ft/s), the same units used by the astronauts.

A. 2.41 ft/s   **B.** 6.78 ft/s

C. 9.95 ft/s   **D.** 10.6 ft/s

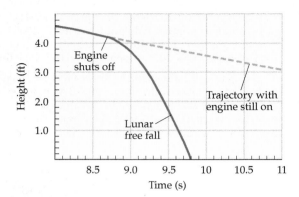

(a)

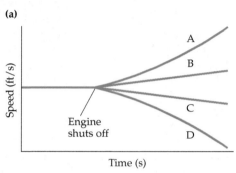

(b)

▲ **FIGURE 2–37** Problems 122, 123, 124, and 125

124. • Which of the speed-versus-time plots in Figure 2–37 (b) correctly represents the speed of the *Apollo 15* lander?

A   B   C   D

125. • Suppose, instead of shutting off the engine, the astronauts had increased its thrust, giving the lander a small, but constant, upward acceleration. Which speed-versus-time plot in Figure 2–37 (b) would describe this situation?

A   B   C   D

INTERACTIVE PROBLEMS

126. •• **Referring to Example 2–9** Suppose the speeder (red car) is traveling with a constant speed of 25 m/s, and that the maximum acceleration of the police car (blue car) is 3.8 m/s^2. If the police car is to start from rest and catch the speeder in 15 s or less, what is the maximum head-start distance the speeder can have? Measure time from the moment the police car starts.

127. •• **Referring to Example 2–9** The speeder passes the position of the police car with a constant speed of 15 m/s. The police car immediately starts from rest and pursues the speeder with constant acceleration. What acceleration must the police car have if it is to catch the speeder in 7.0 s? Measure time from the moment the police car starts.

128. •• **IP Referring to Example 2–12 (a)** In Example 2–12, the bag of sand is released at 20.0 m and reaches a maximum height of 22 m. If the bag had been released at 30.0 m instead, with everything else remaining the same, would its maximum height be 32 m, greater than 32 m, or less than 32 m? **(b)** Find the speed of the bag just before it lands when it is released from 30.0 m.

129. •• **Referring to Example 2–12** Suppose the balloon is descending with a constant speed of 4.2 m/s when the bag of sand comes loose at a height of 35 m. **(a)** How long is the bag in the air? **(b)** What is the speed of the bag when it is 15 m above the ground?

3 Vectors in Physics

The points of the compass have long been used as a framework for indicating directions. The compass shown here was produced by Gowin Knight (1713–1772), whose improved designs were adopted by the Royal Navy in 1752. In physics, we more frequently indicate directions with *x* and *y* rather than N, S, E, and W. Either way, specifying a direction as well as a magnitude is essential to defining one of the physicist's basic tools, the vector.

Of all the mathematical tools used in this book, perhaps none is more important than the vector. In the next chapter, for example, we use vectors to extend our study of motion from one dimension to two dimensions. More generally, vectors are *indispensable* when a physical quantity has a direction associated with it. Suppose, for example, that a pilot wants to fly from Denver to Dallas. If the air is still, the pilot can simply head the plane toward the destination. If there is a wind blowing from west to east, however, the pilot must use vectors to determine the correct heading so that the plane and its passengers will arrive in Dallas and not Little Rock.

In this chapter we discuss what a vector is, how it differs from a scalar, and how it can represent a physical quantity. We also show how to find the components of a vector and how to add and subtract vectors. All of these techniques are used time and again throughout the book. Other useful aspects of vectors, such as how to multiply them, will be presented in later chapters when the need arises.

▲ **FIGURE 3–1 Distance and direction**
If you know only that the library is 0.5 mi from you, it could lie anywhere on a circle of radius 0.5 mi. If, instead, you are told the library is 0.5 mi northwest, you know its precise location.

▲ The information given by this sign includes both a distance and a direction for each city. In effect, the sign defines a displacement vector for each of these destinations.

3–1 Scalars Versus Vectors

Numbers can represent many quantities in physics. For example, a numerical value, together with the appropriate units, can specify the volume of a container, the temperature of the air, or the time of an event. In physics, a number with its units is referred to as a **scalar**:

- A scalar is a number with units. It can be positive, negative, or zero.

Sometimes, however, a scalar isn't enough to adequately describe a physical quantity—in many cases, a direction is needed as well. For example, suppose you're walking in an unfamiliar city and you want directions to the library. You ask a passerby, "Do you know where the library is?" If the person replies "Yes," and walks on, he hasn't been too helpful. If he says, "Yes, it is half a mile from here," that is more helpful, but you still don't know where it is. The library could be anywhere on a circle of radius one-half mile, as shown in **Figure 3–1**. To pin down the location, you need a reply such as, "Yes, the library is half a mile northwest of here." With both a distance *and* a direction, you know the location of the library.

Thus, if you walk northwest for half a mile you arrive at the library, as indicated by the upper left arrow in Figure 3–1. The arrow points in the direction traveled, and its **magnitude,** 0.5 mi in this case, represents the distance covered. In general, a quantity that is specified by both a *magnitude* and a *direction* is represented by a **vector**:

- A vector is a mathematical quantity with both a direction and a magnitude.

In the example of walking to the library, the vector corresponding to the trip is the displacement vector. Other examples of vector quantities are the velocity and the acceleration of an object. For example, the magnitude of a velocity vector is its speed, and its direction is the direction of motion, as we shall see later in this chapter.

When we indicate a vector on a diagram or a sketch, we draw an arrow, as in Figure 3–1. To indicate a vector with a written symbol, we use **boldface** for the vector itself, with a small arrow above it to remind us of its vector nature, and *italic* for its magnitude. Thus, for example, the upper-left vector in Figure 3–1 is designated by the symbol $\vec{r}$, and its magnitude is $r = 0.5$ mi. (When we represent a vector in a graph, we sometimes label it with the corresponding boldface symbol, and sometimes with the appropriate magnitude.) It is common in handwritten material to draw a small arrow over the vector's symbol, which is very similar to the way vectors are represented in this text.

3–2 The Components of a Vector

When we discussed directions for finding a library in the previous section, we pointed out that knowing the magnitude and direction angle—0.5 mi northwest—gives its precise location. We left out one key element in actually *getting* to the library, however. In most cities it would not be possible to simply walk in a straight line for 0.5 mi directly to the library, since to do so would take you through buildings where there are no doors, through people's backyards, and through all kinds of other obstructions. In fact, if the city streets are laid out along north–south and east–west directions, you might instead walk west for a certain distance, then turn and proceed north an equal distance until you reach the library, as illustrated in **Figure 3–2**. What you have just done is "resolved" displacement vector $\vec{r}$ between you and the library into east–west and north–south "components."

In general, to find the components of a vector we need to set up a coordinate system. In two dimensions we choose an origin, O, and a positive direction for both the x and the y axes, as in **Figure 3–3**. If the system were three-dimensional, we would also indicate a z axis.

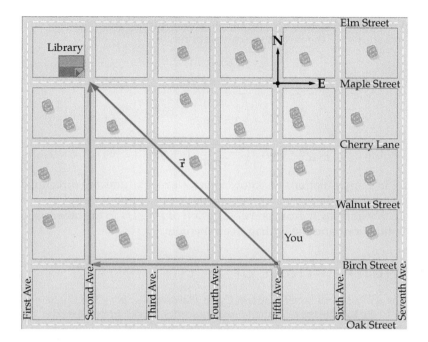

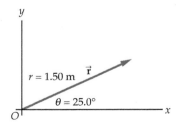

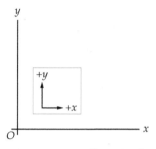

◀ **FIGURE 3–2 A walk along city streets to the library**

By taking the indicated path, we have "resolved" the vector $\vec{r}$ into east–west and north–south components.

▲ **FIGURE 3–3 A two-dimensional coordinate system**

The positive x and y directions are indicated in this shorthand form.

PROBLEM-SOLVING NOTE

A Vector and Its Components

Given the magnitude and direction of a vector, find its components:

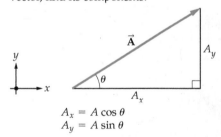

$$A_x = A \cos \theta$$
$$A_y = A \sin \theta$$

Given the components of a vector, find its magnitude and direction:

$$A = \sqrt{A_x^2 + A_y^2}$$
$$\theta = \tan^{-1}\frac{A_y}{A_x}$$

Now, a vector is defined by its magnitude (indicated by the length of the arrow representing the vector) and its direction. For example, suppose an ant leaves its nest at the origin and, after foraging for some time, is at the location given by the vector $\vec{r}$ in **Figure 3–4 (a)**. This vector has a magnitude $r = 1.50$ m and points in a direction $\theta = 25.0°$ above the x axis. Equivalently, $\vec{r}$ can be defined by saying that it extends a distance r_x in the x direction and a distance r_y in the y direction, as shown in **Figure 3–4 (b)**. The quantities r_x and r_y are referred to as the x and y **scalar components** of the vector $\vec{r}$.

We can find r_x and r_y by using standard trigonometric relations, as summarized in the Problem-Solving Note on this page. Referring to Figure 3–4 (b), we see that

$$r_x = r \cos 25.0° = (1.50 \text{ m})(0.906) = 1.36 \text{ m}$$

and

$$r_y = r \sin 25.0° = (1.50 \text{ m})(0.423) = 0.634 \text{ m}$$

Thus, we can say that the ant's final displacement is equivalent to what it would be if the ant had simply walked 1.36 m in the x direction and then 0.634 m in the y direction.

To show the equivalence of these two ways of describing a vector, let's start with the components of $\vec{r}$, as determined previously, and use them to calculate the magnitude r and the angle θ. First, note that r_x, r_y, and r form a right triangle with r as the hypotenuse. Thus, we can use the Pythagorean theorem (Appendix A) to find r in terms of r_x and r_y. This gives

$$r = \sqrt{r_x^2 + r_y^2} = \sqrt{(1.36 \text{ m})^2 + (0.634 \text{ m})^2} = \sqrt{2.25 \text{ m}^2} = 1.50 \text{ m}$$

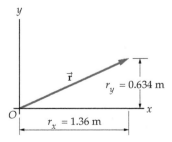

(a) A vector defined in terms of its length and direction angle

(b) The same vector defined in terms of its x and y components

◀ **FIGURE 3–4 A vector and its scalar components**

(a) The vector $\vec{r}$ is defined by its length ($r = 1.50$ m) and its direction angle ($\theta = 25.0°$) measured counterclockwise from the positive x axis. **(b)** Alternatively, the vector $\vec{r}$ can be defined by its x component, $r_x = 1.36$ m, and its y component, $r_y = 0.634$ m.

as expected. Second, we can use any two sides of the triangle to obtain the angle θ, as shown in the next three calculations:

$$\theta = \sin^{-1}\left(\frac{0.634 \text{ m}}{1.50 \text{ m}}\right) = \sin^{-1}(0.423) = 25.0°$$

$$\theta = \cos^{-1}\left(\frac{1.36 \text{ m}}{1.50 \text{ m}}\right) = \cos^{-1}(0.907) = 25.0°$$

$$\theta = \tan^{-1}\left(\frac{0.634 \text{ m}}{1.36 \text{ m}}\right) = \tan^{-1}(0.466) = 25.0°$$

In some situations we know a vector's magnitude and direction; in other cases we are given the vector's components. You will find it useful to be able to convert quickly and easily from one description of a vector to the other using trigonometric functions and the Pythagorean theorem.

EXAMPLE 3–1 DETERMINING THE HEIGHT OF A CLIFF

 REAL-WORLD PHYSICS In the Jules Verne novel *Mysterious Island*, Captain Cyrus Harding wants to find the height of a cliff. He stands with his back to the base of the cliff, then marches straight away from it for 5.00×10^2 ft. At this point he lies on the ground and measures the angle from the horizontal to the top of the cliff. If the angle is 34.0°, **(a)** how high is the cliff? **(b)** What is the straight-line distance from Captain Harding to the top of the cliff?

PICTURE THE PROBLEM
Our sketch shows Cyrus Harding making his measurement of the angle, $\theta = 34.0°$, to the top of the cliff. The relevant triangle for this problem is also indicated. Note that the opposite side of the triangle is the height of the cliff, h; the adjacent side is the distance from the base of the cliff to Harding, $b = 5.00 \times 10^2$ ft; and finally, the hypotenuse is the distance, d, from Harding to the top of the cliff.

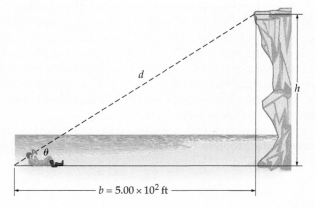

STRATEGY
The tangent of θ is the height of the triangle divided by the base: $\tan \theta = h/b$. Since we know both θ and the base, we can find the height using this relation. Similarly, the distance from Harding to the top of the cliff can be obtained by solving $\cos \theta = b/d$ for d.

SOLUTION

Part (a)

1. Use $\tan \theta = h/b$ to solve for the height of the cliff, h:

$$h = b \tan \theta = (5.00 \times 10^2 \text{ ft}) \tan 34.0° = 337 \text{ ft}$$

Part (b)

2. Similarly, use $\cos \theta = b/d$ to solve for the distance d from Captain Harding to the top of the cliff:

$$d = \frac{b}{\cos \theta} = \frac{5.00 \times 10^2 \text{ ft}}{\cos 34.0°} = 603 \text{ ft}$$

INSIGHT
An alternative way to solve part (b) is to use the Pythagorean theorem:

$$d = \sqrt{h^2 + b^2} = \sqrt{(337 \text{ ft})^2 + (5.00 \times 10^2 \text{ ft})^2} = 603 \text{ ft}$$

Thus, if we let $\vec{r}$ denote the vector from Cyrus Harding to the top of the cliff, as shown here, its magnitude is 603 ft and its direction is 34.0° above the x axis. Alternatively, the x component of $\vec{r}$ is 5.00×10^2 ft and its y component is 337 ft.

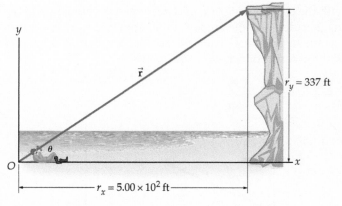

PRACTICE PROBLEM
What angle would Cyrus Harding have found if he had walked 6.00×10^2 ft from the cliff to make his measurement?
[**Answer:** $\theta = 29.3°$]

Some related homework problems: Problem 5, Problem 17

EXERCISE 3–1

a. Find A_x and A_y for the vector $\vec{A}$ with magnitude and direction given by $A = 3.5$ m and $\theta = 66°$, respectively.

b. Find B and θ for the vector $\vec{B}$ with components $B_x = 75.5$ m and $B_y = 6.20$ m.

SOLUTION

a. $A_x = 1.4$ m, $A_y = 3.2$ m

b. $B = 75.8$ m, $\theta = 4.69°$

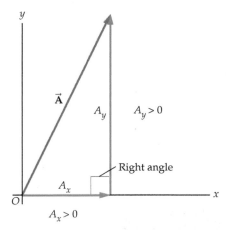

▲ **FIGURE 3–5** **A vector whose x and y components are positive**

Next, how do you determine the correct signs for the x and y components of a vector? This can be done by considering the right triangle formed by A_x, A_y, and $\vec{A}$, as shown in **Figure 3–5**. To determine the sign of A_x, start at the tail of the vector and move along the x axis toward the right angle. If you are moving in the positive x direction, then A_x is positive ($A_x > 0$); if you are moving in the negative x direction, then A_x is negative ($A_x < 0$). For the y component, start at the right angle and move toward the tip of the arrow. A_y is positive or negative depending on whether you are moving in the positive or negative y direction.

For example, consider the vector shown in **Figure 3–6 (a)**. In this case, $A_x > 0$ and $A_y < 0$, as indicated in the figure. Similarly, the signs of A_x and A_y are given in **Figure 3–6 (b, c, d)** for the vectors shown there. Be sure to verify each of these cases by applying the rules just given. As we continue our study of physics, it is important to be able to find the components of a vector *and* to assign to them the correct signs.

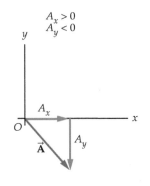

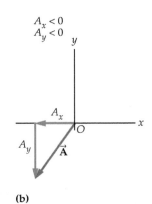

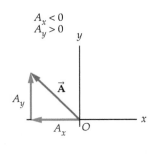

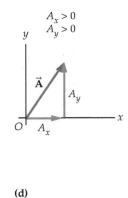

(a)   (b)   (c)   (d)

▲ **FIGURE 3–6** **Examples of vectors with components of different signs**

To determine the signs of a vector's components, it is only necessary to observe the direction in which they point. For example, in part (a) the x component points in the positive direction; hence $A_x > 0$. Similarly, the y component in part (a) points in the negative y direction; therefore $A_y < 0$.

EXERCISE 3–2

The vector $\vec{A}$ has a magnitude of 7.25 m. Find its components for direction angles of

a. $\theta = 5.00°$ c. $\theta = 245°$

b. $\theta = 125°$ d. $\theta = 335°$

SOLUTION

a. $A_x = 7.22$ m, $A_y = 0.632$ m

b. $A_x = -4.16$ m, $A_y = 5.94$ m

c. $A_x = -3.06$ m, $A_y = -6.57$ m

d. $A_x = 6.57$ m, $A_y = -3.06$ m

Be careful when using your calculator to determine the direction angle, θ, because you may need to add 180° to get the correct angle, as measured counterclockwise from the positive x axis. For example, if $A_x = -0.50$ m and $A_y = 1.0$ m, your calculator will give the following result:

$$\theta = \tan^{-1}\left(\frac{1.0 \text{ m}}{-0.50 \text{ m}}\right) = \tan^{-1}(-2.0) = -63°$$

Does this angle correspond to the specified vector? The way to check is to sketch $\vec{A}$. When you do, your drawing is similar to Figure 3–6 (c), and thus the direction angle of $\vec{A}$ should be between 90° and 180°. To obtain the correct angle, add 180° to the calculator's result:

$$\theta = -63° + 180° = 117°$$

This, in fact, is the direction angle for the vector $\vec{A}$.

EXERCISE 3–3

The vector $\vec{B}$ has components $B_x = -2.10$ m and $B_y = -1.70$ m. Find the direction angle, θ, for this vector.

SOLUTION

$$\tan^{-1}[(-1.70 \text{ m})/(-2.10 \text{ m})] = \tan^{-1}(1.70/2.10) = 39.0°, \theta = 39.0 + 180° = 219°$$

Finally, in many situations the direction of a vector $\vec{A}$ is given by the angle θ, measured relative to the x axis, as in **Figure 3–7 (a)**. In these cases we know that

$$A_x = A \cos \theta$$

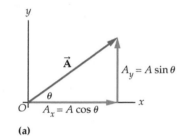

and

$$A_y = A \sin \theta$$

On the other hand, we are sometimes given the angle between the vector and the y axis, as in **Figure 3–7 (b)**. If we call this angle θ', then it follows that

$$A_x = A \sin \theta'$$

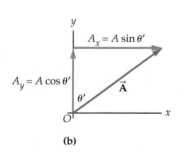

and

$$A_y = A \cos \theta'$$

These two seemingly different results are actually in complete agreement. Note that $\theta + \theta' = 90°$, or $\theta' = 90° - \theta$. If we use the trigonometric identities given in Appendix A, we find

$$A_x = A \sin \theta' = A \sin(90° - \theta) = A \cos \theta$$

and

$$A_y = A \cos \theta' = A \cos(90° - \theta) = A \sin \theta$$

▲ **FIGURE 3–7 Vector direction angles**
Vector $\vec{A}$ and its components in terms of **(a)** the angle relative to the x axis and **(b)** the angle relative to the y axis.

EXERCISE 3–4

If a vector's direction angle relative to the x axis is 35°, then its direction angle relative to the y axis is 55°. Find the components of a vector $\vec{A}$ of magnitude 5.2 m in terms of

a. its direction relative to the x axis, and

b. its direction relative to the y axis.

SOLUTION

a. $A_x = (5.2 \text{ m}) \cos 35° = 4.3$ m, $A_y = (5.2 \text{ m}) \sin 35° = 3.0$ m
b. $A_x = (5.2 \text{ m}) \sin 55° = 4.3$ m, $A_y = (5.2 \text{ m}) \cos 55° = 3.0$ m

3–3 Adding and Subtracting Vectors

One important reason for determining the components of a vector is that they are useful in adding and subtracting vectors. In this section we begin by defining vector addition graphically, and then show how the same addition can be performed more concisely and accurately with components.

Adding Vectors Graphically

One day you open an old chest in the attic and find a treasure map inside. To locate the treasure, the map says that you must "Go to the sycamore tree in the backyard, march 5 paces north, then 3 paces east." If these two displacements are represented by the vectors $\vec{A}$ and $\vec{B}$ in **Figure 3–8**, the total displacement from the tree to the treasure is given by the vector $\vec{C}$. We say that $\vec{C}$ is the *vector sum* of $\vec{A}$ and $\vec{B}$; that is, $\vec{C} = \vec{A} + \vec{B}$. In general, vectors are added graphically according to the following rule:

- To add the vectors $\vec{A}$ and $\vec{B}$, place the tail of $\vec{B}$ at the head of $\vec{A}$. The sum, $\vec{C} = \vec{A} + \vec{B}$, is the vector extending from the tail of $\vec{A}$ to the head of $\vec{B}$.

If the instructions to find the treasure were a bit more complicated—5 paces north, 3 paces east, then 4 paces southeast, for example—the path from the sycamore tree to the treasure would be like that shown in **Figure 3–9**. In this case, the total displacement, $\vec{D}$, is the sum of the three vectors $\vec{A}$, $\vec{B}$, and $\vec{C}$; that is, $\vec{D} = \vec{A} + \vec{B} + \vec{C}$. It follows that to add more than two vectors, we just keep placing the vectors head-to-tail, head-to-tail, and then draw a vector from the tail of the first vector to the head of the last vector, as in Figure 3–9.

In order to place a given pair of vectors head-to-tail, it may be necessary to move the corresponding arrows. This is fine, as long as you don't change their length or their direction. After all, a vector is defined by its length and direction; if these are unchanged, so is the vector.

- A vector is defined by its magnitude and direction, regardless of its location.

▲ To a good approximation, these snow geese are all moving in the same direction with the same speed. As a result, their velocity vectors are equal, even though their positions are different.

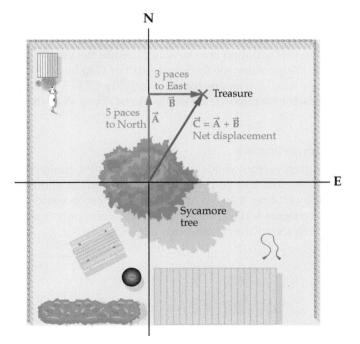

▲ **FIGURE 3–8 The sum of two vectors**
To go from the sycamore tree to the treasure, one must first go 5 paces north ($\vec{A}$) and then 3 paces east ($\vec{B}$). The net displacement from the tree to the treasure is $\vec{C} = \vec{A} + \vec{B}$.

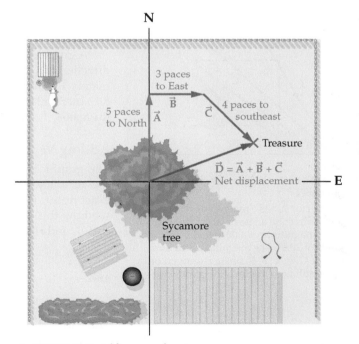

▲ **FIGURE 3–9 Adding several vectors**
Searching for a treasure that is 5 paces north ($\vec{A}$), 3 paces east ($\vec{B}$), and 4 paces southeast ($\vec{C}$) of the sycamore tree. The net displacement from the tree to the treasure is $\vec{D} = \vec{A} + \vec{B} + \vec{C}$.

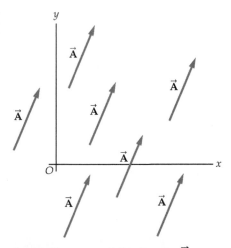

▲ **FIGURE 3–10 Identical vectors $\vec{A}$ at different locations**

A vector is defined by its direction and length; its location is immaterial.

For example, in **Figure 3–10** all of the vectors are the same, even though they are at different locations on the graph.

As an example of moving vectors, consider two vectors, $\vec{A}$ and $\vec{B}$, and their vector sum, $\vec{C}$:

$$\vec{C} = \vec{A} + \vec{B}$$

as illustrated in **Figure 3–11 (a)**. By moving the arrow representing $\vec{B}$ so that its tail is at the origin, and moving the arrow for $\vec{A}$ so that its tail is at the head of $\vec{B}$, we obtain the construction shown in **Figure 3–11 (b)**. From this graph we see that $\vec{C}$, which is $\vec{A} + \vec{B}$, is also equal to $\vec{B} + \vec{A}$:

$$\vec{C} = \vec{A} + \vec{B} = \vec{B} + \vec{A}$$

That is, the sum of vectors is independent of the order in which the vectors are added.

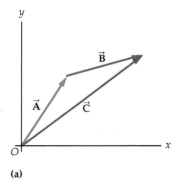

(a)

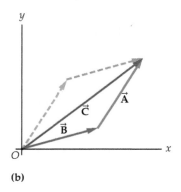

(b)

▲ **FIGURE 3–11 $\vec{A} + \vec{B} = \vec{B} + \vec{A}$**
The vector $\vec{C}$ is equal to **(a)** $\vec{A} + \vec{B}$ and **(b)** $\vec{B} + \vec{A}$. Note also that $\vec{C}$ is the diagonal of the parallelogram formed by the vectors $\vec{A}$ and $\vec{B}$. For this reason, this method of vector addition is referred to as the "parallelogram method."

Now, suppose that $\vec{A}$ has a magnitude of 5.00 m and a direction angle of 60.0° above the x axis, and that $\vec{B}$ has a magnitude of 4.00 m and a direction angle of 20.0° above the x axis. These two vectors and their sum, $\vec{C}$, are shown in **Figure 3–12**. The question is: What are the length and direction angle of $\vec{C}$?

A graphical way to answer this question is to simply measure the length and direction of $\vec{C}$ in Figure 3–12. With a ruler, we find the length of $\vec{C}$ to be approximately 1.75 times the length of $\vec{A}$, which means that $\vec{C}$ is roughly 1.75 (5.00 m) ≐ 8.75 m. Similarly, with a protractor we measure the angle θ to be about 45.0° above the x axis.

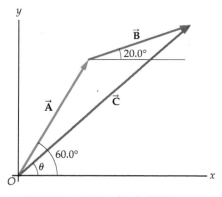

▲ **FIGURE 3–12 Graphical addition of vectors**

The vector $\vec{A}$ has a magnitude of 5.00 m and a direction angle of 60.0°; the vector $\vec{B}$ has a magnitude of 4.00 m and a direction angle of 20.0°. The magnitude and direction of $\vec{C} = \vec{A} + \vec{B}$ can be measured on the graph with a ruler and a protractor.

Adding Vectors Using Components

The graphical method of adding vectors yields approximate results, limited by the accuracy with which the vectors can be drawn and measured. In contrast, exact results can be obtained by adding $\vec{A}$ and $\vec{B}$ in terms of their components. To see how this is done, consider **Figure 3–13 (a)**, which shows the components of $\vec{A}$ and $\vec{B}$, and **Figure 3–13 (b)**, which shows the components of $\vec{C}$. Clearly,

$$C_x = A_x + B_x$$

and

$$C_y = A_y + B_y$$

Thus, to add vectors, you simply add the components.

Returning to our example in Figure 3–12, the components of $\vec{A}$ and $\vec{B}$ are

$$A_x = (5.00 \text{ m}) \cos 60.0° = 2.50 \text{ m} \quad A_y = (5.00 \text{ m}) \sin 60.0° = 4.33 \text{ m}$$

and

$$B_x = (4.00 \text{ m}) \cos 20.0° = 3.76 \text{ m} \quad B_y = (4.00 \text{ m}) \sin 20.0° = 1.37 \text{ m}$$

Adding component by component yields the components of $\vec{C} = \vec{A} + \vec{B}$:

$$C_x = A_x + B_x = 2.50\text{ m} + 3.76\text{ m} = 6.26\text{ m}$$

and

$$C_y = A_y + B_y = 4.33\text{ m} + 1.37\text{ m} = 5.70\text{ m}$$

With these results, we can now find *precise* values for C, the magnitude of vector $\vec{C}$, and its direction angle θ. In particular,

$$C = \sqrt{C_x{}^2 + C_y{}^2} = \sqrt{(6.26\text{ m})^2 + (5.70\text{ m})^2} = \sqrt{71.7\text{ m}^2} = 8.47\text{ m}$$

and

$$\theta = \tan^{-1}\left(\frac{C_y}{C_x}\right) = \tan^{-1}\left(\frac{5.70\text{ m}}{6.26\text{ m}}\right) = \tan^{-1}(0.911) = 42.3°$$

Note that these exact values are in rough agreement with the approximate results found by graphical addition.

In the future, we will always add vectors using components—graphical addition is useful primarily as a rough check on the results obtained with components.

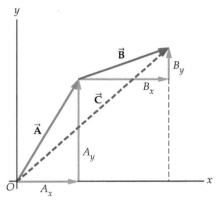

(a)

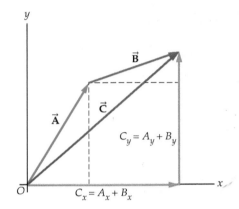

(b)

▲ **FIGURE 3–13 Component addition of vectors**
(a) The x and y components of $\vec{A}$ and $\vec{B}$.
(b) The x and y components of $\vec{C}$. Notice that $C_x = A_x + B_x$ and $C_y = A_y + B_y$.

ACTIVE EXAMPLE 3–1   TREASURE HUNT: FIND THE DIRECTION AND MAGNITUDE

What are the magnitude and direction of the total displacement for the treasure hunt illustrated in Figure 3–9? Assume each pace is 0.750 m in length.

SOLUTION *(Test your understanding by performing the calculations indicated in each step.)*

To define a convenient notation, let the first 5 paces be represented by $\vec{A}$, the next 3 paces by $\vec{B}$, and the final 4 paces by $\vec{C}$. The total displacement, then, is $\vec{D} = \vec{A} + \vec{B} + \vec{C}$.

1. Find the components of $\vec{A}$: $A_x = 0,\ A_y = 3.75\text{ m}$

2. Find the components of $\vec{B}$: $B_x = 2.25\text{ m},\ B_y = 0$

3. Find the components of $\vec{C}$: $C_x = 2.12\text{ m},\ C_y = -2.12\text{ m}$

4. Sum the components of $\vec{A}$, $\vec{B}$, and $\vec{C}$ to find the components of $\vec{D}$: $D_x = 4.37\text{ m},\ D_y = 1.63\text{ m}$

5. Determine D and θ: $D = 4.66\text{ m},\ \theta = 20.5°$

YOUR TURN

If the length of each pace is decreased by a factor of two, to 0.375 m, by what factors do you expect D and θ to change? Verify your answers with a numerical calculation.

*(Answers to **Your Turn** problems are given in the back of the book.)*

Subtracting Vectors

Next, how do we subtract vectors? Suppose, for example, that we would like to determine the vector $\vec{D}$, where

$$\vec{D} = \vec{A} - \vec{B}$$

and $\vec{A}$ and $\vec{B}$ are the vectors shown in Figure 3–12. To find $\vec{D}$, we start by rewriting it as follows:

$$\vec{D} = \vec{A} + (-\vec{B})$$

That is, $\vec{D}$ is the sum of $\vec{A}$ and $-\vec{B}$. Now the negative of a vector has a very simple graphical interpretation:

- The negative of a vector is represented by an arrow of the same length as the original vector, but pointing in the opposite direction. That is, multiplying a vector by minus one *reverses its direction*.

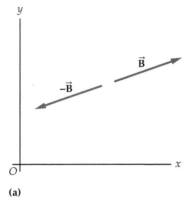

(a)

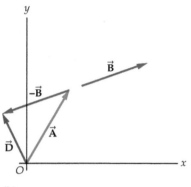

(b)

▲ **FIGURE 3–14 Vector subtraction**
(a) The vector $\vec{B}$ and its negative $-\vec{B}$.
(b) A vector construction for
$\vec{D} = \vec{A} - \vec{B}$.

For example, the vectors $\vec{B}$ and $-\vec{B}$ are indicated in **Figure 3–14 (a)**. Thus, to subtract $\vec{B}$ from $\vec{A}$, simply reverse the direction of $\vec{B}$ and add it to $\vec{A}$, as indicated in **Figure 3–14 (b)**.

In terms of components, you subtract vectors by simply subtracting the components. For example, if

$$\vec{D} = \vec{A} - \vec{B}$$

then

$$D_x = A_x - B_x$$

and

$$D_y = A_y - B_y$$

Once the components of $\vec{D}$ are found, its magnitude and direction angle can be calculated as usual.

EXERCISE 3–5

    a. For the vectors given in Figure 3–12, find the components of $\vec{D} = \vec{A} - \vec{B}$.
    b. Find D and θ and compare with the vector $\vec{D}$ shown in Figure 3–14 (b).

SOLUTION

    a. $D_x = -1.26$ m, $D_y = 2.96$ m
    b. $D = 3.22$ m, $\theta = -66.9° + 180° = 113°$. In Figure 3–14 (b) we see that $\vec{D}$ is shorter than $\vec{B}$, which has a magnitude of 4.00 m, and its direction angle is somewhat greater than 90°, in agreement with our numerical results.

3–4 Unit Vectors

Unit vectors provide a convenient way of expressing an arbitrary vector in terms of its components, as we shall see. But first, let's define what we mean by a unit vector. In particular, the unit vectors $\hat{x}$ and $\hat{y}$ are defined to be dimensionless vectors of unit magnitude pointing in the positive x and y directions, respectively:

- The x unit vector, $\hat{x}$, is a dimensionless vector of unit length pointing in the positive x direction.
- The y unit vector, $\hat{y}$, is a dimensionless vector of unit length pointing in the positive y direction.

Figure 3–15 shows $\hat{x}$ and $\hat{y}$ on a two-dimensional coordinate system. Since unit vectors have no physical dimensions—like mass, length, or time—they are used to specify direction only.

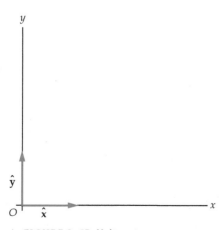

▲ **FIGURE 3–15 Unit vectors**
The unit vectors $\hat{x}$ and $\hat{y}$ point in the positive x and y directions, respectively.

Multiplying Unit Vectors by Scalars

To see the utility of unit vectors, consider the effect of multiplying a vector by a scalar. For example, multiplying a vector by 3 increases its magnitude by a factor of 3, but does not change its direction, as shown in **Figure 3–16**. Multiplying by -3 increases the magnitude by a factor of 3 *and* reverses the direction of the vector. This is also shown in Figure 3–16. In the case of unit vectors—which have a magnitude of 1 and are dimensionless—multiplication by a scalar results in a vector with the same magnitude and dimensions as the scalar.

For example, if a vector $\vec{A}$ has the scalar components $A_x = 5$ m and $A_y = 3$ m, we can write it as

$$\vec{A} = (5\text{ m})\hat{x} + (3\text{ m})\hat{y}$$

We refer to the quantities $(5 \text{ m})\hat{\mathbf{x}}$ and $(3 \text{ m})\hat{\mathbf{y}}$ as the x and y **vector components** of the vector $\vec{\mathbf{A}}$. In general, an arbitrary two-dimensional vector $\vec{\mathbf{A}}$ can always be written as the sum of a vector component in the x direction and a vector component in the y direction:

$$\vec{\mathbf{A}} = A_x\hat{\mathbf{x}} + A_y\hat{\mathbf{y}}$$

This is illustrated in **Figure 3–17 (a)**. An equivalent way of representing the vector components of a vector is illustrated in **Figure 3–17 (b)**. In this case we see that the vector components are the *projection* of a vector onto the x and y axes. The sign of the vector components is positive if they point in the positive x or y direction, and negative if they point in the negative x or y direction. This is how vector components will generally be shown in later chapters.

Finally, note that vector addition and subtraction are straightforward with unit vector notation:

$$\vec{\mathbf{C}} = \vec{\mathbf{A}} + \vec{\mathbf{B}} = (A_x + B_x)\hat{\mathbf{x}} + (A_y + B_y)\hat{\mathbf{y}}$$

and

$$\vec{\mathbf{D}} = \vec{\mathbf{A}} - \vec{\mathbf{B}} = (A_x - B_x)\hat{\mathbf{x}} + (A_y - B_y)\hat{\mathbf{y}}$$

Clearly, unit vectors provide a useful way to keep track of the x and y components of a vector.

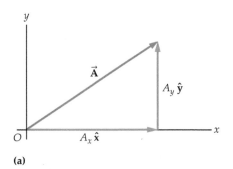

(a)

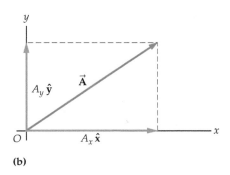

(b)

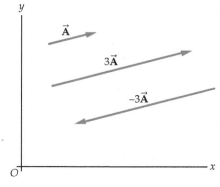

▲ **FIGURE 3–16 Multiplying a vector by a scalar**
Multiplying a vector by a positive scalar different from 1 will change the length of the vector but leave its direction the same. If the vector is multiplied by a negative scalar its direction is reversed.

◀ **FIGURE 3–17 Vector components**
(a) A vector $\vec{\mathbf{A}}$ can be written in terms of unit vectors as $\vec{\mathbf{A}} = A_x\hat{\mathbf{x}} + A_y\hat{\mathbf{y}}$.
(b) Vector components can be thought of as the projection of the vector onto the x and y axes. This method of representing vector components will be used frequently in subsequent chapters.

3–5 Position, Displacement, Velocity, and Acceleration Vectors

In Chapter 2 we discussed four different one-dimensional vectors: position, displacement, velocity, and acceleration. Each of these quantities had a direction associated with it, indicated by its sign; positive meant in the positive direction, negative meant in the negative direction. Now we consider these vectors again, this time in two dimensions, where the possibilities for direction are not so limited.

Position Vectors

To begin, imagine a two-dimensional coordinate system, as in **Figure 3–18**. Position is indicated by a vector from the origin to the location in question. We refer to the position vector as $\vec{\mathbf{r}}$; its units are meters, m.

Definition: Position Vector, $\vec{\mathbf{r}}$

position vector $= \vec{\mathbf{r}}$

SI unit: meter, m

3–1

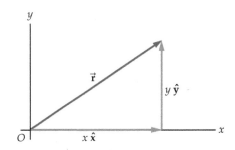

▲ **FIGURE 3–18 Position vector**
The position vector $\vec{\mathbf{r}}$ points from the origin to the current location of an object. The x and y vector components of $\vec{\mathbf{r}}$ are $x\hat{\mathbf{x}}$ and $y\hat{\mathbf{y}}$, respectively.

In terms of unit vectors, the position vector is simply $\vec{\mathbf{r}} = x\hat{\mathbf{x}} + y\hat{\mathbf{y}}$.

A map can be used to determine the direction and magnitude of the displacement vector from your initial position to your destination.

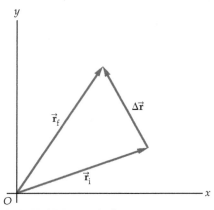

▲ **FIGURE 3–19 Displacement vector**
The displacement vector $\Delta\vec{r}$ is the change in position. It points from the head of the initial position vector $\vec{r}_i$ to the head of the final position vector $\vec{r}_f$. Thus $\vec{r}_f = \vec{r}_i + \Delta\vec{r}$ or $\Delta\vec{r} = \vec{r}_f - \vec{r}_i$.

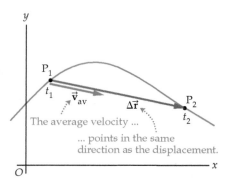

▲ **FIGURE 3–20 Average velocity vector**
The average velocity, $\vec{v}_{av}$, points in the same direction as the displacement, $\Delta\vec{r}$, for any given interval of time.

Displacement Vectors

Now, suppose that initially you are at the location indicated by the position vector $\vec{r}_i$, and that later you are at the final position represented by the position vector $\vec{r}_f$. Your displacement vector, $\Delta\vec{r}$, is the change in position:

> **Definition: Displacement Vector, $\Delta\vec{r}$**
>
> $$\Delta\vec{r} = \vec{r}_f - \vec{r}_i$$ 3–2
>
> SI unit: meter, m

Rearranging this definition slightly, we see that

$$\vec{r}_f = \vec{r}_i + \Delta\vec{r}$$

That is, the final position is equal to the initial position plus the change in position. This is illustrated in **Figure 3–19**, where we see that $\Delta\vec{r}$ extends from the head of $\vec{r}_i$ to the head of $\vec{r}_f$.

Velocity Vectors

Next, the average velocity vector is defined as the displacement vector $\Delta\vec{r}$ divided by the elapsed time Δt.

> **Definition: Average Velocity Vector, $\vec{v}_{av}$**
>
> $$\vec{v}_{av} = \frac{\Delta\vec{r}}{\Delta t}$$ 3–3
>
> SI unit: meter per second, m/s

Since $\Delta\vec{r}$ is a vector, it follows that $\vec{v}_{av}$ is also a vector; it is the vector $\Delta\vec{r}$ times the scalar $(1/\Delta t)$. Thus $\vec{v}_{av}$ is parallel to $\Delta\vec{r}$ and has the units m/s.

EXERCISE 3–6

A dragonfly is observed initially at the position $\vec{r}_i = (2.00 \text{ m})\hat{x} + (3.50 \text{ m})\hat{y}$. Three seconds later it is at the position $\vec{r}_f = (-3.00 \text{ m})\hat{x} + (5.50 \text{ m})\hat{y}$. What was the dragonfly's average velocity during this time?

SOLUTION

$$\vec{v}_{av} = (\vec{r}_f - \vec{r}_i)/\Delta t = [(-5.00 \text{ m})\hat{x} + (2.00 \text{ m})\hat{y}]/(3.00 \text{ s})$$
$$= (-1.67 \text{ m/s})\hat{x} + (0.667 \text{ m/s})\hat{y}$$

To help visualize $\vec{v}_{av}$, imagine a particle moving in two dimensions along the blue path shown in **Figure 3–20**. If the particle is at point P_1 at time t_1, and at P_2 at time t_2, its displacement is indicated by the vector $\Delta\vec{r}$. The average velocity is parallel to $\Delta\vec{r}$, as indicated in Figure 3–20. It makes sense physically that $\vec{v}_{av}$ is parallel to $\Delta\vec{r}$; after all, on *average* you have moved in the direction of $\Delta\vec{r}$ during the time from t_1 to t_2. To put it another way, a particle that starts at P_1 at the time t_1 and moves with the velocity $\vec{v}_{av}$ until the time t_2 will arrive in precisely the same location as the particle that follows the blue path.

By considering smaller and smaller time intervals, as in **Figure 3–21**, it is possible to calculate the instantaneous velocity vector:

> **Definition: Instantaneous Velocity Vector, $\vec{v}$**
>
> $$\vec{v} = \lim_{\Delta t \to 0} \frac{\Delta\vec{r}}{\Delta t}$$ 3–4
>
> SI unit: meter per second, m/s

As can be seen in Figure 3–21, the instantaneous velocity at a given time is tangential to the path of the particle at that time. In addition, the magnitude of the velocity vector is the speed of the particle. Thus, the instantaneous velocity vector tells you both how fast a particle is moving and in what direction.

EXERCISE 3–7

Find the speed and direction of motion for a rainbow trout whose velocity is $\vec{v} = (3.7 \text{ m/s})\hat{x} + (-1.3 \text{ m/s})\hat{y}$.

SOLUTION

$$\text{speed} = v = \sqrt{(3.7 \text{ m/s})^2 + (-1.3 \text{ m/s})^2} = 3.9 \text{ m/s}, \theta = \tan^{-1}\left(\frac{-1.3 \text{ m/s}}{3.7 \text{ m/s}}\right) = -19°,$$

that is, 19° below the x axis.

Acceleration Vectors

Finally, the average acceleration vector over an interval of time, Δt, is defined as the change in the velocity vector, $\Delta\vec{v}$, divided by the scalar Δt.

Definition: Average Acceleration Vector, $\vec{a}_{av}$

$$\vec{a}_{av} = \frac{\Delta\vec{v}}{\Delta t} \qquad\qquad 3\text{–}5$$

SI unit: meter per second per second, m/s^2

An example is given in **Figure 3–22**, where we show the initial and final velocity vectors corresponding to two different times. Since the change in velocity is defined as

$$\Delta\vec{v} = \vec{v}_f - \vec{v}_i$$

it follows that

$$\vec{v}_f = \vec{v}_i + \Delta\vec{v}$$

as indicated in Figure 3–22. Thus, $\Delta\vec{v}$ is the vector extending from the head of $\vec{v}_i$ to the head of $\vec{v}_f$, just as $\Delta\vec{r}$ extends from the head of $\vec{r}_i$ to the head of $\vec{r}_f$ in Figure 3–19. The direction of $\vec{a}_{av}$ is the direction of $\Delta\vec{v}$, as shown in **Figure 3–22(b)**.

Can an object accelerate if its speed is constant? Absolutely—if its direction changes. Consider a car driving with a constant speed on a circular track, as

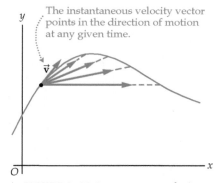

▲ **FIGURE 3–21 Instantaneous velocity vector**

The instantaneous velocity vector $\vec{v}$ is obtained by calculating the average velocity vector over smaller and smaller time intervals. In the limit of vanishingly small time intervals, the average velocity approaches the instantaneous velocity, which points in the direction of motion.

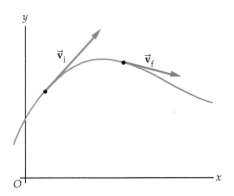

(a) The instantaneous velocity at two different times

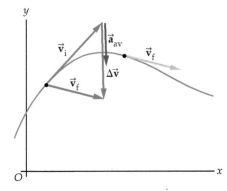

(b) The average acceleration points in the same direction as the change in velocity

▲ **FIGURE 3–22 Average acceleration vector**

(a) As a particle moves along the blue path its velocity changes in magnitude and direction. At the time t_i the velocity is $\vec{v}_i$; at the time t_f the velocity is $\vec{v}_f$. **(b)** The average acceleration vector $\vec{a}_{av} = \Delta\vec{v}/\Delta t$ points in the direction of the change in velocity vector $\Delta\vec{v}$. We obtain $\Delta\vec{v}$ by moving $\vec{v}_f$ so that its tail coincides with the tail of $\vec{v}_i$, and then drawing the arrow that connects the head of $\vec{v}_i$ to the head of $\vec{v}_f$. Note that $\vec{a}_{av}$ need not point in the direction of motion, and in general it doesn't.

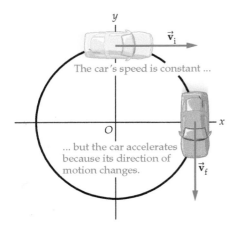

The car's speed is constant ...

... but the car accelerates because its direction of motion changes.

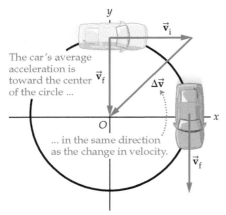

The car's average acceleration is toward the center of the circle ...

... in the same direction as the change in velocity.

▲ **FIGURE 3-23** **Average acceleration for a car traveling in a circle with constant speed** Although the speed of this car never changes, it is still accelerating—due to the change in its direction of motion. For the time interval depicted, the car's average acceleration is in the direction of $\Delta\vec{v}$, which is toward the center of the circle. (As we shall see in Chapter 6, the car's acceleration is always toward the center of the circle.)

shown in **Figure 3-23**. Suppose that the initial velocity of the car is $\vec{v}_i = (12 \text{ m/s})\hat{x}$, and that 10.0 s later its final velocity is $\vec{v}_f = (-12 \text{ m/s})\hat{y}$. Note that the speed is 12 m/s in each case, but the velocity is different because the *direction* has changed. Calculating the average acceleration, we find a nonzero acceleration:

$$\vec{a}_{av} = \frac{\Delta\vec{v}}{\Delta t} = \frac{\vec{v}_f - \vec{v}_i}{10.0 \text{ s}}$$

$$= \frac{(-12 \text{ m/s})\hat{y} - (12 \text{ m/s})\hat{x}}{10.0 \text{ s}} = (-1.2 \text{ m/s}^2)\hat{x} + (-1.2 \text{ m/s}^2)\hat{y}$$

Thus, a change in direction is just as important as a change in speed in producing an acceleration. We shall study circular motion in detail in Chapter 6.

Finally, by going to infinitesimally small time intervals, $\Delta t \rightarrow 0$, we can define the instantaneous acceleration:

> **Definition: Instantaneous Acceleration Vector, $\vec{a}$**
>
> $$\vec{a} = \lim_{\Delta t \rightarrow 0} \frac{\Delta\vec{v}}{\Delta t}$$
>
> SI unit: meter per second per second, m/s^2

3–6

ACTIVE EXAMPLE 3-2 FIND THE AVERAGE ACCELERATION

A car is traveling northwest at 9.00 m/s. Eight seconds later it has rounded a corner and is now heading north at 15.0 m/s. What are the magnitude and direction of its average acceleration during those 8.00 seconds?

Let the positive x direction be east, and the positive y direction be north.

SOLUTION (Test your understanding by performing the calculations indicated in each step.)

1. Write out $\vec{v}_i$: $\vec{v}_i = (-6.36 \text{ m/s})\hat{x} + (6.36 \text{ m/s})\hat{y}$
2. Write out $\vec{v}_f$: $\vec{v}_f = (15.0 \text{ m/s})\hat{y}$
3. Calculate $\Delta\vec{v}$: $\Delta\vec{v} = (6.36 \text{ m/s})\hat{x} + (8.64 \text{ m/s})\hat{y}$
4. Find $\vec{a}_{av}$: $\vec{a}_{av} = (0.795 \text{ m/s}^2)\hat{x} + (1.08 \text{ m/s}^2)\hat{y}$
5. Determine a_{av} and θ: $a_{av} = 1.34 \text{ m/s}^2, \theta = 53.6°$ north of east

YOUR TURN
Find the magnitude and direction of the average acceleration if the same change in velocity occurs in 4.00 s rather than 8.00 s.

*(Answers to **Your Turn** problems are given in the back of the book.)*

▶ The velocities of these cyclists change in both magnitude and direction as they slow to negotiate a series of sharp curves and then speed up again. Both kinds of velocity change involve an acceleration.

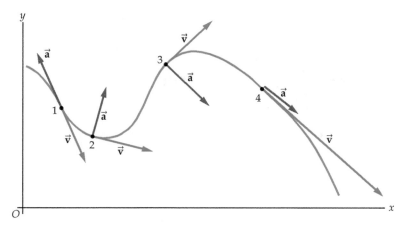

◀ **FIGURE 3–24 Velocity and acceleration vectors for a particle moving along a winding path**
The acceleration of a particle need not point in the direction of motion. At point (1) the particle is slowing down, at (2) it is turning to the left, at (3) it is turning to the right, and, finally, at point (4) it is speeding up.

Note carefully the following critical distinctions between the velocity vector and the acceleration vector:

- The velocity vector, $\vec{v}$, is always in the direction of a particle's motion.
- The acceleration vector, $\vec{a}$, can point in directions other than the direction of motion, and in general it does.

An example of a particle's motion, showing the velocity and acceleration vectors at various times, is presented in **Figure 3–24**.

Note that in all cases the velocity is tangential to the motion, though the acceleration points in various directions. When the acceleration is perpendicular to the velocity of an object, as at points (2) and (3) in Figure 3–24, its speed remains constant while its direction of motion changes. At points (1) and (4) in Figure 3–24 the acceleration is antiparallel (opposite) or parallel to the velocity of the object, respectively. In such cases, the direction of motion remains the same while the speed changes. Throughout the next chapter we shall see further examples of motion in which the velocity and acceleration are in different directions.

3–6 Relative Motion

A good example of the use of vectors is in the description of relative motion. Suppose, for example, that you are standing on the ground as a train goes by at 15.0 m/s, as shown in **Figure 3–25**. Inside the train, a free-riding passenger is walking in the forward direction at 1.2 m/s relative to the train. How fast is the passenger moving relative to you? Clearly, the answer is 1.2 m/s + 15.0 m/s = 16.2 m/s. What if the passenger had been walking with the same speed, but toward the back of the train? In this case, you would see the passenger going by with a speed of −1.2 m/s + 15.0 m/s = 13.8 m/s.

Let's generalize these results. Call the velocity of the *train* relative to the ground $\vec{v}_{tg}$, the velocity of the *passenger* relative to the *train* $\vec{v}_{pt}$, and the velocity of the *passenger* relative to the *ground* $\vec{v}_{pg}$. As we saw in the previous paragraph, the velocity of the *passenger* relative to the *ground* is

$$\vec{v}_{pg} = \vec{v}_{pt} + \vec{v}_{tg} \qquad 3–7$$

This vector addition is illustrated in **Figure 3–26** for the two cases we discussed.

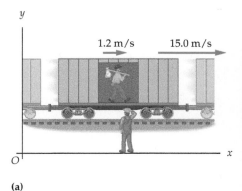

(a)

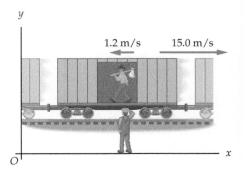

(b)

▶ **FIGURE 3–25 Relative velocity of a passenger on a train with respect to a person on the ground**
(a) The passenger walks toward the front of the train. (b) The passenger walks toward the rear of the train.

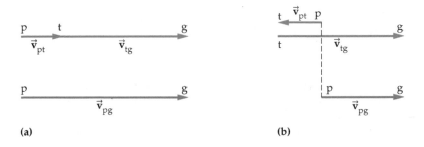

(a)

(b)

◀ **FIGURE 3–26 Adding velocity vectors**
Vector addition to find the velocity of the passenger with respect to the ground for (a) Figure 3–25 (a) and (b) Figure 3–25 (b).

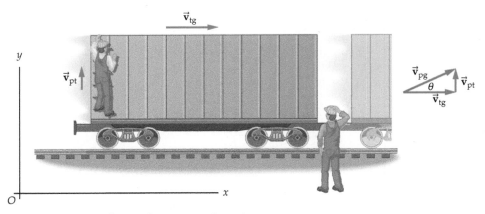

▲ **FIGURE 3–27 Relative velocity in two dimensions**
A person climbs up a ladder on a moving train with velocity $\vec{\mathbf{v}}_{pt}$ relative to the train. If the train moves relative to the ground with a velocity $\vec{\mathbf{v}}_{tg}$, the velocity of the person on the train relative to the ground is $\vec{\mathbf{v}}_{pg} = \vec{\mathbf{v}}_{pt} + \vec{\mathbf{v}}_{tg}$.

Though this example dealt with one-dimensional motion, Equation 3–7 is valid for velocity vectors pointing in arbitrary directions. For example, instead of walking on the car's floor, the passenger might be climbing a ladder to the roof of the car, as in **Figure 3–27**. In this case $\vec{\mathbf{v}}_{pt}$ is vertical, $\vec{\mathbf{v}}_{tg}$ is horizontal, and $\vec{\mathbf{v}}_{pg}$ is simply the vector sum $\vec{\mathbf{v}}_{pt} + \vec{\mathbf{v}}_{tg}$.

EXERCISE 3–8

Suppose the passenger in Figure 3–27 is climbing a vertical ladder with a speed of 0.20 m/s, and the train is slowly coasting forward at 0.70 m/s. Find the speed and direction of the passenger relative to the ground.

SOLUTION

$$\vec{\mathbf{v}}_{pg} = (0.70 \text{ m/s})\hat{\mathbf{x}} + (0.20 \text{ m/s})\hat{\mathbf{y}}; \text{ thus}$$

$$v_{pg} = \sqrt{(0.70 \text{ m/s})^2 + (0.20 \text{ m/s})^2} = 0.73 \text{ m/s}, \theta = \tan^{-1}(0.20/0.70) = 16°$$

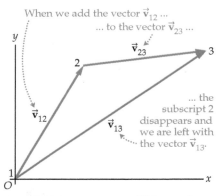

When we add the vector $\vec{\mathbf{v}}_{12}$ ...
... to the vector $\vec{\mathbf{v}}_{23}$ ...
... the subscript 2 disappears and we are left with the vector $\vec{\mathbf{v}}_{13}$.

▲ **FIGURE 3–28 Vector addition used to determine relative velocity**

Note that the subscripts in Equation 3–7 follow a definite pattern. On the left-hand side of the equation we have the subscripts pg. On the right-hand side we have two sets of subscripts, pt and tg; note that a pair of t's has been inserted between the p and the g. This pattern always holds for any relative motion problem, though the subscripts will be different when referring to different objects. Thus, we can say quite generally that

$$\vec{\mathbf{v}}_{13} = \vec{\mathbf{v}}_{12} + \vec{\mathbf{v}}_{23} \qquad \text{3–8}$$

where, in the train example, we can identify 1 as the *passenger*, 2 as the *train*, and 3 as the *ground*.

The vector addition in Equation 3–8 is shown in **Figure 3–28**. For convenience in seeing how the subscripts are ordered in the equation, we have labeled the tail of each vector with its first subscript and the head of each vector with its second subscript.

One final note about velocities and their subscripts: Reversing the subscripts reverses the velocity. This is indicated in **Figure 3–29**, where we see that

$$\vec{\mathbf{v}}_{ba} = -\vec{\mathbf{v}}_{ab}$$

Physically, what we are saying is that if you are riding in a car due *north* at 20 m/s relative to the ground, then the ground, relative to you, is moving due *south* at 20 m/s.

Let's apply these results to a two-dimensional example.

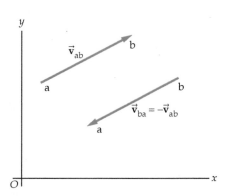

▲ **FIGURE 3–29 Reversing the subscripts of a velocity reverses the corresponding velocity vector**

EXAMPLE 3–2   CROSSING A RIVER

 REAL-WORLD PHYSICS   You are riding in a boat whose speed relative to the water is 6.1 m/s. The boat points at an angle of 25° upstream on a river flowing at 1.4 m/s. **(a)** What is your velocity relative to the ground? **(b)** Suppose the speed of the boat relative to the water remains the same, but the direction in which it points is changed. What angle is required for the boat to go straight across the river?

PICTURE THE PROBLEM
We choose the x axis to be perpendicular to the river, and the y axis to point upstream. With these choices the velocity of the boat relative to the water is 25° above the x axis. In addition, the velocity of the water relative to the ground has a magnitude of 1.4 m/s and points in the negative y direction.

STRATEGY
If the water were still, the boat would move in the direction in which it is pointed. With the water flowing downstream, as shown, the boat will move in a direction closer to the x axis. **(a)** To find the velocity of the boat we use $\vec{v}_{13} = \vec{v}_{12} + \vec{v}_{23}$ with 1 referring to the boat (b), 2 referring to the water (w), and 3 referring to the ground (g). **(b)** To go "straight across the river" means that the velocity of the boat relative to the ground should be in the x direction. Thus, we choose the angle θ that cancels the y component of velocity.

INTERACTIVE FIGURE (MP)™

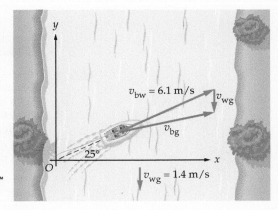

SOLUTION

Part (a)

1. Rewrite $\vec{v}_{13} = \vec{v}_{12} + \vec{v}_{23}$ with $1 \rightarrow$ b, $2 \rightarrow$ w, and $3 \rightarrow$ g:

$$\vec{v}_{bg} = \vec{v}_{bw} + \vec{v}_{wg}$$

2. From our sketch we see that the water flows at 1.4 m/s in the negative y direction relative to the ground:

$$\vec{v}_{wg} = (-1.4 \text{ m/s})\hat{y}$$

3. The velocity of the boat relative to the water is given in the problem statement:

$$\vec{v}_{bw} = (6.1 \text{ m/s}) \cos 25° \, \hat{x} + (6.1 \text{ m/s}) \sin 25° \, \hat{y}$$
$$= (5.5 \text{ m/s})\hat{x} + (2.6 \text{ m/s})\hat{y}$$

4. Carry out the vector sum in Step 1 to find $\vec{v}_{bg}$:

$$\vec{v}_{bg} = (5.5 \text{ m/s})\hat{x} + (2.6 \text{ m/s} - 1.4 \text{ m/s})\hat{y}$$
$$= (5.5 \text{ m/s})\hat{x} + (1.2 \text{ m/s})\hat{y}$$

Part (b)

5. To cancel the y component of $\vec{v}_{bg}$, we choose the angle θ that gives 1.4 m/s for the y component of $\vec{v}_{bw}$:

$$(6.1 \text{ m/s}) \sin \theta = 1.4 \text{ m/s}$$

6. Solve for θ. With this angle, we see that the y component of $\vec{v}_{bg}$ in Step 4 will be zero:

$$\theta = \sin^{-1}(1.4/6.1) = 13°$$

INSIGHT
(a) Note that the speed of the boat relative to the ground is $\sqrt{(5.5 \text{ m/s})^2 + (1.2 \text{ m/s})^2} = 5.6$ m/s, and the direction angle is $\theta = \tan^{-1}(1.2/5.5) = 12°$ upstream. **(b)** The speed of the boat in this case is equal to the x component of its velocity, since the y component is zero. Therefore, its speed is $(6.1 \text{ m/s}) \cos 13° = 5.9$ m/s.

PRACTICE PROBLEM
Find the speed and direction of the boat relative to the ground if the river flows at 4.5 m/s. [**Answer:** $v_{bg} = 5.8$ m/s, $\theta = -19°$. In this case, a person on the ground sees the boat going slowly downstream, even though the boat itself points upstream.]

Some related homework problems: Problem 50, Problem 53, Problem 55

Suppose the problem had been to find the velocity of the boat relative to the water so that it goes straight across the river at 5.0 m/s. That is, we want to find $\vec{v}_{bw}$ such that $\vec{v}_{bg} = (5.0 \text{ m/s})\hat{x}$. One approach is to simply solve $\vec{v}_{bg} = \vec{v}_{bw} + \vec{v}_{wg}$ for $\vec{v}_{bw}$, which gives

$$\vec{v}_{bw} = \vec{v}_{bg} - \vec{v}_{wg} \qquad\qquad 3\text{–}9$$

Another approach is to go back to our general relation, $\vec{v}_{13} = \vec{v}_{12} + \vec{v}_{23}$ and choose 1 to be the *b*oat, 2 to be the *g*round, and 3 to be the *w*ater. With these substitutions we find

$$\vec{v}_{bw} = \vec{v}_{bg} + \vec{v}_{gw}$$

This is the same as Equation 3–9, since $\vec{v}_{gw} = -\vec{v}_{wg}$. In either case, the desired velocity of the boat relative to the water is

$$\vec{v}_{bw} = (5.0\,\text{m/s})\hat{x} + (1.4\,\text{m/s})\hat{y}$$

which corresponds to a speed of 5.2 m/s and a direction angle of 16° upstream.

THE BIG PICTURE | PUTTING PHYSICS IN CONTEXT

LOOKING BACK

In Chapter 2 we indicated direction with + and – signs, since only two directions were possible. With the results from this chapter we can now deal with quantities that point in any direction at all.

The vector quantities we have considered so far are position, displacement, velocity, and acceleration. These quantities are important throughout our study of mechanics.

LOOKING AHEAD

In Chapter 4 we will consider kinematics in two dimensions. As we shall see, the vectors developed in this chapter will play a key role in that study. In particular, vectors will allow us to analyze two-dimensional motion as a combination of two completely independent one-dimensional motions.

In Chapter 5 we will introduce one of the most important concepts in all of physics—force. It is a vector quantity. Other important vector quantities to be introduced in later chapters include linear momentum (Chapter 9), angular momentum (Chapter 11), electric field (Chapter 19), and magnetic field (Chapter 22).

CHAPTER SUMMARY

3–1 SCALARS VERSUS VECTORS

Scalar

A number with appropriate units. Examples of scalar quantities include time and length.

Vector

A quantity with both a magnitude and a direction. Examples include displacement, velocity, and acceleration.

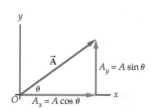

3–2 THE COMPONENTS OF A VECTOR

x Component of Vector $\vec{A}$

$A_x = A \cos \theta$, where θ is measured relative to the x axis.

y Component of Vector $\vec{A}$

$A_y = A \sin \theta$, where θ is measured relative to the x axis.

Sign of the Components

A_x is positive if $\vec{A}$ points in the positive x direction, and negative if it points in the negative x direction. Similar remarks apply to A_y.

Magnitude of Vector $\vec{A}$

The magnitude of $\vec{A}$ is $A = \sqrt{A_x{}^2 + A_y{}^2}$.

Direction Angle of Vector $\vec{A}$

The direction angle of $\vec{A}$ is $\theta = \tan^{-1}(A_y/A_x)$, where θ is measured relative to the x axis.

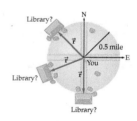

3-3   ADDING AND SUBTRACTING VECTORS

Graphical Method

To add $\vec{\mathbf{A}}$ and $\vec{\mathbf{B}}$, place them so that the tail of $\vec{\mathbf{B}}$ is at the head of $\vec{\mathbf{A}}$. The sum $\vec{\mathbf{C}} = \vec{\mathbf{A}} + \vec{\mathbf{B}}$ is the arrow from the tail of $\vec{\mathbf{A}}$ to the head of $\vec{\mathbf{B}}$. See Figure 3–8.

To find $\vec{\mathbf{A}} - \vec{\mathbf{B}}$, place $\vec{\mathbf{A}}$ and $-\vec{\mathbf{B}}$ head-to-tail and draw an arrow from the tail of $\vec{\mathbf{A}}$ to the head of $-\vec{\mathbf{B}}$. See Figure 3–14.

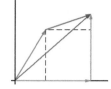

Component Method

If $\vec{\mathbf{C}} = \vec{\mathbf{A}} + \vec{\mathbf{B}}$, then $C_x = A_x + B_x$ and $C_y = A_y + B_y$. If $\vec{\mathbf{C}} = \vec{\mathbf{A}} - \vec{\mathbf{B}}$, then $C_x = A_x - B_x$ and $C_y = A_y - B_y$.

3-4   UNIT VECTORS

x Unit Vector

Written $\hat{\mathbf{x}}$, the x unit vector is a dimensionless vector of unit length in the positive x direction.

y Unit Vector

Written $\hat{\mathbf{y}}$, the y unit vector is a dimensionless vector of unit length in the positive y direction.

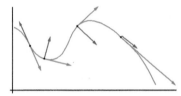

Vector Addition

$$\vec{\mathbf{A}} + \vec{\mathbf{B}} = (A_x + B_x)\hat{\mathbf{x}} + (A_y + B_y)\hat{\mathbf{y}}$$

3-5   POSITION, DISPLACEMENT, VELOCITY, AND ACCELERATION VECTORS

Position Vector

The position vector $\vec{\mathbf{r}}$ points from the origin to a particle's location.

Displacement Vector

The displacement vector $\Delta\vec{\mathbf{r}}$ is the change in position; $\Delta\vec{\mathbf{r}} = \vec{\mathbf{r}}_f - \vec{\mathbf{r}}_i$.

Velocity Vector

The velocity vector $\vec{\mathbf{v}}$ points in the direction of motion and has a magnitude equal to the speed.

Acceleration Vector

The acceleration vector $\vec{\mathbf{a}}$ indicates how quickly and in what direction the velocity is changing. It need not point in the direction of motion.

3-6   RELATIVE MOTION

Velocity of Object 1 Relative to Object 3

$\vec{\mathbf{v}}_{13} = \vec{\mathbf{v}}_{12} + \vec{\mathbf{v}}_{23}$, where object 2 can be anything.

Reversing the Subscripts on a Velocity

$\vec{\mathbf{v}}_{12} = -\vec{\mathbf{v}}_{21}$.

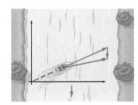

PROBLEM-SOLVING SUMMARY

Type of Problem	Relevant Physical Concepts	Related Examples
Add or subtract vectors.	Resolve the vectors into x and y components, then add or subtract the components.	Active Example 3–1 Exercise 3–5
Calculate the average velocity.	Divide the displacement, $\Delta\vec{\mathbf{r}}$, by the elapsed time, Δt.	Exercise 3–6
Calculate the average acceleration.	Divide the change in velocity, $\Delta\vec{\mathbf{v}}$, by the elapsed time, Δt.	Active Example 3–2
Find the relative velocity of object 1 with respect to object 3.	Use $\vec{\mathbf{v}}_{13} = \vec{\mathbf{v}}_{12} + \vec{\mathbf{v}}_{23}$ with the appropriate choices for 1, 2, and 3.	Example 3–2 Exercise 3–8

CONCEPTUAL QUESTIONS

For instructor-assigned homework, go to www.masteringphysics.com

(Answers to odd-numbered Conceptual Questions can be found in the back of the book.)

1. For the following quantities, indicate which is a scalar and which is a vector: **(a)** the time it takes for you to run the 100-yard dash; **(b)** your displacement after running the 100-yard dash; **(c)** your average velocity while running; **(d)** your average speed while running.

2. Which, if any, of the vectors shown in **Figure 3–30** are equal?

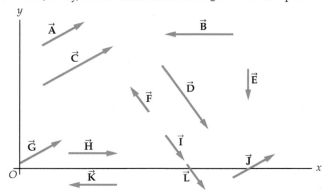

▲ **FIGURE 3–30** Conceptual Question 2

3. Given that $\vec{A} + \vec{B} = 0$, **(a)** how does the magnitude of $\vec{B}$ compare with the magnitude of $\vec{A}$? **(b)** How does the direction of $\vec{B}$ compare with the direction of $\vec{A}$?

4. Can a component of a vector be greater than the vector's magnitude?

5. Suppose that $\vec{A}$ and $\vec{B}$ have nonzero magnitude. Is it possible for $\vec{A} + \vec{B}$ to be zero?

6. Can a vector with zero magnitude have one or more components that are nonzero? Explain.

7. Given that $\vec{A} + \vec{B} = \vec{C}$, and that $A^2 + B^2 = C^2$, how are $\vec{A}$ and $\vec{B}$ oriented relative to one another?

8. Given that $\vec{A} + \vec{B} = \vec{C}$, and that $A + B = C$, how are $\vec{A}$ and $\vec{B}$ oriented relative to one another?

9. Given that $\vec{A} + \vec{B} = \vec{C}$, and that $A - B = C$, how are $\vec{A}$ and $\vec{B}$ oriented relative to one another?

10. Vector $\vec{A}$ has x and y components of equal magnitude. What can you say about the possible directions of $\vec{A}$?

11. The components of a vector $\vec{A}$ satisfy the relation $A_x = -A_y \neq 0$. What are the possible directions of $\vec{A}$?

12. Use a sketch to show that two vectors of unequal magnitude cannot add to zero, but that three vectors of unequal magnitude can.

13. Rain is falling vertically downward and you are running for shelter. To keep driest, should you hold your umbrella vertically, tilted forward, or tilted backward? Explain.

14. When sailing, the wind feels stronger when you sail upwind ("beating") than when you are sailing downwind ("running"). Explain.

PROBLEMS AND CONCEPTUAL EXERCISES

Note: Answers to odd-numbered Problems and Conceptual Exercises can be found in the back of the book. **IP** *denotes an integrated problem, with both conceptual and numerical parts;* **BIO** *identifies problems of biological or medical interest;* **CE** *indicates a conceptual exercise.* **Predict/Explain** *problems ask for two responses:* **(a)** *your prediction of a physical outcome, and* **(b)** *the best explanation among three provided. On all problems, red bullets (•, ••, •••) are used to indicate the level of difficulty.*

SECTION 3–2 THE COMPONENTS OF A VECTOR

1. • **CE** Suppose that each component of a certain vector is doubled. **(a)** By what multiplicative factor does the magnitude of the vector change? **(b)** By what multiplicative factor does the direction angle of the vector change?

2. • **CE** Rank the vectors in **Figure 3–31** in order of increasing magnitude.

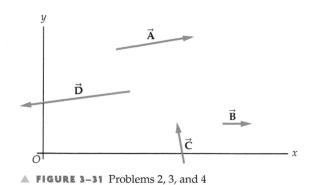

▲ **FIGURE 3–31** Problems 2, 3, and 4

3. • **CE** Rank the vectors in Figure 3–31 in order of increasing value of their x component.

4. • **CE** Rank the vectors in Figure 3–31 in order of increasing value of their y component.

5. • The press box at a baseball park is 32.0 ft above the ground. A reporter in the press box looks at an angle of 15.0° below the horizontal to see second base. What is the horizontal distance from the press box to second base?

6. • You are driving up a long, inclined road. After 1.2 miles you notice that signs along the roadside indicate that your elevation has increased by 530 ft. **(a)** What is the angle of the road above the horizontal? **(b)** How far do you have to drive to gain an additional 150 ft of elevation?

7. • **A One-Percent Grade** A road that rises 1 ft for every 100 ft traveled horizontally is said to have a 1% grade. Portions of the Lewiston grade, near Lewiston, Idaho, have a 6% grade. At what angle is this road inclined above the horizontal?

8. • Find the x and y components of a position vector $\vec{r}$ of magnitude $r = 75$ m, if its angle relative to the x axis is **(a)** 35.0° and **(b)** 65.0°.

9. • A baseball "diamond" **(Figure 3–32)** is a square with sides 90 ft in length. If the positive x axis points from home plate to first base, and the positive y axis points from home plate to third base, find the displacement vector of a base runner who has just hit **(a)** a double, **(b)** a triple, or **(c)** a home run.

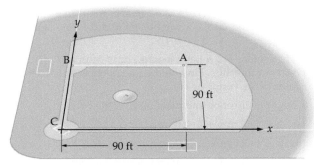

▲ **FIGURE 3–32** Problem 9

10. •• A lighthouse that rises 49 ft above the surface of the water sits on a rocky cliff that extends 19 ft from its base, as shown in **Figure 3–33**. A sailor on the deck of a ship sights the top of the lighthouse at an angle of 30.0° above the horizontal. If the sailor's eye level is 14 ft above the water, how far is the ship from the rocks?

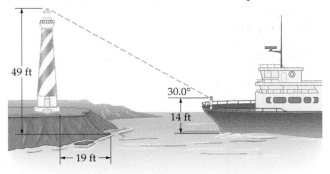

▲ **FIGURE 3–33** Problem 10

11. •• H_2O A water molecule is shown schematically in **Figure 3–34**. The distance from the center of the oxygen atom to the center of a hydrogen atom is 0.96 Å, and the angle between the hydrogen atoms is 104.5°. Find the center-to-center distance between the hydrogen atoms. (1 Å = 10^{-10} m.)

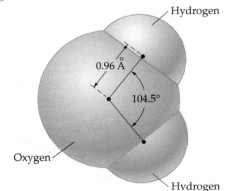

▲ **FIGURE 3–34** Problem 11

12. •• **IP** The x and y components of a vector $\vec{r}$ are $r_x = 14$ m and $r_y = -9.5$ m, respectively. Find **(a)** the direction and **(b)** the magnitude of the vector $\vec{r}$. **(c)** If both r_x and r_y are doubled, how do your answers to parts (a) and (b) change?

13. •• **IP The Longitude Problem** In 1755, John Harrison (1693–1776) completed his fourth precision chronometer, the H4, which eventually won the celebrated Longitude Prize. (For the human drama behind the Longitude Prize, see *Longitude*, by Dava Sobel.) When the minute hand of the H4 indicated 10 minutes past the hour, it extended 3.0 cm in the horizontal direction. **(a)** How long was the H4's minute hand? **(b)** At 10 minutes past the hour,

Not just a watch! The Harrison H4. (Problem 13)

was the extension of the minute hand in the vertical direction more than, less than, or equal to 3.0 cm? Explain. **(c)** Calculate the vertical extension of the minute hand at 10 minutes past the hour.

14. •• You drive a car 680 ft to the east, then 340 ft to the north. **(a)** What is the magnitude of your displacement? **(b)** Using a sketch, estimate the direction of your displacement. **(c)** Verify your estimate in part (b) with a numerical calculation of the direction.

15. •• Vector $\vec{A}$ has a magnitude of 50 units and points in the positive x direction. A second vector, $\vec{B}$, has a magnitude of 120 units and points at an angle of 70° below the x axis. Which vector has **(a)** the greater x component, and **(b)** the greater y component?

16. •• A treasure map directs you to start at a palm tree and walk due north for 15.0 m. You are then to turn 90° and walk 22.0 m; then turn 90° again and walk 5.00 m. Give the distance from the palm tree, and the direction relative to north, for each of the four possible locations of the treasure.

17. •• A whale comes to the surface to breathe and then dives at an angle of 20.0° below the horizontal **(Figure 3–35)**. If the whale continues in a straight line for 150 m, **(a)** how deep is it, and **(b)** how far has it traveled horizontally?

▲ **FIGURE 3–35** Problem 17

SECTION 3–3 ADDING AND SUBTRACTING VECTORS

18. • **CE** Consider the vectors $\vec{A}$ and $\vec{B}$ shown in **Figure 3–36**. Which of the other four vectors in the figure ($\vec{C}, \vec{D}, \vec{E}$, and $\vec{F}$) best represents the *direction* of **(a)** $\vec{A} + \vec{B}$, **(b)** $\vec{A} - \vec{B}$, and **(c)** $\vec{B} - \vec{A}$,?

19. • **CE** Refer to **Figure 3–36** for the following questions: **(a)** Is the magnitude of $\vec{A} + \vec{D}$ greater than, less than, or equal to the magnitude of $\vec{A} + \vec{E}$? **(b)** Is the magnitude of $\vec{A} + \vec{E}$ greater than, less than, or equal to the magnitude of $\vec{A} + \vec{F}$?

20. • A vector $\vec{A}$ has a magnitude of 40.0 m and points in a direction 20.0° below the positive x axis. A second vector, $\vec{B}$, has a magnitude of 75.0 m and points in a direction 50.0° above the positive x axis. **(a)** Sketch the vectors $\vec{A}, \vec{B}$, and $\vec{C} = \vec{A} + \vec{B}$. **(b)** Using the component method of vector addition, find the magnitude and direction of the vector $\vec{C}$.

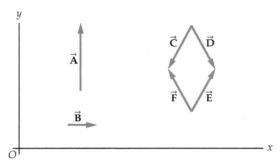

▲ **FIGURE 3–36** Problems 18 and 19

21. • An air traffic controller observes two airplanes approaching the airport. The displacement from the control tower to plane 1 is given by the vector $\vec{A}$, which has a magnitude of 220 km and points in a direction 32° north of west. The displacement from the control tower to plane 2 is given by the vector $\vec{B}$, which has a magnitude of 140 km and points 65° east of north. **(a)** Sketch the vectors $\vec{A}$, $-\vec{B}$, and $\vec{D} = \vec{A} - \vec{B}$. Notice that $\vec{D}$ is the displacement from plane 2 to plane 1. **(b)** Find the magnitude and direction of the vector $\vec{D}$.

22. • The initial velocity of a car, $\vec{v}_i$, is 45 km/h in the positive x direction. The final velocity of the car, $\vec{v}_f$, is 66 km/h in a direction that points 75° above the positive x axis. **(a)** Sketch the vectors $-\vec{v}_i$, $\vec{v}_f$, and $\Delta \vec{v} = \vec{A}_f - \vec{A}_i$. **(b)** Find the magnitude and direction of the change in velocity, $\Delta \vec{v}$.

23. •• Vector $\vec{A}$ points in the positive x direction and has a magnitude of 75 m. The vector $\vec{C} = \vec{A} + \vec{B}$ points in the positive y direction and has a magnitude of 95 m. **(a)** Sketch $\vec{A}$, $\vec{B}$, and $\vec{C}$. **(b)** Estimate the magnitude and direction of the vector $\vec{B}$. **(c)** Verify your estimate in part (b) with a numerical calculation.

24. •• Vector $\vec{A}$ points in the negative x direction and has a magnitude of 22 units. The vector $\vec{B}$ points in the positive y direction. **(a)** Find the magnitude of $\vec{B}$ if $\vec{A} + \vec{B}$ has a magnitude of 37 units. **(b)** Sketch $\vec{A}$ and $\vec{B}$.

25. •• Vector $\vec{A}$ points in the negative y direction and has a magnitude of 5 units. Vector $\vec{B}$ has twice the magnitude and points in the positive x direction. Find the direction and magnitude of **(a)** $\vec{A} + \vec{B}$, **(b)** $\vec{A} - \vec{B}$, and **(c)** $\vec{B} - \vec{A}$.

26. •• A basketball player runs down the court, following the path indicated by the vectors $\vec{A}$, $\vec{B}$, and $\vec{C}$ in **Figure 3–37**. The magnitudes of these three vectors are $A = 10.0$ m, $B = 20.0$ m, and $C = 7.0$ m. Find the magnitude and direction of the net displacement of the player using **(a)** the graphical method and **(b)** the component method of vector addition. Compare your results.

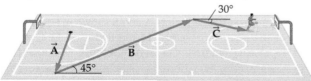

▲ **FIGURE 3–37** Problem 26

SECTION 3–4 UNIT VECTORS

27. • A particle undergoes a displacement $\Delta \vec{r}$ of magnitude 54 m in a direction 42° below the x axis. Express $\Delta \vec{r}$ in terms of the unit vectors $\hat{x}$ and $\hat{y}$.

28. • A vector has a magnitude of 3.50 m and points in a direction that is 145° counterclockwise from the x axis. Find the x and y components of this vector.

29. • A vector $\vec{A}$ has a length of 6.1 m and points in the negative x direction. Find **(a)** the x component and **(b)** the magnitude of the vector $-3.7\,\vec{A}$.

30. • The vector $-5.2\,\vec{A}$ has a magnitude of 34 m and points in the positive x direction. Find **(a)** the x component and **(b)** the magnitude of the vector $\vec{A}$.

31. • Find the direction and magnitude of the vectors.
  (a) $\vec{A} = (5.0 \text{ m})\hat{x} + (-2.0 \text{ m})\hat{y}$,
  (b) $\vec{B} = (-2.0 \text{ m})\hat{x} + (5.0 \text{ m})\hat{y}$, and **(c)** $\vec{A} + \vec{B}$.

32. • Find the direction and magnitude of the vectors.
  (a) $\vec{A} = (25 \text{ m})\hat{x} + (-12 \text{ m})\hat{y}$,
  (b) $\vec{B} = (2.0 \text{ m})\hat{x} + (15 \text{ m})\hat{y}$, and **(c)** $\vec{A} + \vec{B}$.

33. • For the vectors given in Problem 32, express **(a)** $\vec{A} - \vec{B}$ and **(b)** $\vec{B} - \vec{A}$ in unit vector notation.

34. • Express each of the vectors in **Figure 3–38** in unit vector notation.

35. •• Referring to the vectors in Figure 3–38, express the sum $\vec{A} + \vec{B} + \vec{C}$ in unit vector notation.

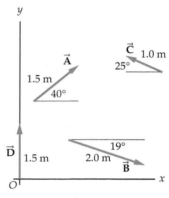

▲ **FIGURE 3–38** Problems 34 and 35

SECTION 3–5 POSITION, DISPLACEMENT, VELOCITY, AND ACCELERATION VECTORS

36. • **CE** The blue curves shown in **Figure 3–39** display the constant-speed motion of two different particles in the x-y plane. For each of the eight vectors in Figure 3–39, state whether it is **(a)** a position vector, **(b)** a velocity vector, or **(c)** an acceleration vector for the particles.

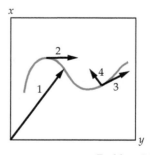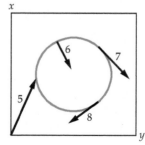

▲ **FIGURE 3–39** Problem 36

37. • **IP Moving the Knight** Two of the allowed chess moves for a knight are shown in **Figure 3–40**. **(a)** Is the magnitude of displacement 1 greater than, less than, or equal to the magnitude of displacement 2? Explain. **(b)** Find the magnitude and direction of the knight's displacement for each of the two moves. Assume that the checkerboard squares are 3.5 cm on a side.

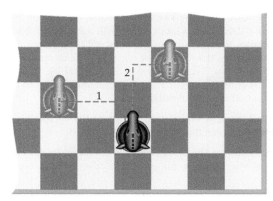

▲ **FIGURE 3–40** Problem 37

38. • **IP** In its daily prowl of the neighborhood, a cat makes a displacement of 120 m due north, followed by a 72-m displacement due west. **(a)** Find the magnitude and direction of the displacement required for the cat to return home. **(b)** If, instead, the cat had first prowled 72 m west and then 120 m north, how would this affect the displacement needed to bring it home? Explain.

39. • If the cat in Problem 38 takes 45 minutes to complete the 120-m displacement and 17 minutes to complete the 72-m displacement, what are the magnitude and direction of its average velocity during this 62-minute period of time?

40. • What are the direction and magnitude of your total displacement if you have traveled due west with a speed of 27 m/s for 125 s, then due south at 14 m/s for 66 s?

41. •• You drive a car 1500 ft to the east, then 2500 ft to the north. If the trip took 3.0 minutes, what were the direction and magnitude of your average velocity?

42. •• **IP** A jogger runs with a speed of 3.25 m/s in a direction 30.0° above the x axis. **(a)** Find the x and y components of the jogger's velocity. **(b)** How will the velocity components found in part (a) change if the jogger's speed is halved?

43. •• You throw a ball upward with an initial speed of 4.5 m/s. When it returns to your hand 0.92 s later, it has the same speed in the downward direction (assuming air resistance can be ignored). What was the average acceleration vector of the ball?

44. •• A skateboarder rolls from rest down an inclined ramp that is 15.0 m long and inclined above the horizontal at an angle of $\theta = 20.0°$. When she reaches the bottom of the ramp 3.00 s later her speed is 10.0 m/s. Show that the average acceleration of the skateboarder is $g \sin \theta$, where $g = 9.81$ m/s^2.

45. •• Consider a skateboarder who starts from rest at the top of a ramp that is inclined at an angle of 17.5° to the horizontal. Assuming that the skateboarder's acceleration is $g \sin 17.5°$, find his speed when he reaches the bottom of the ramp in 3.25 s.

46. ••• **IP The Position of the Moon** Relative to the center of the Earth, the position of the Moon can be approximated by

$$\vec{\mathbf{r}} = (3.84 \times 10^8 \text{ m}) \{\cos[(2.46 \times 10^{-6} \text{ radians/s})t]\hat{\mathbf{x}}$$
$$+ \sin[(2.46 \times 10^{-6} \text{ radians/s})t]\hat{\mathbf{y}}\}$$

where t is measured in seconds. **(a)** Find the magnitude and direction of the Moon's average velocity between $t = 0$ and $t = 7.38$ days. (This time is one-quarter of the 29.5 days it takes the Moon to complete one orbit.) **(b)** Is the instantaneous speed of the Moon greater than, less than, or the same as the average speed found in part (a)? Explain.

47. ••• **The Velocity of the Moon** The velocity of the Moon relative to the center of the Earth can be approximated by

$$\vec{\mathbf{v}} = (945 \text{ m/s}) \{-\sin[(2.46 \times 10^{-6} \text{ radians/s})t]\hat{\mathbf{x}}$$
$$+ \cos[(2.46 \times 10^{-6} \text{ radians/s})t]\hat{\mathbf{y}}\}$$

where t is measured in seconds. To approximate the instantaneous acceleration of the Moon at $t = 0$, calculate the magnitude and direction of the average acceleration between the times **(a)** $t = 0$ and $t = 0.100$ days and **(b)** $t = 0$ and $t = 0.0100$ days. (The time required for the Moon to complete one orbit is 29.5 days.)

SECTION 3–6 RELATIVE MOTION

48. • **CE** The accompanying photo shows a KC-10A Extender using a boom to refuel an aircraft in flight. If the velocity of the KC-10A is 125 m/s due east relative to the ground, what is the velocity of the aircraft being refueled relative to **(a)** the ground, and **(b)** the KC-10A?

Air-to-air refueling. (Problem 48)

49. • As an airplane taxies on the runway with a speed of 16.5 m/s, a flight attendant walks toward the tail of the plane with a speed of 1.22 m/s. What is the flight attendant's speed relative to the ground?

50. • Referring to part (a) of Example 3–2, find the time it takes for the boat to reach the opposite shore if the river is 35 m wide.

51. •• As you hurry to catch your flight at the local airport, you encounter a moving walkway that is 85 m long and has a speed of 2.2 m/s relative to the ground. If it takes you 68 s to cover 85 m when walking on the ground, how long will it take you to cover the same distance on the walkway? Assume that you walk with the same speed on the walkway as you do on the ground.

52. •• In Problem 51, how long would it take you to cover the 85-m length of the walkway if, once you get on the walkway, you immediately turn around and start walking in the opposite direction with a speed of 1.3 m/s relative to the walkway?

53. •• **IP** The pilot of an airplane wishes to fly due north, but there is a 65-km/h wind blowing toward the east. **(a)** In what direction should the pilot head her plane if its speed relative to the air is 340 km/h? **(b)** Draw a vector diagram that illustrates your result in part (a). **(c)** If the pilot decreases the air speed of the plane, but still wants to head due north, should the angle found in part (a) be increased or decreased?

54. •• A passenger walks from one side of a ferry to the ~~other~~ approaches a dock. If the passenger's velocity is 1.~~?~~ north relative to the ferry, and 4.50 m/s at an angle ~~?~~ of north relative to the water, what are the directi~~on~~ nitude of the ferry's velocity relative to the water?

55. •• You are riding on a Jet Ski at an angle of 35° upstream on a river flowing with a speed of 2.8 m/s. If your velocity relative to the ground is 9.5 m/s at an angle of 20.0° upstream, what is the speed of the Jet Ski relative to the water? (*Note*: Angles are measured relative to the x axis shown in Example 3–2.)

56. •• **IP** In Problem 55, suppose the Jet Ski is moving at a speed of 12 m/s relative to the water. **(a)** At what angle must you point the Jet Ski if your velocity relative to the ground is to be perpendicular to the shore of the river? **(b)** If you increase the speed of the Jet Ski relative to the water, does the angle in part (a) increase, decrease, or stay the same? Explain. (*Note*: Angles are measured relative to the x axis shown in Example 3–2.)

57. ••• **IP** Two people take identical Jet Skis across a river, traveling at the same speed relative to the water. Jet Ski A heads directly across the river and is carried downstream by the current before reaching the opposite shore. Jet Ski B travels in a direction that is 35° upstream and arrives at the opposite shore directly across from the starting point. **(a)** Which Jet Ski reaches the opposite shore in the least amount of time? **(b)** Confirm your answer to part (a) by finding the ratio of the time it takes for the two Jet Skis to cross the river. (*Note*: Angles are measured relative to the x axis shown in Example 3–2.)

GENERAL PROBLEMS

58. • **CE Predict/Explain** Consider the vectors $\vec{A} = (1.2 \text{ m})\hat{x}$ and $\vec{B} = (-3.4 \text{ m})\hat{x}$. **(a)** Is the magnitude of vector $\vec{A}$ greater than, less than, or equal to the magnitude of vector $\vec{B}$? **(b)** Choose the *best explanation* from among the following:
  I. The number 3.4 is greater than the number 1.2.
  II. The component of $\vec{B}$ is negative.
  III. The vector $\vec{A}$ points in the positive x direction.

59. • **CE Predict/Explain** Two vectors are defined as follows: $\vec{A} = (-2.2 \text{ m})\hat{x}$ and $\vec{B} = (1.4 \text{ m})\hat{y}$. **(a)** Is the magnitude of $1.4 \vec{A}$ greater than, less than, or equal to the magnitude of $2.2 \vec{B}$? **(b)** Choose the *best explanation* from among the following:
  I. The vector $\vec{A}$ has a negative component.
  II. A number and its negative have the same magnitude.
  III. The vectors $1.4 \vec{A}$ and $2.2 \vec{B}$ point in opposite directions.

60. • You slide a box up a loading ramp that is 10.0 ft long. At the top of the ramp the box has risen a height of 3.00 ft. What is the angle of the ramp above the horizontal?

61. • Find the direction and magnitude of the vector $2\vec{A} + \vec{B}$, where $\vec{A} = (12.1 \text{ m})\hat{x}$ and $\vec{B} = (-32.2 \text{ m})\hat{y}$.

62. •• **CE** The components of a vector $\vec{A}$ satisfy $A_x < 0$ and $A_y < 0$. Is the direction angle of $\vec{A}$ between 0° and 90°, between 90° and 180°, between 180° and 270°, or between 270° and 360°?

63. •• **CE** The components of a vector $\vec{B}$ satisfy $B_x > 0$ and $B_y < 0$. Is the direction angle of $\vec{B}$ between 0° and 90°, between 90° and 180°, between 180° and 270°, or between 270° and 360°?

64. •• It is given that $\vec{A} - \vec{B} = (-51.4 \text{ m})\hat{x}$, $\vec{C} = (62.2 \text{ m})\hat{x}$, and $\vec{A} + \vec{B} + \vec{C} = (13.8 \text{ m})\hat{x}$. Find the vectors $\vec{A}$ and $\vec{B}$.

65. •• **IP** Two students perform an experiment with a train and a ball. Michelle rides on a flatcar pulled at 8.35 m/s by a train on a straight, horizontal track; Gary stands at rest on the ground near the tracks. When Michelle throws the ball with an initial angle of 65.0° above the horizontal, from her point of view, Gary sees the ball rise straight up and back down above a fixed point on the ground. **(a)** Did Michelle throw the ball toward the front of the train or toward the rear of the train? Explain. **(b)** What was the initial speed of Michelle's throw? **(c)** What was the initial [spee]d of the ball as seen by Gary?

66. •• An off-roader explores the open desert in her Hummer. First she drives 25° west of north with a speed of 6.5 km/h for 15 minutes, then due east with a speed of 12 km/h for 7.5 minutes. She completes the final leg of her trip in 22 minutes. What are the direction and speed of travel on the final leg? (Assume her speed is constant on each leg, and that she returns to her starting point at the end of the final leg.)

67. •• Find the x, y, and z components of the vector $\vec{A}$ shown in **Figure 3–41**, given that $A = 65$ m.

68. •• A football is thrown horizontally with an initial velocity of $(16.6 \text{ m/s})\hat{x}$. Ignoring air resistance, the average acceleration

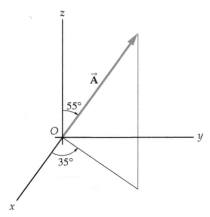

▲ **FIGURE 3–41** Problem 67

of the football over any period of time is $(-9.81 \text{ m/s}^2)\hat{y}$. **(a)** Find the velocity vector of the ball 1.75 s after it is thrown. **(b)** Find the magnitude and direction of the velocity at this time.

69. •• As a function of time, the velocity of the football described in Problem 68 can be written as $\vec{v} = (16.6 \text{ m/s})\hat{x} - [(9.81 \text{ m/s}^2)t]\hat{y}$. Calculate the average acceleration vector of the football for the time periods **(a)** $t = 0$ to $t = 1.00$ s, **(b)** $t = 0$ to $t = 2.50$ s, and **(c)** $t = 0$ to $t = 5.00$ s. (If the acceleration of an object is constant, its average acceleration is the same for all time periods.)

70. •• Two airplanes taxi as they approach the terminal. Plane 1 taxies with a speed of 12 m/s due north. Plane 2 taxies with a speed of 7.5 m/s in a direction 20° north of west. **(a)** What are the direction and magnitude of the velocity of plane 1 relative to plane 2? **(b)** What are the direction and magnitude of the velocity of plane 2 relative to plane 1?

71. •• A shopper at the supermarket follows the path indicated by vectors $\vec{A}, \vec{B}, \vec{C}$, and $\vec{D}$ in **Figure 3–42**. Given that the

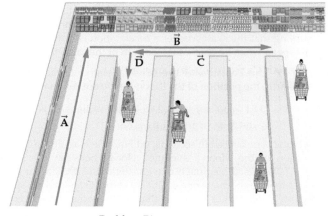

▲ **FIGURE 3–42** Problem 71

vectors have the magnitudes $A = 51$ ft, $B = 45$ ft, $C = 35$ ft, and $D = 13$ ft, find the total displacement of the shopper using **(a)** the graphical method and **(b)** the component method of vector addition. Give the direction of the displacement relative to the direction of vector $\vec{A}$.

72. •• Initially, a particle is moving at 4.10 m/s at an angle of 33.5° above the horizontal. Two seconds later, its velocity is 6.05 m/s at an angle of 59.0° below the horizontal. What was the particle's average acceleration during these 2.00 seconds?

73. •• A passenger on a stopped bus notices that rain is falling vertically just outside the window. When the bus moves with constant velocity, the passenger observes that the falling raindrops are now making an angle of 15° with respect to the vertical. **(a)** What is the ratio of the speed of the raindrops to the speed of the bus? **(b)** Find the speed of the raindrops, given that the bus is moving with a speed of 18 m/s.

74. •• **A Big Clock** The clock that rings the bell known as Big Ben has an hour hand that is 9.0 feet long and a minute hand that is 14 feet long, where the distance is measured from the center of the clock to the tip of each hand. What is the tip-to-tip distance between these two hands when the clock reads 12 minutes after four o'clock?

75. •• **IP** Suppose we orient the x axis of a two-dimensional coordinate system along the beach at Waikiki. Waves approaching the beach have a velocity relative to the shore given by $\vec{v}_{ws} = (1.3 \text{ m/s})\hat{y}$. Surfers move more rapidly than the waves, but at an angle to the beach. The angle is chosen so that the surfers approach the shore with the same speed as the waves. **(a)** If a surfer has a speed of 7.2 m/s relative to the shore, what is her direction of motion relative to the positive x axis? **(b)** What is the surfer's velocity relative to the wave? **(c)** If the surfer's speed is increased, will the angle in part (a) increase or decrease? Explain.

76. ••• **IP** Referring to Example 3–2, **(a)** what heading must the boat have if it is to land directly across the river from its starting point? **(b)** How much time is required for this trip if the river is 25.0 m wide? **(c)** Suppose the speed of the boat is increased, but it is still desired to land directly across from the starting point. Should the boat's heading be more upstream, more downstream, or the same as in part (a)? Explain.

77. ••• Vector $\vec{A}$ points in the negative x direction. Vector $\vec{B}$ points at an angle of 30.0° above the positive x axis. Vector $\vec{C}$ has a magnitude of 15 m and points in a direction 40.0° below the positive x axis. Given that $\vec{A} + \vec{B} + \vec{C} = 0$, find the magnitudes of $\vec{A}$ and $\vec{B}$.

78. ••• As two boats approach the marina, the velocity of boat 1 relative to boat 2 is 2.15 m/s in a direction 47.0° east of north. If boat 1 has a velocity that is 0.775 m/s due north, what is the velocity (magnitude and direction) of boat 2?

PASSAGE PROBLEMS

BIO Motion Camouflage in Dragonflies

Dragonflies, whose ancestors were once the size of hawks, have prowled the skies in search of small flying insects for over 250 million years. Faster and more maneuverable than any other insect, they even fold their front two legs in flight and tuck them behind their head to be as streamlined as possible. They also employ an intriguing stalking strategy known as "motion camouflage" to approach their prey almost undetected.

The basic idea of motion camouflage is for the dragonfly to move in such a way that the line of sight from the prey to the dragonfly is always in the same direction. Moving in this way, the dragonfly appears almost motionless to its prey, as if it were

an object at infinity. Eventually the prey notices the dragonfly has grown in size and is therefore closer, but by that time it's too late for it to evade capture.

A typical capture scenario is shown in **Figure 3–43**, where the prey moves in the positive y direction with the constant speed $v_p = 0.750$ m/s, and the dragonfly moves at an angle $\theta = 48.5°$ to the x axis with the constant speed v_d. If the dragonfly chooses its speed correctly, the line of sight from the prey to the dragonfly will always be in the same direction—parallel to the x axis in this case.

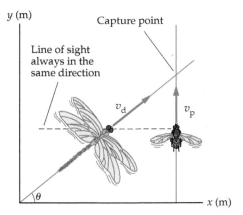

▲ **FIGURE 3–43** Problems 79, 80, 81, and 82

79. • What speed must the dragonfly have if the line of sight, which is parallel to the x axis initially, is to remain parallel to the x axis?

   A. 0.562 m/s   **B.** 0.664 m/s

   C. 1.00 m/s   **D.** 1.13 m/s

80. • Suppose the dragonfly now approaches its prey along a path with $\theta > 48.5°$, but it still keeps the line of sight parallel to the x axis. Is the speed of the dragonfly in this new case greater than, less than, or equal to its speed in Problem 79?

81. • What is the correct "motion camouflage" speed of approach for a dragonfly pursuing its prey at the angle $\theta = 68.5°$?

   A. 0.295 m/s   **B.** 0.698 m/s

   C. 0.806 m/s   **D.** 2.05 m/s

82. •• If the dragonfly approaches its prey with a speed of 0.950 m/s, what angle θ is required to maintain a constant line of sight parallel to the x axis?

   A. 37.9°   **B.** 38.3°

   C. 51.7°   **D.** 52.1°

INTERACTIVE PROBLEMS

83. •• **IP Referring to Example 3–2** Suppose the speed of the boat relative to the water is 7.0 m/s. **(a)** At what angle to the x axis must the boat be headed if it is to land directly across the river from its starting position? **(b)** If the speed of the boat relative to the water is increased, will the angle needed to go directly across the river increase, decrease, or stay the same? Explain.

84. ••• **Referring to Example 3–2** Suppose the boat has a speed of 6.7 m/s relative to the water, and that the dock on the opposite shore of the river is at the location $x = 55$ m and $y = 28$ m relative to the starting point of the boat. **(a)** At what angle relative to the x axis must the boat be pointed in order to reach the other dock? **(b)** With the angle found in part (a), what is the speed of the boat relative to the ground?

4 Two-Dimensional Kinematics

When you hear the word "projectile," you probably think of an artillery shell or perhaps a home run into the upper deck. But as we'll see in this chapter, the term applies to any object moving under the influence of gravity alone. For example, each of these juggling balls undergoes projectile motion as it moves from one hand to the other. In this chapter we will explore the physical laws that govern such motion, and will learn—among other things—that these balls follow a parabolic path.

We now extend our study of kinematics to motion in two dimensions. This allows us to consider a much wider range of physical phenomena observed in everyday life. Of particular interest is **projectile motion,** the motion of objects that are initially launched—or "projected"—and that then continue moving under the influence of gravity alone. Examples of projectile motion include balls thrown from one person to another, water spraying from a hose, salmon leaping over rapids, and divers jumping from the cliffs of Acapulco.

The main idea of this chapter is quite simple: Horizontal and vertical motions are independent. That's it. For example, a ball thrown horizontally with a speed v continues to move with the same speed v in the horizontal direction, even as it falls with an increasing speed in the vertical direction. Similarly, the time of fall is the same whether a ball is dropped from rest straight down, or thrown horizontally. Simply put, each motion continues as if the other motion were not present.

This chapter develops and applies the idea of independence of motion to many common physical systems.

4–1 Motion in Two Dimensions

In this section we develop equations of motion to describe objects moving in two dimensions. First, we consider motion with constant velocity, determining x and y as functions of time. Next, we investigate motion with constant acceleration. We show that the one-dimensional kinematic equations of Chapter 2 can be extended in a straightforward way to apply to two dimensions.

Constant Velocity

To begin, consider the simple situation shown in **Figure 4–1**. A turtle starts at the origin at $t = 0$ and moves with a constant speed $v_0 = 0.26$ m/s in a direction $25°$ above the x axis. How far has the turtle moved in the x and y directions after 5.0 seconds?

First, note that the turtle moves in a straight line a distance

$$d = v_0 t = (0.26 \text{ m/s})(5.0 \text{ s}) = 1.3 \text{ m}$$

as indicated in **Figure 4–1(a)**. From the definitions of sine and cosine given in the previous chapter, we see that

$$x = d \cos 25° = 1.2 \text{ m}$$
$$y = d \sin 25° = 0.55 \text{ m}$$

An alternative way to approach this problem is to treat the x and y motions separately. First, we determine the speed of the turtle in each direction. Referring to **Figure 4–1(b)**, we see that the x component of velocity is

$$v_{0x} = v_0 \cos 25° = 0.24 \text{ m/s}$$

and the y component is

$$v_{0y} = v_0 \sin 25° = 0.11 \text{ m/s}$$

Next, we find the distance traveled by the turtle in the x and y directions by multiplying the speed in each direction by the time:

$$x = v_{0x} t = (0.24 \text{ m/s})(5.0 \text{ s}) = 1.2 \text{ m}$$

and

$$y = v_{0y} t = (0.11 \text{ m/s})(5.0 \text{ s}) = 0.55 \text{ m}$$

This is in agreement with our previous results. To summarize, we can think of the turtle's actual motion as a combination of separate x and y motions.

In general, the turtle might start at a position $x = x_0$ and $y = y_0$ at time $t = 0$. In this case, we have

$$x = x_0 + v_{0x} t \qquad\qquad 4\text{--}1$$

and

$$y = y_0 + v_{0y} t \qquad\qquad 4\text{--}2$$

as the x and y equations of motion.

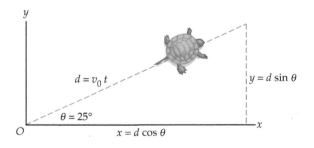

(a)

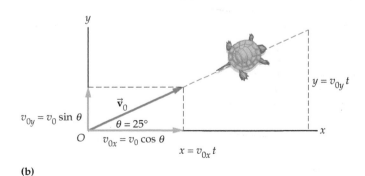

(b)

▲ **FIGURE 4–1 Constant velocity**
A turtle walks from the origin with a speed of $v_0 = 0.26$ m/s. **(a)** In a time t the turtle moves through a straight-line distance of $d = v_0 t$; thus the x and y displacements are $x = d \cos \theta$, $y = d \sin \theta$. **(b)** Equivalently, the turtle's x and y components of velocity are $v_{0x} = v_0 \cos \theta$ and $v_{0y} = v_0 \sin \theta$; hence $x = v_{0x} t$ and $y = v_{0y} t$.

Compare these equations with Equation 2–11, $x = x_0 + v_0 t + \frac{1}{2}at^2$, which gives position as a function of time in one dimension. When acceleration is zero, as it is for the turtle, Equation 2–11 reduces to $x = x_0 + v_0 t$. Replacing v_0 with the x component of the velocity, v_{0x}, yields Equation 4–1. Similarly, replacing each x in Equation 4–1 with y converts it to Equation 4–2, the y equation of motion.

A situation illustrating the use of Equations 4–1 and 4–2 is given in Example 4–1.

EXAMPLE 4–1   **THE EAGLE DESCENDS**

An eagle perched on a tree limb 19.5 m above the water spots a fish swimming near the surface. The eagle pushes off from the branch and descends toward the water. By adjusting its body in flight, the eagle maintains a constant speed of 3.10 m/s at an angle of 20.0° below the horizontal. **(a)** How long does it take for the eagle to reach the water? **(b)** How far has the eagle traveled in the horizontal direction when it reaches the water?

PICTURE THE PROBLEM

We set up our coordinate system so that the eagle starts at $x_0 = 0$ and $y_0 = h = 19.5$ m. The water level is $y = 0$. As indicated in our sketch, $v_{0x} = v_0 \cos\theta$ and $v_{0y} = -v_0 \sin\theta$, where $v_0 = 3.10$ m/s and $\theta = 20.0°$. Notice that both components of the eagle's velocity are constant, and therefore the equations of motion given in Equations 4–1 and 4–2 apply.

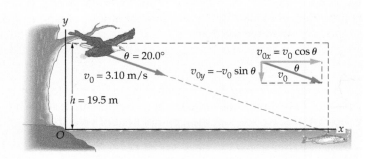

STRATEGY

As usual in such problems, it is best to treat the eagle's flight as a combination of separate x and y motions. Since we are given the constant speed of the eagle, and the angle at which it descends, we can find the x and y components of its velocity. We then use the y equation of motion, $y = y_0 + v_{0y}t$, to find the time t when the eagle reaches the water. Finally, we use this value of t in the x equation of motion, $x = x_0 + v_{0x}t$, to find the horizontal distance the bird travels.

SOLUTION

Part (a)

1. Begin by determining v_{0x} and v_{0y}:

$$v_{0x} = v_0 \cos\theta = (3.10 \text{ m/s}) \cos 20.0° = 2.91 \text{ m/s}$$
$$v_{0y} = -v_0 \sin\theta = -(3.10 \text{ m/s}) \sin 20.0° = -1.06 \text{ m/s}$$

2. Now, set $y = 0$ in $y = y_0 + v_{0y}t$ and solve for t:

$$y = y_0 + v_{0y}t = h + v_{0y}t = 0$$

$$t = -\frac{h}{v_{0y}} = -\frac{19.5 \text{ m}}{(-1.06 \text{ m/s})} = 18.4 \text{ s}$$

Part (b)

3. Substitute $t = 18.4$ s into $x = x_0 + v_{0x}t$ to find x:

$$x = x_0 + v_{0x}t = 0 + (2.91 \text{ m/s})(18.4 \text{ s}) = 53.5 \text{ m}$$

INSIGHT

Notice how the two minus signs in Step 2 combine to give a positive time. One minus sign comes from setting $y = 0$, the other from the fact that v_{0y} is negative. No matter where we choose the origin, or what direction we choose to be positive, the time will always have the same value.

As mentioned in the problem statement, the eagle cannot travel in a straight line by simply dropping from the tree limb—it has to adjust its wings and tail to produce enough lift to balance the force of gravity. Airplanes do the same thing when they adjust their flight surfaces to make a smooth landing.

PRACTICE PROBLEM

What is the location of the eagle 2.00 s after it takes flight?   [**Answer:** $x = 5.82$ m, $y = 17.4$ m]

Some related homework problems: Problem 2, Problem 3

Constant Acceleration

To study motion with constant acceleration in two dimensions we repeat what was done in one dimension in Chapter 2, but with separate equations for both x and y. For example, to obtain x as a function of time we start with $x = x_0 + v_0 t + \frac{1}{2}at^2$ (Equation 2–11), and replace both v_0 and a with the corresponding x components, v_{0x} and a_x. This gives

$$x = x_0 + v_{0x}t + \frac{1}{2}a_x t^2 \qquad \text{4–3(a)}$$

To obtain y as a function of time, we write y in place of x in Equation 4–3(a):

$$y = y_0 + v_{0y}t + \tfrac{1}{2}a_yt^2 \qquad\qquad \text{4–3(b)}$$

These are the position-versus-time equations of motion for two dimensions. (In three dimensions we introduce a third coordinate direction and label it z. We would then simply replace x with z in Equation 4–3(a) to obtain z as a function of time.)

The same approach gives velocity as a function of time. Start with Equation 2–7, $v = v_0 + at$, and write it in terms of x and y components. This yields

$$v_x = v_{0x} + a_xt \qquad\qquad \text{4–4(a)}$$

$$v_y = v_{0y} + a_yt \qquad\qquad \text{4–4(b)}$$

Note that we simply repeat everything we did for one dimension, only now with separate equations for the x and y components.

Finally, we can write $v^2 = v_0^2 + 2a\Delta x$ in terms of components as well:

$$v_x^2 = v_{0x}^2 + 2a_x\Delta x \qquad\qquad \text{4–5(a)}$$

$$v_y^2 = v_{0y}^2 + 2a_y\Delta y \qquad\qquad \text{4–5(b)}$$

The following table summarizes our results:

Table 4–1   Constant-Acceleration Equations of Motion

Position as a function of time	Velocity as a function of time	Velocity as a function of position
$x = x_0 + v_{0x}t + \tfrac{1}{2}a_xt^2$	$v_x = v_{0x} + a_xt$	$v_x^2 = v_{0x}^2 + 2a_x\Delta x$
$y = y_0 + v_{0y}t + \tfrac{1}{2}a_yt^2$	$v_y = v_{0y} + a_yt$	$v_y^2 = v_{0y}^2 + 2a_y\Delta y$

These are the fundamental equations that will be used to obtain *all* of the results presented throughout the rest of this chapter. Though it may appear sometimes that we are writing new sets of equations for different special cases, the equations aren't new—what we are actually doing is simply writing these equations again, but with specific values substituted for the constants that appear in them.

EXAMPLE 4–2   A HUMMER ACCELERATES

A hummingbird is flying in such a way that it is initially moving vertically with a speed of 4.6 m/s and accelerating horizontally at 11 m/s^2. Assuming the bird's acceleration remains constant for the time interval of interest, find **(a)** the horizontal and vertical distances through which it moves in 0.55 s and **(b)** its x and y velocity components at $t = 0.55$ s.

PICTURE THE PROBLEM

In our sketch we have placed the origin of a two-dimensional coordinate system at the location of the hummingbird at the initial time, $t = 0$. In addition, we have chosen the initial direction of motion to be in the positive y direction, and the direction of acceleration to be in the positive x direction. As a result, it follows that $x_0 = y_0 = 0$, $v_{0x} = 0$, $v_{0y} = 4.6$ m/s, $a_x = 11$ m/s^2, and $a_y = 0$. As the hummingbird moves upward, its x component of velocity increases, resulting in a curved path, as shown.

STRATEGY

(a) Since we want to relate position and time, we find the horizontal position of the hummingbird using $x = x_0 + v_{0x}t + \tfrac{1}{2}a_xt^2$, and the vertical position using $y = y_0 + v_{0y}t + \tfrac{1}{2}a_yt^2$. **(b)** The velocity components as a function of time can be found using $v_x = v_{0x} + a_xt$ and $v_y = v_{0y} + a_yt$.

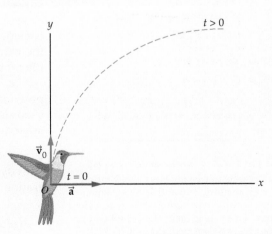

CONTINUED ON NEXT PAGE

CONTINUED FROM PREVIOUS PAGE

SOLUTION

Part (a)

1. Use $x = x_0 + v_{0x}t + \frac{1}{2}a_x t^2$ to find x at $t = 0.55$ s: $x = x_0 + v_{0x}t + \frac{1}{2}a_x t^2 = 0 + 0 + \frac{1}{2}(11 \text{ m/s}^2)(0.55 \text{ s})^2 = 1.7 \text{ m}$

2. Use $y = y_0 + v_{0y}t + \frac{1}{2}a_y t^2$ to find y at $t = 0.55$ s: $y = y_0 + v_{0y}t + \frac{1}{2}a_y t^2 = 0 + (4.6 \text{ m/s})(0.55 \text{ s}) + 0 = 2.5 \text{ m}$

Part (b)

3. Use $v_x = v_{0x} + a_x t$ to find v_x at $t = 0.55$ s: $v_x = v_{0x} + a_x t = 0 + (11 \text{ m/s}^2)(0.55 \text{ s}) = 6.1 \text{ m/s}$

4. Use $v_y = v_{0y} + a_y t$ to find v_y at $t = 0.55$ s: $v_y = v_{0y} + a_y t = 4.6 \text{ m/s} + (0)(0.55 \text{ s}) = 4.6 \text{ m/s}$

INSIGHT

In 0.55 s the hummingbird moves 1.7 m horizontally and 2.5 m vertically. The horizontal position of the bird will eventually increase more rapidly with time than the vertical position, due to the t^2 dependence of x as compared with the t dependence of y. This results in a curved, parabolic path for the hummingbird, as shown in our sketch. The bird's velocity at 0.55 s is $v = \sqrt{v_x^2 + v_y^2} = \sqrt{(6.1 \text{ m/s})^2 + (4.6 \text{ m/s})^2} = 7.6 \text{ m/s}$ at an angle of $\theta = \tan^{-1}(v_y/v_x) = \tan^{-1}[(4.6 \text{ m/s})/(6.1 \text{ m/s})] = 37°$ above the x axis. It's clear the angle of flight must be less than 45° at this time, since the x component of velocity is greater than the y component.

PRACTICE PROBLEM

How much time is required for the hummingbird to move 2.0 m horizontally from its initial position?   [**Answer:** $t = 0.60$ s]

Some related homework problems: Problem 4, Problem 5, Problem 62

4–2 Projectile Motion: Basic Equations

We now apply the independence of horizontal and vertical motions to projectiles. Just what do we mean by a projectile? Well, a **projectile** is an object that is thrown, kicked, batted, or otherwise launched into motion and then allowed to follow a path determined solely by the influence of gravity. As you might expect, this covers a wide variety of physical systems.

In studying projectile motion we make the following assumptions:

- air resistance is ignored
- the acceleration due to gravity is constant, downward, and has a magnitude equal to $g = 9.81 \text{ m/s}^2$
- the Earth's rotation is ignored

Air resistance can be significant when a projectile moves with relatively high speed or if it encounters a strong wind. In many everyday situations, however, like tossing a ball to a friend or dropping a book, air resistance is relatively insignificant. As for the acceleration due to gravity, $g = 9.81 \text{ m/s}^2$, this value varies slightly from place to place on the Earth's surface and decreases with increasing altitude. In addition, the rotation of the Earth can be significant when considering projectiles that cover great distances. Little error is made in ignoring the variation of g or the rotation of the Earth, however, in the examples of projectile motion considered in this chapter.

Let's incorporate these assumptions into the equations of motion given in the previous section. Suppose, as in **Figure 4–2**, that the x axis is horizontal and the y axis is vertical, with the positive direction upward. Since downward is the negative direction, it follows that

$$a_y = -9.81 \text{ m/s}^2 = -g$$

Gravity causes no acceleration in the x direction. Thus, the x component of acceleration is zero:

$$a_x = 0$$

With these acceleration components substituted into the fundamental constant-acceleration equations of motion (Table 4–1) we find:

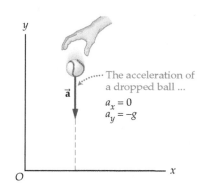

The acceleration of a dropped ball ...
$a_x = 0$
$a_y = -g$

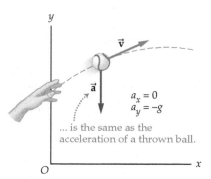

$a_x = 0$
$a_y = -g$

... is the same as the acceleration of a thrown ball.

▲ **FIGURE 4–2 Acceleration in free fall**
All objects in free fall have acceleration components $a_x = 0$ and $a_y = -g$ when the coordinate system is chosen as shown here. This is true regardless of whether the object is dropped, thrown, kicked, or otherwise set into motion.

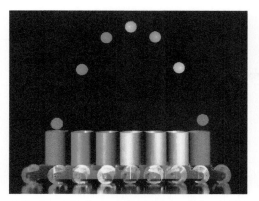

▲ In the multiple-exposure photo at left, a ball is projected upward from a moving cart. The ball retains its initial horizontal velocity; as a result, it follows a parabolic path and remains directly above the cart at all times. When the ball lands, it falls back into the cart, just as it would if the cart had been at rest. (In this sequence, the exposures were made at equal time intervals with light of different colors, making it easier to follow the relative motion of the ball and the cart.) In the photo at right, the pilot ejection seat of a jet fighter is being ground-tested. Here too the horizontal and vertical motions are independent; thus, the test dummy is still almost directly above the cockpit from which it was ejected. Note, however, that air resistance is beginning to reduce the dummy's horizontal velocity. Eventually, it will fall far behind the speeding plane.

Projectile Motion ($a_x = 0$, $a_y = -g$)

$$x = x_0 + v_{0x}t \qquad v_x = v_{0x} \qquad v_x^2 = v_{0x}^2$$
$$y = y_0 + v_{0y}t - \tfrac{1}{2}gt^2 \qquad v_y = v_{0y} - gt \qquad v_y^2 = v_{0y}^2 - 2g\Delta y$$

4–6

Note that in these expressions the positive y direction is upward and the quantity g is positive. All of our studies of *projectile motion* will use Equations 4–6 as our fundamental equations—again, special cases will simply correspond to substituting specific values for the constants.

A simple demonstration illustrates the independence of horizontal and vertical motions in projectile motion. First, while standing still, drop a rubber ball to the floor and catch it on the rebound. Note that the ball goes straight down, lands near your feet, and returns almost to the level of your hand in about a second.

Next, walk—or roller skate—with constant speed before dropping the ball, then observe its motion carefully. To you, its motion looks the same as before: It goes straight down, lands near your feet, bounces straight back up, and returns in about one second. This is illustrated in **Figure 4–3**. The fact that you were moving in the horizontal direction the whole time had no effect on the ball's vertical motion—the motions were independent.

To an observer who sees you walking by, the ball follows a curved path, as shown. The precise shape of this curved path is determined in the next section.

PROBLEM-SOLVING NOTE

Acceleration of a Projectile

When the x axis is chosen to be horizontal and the y axis points vertically upward, it follows that the acceleration of an ideal projectile is $a_x = 0$ and $a_y = -g$.

The moving person sees the ball fall straight down below her hand ...

... but a stationary observer sees the ball follow a curved path.

▲ **FIGURE 4–3 Independence of vertical and horizontal motions**
When you drop a ball while walking, running, or skating with constant velocity, it appears to you to drop straight down from the point where you released it. To a person at rest, the ball follows a curved path that combines horizontal and vertical motions.

▲ This rollerblader may not be thinking about independence of motion, but the ball she released illustrates the concept perfectly; it continues to move horizontally with constant speed—even though she's no longer touching it—at the same time that it accelerates vertically downward.

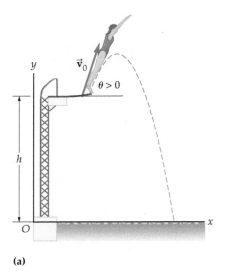
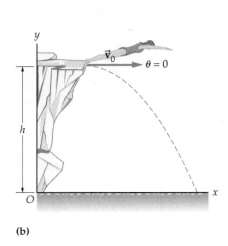

(a)   (b)

▲ **FIGURE 4–4 Launch angle of a projectile**
(a) A projectile launched at an angle above the horizontal, $\theta > 0$. A launch below the horizontal would correspond to $\theta < 0$. **(b)** A projectile launched horizontally, $\theta = 0$. In this section we consider $\theta = 0$. The next section deals with $\theta \neq 0$.

4–3 Zero Launch Angle

A special case of some interest is a projectile launched horizontally, so that the angle between the initial velocity and the horizontal is $\theta = 0$. We devote this section to a brief look at this type of motion.

Equations of Motion

Suppose you are walking with a speed v_0 when you release a ball from a height h, as discussed in the previous section. If we choose ground level to be $y = 0$ and the release point to be directly above the origin, the initial position of the ball is given by

$$x_0 = 0$$

and

$$y_0 = h$$

This is illustrated in Figure 4–3.

The initial velocity is horizontal, corresponding to $\theta = 0$ in **Figure 4–4**. As a result, the x component of the initial velocity is simply the initial speed:

$$v_{0x} = v_0 \cos 0° = v_0$$

and the y component of the initial velocity is zero:

$$v_{0y} = v_0 \sin 0° = 0$$

Substituting these specific values into our fundamental equations for projectile motion (Equations 4–6) gives the following simplified results for zero launch angle ($\theta = 0$):

$$
\begin{array}{lll}
x = v_0 t & v_x = v_0 = \text{constant} & v_x^2 = v_0^2 = \text{constant} \\
y = h - \tfrac{1}{2}g t^2 & v_y = -gt & v_y^2 = -2g\Delta y
\end{array}
\qquad 4\text{–}7
$$

Note that the x component of velocity remains the same for all time and that the y component steadily decreases with time. As a result, x increases linearly with time, and y decreases with a t^2 dependence. Snapshots of this motion at equal time intervals are shown in **Figure 4–5**.

Horizontal motion is uniform—
equal distance in equal time.

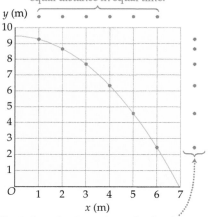

Vertical motion is accelerated—the object goes farther in each successive interval.

▲ **FIGURE 4–5 Trajectory of a projectile launched horizontally**
In this plot, the projectile was launched from a height of 9.5 m with an initial speed of 5.0 m/s. The positions shown in the plot correspond to the times $t = 0.20$ s, 0.40 s, 0.60 s, ... Note the uniform motion in the x direction, and the accelerated motion in the y direction.

PROBLEM-SOLVING NOTE

Identify Initial Conditions

The launch point of a projectile determines x_0 and y_0. The initial velocity of a projectile determines v_{0x} and v_{0y}.

EXAMPLE 4-3   DROPPING A BALL

A person skateboarding with a constant speed of 1.30 m/s releases a ball from a height of 1.25 m above the ground. Given that $x_0 = 0$ and $y_0 = h = 1.25$ m, find x and y for **(a)** $t = 0.250$ s and **(b)** $t = 0.500$ s. **(c)** Find the velocity, speed, and direction of motion of the ball at $t = 0.500$ s.

PICTURE THE PROBLEM
The ball starts at $x_0 = 0$ and $y_0 = h = 1.25$ m. Its initial velocity is horizontal, therefore $v_{0x} = v_0 = 1.30$ m/s and $v_{0y} = 0$. In addition, it accelerates with the acceleration due to gravity in the negative y direction, $a_y = -g$, and moves with constant speed in the x direction, $a_x = 0$.

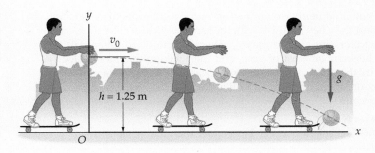

STRATEGY
The x and y positions are given by $x = v_0 t$ and $y = h - \frac{1}{2}gt^2$, respectively. We simply substitute time into these expressions. Similarly, the velocity components are $v_x = v_0$ and $v_y = -gt$.

SOLUTION

Part (a)

1. Substitute $t = 0.250$ s into the x and y equations of motion:

$$x = v_0 t = (1.30 \text{ m/s})(0.250 \text{ s}) = 0.325 \text{ m}$$
$$y = h - \frac{1}{2}gt^2$$
$$= 1.25 \text{ m} - \frac{1}{2}(9.81 \text{ m/s}^2)(0.250 \text{ s})^2 = 0.943 \text{ m}$$

Part (b)

2. Substitute $t = 0.500$ s into the x and y equations of motion. Note that the ball is only about an inch above the ground at this time:

$$x = v_0 t = (1.30 \text{ m/s})(0.500 \text{ s}) = 0.650 \text{ m}$$
$$y = h - \frac{1}{2}gt^2$$
$$= 1.25 \text{ m} - \frac{1}{2}(9.81 \text{ m/s}^2)(0.500 \text{ s})^2 = 0.0238 \text{ m}$$

Part (c)

3. First, calculate the x and y components of the velocity at $t = 0.500$ s using $v_x = v_0$ and $v_y = -gt$:

$$v_x = v_0 = 1.30 \text{ m/s}$$
$$v_y = -gt = -(9.81 \text{ m/s}^2)(0.500 \text{ s}) = -4.91 \text{ m/s}$$

4. Use these components to determine $\vec{v}$, v, and θ:

$$\vec{v} = (1.30 \text{ m/s})\hat{x} + (-4.91 \text{ m/s})\hat{y}$$
$$v = \sqrt{v_x^2 + v_y^2}$$
$$= \sqrt{(1.30 \text{ m/s})^2 + (-4.91 \text{ m/s})^2} = 5.08 \text{ m/s}$$
$$\theta = \tan^{-1}\frac{v_y}{v_x} = \tan^{-1}\frac{(-4.91 \text{ m/s})}{1.30 \text{ m/s}} = -75.2°$$

INSIGHT
Note that the x position of the ball does not depend on the acceleration of gravity, g, and that its y position does not depend on the initial horizontal speed of the ball, v_0. For example, if the person is running when he drops the ball, the ball is moving faster in the horizontal direction, and it keeps up with the person when it is dropped. Its vertical motion doesn't change at all, however; it drops to the ground in exactly the same time and bounces back to the same height as before.

PRACTICE PROBLEM
How long does it take for the ball to land? [**Answer:** Referring to the results of part (b), it is clear that the time of landing is slightly greater than 0.500 s. Setting $y = 0$ gives a precise answer; $t = \sqrt{2h/g} = 0.505$ s.]

Some related homework problems: Problem 15, Problem 16, Problem 20

CONCEPTUAL CHECKPOINT 4–1 COMPARE SPLASHDOWN SPEEDS

Two youngsters dive off an overhang into a lake. Diver 1 drops straight down, diver 2 runs off the cliff with an initial horizontal speed v_0. Is the splashdown speed of diver 2 **(a)** greater than, **(b)** less than, or **(c)** equal to the splashdown speed of diver 1?

REASONING AND DISCUSSION

Note that neither diver has an initial y component of velocity, and that they both fall with the same vertical acceleration—the acceleration due to gravity. Therefore, the two divers fall for the same amount of time, and their y components of velocity are the same at splashdown. Since diver 2 also has a nonzero x component of velocity, unlike diver 1, the speed of diver 2 is greater.

ANSWER

(a) The speed of diver 2 is greater than that of diver 1.

▲ Lava bombs (top) and fountain jets (bottom) trace out parabolic paths, as is typical in projectile motion. The trajectories are only slightly altered by air resistance.

Parabolic Path

Just what is the shape of the curved path followed by a projectile launched horizontally? This can be found by combining $x = v_0 t$ and $y = h - \frac{1}{2}gt^2$, which allows us to express y in terms of x. First, solve for time using the x equation. This gives

$$t = x/v_0$$

Next, substitute this result into the y equation to eliminate t:

$$y = h - \frac{1}{2}g\left(\frac{x}{v_0}\right)^2 = h - \left(\frac{g}{2v_0{}^2}\right)x^2 \qquad \text{4–8}$$

Note that y has the form

$$y = a + bx^2$$

where $a = h = $ constant and $b = -g/2v_0{}^2 = $ constant. This is the equation of a parabola that curves downward, a characteristic shape in projectile motion.

Landing Site

Where does a projectile land if it is launched horizontally with a speed v_0 from a height h?

The most direct way to answer this question is to set $y = 0$ in Equation 4–8, since $y = 0$ corresponds to ground level. This gives

$$0 = h - \left(\frac{g}{2v_0{}^2}\right)x^2$$

Solving for x yields the landing site:

$$x = v_0 \sqrt{\frac{2h}{g}} \qquad \text{4–9}$$

Note that we have chosen the positive sign for the square root since the projectile was launched in the positive x direction, and hence lands at a positive value of x.

A useful alternative approach is to find the time of landing with the kinematic relations given in Equation 4–7, and then substitute this time into $x = v_0 t$. This approach is illustrated in the next Example.

EXAMPLE 4–4   JUMPING A CREVASSE

A mountain climber encounters a crevasse in an ice field. The opposite side of the crevasse is 2.75 m lower, and is separated horizontally by a distance of 4.10 m. To cross the crevasse, the climber gets a running start and jumps in the horizontal direction. **(a)** What is the minimum speed needed by the climber to safely cross the crevasse? If, instead, the climber's speed is 6.00 m/s, **(b)** where does the climber land, and **(c)** what is the climber's speed on landing?

PICTURE THE PROBLEM

The mountain climber jumps from $x_0 = 0$ and $y_0 = h = 2.75$ m. The landing site for part (a) is $x = w = 4.10$ m and $y = 0$. Note that the y position of the climber *decreases* by h, and therefore $\Delta y = -h = -2.75$ m. As for the initial velocity, we are given that $v_{0x} = v_0$ and $v_{0y} = 0$. Finally, with our choice of coordinates it follows that $a_x = 0$ and $a_y = -g$.

STRATEGY

We can model the climber as a projectile, and apply our equations for projectile motion with a horizontal launch.

a. From Equations 4–7 we have that $x = v_0 t$ and $y = h - \frac{1}{2}gt^2$. Setting $y = 0$ determines the time of landing. Using this time in the x equation gives the horizontal landing position in terms of the initial speed.

b. We can now use the relation from part (a) to find x in terms of $v_0 = 6.00$ m/s.

c. We already know v_x, since it remains constant, and we can calculate v_y using $v_y{}^2 = -2g\Delta y$ (Equations 4–7). With the velocity components known, we can use the Pythagorean theorem to find the speed.

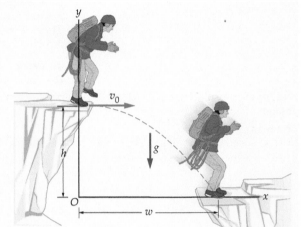

SOLUTION

Part (a)

1. Set $y = h - \frac{1}{2}gt^2$ equal to zero (landing condition) and solve for the corresponding time t:

$$y = h - \tfrac{1}{2}gt^2 = 0$$
$$t = \sqrt{\frac{2h}{g}}$$

2. Substitute this expression for t into the x equation of motion, $x = v_0 t$, and solve for the speed, v_0:

$$x = v_0 t = v_0\sqrt{\frac{2h}{g}} \quad \text{or} \quad v_0 = x\sqrt{\frac{g}{2h}}$$

3. Substitute numerical values in this expression:

$$v_0 = x\sqrt{\frac{g}{2h}} = (4.10\text{ m})\sqrt{\frac{9.81\text{ m/s}^2}{2(2.75\text{ m})}} = 5.48\text{ m/s}$$

Part (b)

4. Substitute $v_0 = 6.00$ m/s into the expression for x obtained in Step 2, $x = v_0\sqrt{2h/g}$:

$$x = v_0\sqrt{\frac{2h}{g}} = (6.00\text{ m/s})\sqrt{\frac{2(2.75\text{ m})}{9.81\text{ m/s}^2}} = 4.49\text{ m}$$

Part (c)

5. Use the fact that the x component of velocity does not change to determine v_x, and use $v_y{}^2 = -2g\Delta y$ to determine v_y. For v_y, note that we choose the minus sign for the square root because the climber is moving downward:

$$v_x = v_0 = 6.00\text{ m/s}$$
$$v_y = \pm\sqrt{-2g\Delta y}$$
$$= -\sqrt{-2(9.81\text{ m/s}^2)(-2.75\text{ m})} = -7.35\text{ m/s}$$

6. Use the Pythagorean theorem to determine the speed:

$$v = \sqrt{v_x{}^2 + v_y{}^2}$$
$$= \sqrt{(6.00\text{ m/s})^2 + (-7.35\text{ m/s})^2} = 9.49\text{ m/s}$$

INSIGHT

The minimum speed needed to safely cross the crevasse is 5.48 m/s. If the initial horizontal speed is 6.00 m/s, the climber will land 4.49 m − 4.10 m = 0.39 m beyond the edge of the crevasse with a speed of 9.49 m/s.

PRACTICE PROBLEM

(a) When the climber's speed is the minimum needed to cross the crevasse, $v_0 = 5.48$ m/s, how long is the climber in the air? **(b)** How long is the climber in the air when $v_0 = 6.00$ m/s?   [**Answer: (a)** $t = x/v_0 = (4.10\text{ m})/(5.48\text{ m/s}) = 0.748$ s. **(b)** $t = x/v_0 = (4.49\text{ m})/(6.00\text{ m/s}) = 0.748$ s. The times are the same! The answer to both parts is simply the time needed to fall through a height h; $t = \sqrt{2h/g} = 0.748$ s.]

Some related homework problems: Problem 11, Problem 12, Problem 17

Projectile problems can be solved by breaking the problem into its x and y components, and then solving for the motion of each component separately.

CONCEPTUAL CHECKPOINT 4–2 MINIMUM SPEED

If the height h is increased in the previous example but the width w remains the same, does the minimum speed needed to cross the crevasse **(a)** increase, **(b)** decrease, or **(c)** stay the same?

REASONING AND DISCUSSION

If the height is greater, the time of fall is also greater. Since the climber is in the air for a greater time, the horizontal distance covered for a given initial speed is also greater. Thus, if the width of the crevasse is the same, a lower initial speed allows for a safe crossing.

ANSWER

(b) The minimum speed decreases.

4–4 General Launch Angle

We now consider the more general case of a projectile launched at an arbitrary angle with respect to the horizontal. This means we can no longer use the simplifications associated with zero launch angle. As always, we return to our basic equations for projectile motion (Equations 4–6), and this time we simply let θ be nonzero.

Figure 4–6 (a) shows a projectile launched with an initial speed v_0 at an angle θ above the horizontal. Since the projectile starts at the origin, the initial x and y positions are zero:

$$x_0 = y_0 = 0$$

The components of the initial velocity are determined as indicated in **Figure 4–6 (b)**:

$$v_{0x} = v_0 \cos \theta$$

and

$$v_{0y} = v_0 \sin \theta$$

As a quick check, note that if $\theta = 0$, then $v_{0x} = v_0$ and $v_{0y} = 0$. Similarly, if $\theta = 90°$ we find $v_{0x} = 0$ and $v_{0y} = v_0$. These checks are depicted in **Figure 4–6 (c)**.

Substituting these results into the basic equations for projectile motion yields the following results for a general launch angle:

$$x = (v_0 \cos \theta)t \qquad v_x = v_0 \cos \theta \qquad v_x^2 = v_0^2 \cos^2 \theta$$
$$y = (v_0 \sin \theta)t - \tfrac{1}{2}gt^2 \qquad v_y = v_0 \sin \theta - gt \qquad v_y^2 = v_0^2 \sin^2 \theta - 2g\Delta y$$

4–10

Note that these equations, which are valid for any launch angle, reduce to the simpler Equations 4–7 when we set $\theta = 0$ and $y_0 = h$. In the next two Exercises, we use Equations 4–10 to calculate a projectile's position and velocity for three equally spaced times.

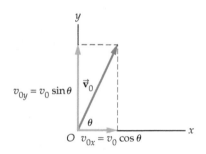

(a)

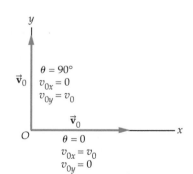

(b)

(c)

▲ **FIGURE 4–6 Projectile with an arbitrary launch angle**
(a) A projectile launched from the origin at an angle θ above the horizontal.
(b) The x and y components of the initial velocity. **(c)** Velocity components in the limits $\theta = 0$ and $\theta = 90°$.

EXERCISE 4–1

A projectile is launched from the origin with an initial speed of 20.0 m/s at an angle of 35.0° above the horizontal. Find the x and y positions of the projectile at times **(a)** $t = 0.500$ s, **(b)** $t = 1.00$ s, and **(c)** $t = 1.50$ s.

SOLUTION

   a. $x = 8.19$ m, $y = 4.51$ m,

   b. $x = 16.4$ m, $y = 6.57$ m,

   c. $x = 24.6$ m, $y = 6.17$ m. Note that x increases steadily; y increases, then decreases.

EXERCISE 4-2

Referring to Exercise 4–1, find the velocity of the projectile at times **(a)** $t = 0.500$ s, **(b)** $t = 1.00$ s, and **(c)** $t = 1.50$ s.

SOLUTION

a. $\vec{v} = (16.4 \text{ m/s})\hat{x} + (6.57 \text{ m/s})\hat{y}$,

b. $\vec{v} = (16.4 \text{ m/s})\hat{x} + (1.66 \text{ m/s})\hat{y}$,

c. $\vec{v} = (16.4 \text{ m/s})\hat{x} + (-3.24 \text{ m/s})\hat{y}$.

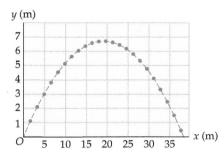

▲ FIGURE 4–7 Snapshots of a trajectory
This plot shows a projectile launched from the origin with an initial speed of 20.0 m/s at an angle of 35.0° above the horizontal. The positions shown in the plot correspond to the times $t = 0.1$ s, 0.2 s, 0.3 s, ... Red dots mark the positions considered in Exercises 4–1 and 4–2.

Figure 4–7 shows the projectile referred to in the previous Exercises for a series of times spaced by 0.10 s. Note that the points in Figure 4–7 are not evenly spaced in terms of position, even though they are evenly spaced in time. In fact, the points bunch closer together at the top of the trajectory, showing that a comparatively large fraction of the flight time is spent near the highest point. This is why it seems that a basketball player soaring toward a slam dunk, or a ballerina performing a grand jeté, is "hanging" in air.

▲ "Hanging" in air near the peak of a jump requires no special knack—in fact, it's an unavoidable consequence of the laws of physics. This phenomenon, which makes big leapers (such as deer and dancers) look particularly graceful, can also make life more dangerous for salmon fighting their way upstream to spawn.

EXAMPLE 4-5 | A ROUGH SHOT

Chipping from the rough, a golfer sends the ball over a 3.00-m-high tree that is 14.0 m away. The ball lands at the same level from which it was struck after traveling a horizontal distance of 17.8 m—on the green, of course. **(a)** If the ball left the club 54.0° above the horizontal and landed on the green 2.24 s later, what was its initial speed? **(b)** How high was the ball when it passed over the tree?

PICTURE THE PROBLEM
Our sketch shows the ball taking flight from the origin, $x_0 = y_0 = 0$, with a launch angle of 54.0°, and arcing over the tree. The individual points along the parabolic trajectory correspond to equal time intervals.

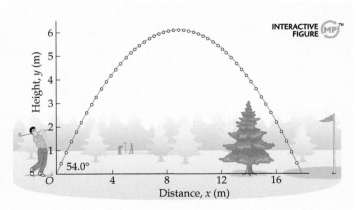

STRATEGY

a. Since the projectile moves with constant speed in the x direction, the x component of velocity is simply horizontal distance divided by time. Knowing v_x and θ, we can find v_0 from $v_x = v_0 \cos \theta$.

b. We can use $x = (v_0 \cos \theta)t$ to find the time when the ball is at $x = 14.0$ m. Substituting this time into $y = (v_0 \sin \theta)t - \frac{1}{2}gt^2$ gives the height.

SOLUTION

Part (a)

1. Divide the horizontal distance, d, by the time of flight, t, to obtain v_x:

$$v_x = \frac{d}{t} = \frac{17.8 \text{ m}}{2.24 \text{ s}} = 7.95 \text{ m/s}$$

CONTINUED ON NEXT PAGE

CONTINUED FROM PREVIOUS PAGE

2. Use $v_x = v_0 \cos \theta$ to find v_0, the initial speed:

$$v_x = v_0 \cos \theta \quad \text{or} \quad v_0 = \frac{v_x}{\cos \theta} = \frac{7.95 \text{ m/s}}{\cos 54.0°} = 13.5 \text{ m/s}$$

Part (b)

3. Use $x = (v_0 \cos \theta)t$ to find the time when $x = 14.0$ m. Recall that $x_0 = 0$:

$$x = (v_0 \cos \theta)t \quad \text{or} \quad t = \frac{x}{v_0 \cos \theta} = \frac{14.0 \text{ m}}{7.95 \text{ m/s}} = 1.76 \text{ s}$$

4. Evaluate $y = (v_0 \sin \theta)t - \frac{1}{2}gt^2$ at the time found in Step 3. Recall that $y_0 = 0$:

$$y = (v_0 \sin \theta)t - \frac{1}{2}gt^2$$
$$= [(13.5 \text{ m/s}) \sin 54.0°](1.76 \text{ s}) - \frac{1}{2}(9.81 \text{ m/s}^2)(1.76 \text{ s})^2$$
$$= 4.03 \text{ m}$$

INSIGHT
The ball clears the top of the tree by 1.03 m and lands on the green 0.48 s later. When it lands, its speed (in the absence of air resistance) is again 13.5 m/s—the same as when it was launched. This result will be verified in the next section.

PRACTICE PROBLEM
What are the speed and direction of the ball when it passes over the tree?   [**Answer:** To find the ball's speed and direction, note that $v_x = 7.95$ m/s and $v_y = v_0 \sin \theta - gt = -6.34$ m/s. It follows that $v = \sqrt{v_x^2 + v_y^2} = 10.2$ m/s and $\theta = \tan^{-1}(v_y/v_x) = -38.6°$.]

Some related homework problems: Problem 31, Problem 39

ACTIVE EXAMPLE 4–1   AN ELEVATED GREEN

A golfer hits a ball from the origin with an initial speed of 30.0 m/s at an angle of 50.0° above the horizontal. The ball lands on a green that is 5.00 m above the level where the ball was struck.

a. How long is the ball in the air?

b. How far has the ball traveled in the horizontal direction when it lands?

c. What are the speed and direction of motion of the ball just before it lands?

SOLUTION   *(Test your understanding by performing the calculations indicated in each step.)*

Part (a)

1. Let $y = (v_0 \sin \theta)t - \frac{1}{2}gt^2 = 5.00$ m and solve for t: $t = 0.229$ s, 4.46 s

2. When $t = 0.229$ s, the ball is moving upward; when $t = 4.46$ s, the ball is on the way down. Choose the later time: $t = 4.46$ s

Part (b)

3. Substitute $t = 4.46$ s into $x = (v_0 \cos \theta)t$: $x = 86.0$ m

Part (c)

4. Use $v_x = v_0 \cos \theta$ to calculate v_x: $v_x = 19.3$ m/s

5. Substitute $t = 4.46$ s into $v_y = v_0 \sin \theta - gt$ to find v_y: $v_y = -20.8$ m/s

6. Calculate v and θ: $v = 28.4$ m/s, $\theta = -47.1°$

YOUR TURN
How long is the ball in the air if the green is 5.00 m *below* the level where the ball was struck?

*(Answers to **Your Turn** problems are given in the back of the book.)*

The next Example presents a classic situation in which two projectiles collide. One projectile is launched from the origin, and thus its equations of motion are given by Equations 4–10. The second projectile is simply dropped from a height, which is a special case of the equations of motion in Equations 4–7 with $v_0 = 0$.

EXAMPLE 4-6 A LEAP OF FAITH

A trained dolphin leaps from the water with an initial speed of 12.0 m/s. It jumps directly toward a ball held by the trainer a horizontal distance of 5.50 m away and a vertical distance of 4.10 m above the water. In the absence of gravity the dolphin would move in a straight line to the ball and catch it, but because of gravity the dolphin follows a parabolic path well below the ball's initial position, as shown in the sketch. If the trainer releases the ball the instant the dolphin leaves the water, show that the dolphin and the falling ball meet.

PICTURE THE PROBLEM

In our sketch we have the dolphin leaping from the water at the origin $x_0 = y_0 = 0$ with an angle above the horizontal given by $\theta = \tan^{-1}(h/d)$. The initial position of the ball is $x_0 = d = 5.50$ m and $y_0 = h = 4.10$ m, and its initial velocity is zero. The ball drops straight down with the acceleration of gravity, $a_y = -g$.

STRATEGY

We want to show that when the dolphin is at $x = d$, its height above the water is the same as the height of the ball above the water. To do this we first find the time when the dolphin is at $x = d$, then calculate y for the dolphin at this time. Next, we calculate y of the ball at the same time and then check to see if they are equal.

Since the ball drops from rest from a height h, its y equation of motion is $y = h - \frac{1}{2}gt^2$, as in Equations 4–7 in Section 4–3.

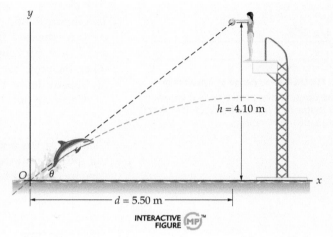

$h = 4.10$ m

$d = 5.50$ m

INTERACTIVE FIGURE (MP)™

SOLUTION

1. Calculate the angle at which the dolphin leaves the water:

$$\theta = \tan^{-1}\left(\frac{h}{d}\right) = \tan^{-1}\left(\frac{4.10 \text{ m}}{5.50 \text{ m}}\right) = 36.7°$$

2. Use this angle and the initial speed to find the time t when the x position of the dolphin, x_d, is equal to 5.50 m. The x equation of motion is $x_d = (v_0 \cos \theta)t$:

$$x_d = (v_0 \cos \theta)t = [(12.0 \text{ m/s}) \cos 36.7°]t = (9.62 \text{ m/s})t$$
$$= 5.50 \text{ m}$$
$$t = \frac{5.50 \text{ m}}{9.62 \text{ m/s}} = 0.572 \text{ s}$$

3. Evaluate the y position of the dolphin, y_d, at $t = 0.572$ s. The y equation of motion is $y_d = (v_0 \sin \theta)t - \frac{1}{2}gt^2$:

$$y_d = (v_0 \sin \theta)t - \frac{1}{2}gt^2$$
$$= [(12.0 \text{ m/s}) \sin 36.7°](0.572 \text{ s}) - \frac{1}{2}(9.81 \text{ m/s}^2)(0.572 \text{ s})^2$$
$$= 4.10 \text{ m} - 1.60 \text{ m} = 2.50 \text{ m}$$

4. Finally, evaluate the y position of the ball, y_b, at $t = 0.572$ s. The ball's equation of motion is $y_b = h - \frac{1}{2}gt^2$:

$$y_b = h - \frac{1}{2}gt^2 = 4.10 \text{ m} - \frac{1}{2}(9.81 \text{ m/s}^2)(0.572 \text{ s})^2$$
$$= 4.10 \text{ m} - 1.60 \text{ m} = 2.50 \text{ m}$$

INSIGHT

In the absence of gravity, both the dolphin and the ball would be at $x = 5.50$ m and $y = 4.10$ m at $t = 0.572$ s. Because of gravity, however, the dolphin and the ball fall below their zero-gravity positions—and by the same amount, 1.60 m. In fact, from the point of view of the dolphin, the ball is always at the same angle of 36.7° above the horizontal until it is caught.

This is shown in the accompanying plot, where the red dots show the position of the ball at ten equally spaced times, and the blue dots show the position of the dolphin at the corresponding times. In addition, the dashed lines from the dolphin to the ball all make the same angle with the horizontal, 36.7°.

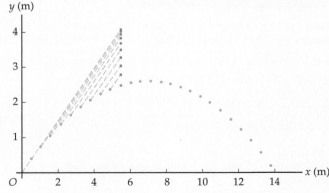

PRACTICE PROBLEM

At what height does the dolphin catch the ball if it leaves the water with an initial speed of 8.00 m/s? [**Answer:** $y_d = y_b = 0.493$ m. If the dolphin's initial speed is less than 7.50 m/s, it reenters the water before catching the ball.]

Some related homework problems: Problem 31, Problem 40

▲ **FIGURE 4–8 Range of a projectile**
The range R of a projectile is the horizontal distance it travels between its takeoff and landing positions.

4–5 Projectile Motion: Key Characteristics

We conclude this chapter with a brief look at some additional characteristics of projectile motion that are both interesting and useful. In all cases our results follow as a direct consequence of the fundamental kinematic equations (Equations 4–10) describing projectile motion.

Range

The **range**, R, of a projectile is the horizontal distance it travels before landing. We consider the case shown in **Figure 4–8**, where the initial and final elevations are the same ($y = 0$). One way to obtain the range, then, is as follows: (i) Find the time when the projectile lands by setting $y = 0$ in the expression $y = (v_0 \sin \theta)t - \frac{1}{2}gt^2$; (ii) Substitute the time found in (i) into the x equation of motion.

Carrying out the first part of the calculation yields the following:

$$(v_0 \sin \theta)t - \tfrac{1}{2}gt^2 = 0 \quad \text{or} \quad (v_0 \sin \theta)t = \tfrac{1}{2}gt^2$$

Clearly, $t = 0$ is a solution to this equation—corresponding to the initial condition—but the solution we seek is a time that is greater than zero. We can find the desired time by dividing both sides of the equation by t. This gives

$$(v_0 \sin \theta) = \tfrac{1}{2}gt \quad \text{or} \quad t = \left(\frac{2v_0}{g}\right)\sin \theta \qquad \text{4–11}$$

This is the time when the projectile lands—also known as the time of flight.

Now, substitute this time into $x = (v_0 \cos \theta)t$ to find the value of x when the projectile lands:

$$x = (v_0 \cos \theta)t = (v_0 \cos \theta)\left(\frac{2v_0}{g}\right)\sin \theta = \left(\frac{2v_0^2}{g}\right)\sin \theta \cos \theta$$

This value of x is the range, R, thus

$$R = \left(\frac{2v_0^2}{g}\right)\sin \theta \cos \theta$$

Using the trigonometric identity $\sin 2\theta = 2 \sin \theta \cos \theta$, as given in Appendix A, we can write this more compactly as follows:

$$R = \left(\frac{v_0^2}{g}\right)\sin 2\theta \quad \text{(same initial and final elevation)} \qquad \text{4–12}$$

PROBLEM-SOLVING NOTE

Use the Same Math Regardless of the Initial Conditions

Once an object is launched, its trajectory follows the kinematic equations of motion, regardless of specific differences in the initial conditions. Thus, our equations of motion can be used to derive any desired characteristic of projectile motion, including range, symmetry, and maximum height.

ACTIVE EXAMPLE 4–2   FIND THE INITIAL SPEED

A football game begins with a kickoff in which the ball travels a horizontal distance of 45 yd and lands on the ground. If the ball was kicked at an angle of 40.0° above the horizontal, what was its initial speed?

SOLUTION *(Test your understanding by performing the calculations indicated in each step.)*

1. Solve Equation 4–12 for the initial speed v_0: $v_0 = \sqrt{gR/\sin 2\theta}$

2. Convert the range to meters: $R = 41$ m

3. Substitute numerical values: $v_0 = 20$ m/s

INSIGHT
Note that we choose the positive square root in Step 1 because we are interested only in the *speed* of the ball, which is always positive.

YOUR TURN
Suppose the initial speed of the ball is increased by 10%, to 22 m/s. By what percentage does the range increase?

*(Answers to **Your Turn** problems are given in the back of the book.)*

Note that R depends inversely on the acceleration of gravity, g—thus the smaller g, the larger the range. For example, a projectile launched on the Moon, where the acceleration of gravity is only about $1/6$ that on Earth, travels about six times as far as it would on Earth. It was for this reason that astronaut Alan Shepard simply couldn't resist the temptation of bringing a golf club and ball with him on the third lunar landing mission in 1971. He ambled out onto the Fra Mauro Highlands and became the first person to hit a tee shot on the Moon. His distance was undoubtedly respectable—unfortunately, his ball landed in a sand trap.

Now, what launch angle gives the greatest range? From Equation 4–12 we see that R varies with angle as $\sin 2\theta$; thus R is largest when $\sin 2\theta$ is largest—that is, when $\sin 2\theta = 1$. Since $\sin 90° = 1$, it follows that $\theta = 45°$ gives the maximum range. Thus

$$R_{max} = \frac{v_0^2}{g} \qquad \text{4–13}$$

As expected, the range (Equation 4–12) and maximum range (Equation 4–13) depend strongly on the initial speed of the projectile—they are both proportional to v_0^2.

Note that these results are specifically for the case where a projectile lands at the same level from which it was launched. If a projectile lands at a higher level, for example, the launch angle that gives maximum range is greater than $45°$, and if it lands at a lower level, the angle for maximum range is less than $45°$.

Finally, the range given here applies only to the ideal case of no air resistance. In cases where air resistance is significant, as in the flight of a rapidly moving golf ball, for example, the overall range of the ball is reduced. In addition, the maximum range occurs for a launch angle less than $45°$ (**Figure 4–9**). The reason is that with a smaller launch angle the golf ball is in the air for less time, giving air resistance less time to affect its flight.

Symmetry in Projectile Motion

There are many striking symmetries in projectile motion, beginning with the graceful symmetry of the parabola itself. As a first example, recall that earlier in this section, in Equation 4–11, we found the time when a projectile lands:

$$t = \left(\frac{2v_0}{g}\right) \sin \theta$$

Now, by symmetry, the time it takes a projectile to reach its highest point (in the absence of air resistance) should be just half this time. After all, the projectile moves in the x direction with constant speed, and the highest point—by symmetry—occurs at $x = \frac{1}{2} R$.

This all seems reasonable, but is there another way to check? Well, at the highest point the projectile is moving horizontally, thus its y component of velocity is zero. Let's find the time when $v_y = 0$ and compare with the time to land:

$$v_y = v_{0y} - gt = v_0 \sin \theta - gt = 0$$

$$t = \left(\frac{v_0}{g}\right) \sin \theta \qquad \text{4–14}$$

As expected from symmetry, the time at the highest point is one-half the time at landing.

There is another interesting symmetry concerning speed. Recall that when a projectile is launched, its y component of velocity is $v_y = v_0 \sin \theta$. When the projectile lands, at time $t = (2v_0/g) \sin \theta$, its y component of velocity is

$$v_y = v_0 \sin \theta - gt = v_0 \sin \theta - g\left(\frac{2v_0}{g}\right) \sin \theta = -v_0 \sin \theta$$

REAL-WORLD PHYSICS
Golf on the Moon

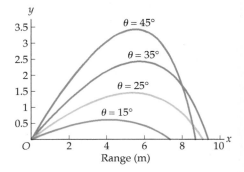

▲ **FIGURE 4–9 Projectiles with air resistance**
Projectiles with the same initial speed but different launch angles showing the effects of air resistance. Notice that the maximum range occurs for a launch angle less than $45°$, and that the projectiles return to the ground at a steeper angle than the launch angle.

▲ To be successful, a juggler must master the behavior of projectile motion. Physicist Richard Feynman shows that just knowing the appropriate equations is not enough; one must also practice. In this sense, learning to juggle is similar to learning to solve physics problems.

This is exactly the opposite of the y component of the velocity when it was launched. Since the x component of velocity is always the same, it follows that when the projectile lands, its speed, $v = \sqrt{v_x{}^2 + v_y{}^2}$, is the same as when it was launched—as one might expect from symmetry.

The velocities are different, however, since the direction of motion is different at launch and landing. Even so, there is still a symmetry—the initial velocity is *above* the horizontal by the angle θ; the landing velocity is *below* the horizontal by the same angle θ.

So far, these results have referred to launching and landing, which both occur at $y = 0$. The same symmetry extends to any level, though. That is, at a given height the speed of a projectile is the same on the way up as on the way down. In addition, the angle of the velocity above the horizontal on the way up is the same as the angle below the horizontal on the way down. This is illustrated in **Figure 4–10** and in the next Conceptual Checkpoint.

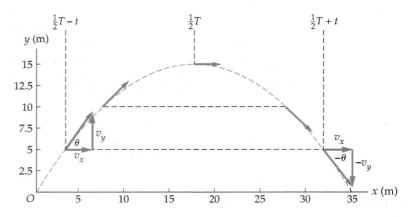

▲ **FIGURE 4–10 Velocity vectors for a projectile launched at the origin**
At a given height the speed (length of velocity vector) is the same on the way up as on the way down. The direction of motion on the way up is above the horizontal by the same amount that it is below the horizontal on the way down. In this case, the total time of flight is T, and the greatest height is reached at the time $T/2$. Notice that the speed is the same at the time $(T/2) - t$ as it is at the time $(T/2) + t$.

CONCEPTUAL CHECKPOINT 4–3   COMPARE LANDING SPEEDS

You and a friend stand on a snow-covered roof. You both throw snowballs with the same initial speed, but in different directions. You throw your snowball downward, at 40° *below* the horizontal; your friend throws her snowball upward, at 40° *above* the horizontal. When the snowballs land on the ground, is the speed of your snowball **(a)** greater than, **(b)** less than, or **(c)** the same as the speed of your friend's snowball?

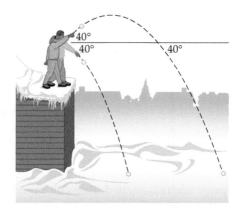

REASONING AND DISCUSSION
One consequence of symmetry in projectile motion is that when your friend's snowball returns to the level of the throw, its speed will be the same as the initial speed. In addition, it will be moving downward, at 40° below the horizontal. From that point on its motion is the same as that of your snowball; thus it lands with the same speed.

What if you throw your snowball horizontally? Or suppose you throw it straight down? In either case, the final speed is unchanged! In fact, for a given initial speed, the speed on landing simply doesn't depend on the direction in which you throw the ball. This is shown in Homework Problems 35 and 76. We return to this point in Chapter 8 when we discuss potential energy and energy conservation.

ANSWER
(c) The snowballs have the same speed.

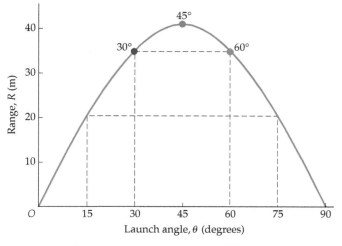

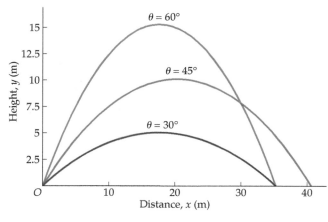

(a) Launch angles that are greater or less than 45° by the same amount give the same range.

(b) Projectiles with $\theta = 30°$ and $\theta = 60°$ follow different paths but have the same range.

▲ **FIGURE 4–11 Range and launch angle in the absence of air resistance**
(a) A plot of range versus launch angle for a projectile launched with an initial speed of 20 m/s. Note that the maximum range occurs at $\theta = 45°$. Launch angles equally greater than or less than 45°, such as 30° and 60°, give the same range. **(b)** Trajectories of projectiles with initial speeds of 20 m/s and launch angles of 60°, 45°, and 30°. The projectiles with launch angles of 30° and 60° land at the same location.

As our final example of symmetry, consider the range R. A plot of R versus launch angle θ is shown in **Figure 4–11 (a)** for $v_0 = 20$ m/s. Note that in the absence of air resistance, R is greatest at $\theta = 45°$, as pointed out previously. In addition, we can see from the figure that the range for angles equally above or below 45° is the same. For example, if air resistance is negligible, the range for $\theta = 30°$ is the same as the range for $\theta = 60°$, as we can see in both parts (a) and (b) of Figure 4–11.

Symmetries such as these are just some of the many reasons why physicists find physics to be "beautiful" and "aesthetically pleasing." Discovering such patterns and symmetries in nature is really what physics is all about. A physicist does not consider the beauty of projectile motion to be diminished by analyzing it in detail. Just the opposite—detailed analysis reveals deeper, more subtle, and sometimes unexpected levels of beauty.

Maximum Height

Let's follow up on an observation made earlier in this section, namely, that a projectile is at maximum height when its y component of velocity is zero. In fact, we will use this observation to determine the maximum height of an arbitrary projectile. This can be accomplished with the following two-step calculation: (i) Find the time when $v_y = 0$; (ii) Substitute this time into the y-versus-t equation of motion, $y = (v_0 \sin \theta)t - \frac{1}{2}gt^2$. This calculation is carried out in the next Example.

▲ An archerfish would have trouble procuring its lunch without an instinctive grasp of projectile motion.

EXAMPLE 4–7 WHAT A SHOT!

The archerfish hunts by dislodging an unsuspecting insect from its resting place with a stream of water expelled from the fish's mouth. Suppose the archerfish squirts water with an initial speed of 2.30 m/s at an angle of 19.5° above the horizontal. When the stream of water reaches a beetle on a leaf at height h above the water's surface, it is moving horizontally.

a. How much time does the beetle have to react?

b. What is the height h of the beetle?

c. What is the horizontal distance d between the fish and the beetle when the water is launched?

CONTINUED ON NEXT PAGE

CONTINUED FROM PREVIOUS PAGE

PICTURE THE PROBLEM

Our sketch shows the fish squirting water from the origin, $x_0 = y_0 = 0$, and the beetle at $x = d, y = h$. The stream of water starts off with a speed $v_0 = 2.30$ m/s at an angle $\theta = 19.5°$ above the horizontal. Note that the water is moving horizontally when it reaches the beetle.

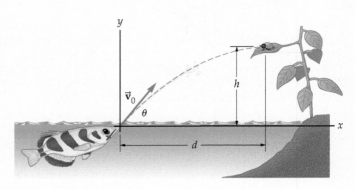

STRATEGY

a. Because the stream of water is moving horizontally when it reaches the beetle, it is at the top of its parabolic trajectory, as can be seen in Figure 4–10. This means that its y component of velocity is zero. Therefore, we can set $v_y = 0$ in $v_y = v_0 \sin \theta - gt$ and solve for the time t.

b. To find the maximum height of the stream of water, and of the beetle, we substitute the time found in part (a) into $y = (v_0 \sin \theta)t - \frac{1}{2}gt^2$.

c. Similarly, we can find the horizontal distance d by substituting the time from part (a) into $x = (v_0 \cos \theta)t$.

SOLUTION

Part (a)

1. Set $v_y = v_0 \sin \theta - gt$ equal to zero and solve for the corresponding time t:

$$v_y = v_{0y} - gt = v_0 \sin \theta - gt = 0$$
$$t = \frac{v_0 \sin \theta}{g}$$

2. Substitute numerical values to determine the reaction time:

$$t = \frac{v_0 \sin \theta}{g} = \frac{(2.30 \text{ m/s}) \sin 19.5°}{9.81 \text{ m/s}^2} = 0.0783 \text{ s}$$

Part (b)

3. To calculate the height, we substitute $t = (v_0 \sin \theta)/g$ into $y = (v_0 \sin \theta)t - \frac{1}{2}gt^2$:

$$y = (v_0 \sin \theta)\left(\frac{v_0 \sin \theta}{g}\right) - \frac{1}{2}g\left(\frac{v_0 \sin \theta}{g}\right)^2 = \frac{(v_0 \sin \theta)^2}{2g}$$

4. Substitute numerical values to find the height h:

$$h = \frac{(v_0 \sin \theta)^2}{2g} = \frac{[(2.30 \text{ m/s}) \sin 19.5°]^2}{2(9.81 \text{ m/s}^2)} = 0.0300 \text{ m}$$

Part (c)

5. We can find the horizontal distance d using x as a function of time, $x = (v_0 \cos \theta)t$:

$$x = (v_0 \cos \theta)t$$
$$d = [(2.30 \text{ m/s}) \cos 19.5°](0.0783 \text{ s}) = 0.170 \text{ m}$$

INSIGHT

To hit the beetle, the fish aims 19.5° above the horizontal. For comparison, note that the straight-line angle to the beetle is $\tan^{-1}(0.0300/0.170) = 10.0°$. Therefore, the fish cannot aim directly at its prey if it wants a meal.

Finally, note that by working symbolically in Step 3 we have derived a general result for the maximum height of a projectile. In particular, we find $y_{max} = (v_0 \sin \theta)^2/2g$, a result that is valid for any launch speed and angle. As a check of our result, note that if we launch a projectile straight upward ($\theta = 90°$), the maximum height is $y_{max} = v_0^2/2g$. Comparing with the one-dimensional kinematics of Chapter 2, if an object is thrown straight upward with an initial speed v_0, and the object accelerates downward with the acceleration of gravity, $a = -g$, it comes to rest ($v = 0$) after covering a vertical distance Δy given by $0 = v_0^2 + 2(-g)\Delta y$. Solving for the distance yields $\Delta y = v_0^2/2g = y_{max}$. This is an example of the internal consistency that characterizes all of physics.

PRACTICE PROBLEM

How far does the stream of water go if it happens to miss the beetle?   [**Answer:** By symmetry, the distance d is half the range. Thus the stream of water travels a distance $R = 2d = 0.340$ m.]

Some related homework problems: Problem 81, Problem 82

THE BIG PICTURE   PUTTING PHYSICS IN CONTEXT

LOOKING BACK

This chapter provides a number of opportunities to use the vector methods developed in Chapter 3. In Section 4–4, for example, we resolve a velocity vector into its x and y components, and then use the components in Equations 4–10.

The equations of one-dimensional kinematics derived in Chapter 2 are used again in this chapter, even though we are now studying kinematics in two dimensions. For example, the equations in Table 4–1 are the same as those used in Chapter 2, only now applied individually to the x and y directions.

LOOKING AHEAD

The basic idea behind projectile motion will be used again in Chapter 12, when we consider orbital motion. See, in particular, the illustration presented in Section 12–1.

Two-dimensional kinematics comes up again when we study the motion of charged particles (like electrons) in electric fields. To see the connection, compare Figures 19–41 and 22–10 (a) with the person jumping a crevasse in Example 4–4. The same basic principles apply.

CHAPTER SUMMARY

4–1 MOTION IN TWO DIMENSIONS

Independence of Motion

Components of motion in the x and y directions can be treated independently of one another. Thus, two-dimensional motion with constant acceleration is described by the same kinematic equations derived in Chapter 2, only now written in terms of x and y components.

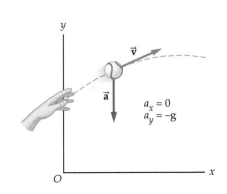

4–2 PROJECTILE MOTION: BASIC EQUATIONS

Projectile motion refers to the path of an object after it is thrown, kicked, batted, or otherwise launched into the air. For the ideal case, we assume no air resistance and a constant downward acceleration of magnitude g.

Acceleration Components

In projectile motion, with the x axis horizontal and the y axis upward, the components of the acceleration of gravity are

$$a_x = 0$$
$$a_y = -g$$

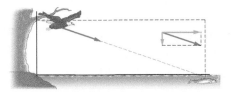

x and y as Functions of Time

The x and y equations of motion are

$$x = x_0 + v_{0x}t$$
$$y = y_0 + v_{0y}t - \tfrac{1}{2}gt^2$$

4–6

v_x and v_y as Functions of Time

The velocity components vary with time as follows:

$$v_x = v_{0x}$$
$$v_y = v_{0y} - gt$$

4–6

v_x and v_y as Functions of Displacement

v_x and v_y vary with displacement as

$$v_x{}^2 = v_{0x}{}^2$$
$$v_y{}^2 = v_{0y}{}^2 - 2g\Delta y$$

4–6

4-3 ZERO LAUNCH ANGLE

Equations of Motion

A projectile launched horizontally from $x_0 = 0$, $y_0 = h$ with an initial speed v_0 has the following equations of motion:

$$x = v_0 t \qquad v_x = v_0 \qquad v_x^2 = v_0^2$$
$$y = h - \tfrac{1}{2}gt^2 \qquad v_y = -gt \qquad v_y^2 = -2g\Delta y$$

4–7

Parabolic Path

The path followed by a projectile launched horizontally with an initial speed v_0 is described by

$$y = h - \left(\frac{g}{2v_0^2}\right)x^2$$

4–8

This path is a parabola.

Landing Site

The landing site of a projectile launched horizontally is

$$x = v_0\sqrt{\frac{2h}{g}}$$

4–9

In this expression, v_0 is the initial speed and h is the initial height. Note that this result is simply the speed in the x direction multiplied by the time of fall.

4-4 GENERAL LAUNCH ANGLE

Launch from the Origin

The equations of motion for a launch from the origin with an initial speed v_0 at an angle of θ with respect to the horizontal are

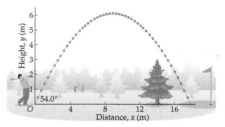

$$x = (v_0\cos\theta)t \qquad v_x = v_0\cos\theta \qquad v_x^2 = v_0^2\cos^2\theta$$
$$y = (v_0\sin\theta)t - \tfrac{1}{2}gt^2 \qquad v_y = v_0\sin\theta - gt \qquad v_y^2 = v_0^2\sin^2\theta - 2g\Delta y$$

4–10

4-5 PROJECTILE MOTION: KEY CHARACTERISTICS

Range

The range of a projectile launched from the origin with an initial speed v_0 and a launch angle θ is

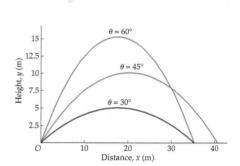

$$R = \left(\frac{v_0^2}{g}\right)\sin 2\theta$$

4–12

This expression applies only to projectiles that land at the same level from which they were launched.

Symmetry

Projectile motion exhibits many symmetries. For example, the speed of a projectile depends only on its height and not on whether it is moving upward or downward.

Maximum Height

The maximum height of a projectile above its launch site is

$$y_{\text{max}} = \frac{v_0^2\sin^2\theta}{2g}$$

In this equation, v_0 is the initial speed and θ is the launch angle.

PROBLEM-SOLVING SUMMARY

Type of Problem	Relevant Physical Concepts	Related Examples
Study two-dimensional motion with constant acceleration.	Motion in the x direction is independent of motion in the y direction. This is the basis for the equations of motion given in Table 4–1. Note that these equations are the same as the kinematic equations of Chapter 2, only written in terms of x and y components.	Examples 4–1, 4–2
Find the location and velocity of a projectile launched horizontally.	When a projectile is launched horizontally with a speed v_0 its initial velocity components are $v_{0x} = v_0$ and $v_{0y} = 0$. Make these substitutions in the equations of projectile motion given in Equations 4–6.	Examples 4–3, 4–4 Conceptual Check-points 4–1, 4–2
Find the location and velocity of a projectile launched with an arbitrary launch angle.	If a projectile is launched at an angle θ, its initial velocity components are $v_{0x} = v_0 \cos\theta$ and $v_{0y} = v_0 \sin\theta$. Make these substitutions in the equations of projectile motion given in Equations 4–6.	Examples 4–5, 4–6, 4–7 Active Examples 4–1, 4–2

CONCEPTUAL QUESTIONS

For instructor-assigned homework, go to www.masteringphysics.com

(Answers to odd-numbered Conceptual Questions can be found in the back of the book.)

1. What is the acceleration of a projectile when it reaches its highest point? What is its acceleration just before and just after reaching this point?

2. A projectile is launched with an initial speed of v_0 at an angle θ above the horizontal. It lands at the same level from which it was launched. What was its average velocity between launch and landing? Explain.

3. A projectile is launched from level ground. When it lands, its direction of motion has rotated clockwise through 60°. What was the launch angle? Explain.

4. In a game of baseball, a player hits a high fly ball to the outfield. **(a)** Is there a point during the flight of the ball where its velocity is parallel to its acceleration? **(b)** Is there a point where the ball's velocity is perpendicular to its acceleration? Explain in each case.

5. A projectile is launched with an initial velocity of $\vec{v} = (4 \text{ m/s})\hat{x} + (3 \text{ m/s})\hat{y}$. What is the velocity of the projectile when it reaches its highest point? Explain.

6. A projectile is launched from a level surface with an initial velocity of $\vec{v} = (2 \text{ m/s})\hat{x} + (4 \text{ m/s})\hat{y}$. What is the velocity of the projectile just before it lands? Explain.

7. Do projectiles for which air resistance is nonnegligible, such as a bullet fired from a rifle, have maximum range when the launch angle is greater than, less than, or equal to 45°? Explain.

8. Two projectiles are launched from the same point at the same angle above the horizontal. Projectile 1 reaches a maximum height twice that of projectile 2. What is the ratio of the initial speed of projectile 1 to the initial speed of projectile 2? Explain.

9. A child rides on a pony walking with constant velocity. The boy leans over to one side and a scoop of ice cream falls from his ice cream cone. Describe the path of the scoop of ice cream as seen by **(a)** the child and **(b)** his parents standing on the ground nearby.

10. Driving down the highway, you find yourself behind a heavily loaded tomato truck. You follow close behind the truck, keeping the same speed. Suddenly a tomato falls from the back of the truck. Will the tomato hit your car or land on the road, assuming you continue moving with the same speed and direction? Explain.

11. A projectile is launched from the origin of a coordinate system where the positive x axis points horizontally to the right and the positive y axis points vertically upward. What was the projectile's launch angle with respect to the x axis if, at its highest point, its direction of motion has rotated **(a)** clockwise through 50° or **(b)** counterclockwise through 30°? Explain.

PROBLEMS AND CONCEPTUAL EXERCISES

Note: Answers to odd-numbered Problems and Conceptual Exercises can be found in the back of the book. **IP** *denotes an integrated problem, with both conceptual and numerical parts;* **BIO** *identifies problems of biological or medical interest;* **CE** *indicates a conceptual exercise.* **Predict/Explain** *problems ask for two responses:* **(a)** *your prediction of a physical outcome, and* **(b)** *the best explanation among three provided. On all problems, red bullets* (•, ••, •••) *are used to indicate the level of difficulty.*

(Air resistance should be ignored in the problems for this chapter, unless specifically stated otherwise.)

SECTION 4–1   MOTION IN TWO DIMENSIONS

1. • **CE Predict/Explain** As you walk briskly down the street, you toss a small ball into the air. **(a)** If you want the ball to land in your hand when it comes back down, should you toss the ball straight upward, in a forward direction, or in a backward direction, relative to your body?

(b) Choose the *best explanation* from among the following:
  I. If the ball is thrown straight up you will leave it behind.
  II. You have to throw the ball in the direction you are walking.
  III. The ball moves in the forward direction with your walking speed at all times.

2. • A sailboat runs before the wind with a constant speed of 4.2 m/s in a direction 32° north of west. How far **(a)** west and **(b)** north has the sailboat traveled in 25 min?

3. • As you walk to class with a constant speed of 1.75 m/s, you are moving in a direction that is 18.0° north of east. How much time does it take to change your displacement by **(a)** 20.0 m east or **(b)** 30.0 m north?

4. • Starting from rest, a car accelerates at 2.0 m/s² up a hill that is inclined 5.5° above the horizontal. How far **(a)** horizontally and **(b)** vertically has the car traveled in 12 s?

5. •• **IP** A particle passes through the origin with a velocity of $(6.2 \text{ m/s})\hat{\mathbf{y}}$. If the particle's acceleration is $(-4.4 \text{ m/s}^2)\hat{\mathbf{x}}$, **(a)** what are its x and y positions after 5.0 s? **(b)** What are v_x and v_y at this time? **(c)** Does the speed of this particle increase with time, decrease with time, or increase and then decrease? Explain.

6. •• An electron in a cathode-ray tube is traveling horizontally at 2.10×10^9 cm/s when deflection plates give it an upward acceleration of 5.30×10^{17} cm/s². **(a)** How long does it take for the electron to cover a horizontal distance of 6.20 cm? **(b)** What is its vertical displacement during this time?

7. •• Two canoeists start paddling at the same time and head toward a small island in a lake, as shown in **Figure 4–12**. Canoeist 1 paddles with a speed of 1.35 m/s at an angle of 45° north of east. Canoeist 2 starts on the opposite shore of the lake, a distance of 1.5 km due east of canoeist 1. **(a)** In what direction relative to north must canoeist 2 paddle to reach the island? **(b)** What speed must canoeist 2 have if the two canoes are to arrive at the island at the same time?

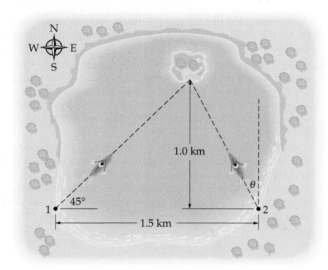

▲ **FIGURE 4–12** Problem 7

SECTION 4–3 ZERO LAUNCH ANGLE

8. • **CE Predict/Explain** Two divers run horizontally off the edge of a low cliff. Diver 2 runs with twice the speed of diver 1. **(a)** When the divers hit the water, is the horizontal distance covered by diver 2 twice as much, four times as much, or equal to the horizontal distance covered by diver 1? **(b)** Choose the *best explanation* from among the following:
   I. The drop time is the same for both divers.
   II. Drop distance depends on t^2.
   III. All divers in free fall cover the same distance.

9. • **CE Predict/Explain** Two youngsters dive off an overhang into a lake. Diver 1 drops straight down, and diver 2 runs off the cliff with an initial horizontal speed v_0. **(a)** Is the splash-down speed of diver 2 greater than, less than, or equal to the splashdown speed of diver 1? **(b)** Choose the *best explanation* from among the following:
   I. Both divers are in free fall, and hence they will have the same splashdown speed.
   II. The divers have the same vertical speed at splashdown, but diver 2 has the greater horizontal speed.
   III. The diver who drops straight down gains more speed than the one who moves horizontally.

10. • An archer shoots an arrow horizontally at a target 15 m away. The arrow is aimed directly at the center of the target, but it hits 52 cm lower. What was the initial speed of the arrow?

11. • **Victoria Falls** The great, gray-green, greasy Zambezi River flows over Victoria Falls in south central Africa. The falls are approximately 108 m high. If the river is flowing horizontally at 3.60 m/s just before going over the falls, what is the speed of the water when it hits the bottom? Assume the water is in free fall as it drops.

12. • A diver runs horizontally off the end of a diving board with an initial speed of 1.85 m/s. If the diving board is 3.00 m above the water, what is the diver's speed just before she enters the water?

13. • An astronaut on the planet Zircon tosses a rock horizontally with a speed of 6.95 m/s. The rock falls through a vertical distance of 1.40 m and lands a horizontal distance of 8.75 m from the astronaut. What is the acceleration of gravity on Zircon?

14. •• **IP Pitcher's Mounds** Pitcher's mounds are raised to compensate for the vertical drop of the ball as it travels a horizontal distance of 18 m to the catcher. **(a)** If a pitch is thrown horizontally with an initial speed of 32 m/s, how far does it drop by the time it reaches the catcher? **(b)** If the speed of the pitch is increased, does the drop distance increase, decrease, or stay the same? Explain. **(c)** If this baseball game were to be played on the Moon, would the drop distance increase, decrease, or stay the same? Explain.

15. •• Playing shortstop, you pick up a ground ball and throw it to second base. The ball is thrown horizontally, with a speed of 22 m/s, directly toward point A (**Figure 4–13**). When the ball reaches the second baseman 0.45 s later, it is caught at point B. **(a)** How far were you from the second baseman? **(b)** What is the distance of vertical drop, AB?

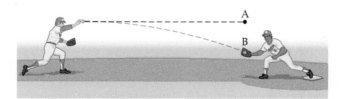

▲ **FIGURE 4–13** Problem 15

16. •• **IP** A crow is flying horizontally with a constant speed of 2.70 m/s when it releases a clam from its beak (**Figure 4–14**). The clam lands on the rocky beach 2.10 s later. Just before the clam lands, what is **(a)** its horizontal component of velocity, and **(b)** its vertical component of velocity? **(c)** How would your answers to parts (a) and (b) change if the speed of the crow were increased? Explain.

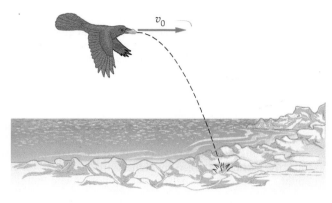

▲ **FIGURE 4–14** Problem 16

17. •• A mountain climber jumps a 2.8-m-wide crevasse by leaping horizontally with a speed of 7.8 m/s. **(a)** If the climber's direction of motion on landing is −45°, what is the height difference between the two sides of the crevasse? **(b)** Where does the climber land?

18. •• **IP** A white-crowned sparrow flying horizontally with a speed of 1.80 m/s folds its wings and begins to drop in free fall. **(a)** How far does the sparrow fall after traveling a horizontal distance of 0.500 m? **(b)** If the sparrow's initial speed is increased, does the distance of fall increase, decrease, or stay the same?

19. •• **Pumpkin Toss** In Denver, children bring their old jack-o-lanterns to the top of a tower and compete for accuracy in hitting a target on the ground (**Figure 4–15**). Suppose that the tower is 9.0 m high and that the bull's-eye is a horizontal distance of 3.5 m from the launch point. If the pumpkin is thrown horizontally, what is the launch speed needed to hit the bull's-eye?

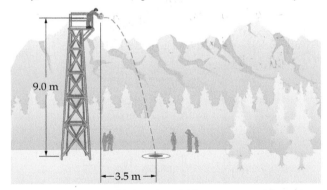

▲ **FIGURE 4–15** Problems 19 and 20

20. •• If, in the previous problem, a jack-o-lantern is given an initial horizontal speed of 3.3 m/s, what are the direction and magnitude of its velocity **(a)** 0.75 s later, and **(b)** just before it lands?

21. •• Fairgoers ride a Ferris wheel with a radius of 5.00 m (**Figure 4–16**). The wheel completes one revolution every 32.0 s. **(a)** What is the average speed of a rider on this Ferris wheel? **(b)** If a rider accidentally drops a stuffed animal at the top of the wheel, where does it land relative to the base of the ride? (Note: The bottom of the wheel is 1.75 m above the ground.)

22. •• **IP** A swimmer runs horizontally off a diving board with a speed of 3.32 m/s and hits the water a horizontal distance of 1.78 m from the end of the board. **(a)** How high above the water was the diving board? **(b)** If the swimmer runs off the board

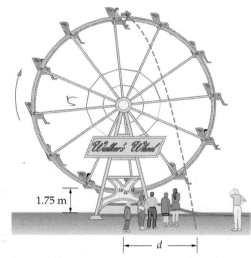

▲ **FIGURE 4–16** Problems 21 and 42

with a reduced speed, does it take more, less, or the same time to reach the water?

23. •• **Baseball and the Washington Monument** On August 25, 1894, Chicago catcher William Schriver caught a baseball thrown from the top of the Washington Monument (555 ft, 898 steps). **(a)** If the ball was thrown horizontally with a speed of 5.00 m/s, where did it land? **(b)** What were the ball's speed and direction of motion when caught?

24. ••• A basketball is thrown horizontally with an initial speed of 4.20 m/s (**Figure 4–17**). A straight line drawn from the release point to the landing point makes an angle of 30.0° with the horizontal. What was the release height?

▲ **FIGURE 4–17** Problem 24

25. ••• **IP** A ball rolls off a table and falls 0.75 m to the floor, landing with a speed of 4.0 m/s. **(a)** What is the acceleration of the ball just before it strikes the ground? **(b)** What was the initial speed of the ball? **(c)** What initial speed must the ball have if it is to land with a speed of 5.0 m/s?

SECTION 4–4 GENERAL LAUNCH ANGLE

26. • **CE** A certain projectile is launched with an initial speed v_0. At its highest point its speed is $\frac{1}{2}v_0$. What was the launch angle of the projectile?

A. 30° **B.** 45° **C.** 60° **D.** 75°

27. • **CE** Three projectiles (A, B, and C) are launched with the same initial speed but with different launch angles, as shown in **Figure 4–18**. Rank the projectiles in order of increasing **(a)** horizontal component of initial velocity and **(b)** time of flight. Indicate ties where appropriate.

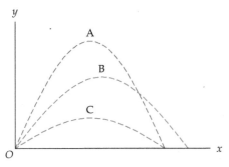

▲ **FIGURE 4–18** Problem 27

28. • **CE** Three projectiles (A, B, and C) are launched with different initial speeds so that they reach the same maximum height, as shown in **Figure 4–19**. Rank the projectiles in order of increasing **(a)** initial speed and **(b)** time of flight. Indicate ties where appropriate.

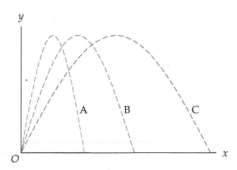

▲ **FIGURE 4–19** Problem 28

29. • A second baseman tosses the ball to the first baseman, who catches it at the same level from which it was thrown. The throw is made with an initial speed of 18.0 m/s at an angle of 37.5° above the horizontal. **(a)** What is the horizontal component of the ball's velocity just before it is caught? **(b)** How long is the ball in the air?

30. • Referring to the previous problem, what are the *y* component of the ball's velocity and its direction of motion just before it is caught?

31. • A cork shoots out of a champagne bottle at an angle of 35.0° above the horizontal. If the cork travels a horizontal distance of 1.30 m in 1.25 s, what was its initial speed?

32. • A soccer ball is kicked with a speed of 9.85 m/s at an angle of 35.0° above the horizontal. If the ball lands at the same level from which it was kicked, how long was it in the air?

33. •• In a game of basketball, a forward makes a bounce pass to the center. The ball is thrown with an initial speed of 4.3 m/s at an angle of 15° below the horizontal. It is released 0.80 m above the floor. What horizontal distance does the ball cover before bouncing?

34. •• Repeat the previous problem for a bounce pass in which the ball is thrown 15° *above* the horizontal.

35. •• **IP** Snowballs are thrown with a speed of 13 m/s from a roof 7.0 m above the ground. Snowball A is thrown straight down-ward; snowball B is thrown in a direction 25° above the horizontal. **(a)** Is the landing speed of snowball A greater than, less than, or the same as the landing speed of snowball B? Explain. **(b)** Verify your answer to part (a) by calculating the landing speed of both snowballs.

36. •• In the previous problem, find the direction of motion of the two snowballs just before they land.

37. •• A golfer gives a ball a maximum initial speed of 34.4 m/s. **(a)** What is the longest possible hole-in-one for this golfer? Neglect any distance the ball might roll on the green and assume that the tee and the green are at the same level. **(b)** What is the minimum speed of the ball during this hole-in-one shot?

38. •• What is the highest tree the ball in the previous problem could clear on its way to the longest possible hole-in-one?

39. •• The "hang time" of a punt is measured to be 4.50 s. If the ball was kicked at an angle of 63.0° above the horizontal and was caught at the same level from which it was kicked, what was its initial speed?

40. •• In a friendly game of handball, you hit the ball essentially at ground level and send it toward the wall with a speed of 18 m/s at an angle of 32° above the horizontal. **(a)** How long does it take for the ball to reach the wall if it is 3.8 m away? **(b)** How high is the ball when it hits the wall?

41. •• **IP** In the previous problem, **(a)** what are the magnitude and direction of the ball's velocity when it strikes the wall? **(b)** Has the ball reached the highest point of its trajectory at this time? Explain.

42. •• A passenger on the Ferris wheel described in Problem 21 drops his keys when he is on the way up and at the 10 o'clock position. Where do the keys land relative to the base of the ride?

43. •• On a hot summer day, a young girl swings on a rope above the local swimming hole (**Figure 4–20**). When she lets go of the rope her initial velocity is 2.25 m/s at an angle of 35.0° above the horizontal. If she is in flight for 0.616 s, how high above the water was she when she let go of the rope?

▲ **FIGURE 4–20** Problem 43

44. •• A certain projectile is launched with an initial speed v_0. At its highest point its speed is $v_0/4$. What was the launch angle?

SECTION 4–5 PROJECTILE MOTION: KEY CHARACTERISTICS

45. • **Punkin Chunkin** In Sussex County, Delaware, a post-Halloween tradition is "Punkin Chunkin," in which contestants build cannons, catapults, trebuchets, and other devices to launch pumpkins and compete for the greatest distance. Though hard to believe, pumpkins have been projected a distance of 4086 feet in this contest. What is the minimum initial speed needed for such a shot?

46. • A dolphin jumps with an initial velocity of 12.0 m/s at an angle of 40.0° above the horizontal. The dolphin passes through the center of a hoop before returning to the water. If the dolphin is moving horizontally when it goes through the hoop, how high above the water is the center of the hoop?

47. • A player passes a basketball to another player who catches it at the same level from which it was thrown. The initial speed of the ball is 7.1 m/s, and it travels a distance of 4.6 m. What were **(a)** the initial direction of the ball and **(b)** its time of flight?

48. • A golf ball is struck with a five iron on level ground. It lands 92.2 m away 4.30 s later. What were **(a)** the direction and **(b)** the magnitude of the initial velocity?

49. • **A Record Toss** Babe Didrikson holds the world record for the longest baseball throw (296 ft) by a woman. For the following questions, assume that the ball was thrown at an angle of 45.0° above the horizontal, that it traveled a horizontal distance of 296 ft, and that it was caught at the same level from which it was thrown. **(a)** What was the ball's initial speed? **(b)** How long was the ball in the air?

50. • In the photograph to the left on page 87, suppose the cart that launches the ball is 11 cm high. Estimate **(a)** the launch speed of the ball and **(b)** the time interval between successive stroboscopic exposures.

51. •• **CE Predict/Explain** You throw a ball into the air with an initial speed of 10 m/s at an angle of 60° above the horizontal. The ball returns to the level from which it was thrown in the time T. **(a)** Referring to **Figure 4–21**, which of the plots (A, B, or C) best represents the speed of the ball as a function of time? **(b)** Choose the *best explanation* from among the following:
  I. Gravity causes the ball's speed to increase during its flight.
  II. The ball has zero speed at its highest point.
  III. The ball's speed decreases during its flight, but it doesn't go to zero.

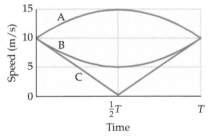

▲ **FIGURE 4–21** Problem 51

52. •• **IP Volcanoes on Io** Astronomers have discovered several volcanoes on Io, a moon of Jupiter. One of them, named Loki,

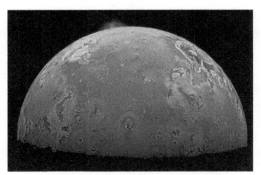

A volcano on Io, the innermost moon of Jupiter, displays the characteristic features of projectile motion. (Problem 52)

ejects lava to a maximum height of 2.00×10^5 m. **(a)** What is the initial speed of the lava? (The acceleration of gravity on Io is 1.80 m/s².) **(b)** If this volcano were on Earth, would the maximum height of the ejected lava be greater than, less than, or the same as on Io? Explain.

53. •• **IP** A soccer ball is kicked with an initial speed of 10.2 m/s in a direction 25.0° above the horizontal. Find the magnitude and direction of its velocity **(a)** 0.250 s and **(b)** 0.500 s after being kicked. **(c)** Is the ball at its greatest height before or after 0.500 s? Explain.

54. •• A second soccer ball is kicked with the same initial speed as in Problem 53. After 0.750 s it is at its highest point. What was its initial direction of motion?

55. •• **IP** A golfer tees off on level ground, giving the ball an initial speed of 46.5 m/s and an initial direction of 37.5° above the horizontal. **(a)** How far from the golfer does the ball land? **(b)** The next golfer in the group hits a ball with the same initial speed but at an angle above the horizontal that is greater than 45.0°. If the second ball travels the same horizontal distance as the first ball, what was its initial direction of motion? Explain.

56. •• **IP** One of the most popular events at Highland games is the hay toss, where competitors use a pitchfork to throw a bale of hay over a raised bar. Suppose the initial velocity of a bale of hay is $\vec{v} = (1.12 \text{ m/s})\hat{x} + (8.85 \text{ m/s})\hat{y}$. **(a)** After what minimum time is its speed equal to 5.00 m/s? **(b)** How long after the hay is tossed is it moving in a direction that is 45.0° below the horizontal? **(c)** If the bale of hay is tossed with the same initial speed, only this time straight upward, will its time in the air increase, decrease, or stay the same? Explain.

GENERAL PROBLEMS

57. • **CE** Child 1 throws a snowball horizontally from the top of a roof; child 2 throws a snowball straight down. Once in flight, is the acceleration of snowball 2 greater than, less than, or equal to the acceleration of snowball 1?

58. • **CE** The penguin to the left in the accompanying photo is about to land on an ice floe. Just before it lands, is its speed greater than, less than, or equal to its speed when it left the water?

This penguin behaves much like a projectile from the time it leaves the water until it touches down on the ice. (Problem 58)

59. • **CE Predict/Explain** A person flips a coin into the air and it lands on the ground a few feet away. **(a)** If the person were to perform an identical coin flip on an elevator rising with constant speed, would the coin's time of flight be greater than, less than, or equal to its time of flight when the person was at rest? **(b)** Choose the *best explanation* from among the following:
  I. The floor of the elevator is moving upward, and hence it catches up with the coin in mid flight.

II. The coin has the same upward speed as the elevator when it is tossed, and the elevator's speed doesn't change during the coin's flight.

III. The coin starts off with a greater upward speed because of the elevator, and hence it reaches a greater height.

60. • **CE Predict/Explain** Suppose the elevator in the previous problem is rising with a constant upward acceleration, rather than constant velocity. **(a)** In this case, would the coin's time of flight be greater than, less than, or equal to its time of flight when the person was at rest? **(b)** Choose the *best explanation* from among the following:

I. The coin has the same acceleration once it is tossed, whether the elevator accelerates or not.

II. The elevator's upward speed increases during the coin's flight, and hence it catches up with the coin at a greater height than before.

III. The coin's downward acceleration is less than before because the elevator's upward acceleration partially cancels it.

61. • A train moving with constant velocity travels 170 m north in 12 s and an undetermined distance to the west. The speed of the train is 32 m/s. **(a)** Find the direction of the train's motion relative to north. **(b)** How far west has the train traveled in this time?

62. • Referring to Example 4–2, find **(a)** the x component and **(b)** the y component of the hummingbird's velocity at the time $t = 0.72$ s. **(c)** What is the bird's direction of travel at this time, relative to the positive x axis?

63. • A racket ball is struck in such a way that it leaves the racket with a speed of 4.87 m/s in the horizontal direction. When the ball hits the court, it is a horizontal distance of 1.95 m from the racket. Find the height of the racket ball when it left the racket.

64. •• **IP** A hot-air balloon rises from the ground with a velocity of $(2.00 \text{ m/s})\hat{y}$. A champagne bottle is opened to celebrate takeoff, expelling the cork horizontally with a velocity of $(5.00 \text{ m/s})\hat{x}$ relative to the balloon. When opened, the bottle is 6.00 m above the ground. **(a)** What is the initial velocity of the cork, as seen by an observer on the ground? Give your answer in terms of the x and y unit vectors. **(b)** What are the speed of the cork and its initial direction of motion as seen by the same observer? **(c)** Determine the maximum height above the ground attained by the cork. **(d)** How long does the cork remain in the air?

65. •• Repeat the previous problem, this time assuming that the balloon is *descending* with a speed of 2.00 m/s.

66. •• **IP** A soccer ball is kicked from the ground with an initial speed of 14.0 m/s. After 0.275 s its speed is 12.9 m/s. **(a)** Give a strategy that will allow you to calculate the ball's initial direction of motion. **(b)** Use your strategy to find the initial direction.

67. •• A particle leaves the origin with an initial velocity $\vec{v} = (2.40 \text{ m/s})\hat{x}$, and moves with constant acceleration $\vec{a} = (-1.90 \text{ m/s}^2)\hat{x} + (3.20 \text{ m/s}^2)\hat{y}$. **(a)** How far does the particle move in the x direction before turning around? **(b)** What is the particle's velocity at this time? **(c)** Plot the particle's position at $t = 0.500$ s, 1.00 s, 1.50 s, and 2.00 s. Use these results to sketch position versus time for the particle.

68. •• When the dried-up seed pod of a scotch broom plant bursts open, it shoots out a seed with an initial velocity of 2.62 m/s at an angle of 60.5° above the horizontal. If the seed pod is 0.455 m above the ground, **(a)** how long does it take for the seed to land? **(b)** What horizontal distance does it cover during its flight?

69. •• Referring to Problem 68, a second seed shoots out from the pod with the same speed but with a direction of motion 30.0° below the horizontal. **(a)** How long does it take for the second seed to land? **(b)** What horizontal distance does it cover during its flight?

70. •• A shot-putter throws the shot with an initial speed of 12.2 m/s from a height of 5.15 ft above the ground. What is the range of the shot if the launch angle is **(a)** 20.0°, **(b)** 30.0°, or **(c)** 40.0°?

71. •• **Pararescue Jumpers** Coast Guard pararescue jumpers are trained to leap from helicopters into the sea to save boaters in distress. The rescuers like to step off their helicopter when it is "ten and ten", which means that it is *ten* feet above the water and moving forward horizontally at *ten* knots. What are **(a)** the speed and **(b)** the direction of motion as a pararescuer enters the water following a ten and ten jump?

72. •• A ball thrown straight upward returns to its original level in 2.75 s. A second ball is thrown at an angle of 40.0° above the horizontal. What is the initial speed of the second ball if it also returns to its original level in 2.75 s?

73. •• **IP** To decide who pays for lunch, a passenger on a moving train tosses a coin straight upward with an initial speed of 4.38 m/s and catches it again when it returns to its initial level. From the point of view of the passenger, then, the coin's initial velocity is $(4.38 \text{ m/s})\hat{y}$. The train's velocity relative to the ground is $(12.1 \text{ m/s})\hat{x}$. **(a)** What is the minimum speed of the coin relative to the ground during its flight? At what point in the coin's flight does this minimum speed occur? Explain. **(b)** Find the initial speed and direction of the coin as seen by an observer on the ground. **(c)** Use the expression for y_{max} derived in Example 4–7 to calculate the maximum height of the coin, as seen by an observer on the ground. **(d)** Calculate the maximum height of the coin from the point of view of the passenger, who sees only one-dimensional motion.

74. •• **IP** A cannon is placed at the bottom of a cliff 61.5 m high. If the cannon is fired straight upward, the cannonball just reaches the top of the cliff. **(a)** What is the initial speed of the cannonball? **(b)** Suppose a second cannon is placed at the top of the cliff. This cannon is fired horizontally, giving its cannonballs the same initial speed found in part (a). Show that the range of this cannon is the same as the maximum range of the cannon at the base of the cliff. (Assume the ground at the base of the cliff is level, though the result is valid even if the ground is not level.)

75. •• **Shot Put Record** The men's world record for the shot put, 23.12 m, was set by Randy Barnes of the United States on May 20, 1990. If the shot was launched from 6.00 ft above the ground at an initial angle of 42.0°, what was its initial speed?

76. •• Referring to Conceptual Checkpoint 4–3, suppose the two snowballs are thrown from an elevation of 15 m with an initial speed of 12 m/s. What is the speed of each ball when it is 5.0 m above the ground?

77. •• **IP** A hockey puck just clears the 2.00-m-high boards on its way out of the rink. The base of the boards is 20.2 m from the point where the puck is launched. **(a)** Given the launch angle of the puck, θ, outline a strategy that you can use to find its initial speed, v_0. **(b)** Use your strategy to find v_0 for $\theta = 15.0°$.

78. •• Referring to Active Example 4–2, suppose the ball is punted from an initial height of 0.750 m. What is the initial speed of the ball in this case?

79. •• **A "Lob" Pass Versus a "Bullet"** A quarterback can throw a receiver a high, lazy "lob" pass or a low, quick "bullet" pass. These passes are indicated by curves 1 and 2, respectively, in **Figure 4–22**. **(a)** The lob pass is thrown with an initial speed of 21.5 m/s and its time of flight is 3.97 s. What is its launch angle?

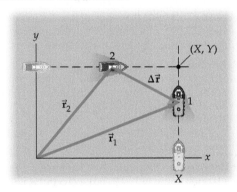

y (m)

▲ **FIGURE 4–22** Problem 79

(b) The bullet pass is thrown with a launch angle of 25.0°. What is the initial speed of this pass? **(c)** What is the time of flight of the bullet pass?

80. ••• **Collision Course** A useful rule of thumb in boating is that if the heading from your boat to a second boat remains constant, the two boats are on a collision course. Consider the two boats shown in **Figure 4–23**. At time $t = 0$, boat 1 is at the location $(X, 0)$ and moving in the positive y direction; boat 2 is at $(0, Y)$ and moving in the positive x direction. The speed of boat 1 is v_1. **(a)** What speed must boat 2 have if the boats are to collide at the point (X, Y)? **(b)** Assuming boat 2 has the speed found in part (a), calculate the displacement from boat 1 to boat 2, $\Delta\vec{r} = \vec{r}_2 - \vec{r}_1$. **(c)** Use your results from part (b) to show that $(\Delta r)_y/(\Delta r)_x = -Y/X$, independent of time. This shows that $\Delta\vec{r} = \vec{r}_2 - \vec{r}_1$ maintains a constant direction until the collision, as specified in the rule of thumb.

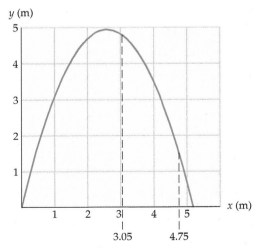

▲ **FIGURE 4–23** Problem 80

81. ••• As discussed in Example 4–7, the archerfish hunts by dislodging an unsuspecting insect from its resting place with a stream of water expelled from the fish's mouth. Suppose the archerfish squirts water with a speed of 2.15 m/s at an angle of 52.0° above the horizontal, and aims for a beetle on a leaf 3.00 cm above the water's surface. **(a)** At what horizontal distance from the beetle should the archerfish fire if it is to hit its target in the least time? **(b)** How much time will the beetle have to react?

82. ••• **(a)** What is the greatest horizontal distance from which the archerfish can hit the beetle, assuming the same squirt speed and direction as in Problem 81? **(b)** How much time does the beetle have to react in this case?

83. ••• Find the launch angle for which the range and maximum height of a projectile are the same.

84. ••• A mountain climber jumps a crevasse of width W by leaping horizontally with speed v_0. **(a)** If the height difference between the two sides of the crevasse is h, what is the minimum value of v_0 for the climber to land safely on the other side? **(b)** In this case, what is the climber's direction of motion on landing?

85. ••• Prove that the landing speed of a projectile is independent of launch angle for a given height of launch.

86. •• **Maximum Height and Range** Prove that the maximum height of a projectile, H, divided by the range of the projectile, R, satisfies the relation $H/R = \frac{1}{4}\tan\theta$.

87. •• **Landing on a Different Level** A projectile fired from $y = 0$ with initial speed v_0 and initial angle θ lands on a different level, $y = h$. Show that the time of flight of the projectile is

$$T = \tfrac{1}{2}T_0\left(1 + \sqrt{1 - \frac{h}{H}}\right)$$

where T_0 is the time of flight for $h = 0$ and H is the maximum height of the projectile.

88. ••• A mountain climber jumps a crevasse by leaping horizontally with speed v_0. If the climber's direction of motion on landing is θ below the horizontal, what is the height difference h between the two sides of the crevasse?

89. •••**IP** Referring to Problem 73, suppose the initial velocity of the coin tossed by the passenger is $\vec{v} = (-2.25 \text{ m/s})\hat{x} + (4.38 \text{ m/s})\hat{y}$. The train's velocity relative to the ground is still $(12.1 \text{ m/s})\hat{x}$. **(a)** What is the minimum speed of the coin relative to the ground during its flight? At what point in the coin's flight does this minimum speed occur? Explain. **(b)** Find the initial speed and direction of the coin as seen by an observer on the ground. **(c)** Use the expression for y_{max} derived in Example 4–7 to calculate the maximum height of the coin, as seen by an observer on the ground. **(d)** Repeat part (c) from the point of view of the passenger. Verify that both observers calculate the same maximum height.

90. ••• **Projectiles: Coming or Going?** Most projectiles continually move farther from the origin during their flight, but this is not the case if the launch angle is greater than $\cos^{-1}(\frac{1}{3}) = 70.5°$. For example, the projectile shown in **Figure 4–24** has a launch angle of 75.0° and an initial speed of 10.1 m/s. During the portion of its motion shown in red, it is moving closer to the origin— it is moving away on the blue portions. Calculate the distance from the origin to the projectile **(a)** at the start of the red portion, **(b)** at the end of the red portion, and **(c)** just before the projectile lands. Notice that the distance for part (b) is the smallest of the three.

y (m)

3.05   4.75

x (m)

▲ **FIGURE 4–24** Problem 90

PASSAGE PROBLEMS

Landing Rovers on Mars

When the twin Mars exploration rovers, *Spirit* and *Opportunity*, set down on the surface of the red planet in January of 2004, their method of landing was both unique and elaborate. After initial braking with retro rockets, the rovers began their long descent through the thin Martian atmosphere on a parachute until they reached an altitude of about 16.7 m. At that point a system of four air bags with six lobes each were inflated, additional retro rocket blasts brought the craft to a virtual standstill, and the rovers detached from their parachutes. After a period of free fall to the surface, with an acceleration of 3.72 m/s^2, the rovers bounced about a dozen times before coming to rest. They then deflated their air bags, righted themselves, and began to explore the surface.

Figure 4–25 shows a rover with its surrounding cushion of air bags making its first contact with the Martian surface. After a typical first bounce the upward velocity of a rover would be 9.92 m/s at an angle of 75.0° above the horizontal. Assume this is the case for the problems that follow.

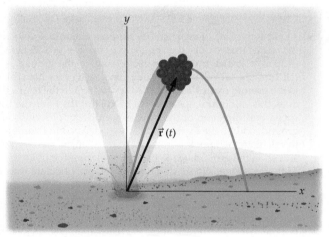

▲ **FIGURE 4–25** Problems 91, 92, 93, and 94

91. • What is the maximum height of a rover between its first and second bounces?

A. 2.58 m   **B.** 4.68 m

C. 12.3 m   **D.** 148 m

92. • How much time elapses between the first and second bounces?

A. 1.38 s   **B.** 2.58 s

C. 5.15 s   **D.** 5.33 s

93. • How far does a rover travel in the horizontal direction between its first and second bounces?

A. 13.2 m   **B.** 49.4 m

C. 51.1 m   **D.** 98.7 m

94. •• What is the average velocity of a rover between its first and second bounces?

A. 0

B. 2.57 m/s in the x direction

C. 9.92 m/s at 75.0° above the x axis

D. 9.58 m/s in the y direction

INTERACTIVE PROBLEMS

95. •• **Referring to Example 4–5 (a)** At what launch angle *greater* than 54.0° does the golf ball just barely miss the top of the tree in front of the green? Assume the ball has an initial speed of 13.5 m/s, and that the tree is 3.00 m high and is a horizontal distance of 14.0 m from the launch point. **(b)** Where does the ball land in the case described in part (a)? **(c)** At what launch angle *less* than 54.0° does the golf ball just barely miss the top of the tree in front of the green? **(d)** Where does the ball land in the case described in part (c)?

96. •• **Referring to Example 4–5** Suppose that the golf ball is launched with a speed of 15.0 m/s at an angle of 57.5° above the horizontal, and that it lands on a green 3.50 m above the level where it was struck. **(a)** What horizontal distance does the ball cover during its flight? **(b)** What increase in initial speed would be needed to increase the horizontal distance in part (a) by 7.50 m? Assume everything else remains the same.

97. •• **Referring to Example 4–6** Suppose the ball is dropped at the horizontal distance of 5.50 m, but from a new height of 5.00 m. The dolphin jumps with the same speed of 12.0 m/s. **(a)** What launch angle must the dolphin have if it is to catch the ball? **(b)** At what height does the dolphin catch the ball in this case? **(c)** What is the minimum initial speed the dolphin must have to catch the ball before it hits the water?

98. •• **IP Referring to Example 4–6** Suppose we change the dolphin's launch angle to 45.0°, but everything else remains the same. Thus, the horizontal distance to the ball is 5.50 m, the drop height is 4.10 m, and the dolphin's launch speed is 12.0 m/s. **(a)** What is the vertical distance between the dolphin and the ball when the dolphin reaches the horizontal position of the ball? We refer to this as the "miss distance." **(b)** If the dolphin's launch speed is reduced, will the miss distance increase, decrease, or stay the same? **(c)** Find the miss distance for a launch speed of 10.0 m/s.

5 Newton's Laws of Motion

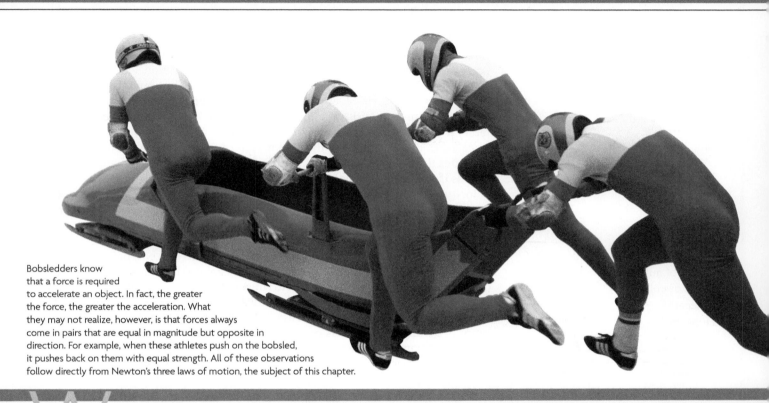

Bobsledders know that a force is required to accelerate an object. In fact, the greater the force, the greater the acceleration. What they may not realize, however, is that forces always come in pairs that are equal in magnitude but opposite in direction. For example, when these athletes push on the bobsled, it pushes back on them with equal strength. All of these observations follow directly from Newton's three laws of motion, the subject of this chapter.

We are all subject to Newton's laws of motion, whether we know it or not. You can't move your body, drive a car, or toss a ball in a way that violates his rules. In short, our very existence is constrained and regulated by these three fundamental statements concerning matter and its motion.

Yet Newton's laws are surprisingly simple, especially when you consider that they apply equally well to galaxies, planets, comets, and yes, even apples falling from trees. In this chapter we present the three laws of Newton, and we show how they can be applied to everyday situations. Using them, we go beyond a simple description of motion, as in kinematics, to a study of the *causes* of motion, referred to as **dynamics.**

With the advent of Newtonian dynamics in 1687, science finally became quantitative and predictive. Edmund Halley, inspired by Newton's laws, used them to predict the return of the comet that today bears his name. In all of recorded history, no one had ever before predicted the appearance of a comet; in fact, they were generally regarded as supernatural apparitions. Though Halley didn't live to see his comet's return, his correct prediction illustrated the power of Newton's laws in a most dramatic and memorable way.

Today, we still recognize Newton's laws as the indispensable foundation for all of physics. It would be nice to say that these laws are the complete story when it comes to analyzing motion, but that is not the case. In the early part of the last century, physicists discovered that Newton's laws must be modified for objects moving at speeds near that of light and for objects comparable in size to atoms. In the world of everyday experience, however, Newton's laws still reign supreme.

5–1 Force and Mass

A **force,** simply put, is a push or a pull. When you push on a box to slide it across the floor, for example, or pull on the handle of a wagon to give a child a ride, you are exerting a force. Similarly, when you hold this book in your hand, you exert an upward force to oppose the downward pull of gravity. If you set the book on a table, the table exerts the same upward force you exerted a moment before. Forces are truly all around us.

Now, when you push or pull on something, there are two quantities that characterize the force you are exerting. The first is the strength or **magnitude** of your force; the second is the **direction** in which you are pushing or pulling. Because a force is determined by both a magnitude and a direction, it is a vector. We consider the vector properties of forces in more detail in Section 5–5.

In general, an object has several forces acting on it at any given time. In the previous example, a book at rest on a table experiences a downward force due to gravity and an upward force due to the table. If you push the book across the table, it also experiences a horizontal force due to your push. The total, or net, force exerted on the book is the vector sum of the individual forces acting on it.

After the net force acting on an object, the second key ingredient in Newton's laws is the **mass** of an object, which is a measure of how difficult it is to change its velocity—to start an object moving if it is at rest, to bring it to rest if it is moving, or to change its direction of motion. For example, if you throw a baseball or catch one thrown to you, the force required is not too great. But if you want to start a car moving or to stop one that is coming at you, the force involved is much greater. It follows that the mass of a car is greater than the mass of a baseball.

In agreement with everyday usage, mass can also be thought of as a measure of the quantity of matter in an object. Thus, it is clear that the mass of an automobile, for example, is much greater than the mass of a baseball, but much less than the mass of Earth. We measure mass in units of kilograms (kg), where one kilogram is defined as the mass of a standard cylinder of platinum-iridium, as discussed in Chapter 1. A list of typical masses is given in Table 5–1.

These properties of force and mass are developed in detail in the next three sections.

TABLE 5–1 Typical Masses in Kilograms (kg)

Earth	5.97×10^{24}
Space shuttle	2,000,000
Blue whale (largest animal on Earth)	178,000
Whale shark (largest fish)	18,000
Elephant (largest land animal)	5400
Automobile	1200
Human (adult)	70
Gallon of milk	3.6
Quart of milk	0.9
Baseball	0.145
Honeybee	0.00015
Bacterium	10^{-15}

5–2 Newton's First Law of Motion

If you've ever stood in line at an airport, pushing your bags forward a few feet at a time, you know that as soon as you stop pushing the bags, they stop moving. Observations such as this often lead to the erroneous conclusion that a force is required for an object to move. In fact, according to Newton's first law of motion, a force is required only to *change* an object's motion.

What is missing in this analysis is the force of friction between the bags and the floor. When you stop pushing the bags, it is not true that they stop moving because they no longer have a force acting on them. On the contrary, there is a rather large *frictional force* between the bags and the floor. It is this force that causes the bags to come to rest.

To see how motion is affected by reducing friction, imagine that you slide on dirt into second base during a baseball game. You won't slide very far before stopping. On the other hand, if you slide with the same initial speed on a sheet of ice—where the friction is much less than on a ball field—you slide considerably farther. If you could reduce the friction more, you would slide even farther.

In the classroom, air tracks allow us to observe motion with practically no friction. An example of such a device is shown in **Figure 5–1**. Note that air is blown through small holes in the track, creating a cushion of air for a small "cart" to ride on. A cart placed at rest on a level track remains at rest—unless you push on it to get it started.

Once set in motion, the cart glides along with constant velocity—constant speed in a straight line—until it hits a bumper at the end of the track. The bumper

Side view

Bumpers

Cart

Air track

End view

Cart

Pressurized
air

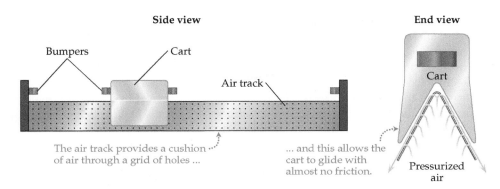

The air track provides a cushion ⋯
of air through a grid of holes …

… and this allows the
cart to glide with
almost no friction.

◀ **FIGURE 5–1** **The air track**
An air track provides a cushion of air
on which a cart can ride with virtually
no friction.

exerts a force on the cart, causing it to change its direction of motion. After bouncing off the bumper, the cart again moves with constant velocity. If the track could be extended to infinite length, and could be made perfectly frictionless, the cart would simply keep moving with constant velocity forever.

Newton's first law of motion summarizes these observations in the following statements:

Newton's First Law
An object at rest remains at rest as long as no net force acts on it.

An object moving with constant velocity continues to move with the same speed and in the same direction as long as no net force acts on it.

Notice the recurring phrase, "no net force," in these statements. It is important to realize that this can mean one of two things: (i) no force acts on the object; or (ii) forces act on the object, but they sum to zero. We shall see examples of the second possibility later in this chapter and again in the next chapter.

Newton's first law, which was first enunciated by Galileo, is also known as the **law of inertia,** which is appropriate since the literal meaning of the word *inertia* is "laziness." Speaking loosely, we can say that matter is "lazy," in that it won't change its motion unless forced to do so. For example, if an object is at rest, it won't start moving on its own. If an object is already moving with constant velocity, it won't alter its speed *or* direction, unless a force causes the change. We call this property of matter its inertia.

According to Newton's first law, being at rest and moving with constant velocity are actually equivalent. To see this, imagine two observers: one is in a train moving with constant velocity; the second is standing next to the tracks, at rest on the ground. The observer in the train places an ice cube on a dinner tray. From that person's point of view—that is, in that person's **frame of reference**—the ice cube has no net force acting on it and it is at rest on the tray. It obeys the first law. In the frame of reference of the observer on the ground, the ice cube has no net force on it and it moves with constant velocity. This also agrees with the first law. Thus Newton's first law holds for both observers: They both see an ice cube with zero net force moving with constant velocity—it's just that for the first observer the constant velocity happens to be zero.

In this example, we say that each observer is in an **inertial frame of reference;** that is, a frame of reference in which the law of inertia holds. In general, if one frame is an inertial frame of reference, then any frame of reference that moves with constant velocity relative to that frame is also an inertial frame of reference. Thus, if an object moves with constant velocity in one inertial frame, it is always possible to find another inertial frame in which the object is at rest. It is in this sense that there really isn't any difference between being at rest and moving with constant velocity. It's all relative—relative to the frame of reference the object is viewed from.

This gives us a more compact statement of the first law:

If the net force on an object is zero, its velocity is constant.

▲ An air track provides a nearly frictionless environment for experiments involving linear motion.

As an example of a frame of reference that is not inertial, imagine that the train carrying the first observer suddenly comes to a halt. From the point of view of that observer, there is still no net force on the ice cube. However, because of the rapid braking, the ice cube flies off the tray. In fact, the ice cube simply continues to move forward with the same constant velocity while the *train* comes to rest. To the observer on the train, it appears that the ice cube has accelerated forward, even though no force acts on it, which is in violation of Newton's first law.

In general, any frame that accelerates relative to an inertial frame is a noninertial frame. The surface of the Earth accelerates slightly, due to its rotational and orbital motions, but since the acceleration is so small, it may be considered an excellent approximation to an inertial frame of reference. Unless specifically stated otherwise, we will always consider the surface of the Earth to be an inertial frame.

5–3 Newton's Second Law of Motion

To hold an object in your hand, you have to exert an upward force to oppose, or "balance," the force of gravity. If you suddenly remove your hand so that the only force acting on the object is gravity, it accelerates downward, as discussed in Chapter 2. This is one example of Newton's second law, which states, basically, that unbalanced forces cause accelerations.

To explore this in more detail, consider a spring scale of the type used to weigh fish. The scale gives a reading of the force, F, exerted by the spring contained within it. If we hang one weight from the scale, it gives a reading that we will call F_1. If two identical weights are attached, the scale reads $F_2 = 2F_1$, as indicated in **Figure 5–2**. With these two forces marked on the scale, we are ready to perform some force experiments.

First, attach the scale to an air-track cart, as in **Figure 5–3**. If we pull with a force F_1, we observe that the cart accelerates at the rate a_1. If we now pull with a force $F_2 = 2F_1$, the acceleration we observe is $a_2 = 2a_1$. Thus, the acceleration is proportional to the force—the greater the force, the greater the acceleration.

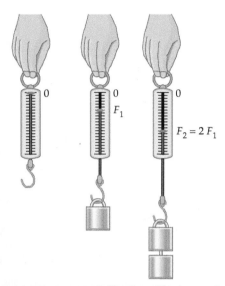

▲ **FIGURE 5–2 Calibrating a "force meter"**
With two weights, the force exerted by the scale is twice the force exerted when only a single weight is attached.

▶ **FIGURE 5–3 Acceleration is proportional to force**
The spring calibrated in Figure 5–2 is used to accelerate a mass on a "frictionless" air track. If the force is doubled, the acceleration is also doubled.

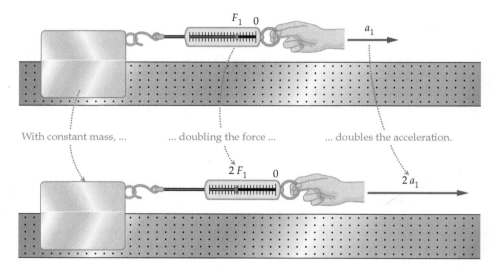

With constant mass, ... doubling the force ...   ... doubles the acceleration.

Second, instead of doubling the force, let's double the mass of the cart by connecting two together, as in **Figure 5–4**. In this case, if we pull with a force F_1 we find an acceleration equal to $\frac{1}{2}a_1$. Thus, the acceleration is inversely proportional to mass—the greater the mass, the less the acceleration.

Combining these results, we find that in this simple case—with just one force in just one direction—the acceleration is given by

$$a = \frac{F}{m}$$

Rearranging the equation yields the form of Newton's law that is perhaps best known, $F = ma$.

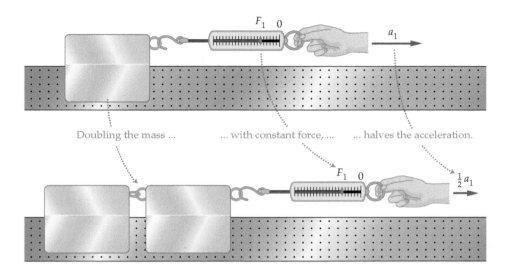

Doubling the mass ...   ... with constant force, ... halves the acceleration.

◀ **FIGURE 5–4 Acceleration is inversely proportional to mass**
If the mass of an object is doubled but the force remains the same, the acceleration is halved.

In general, there may be several forces acting on a given mass, and these forces may be in different directions. Thus, we replace F with the sum of the force vectors acting on a mass:

$$\text{sum of force vectors} = \vec{\mathbf{F}}_{net} = \sum \vec{\mathbf{F}}$$

The notation, $\sum \vec{\mathbf{F}}$, which uses the Greek letter sigma (Σ), is read "sum $\vec{\mathbf{F}}$." Recalling that acceleration is also a vector, we arrive at the formal statement of Newton's second law of motion:

Newton's Second Law

$$\vec{\mathbf{a}} = \frac{\sum \vec{\mathbf{F}}}{m} \qquad \text{or} \qquad \sum \vec{\mathbf{F}} = m\vec{\mathbf{a}} \qquad \qquad 5\text{–}1$$

In words:

If an object of mass m is acted on by a net force $\sum \vec{\mathbf{F}}$, it will experience an acceleration $\vec{\mathbf{a}}$ that is equal to the net force divided by the mass. Because the net force is a vector, the acceleration is also a vector. In fact, the direction of an object's acceleration is the *same* as the direction of the net force acting on it.

One should note that Newton's laws cannot be derived from anything more basic. In fact, this is what we mean by a law of nature. The validity of Newton's laws, and all other laws of nature, comes directly from comparisons with experiment.

In terms of vector components, an equivalent statement of the second law is:

$$\sum F_x = ma_x \qquad \sum F_y = ma_y \qquad \sum F_z = ma_z \qquad 5\text{–}2$$

Note that Newton's second law holds independently for each coordinate direction. This component form of the second law is particularly useful when solving problems.

Let's pause for a moment to consider an important special case of the second law. Suppose an object has zero net force acting upon it. This may be because no forces act on it at all, or because it is acted on by forces whose vector sum is zero. In either case, we can state this mathematically as:

$$\sum \vec{\mathbf{F}} = 0$$

Now, according to Newton's second law, we conclude that the acceleration of this object must be zero:

$$\vec{\mathbf{a}} = \frac{\sum \vec{\mathbf{F}}}{m} = \frac{0}{m} = 0$$

But if an object's acceleration is zero, its velocity must be constant. In other words, if the net force on an object is zero, the object moves with constant velocity. This is

▲ Even though the tugboat exerts a large force on this ship, the ship's acceleration is small. This is because the acceleration of an object is inversely proportional to its mass, and the mass of the ship is enormous. The force exerted on the unfortunate hockey player is much smaller. The resulting acceleration is much larger, however, due to the relatively small mass of the player compared to that of the ship.

Newton's first law. Thus we see that Newton's first and second laws are consistent with one another.

Forces are measured in units called, appropriately enough, the **newton (N).** In particular, one newton is defined as the force required to give one kilogram of mass an acceleration of 1 m/s². Thus,

$$1 \, \text{N} = (1 \, \text{kg})(1 \, \text{m/s}^2) = 1 \, \text{kg} \cdot \text{m/s}^2 \qquad 5\text{–}3$$

In everyday terms, a newton is roughly a quarter of a pound. Note that a force in newtons divided by a mass in kilograms has the units of acceleration:

$$\frac{1 \, \text{N}}{1 \, \text{kg}} = \frac{1 \, \text{kg} \cdot \text{m/s}^2}{1 \, \text{kg}} = 1 \, \text{m/s}^2 \qquad 5\text{–}4$$

Other common units for force are presented in Table 5–2. Typical forces and their magnitudes in newtons are listed in Table 5–3.

TABLE 5–2 Units of Mass, Acceleration, and Force

System of units	Mass	Acceleration	Force
SI	kilogram (kg)	m/s²	newton (N)
cgs	gram (g)	cm/s²	dyne (dyn)
British	slug	ft/s²	pound (lb)

(*Note:* 1 N = 10⁵ dyne = 0.225 lb.)

TABLE 5–3 Typical Forces in Newtons (N)

Main engines of space shuttle	31,000,000
Pulling force of locomotive	250,000
Thrust of jet engine	75,000
Force to accelerate a car	7000
Weight of adult human	700
Weight of an apple	1
Weight of a rose	0.1
Weight of an ant	0.001

EXERCISE 5–1

The net force acting on a Jaguar XK8 has a magnitude of 6800 N. If the car's acceleration is 3.8 m/s², what is its mass?

SOLUTION

Since the net force and the acceleration are always in the same direction, we can replace the vectors in Equation 5–1 with magnitudes. Solving $\Sigma F = ma$ for the mass yields

$$m = \frac{\Sigma F}{a} = \frac{6800 \, \text{N}}{3.8 \, \text{m/s}^2} = 1800 \, \text{kg}$$

The following Conceptual Checkpoint presents a situation in which both Newton's first and second laws play an important role.

CONCEPTUAL CHECKPOINT 5–1   TIGHTENING A HAMMER

The metal head of a hammer is loose. To tighten it, you drop the hammer down onto a table. Should you **(a)** drop the hammer with the handle end down, **(b)** drop the hammer with the head end down, or **(c)** do you get the same result either way?

REASONING AND DISCUSSION

It might seem that since the same hammer hits against the same table in either case, there shouldn't be a difference. Actually, there is.

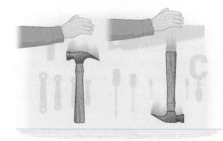

In case (a) the handle of the hammer comes to rest when it hits the table, but the head continues downward until a force acts on it to bring it to rest. The force that acts on it is supplied by the handle, which results in the head being wedged more tightly onto the handle. Since the metal head is heavy, the force wedging it onto the handle is great. In case (b) the head of the hammer comes to rest, but the handle continues to move until a force brings it to rest. The handle is lighter than the head, however; thus the force acting on it is less, resulting in less tightening.

ANSWER

(a) Drop the hammer with the handle end down.

A similar effect occurs when you walk—with each step you take you tamp your head down onto your spine, as when dropping a hammer handle end down.

This causes you to grow shorter during the day! Try it. Measure your height first thing in the morning, then again before going to bed. If you're like many people, you'll find that you have shrunk by an inch or so during the day.

REAL-WORLD PHYSICS: BIO

How walking affects your height

Free-Body Diagrams

When solving problems involving forces and Newton's laws, it is essential to begin by making a sketch that indicates *each and every external force* acting on a given object. This type of sketch is referred to as a **free-body diagram.** If we are concerned only with nonrotational motion, as is the case in this and the next chapter, we treat the object of interest as a point particle and apply each of the forces acting on the object to that point, as **Figure 5–5** shows. Once the forces are drawn, we choose a coordinate system and resolve each force into components. At this point, Newton's second law can be applied to each coordinate direction separately.

PROBLEM-SOLVING NOTE

External Forces

External forces acting on an object fall into two main classes: (i) Forces at the point of contact with another object, and (ii) forces exerted by an external agent, such as gravity.

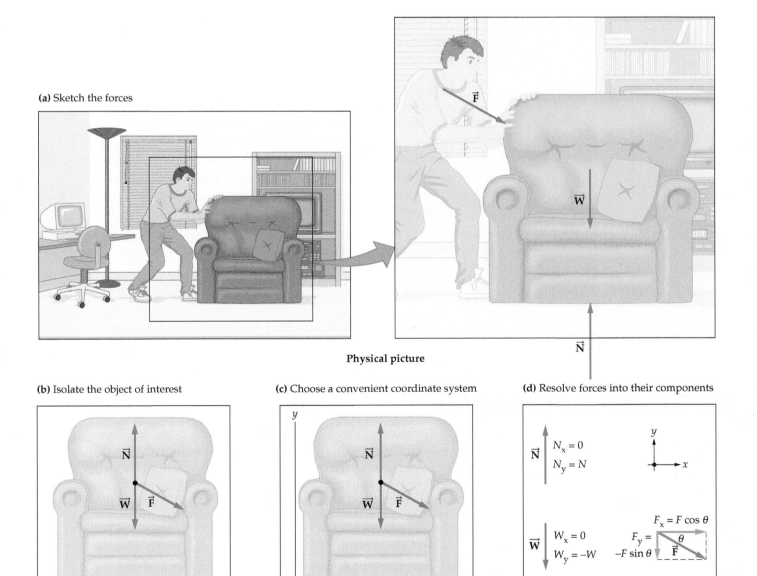

(a) Sketch the forces

$\vec{F}$

$\overline{W}$

$\vec{N}$

Physical picture

(b) Isolate the object of interest

$\vec{N}$

$\overline{W}$ $\vec{F}$

(c) Choose a convenient coordinate system

y

$\vec{N}$

$\overline{W}$ $\vec{F}$

O x

(d) Resolve forces into their components

$\vec{N}$ $\begin{array}{l} N_x = 0 \\ N_y = N \end{array}$

y

x

$\overline{W}$ $\begin{array}{l} W_x = 0 \\ W_y = -W \end{array}$

$F_x = F \cos \theta$

$F_y = -F \sin \theta$ θ $\vec{F}$

Free-body diagram

▲ **FIGURE 5–5 Constructing and using a free-body diagram**

The four basic steps in constructing and using a free-body diagram are illustrated in these sketches. **(a)** Sketch all of the external forces acting on an object of interest. Note that only forces acting *on* the object are shown; none of the forces exerted *by* the object are included. **(b)** Isolate the object and treat it as a point particle. **(c)** Choose a convenient coordinate system. This will often mean aligning a coordinate axis to coincide with the direction of one or more forces in the system. **(d)** Resolve each of the forces into components using the coordinate system of part (c).

For example, in Figure 5–5 there are three external forces acting on the chair. One is the force $\vec{F}$ exerted by the person. In addition, gravity exerts a downward force, $\vec{W}$, which is simply the weight of the chair. Finally, the floor exerts an upward force on the chair that prevents it from falling toward the center of the Earth. This force is referred to as the *normal force*, $\vec{N}$, because it is perpendicular (that is, normal) to the surface of the floor. We will consider the weight and the normal force in greater detail in Sections 5–6 and 5–7, respectively.

We can summarize the steps involved in constructing a free-body diagram as follows:

Sketch the Forces
Identify and sketch all of the external forces acting on an object. Sketching the forces roughly to scale will help in estimating the direction and magnitude of the net force.

Isolate the Object of Interest
Replace the object with a point particle of the same mass. Apply each of the forces acting on the object to that point.

Choose a Convenient Coordinate System
Any coordinate system will work; however, if the object moves in a known direction, it is often convenient to pick that direction for one of the coordinate axes. Otherwise, it is reasonable to choose a coordinate system that aligns with one or more of the forces acting on the object.

Resolve the Forces into Components
Determine the components of each force in the free-body diagram.

Apply Newton's Second Law to Each Coordinate Direction
Analyze motion in each coordinate direction using the component form of Newton's second law, as given in Equation 5–2.

These basic steps are illustrated in Figure 5–5. Note that the figures in this chapter use the labels "Physical picture" to indicate a sketch of the physical situation and "Free-body diagram" to indicate a free-body sketch.

We start by applying this procedure to a simple one-dimensional example, saving two-dimensional systems for Section 5–5. Suppose, for instance, that you hold a book at rest in your hand. What is the magnitude of the upward force that your hand must exert to keep the book at rest? From everyday experience, we expect that the upward force must be equal in magnitude to the weight of the book, but let's see how this result can be obtained directly from Newton's second law.

We begin with a sketch of the physical situation, as shown in **Figure 5–6 (a)**. The corresponding free-body diagram, in **Figure 5–6 (b)**, shows just the book, represented by a point, and the forces acting on it. Note that two forces act on the book: (i) the downward force of gravity, $\vec{W}$, and (ii) the upward force, $\vec{F}$, exerted by your hand. Only the forces acting *on* the book are included in the free-body diagram.

Now that the free-body diagram is drawn, we indicate a coordinate system so that the forces can be resolved into components. In this case all the forces are vertical. Thus we draw a y axis in the vertical direction in Figure 5–6 (b). Note that we have chosen upward to be the positive direction. With this choice, the y components of the forces are $F_y = F$ and $W_y = -W$. It follows that

$$\sum F_y = F - W$$

Using the y component of the second law ($\sum F_y = ma_y$) we find

$$F - W = ma_y$$

Since the book remains at rest, its acceleration is zero. Thus, $a_y = 0$, which gives

$$F - W = ma_y = 0 \quad \text{or} \quad F = W$$

as expected.

Next, we consider a situation where the net force acting on an object is nonzero, meaning that its acceleration is also nonzero.

PROBLEM-SOLVING NOTE

Picture the Problem

In problems involving Newton's laws, it is important to begin with a free-body diagram and to identify all the external forces that act on an object. Once these forces are identified and resolved into their components, Newton's laws can be applied in a straightforward way. It is crucial, however, that only external forces acting on the object be included, and that none of the external forces be omitted.

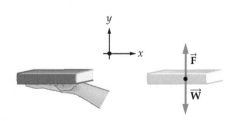

(a) Physical picture   (b) Free-body diagram

▲ **FIGURE 5–6 A book supported in a person's hand**

(a) The physical situation. **(b)** The free-body diagram for the book, showing the two external forces acting on it. We also indicate our choice for a coordinate system.

EXAMPLE 5–1   THREE FORCES

Moe, Larry, and Curly push on a 752-kg boat that floats next to a dock. They each exert an 80.5-N force parallel to the dock. **(a)** What is the acceleration of the boat if they all push in the same direction? Give both direction and magnitude. **(b)** What are the magnitude and direction of the boat's acceleration if Larry and Curly push in the opposite direction to Moe's push?

PICTURE THE PROBLEM

In our sketch we indicate the three relevant forces acting on the boat: $\vec{F}_M$, $\vec{F}_L$, and $\vec{F}_C$. Note that we have chosen the positive x direction to the right, in the direction that all three push for part (a). Therefore, all three forces have a positive x component in part (a). In part (b), however, the forces exerted by Larry and Curly have negative x components.

Physical pictures

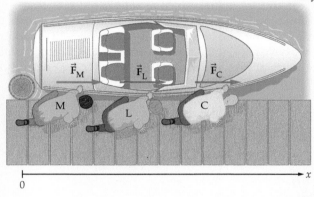
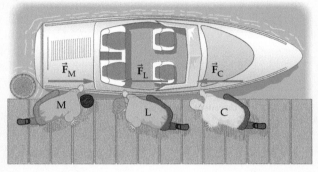

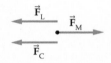

Free-body diagrams

(a)   (b)

STRATEGY

Since we know the mass of the boat and the forces acting on it, we can find the acceleration using $\Sigma F_x = ma_x$. Even though this problem is one-dimensional, it is important to think of it in terms of vector components. For example, when we sum the x components of the forces, we are careful to use the appropriate signs—just as we always do when dealing with vectors.

SOLUTION

Part (a)

1. Write out the x component for each of the three forces:

$$F_{M,x} = F_{L,x} = F_{C,x} = 80.5 \text{ N}$$

2. Sum the x components of force and set equal to ma_x:

$$\sum F_x = F_{M,x} + F_{L,x} + F_{C,x} = 241.5 \text{ N} = ma_x$$

3. Divide by the mass to find a_x. Since a_x is positive, the acceleration is to the right, as expected:

$$a_x = \frac{\sum F_x}{m} = \frac{241.5 \text{ N}}{752 \text{ kg}} = 0.321 \text{ m/s}^2$$

Part (b)

4. Again, start by writing the x component for each force:

$$F_{M,x} = 80.5 \text{ N}$$
$$F_{L,x} = F_{C,x} = -80.5 \text{ N}$$

5. Sum the x components of force and set equal to ma_x:

$$\sum F_x = F_{M,x} + F_{L,x} + F_{C,x}$$
$$= 80.5 \text{ N} - 80.5 \text{ N} - 80.5 \text{ N} = -80.5 \text{ N} = ma_x$$

6. Solve for a_x. In this case a_x is negative, indicating an acceleration to the left:

$$a_x = \frac{\sum F_x}{m} = \frac{-80.5 \text{ N}}{752 \text{ kg}} = -0.107 \text{ m/s}^2$$

INSIGHT

The results of this Example are in agreement with everyday experience: three forces in the same direction cause more acceleration than three forces in opposing directions. The method of using vector components and being careful about their signs gives the expected results in a simple situation like this, and also works in more complicated situations where everyday experience may be of little help.

PRACTICE PROBLEM

If Moe, Larry, and Curly all push to the right with 85.0-N forces, and the boat accelerates at 0.530 m/s², what is its mass? **[Answer: 481 kg]**

Some related homework problems: Problem 2, Problem 4

In some problems, we are given information that allows us to calculate an object's acceleration using the kinematic equations of Chapters 2 and 4. Once the acceleration is known, the second law can be used to find the net force that caused the acceleration.

Astronaut jet packs

For example, suppose that an astronaut uses a jet pack to push a satellite toward the space shuttle. These jet packs, which are known to NASA as Manned Maneuvering Units, or MMUs, are basically small "one-person rockets" strapped to the back of an astronaut's spacesuit. An MMU contains pressurized nitrogen gas that can be released through varying combinations of 24 nozzles spaced around the unit, producing a force of about 10 pounds. The MMUs contain enough propellant for a six-hour EVA (extra-vehicular activity).

We show the physical situation in **Figure 5–7 (a)**, where an astronaut pushes on a 655-kg satellite. The corresponding free-body diagram for the satellite is shown in **Figure 5–7 (b)**. Note that we have chosen the x axis to point in the direction of the push. Now, if the satellite starts at rest and moves 0.675 m after 5.00 seconds of pushing, what is the force, F, exerted on it by the astronaut?

▶ **FIGURE 5–7 An astronaut using a jet pack to push a satellite**
(a) The physical situation. **(b)** The free-body diagram for the satellite. Only one force acts on the satellite, and it is in the positive x direction.

(a) Physical picture   (b) Free-body diagram

Clearly, we would like to use Newton's second law (basically, $\vec{F} = m\vec{a}$) to find the force, but we know only the mass of the satellite, not its acceleration. We can find the acceleration, however, by assuming constant acceleration (after all, the force is constant) and using the kinematic equation relating position to time: $x = x_0 + v_{0x}t + \frac{1}{2}a_xt^2$. We can choose the initial position of the satellite to be $x_0 = 0$, and we are given that it starts at rest, thus $v_{0x} = 0$. Hence,

$$x = \frac{1}{2}a_xt^2$$

Since we know the distance covered in a given time, we can solve for the acceleration:

▲ A technician inspects the landing gear of an airliner in a test of Foamcrete, a solid paving material that is just soft enough to collapse under the weight of an airliner. A plane that has run off the runway will slow safely to a stop as its wheels plow through the crumbling Foamcrete.

$$a_x = \frac{2x}{t^2} = \frac{2(0.675 \text{ m})}{(5.00 \text{ s})^2} = 0.0540 \text{ m/s}^2$$

Now that kinematics has provided the acceleration, we use the x component of the second law to find the force. Only one force acts on the satellite, and its x component is F; thus,

$$\sum F_x = F = ma_x$$

$$F = ma_x = (655 \text{ kg})(0.0540 \text{ m/s}^2) = 35.4 \text{ N}$$

This force corresponds to a push of about 8 lb.

Another problem in which we use kinematics to find the acceleration is presented in the following Active Example.

ACTIVE EXAMPLE 5–1   THE FORCE EXERTED BY FOAMCRETE

Foamcrete is a substance designed to stop an airplane that has run off the end of a runway, without causing injury to passengers. It is solid enough to support a car, but crumbles under the weight of a large airplane. By crumbling, it slows the plane to a safe stop. For example, suppose a 747 jetliner with a mass of 1.75×10^5 kg and an initial speed of 26.8 m/s is slowed to a stop in 122 m. What is the magnitude of the average retarding force $\vec{F}$ exerted by the Foamcrete on the plane?

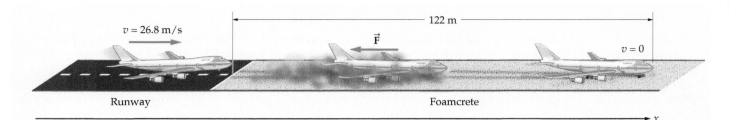

$v = 26.8$ m/s

122 m

$\vec{F}$

$v = 0$

Runway

Foamcrete

x

SOLUTION *(Test your understanding by performing the calculations indicated in each step.)*

1. Use $v^2 = v_0^2 + 2a_x \Delta x$ to find the plane's average acceleration: $a_x = -2.94$ m/s^2

2. Sum the forces in the x direction. Let F represent the magnitude of the force $\vec{F}$: $\sum F_x = -F$

3. Set the sum of forces equal to mass times acceleration: $-F = ma_x$

4. Solve for the magnitude of the average force, F: $F = -ma_x = 5.15 \times 10^5$ N

INSIGHT
Though the plane moves in the positive direction, its acceleration, and the net force exerted on it, are in the negative direction. As a result, the plane's speed decreases with time.

YOUR TURN
Find the plane's stopping distance if the magnitude of the average force exerted by the Foamcrete is doubled.

*(Answers to **Your Turn** problems are given in the back of the book.)*

Note again the care we take with the signs. The plane's acceleration is negative, hence the net force acting on it, $\vec{F}$, is in the negative x direction. On the other hand, the magnitude of the force, F, is positive, as is always the case for magnitudes.

Finally, we end this section with an estimation problem.

EXAMPLE 5-2   PITCH MAN: ESTIMATE THE FORCE ON THE BALL

A pitcher throws a 0.15-kg baseball, accelerating it from rest to a speed of about 90 mi/h. Estimate the force exerted by the pitcher on the ball.

PICTURE THE PROBLEM
We choose the x axis to point in the direction of the pitch. Also indicated in the sketch is the distance over which the pitcher accelerates the ball, Δx. Since we are interested only in the pitch, and not in the subsequent motion of the ball, we ignore the effects of gravity.

Δx

x

0

STRATEGY
We know the mass, so we can find the force with $F_x = ma_x$ if we can estimate the acceleration. To find the acceleration, we start with the fact that $v_0 = 0$ and $v \approx 90$ mi/h. In addition, we can see from the sketch that a reasonable estimate for Δx is about 2.0 m. Combining these results with the kinematic equation $v^2 = v_0^2 + 2a_x\Delta x$ yields the acceleration, which we then use to find the force.

SOLUTION

1. Starting with the fact that 60 mi/h = 1 mi/min, perform a rough back-of-the-envelope conversion of 90 mi/h to meters per second:

$$v \approx 90 \text{ mi/h} = \frac{1.5 \text{ mi}}{\text{min}} \approx \frac{2400 \text{ m}}{60 \text{ s}} = 40 \text{ m/s}$$

2. Solve $v^2 = v_0^2 + 2a_x \Delta x$ for the acceleration, a_x. Use the estimates $\Delta x \approx 2.0$ m and $v \approx 40$ m/s:

$$a_x = \frac{v^2 - v_0^2}{2 \Delta x} \approx \frac{(40 \text{ m/s})^2 - 0}{2(2.0 \text{ m})} = 400 \text{ m/s}^2$$

3. Find the corresponding force with $F_x = ma_x$:

$$F_x = ma_x \approx (0.15 \text{ kg})(400 \text{ m/s}^2) = 60 \text{ N} \approx 10 \text{ lb}$$

INSIGHT
On the one hand, this is a sizable force, especially when you consider that the ball itself weighs only about 1/3 lb. Thus, the pitcher exerts a force on the ball that is about 30 times greater than the force exerted by Earth's gravity. It follows that ignoring gravity during the pitch is a reasonable approximation.

CONTINUED ON NEXT PAGE

CONTINUED FROM PREVIOUS PAGE

On the other hand, you might say that 10 lb isn't that much force for a person to exert. That's true, but this force is being exerted with an average speed of about 20 m/s, which means that the pitcher is actually generating about 1.5 horsepower—a sizable power output for a person. We will cover power in detail in Chapter 7, and relate it to human capabilities.

PRACTICE PROBLEM

What is the approximate speed of the pitch if the force exerted by the pitcher is $\frac{1}{2}(60\ \text{N}) = 30\ \text{N}$? [**Answer:** 30 m/s or 60 mi/h]

Some related homework problems: Problem 5, Problem 8

Another way to find the acceleration is to estimate the amount of time it takes to make the pitch. However, since the pitch is delivered so quickly—about 1/10 s—estimating the time would be more difficult than estimating the distance Δx.

5–4 Newton's Third Law of Motion

Nature never produces just one force at a time; *forces always come in pairs*. In addition, the forces in a pair, which always act on *different objects*, are equal in magnitude and opposite in direction. This is Newton's third law of motion.

Newton's Third Law

For every force that acts on an object, there is a reaction force acting on a different object that is equal in magnitude and opposite in direction.

In a somewhat more specific form:

If object 1 exerts a force $\vec{F}$ on object 2, then object 2 exerts a force $-\vec{F}$ on object 1.

This law, more commonly known by its abbreviated form, "for every action there is an equal and opposite reaction," completes Newton's laws of motion.

Figure 5–8 illustrates some action-reaction pairs. Notice that there is always a reaction force, whether the action force pushes on something hard to move, like a refrigerator, or on something that moves with no friction, like an air-track cart. In some cases, the reaction force tends to be overlooked, as when the Earth exerts a *downward* gravitational force on the space shuttle, and the shuttle exerts an equal and opposite *upward* gravitational force on the Earth. Still, the reaction force always exists.

Another important aspect of the third law is that the action-reaction forces always act on *different* objects. This, again, is illustrated in Figure 5–8. Thus, in drawing a free-body diagram, only one of the action-reaction pair of forces would be drawn for a given object. The other force in the pair would appear in the free-body diagram of a different object. As a result, *the two forces do not cancel*.

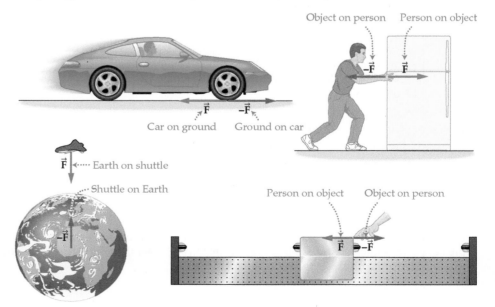

▶ **FIGURE 5–8 Examples of action-reaction force pairs**

For example, consider a car accelerating from rest, as in Figure 5–8. As the car's engine turns the wheels, the tires exert a force on the road. By the third law, the road exerts an equal and opposite force on the car's tires. It is this second force—which acts on the car through its tires—that propels the car forward. The force exerted by the tires on the road does not accelerate the car.

Since the action-reaction forces act on different objects, they generally produce different accelerations. This is the case in the next Example.

EXAMPLE 5–3   TIPPY CANOE

Two groups of canoeists meet in the middle of a lake. After a brief visit, a person in canoe 1 pushes on canoe 2 with a force of 46 N to separate the canoes. If the mass of canoe 1 and its occupants is $m_1 = 150$ kg, and the mass of canoe 2 and its occupants is $m_2 = 250$ kg, **(a)** find the acceleration the push gives to each canoe. **(b)** What is the separation of the canoes after 1.2 s of pushing?

PICTURE THE PROBLEM
We have chosen the positive x direction to point from canoe 1 to canoe 2. With this choice, the force exerted on canoe 2 is $\vec{F}_2 = (+46 \text{ N})\hat{x}$. By Newton's third law, the force exerted on the person in canoe 1, and thus on canoe 1 itself if the person is firmly seated, is $\vec{F}_1 = (-46 \text{ N})\hat{x}$. For convenience, we have placed the origin at the point where the canoes touch.

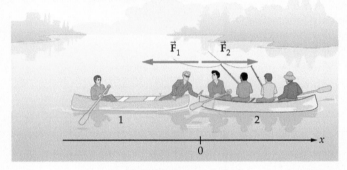

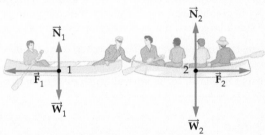

| Physical picture | Free-body diagrams |

STRATEGY
From Newton's third law, the force on canoe 1 is equal in magnitude to the force on canoe 2—the masses of the canoes are different, however, and therefore their accelerations are different as well. **(a)** We can find the acceleration of each canoe by solving $\Sigma F_x = ma_x$ for a_x. **(b)** The kinematic equation relating position to time, $x = x_0 + v_{0x}t + \frac{1}{2}a_xt^2$, can then be used to find the displacement of each canoe.

SOLUTION

Part (a)

1. Use Newton's second law to find the acceleration of canoe 2:

$$a_{2,x} = \frac{\Sigma F_{2,x}}{m_2} = \frac{46 \text{ N}}{250 \text{ kg}} = 0.18 \text{ m/s}^2$$

2. Do the same calculation for canoe 1. Note that the acceleration of canoe 1 is in the negative direction:

$$a_{1,x} = \frac{\Sigma F_{1,x}}{m_1} = \frac{-46 \text{ N}}{150 \text{ kg}} = -0.31 \text{ m/s}^2$$

Part (b)

3. Use $x = x_0 + v_{0x}t + \frac{1}{2}a_xt^2$ to find the position of canoe 2 at $t = 1.2$ s. From the problem statement, we know the canoes start at the origin $(x_0 = 0)$ and at rest $(v_{0x} = 0)$:

$$x_2 = \frac{1}{2}a_{2,x}t^2 = \frac{1}{2}(0.18 \text{ m/s}^2)(1.2 \text{ s})^2 = 0.13 \text{ m}$$

4. Repeat the calculation for canoe 1:

$$x_1 = \frac{1}{2}a_{1,x}t^2 = \frac{1}{2}(-0.31 \text{ m/s}^2)(1.2 \text{ s})^2 = -0.22 \text{ m}$$

5. Subtract the two positions to find the separation of the canoes:

$$x_2 - x_1 = 0.13 \text{ m} - (-0.22 \text{ m}) = 0.35 \text{ m}$$

INSIGHT
The same magnitude of force acts on each canoe; hence the lighter one has the greater acceleration and the greater displacement. If the heavier canoe were replaced by a large ship of great mass, both vessels would still accelerate as a result of the push. However, the acceleration of the large ship would be so small as to be practically imperceptible. In this case, it would appear as if only the canoe moved, whereas, in fact, both vessels move.

PRACTICE PROBLEM
If the mass of canoe 2 is increased, does its acceleration increase, decrease, or stay the same? Check your answer by calculating the acceleration for the case where canoe 2 is replaced by a 25,000-kg ship.   **[Answer:** The acceleration will decrease. In this case, $a = 0.0018 \text{ m/s}^2$.]

Some related homework problems: Problem 18, Problem 19

When objects are touching one another, the action-reaction forces are often referred to as **contact forces.** The behavior of contact forces is explored in the following Conceptual Checkpoint.

CONCEPTUAL CHECKPOINT 5–2 CONTACT FORCES

Two boxes—one large and heavy, the other small and light—rest on a smooth, level floor. You push with a force $\vec{F}$ on either the small box or the large box. Is the contact force between the two boxes **(a)** the same in either case, **(b)** larger when you push on the large box, or **(c)** larger when you push on the small box?

REASONING AND DISCUSSION
Since the same force pushes on the boxes, you might think the force of contact is the same in both cases. It is not. What we can conclude, however, is that the boxes have the same acceleration in either case—the same net force acts on the same total mass, so the same acceleration, a, results.

To find the contact force between the boxes, we focus our attention on each box individually, and note that *Newton's second law must be satisfied for each of the boxes, just as it is for the entire two-box system.* For example, when the external force is applied to the small box, the only force acting on the *large* box (mass m_1) is the contact force; hence, the contact force must have a magnitude equal to $m_1 a$. In the second case, the only force acting on the *small* box (mass m_2) is the contact force, and so the magnitude of the contact force is $m_2 a$. Since m_1 is greater than m_2, it follows that the force of contact is larger when you push on the small box, $m_1 a$, than when you push on the large box, $m_2 a$.

To summarize, the contact force is larger when *it* must push the larger box.

ANSWER
(c) The contact force is larger when you push on the small box.

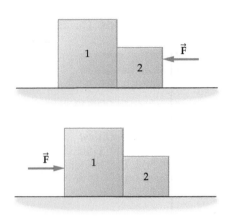

In the next Example, we calculate a numerical value for the contact force in a system similar to that described in Conceptual Checkpoint 5–2. We also show explicitly that Newton's third law is required for a full analysis of this system.

EXAMPLE 5–4 WHEN PUSH COMES TO SHOVE

A box of mass $m_1 = 10.0$ kg rests on a smooth, horizontal floor next to a box of mass $m_2 = 5.00$ kg. If you push on box 1 with a horizontal force of magnitude $F = 20.0$ N, **(a)** what is the acceleration of the boxes? **(b)** What is the force of contact between the boxes?

PICTURE THE PROBLEM
We choose the x axis to be horizontal and pointing to the right. Thus, $\vec{F} = (20.0\text{ N})\hat{x}$. The contact forces are labeled as follows: $\vec{F}_1$ is the contact force exerted on box 1; $\vec{F}_2$ is the contact force exerted on box 2. By Newton's third law, the contact forces have the same magnitude, f, but point in opposite directions. With our coordinate system, we have $\vec{F}_1 = -f\hat{x}$ and $\vec{F}_2 = f\hat{x}$.

Physical picture

Box 1   Box 2

Free-body diagrams

INTERACTIVE FIGURE MP™

STRATEGY

a. Since the two boxes are in contact, they have the same acceleration. We find this acceleration with Newton's second law; that is, we divide the net horizontal force by the total mass of the two boxes.

b. Now let's consider the system consisting solely of box 2. The mass in this case is 5.00 kg, and the only horizontal force acting on the system is $\vec{F}_2$. Thus, we can find f, the magnitude of $\vec{F}_2$, by requiring that box 2 have the acceleration found in part (a).

SOLUTION

Part (a)

1. Find the net horizontal force acting on the two boxes. Note that $\vec{F}_1$ and $\vec{F}_2$ are equal in magnitude but opposite in direction. Hence, they sum to zero; $\vec{F}_1 + \vec{F}_2 = 0$:

$$\sum_{\substack{\text{both}\\\text{boxes}}} F_x = F = 20.0\text{ N}$$

2. Divide the net force by the total mass, $m_1 + m_2$, to find the acceleration of the boxes:

$$a_x = \frac{\sum F_x}{m_1 + m_2} = \frac{20.0\ \text{N}}{(10.0\ \text{kg} + 5.00\ \text{kg})} = \frac{20.0\ \text{N}}{15.0\ \text{kg}} = 1.33\ \text{m/s}^2$$

Part (b)

3. Find the net horizontal force acting on box 2, and set it equal to the mass of box 2 times its acceleration:

$$\sum_{\text{box2}} F_x = F_{2,x} = f = m_2 a_x$$

4. Determine the magnitude of the contact force, f, by substituting numerical values for m_2 and a_x:

$$f = m_2 a_x = (5.00\ \text{kg})(1.33\ \text{m/s}^2) = 6.67\ \text{N}$$

INSIGHT

Since the net horizontal force acting on box 1 is $F - f = 20.0\ \text{N} - 6.67\ \text{N} = 13.3\ \text{N}$, it follows that its acceleration is $(13.3\ \text{N})/(10.0\ \text{kg}) = 1.33\ \text{m/s}^2$. Thus, as expected, box 1 and box 2 have precisely the same acceleration.

If box 2 were not present, the 20.0-N force acting on box 1 would give it an acceleration of $2.00\ \text{m/s}^2$. As it is, the contact force between the boxes slows box 1 so that its acceleration is less than $2.00\ \text{m/s}^2$, and accelerates box 2 so that its acceleration is greater than zero. The precise value of the contact force is simply the value that gives both boxes the same acceleration.

PRACTICE PROBLEM

Suppose the relative positions of the boxes are reversed, so that F pushes on the small box, as shown here. Calculate the contact force for this case, and show that the force is greater than 6.67 N, as expected from Conceptual Checkpoint 5–2. [**Answer:** The contact force in this case is 13.3 N, double its previous value. This follows because the box being pushed has twice the mass of the box that was pushed originally.]

Some related homework problems: Problem 20, Problem 21

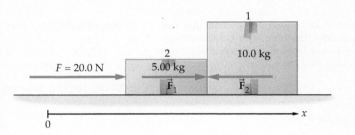

5–5 The Vector Nature of Forces: Forces in Two Dimensions

When we presented Newton's second law in Section 5–3, we said that an object's acceleration is equal to the net force acting on it divided by its mass. For example, if only a single force acts on an object, its acceleration is found to be in the same direction as the force. If more than one force acts on an object, experiments show that its acceleration is in the direction of the vector sum of the forces. Thus forces are indeed vectors, and they exhibit all the vector properties discussed in Chapter 3.

The mass of an object, on the other hand, is simply a positive number with no associated direction. It represents the amount of matter in an object.

As an example of the vector nature of forces, suppose two astronauts are using jet packs to push a 940-kg satellite toward the space shuttle, as shown in **Figure 5–9**. With the coordinate system indicated in the figure, astronaut 1 pushes in the positive x direction and astronaut 2 pushes in a direction 52° above the x axis.

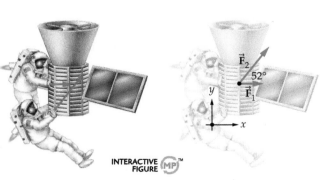

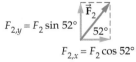

$F_{2,y} = F_2 \sin 52°$

$F_{2,x} = F_2 \cos 52°$

Components of $\vec{F}_2$

Total force

(a) Physical picture   (b) Free-body diagram

◀ **FIGURE 5–9 Two astronauts pushing a satellite with forces that differ in magnitude and direction**

The acceleration of the satellite can be found by calculating a_x and a_y separately, then combining these components to find a and θ.

If astronaut 1 pushes with a force of magnitude $F_1 = 26$ N and astronaut 2 pushes with a force of magnitude $F_2 = 41$ N, what are the magnitude and direction of the satellite's acceleration?

The easiest way to solve a problem like this is to treat each coordinate direction independently of the other, just as we did many times when studying two-dimensional kinematics in Chapter 4. Thus, we first resolve each force into its x and y components. Referring to Figure 5–9, we see that for the x direction

$$F_{1,x} = F_1$$
$$F_{2,x} = F_2 \cos 52°$$

For the y direction

$$F_{1,y} = 0$$
$$F_{2,y} = F_2 \sin 52°$$

Next, we find the acceleration in the x direction by using the x component of Newton's second law:

$$\sum F_x = ma_x$$

Applied to this system, we have

$$\sum F_x = F_{1,x} + F_{2,x} = F_1 + F_2 \cos 52° = 26 \text{ N} + (41 \text{ N}) \cos 52° = 51 \text{ N}$$
$$= ma_x$$

Solving for the acceleration yields

$$a_x = \frac{\sum F_x}{m} = \frac{51 \text{ N}}{940 \text{ kg}} = 0.054 \text{ m/s}^2$$

Similarly, in the y direction we start with

$$\sum F_y = ma_y$$

This gives

$$\sum F_y = F_{1,y} + F_{2,y} = 0 + F_2 \sin 52° = (41 \text{ N}) \sin 52° = 32 \text{ N}$$
$$= ma_y$$

As a result, the y component of acceleration is:

$$a_y = \frac{\sum F_y}{m} = \frac{32 \text{ N}}{940 \text{ kg}} = 0.034 \text{ m/s}^2$$

Thus, the satellite accelerates in both the x and the y directions. Its total acceleration has a magnitude of

$$a = \sqrt{a_x{}^2 + a_y{}^2} = \sqrt{(0.054 \text{ m/s}^2)^2 + (0.034 \text{ m/s}^2)^2} = 0.064 \text{ m/s}^2$$

From Figure 5–9 we expect the total acceleration to be in a direction above the x axis but at an angle less than 52°. Straightforward calculation yields

$$\theta = \tan^{-1}\left(\frac{a_y}{a_x}\right) = \tan^{-1}\left(\frac{0.034 \text{ m/s}^2}{0.054 \text{ m/s}^2}\right) = \tan^{-1}(0.63) = 32°$$

This is the same direction as the total force in Figure 5–9, as expected.

The following Example and Active Example give further practice with resolving force vectors and using Newton's second law in component form.

PROBLEM-SOLVING NOTE

Component-by-Component Application of Newton's Laws

Newton's laws can be applied to each coordinate direction independently of the others. Therefore, when drawing a free-body diagram, be sure to include a coordinate system. Once the forces are resolved into their x and y components, the second law can be solved for each component separately. Working in a component-by-component fashion is the systematic way of using Newton's laws.

EXAMPLE 5–5   JACK AND JILL

Jack and Jill lift upward on a 1.30-kg pail of water, with Jack exerting a force $\vec{F}_1$ of magnitude 7.0 N and Jill exerting a force $\vec{F}_2$ of magnitude 11 N. Jill's force is exerted at an angle of 28° with the vertical, as shown below. **(a)** At what angle θ with respect to the vertical should Jack exert his force if the pail is to accelerate straight upward? **(b)** Determine the acceleration of the pail of water, given that its weight, $\vec{W}$, has a magnitude of 12.8 N. (The simple connection between an object's mass and weight is presented in the next section.)

PICTURE THE PROBLEM

Our physical picture and free-body diagram show the pail and the three forces acting on it, as well as the angles relative to the vertical. In the panels at the right, we show the x and y components of the forces $\vec{F}_1$ and $\vec{F}_2$. Notice, in particular, that $F_{1,x} = -F_1 \sin\theta$ and $F_{1,y} = F_1 \cos\theta$. Similarly, $F_{2,x} = F_2 \sin 28°$ and $F_{2,y} = F_2 \cos 28°$.

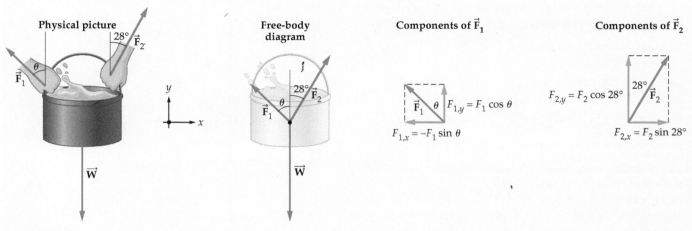

STRATEGY

a. We want the acceleration to be purely vertical. This means that the x component of acceleration must be zero, $a_x = 0$. For a_x to be zero it is necessary that the sum of forces in the x direction be zero, $\Sigma F_x = 0$. Since the x component of $\vec{F}_1$ depends on the angle θ, the equation $\Sigma F_x = 0$ can be used to find θ.

b. Once the appropriate angle is found, we can use it to find the y component of $\vec{F}_1$. Add this result to the y component of $\vec{F}_2$. We're not done yet, though—to find the total y component of the force, ΣF_y, we must also add the weight of the pail, which points in the negative y direction. Finally, divide the total force by the mass of the pail, $m = 1.30$ kg, to obtain its acceleration, $a_y = (\Sigma F_y)/m$.

SOLUTION

Part (a)

1. Begin by writing out the x component of each force. Note that $\vec{W}$ has no x component and that the x component of $\vec{F}_1$ points in the negative x direction:

$$F_{1,x} = -F_1 \sin\theta \qquad F_{2,x} = F_2 \sin 28° \qquad W_x = 0$$

2. Sum the x components of force and set equal to zero. Note that θ is the only unknown in this equation:

$$\sum F_x = -F_1 \sin\theta + F_2 \sin 28° + 0 = ma_x = 0 \text{ or}$$
$$F_1 \sin\theta = F_2 \sin 28°$$

3. Solve for $\sin\theta$ and then for θ:

$$\sin\theta = \frac{F_2 \sin 28°}{F_1} = \frac{(11 \text{ N}) \sin 28°}{7.0 \text{ N}} = 0.74$$
$$\theta = \sin^{-1}(0.74) = 48°$$

Part (b)

4. First, determine the y component of each force. Note that $\vec{W}$ points in the negative y direction and that the y components of both $\vec{F}_1$ and $\vec{F}_2$ are positive:

$$F_{1,y} = F_1 \cos\theta = (7.0 \text{ N}) \cos 48° = 4.7 \text{ N}$$
$$F_{2,y} = F_2 \cos 28° = (11 \text{ N}) \cos 28° = 9.7 \text{ N}$$
$$W_y = -W = -12.8 \text{ N}$$

5. Sum the y components of force and divide by the mass m to obtain the acceleration of the pail of water:

$$\sum F_y = F_1 \cos\theta + F_2 \cos 28° - W$$
$$= 4.7 \text{ N} + 9.7 \text{ N} - 12.8 \text{ N} = 1.6 \text{ N}$$
$$a_y = (\sum F_y)/m = (1.6 \text{ N})/(1.3 \text{ kg}) = 1.2 \text{ m/s}^2$$

INSIGHT

Note that only the y components of $\vec{F}_1$ and $\vec{F}_2$ contribute to the vertical acceleration of the pail. The x components of the applied forces influence only the horizontal motion—they have no effect at all on the vertical acceleration of the pail. In this case the horizontal components of the applied forces cancel, and hence the pail moves straight upward with an acceleration of 1.2 m/s².

Finally, in the next section we shall see that the weight W of an object of mass m is $W = mg$. In this case, $W = (1.3 \text{ kg})(9.81 \text{ m/s}^2) = 12.8$ N.

PRACTICE PROBLEM

At what angle must Jack exert his force for the pail to accelerate straight upward if **(a)** $\vec{F}_2$ is at an angle of 19° with the vertical or **(b)** $\vec{F}_2$ is at an angle of 35° with the vertical?   **[Answer: (a)** 31°, **(b)** 64°**]**

Some related homework problems: Problem 28, Problem 33

ACTIVE EXAMPLE 5–2 FIND THE SPEED OF THE SLED

A 4.60-kg sled is pulled across a smooth ice surface. The force acting on the sled is of magnitude 6.20 N and points in a direction 35.0° above the horizontal. If the sled starts at rest, how fast is it going after being pulled for 1.15 s?

SOLUTION *(Test your understanding by performing the calculations indicated in each step.)*

1. Find the x component of $\vec{F}$: $\qquad F_x = 5.08$ N

2. Apply Newton's second law to the x direction: $\qquad \sum F_x = F_x = ma_x$

3. Solve for the x component of acceleration: $\qquad a_x = 1.10$ m/s^2

4. Use $v_x = v_{0x} + a_x t$ to find the speed of the sled: $\qquad v_x = 1.27$ m/s

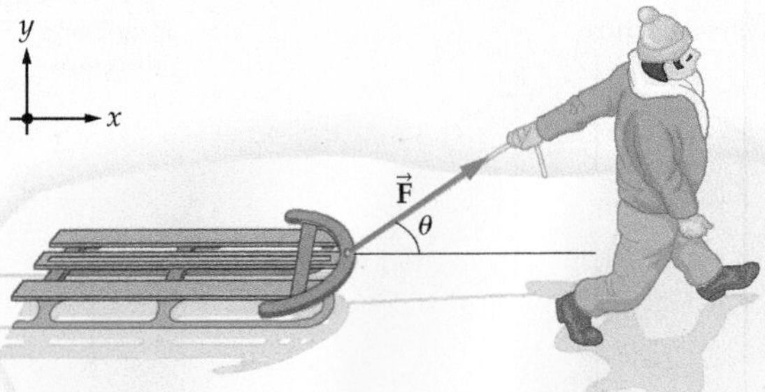

INSIGHT

Note that the y component of $\vec{F}$ has no effect on the acceleration of the sled.

YOUR TURN

Suppose the angle of the force above the horizontal is decreased, and the sled is again pulled from rest for 1.15 s. **(a)** Is the final speed of the sled greater than, less than, or the same as before? Explain. **(b)** Find the final speed of the sled for the case $\theta = 25.0°$.

*(Answers to **Your Turn** problems are given in the back of the book.)*

5–6 Weight

When you step onto a scale to weigh yourself, the scale gives a measurement of the pull of Earth's gravity. This is your weight, W. Similarly, the weight of any object on the Earth's surface is simply the gravitational force exerted on it by the Earth.

- The weight, W, of an object on the Earth's surface is the gravitational force exerted on it by the Earth.

As we know from everyday experience, the greater the mass of an object, the greater its weight. For example, if you put a brick on a scale and weigh it, you might get a reading of 9.0 N. If you put a second, identical brick on the scale—which doubles the mass—you will find a weight of $2(9.0\,\text{N}) = 18$ N. Clearly, there must be a simple connection between weight, W, and mass, m.

To see exactly what this connection is, consider taking one of the bricks just mentioned and letting it drop in free fall. As indicated in **Figure 5–10**, the only force acting on the brick is its weight, W, which is downward. If we choose upward to be the positive direction, we have

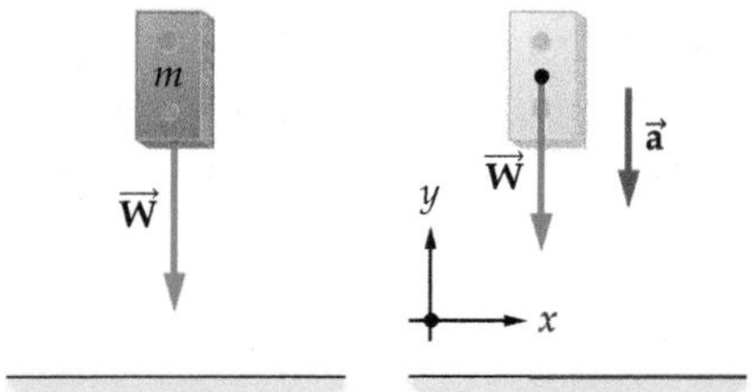

$$\sum F_y = -W$$

In addition, we know from Chapter 2 that the brick moves downward with an acceleration of $g = 9.81$ m/s^2 regardless of its mass. Thus,

$$a_y = -g$$

Using these results in Newton's second law

$$\sum F_y = ma_y$$

we find

$$-W = -mg$$

Therefore, the weight of an object of mass m is $W = mg$:

Physical picture Free-body diagram

▲ FIGURE 5–10 Weight and mass
A brick of mass m has only one force acting on it in free fall—its weight, $\vec{W}$. The resulting acceleration has a magnitude $a = g$; hence $W = mg$.

Definition: Weight, W
$W = mg$
SI unit: newton, N

5–5

Note that there is a clear distinction between weight and mass. Weight is a gravitational force, measured in newtons; mass is a measure of the inertia of an object, and it is given in kilograms. For example, if you were to travel to the Moon, your mass would not change—you would have the same amount of matter in you, regardless of your location. On the other hand, the gravitational force on the Moon's surface is less than the gravitational force on the Earth's surface. As a result, you would weigh less on the Moon than on the Earth, even though your mass is the same.

To be specific, on Earth an 81.0-kg person has a weight given by

$$W_{Earth} = mg_{Earth} = (81.0 \text{ kg})(9.81 \text{ m/s}^2) = 795 \text{ N}$$

In contrast, the same person on the Moon, where the acceleration of gravity is 1.62 m/s^2, weighs only

$$W_{Moon} = mg_{Moon} = (81.0 \text{ kg})(1.62 \text{ m/s}^2) = 131 \text{ N}$$

This is roughly one-sixth the weight on Earth. If, sometime in the future, there is a Lunar Olympics, the Moon's low gravity would be a boon for pole-vaulters, gymnasts, and others.

Finally, since weight is a force—which is a vector quantity—it has both a magnitude and a direction. Its magnitude, of course, is mg, and its direction is simply the direction of gravitational acceleration. Thus, if $\vec{g}$ denotes a vector of magnitude g, pointing in the direction of free-fall acceleration, the weight of an object can be written in vector form as follows:

$$\vec{W} = m\vec{g}$$

We use the weight vector and its magnitude, mg, in the next Example.

▲ At the moment this picture was taken, the acceleration of both climbers was zero because the net force acting on them was zero. In particular, the upward forces exerted on the lower climber by the other climber and the ropes exactly cancel the downward force that gravity exerts on her.

EXAMPLE 5–6   WHERE'S THE FIRE?

The fire alarm goes off, and a 97-kg fireman slides 3.0 m down a pole to the ground floor. Suppose the fireman starts from rest, slides with constant acceleration, and reaches the ground floor in 1.2 s. What was the upward force $\vec{F}$ exerted by the pole on the fireman?

PICTURE THE PROBLEM
Our sketch shows the fireman sliding down the pole and the two forces acting on him: the upward force exerted by the pole, $\vec{F}$, and the downward force of gravity, $\vec{W}$. We choose the positive y direction to be upward, therefore $\vec{F} = F\hat{y}$ and $\vec{W} = (-mg)\hat{y}$. In addition, we choose $y = 0$ to be at ground level.

STRATEGY
The basic idea in approaching this problem is to apply Newton's second law to the y direction: $\Sigma F_y = ma_y$. The acceleration is not given directly, but we can find it using the kinematic equation $y = y_0 + v_{0y}t + \frac{1}{2}a_yt^2$. Substituting the result for a_y into Newton's second law, along with $W_y = -W = -mg$, allows us to solve for the unknown force, $\vec{F}$.

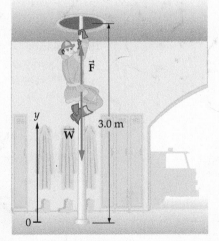

Physical picture

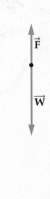

Free-body diagram

SOLUTION

1. Solve $y = y_0 + v_{0y}t + \frac{1}{2}a_yt^2$ for a_y, using the fact that $v_{0y} = 0$:

$$y = y_0 + v_{0y}t + \frac{1}{2}a_yt^2 = y_0 + \frac{1}{2}a_yt^2$$

$$a_y = \frac{2(y - y_0)}{t^2}$$

CONTINUED ON NEXT PAGE

CONTINUED FROM PREVIOUS PAGE

2. Substitute $y = 0$, $y_0 = 3.0$ m, and $t = 1.2$ s to find the acceleration:

$$a_y = \frac{2(0 - 3.0 \text{ m})}{(1.2 \text{ s})^2} = -4.2 \text{ m/s}^2$$

3. Sum the forces in the y direction:

$$\sum F_y = F - mg$$

4. Set the sum of the forces equal to mass times acceleration:

$$F - mg = ma_y$$

5. Solve for F, the y component of the force exerted by the pole. Use the result for F to write the force vector $\vec{F}$:

$$F = mg + ma_y = m(g + a_y)$$
$$= (97 \text{ kg})(9.81 \text{ m/s}^2 - 4.2 \text{ m/s}^2) = 540 \text{ N}$$

$$\vec{F} = (540 \text{ N}) \, \hat{y}$$

INSIGHT

How is it that the pole exerts a force on the fireman? Well, by wrapping his arms and legs around the pole as he slides, the fireman exerts a downward force on the pole. By Newton's third law, the pole exerts an upward force of equal magnitude on the fireman. These forces are due to friction, which we shall study in detail in Chapter 6.

PRACTICE PROBLEM

What is the fireman's acceleration if the force exerted on him by the pole is 650 N? **[Answer:** $a_y = -3.1 \text{ m/s}^2$**]**

Some related homework problems: Problem 36, Problem 40

Apparent Weight

We have all had the experience of riding in an elevator and feeling either heavy or light, depending on its motion. For example, when an elevator moving downward comes to rest by accelerating upward, we feel heavier. On the other hand, we feel lighter when an elevator moving upward comes to rest by accelerating downward. In short, the motion of an elevator can give rise to an **apparent weight** that differs from our true weight. Why?

The reason is that our sensation of weight in this case is due to the force exerted on our feet by the floor of the elevator. If this force is greater than our weight, mg, we feel heavy; if it is less than mg, we feel light.

As an example, imagine you are in an elevator that is moving with an upward acceleration a, as indicated in **Figure 5–11**. Two forces act on you: (i) your weight, W, acting downward; and (ii) the upward normal force exerted on your feet by the floor of the elevator. Let's call the second force W_a, since it represents your apparent weight—that is, W_a is the force that pushes upward on your feet and gives you the sensation of your "weight" pushing down on the floor. We can find W_a by applying Newton's second law to the vertical direction.

To be specific, the sum of the forces acting on you is

$$\sum F_y = W_a - W$$

Physical picture

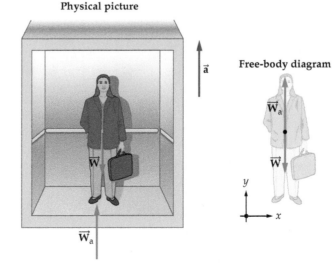

Free-body diagram

▶ **FIGURE 5–11 Apparent weight**
A person rides in an elevator that is accelerating upward. Because the acceleration is upward, the net force must also be upward. As a result, the force exerted on the person by the floor of the elevator, $\vec{W}_a$, must be greater than the person's weight, $\vec{W}$. This means that the person feels heavier than normal.

By Newton's second law, this sum must equal ma_y. Since $a_y = a$, we find

$$W_a - W = ma$$

Solving for the apparent weight, W_a, yields

$$W_a = W + ma$$
$$= mg + ma = m(g + a) \tag{5–6}$$

Note that W_a is greater than your weight, mg, and hence you feel heavier. In fact, your apparent weight is precisely what it would be if you were suddenly "transported" to a planet where the acceleration of gravity is $g + a$ instead of g.

On the other hand, if the elevator accelerates downward, so that $a_y = -a$, your apparent weight is found by simply replacing a with $-a$ in Equation 5–6:

$$W_a = W - ma$$
$$= mg - ma = m(g - a) \tag{5–7}$$

In this case you feel lighter than usual.

We explore these results in the next Example, in which we consider weighing a fish on a scale. The reading on the scale is equal to the upward force it exerts on an object. Thus, the upward force exerted by the scale is the apparent weight, W_a.

EXAMPLE 5–7   HOW MUCH DOES THE SALMON WEIGH?

As part of an attempt to combine physics and biology in the same class, an instructor asks students to weigh a 5.0-kg salmon by hanging it from a fish scale attached to the ceiling of an elevator. What is the apparent weight of the salmon, $\vec{W}_a$, if the elevator **(a)** is at rest, **(b)** moves with an upward acceleration of 2.5 m/s², or **(c)** moves with a downward acceleration of 3.2 m/s²?

PICTURE THE PROBLEM
The free-body diagram for the salmon shows the weight of the salmon, $\vec{W}$, and the force exerted by the scale, $\vec{W}_a$. Note that upward is the positive direction. Therefore, the y component of $\vec{W}$ is $-W = -mg$ and the y component of $\vec{W}_a$ is W_a.

STRATEGY
We know the weight, $W = mg$, and the acceleration, a. To find the apparent weight, W_a, we use $\sum F_y = ma_y$. **(a)** Set $a_y = 0$.
(b) Set $a_y = 2.5$ m/s². **(c)** Set $a_y = -3.2$ m/s².

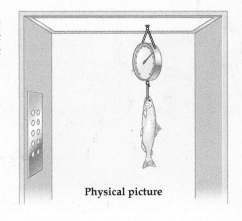

Physical picture

Free-body diagram

SOLUTION
Part (a)

1. Sum the y component of the forces and set equal to mass times the y component of acceleration, with $a_y = 0$:

$$\sum F_y = W_a - W = ma_y = 0$$

2. Solve for W_a, then write the vector $\vec{W}$:

$$W_a = W = mg = (5.0 \text{ kg})(9.81 \text{ m/s}^2) = 49 \text{ N}$$
$$\vec{W}_a = (49 \text{ N})\hat{\mathbf{y}}$$

Part (b)

3. Again, sum the forces and set equal to mass times acceleration, this time with $a_y = a = 2.5$ m/s²:

$$\sum F_y = W_a - W = ma_y = ma$$

4. Solve for W_a, then write the vector $\vec{W}_a$:

$$W_a = W + ma$$
$$= mg + ma = 49 \text{ N} + (5.0 \text{ kg})(2.5 \text{ m/s}^2) = 62 \text{ N}$$
$$\vec{W}_a = (62 \text{ N})\hat{\mathbf{y}}$$

Part (c)

5. Finally, sum the forces and set equal to mass times acceleration, with $a_y = -a = -3.2$ m/s²:

$$\sum F_y = W_a - W = ma_y = -ma$$

CONTINUED ON NEXT PAGE

CONTINUED FROM PREVIOUS PAGE

6. Solve for W_a, then write the vector $\vec{W}_a$:

$$W_a = W - ma$$
$$= mg - ma = 49\,\text{N} - (5.0\,\text{kg})(3.2\,\text{m/s}^2) = 33\,\text{N}$$
$$\vec{W}_a = (33\,\text{N})\hat{y}$$

INSIGHT

When the salmon is at rest, or moving with constant velocity, its acceleration is zero and the apparent weight is equal to the actual weight, mg. In part (b) the apparent weight is greater than the actual weight because the scale must exert an upward force capable not only of supporting the salmon, but of accelerating it upward as well. In part (c) the apparent weight is less than the actual weight. In this case the net force acting on the salmon is downward, and hence its acceleration is downward.

PRACTICE PROBLEM

What is the elevator's acceleration if the scale gives a reading of **(a)** 55 N or **(b)** 45 N?   [**Answer: (a)** $a_y = 1.2\,\text{m/s}^2$, **(b)** $a_y = -0.80\,\text{m/s}^2$]

Some related homework problems: Problem 38, Problem 39

REAL-WORLD PHYSICS: BIO
Simulating weightlessness

▲ Astronaut candidates pose for a floating class picture during weightlessness training aboard the "vomit comet."

Let's return for a moment to Equation 5–7:

$$W_a = m(g - a)$$

This result indicates that a person feels lighter than normal when riding in an elevator with a downward acceleration a. In particular, if the elevator's downward acceleration is g—that is, if the elevator is in free fall—it follows that $W_a = m(g - g) = 0$. Thus, a person feels "weightless" (zero apparent weight) in a freely falling elevator!

NASA uses this effect when training astronauts. Trainees are sent aloft in a KC-135 airplane affectionately known as the "vomit comet" (since many trainees experience nausea along with the weightlessness). To generate an experience of weightlessness, the plane flies on a parabolic path—the same path followed by a projectile in free fall. Each round of weightlessness lasts about half a minute, after which the plane pulls up to regain altitude and start the cycle again. On a typical flight, trainees experience about 40 cycles of weightlessness. Many scenes in the movie *Apollo 13* were shot in 30-second takes aboard the vomit comet.

This idea of free-fall weightlessness applies to more than just the vomit comet. In fact, astronauts in orbit experience weightlessness for the same reason—they and their craft are actually in free fall. As we shall see in detail in Chapter 12 (Gravity), orbital motion is just a special case of free fall.

CONCEPTUAL CHECKPOINT 5–3   ELEVATOR RIDE

If you ride in an elevator moving upward with constant speed, is your apparent weight **(a)** the same as, **(b)** greater than, or **(c)** less than mg?

REASONING AND DISCUSSION

If the elevator is moving in a straight line with constant speed, its acceleration is zero. Now, if the acceleration is zero, the net force must also be zero. Hence, the upward force exerted by the floor of the elevator, W_a, must equal the downward force of gravity, mg. As a result, your apparent weight is equal to mg.

Note that this conclusion agrees with Equations 5–6 and 5–7, with $a = 0$.

ANSWER

(a) Your apparent weight is the same as mg.

5–7 Normal Forces

As you get ready for lunch, you take a can of soup from the cupboard and place it on the kitchen counter. The can is now at rest, which means that its acceleration is zero, so the net force acting on it is also zero. Thus, you know that the

▶ **FIGURE 5–12** **The normal force is perpendicular to a surface**
A can of soup rests on a kitchen counter, which exerts a normal (perpendicular) force, $\vec{N}$, to support it. In the special case shown here, the normal force is equal in magnitude to the weight, $W = mg$, and opposite in direction.

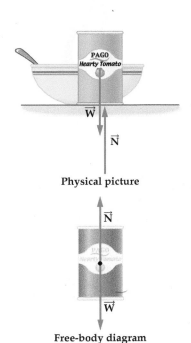

Physical picture

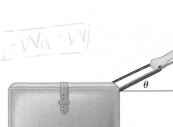

Free-body diagram

downward force of gravity is being opposed by an upward force exerted by the counter, as shown in **Figure 5–12**. As we have mentioned before, this force is referred to as the **normal force, $\vec{N}$**. The reason the force is called normal is that it is *perpendicular to the surface,* and in mathematical terms, *normal* simply means perpendicular.

The origin of the normal force is the interaction between atoms in a solid that act to maintain its shape. When the can of soup is placed on the countertop, for example, it causes an imperceptibly small compression of the surface of the counter. This is similar to compressing a spring, and just like a spring, the countertop exerts a force to oppose the compression. Therefore, the greater the weight placed on the countertop, the greater the normal force it exerts to oppose being compressed.

In the example of the soup can and the countertop, the magnitude of the normal force is equal to the weight of the can. This is a special case, however. In general, the normal force may be greater than or less than the weight of an object.

To see how this can come about, consider pulling a 12.0-kg suitcase across a smooth floor by exerting a force, $\vec{F}$, at an angle θ above the horizontal. The weight of the suitcase is $mg = (12.0 \text{ kg})(9.81 \text{ m/s}^2) = 118 \text{ N}$. The normal force will have a magnitude less than this, however, because the force $\vec{F}$ has an upward component that supports part of the suitcase's weight. To be specific, suppose that $\vec{F}$ has a magnitude of 45.0 N and that $\theta = 20.0°$. What is the normal force exerted by the floor on the suitcase?

The situation is illustrated in **Figure 5–13**, where we show the three forces acting on the suitcase: (i) the weight of the suitcase, $\vec{W}$, (ii) the force $\vec{F}$, and (iii) the normal force, $\vec{N}$. We also indicate a typical coordinate system in the figure, with the x axis horizontal and the y axis vertical. Now, the key to solving a problem like this is to realize that since the suitcase does not move in the y direction, its y component of acceleration is zero; that is, $a_y = 0$. It follows, from Newton's second law, that the sum of the y components of force must also equal zero; that is, $\Sigma F_y = ma_y = 0$. Using this condition, we can solve for the one force that is unknown, $\vec{N}$.

To find $\vec{N}$, then, we start by writing out the y component of each force. For the weight we have $W_y = -mg = -118 \text{ N}$; for the applied force, $\vec{F}$, the y component is $F_y = F \sin 20.0° = (45.0 \text{ N}) \sin 20.0° = 15.4 \text{ N}$; finally, the y component of the normal force is $N_y = N$. Setting the sum of the y components of force equal to zero yields

$$\sum F_y = W_y + F_y + N_y = -mg + F \sin 20.0° + N = 0$$

Solving for N gives

$$N = mg - F \sin 20.0° = 118 \text{ N} - 15.4 \text{ N} = 103 \text{ N}$$

In vector form,

$$\vec{N} = N_y \hat{y} = (103 \text{ N})\hat{y}$$

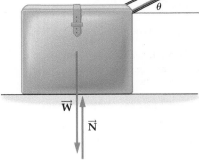

Physical picture

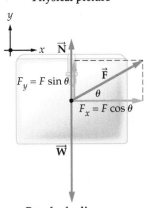

Free-body diagram

▶ **FIGURE 5–13** **The normal force may differ from the weight**
A suitcase is pulled across the floor by an applied force of magnitude F, directed at an angle θ above the horizontal. As a result of the upward component of $\vec{F}$, the normal force $\vec{N}$ will have a magnitude less than the weight of the suitcase.

Thus, as mentioned, the normal force has a magnitude less than $mg = 118$ N because the y component of $\vec{\mathbf{F}}$, $F_y = F \sin 20.0°$, supports part of the weight. In the following Example, however, the applied forces cause the normal force to be greater than the weight.

EXAMPLE 5–8 ICE BLOCK

A 6.0-kg block of ice is acted on by two forces, $\vec{\mathbf{F}}_1$ and $\vec{\mathbf{F}}_2$, as shown in the diagram. If the magnitudes of the forces are $F_1 = 13$ N and $F_2 = 11$ N, find **(a)** the acceleration of the ice and **(b)** the normal force exerted on it by the table.

PICTURE THE PROBLEM

The sketch shows our choice of coordinate system, as well as all the forces acting on the block of ice. Note that $\vec{\mathbf{F}}_1$ has a positive x component and a negative y component; $\vec{\mathbf{F}}_2$ has negative x and y components. The weight and the normal force have only y components, therefore $W_x = 0$, $W_y = -W = -mg$, $N_x = 0$, and $N_y = N$.

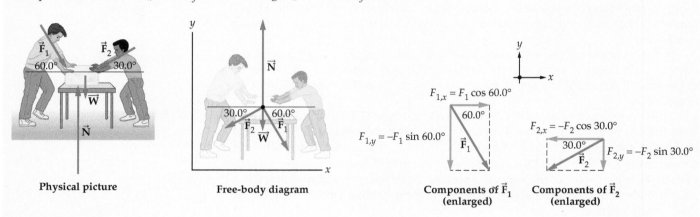

| Physical picture | Free-body diagram | Components of $\vec{\mathbf{F}}_1$ (enlarged) | Components of $\vec{\mathbf{F}}_2$ (enlarged) |

STRATEGY

The basic idea in this problem is to apply Newton's second law to the x and y directions separately. **(a)** The block can accelerate only in the horizontal direction; thus we find the acceleration by solving $\Sigma F_x = ma_x$ for a_x. **(b)** There is no motion in the y direction, and therefore the acceleration in the y direction is zero. Hence, we can find the normal force $\vec{\mathbf{N}}$ by setting $\Sigma F_y = ma_y = 0$.

SOLUTION

Part (a)

1. Write out the x component of each force:
$$F_{1,x} = F_1 \cos 60.0° = (13 \text{ N}) \cos 60.0° = 6.5 \text{ N}$$
$$F_{2,x} = -F_2 \cos 30.0° = -(11 \text{ N}) \cos 30.0° = -9.5 \text{ N}$$
$$N_x = 0 \qquad W_x = 0$$

2. Sum the x components of force:
$$\Sigma F_x = F_{1,x} + F_{2,x} + N_x + W_x$$
$$= 6.5 \text{ N} - 9.5 \text{ N} + 0 + 0 = -3.0 \text{ N}$$

3. Divide by the mass to obtain the acceleration:
$$a_x = \frac{\Sigma F_x}{m} = \frac{-3.0 \text{ N}}{6.0 \text{ kg}} = -0.50 \text{ m/s}^2$$
$$\vec{\mathbf{a}} = (-0.50 \text{ m/s}^2)\hat{\mathbf{x}}$$

Part (b)

4. Write out the y component of each force:
The only force we don't know is the normal. We represent its magnitude by N:
$$F_{1,y} = -F_1 \sin 60° = -(13 \text{ N}) \sin 60.0° = -11 \text{ N}$$
$$F_{2,y} = -F_2 \sin 30° = -(11 \text{ N}) \sin 30.0° = -5.5 \text{ N}$$
$$N_y = N \qquad W_y = -W = -mg$$

5. Sum the y components of force:
$$\Sigma F_y = F_{1,y} + F_{2,y} + N_y + W_y$$
$$= -11 \text{ N} - 5.5 \text{ N} + N - mg$$

6. Set this sum equal to 0 since the acceleration in the *y* direction is zero, and solve for *N*:

$$-11\,\text{N} - 5.5\,\text{N} + N - mg = 0$$
$$N = 11\,\text{N} + 5.5\,\text{N} + mg$$
$$= 11\,\text{N} + 5.5\,\text{N} + (6.0\,\text{kg})(9.81\,\text{m/s}^2) = 75\,\text{N}$$

7. Finally, we write the normal force in vector form:

$$\vec{\mathbf{N}} = (75\,\text{N})\hat{\mathbf{y}}$$

INSIGHT

The block accelerates to the left, even though the force acting to the right, $\vec{\mathbf{F}}_1$, has a greater magnitude than the force acting to the left, $\vec{\mathbf{F}}_2$. This is because $\vec{\mathbf{F}}_2$ has the greater *x* component. Also, note that the normal force is greater in magnitude than the weight, $mg = 59\,\text{N}$.

In general, the normal force exerted by a surface is just as large as is necessary to prevent motion of an object into the surface. If the required force is larger than the material can provide, the surface will break.

PRACTICE PROBLEM

At what angle must $\vec{\mathbf{F}}_2$ be applied if the block of ice is to have zero acceleration?   [**Answer:** $a_x = 0$ implies $F_1 \cos 60.0° = F_2 \cos \theta$. Thus, $\theta = 54°$.]

Some related homework problems: Problem 44, Problem 50

To this point, we have considered surfaces that are horizontal, in which case the normal force is vertical. When a surface is inclined, the normal force is still at right angles to the surface, even though it is no longer vertical. This is illustrated in **Figure 5–14**. (If friction is present, a surface may also exert a force that is parallel to its surface. This will be considered in detail in Chapter 6.)

When choosing a coordinate system for an inclined surface, it is generally best to have the *x* and *y* axes of the system parallel and perpendicular to the surface, respectively, as in **Figure 5–15**. One can imagine the coordinate system to be "bolted down" to the surface, so that when the surface is tilted the coordinate system tilts along with it.

With this choice of coordinate system, there is no motion in the *y* direction, even on the inclined surface, and the normal force points in the positive *y* direction. Thus, the condition that determines the normal force is still $\Sigma F_y = ma_y = 0$, as before. In addition, if the object slides on the surface, its motion is purely in the *x* direction.

Finally, if the surface is inclined by an angle θ, note that the weight—which is still vertically downward—is at the same angle θ with respect to the negative

The normal force is perpendicular to the surface that produces it ...   ... and hence it may or may not be vertical.

▲ **FIGURE 5–14 An object on an inclined surface**

The normal force $\vec{\mathbf{N}}$ is always at right angles to the surface; hence, it is not always in the vertical direction.

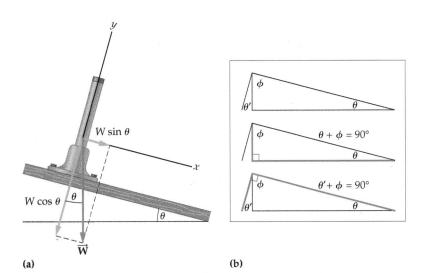

(a)   (b)

◀ **FIGURE 5–15 Components of the weight on an inclined surface**

Whenever a surface is tilted by an angle θ, the weight $\vec{\mathbf{W}}$ makes the same angle θ with respect to the negative *y* axis. This is proven in part (b), where we show that $\theta + \phi = 90°$, and that $\theta' + \phi = 90°$. From these results it follows that $\theta' = \theta$. The component of the weight perpendicular to the surface is $W_y = -W \cos \theta$; the component parallel to the surface is $W_x = W \sin \theta$.

y axis, as shown in Figure 5–15. As a result, the x and y components of the weight are

$$W_x = W \sin \theta = mg \sin \theta \qquad \text{5–8}$$

and

$$W_y = -W \cos \theta = -mg \cos \theta \qquad \text{5–9}$$

Let's quickly check some special cases of these results. First, if $\theta = 0$ the surface is horizontal, and we find $W_x = 0$, $W_y = -mg$, as expected. Second, if $\theta = 90°$ the surface is vertical; therefore, the weight is parallel to the surface, pointing in the positive x direction. In this case, $W_x = mg$ and $W_y = 0$.

The next Example shows how to use the weight components to find the acceleration of an object on an inclined surface.

EXAMPLE 5–9   TOBOGGAN TO THE BOTTOM

A child of mass m rides on a toboggan down a slick, ice-covered hill inclined at an angle θ with respect to the horizontal. **(a)** What is the acceleration of the child? **(b)** What is the normal force exerted on the child by the toboggan?

PICTURE THE PROBLEM
We choose the x axis to be parallel to the slope, with the positive direction pointing downhill. Similarly, we choose the y axis to be perpendicular to the slope, pointing up and to the right. With these choices, the x component of $\vec{W}$ is positive, $W_x = W \sin \theta$, and its y component is negative, $W_y = -W \cos \theta$. Finally, the x component of the normal force is zero, $N_x = 0$, and its y component is positive, $N_y = N$.

STRATEGY
Note that only two forces act on the child: (i) the weight, $\vec{W}$, and (ii) the normal force, $\vec{N}$. **(a)** We find the child's acceleration by solving $\sum F_x = ma_x$ for a_x. **(b)** Because there is no motion in the y direction, the y component of acceleration is zero. Therefore, we can find the normal force by setting $\sum F_y = ma_y = 0$.

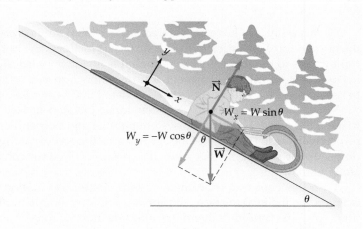

SOLUTION

Part (a)

1. Write out the x components of the forces acting on the child: $N_x = 0 \qquad W_x = W \sin \theta = mg \sin \theta$

2. Sum the x components of the forces and set equal to ma_x: $\sum F_x = N_x + W_x = mg \sin \theta = ma_x$

3. Divide by the mass m to find the acceleration in the x direction: $a_x = \dfrac{\sum F_x}{m} = \dfrac{mg \sin \theta}{m} = g \sin \theta$

Part (b)

4. Write out the y components of the forces acting on the child: $N_y = N \qquad W_y = -W \cos \theta = -mg \cos \theta$

5. Sum the y components of the forces and set the sum equal to zero, since $a_y = 0$: $\sum F_y = N_y + W_y = N - mg \cos \theta$
            $= ma_y = 0$

6. Solve for the magnitude of the normal force, N: $N - mg \cos \theta = 0 \qquad \text{or} \qquad N = mg \cos \theta$

7. Write the normal force in vector form: $\vec{N} = (mg \cos \theta)\hat{y}$

INSIGHT
Note that for θ between 0 and 90° the acceleration of the child is *less* than the acceleration of gravity. This is because only a *component* of the weight is causing the acceleration.

Let's check some special cases of our general result, $a_x = g \sin \theta$. First, let $\theta = 0$. In this case, we find zero acceleration; $a_x = g \sin 0 = 0$. This makes sense because with $\theta = 0$ the hill is actually level, and we don't expect an acceleration. Second, let $\theta = 90°$. In this case, the hill is vertical, and the toboggan should drop straight down in free fall. This also agrees with our general result; $a_x = g \sin 90° = g$.

PRACTICE PROBLEM

What is the child's acceleration if its mass is doubled to $2m$?   **[Answer:** The acceleration is still $a_x = g \sin \theta$. As in free fall, the acceleration produced by gravity is independent of mass.]

Some related homework problems: Problem 45, Problem 49

THE BIG PICTURE   **PUTTING PHYSICS IN CONTEXT**

LOOKING BACK   **LOOKING AHEAD**

The fact that a constant force produces a constant acceleration gives special significance to the discussion of constant acceleration in Chapters 2 and 4.

All forces are vectors, and therefore the ability to use and manipulate vectors confidently is essential to a full and complete understanding of forces. Again, we see the importance of the vector material presented in Chapter 3.

As with two-dimensional kinematics in Chapter 4, where motion in the x and y directions were seen to be independent, the x and y components of force are independent as well. In particular, acceleration in the x direction depends only on the x component of force, and acceleration in the y direction depends only on the y component of force.

Forces are a central theme throughout physics. In particular, we shall see in Chapters 7 and 8 that a force acting on an object over a distance changes its energy.

Another important application of forces is in the study of collisions. Central to this topic is the concept of momentum, a physical quantity that is changed when a force acts on an object over a period of time.

In this chapter we introduced the force law for gravity near the Earth's surface, $F = mg$. The more general law of gravity, valid at any location, is introduced in Chapter 12. Similarly, the force laws for electricity and magnetism are presented in Chapters 19 and 22, respectively.

CHAPTER SUMMARY

5–1   FORCE AND MASS

Force
A push or a pull.

Mass
A measure of the difficulty in accelerating an object. Equivalently, a measure of the quantity of matter in an object.

5–2   NEWTON'S FIRST LAW OF MOTION

First Law (Law of Inertia)
If the net force on an object is zero, its velocity is constant.

Inertial Frame of Reference
Frame of reference in which the first law holds. All inertial frames of reference move with constant velocity relative to one another.

5–3   NEWTON'S SECOND LAW OF MOTION

Second Law
An object of mass m has an acceleration $\vec{a}$ given by the net force $\sum \vec{F}$ divided by m. That is

$$\vec{a} = \sum \vec{F}/m \qquad \text{5–1}$$

Component Form

$$a_x = \sum F_x/m \qquad a_y = \sum F_y/m \qquad a_z = \sum F_z/m \qquad \text{5–2}$$

SI Unit: Newton (N)

$$1\,\text{N} = 1\,\text{kg} \cdot \text{m/s}^2 \qquad \text{5–3}$$

Free-Body Diagram
A sketch showing all external forces acting on an object.

5–4 NEWTON'S THIRD LAW OF MOTION

Third Law

For every force that acts on an object, there is a reaction force acting on a different object that is equal in magnitude and opposite in direction.

Contact Forces

Action-reaction pair of forces produced by physical contact of two objects.

Physical picture

5–5 THE VECTOR NATURE OF FORCES: FORCES IN TWO DIMENSIONS

Forces are vectors.

Newton's second law can be applied to each component of force separately and independently.

5–6 WEIGHT

Gravitational force exerted *by the Earth on an object.*

On the surface of the Earth the weight, W, of an object of mass m has the magnitude

$$W = mg \qquad\qquad 5\text{–}5$$

Apparent Weight

Force felt from contact with the floor or a scale in an accelerating system. For example, the sensation of feeling heavier or lighter in an accelerating elevator.

5–7 NORMAL FORCES

Force exerted by a surface that is *perpendicular* to the surface.

The normal force is equal to the weight of an object only in special cases. In general, the normal force is greater than or less than the object's weight.

PROBLEM-SOLVING SUMMARY

Type of Calculation	Relevant Physical Concepts	Related Examples
Find the acceleration of an object.	Solve Newton's second law for each component of the acceleration; that is, $a_x = \Sigma F_x/m$ and $a_y = \Sigma F_y/m$.	Examples 5–1, 5–3, 5–4, 5–5, 5–8, 5–9 Active Examples 5–1, 5–2
Solve problems involving action-reaction forces.	Apply Newton's third law, being careful to note that the action-reaction forces act on different objects.	Examples 5–3, 5–4
Find the normal force exerted on an object.	Since there is no acceleration in the normal direction, set the sum of the normal components of force equal to zero.	Examples 5–8, 5–9

CONCEPTUAL QUESTIONS

For instructor-assigned homework, go to www.masteringphysics.com

(Answers to odd-numbered Conceptual Questions can be found in the back of the book.)

1. Driving down the road, you hit the brakes suddenly. As a result, your body moves toward the front of the car. Explain, using Newton's laws.

2. You've probably seen pictures of someone pulling a table-cloth out from under glasses, plates, and silverware set out

for a formal dinner. Perhaps you've even tried it yourself. Using Newton's laws of motion, explain how this stunt works.

3. As you read this, you are most likely sitting quietly in a chair. Can you conclude, therefore, that you are at rest? Explain.

4. When a dog gets wet, it shakes its body from head to tail to shed the water. Explain, in terms of Newton's first law, why this works.

A dog uses the principle of inertia to shake water from its coat. (Conceptual Question 4)

5. A young girl slides down a rope. As she slides faster and faster she tightens her grip, increasing the force exerted on her by the rope. What happens when this force is equal in magnitude to her weight? Explain.

6. A drag-racing car accelerates forward because of the force exerted on it by the road. Why, then, does it need an engine? Explain.

7. A block of mass m hangs from a string attached to a ceiling, as shown in **Figure 5–16**. An identical string hangs down from the bottom of the block. Which string breaks if **(a)** the lower string is pulled with a slowly increasing force or **(b)** the lower string is jerked rapidly downward? Explain.

▲ **FIGURE 5–16** Conceptual Question 7

8. An astronaut on a space walk discovers that his jet pack no longer works, leaving him stranded 50 m from the spacecraft. If the jet pack is removable, explain how the astronaut can still use it to return to the ship.

9. Two untethered astronauts on a space walk decide to take a break and play catch with a baseball. Describe what happens as the game of catch progresses.

10. What are the action-reaction forces when a baseball bat hits a fast ball? What is the effect of each force?

11. In **Figure 5–17** Wilbur asks Mr. Ed, the talking horse, to pull a cart. Mr. Ed replies that he would like to, but the laws of nature just won't allow it. According to Newton's third law, he says, if he pulls on the wagon it pulls back on him with an equal force. Clearly, then, the net force is zero and the wagon will stay put. How should Wilbur answer the clever horse?

▲ **FIGURE 5–17** Conceptual Question 11

12. A whole brick has more mass than half a brick, thus the whole brick is harder to accelerate. Why doesn't a whole brick fall more slowly than half a brick? Explain.

13. The force exerted by gravity on a whole brick is greater than the force exerted by gravity on half a brick. Why, then, doesn't a whole brick fall faster than half a brick? Explain.

14. Is it possible for an object at rest to have only a single force acting on it? If your answer is yes, provide an example. If your answer is no, explain why not.

15. Is it possible for an object to be in motion and yet have zero net force acting on it? Explain.

16. A bird cage, with a parrot inside, hangs from a scale. The parrot decides to hop to a higher perch. What can you say about the reading on the scale **(a)** when the parrot jumps, **(b)** when the parrot is in the air, and **(c)** when the parrot lands on the second perch? Assume that the scale responds rapidly so that it gives an accurate reading at all times.

17. Suppose you jump from the cliffs of Acapulco and perform a perfect swan dive. As you fall, you exert an upward force on the Earth equal in magnitude to the downward force the Earth exerts on you. Why, then, does it seem that you are the one doing all the accelerating? Since the forces are the same, why aren't the accelerations?

18. A friend tells you that since his car is at rest, there are no forces acting on it. How would you reply?

19. Since all objects are "weightless" in orbit, how is it possible for an orbiting astronaut to tell if one object has more mass than another object? Explain.

20. To clean a rug, you can hang it from a clothesline and beat it with a tennis racket. Use Newton's laws to explain why beating the rug should have a cleansing effect.

21. If you step off a high board and drop to the water below, you plunge into the water without injury. On the other hand, if you were to drop the same distance onto solid ground, you might break a leg. Use Newton's laws to explain the difference.

22. A moving object is acted on by a net force. Give an example of a situation in which the object moves **(a)** in the same direction as the net force, **(b)** at right angles to the net force, or **(c)** in the opposite direction of the net force.

23. Is it possible for an object to be moving in one direction while the net force acting on it is in another direction? If your answer is yes, provide an example. If your answer is no, explain why not.

24. Since a bucket of water is "weightless" in space, would it hurt to kick the bucket? Explain.

25. In the movie *The Rocketeer*, a teenager discovers a jet-powered backpack in an old barn. The backpack allows him to fly at incredible speeds. In one scene, however, he uses the backpack to rapidly accelerate an old pickup truck that is being chased by "bad guys." He does this by bracing his arms against the cab of the pickup and firing the backpack, giving the truck the acceleration of a drag racer. Is the physics of this scene "Good," "Bad," or "Ugly?" Explain.

26. List three common objects that have a weight of approximately 1 N.

PROBLEMS AND CONCEPTUAL EXERCISES

Note: Answers to odd-numbered Problems and Conceptual Exercises can be found in the back of the book. **IP** *denotes an integrated problem, with both conceptual and numerical parts;* **BIO** *identifies problems of biological or medical interest;* **CE** *indicates a conceptual exercise.* **Predict/Explain** *problems ask for two responses:* **(a)** *your prediction of a physical outcome, and* **(b)** *the best explanation among three provided. On all problems, red bullets (•, ••, •••) are used to indicate the level of difficulty.*

SECTION 5–3 NEWTON'S SECOND LAW OF MOTION

1. • **CE** An object of mass m is initially at rest. After a force of magnitude F acts on it for a time T, the object has a speed v. Suppose the mass of the object is doubled, and the magnitude of the force acting on it is quadrupled. In terms of T, how long does it take for the object to accelerate from rest to a speed v now?

2. • On a planet far, far away, an astronaut picks up a rock. The rock has a mass of 5.00 kg, and on this particular planet its weight is 40.0 N. If the astronaut exerts an upward force of 46.2 N on the rock, what is its acceleration?

3. • In a grocery store, you push a 12.3-kg shopping cart with a force of 10.1 N. If the cart starts at rest, how far does it move in 2.50 s?

4. • You are pulling your little sister on her sled across an icy (frictionless) surface. When you exert a constant horizontal force of 120 N, the sled has an acceleration of 2.5 m/s². If the sled has a mass of 7.4 kg, what is the mass of your little sister?

5. • A 0.53-kg billiard ball initially at rest is given a speed of 12 m/s during a time interval of 4.0 ms. What average force acted on the ball during this time?

6. • A 92-kg water skier floating in a lake is pulled from rest to a speed of 12 m/s in a distance of 25 m. What is the net force exerted on the skier, assuming his acceleration is constant?

7. •• **CE Predict/Explain** You drop two balls of equal diameter from the same height at the same time. Ball 1 is made of metal and has a greater mass than ball 2, which is made of wood. The upward force due to air resistance is the same for both balls. **(a)** Is the drop time of ball 1 greater than, less than, or equal to the drop time of ball 2? **(b)** Choose the *best explanation* from among the following:

  I. The acceleration of gravity is the same for all objects, regardless of mass.

  II. The more massive ball is harder to accelerate.

  III. Air resistance has less effect on the more massive ball.

8. •• **IP** A 42.0-kg parachutist is moving straight downward with a speed of 3.85 m/s. **(a)** If the parachutist comes to rest with constant acceleration over a distance of 0.750 m, what force does the ground exert on her? **(b)** If the parachutist comes to rest over a shorter distance, is the force exerted by the ground greater than, less than, or the same as in part (a)? Explain.

9. •• **IP** In baseball, a pitcher can accelerate a 0.15-kg ball from rest to 98 mi/h in a distance of 1.7 m. **(a)** What is the average force exerted on the ball during the pitch? **(b)** If the mass of the ball is increased, is the force required of the pitcher increased, decreased, or unchanged? Explain.

10. •• A major-league catcher gloves a 92-mi/h pitch and brings it to rest in 0.15 m. If the force exerted by the catcher is 803 N, what is the mass of the ball?

11. •• Driving home from school one day, you spot a ball rolling out into the street (**Figure 5–18**). You brake for 1.20 s, slowing your 950-kg car from 16.0 m/s to 9.50 m/s. **(a)** What was the average force exerted on your car during braking? **(b)** How far did you travel while braking?

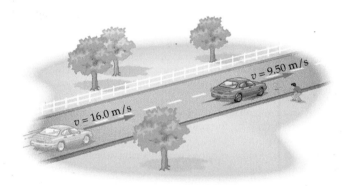

▲ **FIGURE 5–18** Problem 11

12. •• **Stopping a 747** A 747 jetliner lands and begins to slow to a stop as it moves along the runway. If its mass is 3.50×10^5 kg, its speed is 27.0 m/s, and the net braking force is 4.30×10^5 N, **(a)** what is its speed 7.50 s later? **(b)** How far has it traveled in this time?

13. •• **IP** A drag racer crosses the finish line doing 202 mi/h and promptly deploys her drag chute (the small parachute used for braking). **(a)** What force must the drag chute exert on the 891-kg car to slow it to 45.0 mi/h in a distance of 185 m? **(b)** Describe the strategy you used to solve part (a).

SECTION 5–4 NEWTON'S THIRD LAW OF MOTION

14. • **CE Predict/Explain** A small car collides with a large truck. **(a)** Is the magnitude of the force experienced by the car greater than, less than, or equal to the magnitude of the force experienced by the truck? **(b)** Choose the *best explanation* from among the following:

  I. Action-reaction forces always have equal magnitude.

  II. The truck has more mass, and hence the force exerted on it is greater.

  III. The massive truck exerts a greater force on the lightweight car.

15. • **CE Predict/Explain** A small car collides with a large truck. **(a)** Is the acceleration experienced by the car greater than, less than, or equal to the acceleration experienced by the truck? **(b)** Choose the *best explanation* from among the following:
  I. The truck exerts a larger force on the car, giving it the greater acceleration.
  II. Both vehicles experience the same magnitude of force, therefore the lightweight car experiences the greater acceleration.
  III. The greater force exerted on the truck gives it the greater acceleration.

16. • You hold a brick at rest in your hand. **(a)** How many forces act on the brick? **(b)** Identify these forces. **(c)** Are these forces equal in magnitude and opposite in direction? **(d)** Are these forces an action-reaction pair? Explain.

17. • Referring to Problem 16, you are now accelerating the brick upward. **(a)** How many forces act on the brick in this case? **(b)** Identify these forces. **(c)** Are these forces equal in magnitude and opposite in direction? **(d)** Are these forces an action-reaction pair? Explain.

18. •• On vacation, your 1400-kg car pulls a 560-kg trailer away from a stoplight with an acceleration of 1.85 m/s^2. **(a)** What is the net force exerted on the trailer? **(b)** What force does the trailer exert on the car? **(c)** What is the net force acting on the car?

19. •• **IP** A 71-kg parent and a 19-kg child meet at the center of an ice rink. They place their hands together and push. **(a)** Is the force experienced by the child more than, less than, or the same as the force experienced by the parent? **(b)** Is the acceleration of the child more than, less than, or the same as the acceleration of the parent? Explain. **(c)** If the acceleration of the child is 2.6 m/s^2 in magnitude, what is the magnitude of the parent's acceleration?

20. •• A force of magnitude 7.50 N pushes three boxes with masses $m_1 = 1.30 \text{ kg}$, $m_2 = 3.20 \text{ kg}$, and $m_3 = 4.90 \text{ kg}$, as shown in **Figure 5–19**. Find the magnitude of the contact force **(a)** between boxes 1 and 2, and **(b)** between boxes 2 and 3.

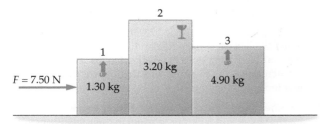

▲ **FIGURE 5–19** Problem 20

21. •• A force of magnitude 7.50 N pushes three boxes with masses $m_1 = 1.30 \text{ kg}$, $m_2 = 3.20 \text{ kg}$, and $m_3 = 4.90 \text{ kg}$, as shown in **Figure 5–20**. Find the magnitude of the contact force **(a)** between boxes 1 and 2, and **(b)** between boxes 2 and 3.

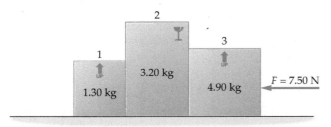

▲ **FIGURE 5–20** Problem 21

22. •• **IP** Two boxes sit side-by-side on a smooth horizontal surface. The lighter box has a mass of 5.2 kg; the heavier box has a mass of 7.4 kg. **(a)** Find the contact force between these boxes when a horizontal force of 5.0 N is applied to the light box. **(b)** If the 5.0-N force is applied to the heavy box instead, is the contact force between the boxes the same as, greater than, or less than the contact force in part (a)? Explain. **(c)** Verify your answer to part (b) by calculating the contact force in this case.

SECTION 5–5   THE VECTOR NATURE OF FORCES

23. • **CE** A skateboarder on a ramp is accelerated by a <u>nonzero</u> net force. For each of the following statements, state whether it is always true, never true, or sometimes true. **(a)** The skateboarder is moving in the direction of the net force. **(b)** The acceleration of the skateboarder is at right angles to the net force. **(c)** The acceleration of the skateboarder is in the same direction as the net force. **(d)** The skateboarder is instantaneously at rest.

24. • **CE** Three objects, A, B, and C, have x and y components of velocity that vary with time as shown in **Figure 5–21**. What is the direction of the net force acting on **(a)** object A, **(b)** object B, and **(c)** object C, as measured from the positive x axis? (All of the nonzero slopes have the same magnitude.)

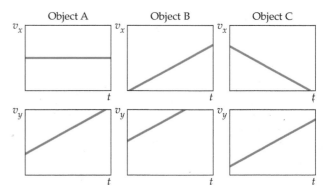

▲ **FIGURE 5–21** Problem 24

25. • A farm tractor tows a 3700-kg trailer up an 18° incline with a steady speed of 3.2 m/s. What force does the tractor exert on the trailer? (Ignore friction.)

26. • A surfer "hangs ten," and accelerates down the sloping face of a wave. If the surfer's acceleration is 3.25 m/s^2 and friction can be ignored, what is the angle at which the face of the wave is inclined above the horizontal?

27. • A shopper pushes a 7.5-kg shopping cart up a 13° incline, as shown in **Figure 5–22**. Find the magnitude of the horizontal force, $\vec{F}$, needed to give the cart an acceleration of 1.41 m/s^2.

▲ **FIGURE 5–22** Problem 27

28. • Two crewmen pull a raft through a lock, as shown in **Figure 5–23**. One crewman pulls with a force of 130 N at an angle of 34° relative to the forward direction of the raft. The second crewman, on the opposite side of the lock, pulls at an angle of 45°. With what force should the second crewman pull so that the net force of the two crewmen is in the forward direction?

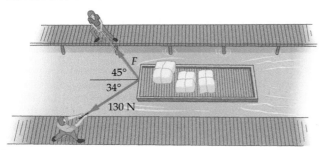

▲ **FIGURE 5–23** Problem 28

29. •• **CE** A hockey puck is acted on by one or more forces, as shown in **Figure 5–24**. Rank the four cases, A, B, C, and D, in order of the magnitude of the puck's acceleration, starting with the smallest. Indicate ties where appropriate.

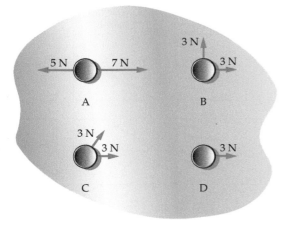

▲ **FIGURE 5–24** Problem 29

30. •• To give a 19-kg child a ride, two teenagers pull on a 3.7-kg sled with ropes, as indicated in **Figure 5–25**. Both teenagers pull with a force of 55 N at an angle of 35° relative to the forward direction, which is the direction of motion. In addition, the snow exerts a retarding force on the sled that points opposite to the direction of motion, and has a magnitude of 57 N. Find the acceleration of the sled and child.

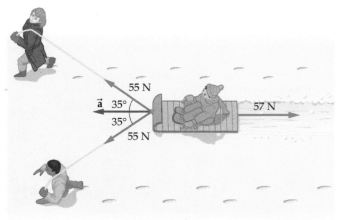

▲ **FIGURE 5–25** Problem 30

31. •• **IP** Before practicing his routine on the rings, a 67-kg gymnast stands motionless, with one hand grasping each ring and his feet touching the ground. Both arms slope upward at an angle of 24° above the horizontal. **(a)** If the force exerted by the rings on each arm has a magnitude of 290 N, and is directed along the length of the arm, what is the magnitude of the force exerted by the floor on his feet? **(b)** If the angle his arms make with the horizontal is greater that 24°, and everything else remains the same, is the force exerted by the floor on his feet greater than, less than, or the same as the value found in part (a)? Explain.

32. •• **IP** A 65-kg skier speeds down a trail, as shown in **Figure 5–26**. The surface is smooth and inclined at an angle of 22° with the horizontal. **(a)** Find the direction and magnitude of the net force acting on the skier. **(b)** Does the net force exerted on the skier increase, decrease, or stay the same as the slope becomes steeper? Explain.

▲ **FIGURE 5–26** Problems 32 and 45

33. •• An object acted on by three forces moves with constant velocity. One force acting on the object is in the positive x direction and has a magnitude of 6.5 N; a second force has a magnitude of 4.4 N and points in the negative y direction. Find the direction and magnitude of the third force acting on the object.

34. •• A train is traveling up a 3.73° incline at a speed of 3.25 m/s when the last car breaks free and begins to coast without friction. **(a)** How long does it take for the last car to come to rest momentarily? **(b)** How far did the last car travel before momentarily coming to rest?

35. •• **The Force Exerted on the Moon Figure 5–27** shows the Earth, Moon, and Sun (not to scale) in their relative positions at the time when the Moon is in its third-quarter phase. Though few people realize it, the force exerted on the Moon by the Sun is actually greater than the force exerted on the Moon by the Earth. In fact, the force exerted on the Moon by the Sun has a magnitude of $F_{SM} = 4.34 \times 10^{20}$ N, whereas the force exerted by the Earth has a magnitude of only $F_{EM} = 1.98 \times 10^{20}$ N. These forces are indicated to scale in Figure 5–27. Find **(a)** the direction and **(b)** the magnitude of the net force acting on the Moon. **(c)** Given that the mass of the Moon is $M_M = 7.35 \times 10^{22}$ kg, find the magnitude of its acceleration at the time of the third-quarter phase.

SECTION 5–6 WEIGHT

36. • You pull upward on a stuffed suitcase with a force of 105 N, and it accelerates upward at 0.705 m/s². What are **(a)** the mass and **(b)** the weight of the suitcase?

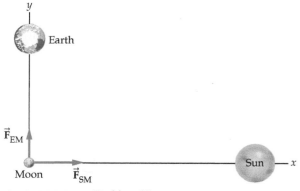

▲ **FIGURE 5–27** Problem 35

37. • **BIO Brain Growth** A newborn baby's brain grows rapidly. In fact, it has been found to increase in mass by about 1.6 mg per minute. **(a)** How much does the brain's weight increase in one day? **(b)** How long does it take for the brain's weight to increase by 0.15 N?

38. • Suppose a rocket launches with an acceleration of 30.5 m/s². What is the apparent weight of an 92-kg astronaut aboard this rocket?

39. • At the bow of a ship on a stormy sea, a crewman conducts an experiment by standing on a bathroom scale. In calm waters, the scale reads 182 lb. During the storm, the crewman finds a maximum reading of 225 lb and a minimum reading of 138 lb. Find **(a)** the maximum upward acceleration and **(b)** the maximum downward acceleration experienced by the crewman.

40. •• **IP** As part of a physics experiment, you stand on a bathroom scale in an elevator. Though your normal weight is 610 N, the scale at the moment reads 730 N. **(a)** Is the acceleration of the elevator upward, downward, or zero? Explain. **(b)** Calculate the magnitude of the elevator's acceleration. **(c)** What, if anything, can you say about the velocity of the elevator? Explain.

41. •• When you weigh yourself on good old *terra firma* (solid ground), your weight is 142 lb. In an elevator your apparent weight is 121 lb. What are the direction and magnitude of the elevator's acceleration?

42. •• **IP BIO Flight of the Samara** A 1.21-g samara—the winged fruit of a maple tree—falls toward the ground with a constant speed of 1.1 m/s (**Figure 5–28**). **(a)** What is the force of air resistance exerted on the samara? **(b)** If the constant speed of descent is greater than 1.1 m/s, is the force of air resistance greater than, less than, or the same as in part (a)? Explain.

$v = 1.1$ m/s

▲ **FIGURE 5–28** Problem 42

43. ••• When you lift a bowling ball with a force of 82 N, the ball accelerates upward with an acceleration a. If you lift with a force of 92 N, the ball's acceleration is $2a$. Find **(a)** the weight of the bowling ball, and **(b)** the acceleration a.

SECTION 5–7 NORMAL FORCES

44. • A 23-kg suitcase is being pulled with constant speed by a handle that is at an angle of 25° above the horizontal. If the normal force exerted on the suitcase is 180 N, what is the force F applied to the handle?

45. • **(a)** Draw a free-body diagram for the skier in Problem 32. **(b)** Determine the normal force acting on the skier.

46. • A 9.3-kg child sits in a 3.7-kg high chair. **(a)** Draw a free-body diagram for the child, and find the normal force exerted by the chair on the child. **(b)** Draw a free-body diagram for the chair, and find the normal force exerted by the floor on the chair.

47. •• **Figure 5–29** shows the normal force as a function of the angle θ for the suitcase shown in Figure 5–13. Determine the magnitude of the force $\vec{F}$ for each of the three curves shown in Figure 5–29. Give your answer in terms of the weight of the suitcase, mg.

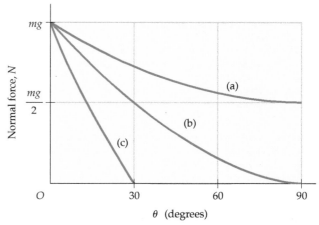

▲ **FIGURE 5–29** Problem 47

48. •• A 5.0-kg bag of potatoes sits on the bottom of a stationary shopping cart. **(a)** Sketch a free-body diagram for the bag of potatoes. **(b)** Now suppose the cart moves with a constant velocity. How does this affect your free-body diagram? Explain.

49. •• **IP (a)** Find the normal force exerted on a 2.9-kg book resting on a surface inclined at 36° above the horizontal. **(b)** If the angle of the incline is reduced, do you expect the normal force to increase, decrease, or stay the same? Explain.

50. •• **IP** A gardener mows a lawn with an old-fashioned push mower. The handle of the mower makes an angle of 35° with the surface of the lawn. **(a)** If a 219-N force is applied along the handle of the 19-kg mower, what is the normal force exerted by the lawn on the mower? **(b)** If the angle between the surface of the lawn and the handle of the mower is increased, does the normal force exerted by the lawn increase, decrease, or stay the same? Explain.

51. ••• An ant walks slowly away from the top of a bowling ball, as shown in **Figure 5–30**. If the ant starts to slip when the normal force on its feet drops below one-half its weight, at what angle θ does slipping begin?

▲ **FIGURE 5–30** Problem 51

GENERAL PROBLEMS

52. • **CE Predict/Explain** Riding in an elevator moving upward with constant speed, you begin a game of darts. **(a)** Do you have to aim your darts higher than, lower than, or the same as when you play darts on solid ground? **(b)** Choose the *best explanation* from among the following:

  I. The elevator rises during the time it takes for the dart to travel to the dartboard.

  II. The elevator moves with constant velocity. Therefore, Newton's laws apply within the elevator in the same way as on the ground.

  III. You have to aim lower to compensate for the upward speed of the elevator.

53. • **CE Predict/Explain** Riding in an elevator moving with a constant upward acceleration, you begin a game of darts. **(a)** Do you have to aim your darts higher than, lower than, or the same as when you play darts on solid ground? **(b)** Choose the *best explanation* from among the following:

  I. The elevator accelerates upward, giving its passengers a greater "effective" acceleration of gravity.

  II. You have to aim lower to compensate for the upward acceleration of the elevator.

  III. Since the elevator moves with a constant acceleration, Newton's laws apply within the elevator the same as on the ground.

54. • **CE** Give the direction of the net force acting on each of the following objects. If the net force is zero, state "zero." **(a)** A car accelerating northward from a stoplight. **(b)** A car traveling southward and slowing down. **(c)** A car traveling westward with constant speed. **(d)** A skydiver parachuting downward with constant speed. **(e)** A baseball during its flight from pitcher to catcher (ignoring air resistance).

55. • **CE Predict/Explain** You jump out of an airplane and open your parachute after an extended period of free fall. **(a)** To decelerate your fall, must the force exerted on you by the parachute be greater than, less than, or equal to your weight? **(b)** Choose the *best explanation* from among the following:

  I. Parachutes can only exert forces that are less than the weight of the skydiver.

  II. The parachute exerts a force exactly equal to the skydiver's weight.

  III. To decelerate after free fall, the net force acting on a skydiver must be upward.

56. • In a tennis serve, a 0.070-kg ball can be accelerated from rest to 36 m/s over a distance of 0.75 m. Find the magnitude of the average force exerted by the racket on the ball during the serve.

57. • A 51.5-kg swimmer with an initial speed of 1.25 m/s decides to coast until she comes to rest. If she slows with constant acceleration and stops after coasting 2.20 m, what was the force exerted on her by the water?

58. •• **CE** Each of the three identical hockey pucks shown in **Figure 5–31** is acted on by a 3-N force. Puck A moves with a speed of 7 m/s in a direction opposite to the force; puck B is instantaneously at rest; puck C moves with a speed of 7 m/s at right angles to the force. Rank the three pucks in order of the magnitude of their acceleration, starting with the smallest. Indicate ties with an equal sign.

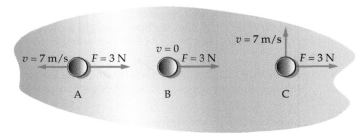

▲ **FIGURE 5–31** Problem 58

59. •• **IP The VASIMR Rocket** NASA plans to use a new type of rocket, a Variable Specific Impulse Magnetoplasma Rocket (VASIMR), on future missions. A VASIMR can produce 1200 N of thrust (force) when in operation. If a VASIMR has a mass of 2.2×10^5 kg, **(a)** what acceleration will it experience? Assume that the only force acting on the rocket is its own thrust, and that the mass of the rocket is constant. **(b)** Over what distance must the rocket accelerate from rest to achieve a speed of 9500 m/s? **(c)** When the rocket has covered one-quarter the acceleration distance found in part (b), is its average speed 1/2, 1/3, or 1/4 its average speed during the final three-quarters of the acceleration distance? Explain.

60. •• An object of mass $m = 5.95$ kg has an acceleration $\vec{a} = (1.17 \text{ m/s}^2)\hat{x} + (-0.664 \text{ m/s}^2)\hat{y}$. Three forces act on this object: $\vec{F}_1$, $\vec{F}_2$, and $\vec{F}_3$. Given that $\vec{F}_1 = (3.22 \text{ N})\hat{x}$ and $\vec{F}_2 = (-1.55 \text{ N})\hat{x} + (2.05 \text{ N})\hat{y}$, find $\vec{F}_3$.

61. •• At the local grocery store, you push a 14.5-kg shopping cart. You stop for a moment to add a bag of dog food to your cart. With a force of 12.0 N, you now accelerate the cart from rest through a distance of 2.29 m in 3.00 s. What was the mass of the dog food?

62. •• **IP BIO The Force of Running** Biomechanical research has shown that when a 67-kg person is running, the force exerted on each foot as it strikes the ground can be as great as 2300 N. **(a)** What is the ratio of the force exerted on the foot by the ground to the person's body weight? **(b)** If the only forces acting on the person are (i) the force exerted by the ground and (ii) the person's weight, what are the magnitude and direction of the person's acceleration? **(c)** If the acceleration found in part (b) acts for 10.0 ms, what is the resulting change in the vertical component of the person's velocity?

63. •• **IP BIO Grasshopper Liftoff** To become airborne, a 2.0-g grasshopper requires a takeoff speed of 2.7 m/s. It acquires this speed by extending its hind legs through a distance of 3.7 cm. **(a)** What is the average acceleration of the grasshopper during takeoff? **(b)** Find the magnitude of the average net force exerted on the grasshopper by its hind legs during takeoff. **(c)** If the mass of the grasshopper increases, does the takeoff acceleration increase, decrease, or stay the same? **(d)** If the mass of the grasshopper increases, does the required takeoff force increase, decrease, or stay the same? Explain.

64. •• **Takeoff from an Aircraft Carrier** On an aircraft carrier, a jet can be catapulted from 0 to 155 mi/h in 2.00 s. If the average force exerted by the catapult is 9.35×10^5 N, what is the mass of the jet?

A jet takes off from the flight deck of an aircraft carrier. (Problem 64)

65. •• **IP** An archer shoots a 0.024-kg arrow at a target with a speed of 54 m/s. When it hits the target, it penetrates to a depth of 0.083 m. **(a)** What was the average force exerted by the target on the arrow? **(b)** If the mass of the arrow is doubled, and the force exerted by the target on the arrow remains the same, by what multiplicative factor does the penetration depth change? Explain.

66. •• An apple of mass $m = 0.13$ kg falls out of a tree from a height $h = 3.2$ m. **(a)** What is the magnitude of the force of gravity, mg, acting on the apple? **(b)** What is the apple's speed, v, just before it lands? **(c)** Show that the force of gravity times the height, mgh, is equal to $\frac{1}{2}mv^2$. (We shall investigate the significance of this result in Chapter 8.) Be sure to show that the dimensions are in agreement as well as the numerical values.

67. •• An apple of mass $m = 0.22$ kg falls from a tree and hits the ground with a speed of $v = 14$ m/s. **(a)** What is the magnitude of the force of gravity, mg, acting on the apple? **(b)** What is the time, t, required for the apple to reach the ground? **(c)** Show that the force of gravity times the time, mgt, is equal to mv. (We shall investigate the significance of this result in Chapter 9.) Be sure to show that the dimensions are in agreement as well as the numerical values.

68. •• **BIO The Fall of _T. rex_** Paleontologists estimate that if a _Tyrannosaurus rex_ were to trip and fall, it would have experienced a force of approximately 260,000 N acting on its torso when it hit the ground. Assuming the torso has a mass of 3800 kg, **(a)** find the magnitude of the torso's upward acceleration as it comes to rest. (For comparison, humans lose consciousness with an acceleration of about $7g$.) **(b)** Assuming the torso is in free fall for a distance of 1.46 m as it falls to the ground, how much time is required for the torso to come to rest once it contacts the ground?

69. •• **Deep Space I** The NASA spacecraft _Deep Space I_ was shut down on December 18, 2001, following a three-year journey to the asteroid Braille and the comet Borrelly. This spacecraft used a solar-powered ion engine to produce 0.064 ounces of thrust (force) by stripping electrons from neon atoms and accelerating the resulting ions to 70,000 mi/h. The thrust was only as much as the weight of a couple sheets of paper, but the engine operated continuously for 16,000 hours. As a result, the speed of the spacecraft increased by 7900 mi/h. What was the mass of _Deep Space I_? (Assume that the mass of the neon gas is negligible.)

70. •• Your groceries are in a bag with paper handles. The handles will tear off if a force greater than 51.5 N is applied to them. What is the greatest mass of groceries that can be lifted safely with this bag, given that the bag is raised **(a)** with constant speed, or **(b)** with an acceleration of 1.25 m/s²?

71. •• **IP** While waiting at the airport for your flight to leave, you observe some of the jets as they take off. With your watch you find that it takes about 35 seconds for a plane to go from rest to takeoff speed. In addition, you estimate that the distance required is about 1.5 km. **(a)** If the mass of a jet is 1.70×10^5 kg, what force is needed for takeoff? **(b)** Describe the strategy you used to solve part (a).

72. •• **BIO Gecko Feet** Researchers have found that a gecko's foot is covered with hundreds of thousands of small hairs (_setae_) that allow it to walk up walls and even across ceilings. A single foot pad, which has an area of 1.0 cm², can attach to a wall or ceiling with a force of 11 N. **(a)** How many 250-g geckos could be suspended from the ceiling by a single foot pad? **(b)** Estimate the force per square centimeter that your body exerts on the soles of your shoes, and compare with the 11 N/cm² of the sticky gecko foot.

A Tokay gecko (_Gekko gecko_) shows off its famous feet. (Problem 72)

73. •• Two boxes are at rest on a smooth, horizontal surface. The boxes are in contact with one another. If box 1 is pushed with a force of magnitude $F = 12.00$ N, the contact force between the boxes is 8.50 N; if, instead, box 2 is pushed with the force F, the contact force is 12.00 N − 8.50 N = 3.50 N. In either case, the boxes move together with an acceleration of 1.70 m/s². What is the mass of **(a)** box 1 and **(b)** box 2?

74. ••• **IP** Responding to an alarm, a 102-kg fireman slides down a pole to the ground floor, 3.3 m below. The fireman starts at rest and lands with a speed of 4.2 m/s. **(a)** Find the average force exerted on the fireman by the pole. **(b)** If the landing speed is half that in part (a), is the average force exerted on the fireman by the pole doubled? Explain. **(c)** Find the average force exerted on the fireman by the pole when the landing speed is 2.1 m/s.

75. ••• For a birthday gift, you and some friends take a hot-air balloon ride. One friend is late, so the balloon floats a couple of feet off the ground as you wait. Before this person arrives, the combined weight of the basket and people is 1220 kg, and the balloon is neutrally buoyant. When the late arrival climbs up into the basket, the balloon begins to accelerate downward at 0.56 m/s^2. What was the mass of the last person to climb aboard?

76. ••• A baseball of mass m and initial speed v strikes a catcher's mitt. If the mitt moves a distance Δx as it brings the ball to rest, what is the average force it exerts on the ball?

77. ••• When two people push in the same direction on an object of mass m they cause an acceleration of magnitude a_1. When the same people push in opposite directions, the acceleration of the object has a magnitude a_2. Determine the magnitude of the force exerted by each of the two people in terms of m, a_1, and a_2.

78. ••• An air-track cart of mass $m_1 = 0.14$ kg is moving with a speed $v_0 = 1.3$ m/s to the right when it collides with a cart of mass $m_2 = 0.25$ kg that is at rest. Each cart has a wad of putty on its bumper, and hence they stick together as a result of their collision. Suppose the average contact force between the carts is $F = 1.5$ N during the collision. (a) What is the acceleration of cart 1? Give direction and magnitude. (b) What is the acceleration of cart 2? Give direction and magnitude. (c) How long does it take for both carts to have the same speed? (Once the carts have the same speed the collision is over and the contact force vanishes.) (d) What is the final speed of the carts, v_f? (e) Show that $m_1 v_0$ is equal to $(m_1 + m_2)v_f$. (We shall investigate the significance of this result in Chapter 9.)

PASSAGE PROBLEMS

BIO Increasing Safety in a Collision

Safety experts say that an automobile accident is really a succession of three separate collisions. These can be described as follows: (1) the automobile collides with an obstacle and comes to rest; (2) people within the car continue to move forward until they collide with the interior of the car, or are brought to rest by a restraint system like a seatbelt or an air bag; (3) organs within the occupants' bodies continue to move forward until they collide with the body wall and are brought to rest. Not much can be done about the third collision, but the effects of the first two can be mitigated by increasing the distance over which the car and its occupants are brought to rest.

For example, the severity of the first collision is reduced by building collapsible "crumple zones" into the body of a car, and by placing compressible collision barriers near dangerous obstacles like bridge supports. The second collision is addressed primarily through the use of seatbelts and air bags. These devices reduce the force that acts on an occupant to survivable levels by increasing the distance over which he or she comes to rest. This is illustrated in **Figure 5–32**, where we see the force exerted on a 65.0-kg driver who slows from an initial speed of 18.0 m/s (lower curve) or 36.0 m/s (upper curve) to rest in a distance ranging from 5.00 cm to 1.00 m.

79. • The combination of "crumple zones" and air bags/seatbelts might increase the distance over which a person stops in a collision to as great as 1.00 m. What is the magnitude of the force exerted on a 65.0-kg driver who decelerates from 18.0 m/s to 0.00 m/s over a distance of 1.00 m?

    A. 162 N   **B.** 585 N

    C. 1.05×10^4 N   **D.** 2.11×10^4 N

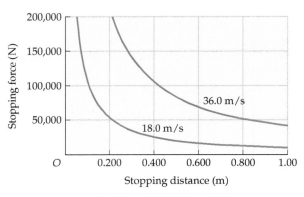

▲ **FIGURE 5–32** Problems 79, 80, 81, and 82

80. • A driver who does not wear a seatbelt continues to move forward with a speed of 18.0 m/s (due to inertia) until something solid like the steering wheel is encountered. The driver now comes to rest in a much shorter distance—perhaps only a few centimeters. Find the magnitude of the net force acting on a 65.0-kg driver who is decelerated from 18.0 m/s to rest in 5.00 cm.

    A. 3240 N   **B.** 1.17×10^4 N

    C. 2.11×10^5 N   **D.** 4.21×10^5 N

81. • Suppose the initial speed of the driver is doubled to 36.0 m/s. If the driver still has a mass of 65.0 kg, and comes to rest in 1.00 m, what is the magnitude of the force exerted on the driver during this collision?

    A. 648 N   **B.** 1170 N

    C. 2.11×10^4 N   **D.** 4.21×10^4 N

82. • If both the speed and stopping distance of a driver are doubled, by what factor does the force exerted on the driver change?

    A. 0.5   **B.** 1

    C. 2   **D.** 4

INTERACTIVE PROBLEMS

83. •• **IP Referring to Example 5–4** Suppose that we would like the contact force between the boxes to have a magnitude of 5.00 N, and that the only thing in the system we are allowed to change is the mass of box 2—the mass of box 1 is 10.0 kg and the applied force is 20.0 N. (a) Should the mass of box 2 be increased or decreased? Explain. (b) Find the mass of box 2 that results in a contact force of magnitude 5.00 N. (c) What is the acceleration of the boxes in this case?

84. •• **Referring to Example 5–4** Suppose the force of 20.0 N pushes on two boxes of unknown mass. We know, however, that the acceleration of the boxes is 1.20 m/s^2 and the contact force has a magnitude of 4.45 N. Find the mass of (a) box 1 and (b) box 2.

85. •• **IP Referring to Figure 5–9** Suppose the magnitude of $\vec{F}_2$ is increased from 41 N to 55 N, and that everything else in the system remains the same. (a) Do you expect the direction of the satellite's acceleration to be greater than, less than, or equal to 32°? Explain. Find (b) the direction and (c) the magnitude of the satellite's acceleration in this case.

86. •• **IP Referring to Figure 5–9** Suppose we would like the acceleration of the satellite to be at an angle of 25°, and that the only quantity we can change in the system is the magnitude of $\vec{F}_1$. (a) Should the magnitude of $\vec{F}_1$ be increased or decreased? Explain. (b) What is the magnitude of the satellite's acceleration in this case?

6 Applications of Newton's Laws

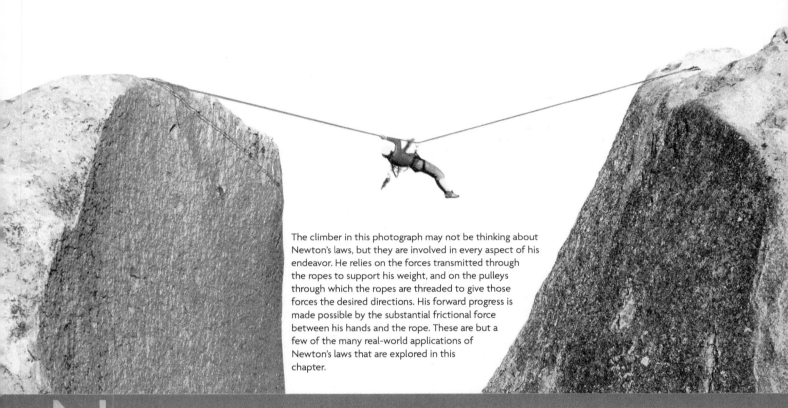

The climber in this photograph may not be thinking about Newton's laws, but they are involved in every aspect of his endeavor. He relies on the forces transmitted through the ropes to support his weight, and on the pulleys through which the ropes are threaded to give those forces the desired directions. His forward progress is made possible by the substantial frictional force between his hands and the rope. These are but a few of the many real-world applications of Newton's laws that are explored in this chapter.

Newton's laws of motion can be applied to an immense variety of systems, a sampling of which was discussed in Chapter 5. In this chapter we extend our discussion of Newton's laws by introducing new types of forces and by considering new classes of systems.

For example, we begin by considering the forces due to friction between two surfaces. As we shall see, the force of friction is different depending on whether the surfaces are in static contact, or are moving relative to one another—an important consideration in antilock braking systems. And though friction may seem like something that should be eliminated, we show that it is actually essential to life as we know it.

Next, we investigate the forces exerted by strings and springs, and show how these forces can safely suspend a mountain climber over a chasm, or cushion the ride of a locomotive. Finally, we consider the key role that force plays in making circular motion possible.

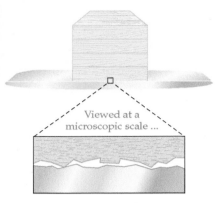

Viewed at a
microscopic scale ...

... even a "smooth" surface is rough.

▲ **FIGURE 6–1 The origin of friction**
Even "smooth" surfaces have irregularities when viewed at the microscopic level. This type of roughness contributes to friction.

6–1 Frictional Forces

In Chapter 5 we always assumed that surfaces were smooth and that objects could slide without resistance to their motion. No surface is perfectly smooth, however. When viewed on the atomic level, even the "smoothest" surface is actually rough and jagged, as indicated in **Figure 6–1**. To slide one such surface across another requires a force large enough to overcome the resistance of microscopic hills and valleys bumping together. This is the origin of the force we call **friction.**

We often think of friction as something that should be reduced, or even eliminated if possible. For example, roughly 20% of the gasoline you buy does nothing but overcome friction within your car's engine. Clearly, reducing that friction would be most desirable.

On the other hand, friction can be helpful—even indispensable—in other situations. Suppose, for example, that you are standing still and then decide to begin walking forward. The force that accelerates you is the force of friction between your shoes and the ground. We simply couldn't walk or run without friction—it's hard enough when friction is merely reduced, as on an icy sidewalk. Similarly, starting or stopping a car, or even turning a corner, all require friction. Friction is an important and common feature of everyday life.

Since friction is caused by the random, microscopic irregularities of a surface, and since it is greatly affected by other factors such as the presence of lubricants, there is no simple "law of nature" for friction. There are, however, some very useful rules of thumb that give us rather accurate, approximate results for calculating frictional forces. In what follows, we describe these rules of thumb for the two types of friction most commonly used in this text—kinetic friction and static friction.

Kinetic Friction

As its name implies, kinetic friction is the friction encountered when surfaces slide against one another with a finite relative speed. The force generated by this friction, which will be designated with the symbol f_k, acts to oppose the sliding motion at the point of contact between the surfaces.

A series of simple experiments illustrates the main characteristics of kinetic friction. First, imagine attaching a spring scale to a rough object, like a brick, and pulling it across a table, as shown in **Figure 6–2**. If the brick moves with constant velocity, Newton's second law tells us that the net force on the brick must be zero. Hence, the force read on the scale, F, has the same magnitude as the force of kinetic friction, f_k. Now, if we repeat the experiment, but this time put a second brick on top of the first, we find that the force needed to pull the brick with constant velocity is doubled, to $2F$.

◀ **FIGURE 6–2 The force of kinetic friction depends on the normal force**

In the top part of the figure, a force F is required to pull the brick with constant speed v. Thus the force of kinetic friction is $f_k = F$. In the bottom part of the figure, the normal force has been doubled, and so has the force of kinetic friction, to $f_k = 2F$.

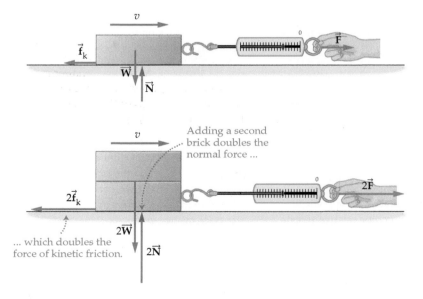

From this experiment we see that when we double the normal force—by stacking up two bricks, for example—the force of kinetic friction is also doubled. In general, the force of kinetic friction is found to be proportional to the magnitude of the normal force, N. Stated mathematically, this observation can be written as follows:

$$f_k = \mu_k N \qquad \text{6–1}$$

The constant of proportionality, μ_k (pronounced "mew sub k"), is referred to as the **coefficient of kinetic friction.** In Figure 6–2 the normal force is equal to the weight of the bricks, but this is a special case. The normal force is greater than the weight if someone pushes down on the bricks, and this would cause more friction, or less than the weight if the bricks are placed on an incline. The former case is considered in several homework problems, and the latter case is considered in Examples 6–2 and 6–3.

Since f_k and N are both forces, and hence have the same units, we see that μ_k is a dimensionless number. The coefficient of kinetic friction is always positive, and typical values range between 0 and 1, as indicated in Table 6–1. The interpretation of μ_k is simple: If $\mu_k = 0.1$, for example, the force of kinetic friction is one-tenth of the normal force. Simply put, the greater μ_k the greater the friction; the smaller μ_k the smaller the friction.

TABLE 6–1 Typical Coefficients of Friction

Materials	Kinetic, μ_k	Static, μ_s
Rubber on concrete (dry)	0.80	1–4
Steel on steel	0.57	0.74
Glass on glass	0.40	0.94
Wood on leather	0.40	0.50
Copper on steel	0.36	0.53
Rubber on concrete (wet)	0.25	0.30
Steel on ice	0.06	0.10
Waxed ski on snow	0.05	0.10
Teflon on Teflon	0.04	0.04
Synovial joints in humans	0.003	0.01

As we know from everyday experience, the force of kinetic friction tends to oppose motion, as shown in Figure 6–2. Thus, $f_k = \mu_k N$ is not a vector equation, because N is perpendicular to the direction of motion. When doing calculations with the force of kinetic friction, we use $f_k = \mu_k N$ to find its magnitude, and we draw its direction so that it is opposite to the direction of motion.

There are two more friction experiments of particular interest. First, suppose that when we pull a brick, we initially pull it at the speed v, then later at the speed $2v$. What forces do we measure? It turns out that the force of kinetic friction is approximately the same in each case—it certainly does not double when we double the speed. Second, let's try standing the brick on end, so that it has a smaller area in contact with the table. If this smaller area is half the previous area, is the force halved? No, the force remains essentially the same, regardless of the area of contact.

We summarize these observations with the following three rules of thumb for kinetic friction:

Rules of Thumb for Kinetic Friction

The force of kinetic friction between two surfaces is:

1. Proportional to the magnitude of the normal force, N, between the surfaces:

$$f_k = \mu_k N$$

2. Independent of the relative speed of the surfaces.

3. Independent of the area of contact between the surfaces.

▲ Friction plays an important role in almost everything we do. Sometimes it is desirable to reduce friction; in other cases we want as much friction as possible. For example, it is more fun to ride on a water slide (upper) if the friction is low. Similarly, an engine operates more efficiently when it is oiled. When running, however, we need friction to help us speed up, slow down, and make turns. The sole of this running shoe (lower), like a car tire, is designed to maximize friction.

Again, these rules are useful and fairly accurate, though they are still only approximate. For simplicity, when we do calculations involving kinetic friction in this text, we will use these rules as if they were exact.

Before we show how to use f_k in calculations, we should make a comment regarding rule 3. This rule often seems rather surprising and counterintuitive. How is it that a larger area of contact doesn't produce a larger force? One way to think about this is to consider that when the area of contact is large, the normal force is spread out over a large area, giving a small force per area, F/A. As a result, the microscopic hills and valleys are not pressed too deeply against one another. On the other hand, if the area is small, the normal force is concentrated in a small region, which presses the surfaces together more firmly, due to the large force per area. The net effect is roughly the same in either case.

Now, let's consider a commonly encountered situation in which kinetic friction plays a decisive role.

EXAMPLE 6–1   PASS THE SALT—PLEASE

Someone at the other end of the table asks you to pass the salt. Feeling quite dashing, you slide the 50.0-g salt shaker in their direction, giving it an initial speed of 1.15 m/s. **(a)** If the shaker comes to rest with constant acceleration in 0.840 m, what is the coefficient of kinetic friction between the shaker and the table? **(b)** How much time is required for the shaker to come to rest if you slide it with an initial speed of 1.32 m/s?

PICTURE THE PROBLEM

We choose the positive x direction to be the direction of motion, and the positive y direction to be upward. Two forces act in the y direction; the shaker's weight, $\vec{W} = -W\hat{y} = -mg\hat{y}$, and the normal force, $\vec{N} = N\hat{y}$. Only one force acts in the x direction: the force of kinetic friction, $\vec{f}_k = -\mu_k N\hat{x}$. Note that the shaker moves through a distance of 0.840 m with an initial speed $v_{0x} = 1.15$ m/s.

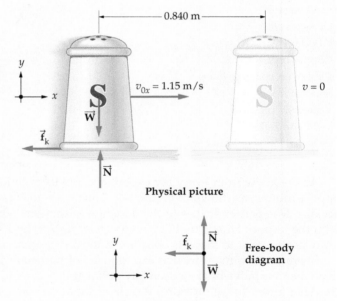

Physical picture

Free-body diagram

STRATEGY

a. Since the frictional force has a magnitude of $f_k = \mu_k N$, it follows that $\mu_k = f_k/N$. Therefore, we need to find the magnitudes of the frictional force, f_k, and the normal force, N. To find f_k we set $\Sigma F_x = ma_x$, and find a_x with the kinematic equation $v_x{}^2 = v_{0x}{}^2 + 2a_x\Delta x$. To find N we set $a_y = 0$ (since there is no motion in the y direction) and solve for N using $\Sigma F_y = ma_y = 0$.

b. The coefficient of kinetic friction is independent of the sliding speed, and hence the acceleration of the shaker is also independent of the speed. As a result, we can use the acceleration from part (a) in the relation $v_x = v_{0x} + a_x t$ to find the sliding time.

SOLUTION

Part (a)

1. Set $\Sigma F_x = ma_x$ to find f_k in terms of a_x:

$$\Sigma F_x = -f_k = ma_x \quad \text{or} \quad f_k = -ma_x$$

2. Determine a_x by using the kinematic equation relating velocity to position, $v_x{}^2 = v_{0x}{}^2 + 2a_x\Delta x$:

$$v_x{}^2 = v_{0x}{}^2 + 2a_x\Delta x$$
$$a_x = \frac{v_x{}^2 - v_{0x}{}^2}{2\Delta x} = \frac{0 - (1.15 \text{ m/s})^2}{2(0.840 \text{ m})} = -0.787 \text{ m/s}^2$$

3. Set $\Sigma F_y = ma_y = 0$ to find the normal force, N:

$$\Sigma F_y = N + (-W) = ma_y = 0 \quad \text{or} \quad N = W = mg$$

4. Substitute $N = mg$ and $f_k = -ma_x$ (with $a_x = -0.787$ m/s^2) into $\mu_k = f_k/N$ to find μ_k:

$$\mu_k = \frac{f_k}{N} = \frac{-ma_x}{mg} = \frac{-a_x}{g} = \frac{-(-0.787 \text{ m/s}^2)}{9.81 \text{ m/s}^2} = 0.0802$$

Part (b)

5. Use $a_x = -0.787 \text{ m/s}^2$, $v_{0x} = 1.32 \text{ m/s}$, and $v_x = 0$ in
$v_x = v_{0x} + a_x t$ to solve for the time, t:

$$v_x = v_{0x} + a_x t \quad \text{or}$$

$$t = \frac{v_x - v_{0x}}{a_x} = \frac{0 - (1.32 \text{ m/s})}{-0.787 \text{ m/s}^2} = 1.68 \text{ s}$$

INSIGHT

Note that m canceled in Step 4, so our result for the coefficient of friction is independent of the shaker's mass. For example, if we were to slide a shaker with twice the mass, but with the same initial speed, it would slide the same distance. It is unlikely this independence would have been apparent if we had worked the problem numerically rather than symbolically. Part (b) shows that the same comments apply to the sliding time—it too is independent of the shaker's mass.

PRACTICE PROBLEM

Given the same initial speed and a coefficient of kinetic friction equal to 0.120, what are **(a)** the acceleration of the shaker, and **(b)** the distance it slides? [**Answer: (a)** $a_x = -1.18 \text{ m/s}^2$, **(b)** 0.560 m]

Some related homework problems: Problem 3, Problem 18

In the next Example we consider a system that is inclined at an angle θ relative to the horizontal. As a result, the normal force responsible for the kinetic friction is less than the weight of the object. To be very clear about how we handle the force vectors in such a case, we begin by resolving each vector into its x and y components.

PROBLEM-SOLVING NOTE

Choice of Coordinate System: Incline

On an incline, align one axis (x) parallel to the surface, and the other axis (y) perpendicular to the surface. That way the motion is in the x direction. Since no motion occurs in the y direction, we know that $a_y = 0$.

EXAMPLE 6–2   MAKING A BIG SPLASH

A trained sea lion slides from rest with constant acceleration down a 3.0-m-long ramp into a pool of water. If the ramp is inclined at an angle of 23° above the horizontal and the coefficient of kinetic friction between the sea lion and the ramp is 0.26, how long does it take for the sea lion to make a splash in the pool?

PICTURE THE PROBLEM

As is usual with inclined surfaces, we choose one axis to be parallel to the surface and the other to be perpendicular to it. In our sketch, the sea lion accelerates in the positive x direction ($a_x > 0$), having started from rest, $v_{0x} = 0$. We are free to choose the initial position of the sea lion to be $x_0 = 0$. There is no motion in the y direction, and therefore $a_y = 0$. Finally, we note from the free-body diagram that $\vec{\mathbf{N}} = N\hat{\mathbf{y}}$, $\vec{\mathbf{f}}_k = -\mu_k N\hat{\mathbf{x}}$, and $\vec{\mathbf{W}} = (mg \sin \theta)\hat{\mathbf{x}} + (-mg \cos \theta)\hat{\mathbf{y}}$.

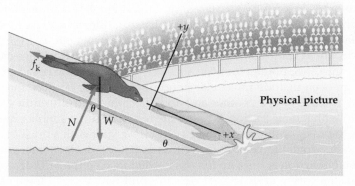

Physical picture

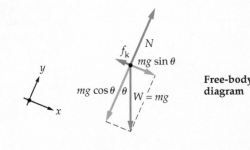

Free-body diagram

STRATEGY

We can use the kinematic equation relating position to time, $x = x_0 + v_{0x} t + \frac{1}{2} a_x t^2$, to find the time of the sea lion's slide. It will be necessary, however, to first determine the acceleration of the sea lion in the x direction, a_x.

To find a_x we apply Newton's second law to the sea lion. First, we can find N by setting $\Sigma F_y = ma_y$ equal to zero (since $a_y = 0$). It is important to start by finding N because we need it to find the force of kinetic friction, $f_k = \mu_k N$. Using f_k in the sum of forces in the x direction, $\Sigma F_x = ma_x$, allows us to solve for a_x and, finally, for the time.

CONTINUED ON NEXT PAGE

CONTINUED FROM PREVIOUS PAGE

SOLUTION

1. We begin by resolving each of the three force vectors into x and y components:

$$N_x = 0 \qquad\qquad N_y = N$$
$$f_{k,x} = -f_k = -\mu_k N \qquad f_{k,y} = 0$$
$$W_x = mg \sin\theta \qquad\qquad W_y = -mg\cos\theta$$

2. Set $\Sigma F_y = ma_y = 0$ to find N:

   We see that N is less than the weight, mg:

$$\Sigma F_y = N - mg\cos\theta = ma_y = 0$$
$$N = mg\cos\theta$$

3. Next, set $\Sigma F_x = ma_x$:

   Note that the mass cancels in this equation:

$$\Sigma F_x = mg\sin\theta - \mu_k$$
$$= mg\sin\theta - \mu_k mg\cos\theta = ma_x$$

4. Solve for the acceleration in the x direction, a_x:

$$a_x = g(\sin\theta - \mu_k\cos\theta)$$
$$= (9.81 \text{ m/s}^2)[\sin 23° - (0.26)\cos 23°]$$
$$= 1.5 \text{ m/s}^2$$

5. Use $x = x_0 + v_{0x}t + \frac{1}{2}a_x t^2$ to find the time when the sea lion reaches the bottom. We choose $x_0 = 0$, and we are given that $v_{0x} = 0$, hence we set $x = \frac{1}{2}a_x t^2 = 3.0$ m and solve for t:

$$x = \frac{1}{2}a_x t^2$$
$$t = \sqrt{\frac{2x}{a_x}} = \sqrt{\frac{2(3.0 \text{ m})}{1.5 \text{ m/s}^2}} = 2.0 \text{ s}$$

INSIGHT

Note that we don't need the sea lion's mass to find the time. On the other hand, if we wanted the magnitude of the force of kinetic friction, $f_k = \mu_k N = \mu_k mg\cos\theta$, the mass would be needed.

It is useful to compare the sliding salt shaker in Example 6–1 with the sliding sea lion in this Example. In the case of the salt shaker, friction is the only force acting along the direction of motion (opposite to the direction of motion, in fact), and it brings the object to rest. Because of the slope on which the sea lion slides, however, it experiences both a component of its weight in the forward direction and the friction force opposite to the motion. Since the component of the weight is the larger of the two forces, the sea lion accelerates down the slope—friction only acts to slow its progress.

PRACTICE PROBLEM

How long would it take the sea lion to reach the water if there were no friction in this system?   [**Answer:** 1.3 s]

Some related homework problems: Problem 11, Problem 72

Static Friction

Static friction tends to keep two surfaces from moving relative to one another. It, like kinetic friction, is due to the microscopic irregularities of surfaces that are in contact. In fact, static friction is typically stronger than kinetic friction because when surfaces are in static contact, their microscopic hills and valleys can nestle down deeply into one another, thus forming a strong connection between the surfaces that may even include molecular bonding. In kinetic friction, the surfaces bounce along relative to one another and don't become as firmly enmeshed.

As we did with kinetic friction, let's use the results of some simple experiments to determine the rules of thumb for static friction. We start with a brick at rest on a table, with no horizontal force pulling on it, as in **Figure 6–3**. Of course, in this case the force of static friction is zero; no force is needed to keep the brick from sliding.

Next, attach a spring scale to the brick and pull with a small force of magnitude F_1, a force small enough that the brick doesn't move. Since the brick is still at rest, it follows that the force of static friction, f_s, is equal in magnitude to the applied force; that is, $f_s = F_1$. Now, increase the applied force to a new value, F_2, which is still small enough that the brick stays at rest. In this case, the force of static friction has also increased so that $f_s = F_2$. If we continue increasing the applied force, we eventually reach a value beyond which the brick starts to move and kinetic friction takes over, as shown in the figure. Thus, there is an upper limit to the force that can be exerted by static friction, and we call this upper limit $f_{s,max}$.

Static friction can have a magnitude of zero ...

$v = 0$

$\vec{f}_s = 0$

... or greater than zero ...

$v = 0$

$\vec{f}_s = -\vec{F}_1$ $\vec{F}_1$

... up to a maximum value.

$v = 0$

$\vec{f}_s = -\vec{F}_2$ $\vec{F}_2$

Once sliding begins, however, the friction is kinetic and has a magnitude less than the maximum value for static friction.

v

$\vec{f}_k$ $\vec{F}$

◀ **FIGURE 6–3 The maximum limit of static friction**

As the force applied to an object increases, so does the force of static friction—up to a certain point. Beyond this maximum value, static friction can no longer hold the object, and it begins to slide. Now kinetic friction takes over.

To summarize, the force of static friction, f_s, can have any value between zero and $f_{s,max}$. This can be written mathematically as follows:

$$0 \leq f_s \leq f_{s,max} \qquad 6\text{--}2$$

Imagine repeating the experiment, only now with a second brick on top of the first. This doubles the normal force and it also doubles the maximum force of static friction. Thus, the maximum force is proportional to the magnitude of the normal force, or

$$f_{s,max} = \mu_s N \qquad 6\text{--}3$$

The constant of proportionality is called μ_s (pronounced "mew sub s"), the **coefficient of static friction.** Note that μ_s, like μ_k, is dimensionless. Typical values are given in Table 6–1. In most cases, μ_s is greater than μ_k, indicating that the force of static friction is greater than the force of kinetic friction, as mentioned. In fact, it is not uncommon for μ_s to be greater than 1, as in the case of rubber in contact with dry concrete.

Finally, two additional comments regarding the nature of static friction: (i) Experiments show that static friction, like kinetic friction, is independent of the area of contact. (ii) The force of static friction is not in the direction of the normal force, thus $f_{s,max} = \mu_s N$ is not a vector relation. The direction of f_s is parallel to the surface of contact, and opposite to the direction the object would move if there were no friction.

These observations are summarized in the following rules of thumb:

Rules of Thumb for Static Friction

The force of static friction between two surfaces has the following properties:

1. It takes on any value between zero and the maximum possible force of static friction, $f_{s,max} = \mu_s N$:

$$0 \leq f_s \leq \mu_s N$$

2. It is independent of the area of contact between the surfaces.

3. It is parallel to the surface of contact, and in the direction that opposes relative motion.

▲ The coefficient of static friction between two surfaces depends on many factors, including whether the surfaces are dry or wet. On the desert floor of Death Valley, California, occasional rains can reduce the friction between rocks and the sandy ground to such an extent that strong winds can move the rocks over considerable distances. This results in linear "rock trails," which record the direction of the winds at different times.

Next, we consider a practical method of determining the coefficient of static friction. As with the last Example, we begin by resolving all relevant force vectors into their x and y components.

EXAMPLE 6-3   SLIGHTLY TILTED

A flatbed truck slowly tilts its bed upward to dispose of a 95.0-kg crate. For small angles of tilt the crate stays put, but when the tilt angle exceeds 23.2°, the crate begins to slide. What is the coefficient of static friction between the bed of the truck and the crate?

PICTURE THE PROBLEM

We align our coordinate system with the incline, and choose the positive x direction to point down the slope. Note that three forces act on the crate: the normal force, $\vec{N} = N\hat{y}$, the force of static friction, $\vec{f}_s = -\mu_s N\hat{x}$, and the weight, $\vec{W} = (mg \sin \theta)\hat{x} + (-mg \cos \theta)\hat{y}$.

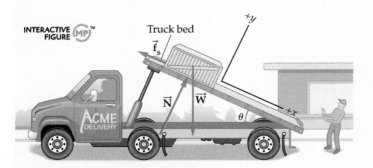

Physical picture

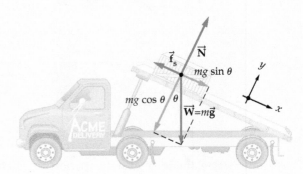

Free-body diagram

STRATEGY

When the crate is on the verge of slipping, but has not yet slipped, its acceleration is zero in both the x and y directions. In addition, "verge of slipping" means that the magnitude of the static friction is at its maximum value, $f_s = f_{s,max} = \mu_s N$. Thus, we set $\Sigma F_y = ma_y = 0$ to find N, then use $\Sigma F_x = ma_x = 0$ to find μ_s.

SOLUTION

1. Resolve the three force vectors acting on the crate into x and y components:

$$N_x = 0 \qquad\qquad N_y = N$$
$$f_{s,x} = -f_{s,max} = -\mu_s N \qquad f_{s,y} = 0$$
$$W_x = mg \sin \theta \qquad\qquad W_y = -mg \cos \theta$$

2. Set $\Sigma F_y = ma_y = 0$, since $a_y = 0$.

$$\sum F_y = N_y + f_{s,y} + W_y = N + 0 - mg \cos \theta = ma_y = 0$$

Solve for the normal force, N:

$$N = mg \cos \theta$$

3. Set $\Sigma F_x = ma_x = 0$, since the crate is at rest, and use the result for N obtained in Step 2:

$$\sum F_x = N_x + f_{s,x} + W_x = ma_x = 0$$
$$= 0 - \mu_s N + mg \sin \theta$$
$$= 0 - \mu_s mg \cos \theta + mg \sin \theta$$

4. Solve the expression for the coefficient of static friction, μ_s:

$$\mu_s mg \cos \theta = mg \sin \theta$$
$$\mu_s = \frac{mg \sin \theta}{mg \cos \theta} = \tan \theta = \tan 23.2° = 0.429$$

INSIGHT

In general, if an object is on the verge of slipping when the surface on which it rests is tilted at an angle θ_c, the coefficient of static friction between the object and the surface is $\mu_s = \tan \theta_c$. Note that this result is independent of the mass of the object. In particular, the critical angle for this crate is precisely the same whether it is filled with feathers or lead bricks.

PRACTICE PROBLEM

Find the magnitude of the force of static friction acting on the crate.   [**Answer:** $f_{s,max} = \mu_s N = 367$ N]

Some related homework problems: Problem 12, Problem 82

◀ The angle that the sloping sides of a sand pile (left) make with the horizontal is determined by the coefficient of static friction between grains of sand, in much the same way that static friction determines the angle at which the crate in Example 6–3 begins to slide. The same basic mechanism determines the angle of the cone-shaped mass of rock debris at the base of a cliff, known as a talus slope (right).

Recall that static friction can have magnitudes less than its maximum possible value. This point is emphasized in the following Active Example.

ACTIVE EXAMPLE 6–1   THE FORCE OF STATIC FRICTION

In the previous Example, what is the magnitude of the force of static friction acting on the crate when the truck bed is tilted at an angle of 20.0°?

SOLUTION *(Test your understanding by performing the calculations indicated in each step.)*

1. Sum the x components of force acting on the crate:

$$\sum F_x = 0 - f_s + mg \sin \theta$$

2. Set this sum equal to zero (since $a_x = 0$) and solve for the magnitude of the static friction force, f_s:

$$f_s = mg \sin \theta$$

3. Substitute numerical values, including $\theta = 20.0°$:

$$f_s = 319 \text{ N}$$

INSIGHT

Notice that the force of static friction in this case has a magnitude (319 N) that is less than the value of 367 N found in the Practice Problem of Example 6–3, even though the coefficient of static friction is precisely the same.

YOUR TURN

At what tilt angle will the force of static friction have a magnitude of 225 N?

*(Answers to **Your Turn** problems are given in the back of the book.)*

Finally, friction often enters into problems dealing with vehicles with rolling wheels. In Conceptual Checkpoint 6–1, we consider which type of friction is appropriate in such cases.

CONCEPTUAL CHECKPOINT 6–1   FRICTION FOR ROLLING TIRES

A car drives with its tires rolling freely. Is the friction between the tires and the road **(a)** kinetic or **(b)** static?

REASONING AND DISCUSSION

A reasonable-sounding answer is that because the car is moving, the friction between its tires and the road must be kinetic friction—but this is not the case.

Actually, the friction is static because the bottom of the tire is in static contact with the road. To understand this, watch your feet as you walk. Even though you are moving, each foot is in static contact with the ground once you step down on it. Your foot doesn't move again until you lift it up and move it forward for the next step. A tire can be thought of as a succession of feet arranged in a circle, each of which is momentarily in static contact with the ground.

ANSWER

(b) The friction between the tires and the road is static friction.

(a) Front wheels locked; rear wheels free to turn

(b) Rear wheels locked; front wheels free to turn

▲ **Static Versus Kinetic Friction** Each of the two photos above shows five images of a toy car as it slides down an inclined surface. **(a)** In this photo the front wheels are locked, and skid on the surface, but the rear wheels roll without slipping. This means the front wheels experience kinetic friction and the rear wheels experience static friction. Because the force of kinetic friction is usually less than the force of static friction, the front wheels go down the incline first, pulling the rear wheels behind. **(b)** The situation is reversed in this photo, and the rear wheels are the ones that skid and experience a smaller frictional force. As a result, the rear wheels slide down the incline more quickly than the front wheels, causing the car to spin around. This change in behavior, which could be dangerous in a real-life situation, illustrates the significant differences between static and kinetic friction.

To summarize, if a car skids, the friction acting on it is kinetic; if its wheels are rolling, the friction is static. Since static friction is generally greater than kinetic friction, it follows that a car can be stopped in less distance if its wheels are rolling (static friction) than if its wheels are locked up (kinetic friction). This is the idea behind the antilock braking systems (ABS) that are available on many cars. When the brakes are applied in a car with ABS, an electronic rotation sensor at each wheel detects whether the wheel is about to start skidding. To prevent skidding, a small computer automatically begins to modulate the hydraulic pressure in the brake lines in short bursts, causing the brakes to release and then reapply in rapid succession. This allows the wheels to continue rotating, even in an emergency stop, and for static friction to determine the stopping distance. **Figure 6–4** shows a comparison of braking distances for cars with and without ABS. An added benefit of ABS is that a driver is better able to steer and control a braking car if its wheels are rotating.

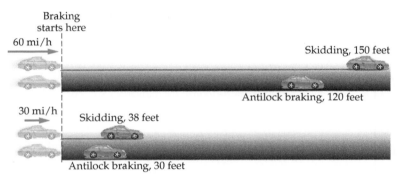

Braking starts here

60 mi/h

Skidding, 150 feet

Antilock braking, 120 feet

30 mi/h

Skidding, 38 feet

Antilock braking, 30 feet

▲ **FIGURE 6–4 Stopping distance with and without ABS**
Antilock braking systems (ABS) allow a car to stop with static friction rather than kinetic friction—even in a case where a person slams on the brakes. As a result, the braking distance is reduced, due to the fact that μ_s is typically greater than μ_k. Professional drivers can beat the performance of ABS by carefully adjusting the force they apply to the brake pedal during a stop, but ABS provides essentially the same performance—within a few percent—for a person who simply pushes the brake pedal to the floor and holds it there.

6–2 Strings and Springs

A common way to exert a force on an object is to pull on it with a string, a rope, a cable, or a wire. Similarly, you can push or pull on an object if you attach it to a spring. In this section we discuss the basic features of strings and springs and how they transmit forces.

Strings and Tension

Imagine picking up a light string and holding it with one end in each hand. If you pull to the right with your right hand with a force T and to the left with your left hand with a force T, the string becomes taut. In such a case, we say that there is a **tension** T in the string. To be more specific, if your friend were to cut the string at some point, the tension T is the force pulling the ends apart, as illustrated in **Figure 6–5**—that is, T is the force your friend would have to exert with each hand to hold the cut ends together. Note that at any given point, the tension pulls equally to the right and to the left.

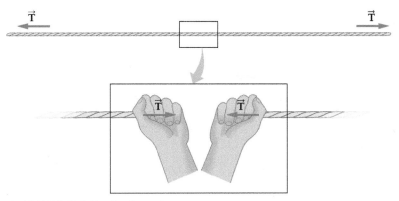

▲ **FIGURE 6–5 Tension in a string**
A string, pulled from either end, has a tension, T. If the string were to be cut at any point, the force required to hold the ends together is T.

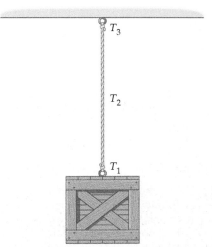

▲ **FIGURE 6–6 Tension in a heavy rope**
Because of the weight of the rope, the tension is noticeably different at points 1, 2, and 3. As the rope becomes lighter, however, the difference in tension decreases. In the limit of a rope of zero mass, the tension is the same throughout the rope.

As an example, consider a rope that is attached to the ceiling at one end, and to a box with a weight of 105 N at the other end, as shown in **Figure 6–6**. In addition, suppose the rope is uniform, and that it has a total weight of 2.00 N. What is the tension in the rope (i) where it attaches to the box, (ii) at its midpoint, and (iii) where it attaches to the ceiling?

First, the rope holds the box at rest; thus, the tension where the rope attaches to the box is simply the weight of the box, $T_1 = 105$ N. At the midpoint of the rope, the tension supports the weight of the box, plus the weight of half the rope. Thus, $T_2 = 105$ N $+ \frac{1}{2}(2.00$ N$) = 106$ N. Similarly, at the ceiling the tension supports the box plus all of the rope, giving a tension of $T_3 = 107$ N. Note that the tension pulls down on the ceiling but pulls up on the box.

From this discussion, we can see that the tension in the rope changes slightly from top to bottom because of the mass of the rope. If the rope had less mass, the difference in tension between its two ends would also be less. In particular, if the rope's mass were to be vanishingly small, the difference in tension would vanish as well. In this text, we will assume that all ropes, strings, wires, and so on are practically massless—unless specifically stated otherwise—and, hence, that the tension is the same throughout their length.

Pulleys are often used to redirect a force exerted by a string, as indicated in **Figure 6–7**. In the ideal case, a pulley has no mass and no friction in its bearings. Thus, *an ideal pulley simply changes the direction of the tension in a string, without changing its magnitude.* If a system contains more than one pulley, however, it is possible to arrange them in such a way as to "magnify a force," even if each pulley itself merely redirects the tension in a string. The traction device considered in the next Example shows one way this can be accomplished in a system that uses three ideal pulleys.

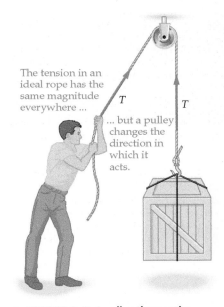

The tension in an ideal rope has the same magnitude everywhere ... T ... but a pulley changes the direction in which it acts. T

▲ **FIGURE 6–7 A pulley changes the direction of a tension**

EXAMPLE 6–4   A BAD BREAK: SETTING A BROKEN LEG WITH TRACTION

A traction device employing three pulleys is applied to a broken leg, as shown in the sketch. The middle pulley is attached to the sole of the foot, and a mass m supplies the tension in the ropes. Find the value of the mass m if the force exerted on the sole of the foot by the middle pulley is to be 165 N.

CONTINUED ON NEXT PAGE

CONTINUED FROM PREVIOUS PAGE

PICTURE THE PROBLEM
Our sketch shows the physical picture as well as the tension forces acting on the middle pulley. Notice that on the upper portion of the rope the tension is $\vec{T}_1 = (T \cos 40.0°)\hat{x} + (T \sin 40.0°)\hat{y}$; on the lower portion it is $\vec{T}_2 = (T \cos 40.0°)\hat{x} + (-T \sin 40.0°)\hat{y}$.

STRATEGY
We begin by noting that the rope supports the hanging mass m. As a result, the tension in the rope, T, must be equal in magnitude to the weight of the mass: $T = mg$.

Next, the pulleys simply change the direction of the tension without changing its magnitude. Therefore, the net force exerted on the sole of the foot is the sum of the tension T at 40.0° above the horizontal plus the tension T at 40.0° below the horizontal. We will calculate the net force component by component.

Once we calculate the net force acting on the foot, we set it equal to 165 N and solve for the tension T. Finally, we find the mass using the relation $T = mg$.

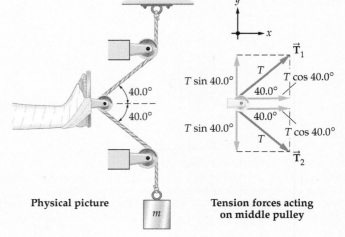

Physical picture   **Tension forces acting on middle pulley**

SOLUTION

1. First, consider the tension that acts upward and to the right on the middle pulley. Resolve this tension into x and y components:

$$T_{1,x} = T \cos 40.0° \qquad T_{1,y} = T \sin 40.0°$$

2. Next, consider the tension that acts downward and to the right on the middle pulley. Resolve this tension into x and y components. Note the minus sign in the y component:

$$T_{2,x} = T \cos 40.0° \qquad T_{2,y} = -T \sin 40.0°$$

3. Sum the x and y components of force acting on the middle pulley. We see that the net force acts only in the x direction, as one might expect from symmetry:

$$\sum F_x = T \cos 40.0° + T \cos 40.0° = 2T \cos 40.0°$$

$$\sum F_y = T \sin 40.0° - T \sin 40.0° = 0$$

4. Step 3 shows that the net force acting on the middle pulley is $2T \cos 40.0°$. Set this force equal to 165 N and solve for T:

$$2T \cos 40.0° = 165 \text{ N}$$

$$T = \frac{165 \text{ N}}{2 \cos 40.0°} = 108 \text{ N}$$

5. Solve for the mass, m, using $T = mg$:

$$T = mg$$

$$m = \frac{T}{g} = \frac{108 \text{ N}}{9.81 \text{ m/s}^2} = 11.0 \text{ kg}$$

INSIGHT
As pointed out earlier, this pulley arrangement "magnifies the force" in the sense that a 108-N weight attached to the rope produces a 165-N force exerted on the foot by the middle pulley. Note that the tension in the rope always has the same value—$T = 108$ N—as expected with ideal pulleys, but because of the arrangement of the pulleys the force applied to the foot by the rope is $2T \cos 40.0° > T$.

In addition, notice that the force exerted on the foot by the middle pulley produces an opposing force in the leg that acts in the direction of the head (a cephalad force), as desired to set a broken leg and keep it straight as it heals.

PRACTICE PROBLEM
(a) Would the required mass m increase or decrease if the angles in this device were changed from 40.0° to 30.0°? (b) Find the mass m for an angle of 30.0°.   [**Answer: (a)** The required mass m would decrease. **(b)** 9.71 kg]

Some related homework problems: Problem 23, Problem 26, Problem 36

CONCEPTUAL CHECKPOINT 6–2   COMPARE THE READINGS ON THE SCALES

The scale at left reads 9.81 N. Is the reading of the scale at right **(a)** greater than 9.81 N, **(b)** equal to 9.81 N, or **(c)** less than 9.81 N?

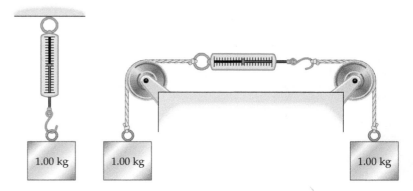

1.00 kg   1.00 kg   1.00 kg

REASONING AND DISCUSSION

Since a pulley simply changes the direction of the tension in a string without changing its magnitude, it is clear that the scale attached to the ceiling reads the same as the scale shown in the figure to the right.

There is no difference, however, between attaching the top end of the scale to something rigid and attaching it to another 1.00-kg hanging mass. In either case, the fact that the scale is at rest means that a force of 9.81 N must be exerted to the left on the top of the scale to balance the 9.81-N force exerted on the lower end of the scale. As a result, the two scales read the same.

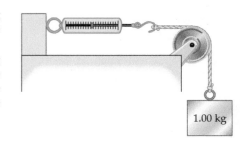

1.00 kg

ANSWER

(b) The reading of the scale at right is equal to 9.81 N.

Springs and Hooke's Law

Suppose you take a spring of length L, as shown in **Figure 6–8 (a)**, and attach it to a block. If you pull on the spring, causing it to stretch to a length $L + x$, the spring pulls on the block with a force of magnitude F. If you increase the length of the spring to $L + 2x$, the force exerted by the spring increases to $2F$. Similarly, if you compress the spring to a length $L - x$, the spring pushes on the block with a force of magnitude F, where F is the same force given previously. As you might expect, compression to a length $L - 2x$ results in a push of magnitude $2F$.

As a result of these experiments, we can say that a spring exerts a force that is proportional to the amount, x, by which it is stretched or compressed. Thus, if F is the magnitude of the spring force, we can say that

$$F = kx$$

In this expression, k is a constant of proportionality, referred to as the **force constant,** or, equivalently, as the **spring constant.** Since F has units of newtons and x has units of meters, it follows that k has units of newtons per meter, or N/m. The larger the value of k, the stiffer the spring.

To be more precise, consider the spring shown in **Figure 6–8 (b)**. Note that we have placed the origin of the x axis at the equilibrium length of the spring—that is, at the position of the spring when no force acts on it. Now, if we stretch the spring so that the end of the spring is at a positive value of x ($x > 0$), we find that the spring exerts a force of magnitude kx in the negative x direction. Thus, the spring force (which has only an x component) can be written as

$$F_x = -kx$$

Similarly, consider compressing the spring so that its end is at a negative value of x ($x < 0$). In this case, the force exerted by the spring is of magnitude kx, and points in the positive x direction, as is shown in Figure 6–8 (b). Again, we can write the spring force as

$$F_x = -kx$$

▶ **FIGURE 6–8 The force exerted by a spring**

When dealing with a spring, it is convenient to choose the origin at the equilibrium (zero force) position. In the cases shown here, the force is strictly in the x direction, and is given by $F_x = -kx$. Note that the minus sign means that the force is opposite to the displacement; that is, the force is restoring.

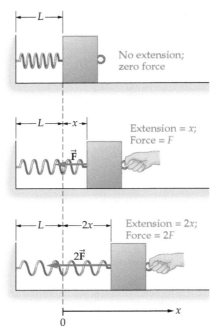

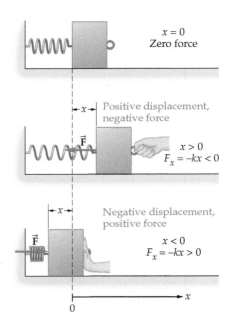

(a) Doubling the extension doubles the force.

(b) The spring force is opposite to the displacement from equilibrium.

▲ Springs come in a variety of sizes and shapes. The large springs on a railroad car (top) are so stiff and heavy that you can't compress or stretch them by hand. Still, three of them are needed to smooth the ride of this car. In contrast, the delicate spiral spring inside a watch (bottom) flexes with even the slightest touch. It exerts enough force, however, to power the equally delicate mechanism of the watch.

To see that this is correct—that is, that F_x is positive in this case—recall that x is negative, which means that $(-x)$ is positive.

This result for the force of a spring is known as Hooke's law, after Robert Hooke (1635–1703). It is really just a good rule of thumb rather than a law of nature. Clearly, it can't work for any amount of stretching. For example, we know that if we stretch a spring far enough it will be permanently deformed, and will never return to its original length. Still, for small stretches or compressions, Hooke's law is quite accurate.

Rules of Thumb for Springs (Hooke's Law)

A spring stretched or compressed by the amount x from its equilibrium length exerts a force whose x component is given by

$$F_x = -kx \text{ (gives magnitude and direction)} \qquad 6\text{–}4$$

If we are interested only in the magnitude of the force associated with a given stretch or compression, we use the somewhat simpler form of Hooke's law:

$$F = kx \text{ (gives magnitude only)} \qquad 6\text{–}5$$

In this text, we consider only **ideal springs**—that is, springs that are massless, and that are assumed to obey Hooke's law exactly.

Since the stretch of a spring and the force it exerts are proportional, we can now see how a spring scale operates. In particular, pulling on the two ends of a scale stretches the spring inside it by an amount proportional to the applied force. Once the scale is calibrated—by stretching the spring with a known, or reference, force—we can use it to measure other unknown forces.

Finally, it is useful to note that Hooke's law, which we've introduced in the context of ideal springs, is particularly important in physics because it applies to so much more than just springs. For example, the forces that hold atoms together are often modeled by Hooke's law—that is, as "interatomic springs"—and these are the forces that are ultimately responsible for the normal force (Chapter 5), vibrations and oscillations (Chapter 13), wave motion (Chapter 14), and even the thermal expansion of solids (Chapter 16). And this just scratches the surface—Hooke's law comes up in one form or another in virtually every field of physics. In the following Active Example, we present a biomedical application of Hooke's law.

ACTIVE EXAMPLE 6–2   NASAL STRIPS

REAL-WORLD PHYSICS: BIO   An increasingly popular device for improving air flow through nasal passages is the nasal strip, which consists of two flat, polyester springs enclosed by an adhesive tape covering. Measurements show that a nasal strip can exert an outward force of 0.22 N on the nose, causing it to expand by 3.5 mm. **(a)** Treating the nose as an ideal spring, find its force constant in newtons per meter. **(b)** How much force would be required to expand the nose by 4.0 mm?

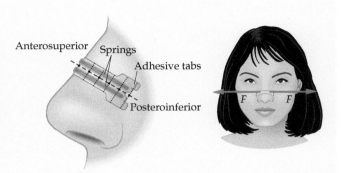

SOLUTION   *(Test your understanding by performing the calculations indicated in each step.)*

Part (a)

1. Solve the magnitude form of Hooke's law, $F = kx$, for the force constant, k: $\quad k = F/x$

2. Substitute numerical values for F and x: $\quad k = 62 \, \text{N/m}$

Part (b)

3. Use $F = kx$ to find the required force: $\quad F = 0.25 \, \text{N}$

INSIGHT
Even though the human nose is certainly not an ideal spring, Hooke's law is still a useful way to model its behavior when dealing with forces and the stretches they cause.

YOUR TURN
Suppose a new nasal strip comes on the market that exerts an outward force of 0.32 N. What expansion of the nose will be caused by this strip?

*(Answers to **Your Turn** problems are given in the back of the book.)*

6–3 Translational Equilibrium

When we say that an object is in **translational equilibrium,** we mean that the net force acting on it is zero:

$$\sum \vec{F} = 0 \qquad\qquad 6\text{–}6$$

From Newton's second law, this is equivalent to saying that the object's acceleration is zero. In two-dimensional systems, translational equilibrium implies two independent conditions: $\Sigma F_x = 0$ and $\Sigma F_y = 0$. In one dimension, only one of these conditions will apply.

Later, in Chapters 10 and 11, we will study objects that have both rotational and linear motions. In such cases, rotational equilibrium will be as important as translation equilibrium. For now, however, when we say equilibrium, we simply mean translational equilibrium.

As a first example, consider the one-dimensional situation illustrated in **Figure 6–9.** Here we see a person lifting a bucket of water from a well by pulling down on a rope that passes over a pulley. If the bucket's mass is m, and it is rising with constant speed v, what is the tension T_1 in the rope attached to the bucket? In addition, what is the tension T_2 in the chain that supports the pulley?

▶ **FIGURE 6–9 Raising a bucket**
A person lifts a bucket of water from the bottom of a well with a constant speed, v. Because the speed is constant, the net force acting on the bucket must be zero.

Physical picture

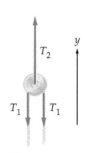

Forces acting on the pulley

Forces acting on the bucket

To answer these questions, we first note that both the bucket and the pulley are in equilibrium; that is, they both have zero acceleration. As a result, the net force on each of them must be zero.

Let's start with the bucket. In Figure 6–9, we see that just two forces act on the bucket: (i) its weight $W = mg$ downward, and (ii) the tension in the rope, T_1 upward. If we take upward to be the positive direction, we can write $\Sigma F_y = 0$ for the bucket as follows:

$$T_1 - mg = 0$$

Therefore, the tension in the rope is $T_1 = mg$. Note that this is also the force the person must exert downward on the rope, as expected.

Next, we consider the pulley. In Figure 6–9, we see that three forces act on it: (i) the tension in the chain, T_2 upward, (ii) the tension in the part of the rope leading to the bucket, T_1 downward, and (iii) the tension in the part of the rope leading to the person, T_1 downward. Note that we don't include the weight of the pulley since we consider it to be ideal; that is, massless and frictionless. If we again take upward to be positive, the statement that the net force acting on the pulley is zero ($\Sigma F_y = 0$) can be written

$$T_2 - T_1 - T_1 = 0$$

It follows that the tension in the chain is $T_2 = 2T_1 = 2mg$, twice the weight of the bucket of water!

In the next Conceptual Checkpoint we consider a slight variation of this situation.

CONCEPTUAL CHECKPOINT 6–3 COMPARING TENSIONS

A person hoists a bucket of water from a well and holds the rope, keeping the bucket at rest, as at left. A short time later, the person ties the rope to the bucket so that the rope holds the bucket in place, as at right. In this case, is the tension in the rope **(a)** greater than, **(b)** less than, or **(c)** equal to the tension in the first case?

REASONING AND DISCUSSION

In the first case (left), the only upward force exerted on the bucket is the tension in the rope. Since the bucket is at rest, the tension must be equal in magnitude to the weight of the bucket. In the second case (right), the two ends of the rope exert equal upward forces on the bucket, hence the tension in the rope is only half the weight of the bucket. To see this more clearly, imagine cutting the bucket in half so that each end of the rope supports half the weight, as indicated in the accompanying diagram.

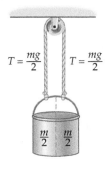

ANSWER

(b) The tension in the second case is less than in the first.

In the next two Examples, we consider two-dimensional systems in which forces act at various angles with respect to one another. Hence, our first step is to resolve the relevant vectors into their x and y components. Following that, we apply the conditions for translational equilibrium, $\Sigma F_x = 0$ and $\Sigma F_y = 0$.

EXAMPLE 6–5   SUSPENDED VEGETATION

To hang a 6.20-kg pot of flowers, a gardener uses two wires—one attached horizontally to a wall, the other sloping upward at an angle of $\theta = 40.0°$ and attached to the ceiling. Find the tension in each wire.

PICTURE THE PROBLEM

We choose a typical coordinate system, with the positive x direction to the right and the positive y direction upward. With this choice, tension 1 is in the positive x direction, $\vec{T}_1 = T_1\hat{x}$, the weight is in the negative y direction, $\vec{W} = -mg\hat{y}$, and tension 2 has a negative x component and a positive y component, $\vec{T}_2 = (-T_2 \cos\theta)\hat{x} + (T_2 \sin\theta)\hat{y}$.

STRATEGY

The pot is at rest, and therefore the net force acting on it is zero. As a result, we can say that (i) $\Sigma F_x = 0$ and (ii) $\Sigma F_y = 0$. These two conditions allow us to determine the magnitude of the two tensions, T_1 and T_2.

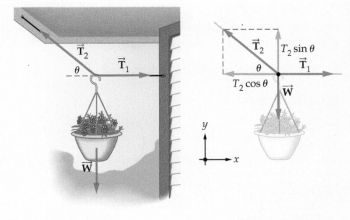

Physical picture   **Free-body diagram**

CONTINUED ON NEXT PAGE

CONTINUED FROM PREVIOUS PAGE

SOLUTION

1. First, resolve each of the forces acting on the pot into x and y components:

$$T_{1,x} = T_1 \qquad\qquad T_{1,y} = 0$$
$$T_{2,x} = -T_2 \cos\theta \qquad T_{2,y} = T_2 \sin\theta$$
$$W_x = 0 \qquad\qquad W_y = -mg$$

2. Now, set $\Sigma F_x = 0$. Note that this condition gives a relation between T_1 and T_2:

$$\Sigma F_x = T_{1,x} + T_{2,x} + W_x = T_1 + (-T_2 \cos\theta) + 0 = 0$$
$$T_1 = T_2 \cos\theta$$

3. Next, set $\Sigma F_y = 0$. This time, the resulting condition determines T_2 in terms of the weight, mg:

$$\Sigma F_y = T_{1,y} + T_{2,y} + W_y = 0 + T_2 \sin\theta + (-mg) = 0$$
$$T_2 \sin\theta = mg$$

4. Use the relation obtained in Step 3 to find T_2:

$$T_2 = \frac{mg}{\sin\theta} = \frac{(6.20\ \text{kg})(9.81\ \text{m/s}^2)}{\sin 40.0°} = 94.6\ \text{N}$$

5. Finally, use the connection between the two tensions (obtained from $\Sigma F_x = 0$) to find T_1:

$$T_1 = T_2 \cos\theta = (94.6\ \text{N}) \cos 40.0° = 72.5\ \text{N}$$

INSIGHT

Notice that even though two wires suspend the pot, they both have tensions *greater* than the pot's weight, $mg = 60.8\ \text{N}$. This is an important point for architects and engineers to consider when designing structures.

PRACTICE PROBLEM

Find T_1 and T_2 if the second wire slopes upward at the angle **(a)** $\theta = 20°$, **(b)** $\theta = 60.0°$, or **(c)** $\theta = 90.0°$.   [**Answer: (a)** $T_1 = 167\ \text{N}$, $T_2 = 178\ \text{N}$ **(b)** $T_1 = 35.1\ \text{N}$, $T_2 = 70.2\ \text{N}$ **(c)** $T_1 = 0$, $T_2 = mg = 60.8\ \text{N}$]

Some related homework problems: Problem 34, Problem 37

ACTIVE EXAMPLE 6–3   THE FORCES IN A LOW-TECH LAUNDRY

A 1.84-kg bag of clothespins hangs in the middle of a clothesline, causing it to sag by an angle $\theta = 3.50°$. Find the tension, T, in the clothesline.

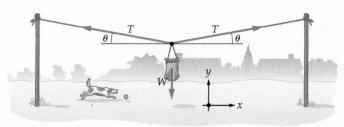

SOLUTION *(Test your understanding by performing the calculations indicated in each step.)*

1. Find the y component for each tension:

$$T_y = T \sin\theta$$

2. Find the y component of the weight:

$$W_y = -mg$$

3. Set $\Sigma F_y = 0$:

$$T \sin\theta + T \sin\theta - mg = 0$$

4. Solve for T:

$$T = mg/(2\sin\theta) = 148\ \text{N}$$

INSIGHT

Note that we only considered the y components of force in our calculation. This is because forces in the x direction automatically balance, due to the symmetry of the system.

YOUR TURN

At what sag angle, θ, will the tension in the clothesline have a magnitude of 175 N?

*(Answers to **Your Turn** problems are given in the back of the book.)*

At 148 N, the tension in the clothesline is quite large, especially when you consider that the weight of the clothespin bag itself is only 18.1 N. The reason for such a large value is that the vertical component of the two tensions is $2T \sin \theta$, which, for $\theta = 3.50°$, is $(0.122)T$. If $(0.122)T$ is to equal the weight of the bag, it is clear that T must be roughly eight times the bag's weight.

If you and a friend were to pull on the two ends of the clothesline, in an attempt to straighten it out, you would find that no matter how hard you pulled, the line would still sag. You may be able to reduce θ to quite a small value, but as you do so the corresponding tension increases rapidly. In principle, it would take an infinite force to completely straighten the line and reduce θ to zero.

On the other hand, if θ were 90°, so that the two halves of the clothesline were vertical, the tension would be $T = mg/(2 \sin 90°) = mg/2$. In this case, each side of the line supports half the weight of the bag, as expected.

6–4 Connected Objects

Interesting applications of Newton's laws arise when we consider accelerating objects that are tied together. Suppose, for example, that a force of magnitude F pulls two boxes—connected by a string—along a frictionless surface, as in **Figure 6–10**. In such a case, the string has a certain tension, T, and the two boxes have the same acceleration, a. Given the masses of the boxes and the applied force F, we would like to determine both the tension in the string and the acceleration of the boxes.

First, sketch the free-body diagram for each box. Box 1 has two horizontal forces acting on it: (i) the tension T to the left, and (ii) the force F to the right. Box 2 has only a single horizontal force, the tension T to the right. If we take the positive direction to be to the right, Newton's second law for the two boxes can be written as follows:

$$F - T = m_1 a_1 = m_1 a \qquad \text{box 1}$$
$$T = m_2 a_2 = m_2 a \qquad \text{box 2} \qquad \qquad \text{6–7}$$

Since the boxes have the same acceleration, a, we have set $a_1 = a_2 = a$.

Next, we can eliminate the tension T by adding the two equations:

$$\begin{aligned} F - T &= m_1 a \\ T &= m_2 a \\ \hline F &= (m_1 + m_2)a \end{aligned}$$

With this result, it is straightforward to solve for the acceleration in terms of the applied force F:

$$a = \frac{F}{m_1 + m_2} \qquad \qquad \text{6–8}$$

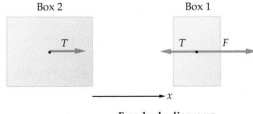

▲ Like the bag of clothespins in Active Example 6–3, this mountain climber is in static equilibrium. Since the ropes suspending the climber are nearly horizontal, the tension in them is significantly greater than the climber's weight.

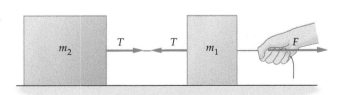

Physical picture

Free-body diagrams
(horizontal components only)

▲ **FIGURE 6–10 Two boxes connected by a string**
The string ensures that the two boxes have the same acceleration. This physical connection results in a mathematical connection, as shown in Equation 6–7. Note that in this case we treat each box as a separate system.

Finally, substitute this expression for a into either of the second-law equations to find the tension. The algebra is simpler if we use the equation for box 2. We find

$$T = m_2 a = \left(\frac{m_2}{m_1 + m_2}\right)F \qquad\qquad 6\text{--}9$$

It is left as an exercise to show that the equation for box 1 gives the same expression for T.

A second way to approach this problem is to treat both boxes together as a single system with a mass $m_1 + m_2$, as shown in **Figure 6–11**. The only *external* horizontal force acting on this system is the applied force F—the two tension forces are now *internal* to the system, and internal forces are not included when applying Newton's second law. As a result, the horizontal acceleration is simply $F/(m_1 + m_2)$, as given in Equation 6–8. This is certainly a quick way to find the acceleration a, but to find the tension T we must still use one of the relations given in Equations 6–7.

In general, we are always free to choose the "system" any way we like—we can choose any individual object, as when we considered box 1 and box 2 separately, or we can choose all the objects together. The important point is that Newton's second law is equally valid no matter what choice we make for the system, as long as we remember to include only forces *external* to *that system* in the corresponding free-body diagram.

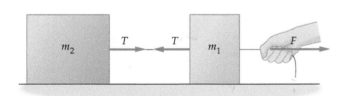

Physical picture

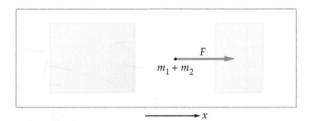

Free-body diagram
(horizontal components only)

▲ **FIGURE 6–11 Two boxes, one system**
In this case we consider the two boxes together as a single system of mass $m_1 + m_2$. The only external horizontal force acting on this system is $\vec{F}$; hence the horizontal acceleration of the system is $a = F/(m_1 + m_2)$, in agreement with Equation 6–8.

CONCEPTUAL CHECKPOINT 6–4 TENSION IN THE STRING

Two masses, m_1 and m_2, are connected by a string that passes over a pulley. Mass m_1 slides without friction on a horizontal tabletop, and mass m_2 falls vertically downward. Both masses move with a constant acceleration of magnitude a. Is the tension in the string **(a)** greater than, **(b)** equal to, or **(c)** less than $m_2 g$?

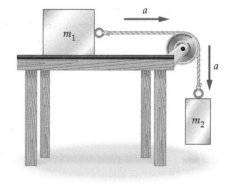

REASONING AND DISCUSSION
First, note that m_2 accelerates downward, which means that the net force acting on it is downward. Only two forces act on m_2, however: the tension in the string (upward) and its weight (downward). Since the net force is downward, the tension in the string must be less than the weight, $m_2 g$.

A common misconception is that since m_2 has to pull m_1 behind it, the tension in the string must be greater than $m_2 g$. Certainly, attaching the string to m_1 has an effect on the tension. If the string were not attached, for example, its tension would be zero. Hence, m_2 pulling on m_1 increases the tension to a value greater than zero, though still less than $m_2 g$.

ANSWER
(c) The tension in the string is less than $m_2 g$.

In the next Example, we verify the qualitative conclusions given in the Conceptual Checkpoint with a detailed calculation. But first, a note about choosing a coordinate system for a problem such as this. Rather than apply the same coordinate system to both masses, it is useful to take into consideration the fact that a pulley simply changes the direction of the tension in a string. With this in mind, we choose a set of axes that "follow the motion" of the string, so that both masses accelerate in the positive x direction with accelerations of equal magnitude. Example 6–6 illustrates the use of this type of coordinate system.

PROBLEM-SOLVING NOTE

Choice of Coordinate System: Connected Objects

If two objects are connected by a string passing over a pulley, let the coordinate system follow the direction of the string. With this choice, both objects have accelerations of the same magnitude and in the same coordinate direction.

EXAMPLE 6–6   CONNECTED BLOCKS

A block of mass m_1 slides on a frictionless tabletop. It is connected to a string that passes over a pulley and suspends a mass m_2. Find **(a)** the acceleration of the masses and **(b)** the tension in the string.

PICTURE THE PROBLEM
Our coordinate system follows the motion of the string so that both masses move in the positive x direction. Since the masses are connected, their accelerations have the same magnitude. Thus, $a_{1,x} = a_{2,x} = a$. In addition, note that the tension, $\vec{T}$, is in the positive x direction for mass 1, but in the negative x direction for mass 2. Its magnitude, T, is the same for each mass, however. Finally, the weight of mass 2, W_2, acts in the positive x direction, whereas the weight of mass 1 is offset by the normal force, N.

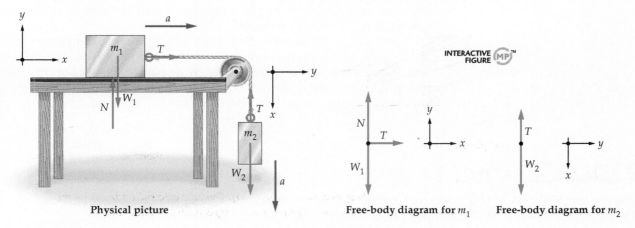

Physical picture   Free-body diagram for m_1 Free-body diagram for m_2

STRATEGY
Applying Newton's second law to the two masses yields the following relations: For mass 1, $\Sigma F_{1,x} = T = m_1 a_{1,x} = m_1 a$ and for mass 2, $\Sigma F_{2,x} = m_2 g - T = m_2 a_{2,x} = m_2 a$. These two equations can be solved for the two unknowns, a and T.

SOLUTION

Part (a)

1. First, write $\Sigma F_{1,x} = m_1 a$. Note that the only force acting on m_1 in the x direction is T:

$$\sum F_{1,x} = T = m_1 a$$
$$T = m_1 a$$

2. Next, write $\Sigma F_{2,x} = m_2 a$. In this case, two forces act in the x direction: $W_2 = m_2 g$ (positive direction) and T (negative direction):

$$\sum F_{2,x} = m_2 g - T = m_2 a$$
$$m_2 g - T = m_2 a$$

3. Sum the two relations obtained to eliminate T:

$$\begin{array}{r} T = m_1 a \\ \underline{m_2 g - T = m_2 a} \\ m_2 g = (m_1 + m_2)a \end{array}$$

4. Solve for a:

$$a = \left(\frac{m_2}{m_1 + m_2}\right)g$$

CONTINUED ON NEXT PAGE

CONTINUED FROM PREVIOUS PAGE

Part (b)

5. Substitute a into the first relation ($T = m_1a$) to find T:

$$T = m_1a = \left(\frac{m_1m_2}{m_1 + m_2}\right)g$$

INSIGHT

We could just as well have determined T using $m_2g - T = m_2a$, though the algebra is a bit messier. Also, note that $a = 0$ if $m_2 = 0$, and that $a = g$ if $m_1 = 0$, as expected. Similarly, $T = 0$ if either m_1 or m_2 is zero. This type of check, where you connect equations with physical situations, is one of the best ways to increase your understanding of physics.

PRACTICE PROBLEM

Find the tension for the case $m_1 = 1.50$ kg and $m_2 = 0.750$ kg, and compare the tension to m_2g. [**Answer:** $a = 3.27$ m/s^2, $T = 4.91$ N $< m_2g = 7.36$ N]

Some related homework problems: Problem 44, Problem 48

Conceptual Checkpoint 6–4 shows that the tension in the string should be less than m_2g. Let's rewrite our solution for T to show that this is indeed the case. From Example 6–6 we have

$$T = \left(\frac{m_1m_2}{m_1 + m_2}\right)g = \left(\frac{m_1}{m_1 + m_2}\right)m_2g$$

Since the ratio $m_1/(m_1 + m_2)$ is always less than 1 (as long as m_2 is nonzero), it follows that $T < m_2g$, as expected.

We conclude this section with a classic system that can be used to measure the acceleration of gravity. It is referred to as Atwood's machine, and it is basically two blocks of different mass connected by a string that passes over a pulley. The resulting acceleration of the blocks is related to the acceleration of gravity by a relatively simple expression, which we derive in the following Example.

EXAMPLE 6–7   ATWOOD'S MACHINE

Atwood's machine consists of two masses connected by a string that passes over a pulley, as shown below. Find the acceleration of the masses for general m_1 and m_2, and evaluate for the specific case $m_1 = 3.1$ kg, $m_2 = 4.4$ kg.

PICTURE THE PROBLEM

Our sketch shows Atwood's machine, along with our choice of coordinate directions for the two blocks. Note that both blocks accelerate in the positive x direction with accelerations of equal magnitude, a. From the free-body diagrams we can see that for mass 1 the weight is in the negative x direction and the tension is in the positive x direction. For mass 2, the tension is in the negative x direction and the weight is in the positive x direction. The tension has the same magnitude T for both masses, but their weights are different.

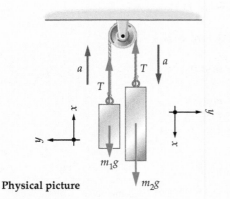

Physical picture

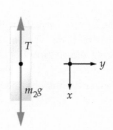

Free-body diagram for m_1   **Free-body diagram for m_2**

STRATEGY

To find the acceleration of the blocks, we follow the same strategy given in the previous Example. In particular, we start by applying Newton's second law to each block individually, using the fact that $a_{1,x} = a_{2,x} = a$. This gives two equations, both involving the tension T and the acceleration a. Eliminating T allows us to solve for the acceleration.

SOLUTION

1. Begin by writing out the expression $\Sigma F_{1,x} = m_1 a$.
   Note that two forces act in the x direction; T
   (positive direction) and $m_1 g$ (negative direction):

$$\Sigma F_{1,x} = T - m_1 g = m_1 a$$

2. Next, write out $\Sigma F_{2,x} = m_2 a$. The two forces
   acting in the x direction in this case are $m_2 g$
   (positive direction) and T (negative direction):

$$\Sigma F_{2,x} = m_2 g - T = m_2 a$$

3. Sum the two relations obtained above to eliminate T:

$$T - m_1 g = m_1 a$$
$$\underline{m_2 g - T = m_2 a}$$
$$(m_2 - m_1)g = (m_1 + m_2)a$$

4. Solve for a:

$$a = \left(\frac{m_2 - m_1}{m_1 + m_2}\right)g$$

5. To evaluate the acceleration, substitute numerical
   values for the masses and for g:

$$a = \left(\frac{m_2 - m_1}{m_1 + m_2}\right)g$$
$$= \left(\frac{4.4 \text{ kg} - 3.1 \text{ kg}}{3.1 \text{ kg} + 4.4 \text{ kg}}\right)(9.81 \text{ m/s}^2) = 1.7 \text{ m/s}^2$$

INSIGHT

Since m_2 is greater than m_1, we find that the acceleration is positive, meaning that the masses accelerate in the positive x direction. On the other hand, if m_1 were greater than m_2, we would find that a is negative, indicating that the masses accelerate in the negative x direction. Finally, if $m_1 = m_2$ we have $a = 0$, as expected.

PRACTICE PROBLEM

If m_1 is increased by a small amount, does the acceleration of the blocks increase, decrease, or stay the same? Check your answer by evaluating the acceleration for $m_1 = 3.3$ kg.   [**Answer:** If m_1 is increased only slightly, the acceleration will decrease. For $m_1 = 3.3$ kg, we find $a = 1.4 \text{ m/s}^2$.]

Some related homework problems: Problem 48, Problem 50

6–5 Circular Motion

According to Newton's second law, if no force acts on an object, it will move with constant speed in a constant direction. A force is required to change the speed, the direction, or both. For example, if you drive a car with constant speed on a circular track, the direction of the car's motion changes continuously. A force must act on the car to cause this change in direction. We would like to know two things about a force that causes circular motion: what is its direction, and what is its magnitude?

First, let's consider the direction of the force. Imagine swinging a ball tied to a string in a circle about your head, as shown in **Figure 6–12**. As you swing the ball, you feel a tension in the string pulling outward. Of course, on the other end of the string, where it attaches to the ball, the tension pulls inward, toward the center of the circle. Thus, the force the ball experiences is a force that is always directed toward the center of the circle. In summary,

> To make an object move in a circle with constant speed, a force must act on it that is directed toward the center of the circle.

Since the ball is acted on by a *force* toward the center of the circle, it follows that it must be *accelerating* toward the center of the circle. This might seem odd at

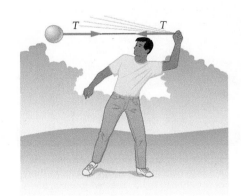

▲ **FIGURE 6–12 Swinging a ball in a circle**
The tension in the string pulls outward on the person's hand and pulls inward on the ball.

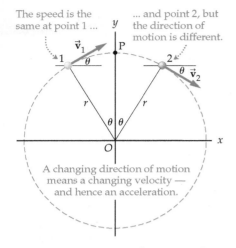

The speed is the same at point 1 ...

... and point 2, but the direction of motion is different.

A changing direction of motion means a changing velocity — and hence an acceleration.

▲ **FIGURE 6–13 A particle moving with constant speed in a circular path centered on the origin**

The speed of the particle is constant, but its velocity is constantly changing direction. Because the velocity changes, the particle is accelerating.

TABLE 6.2 $\dfrac{\sin \theta}{\theta}$ for Values of θ Approaching Zero

θ, radians	$\dfrac{\sin \theta}{\theta}$
1.00	0.841
0.500	0.959
0.250	0.990
0.125	0.997
0.0625	0.999

▲ The people enjoying this carnival ride are experiencing a centripetal acceleration of roughly 10 m/s^2 directed inward, toward the axis of rotation. The force needed to produce this acceleration, which keeps the riders moving in a circular path, is provided by the horizontal component of the tension in the chains.

first: How can a ball that moves with constant speed have an acceleration? The answer is that acceleration is produced whenever the speed or direction of the velocity changes—and in circular motion, the direction changes continuously. The resulting center-directed acceleration is called **centripetal acceleration** (centripetal is from the Latin for "center seeking").

Let's calculate the magnitude of the centripetal acceleration, a_{cp}, for an object moving with a constant speed v in a circle of radius r. **Figure 6–13** shows the circular path of an object, with the center of the circle at the origin. To calculate the acceleration at the top of the circle, at point P, we first calculate the average acceleration from point 1 to point 2:

$$\vec{a}_{av} = \frac{\Delta \vec{v}}{\Delta t} = \frac{\vec{v}_2 - \vec{v}_1}{\Delta t} \qquad 6\text{–}10$$

The instantaneous acceleration at P is the limit of $\vec{a}_{av}$ as points 1 and 2 move closer to P.

Referring to Figure 6–13, we see that $\vec{v}_1$ is at an angle θ above the horizontal, and $\vec{v}_2$ is at an angle θ below the horizontal. Both $\vec{v}_1$ and $\vec{v}_2$ have a magnitude v. Therefore, we can write the two velocities in vector form as follows:

$$\vec{v}_1 = (v \cos \theta)\hat{x} + (v \sin \theta)\hat{y}$$
$$\vec{v}_2 = (v \cos \theta)\hat{x} + (-v \sin \theta)\hat{y}$$

Substituting these results into $\vec{a}_{av}$ gives

$$\vec{a}_{av} = \frac{\vec{v}_2 - \vec{v}_1}{\Delta t} = \frac{-2v \sin \theta}{\Delta t}\hat{y} \qquad 6\text{–}11$$

Note that $\vec{a}_{av}$ points in the negative y direction—which, at point P, is toward the center of the circle.

To complete the calculation, we need Δt, the time it takes the object to go from point 1 to point 2. Since the object's speed is v, and the distance from point 1 to point 2 is $d = r(2\theta)$ where θ is measured in radians (see Appendix A, page A-2 for a discussion of radians and degrees), we find

$$\Delta t = \frac{d}{v} = \frac{2r\theta}{v} \qquad 6\text{–}12$$

Combining this result for Δt with the previous result for $\vec{a}_{av}$ gives

$$\vec{a}_{av} = \frac{-2v \sin \theta}{(2r\theta/v)}\hat{y} = -\frac{v^2}{r}\left(\frac{\sin \theta}{\theta}\right)\hat{y} \qquad 6\text{–}13$$

To find $\vec{a}$ at point P, we let points 1 and 2 approach P, which means letting θ go to zero. Table 6–2 shows that as θ goes to zero ($\theta \to 0$), the ratio $(\sin \theta)/\theta$ goes to 1:

$$\frac{\sin \theta}{\theta} \xrightarrow[\text{as } \theta \to 0]{} 1$$

Finally, then, the instantaneous acceleration at point P is

$$\vec{a} = -\frac{v^2}{r}\hat{y} = -a_{cp}\hat{y} \qquad 6\text{–}14$$

As mentioned, the direction of the acceleration is toward the center of the circle, and now we see that its magnitude is

$$a_{cp} = \frac{v^2}{r} \qquad 6\text{–}15$$

We can summarize these results as follows:

- When an object moves in a circle of radius r with constant speed v, its centripetal acceleration is $a_{cp} = v^2/r$.
- A force must be applied to an object to give it circular motion. For an object of mass m, the net force acting on it must have a magnitude given by

$$f_{cp} = ma_{cp} = m\frac{v^2}{r} \qquad 6\text{–}16$$

and must be directed toward the center of the circle.

Note that the **centripetal force,** f_{cp}, can be produced in any number of ways. For example, f_{cp} might be the tension in a string, as in the example with the ball, or it might be due to friction between tires and the road, as when a car turns a corner. In addition, f_{cp} could be the force of gravity causing a satellite, or the Moon, to orbit the Earth. Thus, f_{cp} is a force that must be present to cause circular motion, but the specific cause of f_{cp} varies from system to system.

We now show how these results for centripetal force and centripetal acceleration can be applied in practice.

PROBLEM-SOLVING NOTE

Choice of Coordinate System: Circular Motion

In circular motion, it is convenient to choose the coordinate system so that one axis points toward the center of the circle. Then, we know that the acceleration in that direction must be $a_{cp} = v^2/r$.

EXAMPLE 6–8   ROUNDING A CORNER

A 1200-kg car rounds a corner of radius $r = 45$ m. If the coefficient of static friction between the tires and the road is $\mu_s = 0.82$, what is the greatest speed the car can have in the corner without skidding?

PICTURE THE PROBLEM
In the first sketch we show a bird's-eye view of the car as it moves along its circular path. The next sketch shows the car moving directly toward the observer. Note that we have chosen the positive x direction to point toward the center of the circular path, and the positive y axis to point vertically upward. We also indicate the three forces acting on the car: gravity, $\vec{W} = -W\hat{y} = -mg\hat{y}$; the normal force, $\vec{N} = N\hat{y}$; and the force of static friction, $\vec{f}_s = \mu_s N\hat{x}$.

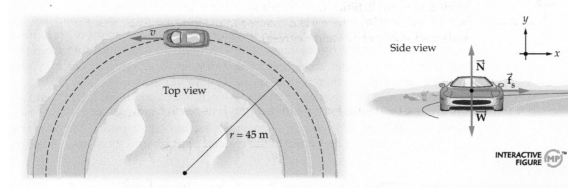

Top view

$r = 45$ m

Side view

INTERACTIVE FIGURE

STRATEGY
In this system, the force of static friction provides the centripetal force required for the car to move in a circular path. That is why the force of friction is at right angles to the car's direction of motion; it is directed toward the center of the circle. In addition, the friction in this case is static because the car's tires are rolling without slipping—always making static contact with the ground. Finally, if the car moves faster, more centripetal force (i.e., more friction) is required. Thus, the greatest speed for the car corresponds to the maximum static friction, $f_s = \mu_s N$. Hence, if we set $\mu_s N$ equal to the centripetal force, $ma_{cp} = mv^2/r$, we can solve for v.

SOLUTION

1. Sum the x components of force to relate the force of static friction to the centripetal acceleration of the car:

$$\sum F_x = f_s = ma_x$$

2. Since the car moves in a circular path, with the center of the circle in the x direction, it follows that $a_x = a_{cp} = v^2/r$. Make this substitution, along with $f_s = \mu_s N$ for the force of static friction:

$$\mu_s N = ma_{cp} = m\frac{v^2}{r}$$

CONTINUED ON NEXT PAGE

CONTINUED FROM PREVIOUS PAGE

3. Next, set the sum of the y components of force equal to zero, since $a_y = 0$: $\sum F_y = N - W = ma_y = 0$

4. Solve for the normal force: $N = W = mg$

5. Substitute the result $N = mg$ in Step 2 and solve for v. Notice that the mass of the car cancels: $\mu_s mg = m\dfrac{v^2}{r}$

   $v = \sqrt{\mu_s rg}$

6. Substitute numerical values to determine v: $v = \sqrt{(0.82)(45\text{ m})(9.81\text{ m/s}^2)} = 19\text{ m/s}$

INSIGHT
Note that the maximum speed is less if the radius is smaller (tighter corner) or if μ_s is smaller (slick road). The mass of the vehicle, however, is irrelevant. For example, the maximum speed is precisely the same for a motorcycle rounding this corner as it is for a large, heavily loaded truck.

PRACTICE PROBLEM
Suppose the situation described in this Example takes place on the Moon, where the acceleration of gravity is less than it is on Earth. If a lunar rover goes around this same corner, is its maximum speed greater than, less than, or the same as the result found in Step 4? To check your answer, find the maximum speed for a lunar rover when it rounds a corner with $r = 45$ m and $\mu_s = 0.82$. (On the Moon, $g = 1.62$ m/s^2.)   [**Answer:** The maximum speed will be less. On the Moon we find $v = 7.7$ m/s.]

Some related homework problems: Problem 55, Problem 57, Problem 61

REAL-WORLD PHYSICS

Skids and banked roadways

If you try to round a corner too rapidly, you may experience a skid; that is, your car may begin to slide sideways across the road. A common bit of road wisdom is that you should turn in the direction of the skid to regain control—which, to most people, sounds counterintuitive. The advice is sound, however. Suppose, for example, that you are turning to the left and begin to skid to the right. If you turn more sharply to the left to try to correct for the skid, you simply reduce the turning radius of your car, r. The result is that the centripetal acceleration, v^2/r, becomes larger, and an even larger force would be required from the road to make the turn. The tendency to skid would therefore be increased. On the other hand, if you turn slightly to the right when you start to skid, you *increase* your turning radius and the centripetal acceleration decreases. In this case your car may stop skidding, and you can then regain control of your vehicle.

You may also have noticed that many roads are tilted, or banked, when they round a corner. The same type of banking is observed on many automobile racetracks as well. Next time you drive around a banked curve, notice that the banking tilts you in toward the center of the circular path you are following. This is by

▲ The steeply banked track at the Talladega Speedway in Alabama (left) helps to keep the rapidly moving cars from skidding off along a tangential path. Even when there is no solid roadway, however, banking can still help—airplanes bank when making turns (center) to keep from "skidding" sideways. Banking is beneficial in another way as well. Occupants of cars on a banked roadway or of a banking airplane feel no sideways force when the banking angle is just right, so turns become a safer and more comfortable experience. For this reason, some trains use hydraulic suspension systems to bank when rounding corners (right), even though the tracks themselves are level.

design. On a banked curve, the normal force exerted by the road contributes to the required centripetal force. If the tilt angle is just right, the normal force provides all of the centripetal force so that the car can negotiate the curve even if there is no friction between its tires and the road. The next Example determines the optimum banking angle for a given speed and given radius of turn.

EXAMPLE 6–9   **BANK ON IT**

If a roadway is banked at the proper angle, a car can round a corner without any assistance from friction between the tires and the road. Find the appropriate banking angle for a 900-kg car traveling at 20.5 m/s in a turn of radius 85.0 m.

PICTURE THE PROBLEM

Note that we choose the positive y axis to point vertically upward and the positive x direction to point toward the center of the circular path. Since $\vec{N}$ is perpendicular to the banked roadway, it is at an angle θ to the y axis. Therefore, $\vec{N} = (N \sin\theta)\hat{x} + (N \cos\theta)\hat{y}$ and $\vec{W} = -W\hat{y} = -mg\hat{y}$.

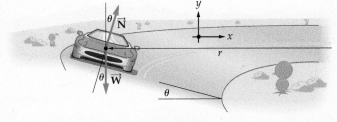

STRATEGY

In order for the car to move in a circular path, there must be a force acting on it in the positive x direction. Since the weight $\vec{W}$ has no x component, it follows that the normal force $\vec{N}$ must supply the needed centripetal force. Thus, we find N by setting $\Sigma F_y = ma_y = 0$, since there is no motion in the y direction. Then we use N in $\Sigma F_x = ma_x = mv^2/r$ to find the angle θ.

SOLUTION

1. Start by determining N from the condition $\Sigma F_y = 0$:

$$\sum F_y = N \cos\theta - W = 0$$

$$N = \frac{W}{\cos\theta} = \frac{mg}{\cos\theta}$$

2. Next, set $\Sigma F_x = mv^2/r$:

$$\sum F_x = N \sin\theta$$

$$= ma_x = ma_{cp} = m\frac{v^2}{r}$$

3. Substitute $N = mg/\cos\theta$ (from $\Sigma F_y = 0$, Step 1) and solve for θ, using the fact that $\sin\theta/\cos\theta = \tan\theta$. Notice that, once again, the mass of the car cancels:

$$N \sin\theta = \frac{mg}{\cos\theta}\sin\theta = m\frac{v^2}{r}$$

$$\tan\theta = \frac{v^2}{gr} \quad \text{or} \quad \theta = \tan^{-1}\left(\frac{v^2}{gr}\right)$$

4. Substitute numerical values to determine θ:

$$\theta = \tan^{-1}\left[\frac{(20.5 \text{ m/s})^2}{(9.81 \text{ m/s}^2)(85.0 \text{ m})}\right] = 26.7°$$

INSIGHT

The symbolic result in Step 3 shows that the banking angle increases with increasing speed and decreasing radius of turn, as one would expect.

From the point of view of a passenger, the experience of rounding a properly banked corner is basically the same as riding on a level road—there are no "sideways forces" to make the turn uncomfortable. There is one small difference, however—the passenger feels heavier due to the increased normal force.

PRACTICE PROBLEM

A turn of radius 65 m is banked at 30.0°. What speed should a car have in order to make the turn with no assistance from friction? [**Answer:** $v = 19$ m/s]

Some related homework problems: Problem 58, Problem 107

If you've ever driven through a dip in the road, you know that you feel momentarily heavier near the bottom of the dip, just like a passenger in Example 6–9. This change in apparent weight is due to the approximately circular motion of the car, as we show next.

ACTIVE EXAMPLE 6-4 FIND THE NORMAL FORCE

While driving along a country lane with a constant speed of 17.0 m/s, you encounter a dip in the road. The dip can be approximated as a circular arc, with a radius of 65.0 m. What is the normal force exerted by a car seat on an 80.0-kg passenger when the car is at the bottom of the dip?

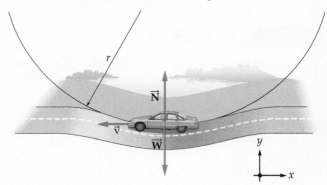

SOLUTION *(Test your understanding by performing the calculations indicated in each step.)*

1. Write $\Sigma F_y = ma_y$ for the passenger: $N - mg = ma_y$

2. Replace a_y with the centripetal acceleration: $a_y = v^2/r$

3. Solve for N: $N = mg + mv^2/r$

4. Substitute numerical values: $N = 1140\ \text{N}$

INSIGHT

At the bottom of the dip the normal force is greater than the weight of the passenger, since it must also supply the centripetal force. As a result, the passenger feels heavier than usual. In this case, the 80.0-kg passenger feels as if his mass has increased by 45%, to 116 kg!

The same physics applies to a jet pilot who pulls a plane out of a high-speed dive. In that case, the magnitude of the effect can be much larger, resulting in a decrease of blood flow to the brain and eventually to loss of consciousness. Here's a case where basic physics really can be a matter of life and death.

YOUR TURN

At what speed will the magnitude of the normal force be equal to 1250 N?

(Answers to **Your Turn** *problems are given in the back of the book.)*

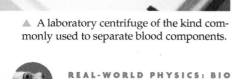

▲ A laboratory centrifuge of the kind commonly used to separate blood components.

REAL-WORLD PHYSICS: BIO

Centrifuges and ultracentrifuges

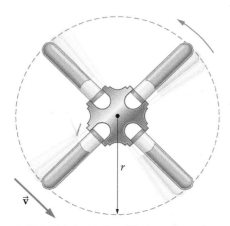

▲ **FIGURE 6-14 Simplified top view of a centrifuge in operation**

A similar calculation can be applied to a car going over the top of a bump. In that case, circular motion results in a reduced apparent weight.

Finally, we determine the acceleration produced in a **centrifuge,** a common device in biological and medical laboratories that uses large centripetal accelerations to perform such tasks as separating red and white blood cells from serum. A simplified top view of a centrifuge is shown in **Figure 6-14.**

EXERCISE 6-1

The centrifuge in Figure 6-14 rotates at a rate that gives the bottom of the test tube a linear speed of 89.3 m/s. If the bottom of the test tube is 8.50 cm from the axis of rotation, what is the centripetal acceleration experienced there?

SOLUTION

Applying the relation $a_{cp} = v^2/r$ yields

$$a_{cp} = \frac{v^2}{r} = \frac{(89.3\ \text{m/s})^2}{0.0850\ \text{m}} = 93,800\ \text{m/s}^2 = 9560g$$

In this expression, g is the acceleration of gravity, 9.81 m/s².

Thus, a centrifuge can produce centripetal accelerations that are many thousand times greater than the acceleration of gravity. In fact, devices referred to as **ultracentrifuges** can produce accelerations as great as 1 million g. Even in the relatively modest case considered in Exercise 6–1, the forces involved in a centrifuge can be quite significant. For example, if the contents of the test tube have a mass of 12.0 g, the centripetal force that must be exerted by the bottom of the tube is $(0.0120 \text{ kg})(9560 \text{ } g) = 1130$ N, or about 250 lb!

Finally, an object moving in a circular path may increase or decrease its speed. In such a case, the object has both an acceleration tangential to its path that changes its speed, $\vec{a}_t$, and a centripetal acceleration perpendicular to its path, $\vec{a}_{cp}$, that changes its direction of motion. Such a situation is illustrated in **Figure 6–15**. The total acceleration of the object is the vector sum of $\vec{a}_t$ and $\vec{a}_{cp}$. We will explore this case more fully in Chapter 10.

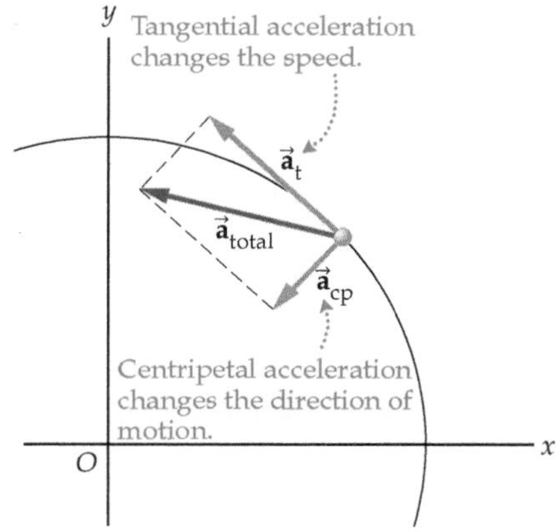

▲ **FIGURE 6–15 A particle moving in a circular path with tangential acceleration**
In this case, the particle's speed is increasing at the rate given by a_t.

THE BIG PICTURE PUTTING PHYSICS IN CONTEXT

LOOKING BACK

The equations of kinematics from Chapters 2 and 4 proved useful again in this chapter. See, in particular, Examples 6–1 and 6–2.

The discussion related to Figure 5–15 about angles on an inclined surface came into play when identifying the angles in Examples 6–2 and 6–9.

Our derivation of the direction and magnitude of centripetal acceleration (Section 6–5) made extensive use of our knowledge of vectors and how to resolve them into components.

LOOKING AHEAD

Our discussion of springs, and Hooke's law in particular, will be of importance when we consider oscillations in Chapter 13.

The basic ideas of translational equilibrium (Section 6–3) will be extended to more general objects in Chapter 11.

Circular motion will come up again in a number of situations, but especially when we consider orbital motion in Chapter 12 and the Bohr model of the hydrogen atom in Chapter 31.

CHAPTER SUMMARY

6–1 FRICTIONAL FORCES

Frictional forces are due to the microscopic roughness of surfaces in contact. As a rule of thumb, friction is independent of the area of contact and independent of the relative speed of the surfaces.

Kinetic Friction
Friction experienced by surfaces that are in contact and moving relative to one another. The force of kinetic friction is given by

$$f_k = \mu_k N \qquad \text{6–1}$$

In this expression, μ_k is the coefficient of kinetic friction and N is the magnitude of the normal force.

Static Friction
Friction experienced by surfaces that are in static contact. The maximum force of static friction is given by

$$f_{s,max} = \mu_s N \qquad \text{6–3}$$

In this expression, μ_s is the coefficient of static friction and N is the magnitude of the normal force. The force of static friction can have any magnitude between zero and its maximum value.

6–2 STRINGS AND SPRINGS

Strings and springs provide a common way of exerting forces on objects. Ideal strings and springs are massless.

Tension
The force transmitted through a string. The tension is the same throughout the length of an ideal string.

Hooke's Law
The force exerted by an ideal spring stretched by the amount x is

$$F_x = -kx \qquad\qquad 6\text{--}4$$

In words, the force exerted by a spring is proportional to the amount of stretch or compression, and is in the opposite direction.

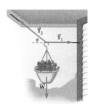

6–3 TRANSLATIONAL EQUILIBRIUM

An object is in translational equilibrium if the net force acting on it is zero. Equivalently, an object is in equilibrium if it has zero acceleration.

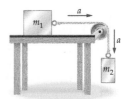

6–4 CONNECTED OBJECTS

Connected objects are linked physically, and hence they are linked mathematically as well. For example, objects connected by strings have the same magnitude of acceleration.

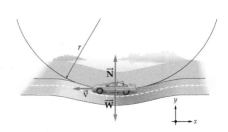

6–5 CIRCULAR MOTION

An object moving with speed v in a circle of radius r has an acceleration of magnitude v^2/r directed toward the center of the circle: This is referred to as the centripetal acceleration, a_{cp}. If the object has a mass m, the force required for the circular motion is

$$f_{cp} = ma_{cp} = mv^2/r \qquad\qquad 6\text{--}16$$

PROBLEM-SOLVING SUMMARY

Type of Calculation	Relevant Physical Concepts	Related Examples
Find the acceleration when kinetic friction is present.	First, find the magnitude of the normal force, N. The corresponding kinetic friction has a magnitude of $f_k = \mu_k N$ and points opposite to the direction of motion. Include this force with the others when applying Newton's second law.	Examples 6–1, 6–2
Solve problems involving static friction.	Start by finding the magnitude of the normal force, N. The corresponding static friction has a magnitude between zero and $\mu_s N$. Its direction opposes motion.	Example 6–3 Active Example 6–1
Find the acceleration and the tension for masses connected by a string.	Apply Newton's second law to each mass separately. This generates two equations, which can be solved for the two unknowns, a and T.	Examples 6–6, 6–7
Solve problems involving circular motion.	Set up the coordinate system so that one axis points to the center of the circle. When applying Newton's second law to that direction, set the acceleration equal to $a_{cp} = v^2/r$.	Examples 6–8, 6–9 Active Example 6–4

CONCEPTUAL QUESTIONS

For instructor-assigned homework, go to www.masteringphysics.com

(Answers to odd-numbered Conceptual Questions can be found in the back of the book.)

1. A clothesline always sags a little, even if nothing hangs from it. Explain.

2. In the *Jurassic Park* sequel, *The Lost World*, a man tries to keep a large vehicle from going over a cliff by connecting a cable from his Jeep to the vehicle. The man then puts the Jeep in gear and spins the rear wheels. Do you expect that spinning the tires will increase the force exerted by the Jeep on the vehicle? Why or why not?

3. When a traffic accident is investigated, it is common for the length of the skid marks to be measured. How could this information be used to estimate the initial speed of the vehicle that left the skid marks?

4. In a car with rear-wheel drive, the maximum acceleration is often less than the maximum deceleration. Why?

5. A train typically requires a much greater distance to come to rest, for a given initial speed, than does a car. Why?

6. Give some everyday examples of situations in which friction is beneficial.

7. At the local farm, you buy a flat of strawberries and place them on the backseat of the car. On the way home, you begin to brake as you approach a stop sign. At first the strawberries stay put, but as you brake a bit harder, they begin to slide off the seat. Explain.

8. It is possible to spin a bucket of water in a vertical circle and have none of the water spill when the bucket is upside down. How would you explain this to members of your family?

9. Water sprays off a rapidly turning bicycle wheel. Why?

10. Can an object be in equilibrium if it is moving? Explain.

11. In a dramatic circus act, a motorcyclist drives his bike around the inside of a vertical circle. How is this possible, considering that the motorcycle is upside down at the top of the circle?

12. The gravitational attraction of the Earth is only slightly less at the altitude of an orbiting spacecraft than it is on the Earth's surface. Why is it, then, that astronauts feel weightless?

13. A popular carnival ride has passengers stand with their backs against the inside wall of a cylinder. As the cylinder begins to spin, the passengers feel as if they are being pushed against the wall. Explain.

14. Referring to Question 13, after the cylinder reaches operating speed, the floor is lowered away, leaving the passengers "stuck" to the wall. Explain.

15. Your car is stuck on an icy side street. Some students on their way to class see your predicament and help out by sitting on the trunk of your car to increase its traction. Why does this help?

16. The parking brake on a car causes the rear wheels to lock up. What would be the likely consequence of applying the parking brake in a car that is in rapid motion? (*Note:* Do *not* try this at home.)

17. **BIO** The foot of your average gecko is covered with billions of tiny hair tips—called spatulae—that are made of keratin, the protein found in human hair. A subtle shift of the electron distribution in both the spatulae and the wall to which a gecko clings produces an adhesive force by means of the van der Waals interaction between molecules. Suppose a gecko uses its spatulae to cling to a vertical windowpane. If you were to describe this situation in terms of a coefficient of static friction, μ_s, what value would you assign to μ_s? Is this a sensible way to model the gecko's feat? Explain.

18. Discuss the physics involved in the spin cycle of a washing machine. In particular, how is circular motion related to the removal of water from the clothes?

19. The gas pedal and the brake pedal are capable of causing a car to accelerate. Can the steering wheel also produce an acceleration? Explain.

20. In the movie *2001: A Space Odyssey*, a rotating space station provides "artificial gravity" for its inhabitants. How does this work?

The rotating space station from the movie *2001: A Space Odyssey* (Conceptual Question 20)

21. When rounding a corner on a bicycle or a motorcycle, the driver leans inward, toward the center of the circle. Why?

22. In *Robin Hood: Prince of Thieves*, starring Kevin Costner, Robin swings between trees on a vine that is on fire. At the lowest point of his swing, the vine burns through and Robin begins to fall. The next shot, from high up in the trees, shows Robin falling straight downward. Would you rate the physics of this scene "Good," "Bad," or "Ugly"? Explain.

PROBLEMS AND CONCEPTUAL EXERCISES

Note: Answers to odd-numbered Problems and Conceptual Exercises can be found in the back of the book. **IP** *denotes an integrated problem, with both conceptual and numerical parts;* **BIO** *identifies problems of biological or medical interest;* **CE** *indicates a conceptual exercise.* **Predict/Explain** *problems ask for two responses:* **(a)** *your prediction of a physical outcome, and* **(b)** *the best explanation among three provided. On all problems, red bullets (•, ••, •••) are used to indicate the level of difficulty.*

SECTION 6–1 FRICTIONAL FORCES

1. • **CE Predict/Explain** You push two identical bricks across a tabletop with constant speed, v, as shown in **Figure 6–16**. In case 1, you place the bricks end to end; in case 2, you stack the bricks one on top of the other. **(a)** Is the force of kinetic friction in case 1 greater than, less than, or equal to the force of kinetic friction in case 2? **(b)** Choose the *best explanation* from among the following:

Case 1   Case 2

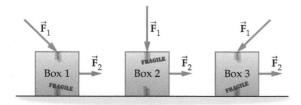

▲ **FIGURE 6–16** Problem 1

    I. The normal force in case 2 is larger, and hence the bricks press down more firmly against the tabletop.
    II. The normal force is the same in the two cases, and friction is independent of surface area.
    III. Case 1 has more surface area in contact with the tabletop, and this leads to more friction.

2. • **CE Predict/Explain** Two drivers traveling side-by-side at the same speed suddenly see a deer in the road ahead of them and begin braking. Driver 1 stops by locking up his brakes and screeching to a halt; driver 2 stops by applying her brakes just to the verge of locking, so that the wheels continue to turn until her car comes to a complete stop. **(a)** All other factors being equal, is the stopping distance of driver 1 greater than, less than, or equal to the stopping distance of driver 2? **(b)** Choose the *best explanation* from among the following:
    I. Locking up the brakes gives the greatest possible braking force.
    II. The same tires on the same road result in the same force of friction.
    III. Locked-up brakes lead to sliding (kinetic) friction, which is less than rolling (static) friction.

3. • A baseball player slides into third base with an initial speed of 4.0 m/s. If the coefficient of kinetic friction between the player and the ground is 0.46, how far does the player slide before coming to rest?

4. • A child goes down a playground slide with an acceleration of 1.26 m/s². Find the coefficient of kinetic friction between the child and the slide if the slide is inclined at an angle of 33.0° below the horizontal.

5. • Hopping into your Porsche, you floor it and accelerate at 12 m/s² without spinning the tires. Determine the minimum coefficient of static friction between the tires and the road needed to make this possible.

6. • When you push a 1.80-kg book resting on a tabletop, it takes 2.25 N to start the book sliding. Once it is sliding, however, it takes only 1.50 N to keep the book moving with constant speed. What are the coefficients of static and kinetic friction between the book and the tabletop?

7. • In Problem 6, what is the frictional force exerted on the book when you push on it with a force of 0.75 N?

8. •• **CE** The three identical boxes shown in **Figure 6–17** remain at rest on a rough, horizontal surface, even though they are acted on by two different forces, $\vec{F}_1$ and $\vec{F}_2$. All of the forces labeled $\vec{F}_1$

have the same magnitude; all of the forces labeled $\vec{F}_2$ are identical to one another. Rank the boxes in order of increasing magnitude of the force static friction between them and the surface. Indicate ties where appropriate.

9. •• **IP** A tie of uniform width is laid out on a table, with a fraction of its length hanging over the edge. Initially, the tie is at rest. **(a)** If the fraction hanging from the table is increased, the tie eventually slides to the ground. Explain. **(b)** What is the coefficient of static friction between the tie and the table if the tie begins to slide when one-fourth of its length hangs over the edge?

10. •• To move a large crate across a rough floor, you push on it with a force *F* at an angle of 21° below the horizontal, as shown in **Figure 6–18**. Find the force necessary to start the crate moving, given that the mass of the crate is 32 kg and the coefficient of static friction between the crate and the floor is 0.57.

▲ **FIGURE 6–18** Problems 10, 11, and 106

11. •• In Problem 10, find the acceleration of the crate if the applied force is 330 N and the coefficient of kinetic friction is 0.45.

12. •• **IP** A 48-kg crate is placed on an inclined ramp. When the angle the ramp makes with the horizontal is increased to 26°, the crate begins to slide downward. **(a)** What is the coefficient of static friction between the crate and the ramp? **(b)** At what angle does the crate begin to slide if its mass is doubled?

13. •• **IP** A 97-kg sprinter wishes to accelerate from rest to a speed of 13 m/s in a distance of 22 m. **(a)** What coefficient of static friction is required between the sprinter's shoes and the track? **(b)** Explain the strategy used to find the answer to part (a).

14. •• **Coffee To Go** A person places a cup of coffee on the roof of her car while she dashes back into the house for a forgotten item. When she returns to the car, she hops in and takes off with the coffee cup still on the roof. **(a)** If the coefficient of static friction between the coffee cup and the roof of the car is 0.24, what is the maximum acceleration the car can have without causing the cup to slide? Ignore the effects of air resistance. **(b)** What is the smallest amount of time in which the person can accelerate the car from rest to 15 m/s and still keep the coffee cup on the roof?

15. •• **IP Force Times Distance I** At the local hockey rink, a puck with a mass of 0.12 kg is given an initial speed of *v* = 5.3 m/s. **(a)** If the coefficient of kinetic friction between the ice and the puck is 0.11, what distance *d* does the puck slide before coming to rest? **(b)** If the mass of the puck is doubled, does the frictional force *F* exerted on the puck increase, decrease, or stay the same? Explain. **(c)** Does the stopping distance of the puck increase, decrease, or stay the same when its mass is doubled? Explain. **(d)** For the situation considered in part (a), show that $Fd = \frac{1}{2}mv^2$.

$\vec{F}_1$ $\vec{F}_1$ $\vec{F}_1$

Box 1 $\vec{F}_2$ FRAGILE Box 2 $\vec{F}_2$ Box 3 $\vec{F}_2$

FRAGILE   FRAGILE

▲ **FIGURE 6–17** Problem 8

(The significance of this result will be discussed in Chapter 7, where we will see that $\frac{1}{2}mv^2$ is the kinetic energy of an object.)

16. •• **IP Force Times Time** At the local hockey rink, a puck with a mass of 0.12 kg is given an initial speed of $v_0 = 6.7$ m/s. **(a)** If the coefficient of kinetic friction between the ice and the puck is 0.13, how much time t does it take for the puck to come to rest? **(b)** If the mass of the puck is doubled, does the frictional force F exerted on the puck increase, decrease, or stay the same? Explain. **(c)** Does the stopping time of the puck increase, decrease, or stay the same when its mass is doubled? Explain. **(d)** For the situation considered in part (a), show that $Ft = mv_0$. (The significance of this result will be discussed in Chapter 9, where we will see that mv is the momentum of an object.)

17. •• **Force Times Distance II** A block of mass $m = 1.95$ kg slides with an initial speed $v_i = 4.33$ m/s on a smooth, horizontal surface. The block now encounters a rough patch with a coefficient of kinetic friction given by $\mu_k = 0.260$. The rough patch extends for a distance $d = 0.125$ m, after which the surface is again frictionless. **(a)** What is the acceleration of the block when it is in the rough patch? **(b)** What is the final speed, v_f, of the block when it exits the rough patch? **(c)** Show that $-Fd = -(\mu_k mg)d = \frac{1}{2}mv_f^2 - \frac{1}{2}mv_i^2$. (The significance of this result will be discussed in Chapter 7, where we will see that $\frac{1}{2}mv^2$ is the kinetic energy of an object.)

18. ••• **IP** The coefficient of kinetic friction between the tires of your car and the roadway is μ. **(a)** If your initial speed is v and you lock your tires during braking, how far do you skid? Give your answer in terms of v, μ, and m, the mass of your car. **(b)** If you double your speed, what happens to the stopping distance? **(c)** What is the stopping distance for a truck with twice the mass of your car, assuming the same initial speed and coefficient of kinetic friction?

SECTION 6–2 STRINGS AND SPRINGS

19. • **CE** A certain spring has a force constant k. **(a)** If this spring is cut in half, does the resulting half spring have a force constant that is greater than, less than, or equal to k? **(b)** If two of the original full-length springs are connected end to end, does the resulting double spring have a force constant that is greater than, less than, or equal to k?

20. • Pulling up on a rope, you lift a 4.35-kg bucket of water from a well with an acceleration of 1.78 m/s². What is the tension in the rope?

21. • When a 9.09-kg mass is placed on top of a vertical spring, the spring compresses 4.18 cm. Find the force constant of the spring.

22. • A 110-kg box is loaded into the trunk of a car. If the height of the car's bumper decreases by 13 cm, what is the force constant of its rear suspension?

23. • A 50.0-kg person takes a nap in a backyard hammock. Both ropes supporting the hammock are at an angle of 15.0° above the horizontal. Find the tension in the ropes.

24. • **IP** A backpack full of books weighing 52.0 N rests on a table in a physics laboratory classroom. A spring with a force constant of 150 N/m is attached to the backpack and pulled horizontally, as indicated in **Figure 6–19**. **(a)** If the spring is pulled until it stretches 2.00 cm and the pack remains at rest, what is the force of friction exerted on the backpack by the table? **(b)** Does your answer to part (a) change if the mass of the backpack is doubled? Explain.

▲ **FIGURE 6–19** Problems 24 and 25

25. • If the 52.0-N backpack in Problem 24 begins to slide when the spring ($k = 150$ N/m) stretches by 2.50 cm, what is the coefficient of static friction between the backpack and the table?

26. •• **IP** The equilibrium length of a certain spring with a force constant of $k = 250$ N/m is 0.18 m. **(a)** What is the magnitude of the force that is required to hold this spring at twice its equilibrium length? **(b)** Is the magnitude of the force required to keep the spring compressed to half its equilibrium length greater than, less than, or equal to the force found in part (a)? Explain.

27. •• **IP** Illinois Jones is being pulled from a snake pit with a rope that breaks if the tension in it exceeds 755 N. **(a)** If Illinois Jones has a mass of 70.0 kg and the snake pit is 3.40 m deep, what is the minimum time that is required to pull our intrepid explorer from the pit? **(b)** Explain why the rope breaks if Jones is pulled from the pit in less time than that calculated in part (a).

28. •• **IP** A spring with a force constant of 120 N/m is used to push a 0.27-kg block of wood against a wall, as shown in **Figure 6–20**. **(a)** Find the minimum compression of the spring needed to keep the block from falling, given that the coefficient of static friction between the block and the wall is 0.46. **(b)** Does your answer to part (a) change if the mass of the block of wood is doubled? Explain.

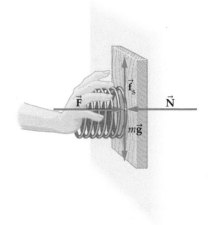

▲ **FIGURE 6–20** Problem 28

29. •• **IP** Your friend's 13.6-g graduation tassel hangs on a string from his rearview mirror. **(a)** When he accelerates from a stoplight, the tassel deflects backward toward the rear of the car. Explain. **(b)** If the tassel hangs at an angle of 6.44° relative to the vertical, what is the acceleration of the car?

30. •• In Problem 29, **(a)** find the tension in the string holding the tassel. **(b)** At what angle to the vertical will the tension in the string be twice the weight of the tassel?

31. •• **IP** A picture hangs on the wall suspended by two strings, as shown in **Figure 6–21**. The tension in string 1 is 1.7 N. **(a)** Is the tension in string 2 greater than, less than, or equal to 1.7 N? Explain. **(b)** Verify your answer to part (a) by calculating the tension in string 2. **(c)** What is the weight of the picture?

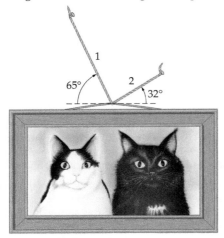

▲ **FIGURE 6–21** Problems 31 and 83

32. •• **Mechanical Advantage** The pulley system shown in **Figure 6–22** is used to lift a 52-kg crate. Note that one chain connects the upper pulley to the ceiling and a second chain connects the lower pulley to the crate. Assuming the masses of the chains, pulleys, and ropes are negligible, determine **(a)** the force $\vec{F}$ required to lift the crate with constant speed, **(b)** the tension in the upper chain, and **(c)** the tension in the lower chain.

▲ **FIGURE 6–22** Problems 32 and 33

33. •• In Problem 32, determine **(a)** the force $\vec{F}$, **(b)** the tension in the upper chain, and **(c)** the tension in the lower chain, given that the crate is rising with an acceleration of 2.3 m/s^2.

SECTION 6–3 TRANSLATIONAL EQUILIBRIUM

34. • Pulling the string on a bow back with a force of 28.7 lb, an archer prepares to shoot an arrow. If the archer pulls in the center of the string, and the angle between the two halves is 138°, what is the tension in the string?

35. • In **Figure 6–23** we see two blocks connected by a string and tied to a wall. The mass of the lower block is 1.0 kg; the mass of the upper block is 2.0 kg. Given that the angle of the incline is

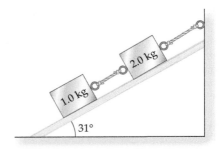

▲ **FIGURE 6–23** Problem 35

31°, find the tensions in **(a)** the string connecting the two blocks and **(b)** the string that is tied to the wall.

36. • **BIO Traction** After a skiing accident, your leg is in a cast and supported in a traction device, as shown in **Figure 6–24**. Find the magnitude of the force $\vec{F}$ exerted by the leg on the small pulley. (By Newton's third law, the small pulley exerts an equal and opposite force on the leg.) Let the mass m be 2.50 kg.

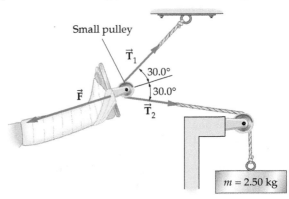

▲ **FIGURE 6–24** Problems 36 and 69

37. • Two blocks are connected by a string, as shown in **Figure 6–25**. The smooth inclined surface makes an angle of 42° with the horizontal, and the block on the incline has a mass of 6.7 kg. Find the mass of the hanging block that will cause the system to be in equilibrium. (The pulley is assumed to be ideal.)

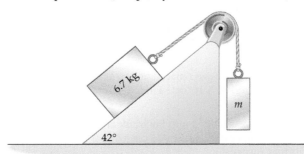

▲ **FIGURE 6–25** Problem 37

38. •• **CE Predict/Explain** **(a)** Referring to the hanging planter in Example 6–5, which of the three graphs (A, B, or C) in **Figure 6–26** shows an accurate plot of the tensions T_1 and T_2 as a function of the angle θ? **(b)** Choose the *best explanation* from among the following:
  I. The two tensions must be equal at some angle between $\theta = 0$ and $\theta = 90°$.
  II. T_2 is greater than T_1 at all angles, and is equal to mg at $\theta = 90°$.
  III. T_2 is less than T_1 at all angles, and is equal to 0 at $\theta = 90°$.

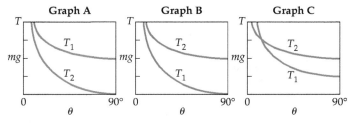

Graph A   Graph B   Graph C

▲ **FIGURE 6–26** Problem 38

39. •• A 0.15-kg ball is placed in a shallow wedge with an opening angle of 120°, as shown in **Figure 6–27**. For each contact point between the wedge and the ball, determine the force exerted on the ball. Assume the system is frictionless.

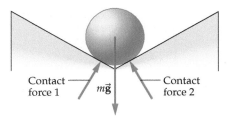

▲ **FIGURE 6–27** Problem 39

40. •• **IP** You want to nail a 1.6-kg board onto the wall of a barn. To position the board before nailing, you push it against the wall with a horizontal force $\vec{F}$ to keep it from sliding to the ground (**Figure 6–28**). **(a)** If the coefficient of static friction between the board and the wall is 0.79, what is the least force you can apply and still hold the board in place? **(b)** What happens to the force of static friction if you push against the wall with a force greater than that found in part (a)?

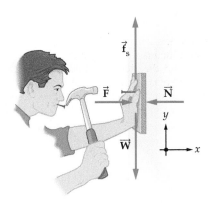

▲ **FIGURE 6–28** Problem 40

41. ••• **BIO The Russell Traction System** To immobilize a fractured femur (the thigh bone), doctors often utilize the Russell traction system illustrated in **Figure 6–29**. Notice that one force is applied directly to the knee, $\vec{F}_1$, while two other forces, $\vec{F}_2$ and $\vec{F}_3$, are applied to the foot. The latter two forces combine to give a force $\vec{F}_2 + \vec{F}_3$ that is transmitted through the lower leg to the knee. The result is that the knee experiences the total force $\vec{F}_{total} = \vec{F}_1 + \vec{F}_2 + \vec{F}_3$. The goal of this traction system is to have $\vec{F}_{total}$ directly in line with the fractured femur, at an angle of 20.0° above the horizontal. Find **(a)** the angle θ required to produce this alignment of $\vec{F}_{total}$ and **(b)** the magnitude of the force, $\vec{F}_{total}$ that is applied to the femur in this case. (Assume the pulleys are ideal.)

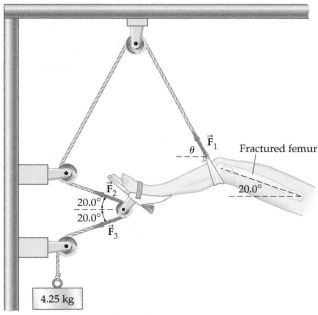

▲ **FIGURE 6–29** Problem 41

SECTION 6–4 CONNECTED OBJECTS

42. • **CE** In Example 6–6 (Connected Blocks), suppose m_1 and m_2 are both increased by a factor of 2. **(a)** Does the acceleration of the blocks increase, decrease, or stay the same? **(b)** Does the tension in the string increase, decrease, or stay the same?

43. • **CE Predict/Explain** Suppose m_1 and m_2 in Example 6–7 (Atwood's Machine) are both increased by 1 kg. Does the acceleration of the blocks increase, decrease, or stay the same? **(b)** Choose the *best explanation* from among the following:

  I. The net force acting on the blocks is the same, but the total mass that must be accelerated is greater.

  II. The difference in the masses is the same, and this is what determines the net force on the system.

  III. The force exerted on each block is greater, leading to an increased acceleration.

44. • Find the acceleration of the masses shown in **Figure 6–30**, given that $m_1 = 1.0$ kg, $m_2 = 2.0$ kg, and $m_3 = 3.0$ kg. Assume the table is frictionless and the masses move freely.

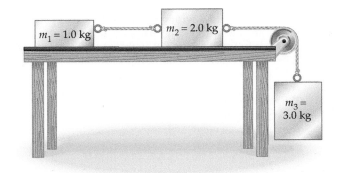

▲ **FIGURE 6–30** Problems 44, 47, and 103

45. • Two blocks are connected by a string, as shown in **Figure 6–31**. The smooth inclined surface makes an angle of 35° with the horizontal, and the block on the incline has a mass of 5.7 kg. The mass of the hanging block is $m = 3.2$ kg. Find **(a)** the direction and **(b)** the magnitude of the hanging block's acceleration.

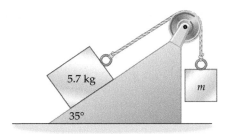

▲ **FIGURE 6–31** Problems 45 and 46

46. • Referring to Problem 45, find **(a)** the direction and **(b)** the magnitude of the hanging block's acceleration if its mass is $m = 4.2$ kg.

47. •• Referring to Figure 6–30, find the tension in the string connecting **(a)** m_1 and m_2 and **(b)** m_2 and m_3. Assume the table is frictionless and the masses move freely.

48. •• **IP** A 3.50-kg block on a smooth tabletop is attached by a string to a hanging block of mass 2.80 kg, as shown in **Figure 6–32**. The blocks are released from rest and allowed to move freely. **(a)** Is the tension in the string greater than, less than, or equal to the weight of the hanging mass? Find **(b)** the acceleration of the blocks and **(c)** the tension in the string.

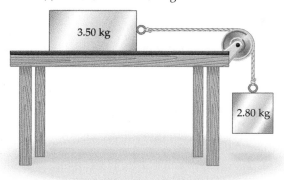

▲ **FIGURE 6–32** Problem 48

49. •• **IP** A 7.7-N force pulls horizontally on a 1.6-kg block that slides on a smooth horizontal surface. This block is connected by a horizontal string to a second block of mass $m_2 = 0.83$ kg on the same surface. **(a)** What is the acceleration of the blocks? **(b)** What is the tension in the string? **(c)** If the mass of block 1 is increased, does the tension in the string increase, decrease, or stay the same?

50. ••• **Buckets and a Pulley** Two buckets of sand hang from opposite ends of a rope that passes over an ideal pulley. One bucket is full and weighs 120 N; the other bucket is only partly filled and weighs 63 N. **(a)** Initially, you hold onto the lighter bucket to keep it from moving. What is the tension in the rope? **(b)** You release the lighter bucket and the heavier one descends. What is the tension in the rope now? **(c)** Eventually the heavier bucket lands and the two buckets come to rest. What is the tension in the rope now?

SECTION 6–5 CIRCULAR MOTION

51. • **CE** Suppose you stand on a bathroom scale and get a reading of 700 N. In principle, would the scale read more, less, or the same if the Earth did not rotate?

52. • **CE** A car drives with constant speed on an elliptical track, as shown in **Figure 6–33**. Rank the points A, B, and C in order of increasing likelihood that the car might skid. Indicate ties where appropriate.

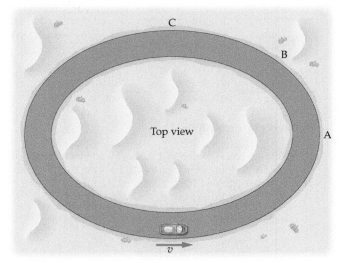

▲ **FIGURE 6–33** Problem 52

53. • **CE** A car is driven with constant speed around a circular track. Answer each of the following questions with "Yes" or "No." **(a)** Is the car's velocity constant? **(b)** Is its speed constant? **(c)** Is the magnitude of its acceleration constant? **(d)** Is the direction of its acceleration constant?

54. • **CE** A puck attached to a string undergoes circular motion on an air table. If the string breaks at the point indicated in **Figure 6–34**, is the subsequent motion of the puck best described by path A, B, C, or D?

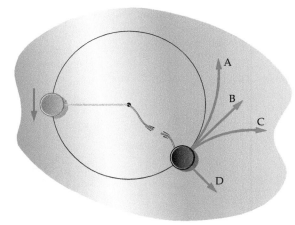

▲ **FIGURE 6–34** Problem 54

55. • When you take your 1300-kg car out for a spin, you go around a corner of radius 59 m with a speed of 16 m/s. The coefficient of static friction between the car and the road is 0.88. Assuming your car doesn't skid, what is the force exerted on it by static friction?

56. • Find the linear speed of the bottom of a test tube in a centrifuge if the centripetal acceleration there is 52,000 times the acceleration of gravity. The distance from the axis of rotation to the bottom of the test tube is 7.5 cm.

57. • **BIO A Human Centrifuge** To test the effects of high acceleration on the human body, the National Aeronautics and Space Administration (NASA) has constructed a large centrifuge at the Manned Spacecraft Center in Houston. In this device, astronauts are placed in a capsule that moves in a circular path with a radius of 15 m. If the astronauts in this centrifuge experience a centripetal acceleration 9.0 times that of gravity, what is the linear speed of the capsule?

58. • A car goes around a curve on a road that is banked at an angle of 33.5°. Even though the road is slick, the car will stay on the road without any friction between its tires and the road when its speed is 22.7 m/s. What is the radius of the curve?

59. •• Jill of the Jungle swings on a vine 6.9 m long. What is the tension in the vine if Jill, whose mass is 63 kg, is moving at 2.4 m/s when the vine is vertical?

60. •• **IP** In Problem 59, **(a)** how does the tension in the vine change if Jill's speed is doubled? Explain. **(b)** How does the tension change if her mass is doubled instead? Explain.

61. •• **IP (a)** As you ride on a Ferris wheel, your apparent weight is different at the top than at the bottom. Explain. **(b)** Calculate your apparent weight at the top and bottom of a Ferris wheel, given that the radius of the wheel is 7.2 m, it completes one revolution every 28 s, and your mass is 55 kg.

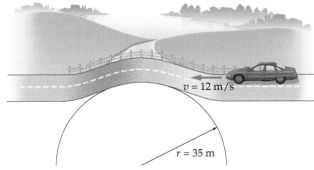

A Ferris Wheel (Problems 61 and 84)

62. •• Driving in your car with a constant speed of 12 m/s, you encounter a bump in the road that has a circular cross section, as indicated in **Figure 6–35**. If the radius of curvature of the bump is 35 m, find the apparent weight of a 67-kg person in your car as you pass over the top of the bump.

$v = 12$ m/s

$r = 35$ m

▲ **FIGURE 6–35** Problems 62 and 63

63. •• Referring to Problem 62, at what speed must you go over the bump if people in your car are to feel "weightless"?

64. •• **IP** You swing a 4.6-kg bucket of water in a vertical circle of radius 1.3 m. **(a)** What speed must the bucket have if it is to complete the circle without spilling any water? **(b)** How does your answer depend on the mass of the bucket?

GENERAL PROBLEMS

65. • **CE** If you weigh yourself on a bathroom scale at the equator, is the reading you get greater than, less than, or equal to the reading you get if you weigh yourself at the North Pole?

66. • **CE** An object moves on a flat surface with an acceleration of constant magnitude. If the acceleration is always perpendicular to the object's direction of motion, **(a)** is the shape of the object's path circular, linear, or parabolic? **(b)** During its motion, does the object's velocity change in direction but not magnitude, change in magnitude but not direction, or change in both magnitude and direction? **(c)** Does its speed increase, decrease, or stay the same?

67. • **CE BIO Maneuvering a Jet** Humans lose consciousness if exposed to prolonged accelerations of more than about 7g. This is of concern to jet fighter pilots, who may experience centripetal accelerations of this magnitude when making high-speed turns. Suppose we would like to decrease the centripetal acceleration of a jet. Rank the following changes in flight path in order of how effective they are in decreasing the centripetal acceleration, starting with the least effective: **A**, decrease the turning radius by a factor of two; **B**, decrease the speed by a factor of three; or **C**, increase the turning radius by a factor of four.

68. • **CE BIO Gravitropism** As plants grow, they tend to align their stems and roots along the direction of the gravitational field. This tendency, which is related to differential concentrations of plant hormones known as auxins, is referred to as *gravitropism*. As an illustration of gravitropism, experiments show that seedlings placed in pots on the rim of a rotating turntable do not grow in the vertical direction. Do you expect their stems to tilt inward—toward the axis of rotation—or outward—away from the axis of rotation?

69. • **BIO** A skateboard accident leaves your leg in a cast and supported by a traction device, as in Figure 6–24. Find the mass *m* that must be attached to the rope if the net force exerted by the small pulley on the foot is to have a magnitude of 37 N.

70. • Find the centripetal acceleration at the top of a test tube in a centrifuge, given that the top is 4.2 cm from the axis of rotation and that its linear speed is 77 m/s.

71. • Find the coefficient of kinetic friction between a 3.85-kg block and the horizontal surface on which it rests if an 850-N/m spring must be stretched by 6.20 cm to pull it with constant speed. Assume that the spring pulls in the horizontal direction.

72. • A child goes down a playground slide that is inclined at an angle of 26.5° below the horizontal. Find the acceleration of the child given that the coefficient of kinetic friction between the child and the slide is 0.315.

73. • When a block is placed on top of a vertical spring, the spring compresses 3.15 cm. Find the mass of the block, given that the force constant of the spring is 1750 N/m.

74. •• **The da Vinci Code** Leonardo da Vinci (1452–1519) is credited with being the first to perform quantitative experiments on friction, though his results weren't known until centuries later, due in part to the secret code (mirror writing) he used in his notebooks. Leonardo would place a block of wood on an inclined

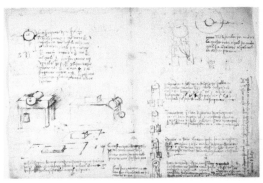

Sketches from the notebooks of Leonardo da Vinci showing experiments he performed on friction (Problem 74)

plane and measure the angle at which the block begins to slide. He reports that the coefficient of static friction was 0.25 in his experiments. At what angle did Leonardo's blocks begin to slide?

75. •• A force of 9.4 N pulls horizontally on a 1.1-kg block that slides on a rough, horizontal surface. This block is connected by a horizontal string to a second block of mass $m_2 = 1.92$ kg on the same surface. The coefficient of kinetic friction is $\mu_k = 0.24$ for both blocks. **(a)** What is the acceleration of the blocks? **(b)** What is the tension in the string?

76. •• You swing a 3.25-kg bucket of water in a vertical circle of radius 0.950 m. At the top of the circle the speed of the bucket is 3.23 m/s; at the bottom of the circle its speed is 6.91 m/s. Find the tension in the rope tied to the bucket at **(a)** the top and **(b)** the bottom of the circle.

77. •• A 14-g coin slides upward on a surface that is inclined at an angle of 18° above the horizontal. The coefficient of kinetic friction between the coin and the surface is 0.23; the coefficient of static friction is 0.35. Find the magnitude and direction of the force of friction **(a)** when the coin is sliding and **(b)** after it comes to rest.

78. •• In Problem 77, the angle of the incline is increased to 25°. Find the magnitude and direction of the force of friction when the coin is **(a)** sliding upward initially and **(b)** sliding back downward later.

79. •• A physics textbook weighing 22 N rests on a table. The coefficient of static friction between the book and the table is $\mu_s = 0.60$; the coefficient of kinetic friction is $\mu_k = 0.40$. You push horizontally on the book with a force that gradually increases from 0 to 15 N, and then slowly decreases to 5.0 N, as indicated in the following table. For each value of the applied force given in the table, give the magnitude of the force of friction and state whether the book is accelerating, decelerating, at rest, or moving with constant speed.

Applied force	Friction force	Motion
0		
5.0 N		
11 N		
15 N		
11 N		
8.0 N		
5.0 N		

80. •• A ball of mass m is placed in a wedge, as shown in **Figure 6–36**, in which the two walls meet at a right angle. Assuming the walls of the wedge are frictionless, determine the magnitude of **(a)** contact force 1 and **(b)** contact force 2.

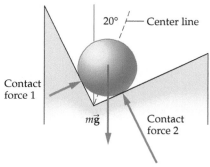

20° — Center line

Contact force 1

$m\vec{g}$

Contact force 2

▲ **FIGURE 6–36** Problem 80

81. •• **IP** The blocks shown in **Figure 6–37** are at rest. **(a)** Find the frictional force exerted on block A given that the mass of block A is 8.82 kg, the mass of block B is 2.33 kg, and the coefficient of

static friction between block A and the surface on which it rests is 0.320. **(b)** If the mass of block A is doubled, does the frictional force exerted on it increase, decrease, or stay the same? Explain.

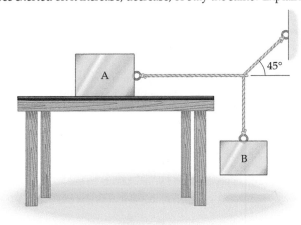

A

45°

B

▲ **FIGURE 6–37** Problems 81 and 82

82. •• In part (a) of Problem 81, what is the maximum mass block B can have and the system still be in equilibrium?

83. •• **IP** A picture hangs on the wall suspended by two strings, as shown in Figure 6–21. The tension in string 2 is 1.7 N. **(a)** Is the tension in string 1 greater than, less than, or equal to 1.7 N? Explain. **(b)** Verify your answer to part (a) by calculating the tension in string 1. **(c)** What is the mass of the picture?

84. •• **IP** Referring to Problem 61, suppose the Ferris wheel rotates fast enough to make you feel "weightless" at the top. **(a)** How many seconds does it take to complete one revolution in this case? **(b)** How does your answer to part (a) depend on your mass? Explain. **(c)** What are the direction and magnitude of your acceleration when you are at the bottom of the wheel? Assume that its rotational speed has remained constant.

85. •• **A Conical Pendulum** A 0.075-kg toy airplane is tied to the ceiling with a string. When the airplane's motor is started, it moves with a constant speed of 1.21 m/s in a horizontal circle of radius 0.44 m, as illustrated in **Figure 6–38**. Find **(a)** the angle the string makes with the vertical and **(b)** the tension in the string.

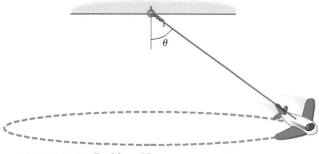

θ

▲ **FIGURE 6–38** Problem 85

86. •• A tugboat tows a barge at constant speed with a 3500-kg cable, as shown in **Figure 6–39**. If the angle the cable makes with the hor-

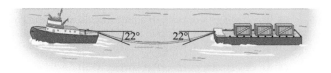

22°   22°

▲ **FIGURE 6–39** Problem 86

izontal where it attaches to the barge and the tugboat is 22°, find the force the cable exerts on the barge in the forward direction.

87. •• **IP** Two blocks, stacked one on top of the other, can move without friction on the horizontal surface shown in **Figure 6–40**. The surface between the two blocks is rough, however, with a coefficient of static friction equal to 0.47. **(a)** If a horizontal force F is applied to the 5.0-kg bottom block, what is the maximum value F can have before the 2.0-kg top block begins to slip? **(b)** If the mass of the top block is increased, does the maximum value of F increase, decrease, or stay the same? Explain.

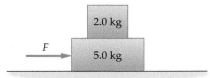

▲ **FIGURE 6–40** Problem 87

88. •• Find the coefficient of kinetic friction between a 4.7-kg block and the horizontal surface on which it rests if an 89-N/m spring must be stretched by 2.2 cm to pull the block with constant speed. Assume the spring pulls in a direction 13° above the horizontal.

89. •• **IP** In a daring rescue by helicopter, two men with a combined mass of 172 kg are lifted to safety. **(a)** If the helicopter lifts the men straight up with constant acceleration, is the tension in the rescue cable greater than, less than, or equal to the combined weight of the men? Explain. **(b)** Determine the tension in the cable if the men are lifted with a constant acceleration of $1.10 \, \text{m/s}^2$.

90. •• At the airport, you pull a 18-kg suitcase across the floor with a strap that is at an angle of 45° above the horizontal. Find **(a)** the normal force and **(b)** the tension in the strap, given that the suitcase moves with constant speed and that the coefficient of kinetic friction between the suitcase and the floor is 0.38.

91. •• **IP** A light spring with a force constant of 13 N/m is connected to a wall and to a 1.2-kg toy bulldozer, as shown in **Figure 6–41**. When the electric motor in the bulldozer is turned on, it stretches the spring for a distance of 0.45 m before its tread begins to slip on the floor. **(a)** Which coefficient of friction (static or kinetic) can be determined from this information? Explain. **(b)** What is the numerical value of this coefficient of friction?

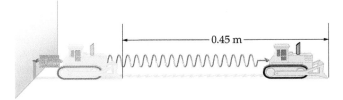

▲ **FIGURE 6–41** Problem 91

92. •• **IP** A 0.16-g spider hangs from the middle of the first thread of its future web. The thread makes an angle of 7.2° with the horizontal on both sides of the spider. **(a)** What is the tension in the thread? **(b)** If the angle made by the thread had been less than 7.2°, would its tension have been greater than, less than, or the same as in part (a)? Explain.

93. •• Find the acceleration the cart in **Figure 6–42** must have in order for the cereal box at the front of the cart not to fall. Assume that the coefficient of static friction between the cart and the box is 0.38.

94. •• **IP Playing a Violin** The tension in a violin string is 2.7 N. When pushed down against the neck of the violin, the string makes an angle of 4.1° with the horizontal. **(a)** With what force must you push down on the string to bring it into contact with the

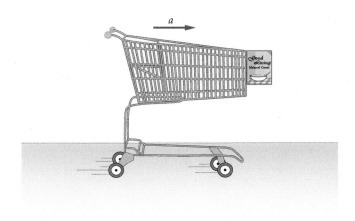

▲ **FIGURE 6–42** Problem 93

neck? **(b)** If the angle were less than 4.1°, would the required force be greater than, less than, or the same as in part (a)? Explain.

95. •• **IP** A pair of fuzzy dice hangs from a string attached to your rearview mirror. As you turn a corner with a radius of 98 m and a constant speed of 27 mi/h, what angle will the dice make with the vertical? Why is it unnecessary to give the mass of the dice?

96. •• Find the tension in each of the two ropes supporting a hammock if one is at an angle of 18° above the horizontal and the other is at an angle of 35° above the horizontal. The person sleeping in the hammock (unconcerned about tensions and ropes) has a mass of 68 kg.

97. •• As your plane circles an airport, it moves in a horizontal circle of radius 2300 m with a speed of 390 km/h. If the lift of the airplane's wings is perpendicular to the wings, at what angle should the plane be banked so that it doesn't tend to slip sideways?

98. •• **IP** A block with a mass of 3.1 kg is placed at rest on a surface inclined at an angle of 45° above the horizontal. The coefficient of static friction between the block and the surface is 0.50, and a force of magnitude F pushes upward on the block, parallel to the inclined surface. **(a)** The block will remain at rest only if F is greater than a minimum value, F_{min}, and less than a maximum value, F_{max}. Explain the reasons for this behavior. **(b)** Calculate F_{min}. **(c)** Calculate F_{max}.

99. •• A mountain climber of mass m hangs onto a rope to keep from sliding down a smooth, ice-covered slope (**Figure 6–43**). Find a formula for the tension in the rope when the slope is inclined at an angle θ above the horizontal. Check your results in the limits $\theta = 0$ and $\theta = 90°$.

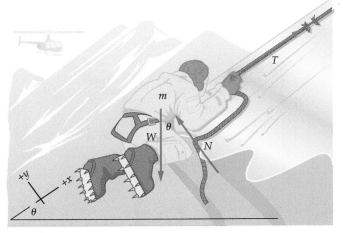

▲ **FIGURE 6–43** Problem 99

100. •• A child sits on a rotating merry-go-round, 2.3 m from its center. If the speed of the child is 2.2 m/s, what is the minimum coefficient of static friction between the child and the merry-go-round that will prevent the child from slipping?

101. ••• A 2.0-kg box rests on a plank that is inclined at an angle of 65° above the horizontal. The upper end of the box is attached to a spring with a force constant of 360 N/m, as shown in **Figure 6–44**. If the coefficient of static friction between the box and the plank is 0.22, what is the maximum amount the spring can be stretched and the box remain at rest?

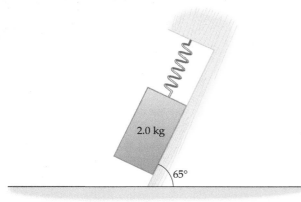

▲ **FIGURE 6–44** Problem 101

102. ••• A wood block of mass m rests on a larger wood block of mass M that rests on a wooden table. The coefficients of static and kinetic friction between all surfaces are μ_s and μ_k, respectively. What is the minimum horizontal force, F, applied to the lower block that will cause it to slide out from under the upper block?

103. ••• Find the tension in each of the two strings shown in Figure 6–30 for general values of the masses. Your answer should be in terms of m_1, m_2, m_3, and g.

104. ••• The coefficient of static friction between a rope and the table on which it rests is μ_s. Find the fraction of the rope that can hang over the edge of the table before it begins to slip.

105. ••• A hockey puck of mass m is attached to a string that passes through a hole in the center of a table, as shown in **Figure 6–45**. The hockey puck moves in a circle of radius r. Tied to the other end of the string, and hanging vertically beneath the table, is a mass M. Assuming the tabletop is perfectly smooth, what speed must the hockey puck have if the mass M is to remain at rest?

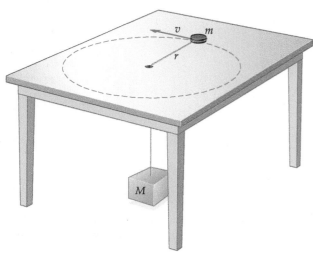

▲ **FIGURE 6–45** Problem 105

106. ••• **The Force Needed to Move a Crate** To move a crate of mass m across a rough floor, you push down on it at an angle θ, as shown in Figure 6–18 for the special case of $\theta = 21°$. **(a)** Find the force necessary to start the crate moving as a function of θ, given that the coefficient of static friction between the crate and the floor is μ_s. **(b)** Show that it is impossible to move the crate, no matter how great the force, if the coefficient of static friction is greater than or equal to $1/\tan\theta$.

107. ••• **IP** A popular ride at amusement parks is illustrated in **Figure 6–46**. In this ride, people sit in a swing that is suspended from a rotating arm. Riders are at a distance of 12 m from the axis of rotation and move with a speed of 25 mi/h. **(a)** Find the centripetal acceleration of the riders. **(b)** Find the angle θ the supporting wires make with the vertical. **(c)** If you observe a ride like that in Figure 6–46, or as shown in the photo on page 170, you will notice that all the swings are at the same angle θ to the vertical, regardless of the weight of the rider. Explain.

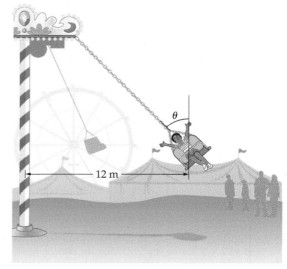

▲ **FIGURE 6–46** Problem 107

108. ••• **A Conveyor Belt** A box is placed on a conveyor belt that moves with a constant speed of 1.25 m/s. The coefficient of kinetic friction between the box and the belt is 0.780. **(a)** How much time does it take for the box to stop sliding relative to the belt? **(b)** How far does the box move in this time?

109. ••• You push a box along the floor against a constant force of friction. When you push with a horizontal force of 75 N, the acceleration of the box is 0.50 m/s²; when you increase the force to 81 N, the acceleration is 0.75 m/s². Find **(a)** the mass of the box and **(b)** the coefficient of kinetic friction between the box and the floor.

110. ••• As part of a circus act, a person drives a motorcycle with constant speed v around the inside of a vertical track of radius r, as indicated in **Figure 6–47**. If the combined mass of the motorcycle and rider is m, find the normal force exerted on the motorcycle by the track at the points **(a)** A, **(b)** B, and **(c)** C.

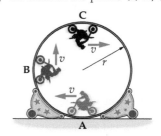

▲ **FIGURE 6–47** Problem 110

PASSAGE PROBLEMS

BIO Nasal Strips

People in all walks of life use nasal strips, or external nasal dilator strips (ENDS), to alleviate a number of respiratory problems. First introduced to eliminate snoring, they are now finding use in a number of other areas. For example, dentists have found that nasal strips help patients breathe better during dental procedures, making the experience considerably more pleasant for both doctor and patient. Surprisingly, horse owners have also discovered the advantage of nasal strips, and have begun to apply large "horse-sized" strips to saddle horses—as well as racing thoroughbreds—to reduce fatigue and lung stress.

One of the great advantages of ENDS is that no drugs are involved; the strips are a purely mechanical device, consisting of two flat, polyester springs enclosed by an adhesive tape covering. When applied to the nose, they exert an outward force that enlarges the nasal passages and reduces the resistance to air flow (see the illustration in Active Example 6–2). The mechanism shown in **Figure 6–48 (a)** is used to measure the behavior of these strips. For example, if a 30-g weight is placed on the moveable platform (of negligible mass), the strip is found to compress from an initial length of 50 mm to a reduced length of 19 mm, as can be seen in **Figure 6–48 (b)**.

111. • On the straight-line segment I in Figure 6–48 (b) we see that increasing the applied mass from 26 g to 44 g results in a

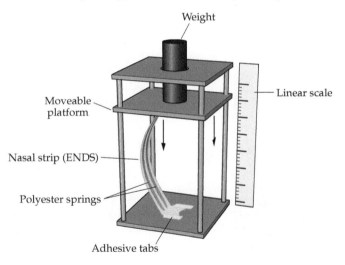

Weight

Moveable platform

Linear scale

Nasal strip (ENDS)

Polyester springs

Adhesive tabs

(a)

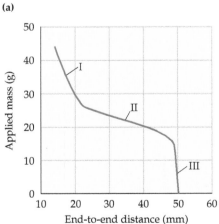

(b)

▲ **FIGURE 6–48** Problems 111, 112, 113, and 114

A thoroughbred racehorse with a nasal strip.
Did it win by a nose?

reduction of the end-to-end distance from 21 mm to 14 mm. What is the force constant in N/m on segment I?

A. 2.6 N/m **B.** 3.8 N/m

C. 9.8 N/m **D.** 25 N/m

112. • Is the force constant on segment II greater than, less than, or equal to the force constant on segment I?

113. • Which of the following is the best estimate for the force constant on segment II?

A. 0.83 N/m **B.** 1.3 N/m

C. 2.5 N/m **D.** 25 N/m

114. • Rank the straight segments I, II, and III in order of increasing "stiffness" of the nasal strip.

INTERACTIVE PROBLEMS

115. •• **IP Referring to Example 6–3** Suppose the coefficients of static and kinetic friction between the crate and the truck bed are 0.415 and 0.382, respectively. **(a)** Does the crate begin to slide at a tilt angle that is greater than, less than, or equal to 23.2°? **(b)** Verify your answer to part (a) by determining the angle at which the crate begins to slide. **(c)** Find the length of time it takes for the crate to slide a distance of 2.75 m when the tilt angle has the value found in part (b).

116. •• **IP Referring to Example 6–3** The crate begins to slide when the tilt angle is 17.5°. When the crate reaches the bottom of the flatbed, after sliding a distance of 2.75 m, its speed is 3.11 m/s. Find **(a)** the coefficient of static friction and **(b)** the coefficient of kinetic friction between the crate and the flatbed.

117. •• **Referring to Example 6–6** Suppose that the mass on the frictionless tabletop has the value $m_1 = 2.45$ kg. **(a)** Find the value of m_2 that gives an acceleration of 2.85 m/s². **(b)** What is the corresponding tension, T, in the string? **(c)** Calculate the ratio T/m_2g and show that it is less than 1, as expected.

118. •• **Referring to Example 6–8 (a)** At what speed will the force of static friction exerted on the car by the road be equal to half the weight of the car? The mass of the car is $m = 1200$ kg, the radius of the corner is $r = 45$ m, and the coefficient of static friction between the tires and the road is $\mu_s = 0.82$. **(b)** Suppose that the mass of the car is now doubled, and that it moves with a speed that again makes the force of static friction equal to half the car's weight. Is this new speed greater than, less than, or equal to the speed in part (a)?

Force, Acceleration, and Motion

Motion does not require a force— but a *change* in motion does. On these pages we explore the connections between forces, as described in Newton's laws, and the types of motion we've studied in the first six chapters.

❶ Objects that experience zero net force obey Newton's first law

If the net force $\vec{F}_{net} = \Sigma\vec{F}$ acting on an object is zero, the object's motion doesn't change—the object either remains at rest or continues to move with constant velocity, as Newton's first law states.

At rest

$\vec{N}$

$\Sigma\vec{F} = 0$
$\vec{a} = 0$

$\vec{W}$

Motion at constant velocity

$\vec{N}$

$\Sigma\vec{F} = 0$
$\vec{a} = 0$

$\vec{W}$

This behavior is consistent with Newton's second law for a net force of zero:

If the net force acting on an object is zero ... $\quad \Sigma\vec{F} = 0,\quad$ then $\quad \vec{a} = \dfrac{\Sigma\vec{F}}{m} = 0 \quad$ ... the object has zero acceleration.

❷ All objects experience forces—the question is whether the object experiences a *net* force

All objects—moving or at rest—are acted on by forces. Even in outer space, objects experience gravitational and other forces. Therefore, the *net* force on the object is the quantity that matters.

Newton's first law seems at odds with our experience: If we stop exerting a force on a moving object, the object usually stops. But that is because we must counter friction and drag forces. In the photo, the net force *on the couch* is zero even though the person exerts a steady push.

$\vec{N}$ $\quad \Sigma\vec{F} = 0$
$\vec{f}_k$ $\quad \vec{a} = 0$

$\vec{F}$

$\vec{W}$

❸ Moving at constant velocity is equivalent to being at rest

When you sit in a jet flying in a straight line, you feel the same as when you are sitting at home, and objects around you behave the same.

From the point of view of physics, *there is no difference* between these situations; Newton's laws hold in both. We say that both represent *inertial frames of reference.*

❹ Objects that experience a nonzero net force obey Newton's second law

A nonzero net force accelerates an object—that is, causes its velocity to change in magnitude, direction, or both. We have studied the following three special types of accelerated motion:

Linear accelerated motion

Projectile motion

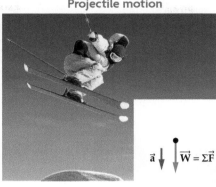

Circular motion

Accelerated motion obeys Newton's second law:

If a nonzero net force acts on an object … $\quad \Sigma\vec{F} \neq 0, \quad$ then $\quad \vec{a} = \dfrac{\Sigma\vec{F}}{m} \neq 0 \quad$ … the object has an acceleration in the direction of the net force that is proportional to $\Sigma\vec{F}$ and inversely proportional to m.

❺ The acceleration points in the direction of the net force

Linear accelerated motion
- Net force is parallel to motion.
- Velocity changes in magnitude but not in direction.

Parabolic motion
- Constant net force acts at angle to motion.
- Velocity changes in both magnitude and direction.

Circular motion (constant speed)
- Net force is constant in magnitude but always points toward the center of the circle. Thus, the net force is always at a right angle to the object's velocity.
- Velocity changes in direction but not in magnitude.

Special case: free fall
Constant downward acceleration $\vec{g}$

Special case: projectile motion
Constant downward acceleration $\vec{g}$

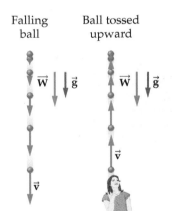

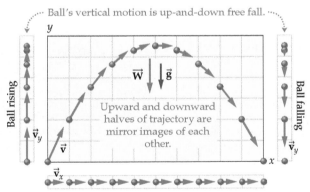

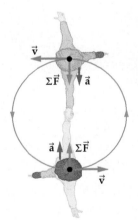

❻ The acceleration magnitude is proportional to F and inversely proportional to m

Doubling the net force acting on an object doubles the object's acceleration ($\vec{a} \propto \vec{F}$).

Doubling the object's mass m *halves* its acceleration ($\vec{a} \propto 1/m$).

mass = m

mass = $2m$

7 Work and Kinetic Energy

We all know intuitively that motion, energy, and work are somehow related. For example, the chemical energy stored in this pitcher's muscles enables him to do work on a baseball. This means, basically, that he exerts a force on it over a distance. The work done on the ball appears as kinetic energy—the energy of motion—and when the ball is caught, its kinetic energy can in turn do work on the catcher. In this chapter we'll give precise definitions of the concepts of work, kinetic energy, and power, and explore the physical relationships among them.

The concept of force is one of the foundations of physics, as we have seen in the previous two chapters. Equally fundamental, though less obvious, is the idea that a force times the displacement through which it acts is also an important physical quantity. We refer to this quantity as the *work* done by a force.

Now, we all know what work means in everyday life: We get up in the morning and go to work, or we "work up a sweat" as we hike a mountain trail. Later in the day we eat lunch, which gives us the "energy" to continue working or to continue our hike. In this chapter we give a precise physical definition of work, and show how it is related to another important physical quantity—the energy of motion, or *kinetic energy*. When these concepts are extended in the next chapter, we are led to the rather sweeping observation that the total amount of energy in the universe remains constant at all times.

7–1 Work Done by a Constant Force

In this section we define work—in the physics sense of the word—and apply our definition to a variety of physical situations. We start with the simplest case; namely, the work done when force and displacement are in the same direction. Later in the section we generalize our definition to include cases where the force and displacement are in arbitrary directions. We conclude with a discussion of the work done on an object when it is acted on by more than one force.

Force in the Direction of Displacement

When we push a shopping cart in a store or pull a suitcase through an airport, we do work. The greater the force, the greater the work; the greater the distance, the greater the work. These simple ideas form the basis for our definition of work.

To be specific, suppose we push a box with a constant force $\vec{F}$, as shown in **Figure 7–1**. If we move the box *in the direction of* $\vec{F}$ through a displacement $\vec{d}$, the **work** W we have done is Fd:

Definition of Work, W, When a Constant Force Is in the Direction of Displacement

$$W = Fd \qquad\qquad 7–1$$

SI unit: newton-meter $(N \cdot m)$ = joule, J

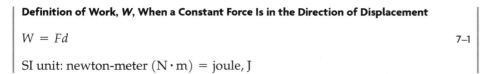
A constant force of magnitude F, ... acting in the direction of a displacement of magnitude d, ... does work $W = Fd$ on the object.

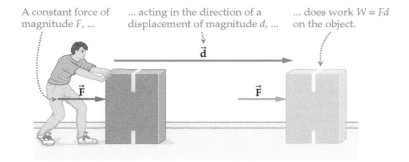
$\vec{d}$

$\vec{F}$ $\vec{F}$

◀ **FIGURE 7–1 Work: constant force in the direction of motion**

A constant force $\vec{F}$ pushes a box through a displacement $\vec{d}$. In this special case, where the force and displacement are in the *same* direction, the work done on the box by the force is $W = Fd$.

Note that work is the product of two magnitudes, and hence it is a scalar. In addition, notice that a small force acting over a large distance gives the same work as a large force acting over a small distance. For example, $W = (1\,N)(400\,m) = (400\,N)(1\,m)$.

The dimensions of work are newtons (force) times meters (distance), or $N \cdot m$. This combination of dimensions is called the **joule** (rhymes with "school," as commonly pronounced) in honor of James Prescott Joule (1818–1889), a dedicated physicist who is said to have conducted physics experiments even while on his honeymoon. We define a joule as follows:

Definition of the Joule, J

$$1 \text{ joule} = 1\,J = 1\,N \cdot m = 1(kg \cdot m/s^2) \cdot m = 1\,kg \cdot m^2/s^2 \qquad\qquad 7–2$$

To get a better feeling for work and the associated units, suppose you exert a force of 82.0 N on the box in Figure 7–1 and move it in the direction of the force through a distance of 3.00 m. The work you have done is

$$W = Fd = (82.0\,N)(3.00\,m) = 246\,N \cdot m = 246\,J$$

Similarly, if you do 5.00 J of work to lift a book through a vertical distance of 0.750 m, the force you exerted on the book is

$$F = \frac{W}{d} = \frac{5.00\,J}{0.750\,m} = \frac{5.00\,N \cdot m}{0.750\,m} = 6.67\,N$$

TABLE 7–1 Typical Values of Work

Activity	Equivalent work (J)
Annual U.S. energy use	8×10^{19}
Mt. St. Helens eruption	10^{18}
Burning one gallon of gas	10^{8}
Human food intake/day	10^{7}
Melting an ice cube	10^{4}
Lighting a 100-W bulb for 1 minute	6000
Heartbeat	0.5
Turning page of a book	10^{-3}
Hop of a flea	10^{-7}
Breaking a bond in DNA	10^{-20}

EXERCISE 7–1

One species of Darwin's finch, *Geospiza magnirostris*, can exert a force of 205 N with its beak as it cracks open a *Tribulus* seed case. If its beak moves through a distance of 0.40 cm during this operation, how much work does the finch do to get the seed?

SOLUTION

$W = Fd = (205 \text{ N})(0.0040 \text{ m}) = 0.82 \text{ J}$

Just how much work is a joule, anyway? Well, you do one joule of work when you lift a gallon of milk through a height of about an inch, or lift an apple a meter. One joule of work lights a 100-watt lightbulb for 0.01 seconds or heats a glass of water 0.00125 degrees Celsius. Clearly, a joule is a modest amount of work in everyday terms. Additional examples of work are listed in Table 7–1.

EXAMPLE 7–1   HEADING FOR THE ER

An intern pushes a 72-kg patient on a 15-kg gurney, producing an acceleration of 0.60 m/s^2. **(a)** How much work does the intern do by pushing the patient and gurney through a distance of 2.5 m? Assume the gurney moves without friction. **(b)** How far must the intern push the gurney to do 140 J of work?

PICTURE THE PROBLEM
Our sketch shows the physical situation for this problem. Note that the force exerted by the intern is in the same direction as the displacement of the gurney; therefore, we know that $W = Fd$.

STRATEGY
We are not given the magnitude of the force F, so we cannot apply Equation 7–1 directly. However, we are given the mass and acceleration of the patient and gurney, from which we can calculate the force with $F = ma$. The work done by the intern is then $W = Fd$.

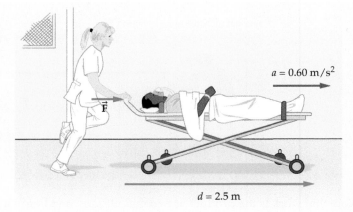

$a = 0.60 \text{ m/s}^2$

$d = 2.5 \text{ m}$

SOLUTION

Part (a)

1. First, find the force F exerted by the intern:

$F = ma = (72 \text{ kg} + 15 \text{ kg})(0.60 \text{ m/s}^2) = 52 \text{ N}$

2. The work done by the intern, W, is the force times the distance:

$W = Fd = (52 \text{ N})(2.5 \text{ m}) = 130 \text{ J}$

Part (b)

3. Use $W = Fd$ to solve for the distance d:

$W = Fd \quad \text{therefore} \quad d = \dfrac{W}{F} = \dfrac{140 \text{ J}}{52 \text{ N}} = 2.7 \text{ m}$

INSIGHT
You might wonder whether the work done by the intern depends on the speed of the gurney. The answer is no. The work done on an object, $W = Fd$, doesn't depend on whether the object moves through the distance d quickly or slowly. What does depend on the speed of the gurney is the *rate* at which work is done, as we discuss in detail in Section 7–4.

PRACTICE PROBLEM
If the total mass of the gurney plus patient is halved and the acceleration is doubled, does the work done by the intern increase, decrease, or remain the same?   [**Answer:** The work remains the same.]

Some related homework problems: Problem 4, Problem 5

Before moving on, let's note an interesting point about our definition of work. It's clear from Equation 7–1 that *the work W is zero if the distance d is zero*—and this is true regardless of how great the force might be. For example, if you push against a solid wall you do no work on it, even though you may become tired from your efforts. Similarly, if you stand in one place holding a 50-pound suitcase in your hand, you do no work on the suitcase. The fact that we become tired when we push against a wall or hold a heavy object is due to the repeated contraction and expansion of individual cells within our muscles. Thus, even when we are "at rest," our muscles are doing mechanical work on the microscopic level.

◀ The weightlifter at left does more work in raising 150 kilograms above her head than Atlas, who is supporting the entire world. Why?

Force at an Angle to the Displacement

In **Figure 7–2** we see a person pulling a suitcase on a level surface with a strap that makes an angle θ with the horizontal—in this case the force is at an angle to the direction of motion. How do we calculate the work now? Well, instead of force times distance, we say that work is the *component* of force in the *direction* of displacement times the magnitude of the displacement. In Figure 7–2, the component of force in the direction of the displacement is $F \cos \theta$ and the magnitude of the displacement is d. Therefore, the work is $F \cos \theta$ times d:

Definition of Work When the Angle Between a Constant Force and the Displacement Is θ

$$W = (F \cos \theta)d = Fd \cos \theta \qquad\qquad 7\text{–}3$$

SI unit: joule, J

Of course, in the case where the force is in the direction of motion, the angle θ is zero; then $W = Fd \cos \theta° = Fd \cdot 1 = Fd$, in agreement with Equation 7–1.

Equally interesting is a situation in which the force and the displacement are at right angles to one another. In this case $\theta = 90°$ and the work done by the force F is zero; $W = Fd \cos 90° = 0$.

This result leads naturally to an alternative way to think about the expression $W = Fd \cos \theta$. In **Figure 7–3** we show the displacement and the force for the suitcase in Figure 7–2. Notice that the displacement is equivalent to a displacement in the

The component of force in the direction of displacement is $F \cos \theta$.
This is the only component of the force that does work.

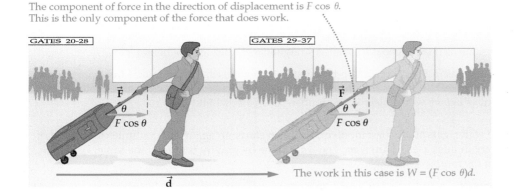

The work in this case is $W = (F \cos \theta)d$.

◀ **FIGURE 7–2 Work: force at an angle to the direction of motion**

A person pulls a suitcase with a strap at an angle θ to the direction of motion. The component of force in the direction of motion is $F \cos \theta$, and the work done by the person is $W = (F \cos \theta)d$.

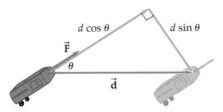

▲ **FIGURE 7–3 Force at an angle to direction of motion: another look**
The displacement of the suitcase in Figure 7–2 is equivalent to a displacement of magnitude $d \cos \theta$ in the direction of the force $\vec{F}$, plus a displacement of magnitude $d \sin \theta$ perpendicular to the force. Only the displacement parallel to the force results in nonzero work, hence the total work done is $F(d \cos \theta)$ as expected.

direction of the force of magnitude $(d \cos \theta)$ *plus* a displacement at right angles to the force of magnitude $(d \sin \theta)$. Since the displacement at right angles to the force corresponds to zero work and the displacement in the direction of the force corresponds to a work $W = F(d \cos \theta)$, it follows that the work done in this case is $Fd \cos \theta$, as given in Equation 7–3. Thus, the work done by a force can be thought of in the following two *equivalent* ways:

(i) *Work is the component of force in the direction of the displacement times the magnitude of the displacement.*

(ii) *Work is the component of displacement in the direction of the force times the magnitude of the force.*

In either of these interpretations, the mathematical expression for work is exactly the same, $W = Fd \cos \theta$, where θ is the angle between the force vector and the displacement vector when they are placed tail-to-tail. This definition of θ is illustrated in Figure 7–3.

Finally, we can also express work as the **dot product** between the vectors $\vec{F}$ and $\vec{d}$; that is, $W = \vec{F} \cdot \vec{d} = Fd \cos \theta$. Note that the dot product, which is always a scalar, is simply the magnitude of one vector times the magnitude of the second vector times the cosine of the angle between them. We discuss the dot product in greater detail in Appendix A.

EXAMPLE 7–2 GRAVITY ESCAPE SYSTEM

REAL-WORLD PHYSICS In a gravity escape system (GES), an enclosed lifeboat on a large ship is deployed by letting it slide down a ramp and then continuing in free fall to the water below. Suppose a 4970-kg lifeboat slides a distance of 5.00 m on a ramp, dropping through a vertical height of 2.50 m. How much work does gravity do on the boat?

PICTURE THE PROBLEM
From our sketch, we see that the force of gravity $m\vec{g}$ and the displacement $\vec{d}$ are at an angle θ relative to one another when placed tail-to-tail, and that θ is also the angle the ramp makes with the vertical. In addition, we note that the vertical height of the ramp is $h = 2.50$ m and the length of the ramp is $d = 5.00$ m.

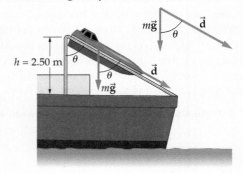

STRATEGY
By definition, the work done on the lifeboat by gravity is $W = Fd \cos \theta$, where $F = mg$, $d = 5.00$ m, and θ is the angle between $m\vec{g}$ and $\vec{d}$. We are not given θ in the problem statement, but from the right triangle that forms the ramp we see that $\cos \theta = h/d$. Once θ is determined from the geometry of our sketch, it is straightforward to calculate W.

SOLUTION

1. First, find the component of $\vec{F} = m\vec{g}$ in the direction of motion:

$$F \cos \theta = (mg)\left(\frac{h}{d}\right)$$
$$= (4970 \text{ kg})(9.81 \text{ m/s}^2)\left(\frac{2.50 \text{ m}}{5.00 \text{ m}}\right) = 24{,}400 \text{ N}$$

2. Multiply by distance to find the work:

$$W = (F \cos \theta)d = (24{,}400 \text{ N})(5.00 \text{ m}) = 122{,}000 \text{ J}$$

3. Alternatively, cancel d algebraically before substituting numerical values:

$$W = Fd \cos \theta = (mg)(d)\left(\frac{h}{d}\right)$$
$$= mgh = (4970 \text{ kg})(9.81 \text{ m/s}^2)(2.50 \text{ m}) = 122{,}000 \text{ J}$$

INSIGHT
The work is simply $W = mgh$, exactly the same as if the lifeboat had fallen straight down through the height h.

Notice that working the problem symbolically, as in Step 3, results in two distinct advantages. First, it makes for a simpler expression for the work. Second, and more importantly, it shows that the distance d cancels; hence the work depends on the height h but not on d. Such a result is not apparent when we work solely with numbers, as in Steps 1 and 2.

PRACTICE PROBLEM
Suppose the lifeboat slides halfway to the water, gets stuck for a moment, and then starts up again and continues to the end of the ramp. What is the work done by gravity in this case? [**Answer:** The work done by gravity is exactly the same, $W = mgh$, independent of how the boat moves down the ramp.]

Some related homework problems: Problem 11, Problem 12

Next, we present a Conceptual Checkpoint that compares the work required to move an object along two different paths.

PATH DEPENDENCE OF WORK

You want to load a box into the back of a truck. One way is to lift it straight up through a height h, as shown, doing a work W_1. Alternatively, you can slide the box up a loading ramp a distance L, doing a work W_2. Assuming the box slides on the ramp without friction, which of the following is correct: **(a)** $W_1 < W_2$, **(b)** $W_1 = W_2$, **(c)** $W_1 > W_2$?

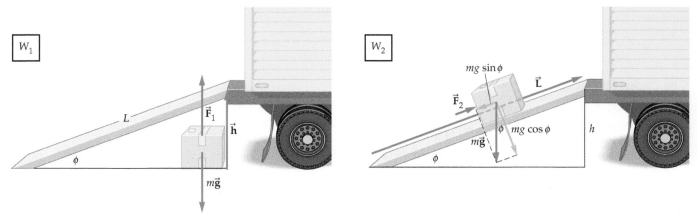

REASONING AND DISCUSSION
You might think that W_2 is less than W_1, since the force needed to slide the box up the ramp, F_2, is less than the force needed to lift it straight up. On the other hand, the distance up the ramp, L, is greater than the vertical distance, h, so perhaps W_2 should be greater than W_1. In fact, these two effects cancel exactly, giving $W_1 = W_2$.

To see this, we first calculate W_1. The force needed to lift the box with constant speed is $F_1 = mg$, and the height is h, therefore $W_1 = mgh$.

Next, the work to slide the box up the ramp with constant speed is $W_2 = F_2L$, where F_2 is the force required to push against the tangential component of gravity. In the figure we see that $F_2 = mg \sin \phi$. The figure also shows that $\sin \phi = h/L$; thus $W_2 = (mg \sin \phi)L = (mg)(h/L)L = mgh = W_1$.

Clearly, the ramp is a useful device—it reduces the *force* required to move the box upward from $F_1 = mg$ to $F_2 = mg(h/L)$. Even so, it doesn't decrease the amount of *work* we need to do. As we have seen, the reduced force on the ramp is offset by the increased distance.

ANSWER
(b) $W_1 = W_2$

Negative Work and Total Work

Work depends on the angle between the force, $\vec{\mathbf{F}}$, and the displacement (or direction of motion), $\vec{\mathbf{d}}$. This dependence gives rise to three distinct possibilities, as shown in **Figure 7–4**:

(i) *Work is positive if the force has a component in the direction of motion* $(-90° < \theta < 90°)$.

(ii) *Work is zero if the force has no component in the direction of motion* $(\theta = \pm 90°)$.

(iii) *Work is negative if the force has a component opposite to the direction of motion* $(90° < \theta < 270°)$.

Thus, whenever we calculate work, we must be careful about its sign and not just assume it to be positive.

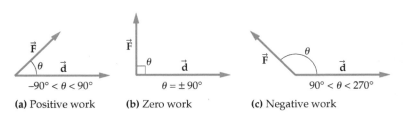

(a) Positive work   **(b)** Zero work   **(c)** Negative work

◀ **FIGURE 7–4 Positive, negative, and zero work**

Work is positive when the force is in the same general direction as the displacement and is negative if the force is generally opposite to the displacement. Zero work is done if the force is at right angles to the displacement.

Be Careful About the Angle θ

In calculating $W = Fd \cos \theta$ be sure that the angle you use in the cosine is the angle between the force and the displacement vectors when they are placed tail to tail. Sometimes θ may be used to label a different angle in a given problem. For example, θ is often used to label the angle of a slope, in which case it may have nothing to do with the angle between the force and the displacement. To summarize: Just because an angle is labeled θ doesn't mean it's automatically the correct angle to use in the work formula.

When more than one force acts on an object, the total work is the sum of the work done by each force separately. Thus, if force $\vec{F}_1$ does work W_1, force $\vec{F}_2$ does work W_2, and so on, the total work is

$$W_{total} = W_1 + W_2 + W_3 + \cdots = \sum W \qquad 7\text{--}4$$

Equivalently, the total work can be calculated by first performing a vector sum of all the forces acting on an object to obtain $\vec{F}_{total}$ and then using our basic definition of work:

$$W_{total} = (F_{total} \cos \theta)d = F_{total}\, d \cos \theta \qquad 7\text{--}5$$

where θ is the angle between $\vec{F}_{total}$ and the displacement $\vec{d}$. In the next two Examples we calculate the total work in each of these ways.

EXAMPLE 7–3   A COASTING CAR I

A car of mass m coasts down a hill inclined at an angle ϕ below the horizontal. The car is acted on by three forces: (i) the normal force $\vec{N}$ exerted by the road, (ii) a force due to air resistance, $\vec{F}_{air}$, and (iii) the force of gravity, $m\vec{g}$. Find the total work done on the car as it travels a distance d along the road.

PICTURE THE PROBLEM

Because ϕ is the angle the slope makes with the horizontal, it is also the angle between $m\vec{g}$ and the downward normal direction, as was shown in Figure 5–15. It follows that the angle between $m\vec{g}$ and the displacement $\vec{d}$ is $\theta = 90° - \phi$. Our sketch also shows that the angle between $\vec{N}$ and $\vec{d}$ is $\theta = 90°$, and the angle between $\vec{F}_{air}$ and $\vec{d}$ is $\theta = 180°$.

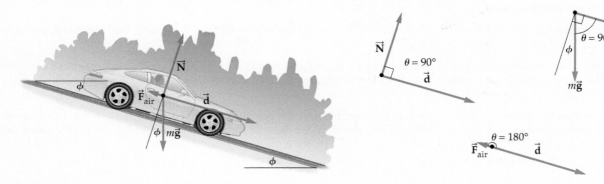

STRATEGY

For each force we calculate the work using $W = Fd \cos \theta$, where θ is the angle between that particular force and the displacement $\vec{d}$. The total work is the sum of the work done by each of the three forces.

SOLUTION

1. We start with the work done by the normal force, $\vec{N}$. From the figure we see that $\theta = 90°$ for this force:

$$W_N = Nd \cos \theta = Nd \cos 90° = Nd(0) = 0$$

2. For the force of air resistance, $\theta = 180°$:

$$W_{air} = F_{air} d \cos 180° = F_{air} d(-1) = -F_{air} d$$

3. For gravity the angle θ is $\theta = 90° - \phi$, as indicated in the figure. Recall that $\cos(90° - \phi) = \sin \phi$ (see Appendix A):

$$W_{mg} = mgd \cos(90° - \phi) = mgd \sin \phi$$

4. The total work is the sum of the individual works:

$$W_{total} = W_N + W_{air} + W_{mg} = 0 - F_{air} d + mgd \sin \phi$$

INSIGHT

The normal force is perpendicular to the motion of the car, and thus does no work. Air resistance points in a direction that opposes the motion, so it does negative work. On the other hand, gravity has a component in the direction of motion; therefore, its work is positive. The physical significance of positive, negative, and zero work will be discussed in detail in the next section.

PRACTICE PROBLEM

Calculate the total work done on a 1550-kg car as it coasts 20.4 m down a hill with $\phi = 5.00°$. Let the force due to air resistance be 15.0 N.   [**Answer:** $W_{total} = W_N + W_{air} + W_{mg} = 0 - F_{air} d + mgd \sin \phi = 0 - 306\,J + 2.70 \times 10^4\,J = 2.67 \times 10^4\,J$]

Some related homework problems: Problem 15, Problem 81

In the previous Example, we showed that the total work can be calculated by finding the work done by each force separately, and then summing the individual works. In the next Example, we take a different approach. We first sum the forces acting on the car to find F_{total}. Once the total force is determined, we calculate the total work using $W_{total} = F_{total}d \cos \theta$.

EXAMPLE 7–4   A COASTING CAR II

Consider the car described in Example 7–3. Calculate the total work done on the car using $W_{total} = F_{total}d \cos \theta$.

PICTURE THE PROBLEM

First, we choose the x axis to point down the slope, and the y axis to be at right angles to the slope. With this choice, there is no acceleration in the y direction, which means that the total force in that direction must be zero. As a result, the total force acting on the car is in the x direction. The magnitude of the total force is $mg \sin \phi - F_{air}$, as can be seen in our sketch.

STRATEGY

We begin by finding the x component of each force vector and then summing them to find the total force acting on the car. As can be seen from the figure, the total force points in the positive x direction; that is, in the same direction as the displacement. Therefore, the angle θ in $W = F_{total}d \cos \theta$ is zero.

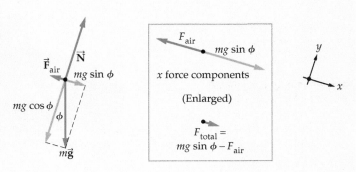

SOLUTION

1. Referring to the figure above, we see that the *magnitude* of the total force is $mg \sin \phi$ minus F_{air}:

$$F_{total} = mg \sin \phi - F_{air}$$

2. The *direction* of $\vec{F}_{total}$ is the same as the direction of $\vec{d}$, thus $\theta = 0°$. We can now calculate W_{total}:

$$W_{total} = F_{total}d \cos \theta = (mg \sin \phi - F_{air})d \cos 0°$$
$$= mgd \sin \phi - F_{air}d$$

INSIGHT

Note that we were careful to calculate both the magnitude and the direction of the total force. The magnitude (which is always positive) gives F_{total} and the direction gives $\theta = 0°$, allowing us to use $W_{total} = F_{total}d \cos \theta$.

PRACTICE PROBLEM

Suppose the total work done on a 1620-kg car as it coasts 25.0 m down a hill with $\phi = 6.00°$ is $W_{total} = 3.75 \times 10^4$ J. Find the magnitude of the force due to air resistance.   [**Answer:** $F_{air}d = -W_{total} + mgd \sin \phi = 4030$ J, thus $F_{air} = (4030\,\text{J})/d = 161$ N]

Some related homework problems: Problem 15, Problem 81

The full significance of positive versus negative work is seen in the next section, where we relate the work done on an object to the change in its speed.

7–2 Kinetic Energy and the Work–Energy Theorem

Suppose you drop an apple. As it falls, gravity does positive work on it, as indicated in **Figure 7–5**, and its speed increases. If you toss the apple upward, gravity does negative work, and the apple slows down. In general, whenever the total work done on an object is positive, its speed increases; when the total work is negative, its speed decreases. In this section we derive an important result, the **work–energy theorem,** which makes this connection between work and change in speed precise.

To begin, consider an apple of mass m falling through the air, and suppose that two forces act on the apple—gravity, $m\vec{g}$, and the average force of air resistance, $\vec{F}_{air}$. The total force acting on the apple, $\vec{F}_{total}$, gives the apple a constant downward acceleration of magnitude

$$a = F_{total}/m$$

Since the total force is downward and the motion is downward, the work done on the apple is positive.

▶ **FIGURE 7–5 Gravitational work**
The work done by gravity on an apple that moves downward is positive. If the apple is in free fall, this positive work will result in an increase in speed. On the other hand, the work done by gravity on an apple that moves upward is negative. If the apple is in free fall, the negative work done by gravity will result in a decrease of speed.

Force is in the direction of displacement ...

... so positive work is done on the apple. $\vec{d}$ $m\vec{g}$

This causes the apple to speed up.

Apple falling: $W > 0$, speed increases

Negative work done on the apple ...

$\vec{d}$ $m\vec{g}$

... causes it to slow down.

Apple tossed upward: $W < 0$, speed decreases

Now, suppose the initial speed of the apple is v_i, and that after falling a distance d its speed increases to v_f. The apple falls with constant acceleration a, hence constant-acceleration kinematics (Equation 2–12) gives

$$v_f^2 = v_i^2 + 2ad$$

or, with a slight rearrangement,

$$2ad = v_f^2 - v_i^2$$

Next, substitute $a = F_{total}/m$ into this equation:

$$2\left(\frac{F_{total}}{m}\right)d = v_f^2 - v_i^2$$

Multiplying both sides by m and dividing by 2 yields

$$F_{total}d = \tfrac{1}{2}mv_f^2 - \tfrac{1}{2}mv_i^2$$

where $F_{total}d$ is simply the total work done on the apple. Thus we find

$$W_{total} = \tfrac{1}{2}mv_f^2 - \tfrac{1}{2}mv_i^2$$

showing that total work is directly related to change in speed, as just mentioned. Note that $W_{total} > 0$ means $v_f > v_i$, $W_{total} < 0$ means $v_f < v_i$, and $W_{total} = 0$ implies that $v_f = v_i$.

The quantity $\tfrac{1}{2}mv^2$ in the equation for W_{total} has a special significance in physics, as we shall see. We call it the **kinetic energy**, K:

PROBLEM-SOLVING NOTE

Work Can Be Positive, Negative, or Zero

When you calculate work, be sure to keep track of whether it is positive or negative. The distinction is important, since positive work increases speed, whereas negative work decreases speed. Zero work, of course, has no effect on speed.

> **Definition of Kinetic Energy, K**
>
> $K = \tfrac{1}{2}mv^2$ 7–6
>
> SI unit: $kg \cdot m^2/s^2 = $ joule, J

In general, the kinetic energy of an object is the energy due to its motion. We measure kinetic energy in joules, the same units as work, and both kinetic energy and work are scalars. Unlike work, however, kinetic energy is never negative. Instead, K is always greater than or equal to zero, independent of the direction of motion or the direction of any forces.

To get a feeling for typical values of kinetic energy, consider your kinetic energy when jogging. Assuming a mass of about 62 kg and a speed of 2.5 m/s, your kinetic energy is $K = \tfrac{1}{2}(62\text{ kg})(2.5\text{ m/s})^2 = 190$ J. Additional examples of kinetic energy are given in Table 7–2.

TABLE 7–2 Typical Kinetic Energies

Source	Approximate kinetic energy (J)
Jet aircraft at 500 mi/h	10^9
Car at 60 mi/h	10^6
Home-run baseball	10^3
Person at walking speed	50
Housefly in flight	10^{-3}

EXERCISE 7–2

A truck moving at 15 m/s has a kinetic energy of 4.2×10^5 J. **(a)** What is the mass of the truck? **(b)** By what multiplicative factor does the kinetic energy of the truck increase if its speed is doubled?

SOLUTION

(a) $K = \frac{1}{2}mv^2$; therefore $m = 2K/v^2 = 3700$ kg. **(b)** Kinetic energy depends on the speed squared, and hence doubling the speed increases the kinetic energy by a factor of four.

In terms of kinetic energy, the work–energy theorem can be stated as follows:

Work–Energy Theorem
The total work done on an object is equal to the change in its kinetic energy:

$$W_{\text{total}} = \Delta K = \tfrac{1}{2}mv_f^2 - \tfrac{1}{2}mv_i^2 \qquad \qquad 7\text{–}7$$

Thus, the work–energy theorem says that when a force acts on an object over a distance—doing work on it—the result is a change in the speed of the object, and hence a change in its energy of motion. Equation 7–7 is the quantitative expression of this connection.

Finally, though we have derived the work–energy theorem for a force that is constant in direction and magnitude, it is valid for any force, as can be shown using the methods of calculus. In fact, the work–energy theorem is completely general, making it one of the more important and fundamental results in physics. It is also a very handy tool for problem solving, as we shall see many times throughout this text.

PROBLEM-SOLVING NOTE

Starts from Rest Means $v_i = 0$

A problem statement that uses a phrase like "starts from rest" or "is raised from rest" is telling you that $v_i = 0$.

EXERCISE 7–3

How much work is required for a 74-kg sprinter to accelerate from rest to 2.2 m/s?

SOLUTION

Since $v_i = 0$, we have $W = \frac{1}{2}mv_f^2 - \frac{1}{2}mv_i^2 = \frac{1}{2}mv_f^2 = \frac{1}{2}(74$ kg$)(2.2$ m/s$)^2 = 180$ J.

We now present a variety of Examples showing how the work–energy theorem is used in practical situations.

EXAMPLE 7–5 HIT THE BOOKS

A 4.10-kg box of books is lifted vertically from rest a distance of 1.60 m with a constant, upward applied force of 52.7 N. Find **(a)** the work done by the applied force, **(b)** the work done by gravity, and **(c)** the final speed of the box.

PICTURE THE PROBLEM

Our sketch shows that the direction of motion of the box is upward. In addition, we see that the applied force, $\vec{F}_{\text{app}}$, is upward and the force of gravity, $m\vec{g}$, is downward. Finally, the box is lifted from rest ($v_i = 0$) through a distance $\Delta y = 1.60$ m.

STRATEGY

The applied force is in the direction of motion, so the work it does, W_{app}, is positive. Gravity is opposite in direction to the motion; thus its work, W_g, is negative. The total work is the sum of W_{app} and W_g, and the final speed of the box is found by applying the work–energy theorem, $W_{\text{total}} = \Delta K$.

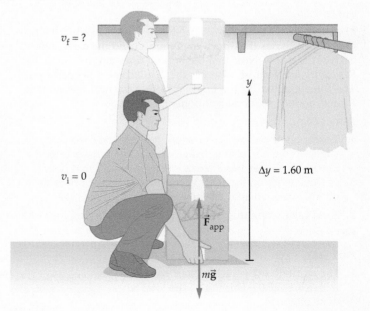

CONTINUED ON NEXT PAGE

CONTINUED FROM PREVIOUS PAGE

SOLUTION

Part (a)

1. First we find the work done by the applied force. In this case, $\theta = 0°$ and the distance is $\Delta y = 1.60$ m:

$$W_{app} = F_{app} \cos 0° \, \Delta y = (52.7 \text{ N})(1)(1.60 \text{ m}) = 84.3 \text{ J}$$

Part (b)

2. Next, we calculate the work done by gravity. The distance is $\Delta y = 1.60$ m, as before, but now $\theta = 180°$:

$$W_g = mg \cos 180° \, \Delta y$$
$$= (4.10 \text{ kg})(9.81 \text{ m/s}^2)(-1)(1.60 \text{ m}) = -64.4 \text{ J}$$

Part (c)

3. The total work done on the box, W_{total}, is the sum of W_{app} and W_g:

$$W_{total} = W_{app} + W_g = 84.3 \text{ J} - 64.4 \text{ J} = 19.9 \text{ J}$$

4. To find the final speed, v_f, we apply the work–energy theorem. Recall that the box started at rest, thus $v_i = 0$:

$$W_{total} = \tfrac{1}{2}mv_f^2 - \tfrac{1}{2}mv_i^2 = \tfrac{1}{2}mv_f^2$$

$$v_f = \sqrt{\frac{2W_{total}}{m}} = \sqrt{\frac{2(19.9 \text{ J})}{4.10 \text{ kg}}} = 3.12 \text{ m/s}$$

INSIGHT

As a check on our result, we can find v_f in a completely different way. First, calculate the acceleration of the box with the result $a = (F_{app} - mg)/m = 3.04$ m/s^2. Next, use this result in the kinematic equation $v^2 = v_0^2 + 2a\Delta y$. With $v_0 = 0$ and $\Delta y = 1.60$ m, we find $v = 3.12$ m/s, in agreement with the results using the work–energy theorem.

PRACTICE PROBLEM

If the box is lifted only a quarter of the distance, is the final speed 1/8, 1/4, or 1/2 of the value found in Step 4? Calculate v_f in this case as a check on your answer. **[Answer:** Since work depends linearly on Δy, and v_f depends on the square root of the work, it follows that the final speed is $\sqrt{1/4} = \tfrac{1}{2}$ the value in Step 4. Letting $\Delta y = (1.60 \text{ m})/4 = 0.400$ m, we find $v_f = \tfrac{1}{2}(3.12 \text{ m/s}) = 1.56 \text{ m/s}.$**]**

Some related homework problems: Problem 19, Problem 24, Problem 25

In the previous Example the initial speed was zero. This is not always the case, of course. The next Example illustrates how to use the work–energy theorem when the initial velocity is nonzero.

EXAMPLE 7–6 PULLING A SLED

A boy exerts a force of 11.0 N at 29.0° above the horizontal on a 6.40-kg sled. Find **(a)** the work done by the boy and **(b)** the final speed of the sled after it moves 2.00 m, assuming the sled starts with an initial speed of 0.500 m/s and slides horizontally without friction.

PICTURE THE PROBLEM

Our sketch shows the direction of motion and the directions of each of the forces. Note that the normal force and the force due to gravity are vertical, whereas the displacement is horizontal. The force exerted by the boy has both a vertical component, $F \sin \theta$, and a horizontal component, $F \cos \theta$.

STRATEGY

a. The forces $\vec{N}$ and $m\vec{g}$ do no work because they are at right angles to the horizontal displacement. The force exerted by the boy, however, has a horizontal component that does positive work on the sled. Therefore, the total work is simply the work done by the boy.

b. After calculating this work, we find v_f by applying the work–energy theorem with $v_i = 0.500$ m/s.

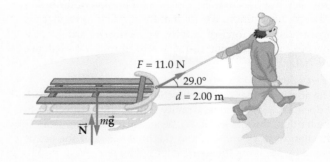

SOLUTION

Part (a)

1. The work done by the boy is $(F \cos \theta)d$, where $\theta = 29.0°$. This is also the total work done on the sled:

$$W_{boy} = (F \cos \theta)d$$
$$= (11.0 \text{ N})(\cos 29.0°)(2.00 \text{ m}) = 19.2 \text{ J} = W_{total}$$

Part (b)

2. Use the work-energy theorem to solve for the final speed:

$$W_{\text{total}} = \Delta K = \tfrac{1}{2}mv_f^2 - \tfrac{1}{2}mv_i^2$$

$$\tfrac{1}{2}mv_f^2 = W_{\text{total}} + \tfrac{1}{2}mv_i^2$$

$$v_f = \sqrt{\frac{2W_{\text{total}}}{m} + v_i^2}$$

3. Substitute numerical values to get the final answer:

$$v_f = \sqrt{\frac{2(19.2\text{ J})}{6.40\text{ kg}} + (0.500\text{ m/s})^2}$$

$$= 2.50\text{ m/s}$$

INSIGHT

If the sled had started from rest, instead of with an initial speed of 0.500 m/s, would its final speed be 2.50 m/s − 0.500 m/s = 2.00 m/s?

No. If the initial speed is zero, then $v_f = \sqrt{\dfrac{2W_{\text{total}}}{m}} = \sqrt{\dfrac{2(19.2\text{ J})}{6.40\text{ kg}}} = 2.45$ m/s. Why don't the speeds add and subtract in a straightforward way? The reason is that the work-energy theorem depends on the *square* of the speeds rather than on v_i and v_f directly.

PRACTICE PROBLEM

Suppose the sled starts with a speed of 0.500 m/s and has a final speed of 2.50 m/s after the boy pulls it through a distance of 3.00 m. What force did the boy exert on the sled? **[Answer:** $F = W_{\text{total}}/(d\cos\theta) = \Delta K/(d\cos\theta) = 7.32$ N**]**

Some related homework problems: Problem 28, Problem 61

The final speeds in the previous Examples could have been found using Newton's laws and the constant-acceleration kinematics of Chapter 2, as indicated in the Insight following Example 7–5. The work-energy theorem provides an alternative method of calculation that is often much easier to apply than Newton's laws. We return to this point in Chapter 8.

PROBLEM-SOLVING NOTE

Be Careful About Linear Reasoning

Though some relations are linear—if you *double* the mass, you *double* the kinetic energy—others are not. For example, if you *double* the speed, you *quadruple* the kinetic energy. Be careful not to jump to conclusions based on linear reasoning.

CONCEPTUAL CHECKPOINT 7–2   COMPARE THE WORK

To accelerate a certain car from rest to the speed v requires the work W_1. The work needed to accelerate the car from v to $2v$ is W_2. Which of the following is correct: **(a)** $W_2 = W_1$, **(b)** $W_2 = 2\,W_1$, **(c)** $W_2 = 3W_1$, **(d)** $W_2 = 4W_1$?

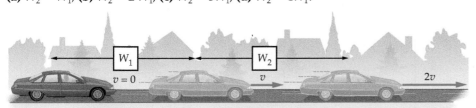

REASONING AND DISCUSSION

A common mistake is to reason that since we increase the speed by the same amount in each case, the work required is the same. It is not, and the reason is that work depends on the speed squared rather than on the speed itself.

To see how this works, first calculate W_1, the work needed to go from rest to a speed v.

From the work-energy theorem, with $v_i = 0$ and $v_f = v$, we find $W_1 = \tfrac{1}{2}mv_f^2 - \tfrac{1}{2}mv_i^2 = \tfrac{1}{2}mv^2$. Similarly, the work needed to go from rest, $v_i = 0$, to a speed $v_f = 2v$, is simply $\tfrac{1}{2}m(2v)^2 = 4\left(\tfrac{1}{2}mv^2\right) = 4W_1$. Therefore, the work needed to increase the speed from v to $2v$ is the difference: $W_2 = 4W_1 - W_1 = 3W_1$.

ANSWER

(c) $W_2 = 3W_1$

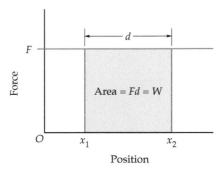

▲ **FIGURE 7–6 Graphical representation of the work done by a constant force**

A constant force F acting through a distance d does a work $W = Fd$. Note that Fd is also equal to the shaded area between the force line and the x axis.

7–3 Work Done by a Variable Force

Thus far we have calculated work only for constant forces, yet most forces in nature vary with position. For example, the force exerted by a spring depends on how far the spring is stretched, and the force of gravity between planets depends on their separation. In this section we show how to calculate the work for a force that varies with position.

First, let's review briefly the case of a constant force, and develop a graphical interpretation of work. **Figure 7–6** shows a constant force plotted versus position, x. If the force acts in the positive x direction and moves an object a distance d, from x_1 to x_2, the work it does is $W = Fd = F(x_2 - x_1)$. Referring to the figure, we see that the work is equal to the shaded area[1] between the force line and the x axis.

Next, consider a force that has the value F_1 from $x = 0$ to $x = x_1$ and a different value F_2 from $x = x_1$ to $x = x_2$, as in **Figure 7–7 (a)**. The work in this case is the sum of the works done by F_1 and F_2. Therefore, $W = F_1 x_1 + F_2(x_2 - x_1)$ which, again, is the area between the force lines and the x axis. Clearly, this type of calculation can be extended to a force with any number of different values, as indicated in **Figure 7–7 (b)**.

If a force varies continuously with position, we can approximate it with a series of constant values that follow the shape of the curve, as shown in **Figure 7–8 (a)**. It follows that the work done by the continuous force is approximately equal to the area of the corresponding rectangles, as **Figure 7–8 (b)** shows. The approximation can be made better by using more rectangles, as illustrated in **Figure 7–8 (c)**. In the

▶ **FIGURE 7–7 Work done by a nonconstant force**

(a) A force with a value F_1 from 0 to x_1 and a value F_2 from x_1 to x_2 does the work $W = F_1 x_1 + F_2(x_2 - x_1)$. This is simply the area of the two shaded rectangles. **(b)** If a force takes on a number of different values, the work it does is still the total area between the force lines and the x axis, just as in part (a).

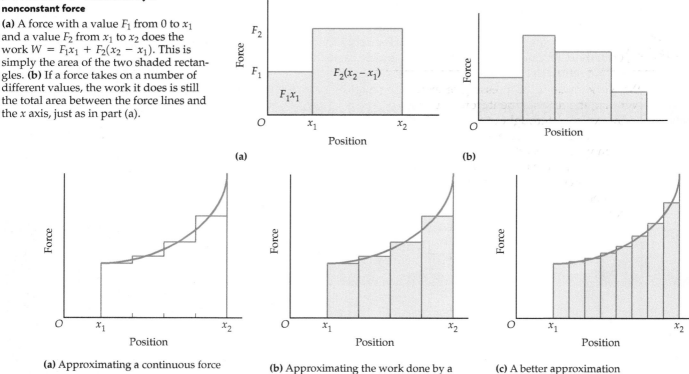

(a) Approximating a continuous force

(b) Approximating the work done by a continuous force

(c) A better approximation

▲ **FIGURE 7–8 Work done by a continuously varying force**

(a) A continuously varying force can be approximated by a series of constant values that follow the shape of the curve. **(b)** The work done by the continuous force is approximately equal to the area of the small rectangles corresponding to the constant values of force shown in part (a). **(c)** In the limit of an infinite number of vanishingly small rectangles, we see that the work done by the force is equal to the area between the force curve and the x axis.

---

[1]Usually, area has the dimensions of (length) × (length), or length². In this case, however, the vertical axis is force and the horizontal axis is distance. As a result, the dimensions of area are (force) × (distance), which in SI units is N · m = J.

limit of an infinite number of vanishingly small rectangles, the area of the rectangles becomes identical to the area under the force curve. Hence this area is the work done by the continuous force. To summarize:

The work done by a force in moving an object from x_1 to x_2 is equal to the corresponding area between the force curve and the x axis.

A case of particular interest is that of a spring. Since the force exerted by a spring is given by $F_x = -kx$ (Section 6–2), it follows that the force we must exert to hold it at the position x is $+kx$. This is illustrated in **Figure 7–9**, where we also show that the corresponding force curve is a straight line extending from the origin. Therefore, the work we do in stretching a spring from $x = 0$ (equilibrium) to the general position x is the shaded, triangular area shown in **Figure 7–10**. This area is equal to $\frac{1}{2}$(base)(height), where in this case the base is x and the height is kx. As a result, the work is $\frac{1}{2}(x)(kx) = \frac{1}{2}kx^2$. Similar reasoning shows that the work needed to compress a spring a distance x is also $\frac{1}{2}kx^2$. Therefore,

Work to Stretch or Compress a Spring a Distance x from Equilibrium

$$W = \tfrac{1}{2}kx^2 \qquad\qquad 7\text{–}8$$

SI unit: joule, J

We can get a feeling for the amount of work required to compress a typical spring in the following Exercise.

EXERCISE 7–4

The spring in a pinball launcher has a force constant of 405 N/m. How much work is required to compress the spring a distance of 3.00 cm?

SOLUTION

$W = \frac{1}{2}kx^2 = \frac{1}{2}(405\ \text{N/m})(0.0300\ \text{m})^2 = 0.182\ \text{J}$

Note that the work done in compressing or expanding a spring varies with the second power of x, the displacement from equilibrium. The consequences of this dependence are explored throughout the rest of this section.

Before we consider a specific example, however, recall that the results for a spring apply to more than just the classic case of a helical coil of wire. In fact, any flexible structure satisfies the relations $F_x = -kx$ and $W = \frac{1}{2}kx^2$, given the appropriate value of the force constant, k, and small enough displacements, x. Several examples were mentioned in Section 6–2.

Here we consider an example from the field of nanotechnology; namely, the cantilevers used in **atomic-force microscopy** (AFM). As we show in Example 7–7, a typical atomic-force cantilever is basically a thin silicon bar about 250 µm in length, supported at one end like a diving board, with a sharp, hanging point at the other end. When the point is pulled across the surface of a material—like an old-fashioned phonograph needle in the groove of a record—individual atoms on the surface cause the point to move up and down, deflecting the cantilever. These deflections, which can be measured by reflecting a laser beam from the top of the cantilever, are then converted into an atomic-level picture of the surface, as shown in the accompanying photograph.

A typical force constant for an AFM cantilever is on the order of 1 N/m, much smaller than the 100–500 N/m force constant of a common lab spring. The implications of this are discussed in the following Example.

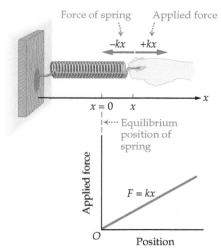

▲ **FIGURE 7–9 Stretching a spring**
The force we must exert on a spring to stretch it a distance x is $+kx$. Thus, applied force versus position for a spring is a straight line of slope k.

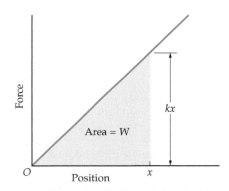

▲ **FIGURE 7–10 Work needed to stretch a spring a distance x**
The work done is equal to the shaded area, which is a right triangle. The area of the triangle is $\frac{1}{2}(x)(kx) = \frac{1}{2}kx^2$.

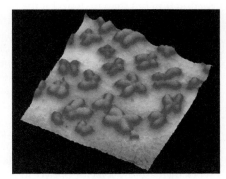

▲ Human chromosomes, as imaged by an atomic-force microscope.

EXAMPLE 7–7 FLEXING AN AFM CANTILEVER

The work required to deflect a typical AFM cantilever by 0.10 nm is 1.2×10^{-20} J. **(a)** What is the force constant of the cantilever, treating it as an ideal spring? **(b)** How much work is required to increase the deflection of the cantilever from 0.10 nm to 0.20 nm?

CONTINUED ON NEXT PAGE

CONTINUED FROM PREVIOUS PAGE

PICTURE THE PROBLEM

The sketch on the left shows the cantilever and its sharp point being dragged across the surface of a material. In the sketch to the right, we show an exaggerated view of the cantilever's deflection, and indicate that it is equivalent to the stretch of an "effective" ideal spring with a force constant k.

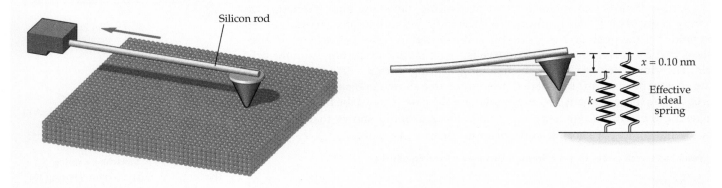

Silicon rod

$x = 0.10$ nm

k

Effective ideal spring

STRATEGY

a. Given that $W = 1.2 \times 10^{-20}$ J for a deflection of $x = 0.10$ nm, we can find the effective force constant k using $W = \frac{1}{2}kx^2$.

b. To find the work required to deflect from $x = 0.10$ nm to $x = 0.20$ nm, $W_{1\rightarrow2}$, we calculate the work to deflect from $x = 0$ to $x = 0.20$ nm, $W_{0\rightarrow2}$, and then subtract the work needed to deflect from $x = 0$ to $x = 0.10$ nm, $W_{0\rightarrow1}$. (Note that we *cannot* simply assume the work to go from $x = 0.10$ nm to $x = 0.20$ nm is the same as the work to go from $x = 0$ to $x = 0.10$ nm.)

SOLUTION

Part (a)

1. Solve $W = \frac{1}{2}kx^2$ for the force constant k:

$$k = \frac{2W}{x^2} = \frac{2(1.2 \times 10^{-20}\,\text{J})}{(0.10 \times 10^{-9}\,\text{m})^2} = 2.4\,\text{N/m}$$

Part (b)

2. First, calculate the work needed to deflect the cantilever from $x = 0$ to $x = 0.20$ nm:

$$W_{0\rightarrow2} = \frac{1}{2}kx^2$$
$$= \frac{1}{2}(2.4\,\text{N/m})(0.2 \times 10^{-9}\,\text{m})^2 = 4.8 \times 10^{-20}\,\text{J}$$

3. Subtract from the above result the work to deflect from $x = 0$ to $x = 0.10$ nm, which the problem statement gives as 1.2×10^{-20} J:

$$W_{1\rightarrow2} = W_{0\rightarrow2} - W_{0\rightarrow1}$$
$$= 4.8 \times 10^{-20}\,\text{J} - 1.2 \times 10^{-20}\,\text{J} = 3.6 \times 10^{-20}\,\text{J}$$

INSIGHT

Our results show that more energy is needed to deflect the cantilever the second 0.10 nm than to deflect it the first 0.10 nm. Why? The reason is that the force of the cantilever increases with distance; thus, the average force over the second 0.10 nm is greater than the average force over the first 0.10 nm. In fact, we can see from the adjacent figure that the average force between 0.10 nm and 0.20 nm (3.6 nN) is three times the average force between 0 and 0.10 nm (1.2 nN). It follows, then, that the work required for the second 0.10 nm is three times the work required for the first 0.10 nm.

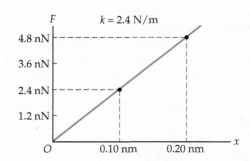

PRACTICE PROBLEM

A second cantilever has half the force constant of the cantilever in this Example. Is the work required to deflect the second cantilever by 0.20 nm greater than, less than, or equal to the work required to deflect the cantilever in this Example by 0.10 nm? [**Answer:** Halving the force constant halves the work, but doubling the deflection quadruples the work. The net effect is that the work increases by a factor of two, to 2.4×10^{-20} J.]

Some related homework problems: Problem 32, Problem 38

An equivalent way to calculate the work for a variable force is to multiply the average force, F_{av}, by the distance, d:

$$W = F_{av}d$$

For a spring that is stretched a distance x from equilibrium the force varies linearly from 0 to kx. Thus, the average force is $F_{av} = \frac{1}{2}kx$, as indicated in **Figure 7–11**. Therefore, the work is

$$W = \tfrac{1}{2}kx(x) = \tfrac{1}{2}kx^2$$

As expected, our result agrees with Equation 7–8.

Finally, when you stretch or compress a spring from its equilibrium position, the work you do is always positive. The work done *by* a spring, however, may be positive or negative, depending on the situation. For example, consider a block sliding to the right with an initial speed v_0 on a smooth, horizontal surface, as shown in **Figure 7–12 (a)**. When the block begins to compress the spring, as in **Figure 7–12 (b)**, the spring exerts a force on the block to the left—that is, opposite to the block's direction of motion. As a result, the spring does *negative* work on the block, which causes the block's speed to decrease. Eventually the negative work done by the spring, $W = -\frac{1}{2}kx^2$, is equal in magnitude to the initial kinetic energy of the block. At this point, **Figure 7–12 (c)**, the block comes to rest momentarily, and $W = \Delta K = K_f - K_i = 0 - K_i = -K_i = -\frac{1}{2}mv_0^2 = -\frac{1}{2}kx^2$. We apply this result in Active Example 7–1.

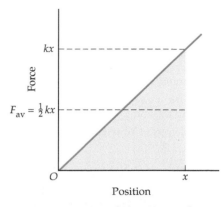

▲ **FIGURE 7–11 Work done in stretching a spring: average force**
The average force of a spring from $x = 0$ to x is $F_{av} = \frac{1}{2}kx$, and the work done is $W = F_{av}d = \frac{1}{2}kx(x) = \frac{1}{2}kx^2$.

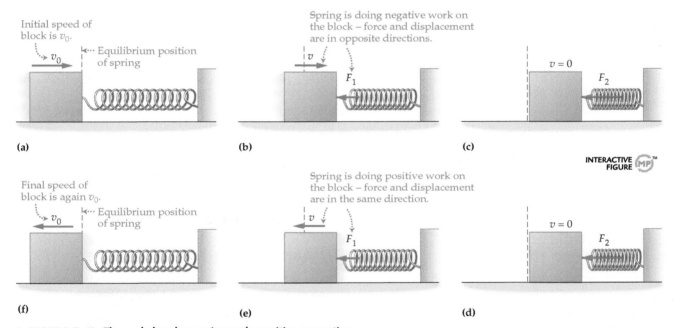

(a)   **(b)**   **(c)**

INTERACTIVE FIGURE (MP)™

(f)   **(e)**   **(d)**

▲ **FIGURE 7–12 The work done by a spring can be positive or negative**
(a) A block slides to the right on a frictionless surface with a speed v_0 until it encounters a spring. **(b)** The spring now exerts a force to the left—opposite to the block's motion—and hence it does negative work on the block. This causes the block's speed to decrease. **(c)** The negative work done by the spring eventually is equal in magnitude to the block's initial kinetic energy, at which point the block comes to rest momentarily. As the spring expands, **(d)** and **(e)**, it does positive work on the block and increases its speed. **(f)** When the block leaves the spring its speed is again equal to v_0.

ACTIVE EXAMPLE 7–1   A BLOCK COMPRESSES A SPRING

Suppose the block in Figure 7–12 (a) has a mass of 1.5 kg and moves with an initial speed of $v_0 = 2.2$ m/s. Find the compression of the spring, whose force constant is 475 N/m, when the block momentarily comes to rest.

SOLUTION *(Test your understanding by performing the calculations indicated in each step.)*

1. Calculate the initial and final kinetic energies of the block: $K_i = 3.6$ J, $K_f = 0$

2. Calculate the change in kinetic energy of the block: $\Delta K = -3.6$ J

3. Set the negative work done by the spring equal to the change in kinetic energy of the block: $-\frac{1}{2}kx^2 = \Delta K = -3.6$ J

4. Solve for the compression, x, and substitute numerical values: $x = 0.12$ m

CONTINUED ON NEXT PAGE

CONTINUED FROM PREVIOUS PAGE

INSIGHT

After the block comes to rest, the spring expands back to its equilibrium position, as shown in **Figures 7–12 (d)–(f)**. During this expansion the force exerted by the spring is in the same direction as the block's motion, and hence it does *positive* work in the amount $W = \frac{1}{2}kx^2$. As a result, the block leaves the spring with the same speed it had initially.

YOUR TURN

Find the compression of the spring for the case where the mass of the block is doubled to 3.0 kg.

*(Answers to **Your Turn** problems are given in the back of the book.)*

7–4 Power

Power is a measure of how *quickly* work is done. To be precise, suppose the work W is performed in the time t. The average power delivered during this time is defined as follows:

Definition of Average Power, P

$$P = \frac{W}{t} \qquad \qquad 7\text{--}10$$

SI unit: J/s = watt, W

For simplicity of notation we drop the usual subscript av for an average quantity and simply understand that the power P refers to an average power unless stated otherwise.

Note that the dimensions of power are joules (work) per second (time). We define one joule per second to be a watt (W), after James Watt (1736–1819), the Scottish engineer and inventor who played a key role in the development of practical steam engines:

$$1 \text{ watt} = 1 \text{ W} = 1 \text{ J/s} \qquad \qquad 7\text{--}11$$

Of course, the watt is the unit of power used to rate the output of lightbulbs. Another common unit of power is the horsepower (hp), which is used to rate the output of car engines. It is defined as follows:

$$1 \text{ horsepower} = 1 \text{ hp} = 746 \text{ W} \qquad \qquad 7\text{--}12$$

Though it sounds like a horse should be able to produce one horsepower, in fact, a horse can generate only about 2/3 hp for sustained periods. The reason for the discrepancy is that when James Watt defined the horsepower—as a way to characterize the output of his steam engines—he purposely chose a unit that was overly generous to the horse, so that potential investors couldn't complain he was overstating the capability of his engines.

To get a feel for the magnitude of the watt and the horsepower, consider the power you might generate when walking up a flight of stairs. Suppose, for example, that an 80.0-kg person walks up a flight of stairs in 20.0 s, and that the altitude gain is 12.0 ft (3.66 m). Referring to Example 7–2 and Conceptual Checkpoint 7–1, we find that the work done by the person is $W = mgh = (80.0 \text{ kg})(9.81 \text{ m/s}^2)(3.66 \text{ m}) = 2870 \text{ J}$. To find the power, we simply divide by the time: $P = W/t = (2870 \text{ J})/(20.0 \text{ s}) = 144 \text{ W} = 0.193 \text{ hp}$. Thus, a leisurely stroll up the stairs requires about 1/5 hp or 150 W. Similarly, the power produced by a sprinter bolting out of the starting blocks is about 1 hp, and the greatest power most people can produce for sustained periods of time is roughly 1/3 to 1/2 hp. Further examples of power are given in Table 7–3.

Human-powered flight is a feat just barely within our capabilities, since the most efficient human-powered airplanes require a steady power output of about 1/3 hp. On August 23, 1977, the *Gossamer Condor*, designed by Paul MacCready and flown by Bryan Allen, became the first human-powered airplane to complete a prescribed one-mile, figure-eight course and claim the Kremer Prize of £50,000. Allen, an accomplished bicycle racer, used bicycle-like pedals to spin the pro-

TABLE 7–3 Typical Values of Power

Source	Approximate power (W)
Hoover Dam	1.34×10^9
Car moving at 40 mi/h	7×10^4
Home stove	1.2×10^4
Sunlight falling on one square meter	1380
Refrigerator	615
Television	200
Person walking up stairs	150
Human brain	20

REAL-WORLD PHYSICS: BIO

Human power output and flight

▲ The *Gossamer Albatross* on its record-breaking flight across the English Channel in 1979. On two occasions the aircraft actually touched the surface of the water, but the pilot was able to maintain control and complete the 22.25-mile flight.

peller. Controlling the slow-moving craft while pedaling at full power was no easy task. Allen also piloted the *Gossamer Albatross*, which, in 1979, became the first (and so far the only) human-powered aircraft to fly across the English Channel. This 22.25-mile flight—from Folkestone, England, to Cap Gris-Nez, France—took 2 hours 49 minutes and required a total energy output roughly equivalent to climbing to the top of the Empire State Building 10 times.

Power output is also an important factor in the performance of a car. For example, suppose it takes a certain amount of work, W, to accelerate a car from 0 to 60 mi/h. If the average power provided by the engine is P, then according to Equation 7–10 the amount of time required to reach 60 mi/h is $t = W/P$. Clearly, the greater the power P, the less the time required to accelerate. Thus, in a loose way of speaking, we can say that the power of a car is a measure of "how fast it can go fast."

EXAMPLE 7–8   PASSING FANCY

To pass a slow-moving truck, you want your fancy 1.30×10^3-kg car to accelerate from 13.4 m/s (30.0 mi/h) to 17.9 m/s (40.0 mi/h) in 3.00 s. What is the minimum power required for this pass?

PICTURE THE PROBLEM
Our sketch shows the car accelerating from an initial speed of $v_i = 13.4$ m/s to a final speed of $v_f = 17.9$ m/s. We assume the road is level, so that no work is done against gravity, and that friction and air resistance may be ignored.

STRATEGY
Power is work divided by time, and work is equal to the change in kinetic energy as the car accelerates. We can determine the change in kinetic energy from the given mass of the car and its initial and final speeds. With this information at hand, we can determine the power with the relation $P = W/t = \Delta K/t$.

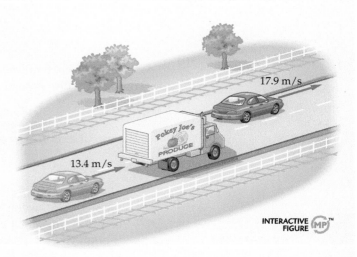

SOLUTION

1. First, calculate the change in kinetic energy:

$$\Delta K = \tfrac{1}{2}mv_f^2 - \tfrac{1}{2}mv_i^2 = \tfrac{1}{2}(1.30 \times 10^3 \text{ kg})(17.9 \text{ m/s})^2$$
$$- \tfrac{1}{2}(1.30 \times 10^3 \text{ kg})(13.4 \text{ m/s})^2$$
$$= 9.16 \times 10^4 \text{ J}$$

2. Divide by time to find the minimum power. (The actual power would have to be greater to overcome frictional losses.):

$$P = \frac{W}{t} = \frac{\Delta K}{t} = \frac{9.16 \times 10^4 \text{ J}}{3.00 \text{ s}} = 3.05 \times 10^4 \text{ W} = 40.9 \text{ hp}$$

INSIGHT
Suppose that your fancy car continues to produce the same 3.05×10^4 W of power as it accelerates from $v = 17.9$ m/s (40.0 mi/h) to $v = 22.4$ ms (50.0 mi/h). Is the time required more than, less than, or equal to 3.00 s? It will take more than 3.00 s. The reason is that ΔK is greater for a change in speed from 40.0 mi/h to 50.0 mi/h than for a change in speed from 30.0 mi/h to 40.0 mi/h, because K depends on speed squared. Since ΔK is greater, the time $t = \Delta K/P$ is also greater.

PRACTICE PROBLEM
Find the time required to accelerate from 40.0 mi/h to 50.0 mi/h with 3.05×10^4 W of power.   [**Answer:** First, $\Delta K = 1.18 \times 10^5$ J. Second, $P = \Delta K/t$ can be solved for time to give $t = \Delta K/P$. Thus, $t = 3.87$ s.]

Some related homework problems: Problem 44, Problem 59

Finally, consider a system in which a car, or some other object, is moving with a constant speed v. For example, a car might be traveling uphill on a road inclined at an angle θ above the horizontal. To maintain a constant speed, the engine must exert a constant force F equal to the combined effects of friction, gravity, and air

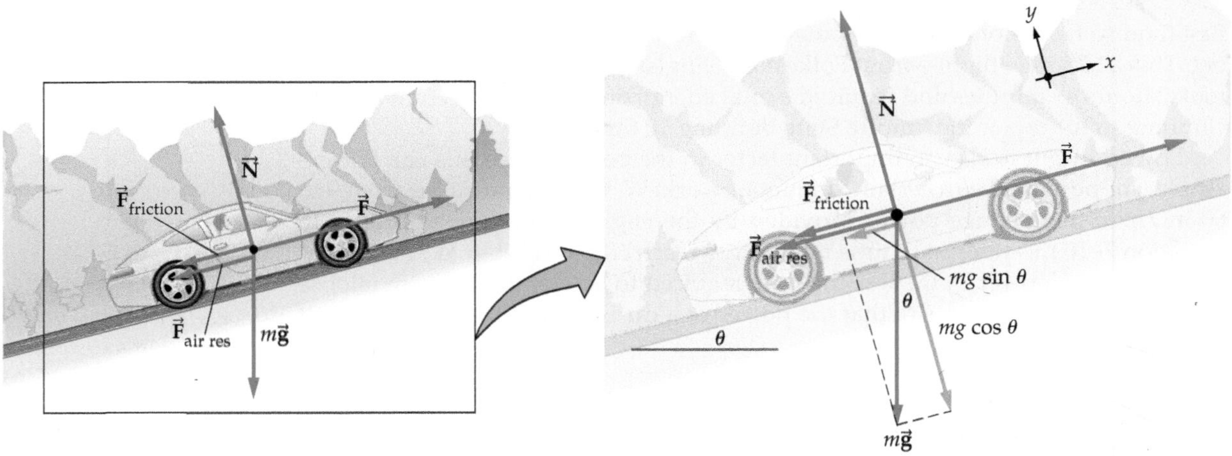

▲ **FIGURE 7–13 Driving up a hill**
A car traveling uphill at constant speed requires a constant force, F, of magnitude $mg \sin \theta + F_{\text{air res}} + F_{\text{friction}}$, applied in the direction of motion.

resistance, as indicated in **Figure 7–13**. Now, as the car travels a distance d, the work done by the engine is $W = Fd$, and the power it delivers is

$$P = \frac{W}{t} = \frac{Fd}{t}$$

Since the car has a constant speed, $v = d/t$, it follows that

$$P = \frac{Fd}{t} = F\left(\frac{d}{t}\right) = Fv \qquad \text{7–13}$$

Note that power is directly proportional to both the force and the speed. For example, suppose you push a heavy shopping cart with a force F. You produce twice as much power when you push at 2 m/s than when you push at 1 m/s, even though you are pushing no harder. It's just that the amount of work you do in a given time period is doubled.

ACTIVE EXAMPLE 7–2   FIND THE MAXIMUM SPEED

It takes a force of 1280 N to keep a 1500-kg car moving with constant speed up a slope of 5.00°. If the engine delivers 50.0 hp to the drive wheels, what is the maximum speed of the car?

SOLUTION *(Test your understanding by performing the calculations indicated in each step.)*

1. Convert the power of 50.0 hp to watts: $P = 3.73 \times 10^4 \, \text{W}$

2. Solve Equation 7–13 for the speed v: $v = P/F$

3. Substitute numerical values for the power and force: $v = 29.1 \, \text{m/s}$

INSIGHT
Thus, the maximum speed of the car on this slope is approximately 65 mi/h.

YOUR TURN
How much power is required for a maximum speed of 32.0 m/s?

*(Answers to **Your Turn** problems are given in the back of the book.)*

THE BIG PICTURE   PUTTING PHYSICS IN CONTEXT

LOOKING BACK

Even though work and kinetic energy are scalar quantities, the idea of vectors, and vector components in particular (Chapter 3), was used in the definition of work in Section 7–1.

The kinematic equations of motion for constant acceleration (Chapters 2 and 4) were used in the derivation of kinetic energy in Section 7–2. In particular, we used the relation between the speed of an object and the distance through which it accelerates.

The basic concepts of force, mass, and acceleration (Chapters 5 and 6) were used throughout this chapter. One particular force, the force exerted by a spring (Chapter 6), played a key role in Section 7–3.

LOOKING AHEAD

In Chapter 8 we introduce the concept of potential energy. The combination of kinetic and potential energy is referred to as the mechanical energy, which will play a central role in our discussion of the conservation of energy.

Collisions are studied in Chapter 9. As we shall see, the kinetic energy before and after a collision is an important characterizing feature. Look for the discussion of elastic versus inelastic collision in particular.

The concept of kinetic energy plays a significant role in many areas of physics. Look for it to reappear when we study rotational motion in Chapter 10, and in Section 10–5 in particular. Kinetic energy is also important when we study ideal gases in Chapter 17—in fact, Section 17–2 is titled Kinetic Theory.

CHAPTER SUMMARY

7–1   WORK DONE BY A CONSTANT FORCE

A force exerted through a distance performs mechanical work.

Force in Direction of Motion
In this, the simplest case, work is force times distance:

$$W = Fd \qquad\qquad 7\text{–}1$$

Force at an Angle θ to Motion
Work is the component of force in the direction of motion, $F \cos \theta$, times distance, d:

$$W = (F \cos \theta)d = Fd \cos \theta \qquad\qquad 7\text{–}3$$

Negative and Total Work
Work is negative if the force opposes the motion; that is, if $\theta > 90°$. If more than one force does work, the total work is the sum of the works done by each force separately:

$$W_{\text{total}} = W_1 + W_2 + W_3 + \cdots \qquad\qquad 7\text{–}4$$

Equivalently, sum the forces first to find F_{total}, then

$$W_{\text{total}} = (F_{\text{total}} \cos \theta)d = F_{\text{total}}\, d \cos \theta \qquad\qquad 7\text{–}5$$

Units
The SI unit of work and energy is the joule, J:

$$1\,\text{J} = 1\,\text{N} \cdot \text{m} \qquad\qquad 7\text{–}2$$

7–2   KINETIC ENERGY AND THE WORK–ENERGY THEOREM

Total work is equal to the change in kinetic energy:

$$W_{\text{total}} = \Delta K = \tfrac{1}{2}mv_{\text{f}}^2 - \tfrac{1}{2}mv_{\text{i}}^2 \qquad\qquad 7\text{–}7$$

Note: To apply this theorem correctly, you must use the *total* work. Kinetic energy is one-half mass times speed squared:

$$K = \tfrac{1}{2}mv^2 \qquad\qquad 7\text{–}6$$

It follows that kinetic energy is always positive or zero.

7–3   WORK DONE BY A VARIABLE FORCE

Work is equal to the area between the force curve and the displacement on the x axis. For the case of a spring force, the work to stretch or compress a distance x from equilibrium is

$$W = \tfrac{1}{2}kx^2 \qquad\qquad 7\text{–}8$$

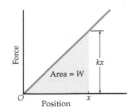

7–4   POWER

Average power is work divided by the time required to do the work:

$$P = \frac{W}{t}$$ 7–10

Equivalently, power is force times speed:

$$P = Fv$$ 7–13

Units

The SI unit of power is the watt, W:

$$1\,\text{W} = 1\,\text{J/s}$$ 7–11

$$746\,\text{W} = 1\,\text{hp}$$ 7–12

PROBLEM-SOLVING SUMMARY

Type of Calculation	Relevant Physical Concepts	Related Examples
Find the work done by a constant force.	Work is defined as force times displacement, $W = Fd$, when F is in the direction of motion. Use $W = (F \cos \theta)d$ when there is an angle θ between the force and the direction of motion.	Examples 7–1 through 7–6
Calculate the change in speed.	The change in kinetic energy is given by the work–energy theorem, $W_{\text{total}} = \Delta K$. From this, the change in speed can be found by recalling that $K = \frac{1}{2}mv^2$. Be sure W_{total} is the total work and that it has the correct sign.	Examples 7–5, 7–6
Calculate the power.	Find the work done, then divide by time: $P = W/t$. Alternatively, find the force, then multiply by the speed: $P = Fv$.	Example 7–8 Active Example 7–2

CONCEPTUAL QUESTIONS

For instructor-assigned homework, go to www.masteringphysics.com

(Answers to odd-numbered Conceptual Questions can be found in the back of the book.)

1. Is it possible to do work on an object that remains at rest?
2. A friend makes the statement, "Only the total force acting on an object can do work." Is this statement true or false? If it is true, state why; if it is false, give a counterexample.
3. A friend makes the statement, "A force that is always perpendicular to the velocity of a particle does no work on the particle." Is this statement true or false? If it is true, state why; if it is false, give a counterexample.
4. The net work done on a certain object is zero. What can you say about its speed?
5. To get out of bed in the morning, do you have to do work? Explain.
6. Give an example of a frictional force doing negative work.
7. Give an example of a frictional force doing positive work.
8. A ski boat moves with constant velocity. Is the net force acting on the boat doing work? Explain.
9. A package rests on the floor of an elevator that is rising with constant speed. The elevator exerts an upward normal force on the package, and hence does positive work on it. Why doesn't the kinetic energy of the package increase?
10. An object moves with constant velocity. Is it safe to conclude that no force acts on the object? Why, or why not?
11. Engine 1 does twice the work of engine 2. Is it correct to conclude that engine 1 produces twice as much power as engine 2? Explain.
12. Engine 1 produces twice the power of engine 2. Is it correct to conclude that engine 1 does twice as much work as engine 2? Explain.

PROBLEMS AND CONCEPTUAL EXERCISES

Note: Answers to odd-numbered Problems and Conceptual Exercises can be found in the back of the book. **IP** *denotes an integrated problem, with both conceptual and numerical parts;* **BIO** *identifies problems of biological or medical interest;* **CE** *indicates a conceptual exercise.* **Predict/Explain** *problems ask for two responses:* **(a)** *your prediction of a physical outcome, and* **(b)** *the best explanation among three provided. On all problems, red bullets (•, ••, •••) are used to indicate the level of difficulty.*

SECTION 7–1   WORK DONE BY A CONSTANT FORCE

1. • **CE** The International Space Station orbits the Earth in an approximately circular orbit at a height of $h = 375$ km above the Earth's surface. In one complete orbit, is the work done by the Earth on the space station positive, negative, or zero? Explain.

2. • **CE** A pendulum bob swings from point I to point II along the circular arc indicated in **Figure 7–14**. **(a)** Is the work done on the bob by gravity positive, negative, or zero? Explain. **(b)** Is the work done on the bob by the string positive, negative, or zero? Explain.

3. • **CE** A pendulum bob swings from point II to point III along the circular arc indicated in Figure 7–14. **(a)** Is the work done on

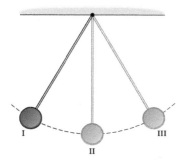

▲ **FIGURE 7–14** Problems 2 and 3

the bob by gravity positive, negative, or zero? Explain. **(b)** Is the work done on the bob by the string positive, negative, or zero? Explain.

4. • A farmhand pushes a 26-kg bale of hay 3.9 m across the floor of a barn. If she exerts a horizontal force of 88 N on the hay, how much work has she done?

5. • Children in a tree house lift a small dog in a basket 4.70 m up to their house. If it takes 201 J of work to do this, what is the combined mass of the dog and basket?

6. • Early one October, you go to a pumpkin patch to select your Halloween pumpkin. You lift the 3.2-kg pumpkin to a height of 1.2 m, then carry it 50.0 m (on level ground) to the check-out stand. **(a)** Calculate the work you do on the pumpkin as you lift it from the ground. **(b)** How much work do you do on the pumpkin as you carry it from the field?

7. • The coefficient of kinetic friction between a suitcase and the floor is 0.272. If the suitcase has a mass of 71.5 kg, how far can it be pushed across the level floor with 642 J of work?

8. •• You pick up a 3.4-kg can of paint from the ground and lift it to a height of 1.8 m. **(a)** How much work do you do on the can of paint? **(b)** You hold the can stationary for half a minute, waiting for a friend on a ladder to take it. How much work do you do during this time? **(c)** Your friend decides against the paint, so you lower it back to the ground. How much work do you do on the can as you lower it?

9. •• IP A tow rope, parallel to the water, pulls a water skier directly behind the boat with constant velocity for a distance of 65 m before the skier falls. The tension in the rope is 120 N. **(a)** Is the work done on the skier by the rope positive, negative, or zero? Explain. **(b)** Calculate the work done by the rope on the skier.

10. •• IP In the situation described in the previous problem, **(a)** is the work done on the boat by the rope positive, negative, or zero? Explain. **(b)** Calculate the work done by the rope on the boat.

11. •• A child pulls a friend in a little red wagon with constant speed. If the child pulls with a force of 16 N for 10.0 m, and the handle of the wagon is inclined at an angle of 25° above the horizontal, how much work does the child do on the wagon?

12. •• A 51-kg packing crate is pulled with constant speed across a rough floor with a rope that is at an angle of 43.5° above the horizontal. If the tension in the rope is 115 N, how much work is done on the crate to move it 8.0 m?

13. •• IP To clean a floor, a janitor pushes on a mop handle with a force of 50.0 N. **(a)** If the mop handle is at an angle of 55° above the horizontal, how much work is required to push the mop 0.50 m? **(b)** If the angle the mop handle makes with the horizontal is increased to 65°, does the work done by the janitor increase, decrease, or stay the same? Explain.

14. •• A small plane tows a glider at constant speed and altitude. If the plane does 2.00×10^5 J of work to tow the glider 145 m and the tension in the tow rope is 2560 N, what is the angle between the tow rope and the horizontal?

15. •• A young woman on a skateboard is pulled by a rope attached to a bicycle. The velocity of the skateboarder is $\vec{v} = (4.1 \text{ m/s})\hat{x}$ and the force exerted on her by the rope is $\vec{F} = (17 \text{ N})\hat{x} + (12 \text{ N})\hat{y}$. **(a)** Find the work done on the skateboarder by the rope in 25 seconds. **(b)** Assuming the velocity of the bike is the same as that of the skateboarder, find the work the rope does on the bicycle in 25 seconds.

16. •• To keep her dog from running away while she talks to a friend, Susan pulls gently on the dog's leash with a constant force given by $\vec{F} = (2.2 \text{ N})\hat{x} + (1.1 \text{ N})\hat{y}$. How much work does she do on the dog if its displacement is **(a)** $\vec{d} = (0.25 \text{ m})\hat{x}$, **(b)** $\vec{d} = (0.25 \text{ m})\hat{y}$, or **(c)** $\vec{d} = (-0.50 \text{ m})\hat{x} + (-0.25 \text{ m})\hat{y}$?

17. •• Water skiers often ride to one side of the center line of a boat, as shown in **Figure 7–15**. In this case, the ski boat is traveling at 15 m/s and the tension in the rope is 75 N. If the boat does 3500 J of work on the skier in 50.0 m, what is the angle θ between the tow rope and the center line of the boat?

▲ **FIGURE 7–15** Problems 17 and 69

SECTION 7–2 KINETIC ENERGY AND THE WORK–ENERGY THEOREM

18. • **CE** A pitcher throws a ball at 90 mi/h and the catcher stops it in her glove. **(a)** Is the work done on the ball by the pitcher positive, negative, or zero? Explain. **(b)** Is the work done on the ball by the catcher positive, negative, or zero? Explain.

19. • How much work is needed for a 73-kg runner to accelerate from rest to 7.7 m/s?

20. • **Skylab's Reentry** When Skylab reentered the Earth's atmosphere on July 11, 1979, it broke into a myriad of pieces. One of the largest fragments was a 1770-kg lead-lined film vault, and it landed with an estimated speed of 120 m/s. What was the kinetic energy of the film vault when it landed?

21. • **IP** A 9.50-g bullet has a speed of 1.30 km/s. **(a)** What is its kinetic energy in joules? **(b)** What is the bullet's kinetic energy if its speed is halved? **(c)** If its speed is doubled?

22. •• **CE Predict/Explain** The work W_0 accelerates a car from 0 to 50 km/h. **(a)** Is the work required to accelerate the car from 50 km/h to 150 km/h equal to $2W_0$, $3W_0$, $8W_0$, or $9W_0$? **(b)** Choose the *best explanation* from among the following:
   I. The work to accelerate the car depends on the speed squared.
   II. The final speed is three times the speed that was produced by the work W_0.
   III. The increase in speed from 50 km/h to 150 km/h is twice the increase in speed from 0 to 50 km/h.

23. •• **CE** Jogger A has a mass m and a speed v, jogger B has a mass $m/2$ and a speed $3v$, jogger C has a mass $3m$ and a speed $v/2$, and jogger D has a mass $4m$ and a speed $v/2$. Rank the joggers in order of increasing kinetic energy. Indicate ties where appropriate.

24. •• **IP** A 0.14-kg pinecone falls 16 m to the ground, where it lands with a speed of 13 m/s. **(a)** With what speed would the pinecone have landed if there had been no air resistance? **(b)** Did air resistance do positive work, negative work, or zero work on the pinecone? Explain.

25. •• In the previous problem, **(a)** how much work was done on the pinecone by air resistance? **(b)** What was the average force of air resistance exerted on the pinecone?

26. •• At $t = 1.0$ s, a 0.40-kg object is falling with a speed of 6.0 m/s. At $t = 2.0$ s, it has a kinetic energy of 25 J. **(a)** What is the kinetic energy of the object at $t = 1.0$ s? **(b)** What is the speed of the object at $t = 2.0$ s? **(c)** How much work was done on the object between $t = 1.0$ s and $t = 2.0$ s?

27. •• After hitting a long fly ball that goes over the right fielder's head and lands in the outfield, the batter decides to keep going past second base and try for third base. The 62.0-kg player begins sliding 3.40 m from the base with a speed of 4.35 m/s. If the player comes to rest at third base, **(a)** how much work was done on the player by friction? **(b)** What was the coefficient of kinetic friction between the player and the ground?

28. •• **IP** A 1100-kg car coasts on a horizontal road with a speed of 19 m/s. After crossing an unpaved, sandy stretch of road 32 m long, its speed decreases to 12 m/s. **(a)** Was the net work done on the car positive, negative, or zero? Explain. **(b)** Find the magnitude of the average net force on the car in the sandy section.

29. •• **IP** **(a)** In the previous problem, the car's speed decreased by 7.0 m/s as it coasted across a sandy section of road 32 m long. If the sandy portion of the road had been only 16 m long, would the car's speed have decreased by 3.5 m/s, more than 3.5 m/s, or less than 3.5 m/s? Explain. **(b)** Calculate the change in speed in this case.

30. •• A 65-kg bicyclist rides his 8.8-kg bicycle with a speed of 14 m/s. **(a)** How much work must be done by the brakes to bring the bike and rider to a stop? **(b)** How far does the bicycle travel if it takes 4.0 s to come to rest? **(c)** What is the magnitude of the braking force?

SECTION 7–3 WORK DONE BY A VARIABLE FORCE

31. • **CE** A block of mass m and speed v collides with a spring, compressing it a distance Δx. What is the compression of the spring if the force constant of the spring is increased by a factor of four?

32. • A spring with a force constant of 3.5×10^4 N/m is initially at its equilibrium length. **(a)** How much work must you do to stretch the spring 0.050 m? **(b)** How much work must you do to compress it 0.050 m?

33. • A 1.2-kg block is held against a spring of force constant 1.0×10^4 N/m, compressing it a distance of 0.15 m. How fast is the block moving after it is released and the spring pushes it away?

34. • Initially sliding with a speed of 2.2 m/s, a 1.8-kg block collides with a spring and compresses it 0.31 m before coming to rest. What is the force constant of the spring?

35. • The force shown in **Figure 7–16** moves an object from $x = 0$ to $x = 0.75$ m. **(a)** How much work is done by the force? **(b)** How much work is done by the force if the object moves from $x = 0.15$ m to $x = 0.60$ m?

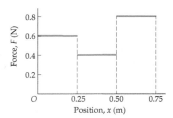

▲ **FIGURE 7–16** Problem 35

36. • An object is acted on by the force shown in **Figure 7–17**. What is the final position of the object if its initial position is $x = 0.40$ m and the work done on it is equal to **(a)** 0.21 J, or **(b)** −0.19 J?

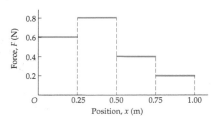

▲ **FIGURE 7–17** Problems 36 and 40

37. •• **CE** A block of mass m and speed v collides with a spring, compressing it a distance Δx. What is the compression of the spring if the mass of the block is halved and its speed is doubled?

38. •• To compress spring 1 by 0.20 m takes 150 J of work. Stretching spring 2 by 0.30 m requires 210 J of work. Which spring is stiffer?

39. •• **IP** It takes 180 J of work to compress a certain spring 0.15 m. **(a)** What is the force constant of this spring? **(b)** To compress the spring an additional 0.15 m, does it take 180 J, more than 180 J, or less than 180 J? Verify your answer with a calculation.

40. •• The force shown in Figure 7–17 acts on a 1.7-kg object whose initial speed is 0.44 m/s and initial position is $x = 0.27$ m. **(a)** Find the speed of the object when it is at the location $x = 0.99$ m. **(b)** At what location would the object's speed be 0.32 m/s?

41. ••• A block is acted on by a force that varies as $(2.0 \times 10^4 \, \text{N/m})x$ for $0 \le x \le 0.21$ m, and then remains constant at 4200 N for larger x. How much work does the force do on the block in moving it **(a)** from $x = 0$ to $x = 0.30$ m, or **(b)** from $x = 0.10$ m to $x = 0.40$ m?

SECTION 7–4 POWER

42. • **CE** Force F_1 does 5 J of work in 10 seconds, force F_2 does 3 J of work in 5 seconds, force F_3 does 6 J of work in 18 seconds, and force F_4 does 25 J of work in 125 seconds. Rank these forces in order of increasing power they produce. Indicate ties where appropriate.

43. • **BIO Climbing the Empire State Building** A new record for running the stairs of the Empire State Building was set on February 3, 2003. The 86 flights, with a total of 1576 steps, was run in 9 minutes and 33 seconds. If the height gain of each step was 0.20 m, and the mass of the runner was 70.0 kg, what was his average power output during the climb? Give your answer in both watts and horsepower.

44. • How many joules of energy are in a kilowatt-hour?

45. • Calculate the power output of a 1.4-g fly as it walks straight up a windowpane at 2.3 cm/s.

46. • An ice cube is placed in a microwave oven. Suppose the oven delivers 105 W of power to the ice cube and that it takes 32,200 J to melt it. How long does it take for the ice cube to melt?

47. • You raise a bucket of water from the bottom of a deep well. If your power output is 108 W, and the mass of the bucket and the water in it is 5.00 kg, with what speed can you raise the bucket? Ignore the weight of the rope.

48. •• In order to keep a leaking ship from sinking, it is necessary to pump 12.0 lb of water each second from below deck up a height of 2.00 m and over the side. What is the minimum horsepower motor that can be used to save the ship?

49. •• **IP** A kayaker paddles with a power output of 50.0 W to maintain a steady speed of 1.50 m/s. (a) Calculate the resistive force exerted by the water on the kayak. (b) If the kayaker doubles her power output, and the resistive force due to the water remains the same, by what factor does the kayaker's speed change?

50. •• **BIO Human-Powered Flight** Human-powered aircraft require a pilot to pedal, as in a bicycle, and produce a sustained power output of about 0.30 hp. The *Gossamer Albatross* flew across the English Channel on June 12, 1979, in 2 h 49 min. (a) How much energy did the pilot expend during the flight? (b) How many Snickers candy bars (280 Cal per bar) would the pilot have to consume to be "fueled up" for the flight? [*Note:* The nutritional calorie, 1 Cal, is equivalent to 1000 calories (1000 cal) as defined in physics. In addition, the conversion factor between calories and joules is as follows: 1 Cal = 1000 cal = 1 kcal = 4186 J.]

51. •• **IP** A grandfather clock is powered by the descent of a 4.35-kg weight. (a) If the weight descends through a distance of 0.760 m in 3.25 days, how much power does it deliver to the clock? (b) To increase the power delivered to the clock, should the time it takes for the mass to descend be increased or decreased? Explain.

52. •• **BIO The Power You Produce** Estimate the power you produce in running up a flight of stairs. Give your answer in horsepower.

53. ••• **IP** A certain car can accelerate from rest to the speed v in T seconds. If the power output of the car remains constant, (a) how long does it take for the car to accelerate from v to $2v$? (b) How fast is the car moving at $2T$ seconds after starting?

GENERAL PROBLEMS

54. • **CE** As the three small sailboats shown in **Figure 7–18** drift next to a dock, because of wind and water currents, students pull on a line attached to the bow and exert forces of equal magnitude F. Each boat drifts through the same distance d. Rank the three boats (A, B, and C) in order of increasing work done on the boat by the force F. Indicate ties where appropriate.

▲ **FIGURE 7–18** Problem 54

55. • **CE** A youngster rides on a skateboard with a speed of 2 m/s. After a force acts on the youngster, her speed is 3 m/s. Was the work done by the force positive, negative, or zero? Explain.

56. • **CE Predict/Explain** A car is accelerated by a constant force, F. The distance required to accelerate the car from rest to the speed v is Δx. (a) Is the distance required to accelerate the car from the speed v to the speed $2v$ equal to Δx, $2\Delta x$, $3\Delta x$, or $4\Delta x$? (b) Choose the *best explanation* from among the following:
I. The final speed is twice the initial speed.
II. The increase in speed is the same in each case.
III. Work is force times distance, and work depends on the speed squared.

57. • **CE** Car 1 has four times the mass of car 2, but they both have the same kinetic energy. If the speed of car 2 is v, is the speed of car 1 equal to $v/4$, $v/2$, $2v$, or $4v$? Explain.

58. • **BIO Muscle Cells** Biological muscle cells can be thought of as nanomotors that use the chemical energy of ATP to produce mechanical work. Measurements show that the active proteins within a muscle cell (such as myosin and actin) can produce a force of about 7.5 pN and displacements of 8.0 nm. How much work is done by such proteins?

59. • When you take a bite out of an apple, you do about 19 J of work. Estimate (a) the force and (b) the power produced by your jaw muscles during the bite.

60. • A Mountain bar has a mass of 0.045 kg and a calorie rating of 210 Cal. What speed would this candy bar have if its kinetic energy were equal to its metabolic energy? [See the note following Problem 50.]

61. • A small motor runs a lift that raises a load of bricks weighing 836 N to a height of 10.7 m in 23.2 s. Assuming that the bricks are lifted with constant speed, what is the minimum power the motor must produce?

62. • You push a 67-kg box across a floor where the coefficient of kinetic friction is $\mu_k = 0.55$. The force you exert is horizontal. (a) How much power is needed to push the box at a speed of 0.50 m/s? (b) How much work do you do if you push the box for 35 s?

63. • **BIO The Beating Heart** The average power output of the human heart is 1.33 watts. (a) How much energy does the heart produce in a day? (b) Compare the energy found in part (a) with the energy required to walk up a flight of stairs. Estimate the height a person could attain on a set of stairs using nothing more than the daily energy produced by the heart.

64. • **The Atmos Clock** The Atmos clock (the so-called perpetual motion clock) gets its name from the fact that it runs off pressure variations in the atmosphere, which drive a bellows containing a mixture of gas and liquid ethyl chloride. Because the power to drive these clocks is so limited, they must be very efficient. In fact, a single 60.0-W lightbulb could power 240 million Atmos clocks simultaneously. Find the amount of energy, in joules, required to run an Atmos clock for one day.

65. •• **CE** The work W_0 is required to accelerate a car from rest to the speed v_0. How much work is required to accelerate the car (a) from rest to the speed $v_0/2$ and (b) from $v_0/2$ to v_0?

66. •• **CE** A work W_0 is required to stretch a certain spring 2 cm from its equilibrium position. (a) How much work is required to stretch the spring 1 cm from equilibrium? (b) Suppose the spring is already stretched 2 cm from equilibrium. How much additional work is required to stretch it to 3 cm from equilibrium?

67. •• After a tornado, a 0.55-g straw was found embedded 2.3 cm into the trunk of a tree. If the average force exerted on the straw by the tree was 65 N, what was the speed of the straw when it hit the tree?

68. •• You throw a glove straight upward to celebrate a victory. Its initial kinetic energy is K and it reaches a maximum height h. What is the kinetic energy of the glove when it is at the height $h/2$?

69. •• The water skier in Figure 7–15 is at an angle of 35° with respect to the center line of the boat, and is being pulled at a constant speed of 14 m/s. If the tension in the tow rope is 90.0 N, **(a)** how much work does the rope do on the skier in 10.0 s? **(b)** How much work does the resistive force of water do on the skier in the same time?

70. •• **IP** A sled with a mass of 5.80 kg is pulled along the ground through a displacement given by $\vec{d} = (4.55 \text{ m})\hat{x}$. (Let the x axis be horizontal and the y axis be vertical.) **(a)** How much work is done on the sled when the force acting on it is $\vec{F} = (2.89 \text{ N})\hat{x} + (0.131 \text{ N})\hat{y}$? **(b)** How much work is done on the sled when the force acting on it is $\vec{F} = (2.89 \text{ N})\hat{x} + (0.231 \text{ N})\hat{y}$? **(c)** If the mass of the sled is increased, does the work done by the forces in parts (a) and (b) increase, decrease, or stay the same? Explain.

71. •• **IP** A 0.19-kg apple falls from a branch 3.5 m above the ground. **(a)** Does the power delivered to the apple by gravity increase, decrease, or stay the same during the time the apple falls to the ground? Explain. Find the power delivered by gravity to the apple when the apple is **(b)** 2.5 m and **(c)** 1.5 m above the ground.

72. •• A juggling ball of mass m is thrown straight upward from an initial height h with an initial speed v_0. How much work has gravity done on the ball **(a)** when it reaches its greatest height, h_{max}, and **(b)** when it reaches ground level? **(c)** Find an expression for the kinetic energy of the ball as it lands.

73. •• The force shown in **Figure 7–19** acts on an object that moves along the x axis. How much work is done by the force as the object moves from **(a)** $x = 0$ to $x = 2.0$ m, **(b)** $x = 1.0$ m to $x = 4.0$ m, and **(c)** $x = 3.5$ m to $x = 1.2$ m?

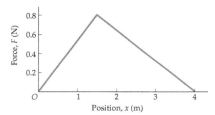

▲ **FIGURE 7–19** Problem 73

74. •• Calculate the power output of a 1.8-g spider as it walks up a windowpane at 2.3 cm/s. The spider walks on a path that is at 25° to the vertical, as illustrated in **Figure 7–20**.

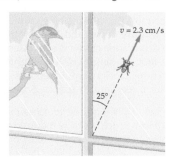

▲ **FIGURE 7–20** Problem 74

75. •• The motor of a ski boat produces a power of 36,600 W to maintain a constant speed of 14.0 m/s. To pull a water skier at the same constant speed, the motor must produce a power of 37,800 W. What is the tension in the rope pulling the skier?

76. •• **Cookie Power** To make a batch of cookies, you mix half a bag of chocolate chips into a bowl of cookie dough, exerting a 21-N force on the stirring spoon. Assume that your force is always in the direction of motion of the spoon. **(a)** What power is needed to move the spoon at a speed of 0.23 m/s? **(b)** How much work do you do if you stir the mixture for 1.5 min?

77. •• **IP** A pitcher accelerates a 0.14-kg hardball from rest to 42.5 m/s in 0.060 s. **(a)** How much work does the pitcher do on the ball? **(b)** What is the pitcher's power output during the pitch? **(c)** Suppose the ball reaches 42.5 m/s in less than 0.060 s. Is the power produced by the pitcher in this case more than, less than, or the same as the power found in part (b)? Explain.

78. •• **Catapult Launcher** A catapult launcher on an aircraft carrier accelerates a jet from rest to 72 m/s. The work done by the catapult during the launch is 7.6×10^7 J. **(a)** What is the mass of the jet? **(b)** If the jet is in contact with the catapult for 2.0 s, what is the power output of the catapult?

79. •• **BIO Brain Power** The human brain consumes about 22 W of power under normal conditions, though more power may be required during exams. **(a)** How long can one Snickers bar (see the note following Problem 50) power the normally functioning brain? **(b)** At what rate must you lift a 3.6-kg container of milk (one gallon) if the power output of your arm is to be 22 W? **(c)** How long does it take to lift the milk container through a distance of 1.0 m at this rate?

80. •• **IP** A 1300-kg car delivers a constant 49 hp to the drive wheels. We assume the car is traveling on a level road and that all frictional forces may be ignored. **(a)** What is the acceleration of this car when its speed is 14 m/s? **(b)** If the speed of the car is doubled, does its acceleration increase, decrease, or stay the same? Explain. **(c)** Calculate the car's acceleration when its speed is 28 m/s.

81. •• **Meteorite** On October 9, 1992, a 27-pound meteorite struck a car in Peekskill, NY, creating a dent about 22 cm deep. If the initial speed of the meteorite was 550 m/s, what was the average force exerted on the meteorite by the car?

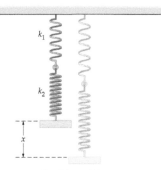

An interplanetary fender bender (Problem 81)

82. ••• **BIO Powering a Pigeon** A pigeon in flight experiences a force of air resistance given approximately by $F = bv^2$, where v is the flight speed and b is a constant. **(a)** What are the units of the constant b? **(b)** What is the largest possible speed of the pigeon if its maximum power output is P? **(c)** By what factor does the largest possible speed increase if the maximum power is doubled?

83. ••• **Springs in Series** Two springs, with force constants k_1 and k_2, are connected in series, as shown in **Figure 7–21**. How much work is required to stretch this system a distance x from the equilibrium position?

▲ **FIGURE 7–21** Problem 83

84. • • • **Springs in Parallel** Two springs, with force constants k_1 and k_2, are connected in parallel, as shown in **Figure 7–22**. How much work is required to stretch this system a distance x from the equilibrium position?

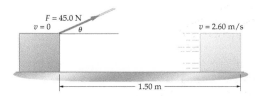

▲ **FIGURE 7–22** Problem 84

85. • • • A block rests on a horizontal frictionless surface. A string is attached to the block, and is pulled with a force of 45.0 N at an angle θ above the horizontal, as shown in **Figure 7–23**. After the block is pulled through a distance of 1.50 m, its speed is 2.60 m/s, and 50.0 J of work has been done on it. **(a)** What is the angle θ? **(b)** What is the mass of the block?

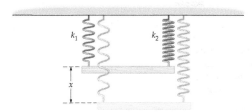

▲ **FIGURE 7–23** Problem 85

PASSAGE PROBLEMS

BIO *Microraptor gui*: **The Biplane Dinosaur**

The evolution of flight is a subject of intense interest in paleontology. Some subscribe to the "cursorial" (or ground-up) hypothesis, in which flight began with ground-dwelling animals running and jumping after prey. Others favor the "arboreal" (or trees-down) hypothesis, in which tree-dwelling animals, like modern-day flying squirrels, developed flight as an extension of gliding from tree to tree.

A recently discovered fossil from the Cretaceous period in China supports the arboreal hypothesis and adds a new element—it suggests that feathers on both the wings and the lower legs and feet allowed this dinosaur, *Microraptor gui*, to glide much like a biplane, as shown in **Figure 7–24 (a)**. Researchers have produced a detailed computer simulation of *Microraptor*, and with its help have obtained the power-versus-speed plot presented in **Figure 7–24 (b)**. This curve shows how much power is required for flight at speeds between 0 and 30 m/s. Notice that the power increases at high speeds, as expected, but is also high for low speeds, where the dinosaur is almost hovering. A minimum of 8.1 W is needed for flight at 10 m/s. The lower horizontal line shows the estimated 9.8-W power output of *Microraptor*, indicating the small range of speeds for which flight would be possible. The upper horizontal line shows the wider range of flight speeds that would be available if *Microraptor* were able to produce 20 W of power.

Also of interest are the two dashed, straight lines labeled 1 and 2. These lines represent constant ratios of power to speed; that is, a constant value for P/v. Referring to Equation 7–13, we see that $P/v = Fv/v = F$, so the lines 1 and 2 correspond to lines of constant force. Line 2 is interesting in that it has the smallest slope that still touches the power-versus-speed curve.

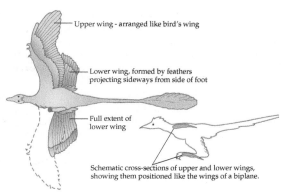

(a) Possible reconstruction of *Microraptor gui* in flight

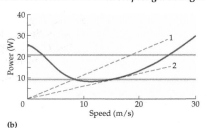

(b)

▲ **FIGURE 7–24** Problems 86, 87, 88, and 89

86. • Estimate the range of flight speeds for *Microraptor gui* if its power output is 9.8 W.

   A. 0–7.7 m/s   **B.** 7.7–15 m/s   **C.** 15–30 m/s   **D.** 0–15 m/s

87. • What approximate range of flight speeds would be possible if *Microraptor gui* could produce 20 W of power?

   A. 0–25 m/s   **B.** 25–30 m/s   **C.** 2.5–25 m/s   **D.** 0–2.5 m/s

88. • • How much energy would *Microraptor* have to expend to fly with a speed of 10 m/s for 1.0 minute?

   A. 8.1 J   **B.** 81 J   **C.** 490 J   **D.** 600 J

89. • Estimate the minimum force that *Microraptor* must exert to fly.

   A. 0.65 N   **B.** 1.3 N   **C.** 1.0 N   **D.** 10 N

INTERACTIVE PROBLEMS

90. • • **Referring to Figure 7–12** Suppose the block has a mass of 1.4 kg and an initial speed of 0.62 m/s. **(a)** What force constant must the spring have if the maximum compression is to be 2.4 cm? **(b)** If the spring has the force constant found in part (a), find the maximum compression if the mass of the block is doubled *and* its initial speed is halved.

91. • • **IP Referring to Figure 7–12** In the situation shown in Figure 7–12 (d), a spring with a force constant of 750 N/m is compressed by 4.1 cm. **(a)** If the speed of the block in Figure 7–12 (f) is 0.88 m/s, what is its mass? **(b)** If the mass of the block is doubled, is the final speed greater than, less than, or equal to 0.44 m/s? **(c)** Find the final speed for the case described in part (b).

92. • • **IP Referring to Example 7–8** Suppose the car has a mass of 1400 kg and delivers 48 hp to the wheels. **(a)** How long does it take for the car to increase its speed from 15 m/s to 25 m/s? **(b)** Would the time required to increase the speed from 5.0 m/s to 15 m/s be greater than, less than, or equal to the time found in part (a)? **(c)** Determine the time required to accelerate from 5.0 m/s to 15 m/s.

8 Potential Energy and Conservation of Energy

Probably everyone has seen a high jumper spring into the air, slow, hang motionless in midair for an instant, and then start to descend, picking up speed on the way. At the top of the trajectory, where has the kinetic energy gone? And how does it reappear as the jumper descends? As we answer these questions, we will find that there are other kinds of energy besides those considered in the last chapter.

One of the greatest accomplishments of physics is the concept of energy and its conservation. To realize, for example, that there is an important physical quantity that we can neither see nor touch is an impressive leap of the imagination. Even more astonishing, however, is the discovery that energy comes in a multitude of forms, and that the sum total of all these forms of energy is a constant. The universe, in short, has a certain amount of energy, and that energy simply ebbs and flows from one form to another, with the total amount remaining fixed.

In this chapter we focus on the conservation of energy, the first "conservation law" to be studied in this text. Though only a handful of conservation laws are known, they are all of central importance in physics. Not only do they give deep insight into the workings of nature, they are also practical tools in problem solving. As we shall see in this chapter, many problems that would be difficult to solve using Newton's laws can be solved with ease using the principle of energy conservation.

8–1 Conservative and Nonconservative Forces

In physics, we classify forces according to whether they are *conservative* or *nonconservative*. The key distinction is that when a **conservative force** acts, the work it does is stored in the form of energy that can be released at a later time. In this section, we sharpen this distinction and explore some examples of conservative and nonconservative forces.

Perhaps the simplest case of a conservative force is gravity. Imagine lifting a box of mass m from the floor to a height h, as in **Figure 8–1**. To lift the box with constant speed, the force you must exert against gravity is mg. Since the upward distance is h, the work you do on the box is $W = mgh$. If you now release the box and allow it to drop back to the floor, gravity does the same work, $W = mgh$, and in the process gives the box an equivalent amount of kinetic energy.

Work done by person = mgh Work done by gravity = mgh

◀ **FIGURE 8–1 Work against gravity**
Lifting a box against gravity with constant speed takes a work mgh. When the box is released, gravity does the same work on the box as it falls. Gravity is a conservative force.

Contrast this with the force of kinetic friction, which is nonconservative. To slide a box of mass m across the floor with constant speed, as shown in **Figure 8–2**, you must exert a force of magnitude $\mu_k N = \mu_k mg$. After sliding the box a distance d, the work you have done is $W = \mu_k mgd$. In this case, when you release the box it simply stays put—friction does no work on it after you let go. Thus, the work done by a **nonconservative force** cannot be recovered later as kinetic energy; instead, it is converted to other forms of energy, such as a slight warming of the floor and box in our example.

The differences between conservative and nonconservative forces are even more apparent if we consider moving an object around a closed path. Consider, for example, the path shown in **Figure 8–3**. If we move a box of mass m along this path, the total work done by gravity is the sum of the work done on each segment of the path; that is, $W_{total} = W_{AB} + W_{BC} + W_{CD} + W_{DA}$. The work done by gravity from A to B and from C to D is zero, since the force is at right angles to the displacement on these segments. Thus $W_{AB} = W_{CD} = 0$. On the segment from B to C, gravity does negative work (displacement and force are in opposite directions),

Work = $\mu_k mgd$

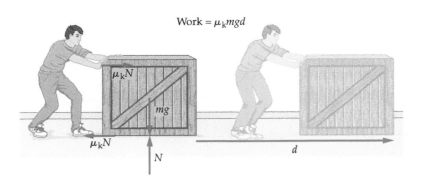

◀ **FIGURE 8–2 Work against friction**
Pushing a box with constant speed against friction takes a work $\mu_k mgd$. When the box is released, it quickly comes to rest and friction does no further work. Friction is a nonconservative force.

▶ **FIGURE 8–3 Work done by gravity on a closed path is zero**

Gravity does no work on the two horizontal segments of the path. On the two vertical segments, the amounts of work done are equal in magnitude but opposite in sign. Therefore, the total work done by gravity on this—or any—closed path is zero.

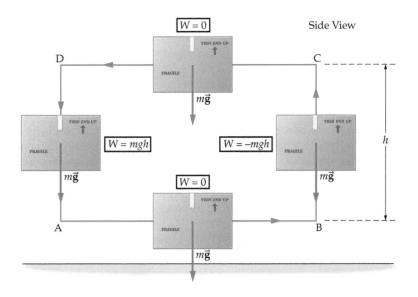

but it does positive work from D to A (displacement and force are in the same direction). Hence, $W_{BC} = -mgh$ and $W_{DA} = mgh$. As a result, the total work done by gravity is zero:

$$W_{total} = 0 + (-mgh) + 0 + mgh = 0$$

With friction, the results are quite different. If we push the box around the closed horizontal path shown in **Figure 8–4**, the total work done by friction does not vanish. In fact, friction does the negative work $W = -f_k d = -\mu_k mgd$ on each segment. Therefore, the total work done by kinetic friction is

$$W_{total} = (-\mu_k mgd) + (-\mu_k mgd) + (-\mu_k mgd) + (-\mu_k mgd) = -4\,\mu_k mgd$$

These results lead to the following definition of a conservative force:

Conservative Force: Definition 1
A conservative force is a force that does zero total work on any closed path.

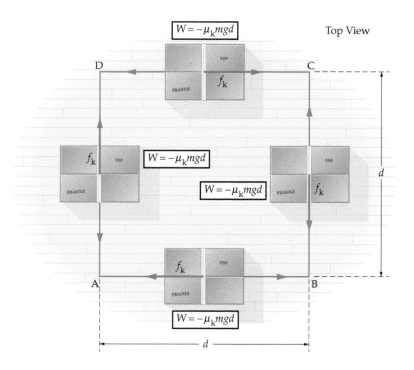

▶ **FIGURE 8–4 Work done by friction on a closed path is nonzero**

The work done by friction when an object moves through a distance d is $-\mu_k mgd$. Thus, the total work done by friction on a closed path is nonzero. In this case, it is equal to $-4\,\mu_k mgd$.

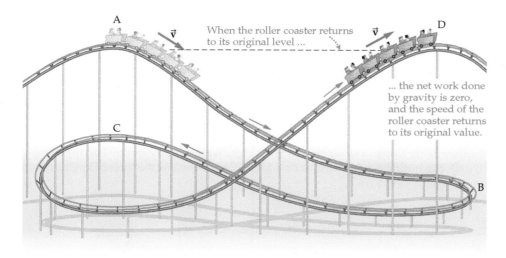

▲ **FIGURE 8–5 Gravity is a conservative force**
If frictional forces can be ignored, a roller coaster car will have the same speed at points A and D, since they are at the same height. Hence, after any complete circuit of the track the speed of the car returns to its initial value. It follows that the change in kinetic energy is zero for a complete circuit, and, therefore, the work done by gravity is also zero.

A roller coaster provides a good illustration of this definition. If a car on a roller coaster has a speed v at point A in **Figure 8–5**, it speeds up as it drops to point B, slows down as it approaches point C, and so on. When the car returns to its original height, at point D, it will again have the speed v, as long as friction and other nonconservative forces can be neglected. Similarly, if the car completes a circuit of the track and returns to point A, it will again have the speed v. Hence, a car's kinetic energy is unchanged ($\Delta K = 0$) after *any* complete circuit of the track. From the work–energy theorem, $W_{\text{total}} = \Delta K$, it follows that the work done by gravity is zero for the closed path of the car, as expected for a conservative force.

This property of conservative forces has interesting consequences. For instance, consider the closed paths shown in **Figure 8–6**. On each of these paths, we know that the work done by a conservative force is zero. Thus, it follows from paths 1 and 2 that $W_{\text{total}} = W_1 + W_2 = 0$, or

$$W_2 = -W_1$$

Similarly, using paths 1 and 3 we have $W_{\text{total}} = W_1 + W_3 = 0$, or

$$W_3 = -W_1$$

As a result, we see that the work done on path 3 is the same as the work done on path 2:

$$W_3 = W_2$$

But paths 2 and 3 are arbitrary, as long as they start at point B and end at point A. This leads to an equivalent definition of a conservative force:

Conservative Force: Definition 2
If the work done by a force in going from an arbitrary point A to an arbitrary point B is *independent of the path* from A to B, the force is conservative.

This definition is given an explicit check in Example 8–1.
Table 8–1 summarizes the different kinds of conservative and nonconservative forces we have encountered thus far in this text.

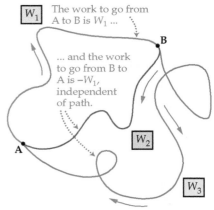

▲ **FIGURE 8–6 The work done by a conservative force is independent of path**
Considering paths 1 and 2, we see that $W_1 + W_2 = 0$, or $W_2 = -W_1$. From paths 1 and 3, however, we see that $W_1 + W_3 = 0$, or $W_3 = -W_1$. It follows, then, that $W_3 = W_2$, since they are both equal to $-W_1$; hence the work done in going from A to B is independent of the path.

TABLE 8–1 Conservative and Nonconservative Forces

Force	Section
Conservative forces	
Gravity	5–6
Spring force	6–2
Nonconservative forces	
Friction	6–1
Tension in a rope, cable, etc.	6–2
Forces exerted by a motor	7–4
Forces exerted by muscles	5–3

EXAMPLE 8–1 DIFFERENT PATHS, DIFFERENT FORCES

(a) A 4.57-kg box is moved with constant speed from A to B along the two paths shown at left below. Calculate the work done by gravity on each of these paths. **(b)** The same box is pushed across a floor from A to B along path 1 and path 2 at right below. If the coefficient of kinetic friction between the box and the surface is $\mu_k = 0.63$, how much work is done by friction along each path?

PICTURE THE PROBLEM

Part (a) of our sketch shows two different paths a box might be taken through in going from point A to point B. Path 1 is indicated by two red lines, indicating a vertical displacement of 1.0 m and a horizontal displacement of 3.0 m. Path 2, indicated in green, consists of two horizontal and two vertical displacements. In this case, we are interested in the work done by gravity. Part (b) shows the same basic paths—path 1 in orange and path 2 in purple—only this time on a rough floor. Here it is the force of kinetic friction that is of interest.

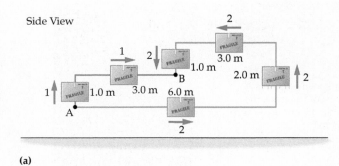

(a)

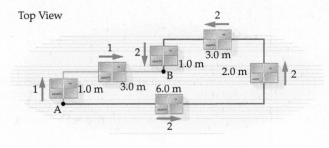

(b)

STRATEGY

To calculate the work for each path, we break it down into segments. Path 1 is made up of two segments, path 2 has four segments.

a. For gravity, the work is zero on horizontal segments. On vertical segments, the work done by gravity is positive when motion is downward and negative when motion is upward.

b. The work done by kinetic friction is negative on all segments of both paths.

SOLUTION

Part (a)

1. Using $W = Fd = mgy$, calculate the work done by gravity along the two segments of path 1:

$$W_1 = -(4.57 \text{ kg})(9.81 \text{ m/s}^2)(1.0 \text{ m}) + 0 = -45 \text{ J}$$

2. In the same way, calculate the work done by gravity along the four segments of path 2:

$$W_2 = 0 - (4.57 \text{ kg})(9.81 \text{ m/s}^2)(2.0 \text{ m})$$
$$+ 0 + (4.57 \text{ kg})(9.81 \text{ m/s}^2)(1.0 \text{ m}) = -45 \text{ J}$$

Part (b)

3. Using $F = \mu_k N$, calculate the work done by kinetic friction along the two segments of path 1:

$$W_1 = -(0.63)(4.57 \text{ kg})(9.81 \text{ m/s}^2)(1.0 \text{ m})$$
$$- (0.63)(4.57 \text{ kg})(9.81 \text{ m/s}^2)(3.0 \text{ m}) = -110 \text{ J}$$

4. Similarly, calculate the work done by kinetic friction along the four segments of path 2:

$$W_2 = -(0.63)(4.57 \text{ kg})(9.81 \text{ m/s}^2)(6.0 \text{ m})$$
$$- (0.63)(4.57 \text{ kg})(9.81 \text{ m/s}^2)(2.0 \text{ m})$$
$$- (0.63)(4.57 \text{ kg})(9.81 \text{ m/s}^2)(3.0 \text{ m})$$
$$- (0.63)(4.57 \text{ kg})(9.81 \text{ m/s}^2)(1.0 \text{ m}) = -340 \text{ J}$$

INSIGHT

As expected, the conservative force of gravity gives the same work in going from A to B, regardless of the path. The work done by kinetic friction, however, is greater on the path of greater length.

PRACTICE PROBLEM

The work done by gravity when the box is moved from point B to a point C is 140 J. Is point C above or below point B? What is the vertical distance between points B and C? **[Answer: Point C is 3.1 m below point B.]**

Some related homework problems: Problem 2, Problem 3

8–2 Potential Energy and the Work Done by Conservative Forces

Work must be done to lift a bowling ball from the floor to a shelf. Once on the shelf, the bowling ball has zero kinetic energy, just as it did on the floor. Even so, the work done in lifting the ball has not been lost. If the ball is allowed to fall from the shelf, gravity does the same amount of work on it as you did to lift it in the first place. As a result, the work you did is "recovered" in the form of kinetic energy. Thus we say that when the ball is lifted to a new position, there is an increase in **potential energy,** U, and that this potential energy can be converted to kinetic energy when the ball falls.

▲ Because gravity is a conservative force, the work done against gravity in lifting these logs (left) can, in principle, all be recovered. If the logs are released, for example, they will acquire an amount of kinetic energy exactly equal to the work done to lift them and to the gravitational potential energy that they gained in being lifted. Friction, by contrast, is a nonconservative force. Some of the work done by this spinning grindstone (right) goes into removing material from the object being ground, while the rest is transformed into sound energy and (especially) heat. Most of this work can never be recovered as kinetic energy.

In a sense, potential energy is a storage system for energy. When we increase the separation between the ball and the ground, the work we do is stored in the form of an increased potential energy. Not only that, but the storage system is perfect, in the sense that the energy is never lost, as long as the separation remains the same. The ball can rest on the shelf for a million years, and still, when it falls, it gains the same amount of kinetic energy.

Work done against friction, however, is not "stored" as potential energy. Instead, it is dissipated into other forms of energy such as heat or sound. The same is true of other nonconservative forces. Only conservative forces have the potential-energy storage system.

Before proceeding, we should point out an interesting difference between kinetic and potential energy. Kinetic energy is given by the expression $K = \frac{1}{2}mv^2$, no matter what force might be involved. On the other hand, each different conservative force has a different expression for its potential energy. To see how this comes about, we turn now to a precise definition of potential energy.

Potential Energy, U

When a conservative force does an amount of work W_c (the subscript c stands for conservative), the corresponding potential energy U is changed according to the following definition:

Definition of Potential Energy, U

$$W_c = U_i - U_f = -(U_f - U_i) = -\Delta U \qquad\qquad 8\text{–}1$$

SI unit: joule, J

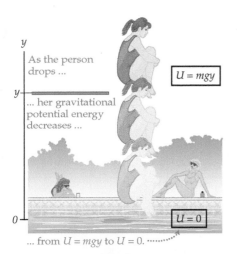

▲ **FIGURE 8–7 Gravitational potential energy**
A person drops from a diving board into a swimming pool. The diving board is at the height y, and the surface of the water is at $y = 0$. We choose the gravitational potential energy to be zero at $y = 0$; hence, the potential energy is mgy at the diving board.

PROBLEM-SOLVING NOTE

Zero of Potential Energy

When working potential energy problems it is important to make a definite choice for the location where the potential energy is to be set equal to zero. Any location can be chosen, but once the choice is made, it must be used consistently.

▲ The $U = 0$ level for the gravitational potential energy of this system can be assigned to the point where the diver starts his dive, to the water level, or to any other level. Regardless of the choice, however, his kinetic energy when he strikes the water will be exactly equal to the difference in gravitational potential energy between his launch and splashdown points.

In words, the work done by a conservative force is equal to the negative of the change in potential energy. For example, when an object falls, gravity does *positive* work on it and its potential energy *decreases*. Similarly, when an object is lifted, gravity does *negative* work and the potential energy *increases*.

Note that since work is a scalar with units of joules, the same is true of potential energy. In addition, our definition determines only the *difference* in potential energy between two points, not the actual value of the potential energy. Hence, we are free to choose the place where the potential energy is zero ($U = 0$) in much the same way we are free to choose the location of the origin in a coordinate system.

Gravity

Let's apply our definition of potential energy to the force of gravity near the Earth's surface. Suppose a person of mass m drops a distance y from a diving board into a pool, as shown in **Figure 8–7**. As the person drops, gravity does the work

$$W_c = mgy$$

Applying the definition given in Equation 8–1, the corresponding change in potential energy is

$$-\Delta U = U_i - U_f = W_c = mgy$$

In this expression, U_i is the potential energy when the diver is on the board, and U_f is the potential energy when the diver enters the water. Rearranging slightly, we have

$$U_i = mgy + U_f \qquad 8\text{--}2$$

Note that U_i is greater than U_f.

As mentioned above, we are free to choose $U = 0$ anywhere we like; *only the difference* in U is important. For example, if you slip and fall to the ground, you hit with the same thud whether you fall in Denver (altitude 1 mile) or in Honolulu (at sea level). It's the difference in height that matters, not the height itself. (The acceleration of gravity does vary slightly with altitude, as we shall see, but the difference is small enough to be unimportant in this case.) The only point to be careful about when choosing a location for $U = 0$ is to be consistent with the choice once it is made.

In general, we choose $U = 0$ in a convenient location. In Figure 8–7, a reasonable place for $U = 0$ is the surface of the water, where $y = 0$; that is, $U_f = 0$. Then, Equation 8–2 becomes $U_i = mgy$. If we omit the subscript on U_i, letting U stand for the potential energy at the arbitrary height y, we have

Gravitational Potential Energy (Near Earth's Surface)

$$U = mgy \qquad 8\text{--}3$$

Note that the gravitational potential energy depends only on the height, y, and is independent of horizontal position.

EXERCISE 8–1

Find the gravitational potential energy of a system consisting of a 65-kg person on a 3.0-m-high diving board. Let $U = 0$ be at water level.

SOLUTION

Substituting $m = 65$ kg and $y = 3.0$ m in Equation 8–3 yields

$$U = mgy = (65 \text{ kg})(9.81 \text{ m/s}^2)(3.0 \text{ m}) = 1900 \text{ J}$$

The next Example considers the change in gravitational potential energy of a mountain climber, given different choices for the location of $U = 0$.

EXAMPLE 8–2   PIKES PEAK OR BUST

An 82.0-kg mountain climber is in the final stage of the ascent of 4301-m-high Pikes Peak. What is the change in gravitational potential energy as the climber gains the last 100.0 m of altitude? Let $U = 0$ be **(a)** at sea level or **(b)** at the top of the peak.

PICTURE THE PROBLEM
Our sketch shows the mountain climber and the last 100.0 m of altitude to be climbed. We choose a typical coordinate system, with the positive y axis upward and the positive x axis to the right.

STRATEGY
The gravitational potential energy of the Earth–climber system depends only on the height y; the path followed in gaining the last 100.0 m of altitude is unimportant. The change in potential energy is $\Delta U = U_f - U_i = mgy_f - mgy_i$, where y_f is the altitude of the peak and y_i is 100.0 m less than y_f.

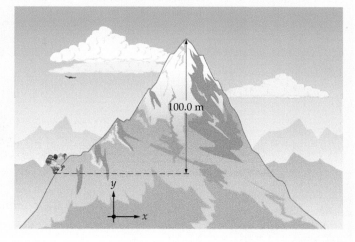

100.0 m

SOLUTION

Part (a)

1. Calculate ΔU with $y_f = 4301$ m and $y_i = 4201$ m:

$$\Delta U = mgy_f - mgy_i$$
$$= (82.0 \text{ kg})(9.81 \text{ m/s}^2)(4301 \text{ m})$$
$$- (82.0 \text{ kg})(9.81 \text{ m/s}^2)(4201 \text{ m}) = 80,400 \text{ J}$$

Part (b)

2. Calculate ΔU with $y_f = 0$ and $y_i = -100.0$ m:

$$\Delta U = mgy_f - mgy_i$$
$$= (82.0 \text{ kg})(9.81 \text{ m/s}^2)(0)$$
$$- (82.0 \text{ kg})(9.81 \text{ m/s}^2)(-100.0 \text{ m}) = 80,400 \text{ J}$$

INSIGHT
As expected, the *change* in gravitational potential energy does not depend on where we choose $U = 0$. Nor does it depend on the path taken between the initial and final points.

PRACTICE PROBLEM
Find the altitude of the climber for which the gravitational potential energy of the Earth–climber system is 1.00×10^5 J less than it is when the climber is at the summit.   [**Answer:** 4180 m]

Some related homework problems: Problem 10, Problem 17

    A single item of food can be converted into a surprisingly large amount of potential energy. This is shown for the case of a candy bar in Example 8–3.

EXAMPLE 8–3   CONVERTING FOOD ENERGY TO MECHANICAL ENERGY

REAL-WORLD PHYSICS: BIO

A candy bar called the Mountain Bar has a calorie content of 212 Cal = 212 kcal, which is equivalent to an energy of 8.87×10^5 J. If an 81.0-kg mountain climber eats a Mountain Bar and magically converts it all to potential energy, what gain of altitude would be possible?

PICTURE THE PROBLEM
We show the mountain climber eating the candy bar at a given level on the mountain, which we can take to be $y = 0$. The altitude gain, then, corresponds to $y = h$.

CONTINUED ON NEXT PAGE

CONTINUED FROM PREVIOUS PAGE

STRATEGY
The initial gravitational potential energy of the Earth–climber system is $U = 0$; the final potential energy is $U = mgh$. To find the altitude gain, set $U = mgh$ equal to the energy provided by the candy bar, 8.87×10^5 J, and solve for h.

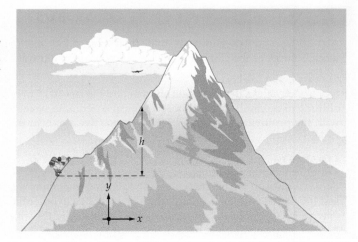

SOLUTION

1. Solve $U = mgh$ for h:

$$U = mgh$$
$$h = \frac{U}{mg}$$

2. Substitute numerical values, with $U = 8.87 \times 10^5$ J:

$$h = \frac{U}{mg} = \frac{8.87 \times 10^5 \text{ J}}{(81.0 \text{ kg})(9.81 \text{ m/s}^2)} = 1120 \text{ m}$$

INSIGHT
This is more than two-thirds of a mile in elevation. Even if we take into account the fact that metabolic efficiency is only about 25%, the height would still be 280 m, or nearly two-tenths of a mile. It's remarkable just how much our bodies can do with so little.

PRACTICE PROBLEM
If the mass of the mountain climber is increased—by adding more items to the backpack, for example—does the possible elevation gain increase, decrease, or stay the same? Calculate the elevation gain for a climber with a mass of 91.0 kg. [**Answer:** The altitude gain will decrease. For $m = 91.0$ kg we find $h = 994$ m.]

Some related homework problems: Problem 10, Problem 17

▲ Because springs, and bungee cords, exert conservative forces, they can serve as energy storage devices. In this case, the stretched bungee cord is beginning to give up the energy it has stored, and to convert that potential energy into kinetic energy as the jumper is pulled rapidly skyward.

We have been careful *not* to say that the potential energy of the mountain climber—or any object—increases when its height increases. The reason is that the potential energy is a property of an entire system, not of its individual parts. The correct statement is that if an object is lifted, the potential energy of the Earth–object system is increased.

Springs

Consider a spring that is stretched from its equilibrium position a distance x. According to Equation 7–8, the work required to cause this stretch is $W = \frac{1}{2}kx^2$. Therefore, if the spring is released—and allowed to move from the stretched position back to the equilibrium position—it will do the same work, $\frac{1}{2}kx^2$. From our definition of potential energy, then, we see that

$$W_c = \tfrac{1}{2}kx^2 = U_i - U_f \qquad \text{8–4}$$

Note that in this case U_f is the potential energy when the spring is at $x = 0$ (equilibrium position), and U_i is the potential energy when the spring is stretched by the amount x.

A convenient choice for $U = 0$ is the equilibrium position of the spring. With this choice we have $U_f = 0$, and Equation 8–4 becomes $U_i = \frac{1}{2}kx^2$. Omitting the subscript i, so that U represents the potential energy of the spring for an arbitrary amount of stretch x, we have

Potential Energy of a Spring

$$U = \tfrac{1}{2}kx^2 \qquad \text{8–5}$$

Since U depends on x^2, which is positive even if x is negative, the potential energy of a spring is always greater than or equal to zero. Thus, a spring's potential energy increases whenever it is displaced from equilibrium.

EXERCISE 8–2

Find the potential energy of a spring with force constant $k = 680$ N/m if it is **(a)** stretched by 5.00 cm or **(b)** compressed by 7.00 cm.

SOLUTION

Substituting $x = 0.0500$ m and $x = -0.0700$ m in Equation 8–5 yields

a. $U = \frac{1}{2}(680 \text{ N/m})(0.0500 \text{ m})^2 = 0.850$ J

b. $U = \frac{1}{2}(680 \text{ N/m})(-0.0700 \text{ m})^2 = 1.67$ J

Finally, comparing Equation 8–3 to Equation 8–5, we see that the potential energies for gravity and for a spring are given by different expressions. As mentioned, each conservative force has its own potential energy.

EXAMPLE 8–4 COMPRESSED ENERGY AND THE JUMP OF A FLEA

When a force of 120.0 N is applied to a certain spring, it causes a stretch of 2.25 cm. What is the potential energy of this spring when it is **(a)** compressed by 3.50 cm or **(b)** expanded by 7.00 cm?

PICTURE THE PROBLEM
The top sketch shows the spring stretched 2.25 cm by the force $F_1 = 120.0$ N. The lower sketch shows the same spring compressed by a second force, F_2, which causes a compression of 3.50 cm. An expansion of the spring by 7.00 cm would look similar to the top sketch.

STRATEGY
From the first piece of information—a certain force causes a certain stretch—we can calculate the force constant using $F = kx$. Once we know k, we find the potential energy for either a compression or an expansion with $U = \frac{1}{2}kx^2$.

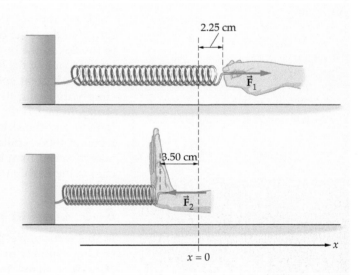

SOLUTION

1. Solve $F = kx$ for the spring constant, k:

$$F = kx$$
$$k = \frac{F}{x} = \frac{120.0 \text{ N}}{0.0225 \text{ m}} = 5330 \text{ N/m}$$

Part (a)

2. Substitute $k = 5330$ N/m and $x = -0.0350$ m into the potential energy expression, $U = \frac{1}{2}kx^2$:

$$U = \frac{1}{2}kx^2 = \frac{1}{2}(5330 \text{ N/m})(-0.0350 \text{ m})^2 = 3.26 \text{ J}$$

Part (b)

3. Substitute $k = 5330$ N/m and $x = 0.0700$ m into the potential energy expression, $U = \frac{1}{2}kx^2$:

$$U = \frac{1}{2}kx^2 = \frac{1}{2}(5330 \text{ N/m})(0.0700 \text{ m})^2 = 13.1 \text{ J}$$

INSIGHT
Though this Example deals with ideal springs, the same basic physics applies to many other real-world situations. A case in point is the jump of a flea, in which a flea can propel itself up to 100 times its body length. The physics behind this feat is the slow

CONTINUED ON NEXT PAGE

CONTINUED FROM PREVIOUS PAGE

accumulation of energy in a "springy" strip of resilin in the coxa of the leg, as shown in the accompanying sketches, and the sudden release of this energy at a later time. Specifically, as the flea's muscles flex the leg, the resilin strip in the coxa is stretched, storing the work done by the muscles in the form of potential energy, $U = \frac{1}{2}kx^2$. Later, when a trigger mechanism unlocks the flexed leg, the energy stored in the resilin is released explosively—rapidly extending the leg and propelling the flea upward. See Problem 89 for a calculation using the force constant of resilin.

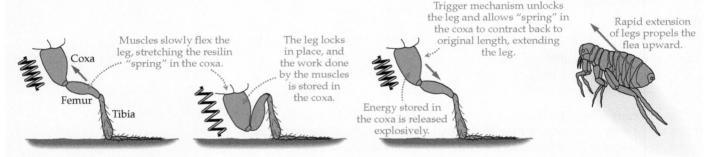

PRACTICE PROBLEM

What stretch is necessary for the spring in this Example to have a potential energy of 5.00 J? [**Answer:** 4.33 cm]

Some related homework problems: Problem 12, Problem 16

The jump of a flea is similar in many respects to the operation of a bow and arrow. In the latter case, the work done in slowly pulling the string back is stored in the flex of the bow. The string is held in place while aim is taken, and then released to allow the bow to return to its original shape. This propels the arrow forward with great speed—a speed many times faster than could be obtained by simply throwing the arrow with the same arm muscles that pulled back on the string. In fact, if the string returns to its original position in 1/1000th the time it took to pull the string back, the power it delivers to the arrow is magnified by a factor of 1000. Similarly, the spring-loaded jump of the flea gives it a much greater takeoff speed than if it relied solely on muscle power. An analogous process occurs in the flash unit of a camera, as we shall see in Chapter 20.

8–3 Conservation of Mechanical Energy

In this section, we show how potential energy can be used as a powerful tool in solving a variety of problems and in gaining greater insight into the workings of physical systems. To do so, we begin by defining the **mechanical energy**, E, as the sum of the potential and kinetic energies of an object:

$$E = U + K \tag{8-6}$$

The significance of mechanical energy is that it is **conserved** in systems involving only conservative forces. By conserved, we mean that its value never changes; that is, $E = $ constant. (In situations where nonconservative forces are involved, the mechanical energy can change, as when friction causes warming by converting mechanical energy to thermal energy. When *all* possible forms of energy are considered, energy is always found to be conserved.)

To show that E is conserved for conservative forces, we start with the work–energy theorem from Chapter 7:

$$W_{\text{total}} = \Delta K = K_f - K_i$$

Suppose for a moment that the system has only a single force and that the force is conservative. If this is the case, then the total work, W_{total}, is the work done by the conservative force, W_c:

$$W_{\text{total}} = W_c$$

From the definition of potential energy, we know that $W_c = -\Delta U = U_i - U_f$. Combining these results, we have

$$W_{total} = W_c$$

$$K_f - K_i = U_i - U_f$$

With a slight rearrangement we find

$$U_f + K_f = U_i + K_i$$

or

$$E_f = E_i$$

Since the initial and final points can be chosen arbitrarily, it follows that E is conserved:

$$E = \text{constant}$$

If the system has more than one conservative force, the only change to these results is to replace U with the sum of potential energies of all the forces.

To summarize:

Conservation of Mechanical Energy

In systems with conservative forces only, the mechanical energy E is conserved; that is, $E = U + K = \text{constant}$.

In terms of physical systems, conservation of mechanical energy means that energy can be converted between potential and kinetic forms, but that the sum remains the same. As an example, in the roller coaster shown in Figure 8–5, the gravitational potential energy decreases as the car approaches point B; as it does, the car's kinetic energy increases by the same amount. From a practical point of view, conservation of mechanical energy means that many physics problems can be solved by what amounts to simple bookkeeping.

For example, consider a key chain of mass m that is dropped to the floor from a height h, as illustrated in **Figure 8–8**. The question is, how fast are the keys moving just before they land? We know how to solve this problem using Newton's laws and kinematics, but now let's see how energy conservation can be used instead.

First, note that the only force acting on the keys is gravity—ignoring air resistance, of course—and that gravity is a conservative force. As a result, we can say

▲ A roller coaster (top) illustrates the conservation of mechanical energy. With every descent, gravitational potential energy is converted into kinetic energy; with every rise, kinetic energy is converted back into gravitational potential energy. If friction is neglected, the total mechanical energy of the car remains constant. The same principle is exploited at a pumped-storage facility, such as this one at the Mormon Flat Dam in Phoenix, Arizona (bottom). When surplus electrical power is available, it is used to pump water uphill into the reservoir. This process, in effect, stores electrical energy as gravitational potential energy. When power demand is high, the stored water is allowed to flow back downhill through the electrical generators in the dam, converting the gravitational energy to kinetic energy and the kinetic energy to electrical energy.

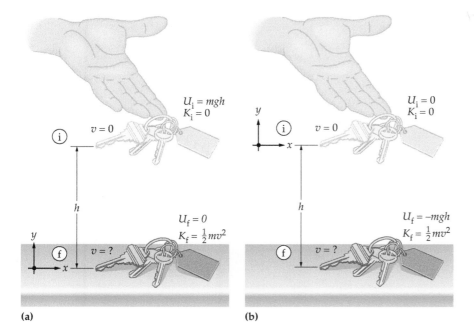

(a) (b)

◀ **FIGURE 8–8 Solving a kinematics problem using conservation of energy**
(a) A set of keys falls to the floor. Ignoring frictional forces, we know that the mechanical energy at points i and f must be equal; $E_i = E_f$. Using this condition, we can find the speed of the keys just before they land. **(b)** The same physical situation as in part (a), except this time we have chosen $y = 0$ to be at the point where the keys are dropped. As before, we set $E_i = E_f$ to find the speed of the keys just before they land. The result is the same.

Conservative Systems

A convenient approach to problems involving energy conservation is to first sketch the system, and then label the initial and final points with i and f, respectively. To apply energy conservation, write out the energy at these two points and set $E_i = E_f$.

that $E = U + K$ is constant during the entire time the keys are falling. To solve the problem, then, we pick two points on the motion of the keys, say i and f in Figure 8–8, and we set the mechanical energy equal at these points:

$$E_i = E_f \qquad\qquad 8\text{–}7$$

Writing this out in terms of potential and kinetic energies, we have

$$U_i + K_i = U_f + K_f \qquad\qquad 8\text{–}8$$

This one equation—which is nothing but bookkeeping—can be used to solve for the one unknown, the final speed.

To be specific, in Figure 8–8 (a) we choose $y = 0$ at ground level, which means that $U_i = mgh$. In addition, the fact that the keys are released from rest means that $K_i = 0$. Similarly, at point f—just before hitting the ground—the energy is all kinetic, and the potential energy is zero; that is, $U_f = 0$, $K_f = \frac{1}{2}mv^2$. Substituting these values into Equation 8–8, we find

$$mgh + 0 = 0 + \tfrac{1}{2}mv^2$$

Canceling m and solving for v yields the same result we get with kinematics:

$$v = \sqrt{2gh}$$

Suppose, instead, that we had chosen $y = 0$ to be at the release point of the keys, as in Figure 8–8 (b), so that the keys land at $y = -h$. Now, when the keys are released, we have $U_i = 0$ and $K_i = 0$, and when they land $U_f = -mgh$ and $K_f = \frac{1}{2}mv^2$. Substituting these results in $U_i + K_i = U_f + K_f$ yields

$$0 + 0 = -mgh + \tfrac{1}{2}mv^2$$

Solving for v gives the same result:

$$v = \sqrt{2gh}$$

Thus, as expected, changing the zero level has no effect on the physical results.

EXAMPLE 8–5 GRADUATION FLING

At the end of a graduation ceremony, graduates fling their caps into the air. Suppose a 0.120-kg cap is thrown straight upward with an initial speed of 7.85 m/s, and that frictional forces can be ignored. **(a)** Use kinematics to find the speed of the cap when it is 1.18 m above the release point. **(b)** Show that the mechanical energy at the release point is the same as the mechanical energy 1.18 m above the release point.

PICTURE THE PROBLEM

In our sketch we choose $y = 0$ to be at the level where the cap is released with an initial speed of 7.85 m/s. In addition, note that we designate the release point as i (initial) and the point at which $y = 1.18$ m as f (final). It is the speed at point f that we wish to find.

STRATEGY

a. The cap is in free fall, which justifies the use of constant-acceleration kinematics. Since we want to relate velocity to position, we use $v_y{}^2 = v_{0y}{}^2 + 2a_y\Delta y$ (Section 2–5). In this case, $v_{0y} = 7.85$ m/s, $\Delta y = 1.18$ m, and $a_y = -g$. Substituting these values gives v_y.

b. At each point we simply calculate $E = U + K$, with $U = mgy$ and $K = \frac{1}{2}mv^2$.

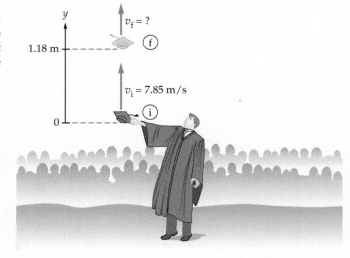

SOLUTION

Part (a)

1. Use kinematics to solve for v_y:

$$v_y^2 = v_{0y}^2 + 2a_y \, \Delta y$$
$$v_y = \pm\sqrt{v_{0y}^2 + 2a_y \, \Delta y}$$

2. Substitute $v_{0y} = 7.85$ m/s, $\Delta y = 1.18$ m, and $a_y = -g$ to find v_y. Choose the plus sign, since we are interested only in the speed:

$$v_y = \sqrt{v_{0y}^2 + 2a_y \, \Delta y}$$
$$= \sqrt{(7.85 \text{ m/s})^2 + 2(-9.81 \text{ m/s}^2)(1.18 \text{ m})} = 6.20 \text{ m/s}$$

Part (b)

3. Calculate E_i. At this point $y_i = 0$ and $v_i = 7.85$ m/s:

$$E_i = U_i + K_i = mgy_i + \tfrac{1}{2}mv_i^2$$
$$= 0 + \tfrac{1}{2}(0.120 \text{ kg})(7.85 \text{ m/s})^2 = 3.70 \text{ J}$$

4. Calculate E_f. At this point $y_f = 1.18$ m and $v_f = 6.20$ m/s:

$$E_f = U_f + K_f = mgy_f + \tfrac{1}{2}mv_f^2$$
$$= (0.120 \text{ kg})(9.81 \text{ m/s}^2)(1.18 \text{ m}) + \tfrac{1}{2}(0.120 \text{ kg})(6.20 \text{ m/s})^2$$
$$= 1.39 \text{ J} + 2.31 \text{ J} = 3.70 \text{ J}$$

INSIGHT

As expected, E_f is equal to E_i. In the remaining Examples in this section we turn this process around; we start with $E_f = E_i$, and use this relation to find a final speed or a final height. As we shall see, this procedure of using energy conservation is a more powerful approach—it actually makes the calculations simpler.

PRACTICE PROBLEM

Use energy conservation to find the height at which the speed of the cap is 5.00 m/s.   [**Answer:** 1.87 m]

Some related homework problems: Problem 30, Problem 31, and Problem 33

An interesting extension of this Example is shown in **Figure 8–9**. In this case, we are given that the speed of the cap is v_i at the height y_i, and we would like to know its speed v_f when it is at the height y_f.

To find v_f, we apply energy conservation to the points i and f:

$$U_i + K_i = U_f + K_f$$

Writing out U and K specifically for these two points yields the following:

$$mgy_i + \tfrac{1}{2}mv_i^2 = mgy_f + \tfrac{1}{2}mv_f^2$$

As before, we cancel m and solve for the unknown speed, v_f:

$$v_f = \sqrt{v_i^2 + 2g(y_i - y_f)}$$

This result is in agreement with the kinematic equation, $v_y^2 = v_{0y}^2 + 2a_y \, \Delta y$.

◀ **FIGURE 8–9 Speed is independent of path**

If the speed of the cap is v_i at the height y_i, its speed is v_f at the height y_f, independent of the path between the two heights. This assumes, of course, that frictional forces can be neglected.

Note that v_f depends only on y_i and y_f, not on the path connecting them. This is because conservative forces such as gravity do work that is path-independent. What this means physically is that the cap has the same speed v_f at the height y_f, whether it goes straight upward or follows some other trajectory, as in Figure 8–9. All that matters is the height difference.

EXAMPLE 8–6   CATCHING A HOME RUN

In the bottom of the ninth inning, a player hits a 0.15-kg baseball over the outfield fence. The ball leaves the bat with a speed of 36 m/s, and a fan in the bleachers catches it 7.2 m above the point where it was hit. Assuming frictional forces can be ignored, find **(a)** the kinetic energy of the ball when it is caught and **(b)** its speed when caught.

PICTURE THE PROBLEM
Our sketch shows the ball's trajectory. We label the hit point i and the catch point f. At point i we choose $y_i = 0$; at point f, then, $y_f = h = 7.2$ m. In addition, we are given that $v_i = 36$ m/s; v_f is to be determined.

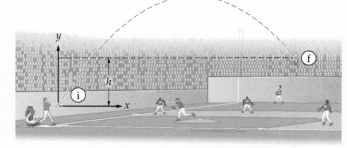

STRATEGY

a. Because frictional forces can be ignored, it follows that the initial mechanical energy is equal to the final mechanical energy; that is, $U_i + K_i = U_f + K_f$. Use this relation to find K_f.

b. Once K_f is determined, use $K_f = \frac{1}{2}mv_f^2$ to find v_f.

SOLUTION

Part (a)

1. Begin by writing U and K for point i:

$$U_i = 0$$
$$K_i = \tfrac{1}{2}mv_i^2 = \tfrac{1}{2}(0.15 \text{ kg})(36 \text{ m/s})^2 = 97 \text{ J}$$

2. Next, write U and K for point f:

$$U_f = mgh = (0.15 \text{ kg})(9.81 \text{ m/s}^2)(7.2 \text{ m}) = 11 \text{ J}$$
$$K_f = \tfrac{1}{2}mv_f^2$$

3. Set the total mechanical energy at point i, $E_i = U_i + K_i$, equal to the total mechanical energy at point f, $E_f = U_f + K_f$, and solve for K_f:

$$U_i + K_i = U_f + K_f$$
$$0 + 97 \text{ J} = 11 \text{ J} + K_f$$
$$K_f = 97 \text{ J} - 11 \text{ J} = 86 \text{ J}$$

Part (b)

4. Use $K_f = \frac{1}{2}mv_f^2$ to find v_f:

$$K_f = \tfrac{1}{2}mv_f^2$$

$$v_f = \sqrt{\frac{2K_f}{m}} = \sqrt{\frac{2(86 \text{ J})}{0.15 \text{ kg}}} = 34 \text{ m/s}$$

INSIGHT
To find the ball's speed when it was caught, we need to know the height of point f, but we don't need to know any details about the ball's trajectory. For example, it is not necessary to know the angle at which the ball leaves the bat or its maximum height.

The histograms to the right show the values of U and K at the points i and f. Notice that the energy of the system is mostly kinetic at the time the ball is caught.

PRACTICE PROBLEM
If the mass of the ball were increased, would the catch speed be greater than, less than, or the same as the value we just found?   [**Answer:** The same. U and K depend on mass in the same way, hence the mass cancels.]

Some related homework problems: Problem 29, Problem 30

The connection between height difference and speeds is explored further in the following Conceptual Checkpoint and Example.

CONCEPTUAL CHECKPOINT 8-1   COMPARE THE FINAL SPEEDS

Swimmers at a water park can enter a pool using one of two frictionless slides of equal height. Slide 1 approaches the water with a uniform slope; slide 2 dips rapidly at first, then levels out. Is the speed v_2 at the bottom of slide 2 **(a)** greater than, **(b)** less than, or **(c)** the same as the speed v_1 at the bottom of slide 1?

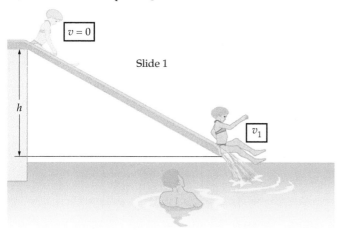

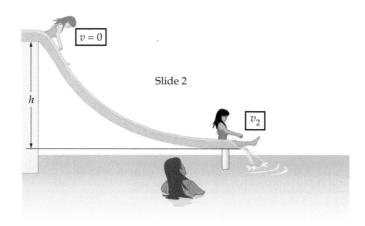

REASONING AND DISCUSSION

In both cases, the same amount of potential energy, *mgh*, is converted to kinetic energy. Since the conversion of gravitational potential energy to kinetic energy is the *only* energy transaction taking place, it follows that the speed is the same for each slide.

Interestingly, although the final speeds are the same, the time required to reach the water is less for slide 2. The reason is that swimmer 2 reaches a high speed early and maintains it, whereas the speed of swimmer 1 increases slowly and steadily.

ANSWER

(c) The speeds are the same.

EXAMPLE 8-7   SKATEBOARD EXIT RAMP

A 55-kg skateboarder enters a ramp moving horizontally with a speed of 6.5 m/s and leaves the ramp moving vertically with a speed of 4.1 m/s. Find the height of the ramp, assuming no energy loss to frictional forces.

PICTURE THE PROBLEM

We choose $y = 0$ to be the level of the bottom of the ramp, thus the gravitational potential energy is zero there. Point i indicates the skateboarder entering the ramp with a speed of 6.5 m/s; point f is the top of the ramp, where the speed is 4.1 m/s.

STRATEGY

To find h, simply set the initial energy, $E_i = U_i + K_i$, equal to the final energy, $E_f = U_f + K_f$.

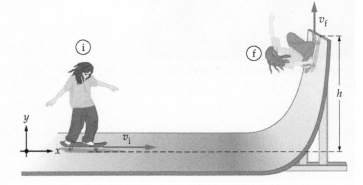

SOLUTION

1. Write expressions for U_i and K_i:

$$U_i = mg \cdot 0 = 0 \qquad K_i = \tfrac{1}{2}mv_i^2$$

2. Write expressions for U_f and K_f:

$$U_f = mgh \qquad K_f = \tfrac{1}{2}mv_f^2$$

CONTINUED ON NEXT PAGE

CONTINUED FROM PREVIOUS PAGE

3. Set the total mechanical energy at point i, $E_i = U_i + K_i$, equal to the total mechanical energy at point f, $E_f = U_f + K_f$:

$$U_i + K_i = U_f + K_f$$
$$0 + \tfrac{1}{2}mv_i^2 = mgh + \tfrac{1}{2}mv_f^2$$

4. Solve for h. Note that m cancels:

$$mgh = \tfrac{1}{2}mv_i^2 - \tfrac{1}{2}mv_f^2$$
$$h = \frac{v_i^2 - v_f^2}{2g}$$

5. Substitute numerical values:

$$h = \frac{(6.5 \text{ m/s})^2 - (4.1 \text{ m/s})^2}{2(9.81 \text{ m/s}^2)} = 1.3 \text{ m}$$

INSIGHT

Note that our value for h is independent of the shape of the ramp—it is equally valid for one with the shape shown here, or one that simply inclines upward at a constant angle. In addition, the height does not depend on the person's mass, as we see in Step 4.

The histograms to the right show U and K to scale at the points i and f, as well as at the maximum height where $K = 0$.

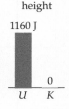

PRACTICE PROBLEM

What is the skateboarder's maximum height above the bottom of the ramp?   [**Answer: 2.2 m**]

Some related homework problems: Problem 29, Problem 33

▲ Does the shape of the slide matter? (See Conceptual Checkpoint 8–1.)

It is interesting to express the equation in Step 3 from Example 8–7 in words. First, the left side of the equation is the initial kinetic energy of the skateboarder, $\tfrac{1}{2}mv_i^2$. This is the initial energy content of the system. At point f the system still has the same amount of energy, only now part of it, mgh, is in the form of gravitational potential energy. The remainder is the final kinetic energy, $\tfrac{1}{2}mv_f^2$.

Conceptual Checkpoint 8–2 considers the effect of a slight change in the initial speed of an object.

CONCEPTUAL CHECKPOINT 8–2   WHAT IS THE FINAL SPEED?

A snowboarder coasts on a smooth track that rises from one level to another. If the snowboarder's initial speed is 4 m/s, the snowboarder just makes it to the upper level and comes to rest. With a slightly greater initial speed of 5 m/s, the snowboarder is still moving to the right on the upper level. Is the snowboarder's final speed in this case **(a)** 1 m/s, **(b)** 2 m/s, or **(c)** 3 m/s?

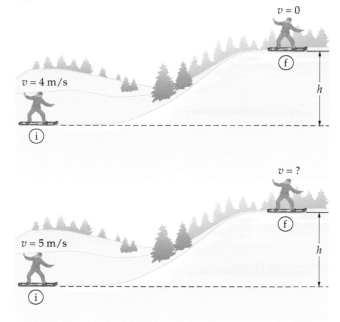

REASONING AND DISCUSSION
A plausible-sounding answer is that since the initial speed is greater by 1 m/s in the second case, the final speed should be greater by 1 m/s as well. Therefore, the answer should be 0 + 1 m/s = 1 m/s. This is incorrect, however.

As surprising as it may seem, an increase in the initial speed from 4 m/s to 5 m/s results in an increase in the final speed from 0 to 3 m/s. This is due to the fact that kinetic energy depends on v^2 rather than v; thus, it is the difference in v^2 that counts. In this case, the initial value of v^2 increases from 16 m²/s² to 25 m²/s², for a total increase of 25 m²/s² − 16 m²/s² = 9 m²/s². The final value of v^2 must increase by the same amount, 9 m²/s² = (3 m/s)². As a result, the final speed is 3 m/s.

ANSWER
(c) The final speed of the snowboarder in the second case is 3 m/s.

Let's check the results of the previous Conceptual Checkpoint with a specific numerical example. Suppose the snowboarder has a mass of 74.0 kg. It follows that in the first case the initial kinetic energy is $K_i = \frac{1}{2}(74.0 \text{ kg})(4.00 \text{ m/s})^2 = 592$ J. At the top of the hill all of this kinetic energy is converted to gravitational potential energy, mgh.

In the second case, the initial speed of the snowboarder is 5.00 m/s; thus, the initial kinetic energy is $K_i = \frac{1}{2}(74.0 \text{ kg})(5.00 \text{ m/s})^2 = 925$ J. When the snowboarder reaches the top of the hill, 592 J of this kinetic energy is converted to gravitational potential energy, leaving the snowboarder with a final kinetic energy of 925 J − 592 J = 333 J. The corresponding speed is given by

$$\frac{1}{2}mv^2 = 333 \text{ J}$$

$$v = \sqrt{\frac{2(333 \text{ J})}{m}} = \sqrt{\frac{2(333 \text{ J})}{74.0 \text{ kg}}} = \sqrt{9.00 \text{ m}^2/\text{s}^2} = 3.00 \text{ m/s}$$

Thus, as expected, the snowboarder in the second case has a final speed of 3.00 m/s.

We conclude this section with two Examples involving springs.

EXAMPLE 8–8 SPRING TIME

A 1.70-kg block slides on a horizontal, frictionless surface until it encounters a spring with a force constant of 955 N/m. The block comes to rest after compressing the spring a distance of 4.60 cm. Find the initial speed of the block. (Ignore air resistance and any energy lost when the block initially contacts the spring.)

PICTURE THE PROBLEM
Point i refers to times before the block makes contact with the spring, which means the block has a speed v and the end of the spring is at $x = 0$. Point f refers to the time when the block has come to rest, and the spring is compressed to $x = -d = -4.60$ cm.

We can choose the center of the block to be the $y = 0$ level. With this choice, the gravitational potential energy of the system is zero at all times.

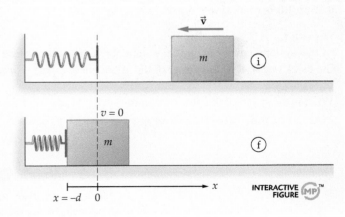

STRATEGY
Set E_i equal to E_f to find the one unknown, v. Note that the initial energy, E_i, is the kinetic energy of the block before it reaches the spring. The final energy, E_f, is the potential energy of the compressed spring.

SOLUTION

1. Write expressions for U_i and K_i. For U, we consider only the potential energy of the spring, $U = \frac{1}{2}kx^2$: $U_i = \frac{1}{2}k \cdot 0^2 = 0$ $K_i = \frac{1}{2}mv^2$

2. Do the same for U_f and K_f: $U_f = \frac{1}{2}k(-d)^2 = \frac{1}{2}kd^2$ $K_f = \frac{1}{2}m \cdot 0^2 = 0$

CONTINUED ON NEXT PAGE

CONTINUED FROM PREVIOUS PAGE

3. Set the initial mechanical energy, $E_i = U_i + K_i$, equal to the final mechanical energy, $E_f = U_f + K_f$, and solve for v:

$$U_i + K_i = U_f + K_f$$

$$0 + \tfrac{1}{2}mv^2 = \tfrac{1}{2}kd^2 + 0$$

$$v = d\sqrt{\frac{k}{m}}$$

4. Substitute numerical values:

$$v = d\sqrt{\frac{k}{m}} = (0.0460 \text{ m})\sqrt{\frac{955 \text{ N/m}}{1.70 \text{ kg}}} = 1.09 \text{ m/s}$$

INSIGHT
After the block comes to rest, the spring expands again, converting its potential energy back into the kinetic energy of the block. When the block leaves the spring, moving to the right, its speed is once again 1.09 m/s.

PRACTICE PROBLEM
What is the compression distance, d, if the block's initial speed is 0.500 m/s? [**Answer:** 2.11 cm]

Some related homework problems: Problem 32, Problem 34

ACTIVE EXAMPLE 8–1 FIND THE SPEED OF THE BLOCK

Suppose the spring and block in Example 8–8 are oriented vertically, as shown here. Initially, the spring is compressed 4.60 cm and the block is at rest. When the block is released, it accelerates upward. Find the speed of the block when the spring has returned to its equilibrium position.

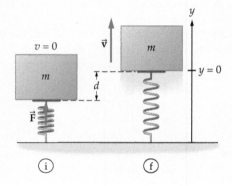

SOLUTION *(Test your understanding by performing the calculations indicated in each step.)*

1. Write an expression for the initial mechanical energy E_i:

$$E_i = U_i + K_i = -mgd + \tfrac{1}{2}kd^2 + 0$$

2. Write an expression for the final mechanical energy E_f:

$$E_f = U_f + K_f = 0 + 0 + \tfrac{1}{2}mv^2$$

3. Set E_i equal to E_f and solve for v:

$$-mgd + \tfrac{1}{2}kd^2 = \tfrac{1}{2}mv^2$$

$$v = \sqrt{kd^2/m - 2gd}$$

4. Substitute numerical values:

$$v = 0.535 \text{ m/s}$$

INSIGHT
In this system, part of the initial potential energy of the spring ($\tfrac{1}{2}kd^2$) goes into increasing the gravitational potential energy of the block (mgd). The remainder of the initial energy, $\tfrac{1}{2}kd^2 - mgd$, is converted into the block's kinetic energy.

YOUR TURN
What is the speed of the block when the spring is only halfway back to its equilibrium position?

*(Answers to **Your Turn** problems are given in the back of the book.)*

8–4 Work Done by Nonconservative Forces

Nonconservative forces change the amount of mechanical energy in a system. They might decrease the mechanical energy by converting it to thermal energy, or increase it by converting muscular work to kinetic or potential energy. In some systems, both types of processes occur at the same time.

To see the connection between the work done by a nonconservative force, W_{nc}, and the mechanical energy, E, we return once more to the work–energy theorem, which says that the *total* work is equal to the change in kinetic energy:

$$W_{total} = \Delta K$$

Suppose, for instance, that a system has one conservative and one nonconservative force. In this case, the total work is the sum of the conservative work W_c and the nonconservative work W_{nc}:

$$W_{total} = W_c + W_{nc}$$

Recalling that conservative work is related to the change in potential energy by the definition given in Equation 8–1, $W_c = -\Delta U$, we have

$$W_{total} = -\Delta U + W_{nc} = \Delta K$$

Solving this relation for the nonconservative work yields

$$W_{nc} = \Delta U + \Delta K$$

Finally, since the total mechanical energy is $E = U + K$, it follows that the *change* in mechanical energy is $\Delta E = \Delta U + \Delta K$. As a result, the nonconservative work is simply the change in mechanical energy:

$$W_{nc} = \Delta E = E_f - E_i \qquad \text{8–9}$$

If more than one nonconservative force acts, we simply add the nonconservative work done by each such force to obtain W_{nc}.

At this point it may be useful to collect the three "working relationships" that have been introduced in the last two chapters:

$$W_{total} = \Delta K$$
$$W_c = -\Delta U \qquad \text{8–10}$$
$$W_{nc} = \Delta E$$

Note that positive nonconservative work increases the total mechanical energy of a system, while negative nonconservative work decreases the mechanical energy—and converts it to other forms. In the next Example, for instance, part of the initial mechanical energy of a leaf is converted to heat and other forms of energy by air resistance as it falls to the ground.

PROBLEM-SOLVING NOTE

Nonconservative Systems

Start by sketching the system and labeling the initial and final points with i and f, respectively. The initial and final mechanical energies are related to the nonconservative work by $W_{nc} = E_f - E_i$.

EXAMPLE 8–9   A LEAF FALLS IN THE FOREST: FIND THE NONCONSERVATIVE WORK

Deep in the forest, a 17.0-g leaf falls from a tree and drops straight to the ground. If its initial height was 5.30 m and its speed on landing was 1.3 m/s, how much nonconservative work was done on the leaf?

PICTURE THE PROBLEM
The leaf drops from rest at a height $y = h = 5.30$ m and lands with a speed $v = 1.3$ m/s at $y = 0$. These two points are labeled i and f, respectively.

STRATEGY
To begin, calculate the initial mechanical energy, E_i, and the final mechanical energy, E_f. Once these energies have been determined, the nonconservative work is $W_{nc} = \Delta E = E_f - E_i$.

SOLUTION

1. Evaluate U_i, K_i, and E_i:

$$U_i = mgh = (0.0170 \text{ kg})(9.81 \text{ m/s}^2)(5.30 \text{ m}) = 0.884 \text{ J}$$
$$K_i = \tfrac{1}{2}m \cdot 0^2 = 0$$
$$E_i = U_i + K_i = 0.884 \text{ J}$$

2. Next, evaluate U_f, K_f, and E_f.

$$U_f = mg \cdot 0 = 0$$
$$K_f = \tfrac{1}{2}mv^2 = \tfrac{1}{2}(0.0170 \text{ kg})(1.3 \text{ m/s})^2 = 0.014 \text{ J}$$
$$E_f = U_f + K_f = 0.014 \text{ J}$$

3. Use $W_{nc} = \Delta E$ to find the nonconservative work:

$$W_{nc} = \Delta E = E_f - E_i = 0.014 \text{ J} - 0.884 \text{ J} = -0.870 \text{ J}$$

CONTINUED ON NEXT PAGE

CONTINUED FROM PREVIOUS PAGE

INSIGHT

Note that most of the initial mechanical energy is dissipated as the leaf falls. This is indicated in the histograms to the right. The small amount that remains (only about 1.6%) appears as the kinetic energy of the leaf just before it lands. If a cherry had fallen from the tree, it would have struck the ground with a considerably greater speed—perhaps five times the speed of the leaf. In that case, the percentage of the initial potential energy remaining as kinetic energy would have been $5^2 = 25$ times greater than the percentage retained by the leaf.

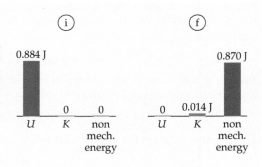

PRACTICE PROBLEM

What was the average nonconservative force exerted on the leaf as it fell? [**Answer:** $W_{nc} = -Fh$, $F = -W_{nc}/h = 0.16$ N, upward]

Some related homework problems: Problem 42, Problem 43

In the following Active Example, we use a knowledge of the nonconservative work to find the depth at which a diver comes to rest.

ACTIVE EXAMPLE 8–2   FIND THE DIVER'S DEPTH

A 95.0-kg diver steps off a diving board and drops into the water 3.00 m below. At some depth d below the water's surface, the diver comes to rest. If the nonconservative work done on the diver is $W_{nc} = -5120$ J, what is the depth, d?

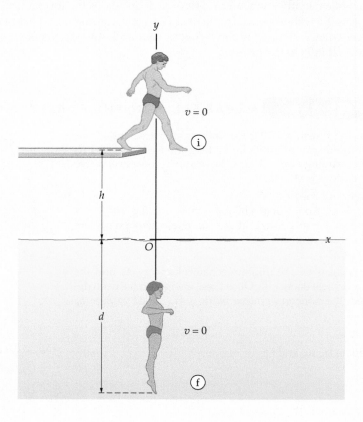

SOLUTION *(Test your understanding by performing the calculations indicated in each step.)*

1. Write the initial mechanical energy, E_i: $E_i = mgh + 0 = mgh$

2. Write the final mechanical energy, E_f: $E_f = mg(-d) + 0 = -mgd$

3. Set W_{nc} equal to ΔE: $W_{nc} = \Delta E = E_f - E_i = -mgd - mgh$

4. Solve for d: $d = -(W_{nc} + mgh)/mg$

5. Substitute numerical values: $d = 2.49$ m

INSIGHT

Another way to write Step 3 is $E_f = E_i + W_{nc}$. In words, this equation says that the final mechanical energy is the initial mechanical energy plus the nonconservative work done on the system. In this case, $W_{nc} < 0$; hence the final mechanical energy is less than the initial mechanical energy.

YOUR TURN

Suppose the diver descends to a depth of 3.50 m. How much nonconservative work is done in this case?

(*Answers to* **Your Turn** *problems are given in the back of the book.*)

We now present a Conceptual Checkpoint that further examines the relationship between nonconservative work and distance.

CONCEPTUAL CHECKPOINT 8–3   JUDGING A PUTT

A golfer badly misjudges a putt, sending the ball only one-quarter of the distance to the hole. The original putt gave the ball an initial speed of v_0. If the force of resistance due to the grass is constant, would an initial speed of **(a)** $2v_0$, **(b)** $3v_0$, or **(c)** $4v_0$ be needed to get the ball to the hole from its original position?

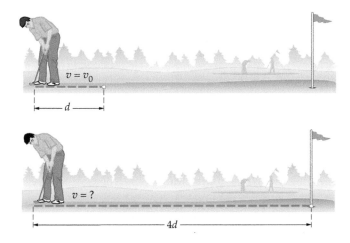

REASONING AND DISCUSSION

In the original putt, the ball started with a kinetic energy of $\frac{1}{2}mv_0^2$ and came to rest in the distance d. The kinetic energy was dissipated by the nonconservative force due to grass resistance, F, which does the work $W_{nc} = -Fd$. Since the change in mechanical energy is $\Delta E = 0 - \frac{1}{2}mv_0^2 = -\frac{1}{2}mv_0^2$, it follows from $W_{nc} = \Delta E$ that $Fd = \frac{1}{2}mv_0^2$. Therefore, to go four times the distance, $4d$, we need to give the ball four times as much kinetic energy. Noting that kinetic energy is proportional to v^2, we see that the initial speed need only be doubled.

ANSWER

(a) The initial speed should be doubled to $2v_0$.

A common example of a nonconservative force is kinetic friction. In the next Example, we show how to include the effects of friction in a system that also includes kinetic energy and gravitational potential energy.

EXAMPLE 8–10 LANDING WITH A THUD

A block of mass $m_1 = 2.40$ kg is connected to a second block of mass $m_2 = 1.80$ kg, as shown here. When the blocks are released from rest, they move through a distance $d = 0.500$ m, at which point m_2 hits the floor. Given that the coefficient of kinetic friction between m_1 and the horizontal surface is $\mu_k = 0.450$, find the speed of the blocks just before m_2 lands.

PICTURE THE PROBLEM
We choose $y = 0$ to be at floor level; therefore, the gravitational potential energy of m_2 is zero when it lands. The potential energy of m_1 doesn't change during this process; it is always m_1gh. Thus, it isn't necessary to know the value of h. Note that we label the beginning and ending points with i and f, respectively.

STRATEGY
Since a nonconservative force (friction) is doing work in this system, we use $W_{nc} = \Delta E = E_f - E_i$. Thus, we must calculate not only the mechanical energies, E_i and E_f, but also the nonconservative work, W_{nc}. Note that E_f can be written in terms of the unknown speed of the blocks just before m_2 lands. Therefore, we can set W_{nc} equal to ΔE and solve for the final speed.

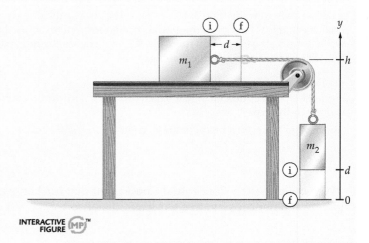

INTERACTIVE FIGURE MP™

SOLUTION

1. Evaluate U_i, K_i, and E_i. Be sure to include contributions from both masses:

$$U_i = m_1gh + m_2gd$$
$$K_i = \tfrac{1}{2}m_1 \cdot 0^2 + \tfrac{1}{2}m_2 \cdot 0^2 = 0$$
$$E_i = U_i + K_i = m_1gh + m_2gd$$

2. Next, evaluate U_f, K_f, and E_f. Note that E_f depends on the unknown speed, v:

$$U_f = m_1gh + 0$$
$$K_f = \tfrac{1}{2}m_1v^2 + \tfrac{1}{2}m_2v^2$$
$$E_f = U_f + K_f = m_1gh + \tfrac{1}{2}m_1v^2 + \tfrac{1}{2}m_2v^2$$

3. Calculate the nonconservative work, W_{nc}. Recall that the force of friction is $f_k = \mu_k N = \mu_k m_1 g$, and that it points opposite to the displacement of distance d:

$$W_{nc} = -f_k d = -\mu_k m_1 g d$$

4. Set W_{nc} equal to $\Delta E = E_f - E_i$. Notice that m_1gh cancels because it occurs in both E_i and E_f:

$$W_{nc} = E_f - E_i$$
$$-\mu_k m_1 g d = \tfrac{1}{2}m_1v^2 + \tfrac{1}{2}m_2v^2 - m_2gd$$

5. Solve for v:

$$v = \sqrt{\frac{2(m_2 - \mu_k m_1)gd}{m_1 + m_2}}$$

6. Substitute numerical values:

$$v = \sqrt{\frac{2[1.80 \text{ kg} - (0.450)(2.40 \text{ kg})](9.81 \text{ m/s}^2)(0.500 \text{ m})}{1.80 \text{ kg} + 2.40 \text{ kg}}}$$
$$= 1.30 \text{ m/s}$$

INSIGHT
Note that Step 4 can be rearranged as follows: $\tfrac{1}{2}m_1v^2 + \tfrac{1}{2}m_2v^2 = m_2gd - \mu_k m_1 g d$. Translating this to words, we can say that the final kinetic energy of the blocks is equal to the initial gravitational potential energy of m_2, minus the energy dissipated by friction.

PRACTICE PROBLEM
Find the coefficient of kinetic friction if the final speed of the blocks is 0.950 m/s.   [**Answer:** $\mu_k = 0.589$]

Some related homework problems: Problem 46, Problem 51, Problem 66, Problem 106

Finally, we present an Active Example for the common situation of a system in which two different nonconservative forces do work.

MARATHON MAN: FIND THE HEIGHT OF THE HILL

An 80.0-kg jogger starts from rest and runs uphill into a stiff breeze. At the top of the hill the jogger has done the work $W_{nc1} = +1.80 \times 10^4$ J, air resistance has done the work $W_{nc2} = -4420$ J, and the jogger's speed is 3.50 m/s. Find the height of the hill.

SOLUTION   *(Test your understanding by performing the calculations indicated in each step.)*

1. Write the initial mechanical energy, E_i: $E_i = U_i + K_i = 0 + 0 = 0$

2. Write the final mechanical energy, E_f: $E_f = U_f + K_f = mgh + \frac{1}{2}mv^2$

3. Set W_{nc} equal to ΔE: $W_{nc} = \Delta E = mgh + \frac{1}{2}mv^2$

4. Use $W_{nc} = \Delta E$ to solve for h: $h = (W_{nc} - \frac{1}{2}mv^2)/mg$

5. Calculate the total nonconservative work: $W_{nc} = W_{nc1} + W_{nc2} = 13{,}600$ J

6. Substitute numerical values to determine h: $h = 16.7$ m

INSIGHT
As usual when dealing with energy calculations, our final result is independent of the shape of the hill.

YOUR TURN
Suppose the jogger's mass had been 90.0 kg rather than 80.0 kg. What would be the height of the hill in this case?

*(Answers to **Your Turn** problems are given in the back of the book.)*

8–5 Potential Energy Curves and Equipotentials

Figure 8–10 shows a metal ball rolling on a roller coaster–like track. Initially the ball is at rest at point A. Since the height at A is $y = h$, the ball's initial mechanical energy is $E_0 = mgh$. If friction and other nonconservative forces can be ignored, the ball's mechanical energy remains fixed at E_0 throughout its motion. Thus,

$$E = U + K = E_0$$

▲ Highways that descend steeply are often provided with escape ramps that enable truck drivers whose brakes fail to bring their rigs to a safe stop. These ramps provide a perfect illustration of the conservation of energy. From a physics point of view, the driver's problem is to get rid of an enormous amount of kinetic energy in the safest possible way. The ramps run uphill, so some of the kinetic energy is simply converted back into gravitational potential energy (just as in a roller coaster). In addition, the ramps are typically surfaced with sand or gravel, allowing much of the initial kinetic energy to be dissipated by friction into other forms of energy, such as sound and heat.

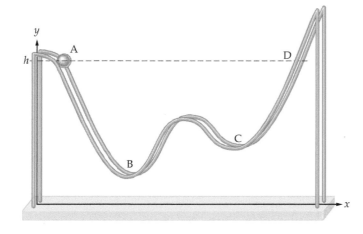

◀ **FIGURE 8–10 A ball rolling on a frictionless track**
The ball starts at A, where $y = h$, with zero speed. Its greatest speed occurs at B. At D, where $y = h$ again, its speed returns to zero.

▶ **FIGURE 8–11** **Gravitational potential energy versus position for the track shown in Figure 8–10**

The shape of the potential energy curve is exactly the same as the shape of the track. In this case, the total mechanical energy is fixed at its initial value, $E_0 = U + K = mgh$. Because the height of the curve is U, by definition, it follows that K is the distance from the curve up to the dashed line at $E_0 = mgh$. Note that K is largest at B. In addition, K vanishes at A and D, which are turning points of the motion.

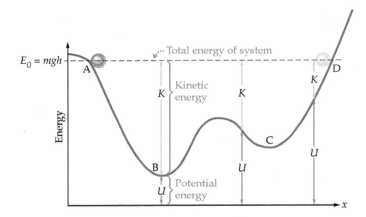

As the ball moves, its potential energy falls and rises in the same way as the track. After all, the gravitational potential energy, $U = mgy$, is directly proportional to the height of the track, y. In a sense, then, the track itself represents a graph of the corresponding potential energy.

This is shown explicitly in **Figure 8–11**, where we plot energy on the vertical axis and x on the horizontal axis. The potential energy U looks just like the track in Figure 8–10. In addition, we plot a horizontal line at the value E_0, indicating the constant energy of the ball. Since the potential energy plus the kinetic energy must always add up to E_0, it follows that K is the amount of energy from the potential energy curve up to the horizontal line at E_0. This is also shown in Figure 8–11.

Examining an energy plot like Figure 8–11 gives a great deal of information about the motion of an object. For example, at point B the potential energy has its lowest value, and thus the kinetic energy is greatest there. At point C the potential energy has increased, indicating a corresponding decrease in kinetic energy. As the ball continues to the right, the potential energy increases until, at point D, it is again equal to the total energy, E_0. At this point the kinetic energy is zero, and the ball comes to rest momentarily. It then "turns around" and begins to move to the left, eventually returning to point A where it again stops, changes direction, and begins a new cycle. Points A and D, then, are referred to as **turning points** of the motion.

Turning points are also seen in the motion of a mass on a spring, as indicated in **Figure 8–12**. Figure 8–12 (a) shows a mass pulled to the position $x = A$, and released from rest; Figure 8–12 (b) shows the potential energy of the system, $U = \frac{1}{2}kx^2$.

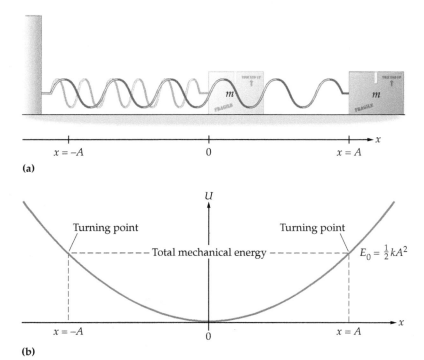

▶ **FIGURE 8–12** **A mass on a spring**

(a) A spring is stretched by an amount A, giving it a potential energy of $U = \frac{1}{2}kA^2$.
(b) The potential energy curve, $U = \frac{1}{2}kx^2$, for the spring in (a). Because the mass starts at rest, its initial mechanical energy is $E_0 = \frac{1}{2}kA^2$. The mass oscillates between $x = A$ and $x = -A$.

Starting the system this way gives it an initial energy $E_0 = \frac{1}{2}kA^2$, shown by the horizontal line in Figure 8–12 (b). As the mass moves to the left, its speed increases, reaching a maximum where the potential energy is lowest, at $x = 0$. If no nonconservative forces act, the mass continues to $x = -A$, where it stops momentarily before returning to $x = A$. This type of **oscillatory motion** will be studied in detail in Chapter 13.

The next Example uses a potential-energy curve to find the speed of an object at a given value of x.

EXAMPLE 8–11   A POTENTIAL PROBLEM

A 1.60-kg object in a conservative system moves along the x axis, where the potential energy is as shown. A physical example would be a bead sliding on a wire with the shape of the potential energy curve. If the object's speed at $x = 0$ is 2.30 m/s, what is its speed at $x = 2.00$ m?

PICTURE THE PROBLEM
The plot shows U as a function of x. The values of U at $x = 0$ and $x = 2.00$ m are 9.35 J and 4.15 J, respectively. It follows that the object's speed at $x = 2.00$ m will be greater than its speed at $x = 0$.

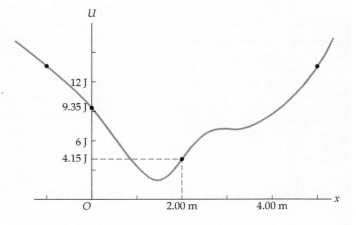

STRATEGY
Since mechanical energy is conserved, we know that the total energy at $x = 0$ $(U_i + K_i)$ is equal to the total energy at $x = 2.00$ m $(U_f + K_f)$.

The problem statement gives U_i, and since we also know the speed at $x = 0$ we can use $K = \frac{1}{2}mv^2$ to calculate the corresponding kinetic energy, K_i. At $x = 2.00$ m we know the potential energy, U_f; hence we can use $U_i + K_i = U_f + K_f$ to solve for K_f. Once the final kinetic energy is known, it is possible to solve for the final speed by once again using $K = \frac{1}{2}mv^2$.

SOLUTION

1. Evaluate U_i, K_i, and E_i at $x = 0$:

$$U_i = 9.35 \text{ J}$$
$$K_i = \tfrac{1}{2}mv_i^2 = \tfrac{1}{2}(1.60 \text{ kg})(2.30 \text{ m/s})^2 = 4.23 \text{ J}$$
$$E_i = U_i + K_i = 9.35 \text{ J} + 4.23 \text{ J} = 13.58 \text{ J}$$

2. Write expressions for U_f, K_f, and E_f at $x = 2.00$ m:

$$U_f = 4.15 \text{ J}$$
$$K_f = \tfrac{1}{2}mv_f^2$$
$$E_f = U_f + K_f = 4.15 \text{ J} + \tfrac{1}{2}mv_f^2$$

3. Set E_f equal to E_i and solve for v_f:

$$4.15 \text{ J} + \tfrac{1}{2}mv_f^2 = 13.58 \text{ J}$$

   Solve for v_f:

$$v_f = \sqrt{\frac{2(13.58 \text{ J} - 4.15 \text{ J})}{m}}$$

4. Substitute the numerical value of the object's mass:

$$v_f = \sqrt{\frac{2(13.58 \text{ J} - 4.15 \text{ J})}{1.60 \text{ kg}}} = 3.43 \text{ m/s}$$

INSIGHT
As we see in Step 1, the total mechanical energy of the system is 13.58 J. This means that turning points for this object occur at values of x where $U = 13.58$ J.

PRACTICE PROBLEM
Using the graph provided, estimate the location of the turning points for this object.   [**Answer:** $x = -1.00$ m and $x = 5.00$ m]

Some related homework problems: Problem 57, Problem 58

Oscillatory motion between turning points is also observed in molecules. If the energy of oscillation is relatively small, as is usual at room temperature, the atoms in a molecule simply vibrate back and forth—like masses connected by a spring. As long as no energy is gained or lost, the molecular oscillations continue unchanged. On the other hand, if the energy of the molecule is increased by

Where the slope is steep ...

Side view of mountain

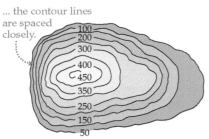

... the contour lines are spaced closely.

100
200
300
400
450
350
250
150
50

Contour map of mountain (from above)

▲ **FIGURE 8–13 A contour map**
A small mountain (top, in side view) is very steep on the left, more gently sloping on the right. A contour map of this mountain (bottom) shows a series of equal-altitude contour lines from 50 ft to 450 ft. Notice that the contour lines are packed close together where the terrain is steep, but are widely spaced where it is more level.

heating, or some other mechanism, the molecule will eventually dissociate—fly apart—as the atoms move to infinite separation.

In some cases, a two-dimensional plot of potential energy contours is useful. For instance, **Figure 8–13** shows a contour map of a hill. Each contour corresponds to a given altitude and, hence, to a given value of the gravitational potential energy. In general, lines corresponding to constant values of potential energy are called **equipotentials.** Since the altitude changes by equal amounts from one contour to the next, it follows that when gravitational equipotentials are packed close together, the corresponding terrain is steep. On the other hand, when the equipotentials are widely spaced, the ground is nearly flat, since a large horizontal distance is required for a given change in altitude. We shall see similar plots with similar interpretations when we study electric potential energy in Chapter 21.

THE BIG PICTURE	**PUTTING PHYSICS IN CONTEXT**
LOOKING BACK	LOOKING AHEAD

The concept of work, first introduced in Chapter 7 as force times distance, is used again in this chapter. For example, we use work in Section 8–1 to illustrate the difference between conservative and nonconservative forces.

Work (Chapter 7) is used again in Section 8–2 to introduce the concept of potential energy, U, and to define its change.

Conservation of energy is one of the key elements in the study of elastic collisions. See, in particular, Section 9–6 and Example 9–7.

The wide-ranging importance of energy conservation is illustrated by its use in the following disparate topics: rotational motion (Section 10–6), gravitation (Section 12–5), oscillatory motion (Section 13–5), fluid dynamics (Section 15–7), and phase changes (Section 17–6).

CHAPTER SUMMARY

8–1 CONSERVATIVE AND NONCONSERVATIVE FORCES

Conservative forces conserve the mechanical energy of a system. Thus, in a conservative system the total mechanical energy remains constant.

Nonconservative forces convert mechanical energy into other forms of energy, or convert other forms of energy into mechanical energy.

Conservative Force, Definition
A conservative force does zero total work on any closed path. In addition, the work done by a conservative force in going from point A to point B is *independent of the path* from A to B.

Examples of Conservative Forces
Gravity, spring.

Nonconservative Force, Definition
The work done by a nonconservative force on a closed path is nonzero. The work is also path-dependent.

Examples of Nonconservative Forces
Friction, air resistance, tension in ropes and cables, forces exerted by muscles and motors.

8–2 POTENTIAL ENERGY AND THE WORK DONE BY CONSERVATIVE FORCES

Potential energy, U, can "store" energy in a system. Energy in the form of potential energy can be converted to kinetic or other forms of energy.

Potential Energy, Definition
The work done by a conservative force is the negative of the change in potential energy:

$$W_c = -\Delta U = U_i - U_f \qquad 8\text{–}1$$

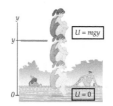

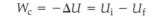

Zero Level

Any location can be chosen for $U = 0$. Once the choice is made, however, it must be used consistently.

Gravity

Choosing $y = 0$ to be the zero level near Earth's surface,

$$U = mgy. \qquad \text{8-3}$$

Spring

Choosing $x = 0$ (the equilibrium position) to be the zero level,

$$U = \tfrac{1}{2}kx^2. \qquad \text{8-5}$$

8–3 CONSERVATION OF MECHANICAL ENERGY

Mechanical energy, E, is conserved in systems with conservative forces only.

Mechanical Energy, Definition

Mechanical energy is the sum of the potential and kinetic energies of a system:

$$E = U + K \qquad \text{8-6}$$

8–4 WORK DONE BY NONCONSERVATIVE FORCES

Nonconservative forces can change the mechanical energy of a system.

Change in Mechanical Energy

The work done by a nonconservative force is equal to the change in the mechanical energy of a system:

$$W_{\mathrm{nc}} = \Delta E = E_{\mathrm{f}} - E_{\mathrm{i}} \qquad \text{8-9}$$

8–5 POTENTIAL ENERGY CURVES AND EQUIPOTENTIALS

A potential energy curve plots U as a function of position.

An equipotential plot shows contours corresponding to constant values of U.

Turning Points

Turning points occur where an object stops momentarily before reversing direction. At turning points the kinetic energy is zero.

Oscillatory Motion

An object moving back and forth between two turning points is said to have oscillatory motion.

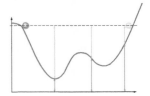

PROBLEM-SOLVING SUMMARY

Type of Calculation	Relevant Physical Concepts	Related Examples
Calculate the gravitational or spring potential energy.	The potential energy for gravity is $U = mgy$; the potential energy for a spring is $U = \tfrac{1}{2}kx^2$.	Examples 8–2, 8–3, 8–4
Apply energy conservation in a system involving gravity.	Choose a horizontal level for $y = 0$, then use $U = mgy$.	Examples 8–6, 8–7 Active Example 8–1
Apply energy conservation in a system involving a spring.	Use $U = \tfrac{1}{2}kx^2$, where x measures the expansion or compression of the spring from its equilibrium position.	Example 8–8, Active Example 8–1
Find the nonconservative work done on a system.	Calculate the initial energy, E_{i}, and the final energy, E_{f}. Then use $W_{\mathrm{nc}} = \Delta E = E_{\mathrm{f}} - E_{\mathrm{i}}$.	Examples 8–9, 8–10, Active Examples 8–2, 8–3

CONCEPTUAL QUESTIONS

For instructor-assigned homework, go to www.masteringphysics.com

(Answers to odd-numbered Conceptual Questions can be found in the back of the book.)

1. Is it possible for the kinetic energy of an object to be negative? Is it possible for the gravitational potential energy of an object to be negative? Explain.

2. An avalanche occurs when a mass of snow slides down a steep mountain slope. Discuss the energy conversions responsible for water vapor rising to form clouds, falling as snow on a mountain, and then sliding down a slope as an avalanche.

3. If the stretch of a spring is doubled, the force it exerts is also doubled. By what factor does the spring's potential energy increase?

4. When a mass is placed on top of a vertical spring, the spring compresses and the mass moves downward. Analyze this system in terms of its mechanical energy.

5. If a spring is stretched so far that it is permanently deformed, its force is no longer conservative. Why?

6. An object is thrown upward to a person on a roof. At what point is the object's kinetic energy at maximum? At what point is the potential energy of the system at maximum? At what locations do these energies have their minimum values?

7. It is a law of nature that the total energy of the universe is conserved. What do politicians mean, then, when they urge "energy conservation"?

8. Discuss the various energy conversions that occur when a person performs a pole vault. Include as many conversions as you can, and consider times before, during, and after the actual vault itself.

How many energy conversions can you identify?
(Conceptual Question 8)

9. Discuss the nature of the work done by the equipment shown in this photo. What types of forces are involved?

Conservative or nonconservative? (Conceptual Question 9)

10. A toy frog consists of a suction cup and a spring. When the suction cup is pressed against a smooth surface, the frog is held down. When the suction cup lets go, the frog leaps into the air. Discuss the behavior of the frog in terms of energy conversions.

11. If the force on an object is zero, does that mean the potential energy of the system is zero? If the potential energy of a system is zero, is the force zero?

12. When a ball is thrown upward, its mechanical energy, $E = mgy + \frac{1}{2}mv^2$, is constant with time if air resistance can be ignored. How does E vary with time if air resistance cannot be ignored?

13. When a ball is thrown upward, it spends the same amount of time on the way up as on the way down—as long as air resistance can be ignored. If air resistance is taken into account, is the time on the way down the same as, greater than, or less than the time on the way up? Explain.

PROBLEMS AND CONCEPTUAL EXERCISES

Note: Answers to odd-numbered Problems and Conceptual Exercises can be found in the back of the book. **IP** *denotes an integrated problem, with both conceptual and numerical parts;* **BIO** *identifies problems of biological or medical interest;* **CE** *indicates a conceptual exercise.* **Predict/Explain** *problems ask for two responses: (a) your prediction of a physical outcome, and (b) the best explanation among three provided. On all problems, red bullets (•, ••, •••) are used to indicate the level of difficulty.*

SECTION 8–1 CONSERVATIVE AND NONCONSERVATIVE FORCES

1. • **CE** The work done by a conservative force is indicated in **Figure 8–14** for a variety of different paths connecting the points A and B. What is the work done by this force **(a)** on path 1 and **(b)** on path 2?

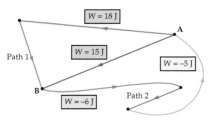

▲ **FIGURE 8–14** Problem 1

2. • Calculate the work done by gravity as a 3.2-kg object is moved from point A to point B in **Figure 8–15** along paths 1, 2, and 3.

3. • Calculate the work done by friction as a 3.7-kg box is slid along a floor from point A to point B in **Figure 8–16** along paths 1, 2, and 3. Assume that the coefficient of kinetic friction between the box and the floor is 0.26.

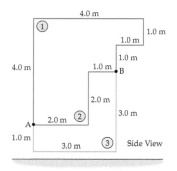

▲ **FIGURE 8–15** Problem 2

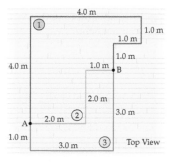

▲ **FIGURE 8–16** Problem 3

4. • **IP** A 4.1-kg block is attached to a spring with a force constant of 550 N/m, as shown in **Figure 8–17**. **(a)** Find the work done by the spring on the block as the block moves from A to B along paths 1 and 2. **(b)** How do your results depend on the mass of the block? Specifically, if you increase the mass, does the work done by the spring increase, decrease, or stay the same? (Assume the system is frictionless.)

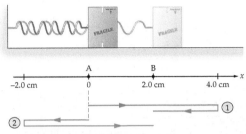

▲ **FIGURE 8–17** Problems 4 and 6

5. • **IP (a)** Calculate the work done by gravity as a 5.2-kg object is moved from A to B in **Figure 8–18** along paths 1 and 2. **(b)** How do your results depend on the mass of the block? Specifically, if you increase the mass, does the work done by gravity increase, decrease, or stay the same?

▲ **FIGURE 8–18** Problem 5

6. •• In the system shown in Figure 8–17, suppose the block has a mass of 2.7 kg, the spring has a force constant of 480 N/m, and the coefficient of kinetic friction between the block and the floor is 0.16. **(a)** Find the work done on the block by the spring and by friction as the block is moved from point A to point B along path 2. **(b)** Find the work done on the block by the spring and by friction if the block is moved directly from point A to point B.

SECTION 8–2 POTENTIAL ENERGY AND THE WORK DONE BY CONSERVATIVE FORCES

7. • **CE Predict/Explain** Ball 1 is thrown to the ground with an initial downward speed; ball 2 is dropped to the ground from rest. Assuming the balls have the same mass and are released from the same height, is the change in gravitational potential energy of ball 1 greater than, less than, or equal to the change in gravitational potential energy of ball 2? **(b)** Choose the *best explanation* from among the following:

  I. Ball 1 has the greater total energy, and therefore more energy can go into gravitational potential energy.

  II. The gravitational potential energy depends only on the mass of the ball and the drop height.

  III. All of the initial energy of ball 2 is gravitational potential energy.

8. • **CE** A mass is attached to the bottom of a vertical spring. This causes the spring to stretch and the mass to move downward. **(a)** Does the potential energy of the spring increase, decrease, or stay the same during this process? Explain. **(b)** Does the gravitational potential energy of the Earth–mass system increase, decrease, or stay the same during this process? Explain.

9. • As an Acapulco cliff diver drops to the water from a height of 46 m, his gravitational potential energy decreases by 25,000 J. What is the diver's weight in newtons?

10. • Find the gravitational potential energy of an 88-kg person standing atop Mt. Everest at an altitude of 8848 m. Use sea level as the location for $y = 0$.

11. • **Jeopardy!** Contestants on the game show *Jeopardy!* depress spring-loaded buttons to "buzz in" and provide the question corresponding to the revealed answer. The force constant on these buttons is about 130 N/m. Estimate the amount of energy it takes—at a minimum—to buzz in.

12. •• **BIO The Wing of the Hawkmoth** Experiments performed on the wing of a hawkmoth (*Manduca sexta*) show that it deflects by a distance of $x = 4.8$ mm when a force of magnitude $F = 3.0$ mN is applied at the tip, as indicated in **Figure 8–19**. Treating the wing as an ideal spring, find **(a)** the force constant of the wing and **(b)** the energy stored in the wing when it is deflected. **(c)** What force must be applied to the tip of the wing to store twice the energy found in part (b)?

Hummingbird hawkmoth (*Manduca sexta*). (Problem 12)

▲ **FIGURE 8–19** Problem 12

13. •• **IP** A vertical spring stores 0.962 J in spring potential energy when a 3.5-kg mass is suspended from it. **(a)** By what multiplicative factor does the spring potential energy change if the mass attached to the spring is doubled? **(b)** Verify your answer to part (a) by calculating the spring potential energy when a 7.0-kg mass is attached to the spring.

14. •• Pushing on the pump of a soap dispenser compresses a small spring. When the spring is compressed 0.50 cm, its potential energy is 0.0025 J. **(a)** What is the force constant of the spring? **(b)** What compression is required for the spring potential energy to equal 0.0084 J?

15. •• A force of 4.1 N is required to stretch a certain spring by 1.4 cm. **(a)** How far must this spring be stretched for its potential energy to be 0.020 J? **(b)** How much stretch is required for the spring potential energy to be 0.080 J?

16. •• **IP** The work required to stretch a certain spring from an elongation of 4.00 cm to an elongation of 5.00 cm is 30.5 J. **(a)** Is the work required to increase the elongation of the spring from 5.00 cm to 6.00 cm greater than, less than, or equal to 30.5 J? Explain. **(b)** Verify your answer to part (a) by calculating the required work.

17. •• A 0.33-kg pendulum bob is attached to a string 1.2 m long. What is the change in the gravitational potential energy of the system as the bob swings from point A to point B in **Figure 8–20**?

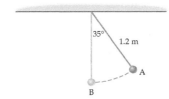

▲ **FIGURE 8–20** Problems 17, 34, 35, and 74

SECTION 8–3 CONSERVATION OF MECHANICAL ENERGY

18. • **CE Predict/Explain** You throw a ball upward and let it fall to the ground. Your friend drops an identical ball straight down to the ground from the same height. Is the change in kinetic energy of your ball greater than, less than, or equal to the change in kinetic energy of your friend's ball? **(b)** Choose the *best explanation* from among the following:
  I. Your friend's ball converts all its initial energy into kinetic energy.
  II. Your ball is in the air longer, which results in a greater change in kinetic energy.
  III. The change in gravitational potential energy is the same for each ball, which means the change in kinetic energy must be the same also.

19. • **CE** Suppose the situation described in Conceptual Checkpoint 8–2 is repeated on the fictional planet Epsilon, where the acceleration due to gravity is less than it is on the Earth. **(a)** Would the height of a hill on Epsilon that causes a reduction in speed from 4 m/s to 0 be greater than, less than, or equal to the height of the corresponding hill on Earth? Explain. **(b)** Consider the hill on Epsilon discussed in part (a). If the initial speed at the bottom of the hill is 5 m/s, will the final speed at the top of the hill be greater than, less than, or equal to 3 m/s? Explain.

20. • **CE Predict/Explain** When a ball of mass m is dropped from rest from a height h, its kinetic energy just before landing is K. Now, suppose a second ball of mass $4m$ is dropped from rest from a height $h/4$. **(a)** Just before ball 2 lands, is its kinetic energy $4K$, $2K$, K, $K/2$, or $K/4$? **(b)** Choose the *best explanation* from among the following:
  I. The two balls have the same initial energy.
  II. The more massive ball will have the greater kinetic energy.
  III. The reduced drop height results in a reduced kinetic energy.

21. • **CE Predict/Explain** When a ball of mass m is dropped from rest from a height h, its speed just before landing is v. Now, suppose a second ball of mass $4m$ is dropped from rest from a height $h/4$. **(a)** Just before ball 2 lands, is its speed $4v$, $2v$, v, $v/2$, or $v/4$? **(b)** Choose the *best explanation* from among the following:
  I. The factors of 4 cancel; therefore, the landing speed is the same.
  II. The two balls land with the same kinetic energy; therefore, the ball of mass $4m$ has the speed $v/2$.
  III. Reducing the height by a factor of 4 reduces the speed by a factor of 4.

22. • **CE** For an object moving along the x axis, the potential energy of the frictionless system is shown in **Figure 8–21**. Suppose the object is released from rest at the point A. Rank the other points

in the figure in increasing order of the object's speed. Indicate ties where appropriate.

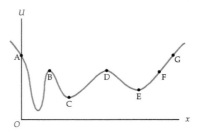

▲ **FIGURE 8–21** Problems 22 and 23

23. • **CE** Referring to Problem 22, suppose the object is released from rest at a point halfway between the points F and G. Rank the other points in the figure in increasing order of the object's speed, if the object can reach that point. Indicate ties where appropriate.

24. • At an amusement park, a swimmer uses a water slide to enter the main pool. If the swimmer starts at rest, slides without friction, and descends through a vertical height of 2.31 m, what is her speed at the bottom of the slide?

25. • In the previous problem, find the swimmer's speed at the bottom of the slide if she starts with an initial speed of 0.840 m/s.

26. • **IP** A player passes a 0.600-kg basketball downcourt for a fast break. The ball leaves the player's hands with a speed of 8.30 m/s and slows down to 7.10 m/s at its highest point. **(a)** Ignoring air resistance, how high above the release point is the ball when it is at its maximum height? **(b)** How would doubling the ball's mass affect the result in part (a)? Explain.

27. •• **CE** Three balls are thrown upward with the same initial speed v_0, but at different angles relative to the horizontal, as shown in **Figure 8–22**. Ignoring air resistance, indicate which of the following statements is correct: At the dashed level, **(A)** ball 3 has the lowest speed; **(B)** ball 1 has the lowest speed; **(C)** all three balls have the same speed; **(D)** the speed of the balls depends on their mass.

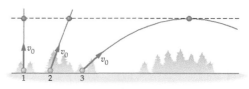

▲ **FIGURE 8–22** Problem 27

28. •• **IP** In a tennis match, a player wins a point by hitting the ball sharply to the ground on the opponent's side of the net. **(a)** If the ball bounces upward from the ground with a speed of 16 m/s, and is caught by a fan in the stands with a speed of 12 m/s, how high above the court is the fan? Ignore air resistance. **(b)** Explain why it is not necessary to know the mass of the tennis ball.

29. •• A 0.21-kg apple falls from a tree to the ground, 4.0 m below. Ignoring air resistance, determine the apple's kinetic energy, K, the gravitational potential energy of the system, U, and the total mechanical energy of the system, E, when the apple's height above the ground is **(a)** 4.0 m, **(b)** 3.0 m, **(c)** 2.0 m, **(d)** 1.0 m, and **(e)** 0 m. Take ground level to be $y = 0$.

30. •• **IP** A 2.9-kg block slides with a speed of 1.6 m/s on a frictionless horizontal surface until it encounters a spring. **(a)** If the block compresses the spring 4.8 cm before coming to rest, what is the force constant of the spring? **(b)** What initial speed should the block have to compress the spring by 1.2 cm?

31. •• A 0.26-kg rock is thrown vertically upward from the top of a cliff that is 32 m high. When it hits the ground at the base of the cliff, the rock has a speed of 29 m/s. Assuming that air resistance can be ignored, find **(a)** the initial speed of the rock and **(b)** the greatest height of the rock as measured from the base of the cliff.

32. •• A 1.40-kg block slides with a speed of 0.950 m/s on a frictionless horizontal surface until it encounters a spring with a force constant of 734 N/m. The block comes to rest after compressing the spring 4.15 cm. Find the spring potential energy, U, the kinetic energy of the block, K, and the total mechanical energy of the system, E, for compressions of **(a)** 0 cm, **(b)** 1.00 cm, **(c)** 2.00 cm, **(d)** 3.00 cm, and **(e)** 4.00 cm.

33. •• A 5.76-kg rock is dropped and allowed to fall freely. Find the initial kinetic energy, the final kinetic energy, and the change in kinetic energy for **(a)** the first 2.00 m of fall and **(b)** the second 2.00 m of fall.

34. •• **IP** Suppose the pendulum bob in Figure 8–20 has a mass of 0.33 kg and is moving to the right at point B with a speed of 2.4 m/s. Air resistance is negligible. **(a)** What is the change in the system's gravitational potential energy when the bob reaches point A? **(b)** What is the speed of the bob at point A? **(c)** If the mass of the bob is increased, does your answer to part (a) increase, decrease, or stay the same? Explain. **(d)** If the mass of the bob is increased, does your answer to part (b) increase, decrease, or stay the same? Explain.

35. •• **IP** In the previous problem, **(a)** what is the bob's kinetic energy at point B? **(b)** At some point the bob will come to rest momentarily. Without doing an additional calculation, determine the change in the system's gravitational potential energy between point B and the point where the bob comes to rest. **(c)** Find the maximum angle the string makes with the vertical as the bob swings back and forth. Ignore air resistance.

36. ••• The two masses in the Atwood's machine shown in **Figure 8–23** are initially at rest at the same height. After they are released, the large mass, m_2, falls through a height h and hits the floor, and the small mass, m_1, rises through a height h. **(a)** Find the speed of the masses just before m_2 lands, giving your answer in terms of m_1, m_2, g, and h. Assume the ropes and pulley have negligible mass and that friction can be ignored. **(b)** Evaluate your answer to part (a) for the case $h = 1.2$ m, $m_1 = 3.7$ kg, and $m_2 = 4.1$ kg.

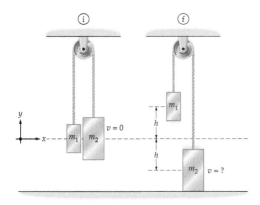

▲ **FIGURE 8–23** Problems 36, 37, 82, and 99

37. ••• In the previous problem, suppose the masses have an initial speed of 0.20 m/s, and that m_2 is moving upward. How high does m_2 rise above its initial position before momentarily coming to rest, given that $m_1 = 3.7$ kg and $m_2 = 4.1$ kg?

SECTION 8–4 WORK DONE BY NONCONSERVATIVE FORCES

38. • **CE** You coast up a hill on your bicycle with decreasing speed. Your friend pedals up the hill with constant speed. **(a)** Ignoring friction, does the mechanical energy of the you–bike–Earth system increase, decrease, or stay the same? Explain. **(b)** Does the mechanical energy of the friend–bike–Earth system increase, decrease, or stay the same? Explain.

39. • **CE Predict/Explain** On reentry, the space shuttle's protective heat tiles become extremely hot. **(a)** Is the mechanical energy of the shuttle–Earth system when the shuttle lands greater than, less than, or the same as when it is in orbit? **(b)** Choose the *best explanation* from among the following:
I. Dropping out of orbit increases the mechanical energy of the shuttle.
II. Gravity is a conservative force.
III. A portion of the mechanical energy has been converted to heat energy.

40. • Catching a wave, a 77-kg surfer starts with a speed of 1.3 m/s, drops through a height of 1.65 m, and ends with a speed of 8.2 m/s. How much nonconservative work was done on the surfer?

41. • At a playground, a 19-kg child plays on a slide that drops through a height of 2.3 m. The child starts at rest at the top of the slide. On the way down, the slide does a nonconservative work of −361 J on the child. What is the child's speed at the bottom of the slide?

42. • Starting at rest at the edge of a swimming pool, a 72.0-kg athlete swims along the surface of the water and reaches a speed of 1.20 m/s by doing the work $W_{nc1} = +161$ J. Find the nonconservative work, W_{nc2}, done by the water on the athlete.

43. • A 17,000-kg airplane lands with a speed of 82 m/s on a stationary aircraft carrier deck that is 115 m long. Find the work done by nonconservative forces in stopping the plane.

44. • **IP** The driver of a 1300-kg car moving at 17 m/s brakes quickly to 11 m/s when he spots a local garage sale. **(a)** Find the change in the car's kinetic energy. **(b)** Explain where the "missing" kinetic energy has gone.

45. •• **CE** You ride your bicycle down a hill, maintaining a constant speed the entire time. **(a)** As you ride, does the gravitational potential energy of the you–bike–Earth system increase, decrease, or stay the same? Explain. **(b)** Does the kinetic energy of you and your bike increase, decrease, or stay the same? Explain. **(c)** Does the mechanical energy of the you–bike–Earth system increase, decrease, or stay the same? Explain.

46. •• Suppose the system in Example 8–10 starts with m_2 moving downward with a speed of 1.3 m/s. What speed do the masses have just before m_2 lands?

47. •• A 42.0-kg seal at an amusement park slides from rest down a ramp into the pool below. The top of the ramp is 1.75 m higher than the surface of the water, and the ramp is inclined at an angle of 35.0° above the horizontal. If the seal reaches the water with a speed of 4.40 m/s, what are **(a)** the work done by kinetic friction and **(b)** the coefficient of kinetic friction between the seal and the ramp?

48. •• A 1.9-kg rock is released from rest at the surface of a pond 1.8 m deep. As the rock falls, a constant upward force of 4.6 N is exerted on it by water resistance. Calculate the nonconservative work, W_{nc}, done by water resistance on the rock, the gravitational potential energy of the system, U, the kinetic energy of the rock, K, and the total mechanical energy of the system, E, when the depth of the rock below the water's surface is **(a)** 0 m, **(b)** 0.50 m, and **(c)** 1.0 m. Let $y = 0$ be at the bottom of the pond.

49. •• A 1250-kg car drives up a hill that is 16.2 m high. During the drive, two nonconservative forces do work on the car: (i) the force of friction, and (ii) the force generated by the car's engine. The work done by friction is -3.11×10^5 J; the work done by the engine is $+6.44 \times 10^5$ J. Find the change in the car's kinetic energy from the bottom of the hill to the top of the hill.

50. •• **IP** An 81.0-kg in-line skater does +3420 J of nonconservative work by pushing against the ground with his skates. In addition, friction does −715 J of nonconservative work on the skater. The skater's initial and final speeds are 2.50 m/s and 1.22 m/s, respectively. **(a)** Has the skater gone uphill, downhill, or remained at the same level? Explain. **(b)** Calculate the change in height of the skater.

51. •• In Example 8–10, suppose the two masses start from rest and are moving with a speed of 2.05 m/s just before m_2 hits the floor. **(a)** If the coefficient of kinetic friction is $\mu_k = 0.350$, what is the distance of travel, d, for the masses? **(b)** How much conservative work was done on this system? **(c)** How much nonconservative work was done on this system? **(d)** Verify the three work relations given in Equations 8–10.

52. •• **IP** A 15,800-kg truck is moving at 12.0 m/s when it starts down a 6.00° incline in the Canadian Rockies. At the start of the descent the driver notices that the altitude is 1630 m. When she reaches an altitude of 1440 m, her speed is 29.0 m/s. Find the change in **(a)** the gravitational potential energy of the system and **(b)** the truck's kinetic energy. **(c)** Is the total mechanical energy of the system conserved? Explain.

53. ••• A 1.80-kg block slides on a rough horizontal surface. The block hits a spring with a speed of 2.00 m/s and compresses it a distance of 11.0 cm before coming to rest. If the coefficient of kinetic friction between the block and the surface is $\mu_k = 0.560$, what is the force constant of the spring?

SECTION 8–5 POTENTIAL ENERGY CURVES AND EQUIPOTENTIALS

54. • **Figure 8–24** shows a potential energy curve as a function of x. In qualitative terms, describe the subsequent motion of an object that starts at rest at point A.

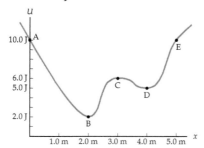

▲ **FIGURE 8–24** Problems 54, 55, 56, and 59

55. • An object moves along the x axis, subject to the potential energy shown in Figure 8–24. The object has a mass of 1.1 kg and starts at rest at point A. **(a)** What is the object's speed at point B? **(b)** At point C? **(c)** At point D? **(d)** What are the turning points for this object?

56. • A 1.34-kg object moves along the x axis, subject to the potential energy shown in Figure 8–24. If the object's speed at point C is 1.25 m/s, what are the approximate locations of its turning points?

57. • A 23-kg child swings back and forth on a swing suspended by 2.5-m-long ropes. Plot the gravitational potential energy of this system as a function of the angle the ropes make with the vertical, assuming the potential energy is zero when the ropes are vertical. Consider angles up to 90° on either side of the vertical.

58. •• Find the turning-point angles in the previous problem if the child has a speed of 0.89 m/s when the ropes are vertical. Indicate the turning points on a plot of the system's potential energy.

59. •• The potential energy of a particle moving along the x axis is shown in Figure 8–24. When the particle is at $x = 1.0$ m it has 3.6 J of kinetic energy. Give approximate answers to the following questions. **(a)** What is the total mechanical energy of the system? **(b)** What is the smallest value of x the particle can reach? **(c)** What is the largest value of x the particle can reach?

60. •• A block of mass $m = 0.95$ kg is connected to a spring of force constant $k = 775$ N/m on a smooth, horizontal surface. **(a)** Plot the potential energy of the spring from $x = -5.00$ cm to $x = 5.00$ cm. **(b)** Determine the turning points of the block if its speed at $x = 0$ is 1.3 m/s.

61. •• A ball of mass $m = 0.75$ kg is thrown straight upward with an initial speed of 8.9 m/s. **(a)** Plot the gravitational potential energy of the block from its launch height, $y = 0$, to the height $y = 5.0$ m. Let $U = 0$ correspond to $y = 0$. **(b)** Determine the turning point (maximum height) of this mass.

62. ••• Two blocks, each of mass m, are connected on a frictionless horizontal table by a spring of force constant k and equilibrium length L. Find the maximum and minimum separation between the two blocks in terms of their maximum speed, v_{max}, relative to the table. (The two blocks always move in opposite directions as they oscillate back and forth about a fixed position.)

GENERAL PROBLEMS

63. • **CE** You and a friend both solve a problem involving a skier going down a slope. When comparing solutions, you notice that your choice for the $y = 0$ level is different than the $y = 0$ level chosen by your friend. Will your answers agree or disagree on the following quantities: **(a)** the skier's potential energy; **(b)** the skier's change in potential energy; **(c)** the skier's kinetic energy?

64. • **CE** A particle moves under the influence of a conservative force. At point A the particle has a kinetic energy of 12 J; at point B the particle is momentarily at rest, and the potential energy of the system is 25 J; at point C the potential energy of the system is 5 J. **(a)** What is the potential energy of the system when the particle is at point A? **(b)** What is the kinetic energy of the particle at point C?

65. • **CE** A leaf falls to the ground with constant speed. Is $U_i + K_i$ for this system greater than, less than, or the same as $U_f + K_f$ for this system? Explain.

66. • **CE** Consider the two-block system shown in Example 8–10. **(a)** As block 2 descends through the distance d, does its mechanical energy increase, decrease, or stay the same? Explain. **(b)** Is the nonconservative work done on block 2 by the tension in the rope positive, negative, or zero? Explain.

67. •• **CE** Taking a leap of faith, a bungee jumper steps off a platform and falls until the cord brings her to rest. Suppose you analyze this system by choosing $y = 0$ at the platform level, and your friend chooses $y = 0$ at ground level. **(a)** Is the jumper's initial potential energy in your calculation greater than, less than, or equal to the same quantity in your friend's calculation? Explain. **(b)** Is the change in the jumper's potential energy in your calculation greater than, less than, or equal to the same quantity in your friend's calculation? Explain.

68. •• **IP** A sled slides without friction down a small, ice-covered hill. If the sled starts from rest at the top of the hill, its speed at the bottom is 7.50 m/s. **(a)** On a second run, the sled starts with a speed of 1.50 m/s at the top. When it reaches the bottom of the hill, is its speed 9.00 m/s, more than 9.00 m/s, or less than 9.00 m/s? Explain. **(b)** Find the speed of the sled at the bottom of the hill after the second run.

69. •• In the previous problem, what is the height of the hill?

70. •• A 68-kg skier encounters a dip in the snow's surface that has a circular cross section with a radius of curvature of 12 m. If the skier's speed at point A in **Figure 8–25** is 8.0 m/s, what is the normal force exerted by the snow on the skier at point B? Ignore frictional forces.

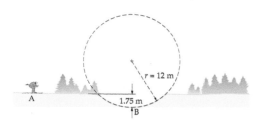

▲ **FIGURE 8–25** Problem 70

71. •• **Running Shoes** The soles of a popular make of running shoe have a force constant of 2.0×10^5 N/m. Treat the soles as ideal springs for the following questions. **(a)** If a 62-kg person stands in a pair of these shoes, with her weight distributed equally on both feet, how much does she compress the soles? **(b)** How much energy is stored in the soles of her shoes when she's standing?

72. •• **Nasal Strips** The force required to flex a nasal strip and apply it to the nose is 0.25 N; the energy stored in the strip when flexed is 0.0022 J. Assume the strip to be an ideal spring for the following calculations. Find **(a)** the distance through which the strip is flexed and **(b)** the force constant of the strip.

73. •• **IP** A pendulum bob with a mass of 0.13 kg is attached to a string with a length of 0.95 m. We choose the potential energy to be zero when the string makes an angle of 90° with the vertical. **(a)** Find the potential energy of this system when the string makes an angle of 45° with the vertical. **(b)** Is the magnitude of the change in potential energy from an angle of 90° to 45° greater than, less than, or the same as the magnitude of the change from 45° to 0°? Explain. **(c)** Calculate the potential energy of the system when the string is vertical.

74. •• Suppose the pendulum bob in Figure 8–20 has a mass of 0.25 kg. **(a)** How much work does gravity do on the bob as it moves from point A to point B? **(b)** From point B to point A? **(c)** How much work does the string do on the bob as it moves from point A to point B? **(d)** From point B to point A?

75. •• An 1865-kg airplane starts at rest on an airport runway at sea level. **(a)** What is the change in mechanical energy of the airplane if it climbs to a cruising altitude of 2420 m and maintains a constant speed of 96.5 m/s? **(b)** What cruising speed would the plane need at this altitude if its increase in kinetic energy is to be equal to its increase in potential energy?

76. •• **IP** At the local playground a child on a swing has a speed of 2.02 m/s when the swing is at its lowest point. **(a)** To what maximum vertical height does the child rise, assuming he sits still and "coasts"? Ignore air resistance. **(b)** How do your results change if the initial speed of the child is halved?

77. •• The water slide shown in **Figure 8–26** ends at a height of 1.50 m above the pool. If the person starts from rest at point A and lands in the water at point B, what is the height h of the water slide? (Assume the water slide is frictionless.)

78. •• If the height of the water slide in Figure 8–26 is $h = 3.2$ m, and the person's initial speed at point A is 0.54 m/s, what is the new horizontal distance between the base of the slide and the splashdown point of the person?

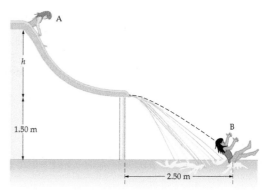

▲ **FIGURE 8–26** Problems 77 and 78

79. •• **IP** A person is to be released from rest on a swing pulled away from the vertical by an angle of 20.0°. The two frayed ropes of the swing are 2.75 m long, and will break if the tension in either of them exceeds 355 N. **(a)** What is the maximum weight the person can have and not break the ropes? **(b)** If the person is released at an angle greater than 20.0°, does the maximum weight increase, decrease, or stay the same? Explain.

80. •• **IP** A car is coasting without friction toward a hill of height h and radius of curvature r. **(a)** What initial speed, v_0, will result in the car's wheels just losing contact with the roadway as the car crests the hill? **(b)** What happens if the initial speed of the car is greater than the value found in part (a)?

81. •• A skateboarder starts at point A in **Figure 8–27** and rises to a height of 2.64 m above the top of the ramp at point B. What was the skateboarder's initial speed at point A?

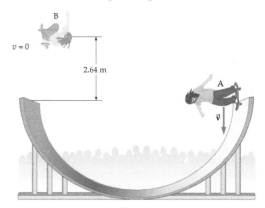

▲ **FIGURE 8–27** Problem 81

82. •• In the Atwood's machine of Problem 36, the mass m_2 remains at rest once it hits the floor, but the mass m_1 continues moving upward. How much higher does m_1 go after m_2 has landed? Give your answer for the case $h = 1.2$ m, $m_1 = 3.7$ kg, and $m_2 = 4.1$ kg.

83. •• An 8.70-kg block slides with an initial speed of 1.56 m/s up a ramp inclined at an angle of 28.4° with the horizontal. The coefficient of kinetic friction between the block and the ramp is 0.62. Use energy conservation to find the distance the block slides before coming to rest.

84. •• Repeat the previous problem for the case of an 8.70-kg block sliding down the ramp, with an initial speed of 1.56 m/s.

85. •• Jeff of the Jungle swings on a 7.6-m vine that initially makes an angle of 37° with the vertical. If Jeff starts at rest and has a mass of 78 kg, what is the tension in the vine at the lowest point of the swing?

86. •• A 1.9-kg block slides down a frictionless ramp, as shown in Figure 8–28. The top of the ramp is 1.5 m above the ground; the bottom of the ramp is 0.25 m above the ground. The block leaves the ramp moving horizontally, and lands a horizontal distance d away. Find the distance d.

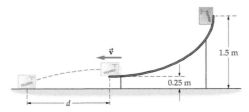

0.25 m

1.5 m

$\vec{v}$

d

▲ **FIGURE 8–28** Problems 86 and 87

87. •• Suppose the ramp in Figure 8–28 is not frictionless. Find the distance d for the case in which friction on the ramp does $-9.7\,\text{J}$ of work on the block before it becomes airborne.

88. •• **BIO Compressing the Ground** A running track at Harvard University uses a surface with a force constant of $2.5 \times 10^5\,\text{N/m}$. This surface is compressed slightly every time a runner's foot lands on it. The force exerted by the foot, according to the Saucony shoe company, has a magnitude of 2700 N for a typical runner. Treating the track's surface as an ideal spring, find **(a)** the amount of compression caused by a foot hitting the track and **(b)** the energy stored briefly in the track every time a foot lands.

89. •• **BIO A Flea's Jump** The resilin in the upper leg (coxa) of a flea has a force constant of about 26 N/m, and when the flea cocks its jumping legs, the resilin in each leg is stretched by approximately 0.10 mm. Given that the flea has a mass of 0.50 mg, and that two legs are used in a jump, estimate the maximum height a flea can attain by using the energy stored in the resilin. (Assume the resilin to be an ideal spring.)

90. ••• **IP** A trapeze artist of mass m swings on a rope of length L. Initially, the trapeze artist is at rest and the rope makes an angle θ with the vertical. **(a)** Find the tension in the rope when it is vertical. **(b)** Explain why your result for part (a) depends on L in the way it does.

91. ••• **IP Tension at the Bottom** A ball of mass m is attached to a string of length L and released from rest at the point A in Figure 8–29. **(a)** Show that the tension in the string when the ball reaches point B is $3mg$, independent of the length l. **(b)** Give a detailed physical explanation for the fact that the tension at point B is independent of the length l.

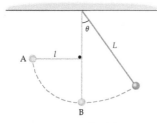

▲ **FIGURE 8–29** Problems 91 and 92

92. ••• **IP** In Figure 8–29, suppose that $L = 0.652\,\text{m}$ and $l = 0.325\,\text{m}$. **(a)** Find the maximum angle the string makes with the vertical when the mass is released from rest at point A and swings as far to the right as it can. **(b)** At the point found in part (a), find the height of the mass above point B. Explain the physical significance of your result. **(c)** Give the angle of part (a) as a general expression in terms of L and l.

93. ••• An ice cube is placed on top of an overturned spherical bowl of radius r, as indicated in Figure 8–30. If the ice cube slides downward from rest at the top of the bowl, at what angle θ does it separate from the bowl? In other words, at what angle does the normal force between the ice cube and the bowl go to zero?

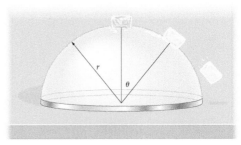

▲ **FIGURE 8–30** Problem 93

94. ••• **IP** The two blocks shown in Figure 8–31 are moving with an initial speed v. **(a)** If the system is frictionless, find the distance d the blocks travel before coming to rest. (Let $U = 0$ correspond to the initial position of block 2.) **(b)** Is the work done on block 2 by the rope positive, negative, or zero? Explain. **(c)** Calculate the work done on block 2 by the rope.

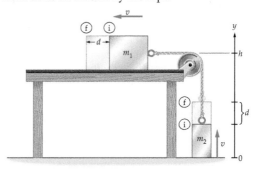

▲ **FIGURE 8–31** Problems 94 and 95

95. ••• **IP** Consider the system shown in Figure 8–31. **(a)** What initial speed v is required if the blocks $m_1 = 2.4\,\text{kg}$ and $m_2 = 1.1\,\text{kg}$ are to travel a distance $d = 6.5\,\text{cm}$ before coming to rest? Assume the coefficient of kinetic friction between m_1 and the tabletop is $\mu_k = 0.25$. **(b)** Is the work done on m_2 by the rope positive, negative, or zero? Explain. **(c)** Calculate the work done on m_2 by the rope.

96. ••• **IP Loop-the-Loop (a)** A block of mass m slides from rest on a frictionless loop-the-loop track, as shown in Figure 8–32. What is the minimum release height, h, required for the block to maintain contact with the track at all times? Give your answer in terms of the radius of the loop, r. **(b)** Explain why the release height obtained in part (a) is independent of the block's mass.

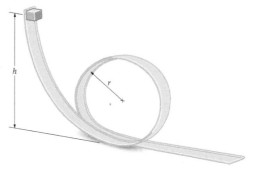

▲ **FIGURE 8–32** Problem 96

97. ••• **Figure 8–33** shows a 1.75-kg block at rest on a ramp of height h. When the block is released, it slides without friction to the bottom of the ramp, and then continues across a surface that is frictionless except for a rough patch of width 10.0 cm that has a coefficient of kinetic friction $\mu_k = 0.640$. Find h such that the block's speed after crossing the rough patch is 3.50 m/s.

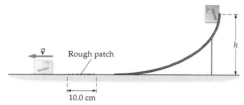

▲ **FIGURE 8–33** Problem 97

98. ••• In **Figure 8–34** a 1.2-kg block is held at rest against a spring with a force constant $k = 730$ N/m. Initially, the spring is compressed a distance d. When the block is released, it slides across a surface that is frictionless except for a rough patch of width 5.0 cm that has a coefficient of kinetic friction $\mu_k = 0.44$. Find d such that the block's speed after crossing the rough patch is 2.3 m/s.

▲ **FIGURE 8–34** Problem 98

99. ••• **IP Using Work and Energy to Calculate Tension** Consider the Atwood's machine shown in Figure 8–23, with $h = 1.2$ m, $m_1 = 3.7$ kg, and $m_2 = 4.1$ kg. In this problem, we show how to calculate the tension in the rope using energy and work, rather than Newton's laws. **(a)** Is the change in mechanical energy for block 2 as it drops through the height h positive, negative, or zero? Explain. **(b)** Use energy conservation applied to the entire system to calculate the change in mechanical energy for block 2 as it drops through the height h. **(c)** Use your answer to part (b), and the known drop height, to find the magnitude of the tension in the rope.

PASSAGE PROBLEMS

BIO The Flight of the Dragonflies

Of all the animals you're likely to see on a summer's day, the most ancient is the dragonfly. In fact, the fossil record for dragonflies extends back over 250 million years, more than twice as long as for birds. Ancient dragonflies could be as large as a hawk, and were surely buzzing around the heads of both *T. Rex* and *Triceratops*.

Dragonflies belong to the order Odonata ("toothed jaws") and the suborder Anisoptera ("different wings"), a reference to the fact that their hindwings are wider front-to-back than their forewings. (Damselflies, in contrast, have forewings and hindwings that are the same.) Although ancient in their lineage, dragonflies are the fastest flying and most acrobatic of all insects; some of their maneuvers subject them to accelerations as great as $20g$.

The properties of dragonfly wings, and how they account for such speed and mobility, have been of great interest to biologists. **Figure 8–35 (a)** shows an experimental setup designed to measure the force constant of Plexiglas models of wings, which are used in wind tunnel tests. A downward force is applied to the model wing at the tip (1 for hindwing, 2 for forewing) or at two-thirds the distance to the tip (3 for hindwing, 4 for forewing). As the force is varied in magnitude, the resulting deflection of the wing is measured. The results are shown in **Figure 8–35 (b)**. Notice that

significant differences are seen between the hindwings and forewings, as one might expect from their different shapes.

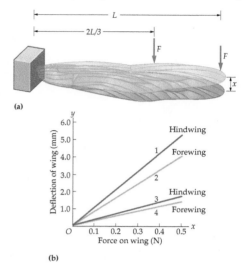

FIGURE 8–35 Problems 100, 101, 102, and 103

100. • Treating the model wing as an ideal spring, what is the force constant of the hindwing when a force is applied to its tip?

A. 94 N/m   **B.** 130 N/m   **C.** 290 N/m   **D.** 330 N/m

101. • What is the force constant of the hindwing when a force is applied at two-thirds the distance from the base of the wing to the tip?

A. 94 N/m   **B.** 130 N/m

C. 290 N/m   **D.** 330 N/m

102. • Which of the wings is "stiffer"?

A. The hindwing.   **B.** The forewing.

C. Depends on where the force is applied.

D. They are equally "stiff."

103. •• How much energy is stored in the forewing when a force at the tip deflects it by 3.5 mm?

A. 0.766 mJ   **B.** 49.0 mJ   **C.** 0.219 J   **D.** 1.70 kJ

INTERACTIVE PROBLEMS

104. •• **IP Referring to Example 8–8** Consider a spring with a force constant of 955 N/m. **(a)** Suppose the mass of the block is 1.70 kg, but its initial speed can be varied. What initial speed is required to give a maximum spring compression of 4.00 cm? **(b)** Suppose the initial speed of the block is 1.09 m/s, but its mass can be varied. What mass is required to give a maximum spring compression of 4.00 cm?

105. •• **Referring to Example 8–8** Suppose the block is released from rest with the spring compressed 5.00 cm. The mass of the block is 1.70 kg and the force constant of the spring is 955 N/m. **(a)** What is the speed of the block when the spring expands to a compression of only 2.50 cm? **(b)** What is the speed of the block after it leaves the spring?

106. •• **Referring to Example 8–10** Suppose we would like the landing speed of block 2 to be increased to 1.50 m/s. **(a)** Should the coefficient of kinetic friction between block 1 and the tabletop be increased or decreased? **(b)** Find the required coefficient of kinetic friction for a landing speed of 1.50 m/s. Note that $m_1 = 2.40$ kg, $m_2 = 1.80$ kg, and $d = 0.500$ m.

Energy: A Breakthrough in Physics

The concept of energy is a surprisingly recent addition to physics—in fact, Galileo and Newton knew nothing about it. Energy was difficult to discover because it can't be seen or touched, and because it takes so many different forms. Nevertheless, energy is central to our modern world.

❶ Energy takes multiple forms

This scene shows a few of the myriad energy transformations that make life possible. Throughout the universe, energy continually changes form and moves from system to system.

Energy from the Sun travels to the Earth as sunlight.

Plants store solar energy in the chemical bonds of food molecules.

Animals convert food energy to many forms. Ultimately, most of it leaves the body as work done on the environment and as heat.

A leaping dog is a projectile, interconverting gravitational potential energy and kinetic energy. A thrown frisbee adds a new twist, trading part of its kinetic energy for lift, which does work to keep the frisbee airborne.

❷ Energy is always conserved; mechanical energy is sometimes conserved

No energy is lost or gained during energy transfers and transformations. Therefore, the total energy of the universe is conserved (stays the same). This is a fundamental law of physics.

Although *energy* is always conserved, *mechanical energy* (kinetic and potential energy) is conserved only by conservative forces such as gravity. If nonconservative forces such as friction do work in a system, some mechanical energy is dissipated to other forms of energy.

Ideal bouncing ball: Energy and mechanical energy both conserved

If only gravity and spring forces did work on a bouncing ball, the ball would bounce to the same height forever—potential and kinetic energy would interconvert with no loss.

Real bouncing ball: Mechanical energy dissipated (but energy conserved)

In a real ball, air drag and friction within the ball gradually dissipate mechanical energy to thermal energy and other forms, so the ball loses height with each bounce.

❸ ... But what *is* energy?

Energy is a very abstract concept—you can define it as *the scalar quantity that is conserved during energy transformations*. This seems hard to grasp until you realize that *money* is just as abstract and

works in much the same way. Money can take many forms—cash, a checking account, a savings account—while its amount doesn't change. You can think of potential energy as money in the bank and of kinetic energy as cash.

The fact that energy is so abstract explains why this fundamental concept didn't become part of physics until about 200 years ago, 120 years *after* Newton formulated his laws.

4 Work done by conservative forces conserves mechanical energy, whereas work done by nonconservative forces dissipates it

Let us use the two cases shown below to explore the equations that relate work to mechanical energy within a given system:

$$W_{tot} = \Delta K \qquad W_c = -(\Delta U) \qquad W_{nc} = \Delta E_{mech}$$

For clarity, on these pages we denote mechanical energy by E_{mech} rather than the usual E.

- $W_{tot} = \Delta K$: This is the work–energy theorem.

- $W_c = -(\Delta U)$: Within a given system, only conservative forces can change the potential energy. *Positive W_c* increases the system's kinetic energy at the expense of potential energy—that is why the ΔU term has a minus sign. (*Negative W_c* results in an *increase* in potential energy.)

- $W_{nc} = \Delta E_{mech}$: Since nonconservative forces in a system act to dissipate mechanical energy to other forms of energy, the work done by these forces equals the change in mechanical energy.

Symbols used on this page:

E_{mech}, $E_{nonmech}$: Mechanical and nonmechanical energy, respectively

E_{tot}: Total energy (mechanical plus nonmechanical)

W_c, W_{nc}: Work done by conservative and nonconservative forces, respectively

W_{tot}: Total work ($W_c + W_{nc}$)

Case 1: Block slides down slippery slope
Only the conservative force of gravity does work on the block

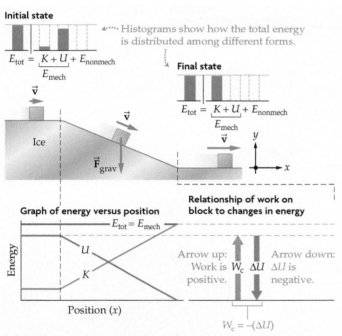

- Initially the system has both kinetic and potential energy.
- The block slides down because the conservative force of gravity does positive work on it, changing the system's potential energy to kinetic energy. (We know the work is positive because the block speeds up.)
- In the final state, the system has only kinetic energy. Mechanical energy has been conserved.

Case 2: Block slides down slope with friction
In addition to gravity, nonconservative friction does work on the block

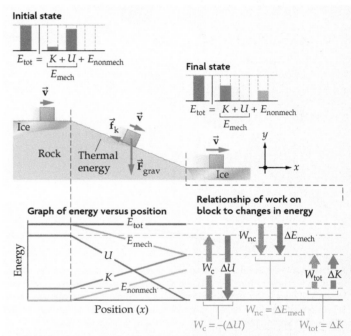

- Initially the system has both kinetic and potential energy.
- The block slides down because gravity does positive work on it, changing the system's potential energy to kinetic energy. At the same time, friction does negative work on the block, dissipating some of its kinetic energy to nonmechanical energy.
- The system's final energy is partly kinetic and partly nonmechanical. Energy has been conserved, but not mechanical energy.

5 Conservation of mechanical energy is useful for solving problems

If nonconservative forces do no work in a system (or if the work they do is negligible compared to that done by conservative forces), you can use energy conservation to predict the system's behavior.

In the case of the water slides at right, it would be nearly impossible to predict a person's final speed using Newton's laws—you would need to know the net force acting at each position along the slide.

To apply energy conservation, all you need to know are the person's initial and final heights.

9 Linear Momentum and Collisions

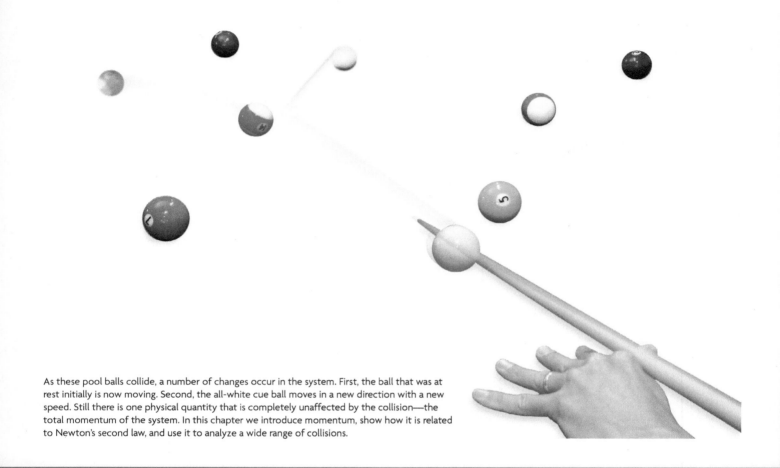

As these pool balls collide, a number of changes occur in the system. First, the ball that was at rest initially is now moving. Second, the all-white cue ball moves in a new direction with a new speed. Still there is one physical quantity that is completely unaffected by the collision—the total momentum of the system. In this chapter we introduce momentum, show how it is related to Newton's second law, and use it to analyze a wide range of collisions.

C onservation laws play a central role in physics. In this chapter we introduce the concept of *momentum* and show that it, like energy, is a conserved quantity. Nothing we can do—in fact, nothing that can occur in nature—can change the total energy or the total momentum of the universe.

As with conservation of energy, we shall see that the conservation of momentum provides a powerful way of approaching a variety of problems that would be extremely difficult to solve using Newton's laws directly. In particular,

problems involving the collision of two or more objects—such as a baseball bat striking a ball or one car bumping into another at an intersection—are especially well suited to a momentum approach. Finally, we introduce the concept of the *center of mass* and show that it allows us to extend many of the results that have been obtained for point particles to systems involving more realistic objects.

9–1 Linear Momentum

Imagine for a moment that you are sitting at rest on a skateboard that can roll without friction on a smooth surface. If you catch a heavy, slow-moving ball tossed to you by a friend, you begin to move. If, on the other hand, your friend tosses you a light, yet fast-moving ball, the net effect may be the same—that is, catching a lightweight ball moving fast enough will cause you to move with the same speed as when you caught the heavy ball.

In physics, the previous observations are made precise by defining a quantity called the **linear momentum, $\vec{p}$**, which is defined as the product of the mass m and velocity $\vec{v}$ of an object:

Definition of Linear Momentum, $\vec{p}$

$$\vec{p} = m\vec{v} \qquad\qquad 9\text{–}1$$

SI unit: kg·m/s

In our example, if the heavy ball has twice the mass of the light ball but the light ball has twice the speed of the heavy ball, the momenta of the two balls are equal in magnitude. We can see from Equation 9–1 that the units of linear momentum are simply the units of mass times the units of velocity: kg·m/s. There is no special shorthand name given to this combination of units.

It is important to note that a constant *linear* momentum $\vec{p}$ is the momentum of an object of mass m that is *moving in a straight line* with a velocity $\vec{v}$. In Chapter 11 we introduce a similar quantity to describe the momentum of an object that rotates. This momentum will be referred to as the *angular momentum*. In general, when we simply say momentum, we are referring to the linear momentum $\vec{p}$. We will always specify angular momentum when referring to the momentum associated with rotation.

Because the velocity $\vec{v}$ is a vector with both a magnitude and a direction, so too is the momentum, $\vec{p} = m\vec{v}$. The next Exercise gives some feeling for the *magnitude* of the momentum, $p = mv$, for everyday objects.

EXERCISE 9–1

(a) A 1180-kg car drives along a city street at 30.0 miles per hour (13.4 m/s). What is the magnitude of the car's momentum? **(b)** A major-league pitcher can give a 0.142-kg baseball a speed of 101 mi/h (45.1 m/s). Find the magnitude of the baseball's momentum.

SOLUTION

a. Using $p = mv$, we find

$$p_\text{c} = m_\text{c}v_\text{c} = (1180\text{ kg})(13.4\text{ m/s}) = 15{,}800\text{ kg·m/s}$$

b. Similarly,

$$p_\text{b} = m_\text{b}v_\text{b} = (0.142\text{ kg})(45.1\text{ m/s}) = 6.40\text{ kg·m/s}$$

As an illustration of the vector nature of momentum, consider the situations shown in **Figures 9–1 (a)** and **(b)**. In Figure 9–1 (a), a 0.10-kg beanbag bear is dropped to the floor, where it hits with a speed of 4.0 m/s and sticks. In Figure 9–1 (b) a 0.10-kg rubber ball also hits the floor with a speed of 4.0 m/s, but in this case the ball bounces upward off the floor. Assuming an ideal rubber ball, its initial upward speed is 4.0 m/s. Now the question in each case is, "What is the change in momentum?"

To approach the problem systematically, we introduce a coordinate system as shown in Figure 9–1. With this choice, we can see that neither object has momentum in the x direction; thus we need only consider the y component of momentum, p_y. The problem, therefore, is one-dimensional; still, we must be careful about the sign of p_y.

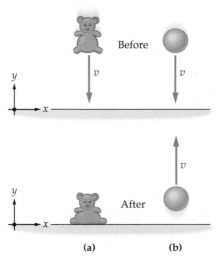

▲ **FIGURE 9–1 Change in momentum**
A beanbag bear and a rubber ball, with the same mass m and the same downward speed v, hit the floor. **(a)** The beanbag bear comes to rest on hitting the floor. Its change in momentum is mv upward. **(b)** The rubber ball bounces upward with a speed v. Its change in momentum is $2mv$ upward.

We begin with the beanbag. Just before hitting the floor, it moves downward (that is, in the negative y direction) with a speed of $v = 4.0$ m/s. Letting m stand for the mass of the beanbag, we find that the initial momentum is

$$p_{y,i} = m(-v)$$

After landing on the floor, the beanbag is at rest; hence, its final momentum is zero:

$$p_{y,f} = m(0) = 0$$

Therefore the change in momentum is

$$\Delta p_y = p_{y,f} - p_{y,i} = 0 - m(-v) = mv$$
$$= (0.10 \text{ kg})(4.0 \text{ m/s}) = 0.40 \text{ kg} \cdot \text{m/s}$$

Note that the change in momentum is positive—that is, in the upward direction. This makes sense because, before the bag landed, it had a negative (downward) momentum in the y direction. In order to increase the momentum from a negative value to zero, it is necessary to add a positive (upward) momentum.

Next, consider the rubber ball in Figure 9–1 (b). Before bouncing, its momentum is

$$p_{y,i} = m(-v)$$

the same as for the beanbag. After bouncing, when the ball is moving in the upward (positive) direction, its momentum is

$$p_{y,f} = mv$$

As a result, the change in momentum for the rubber ball is

$$\Delta p_y = p_{y,f} - p_{y,i} = mv - m(-v) = 2mv$$
$$= 2(0.10 \text{ kg})(4.0 \text{ m/s}) = 0.80 \text{ kg} \cdot \text{m/s}$$

This is *twice* the change in momentum of the beanbag! The reason is that in this case, the momentum in the y direction must first be increased from $-mv$ to 0, then increased again from 0 to mv. For the beanbag, the change was merely from $-mv$ to 0.

Note how important it is to be careful about the vector nature of the momentum and to use the correct sign for p_y. Otherwise, we might have concluded—erroneously—that the rubber ball had zero change in momentum, since the *magnitude* of its momentum was unchanged by the bounce. In fact, its momentum does change due to the change in its *direction* of motion.

One additional point: Since momentum is a vector, the total momentum of a system of objects is the *vector* sum of the momenta of all the objects. That is,

$$\vec{\mathbf{p}}_{\text{total}} = \vec{\mathbf{p}}_1 + \vec{\mathbf{p}}_2 + \vec{\mathbf{p}}_3 + \cdots \qquad 9\text{--}2$$

This is illustrated for the case of three objects in the following Example.

PROBLEM-SOLVING NOTE

Coordinate Systems

Be sure to draw a coordinate system for momentum problems, even if the problem is only one-dimensional. It is important to use the coordinate system to assign the correct sign to velocities and momenta in the system.

EXAMPLE 9–1 DUCK, DUCK, GOOSE: ADDING MOMENTA

At a city park, a person throws some bread into a duck pond. Two 4.00-kg ducks and a 9.00-kg goose paddle rapidly toward the bread, as shown in our sketch. If the ducks swim at 1.10 m/s, and the goose swims with a speed of 1.30 m/s, find the magnitude and direction of the total momentum of the three birds.

PICTURE THE PROBLEM

In our sketch we place the origin where the bread floats on the water. Note that duck 1 swims in the positive x direction, duck 2 swims in the negative y direction, and the goose swims in the positive y direction. Therefore, $\vec{\mathbf{p}}_{d1} = m_d v_d \hat{\mathbf{x}}$, $\vec{\mathbf{p}}_{d2} = -m_d v_d \hat{\mathbf{y}}$, and $\vec{\mathbf{p}}_g = m_g v_g \hat{\mathbf{y}}$, where $v_d = 1.10$ m/s, $m_d = 4.00$ kg, $v_g = 1.30$ m/s, and $m_g = 9.00$ kg. The total momentum, $\vec{\mathbf{p}}_{\text{total}}$, points at an angle θ relative to the positive x axis.

STRATEGY

Write the momentum of each bird as a vector, using unit vectors in the x and y directions. Next, sum these vectors component by component to find the total momentum. Finally, use the components of the total momentum to calculate its magnitude and direction.

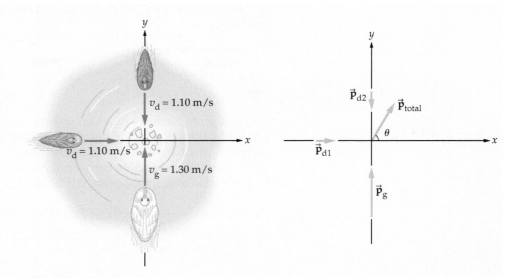

SOLUTION

1. Use x and y unit vectors to express the momentum of each bird in vector form:

$$\vec{\mathbf{p}}_{d1} = m_d v_d \hat{\mathbf{x}} = (4.00 \text{ kg})(1.10 \text{ m/s})\hat{\mathbf{x}}$$
$$= (4.40 \text{ kg} \cdot \text{m/s})\hat{\mathbf{x}}$$
$$\vec{\mathbf{p}}_{d2} = -m_d v_d \hat{\mathbf{y}} = -(4.00 \text{ kg})(1.10 \text{ m/s})\hat{\mathbf{y}}$$
$$= -(4.40 \text{ kg} \cdot \text{m/s})\hat{\mathbf{y}}$$
$$\vec{\mathbf{p}}_g = m_g v_g \hat{\mathbf{y}} = (9.00 \text{ kg})(1.30 \text{ m/s})\hat{\mathbf{y}}$$
$$= (11.7 \text{ kg} \cdot \text{m/s})\hat{\mathbf{y}}$$

2. Sum the momentum vectors to obtain the total momentum:

$$\vec{\mathbf{p}}_{total} = \vec{\mathbf{p}}_{d1} + \vec{\mathbf{p}}_{d2} + \vec{\mathbf{p}}_g$$
$$= (4.40 \text{ kg} \cdot \text{m/s})\hat{\mathbf{x}} + [-4.40 \text{ kg} \cdot \text{m/s} + 11.7 \text{ kg} \cdot \text{m/s}]\hat{\mathbf{y}}$$
$$= (4.40 \text{ kg} \cdot \text{m/s})\hat{\mathbf{x}} + (7.30 \text{ kg} \cdot \text{m/s})\hat{\mathbf{y}}$$

3. Calculate the magnitude of the total momentum:

$$p_{total} = \sqrt{p_{total,x}^2 + p_{total,y}^2}$$
$$= \sqrt{(4.40 \text{ kg} \cdot \text{m/s})^2 + (7.30 \text{ kg} \cdot \text{m/s})^2}$$
$$= 8.52 \text{ kg} \cdot \text{m/s}$$

4. Calculate the direction of the total momentum:

$$\theta = \tan^{-1}\left(\frac{p_{total,y}}{p_{total,x}}\right) = \tan^{-1}\left(\frac{7.30 \text{ kg} \cdot \text{m/s}}{4.40 \text{ kg} \cdot \text{m/s}}\right) = 58.9°$$

INSIGHT

Note that the momentum of each bird depends only on its mass and velocity; it is independent of the bird's location. In addition, we observe that the magnitude of the total momentum is less than the sum of the magnitudes of each bird's momentum individually. This is generally the case when dealing with vector addition—the only exception is when all vectors point in the same direction.

PRACTICE PROBLEM

Should the speed of the goose be increased or decreased if the total momentum of the three birds is to point in the positive x direction? Verify your answer by calculating the required speed. [**Answer:** The goose's speed must be decreased. Setting the momentum of the goose equal to minus the momentum of duck 2 yields $v_g = 0.489$ m/s.]

Some related homework problems: Problem 1, Problem 2, Problem 3

9–2 Momentum and Newton's Second Law

In Chapter 5 we introduced Newton's second law:

$$\sum \vec{\mathbf{F}} = m\vec{\mathbf{a}}$$

As mentioned, this expression is valid only for objects that have constant mass. The more general law, which holds even if the mass changes, is expressed in terms of momentum. In fact, Newton's original statement of the second law was in just this form:

Newton's Second Law

$$\sum \vec{F} = \frac{\Delta \vec{p}}{\Delta t} \qquad 9\text{--}3$$

That is, the net force acting on an object is equal to the change in its momentum divided by the time interval during which the change occurs—in other words, the net force is the rate of change of momentum with time.

To show the connection between these two statements of the second law, consider the change in momentum, $\Delta \vec{p}$. Since $\vec{p} = m\vec{v}$, we have

$$\Delta \vec{p} = \vec{p}_f - \vec{p}_i = m_f \vec{v}_f - m_i \vec{v}_i$$

However, if the mass is constant, so that $m_f = m_i = m$, it follows that the change in momentum is simply m times $\Delta \vec{v}$:

$$\Delta \vec{p} = m_f \vec{v}_f - m_i \vec{v}_i = m(\vec{v}_f - \vec{v}_i) = m \Delta \vec{v}$$

As a result, Newton's second law, for objects of constant mass, can be written as follows:

$$\sum \vec{F} = \frac{\Delta \vec{p}}{\Delta t} = m \frac{\Delta \vec{v}}{\Delta t}$$

Finally, recall that acceleration is the rate of change of velocity with time:

$$\vec{a} = \frac{\Delta \vec{v}}{\Delta t}$$

Therefore, we can write Equation 9–3 as

$$\sum \vec{F} = \frac{\Delta \vec{p}}{\Delta t} = m\vec{a} \qquad 9\text{--}4$$

Hence, the two statements are equivalent if the mass is constant.

It should be noted, however, that $\sum \vec{F} = \Delta \vec{p}/\Delta t$ is the general form of Newton's second law, and that it is valid no matter how the mass may vary. In the remainder of this chapter we use this form of the second law to investigate the connections between forces and changes in momentum.

9–3 Impulse

The pitcher delivers a fastball, the batter takes a swing, and with a crack of the bat the ball that was approaching home plate at 95.0 mi/h is now heading toward the pitcher at 115 mi/h. In the language of physics, we say that the bat has delivered an **impulse, $\vec{I}$,** to the ball.

During the brief time the ball and bat are in contact—perhaps as little as a thousandth of a second—the force between them rises rapidly to a large value, as shown in **Figure 9–2**, then falls back to zero as the ball takes flight. It would be almost impossible, of course, to describe every detail of the way the force varies with time. Instead, we focus on the average force exerted by the bat, $\vec{F}_{av}$, which is also shown in Figure 9–2. The impulse, then, is defined to be $\vec{F}_{av}$ times the length of time, Δt, that the ball and bat are in contact, which is simply the area under the force-versus-time curve:

Definition of Impulse, $\vec{I}$

$$\vec{I} = \vec{F}_{av} \Delta t \qquad 9\text{--}5$$

SI unit: $N \cdot s = kg \cdot m/s$

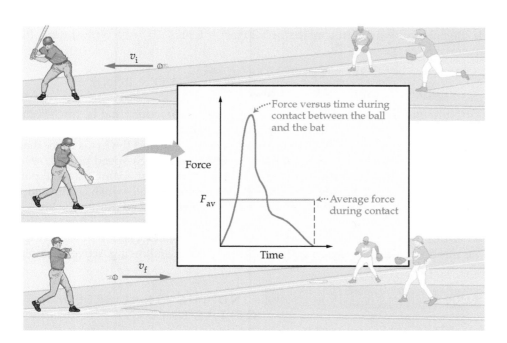

The force between two objects that collide, as when a bat hits a baseball, rises rapidly to very large values, then drops again to zero in a matter of milliseconds. Rather than try to describe the complex behavior of the force, we focus on its average value, F_{av}. Note that the area under the F_{av} rectangle is the same as the area under the actual force curve.

Note that impulse is a vector and that it points in the same direction as the average force. In addition, its units are $\text{N} \cdot \text{s} = (\text{kg} \cdot \text{m/s}^2) \cdot \text{s} = \text{kg} \cdot \text{m/s}$, the same as the units of momentum.

It is no accident that impulse and momentum have the same units. In fact, rearranging Newton's second law, Equation 9–3, we see that the average force times Δt is simply the change in momentum of the ball due to the bat:

$$\vec{\mathbf{F}}_{av} = \frac{\Delta \vec{\mathbf{p}}}{\Delta t}$$

$$\vec{\mathbf{F}}_{av} \, \Delta t = \Delta \vec{\mathbf{p}}$$

Hence, in general, impulse is just the change in momentum:

Momentum–Impulse Theorem

$$\vec{\mathbf{I}} = \vec{\mathbf{F}}_{av} \, \Delta t = \Delta \vec{\mathbf{p}} \qquad\qquad 9\text{–}6$$

For instance, if we know the impulse delivered to an object—that is, its change in momentum—and the time interval during which the change occurs, we can find the average force that caused the impulse.

As an example, let's calculate the impulse given to the baseball considered at the beginning of this section, as well as the average force between the ball and the bat. First, set up a coordinate system with the positive x axis pointing from home plate toward the pitcher's mound, as indicated in **Figure 9–3**. If the ball's mass is 0.145 kg, its initial momentum—which is in the negative x direction—is

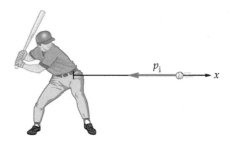

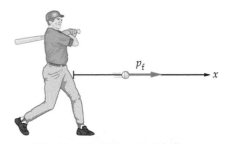

▲ **FIGURE 9–3 Hitting a baseball**
A batter hits a ball, sending it back toward the pitcher's mound. The impulse delivered to the ball by the bat changes the ball's momentum from $-p_i\hat{\mathbf{x}}$ to $p_f\hat{\mathbf{x}}$.

REAL-WORLD PHYSICS

The force between a ball and a bat

$$\vec{\mathbf{p}}_i = -mv_i\hat{\mathbf{x}} = -(0.145 \text{ kg})(95.0 \text{ mi/h})\left(\frac{0.447 \text{ m/s}}{1 \text{ mi/h}}\right)\hat{\mathbf{x}} = -(6.16 \text{ kg} \cdot \text{m/s})\hat{\mathbf{x}}$$

Immediately after the hit, the ball's final momentum is in the positive x direction:

$$\vec{\mathbf{p}}_f = mv_f\hat{\mathbf{x}} = (0.145 \text{ kg})(115 \text{ mi/h})\left(\frac{0.447 \text{ m/s}}{1 \text{ mi/h}}\right)\hat{\mathbf{x}} = (7.45 \text{ kg} \cdot \text{m/s})\hat{\mathbf{x}}$$

The impulse, then, is

$$\vec{\mathbf{I}} = \Delta \vec{\mathbf{p}} = \vec{\mathbf{p}}_f - \vec{\mathbf{p}}_i = [7.45 \text{ kg} \cdot \text{m/s} - (-6.16 \text{ kg} \cdot \text{m/s})]\hat{\mathbf{x}} = (13.6 \text{ kg} \cdot \text{m/s})\hat{\mathbf{x}}$$

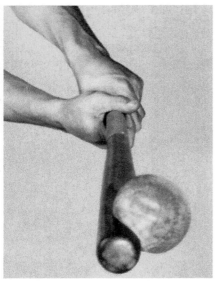

© Harold and Esther Edgerton Foundation, 2007, courtesy of Palm Press, Inc.

▲ When a softball is hit by a bat (top), an enormous force (thousands of newtons) acts for a very short period of time—perhaps only a few ms. During this time, the ball is dramatically deformed by the impact. To keep the same thing from happening to a pole vaulter, who must fall nearly 20 feet after clearing the bar (bottom), a deeply padded landing area is provided. The change in the pole vaulter's momentum as he is brought to a stop, $mv = F\Delta t$, is the same whether he lands on a mat or on concrete. However, the padding is very yielding, greatly prolonging the time Δt during which he is in contact with the mat. The corresponding force on the vaulter is thus markedly decreased.

If the ball and bat are in contact for $1.20 \text{ ms} = 1.20 \times 10^{-3}$ s, a typical time, the average force is

$$\vec{F}_{av} = \frac{\Delta \vec{p}}{\Delta t} = \frac{\vec{I}}{\Delta t} = \frac{(13.6 \text{ kg} \cdot \text{m/s})\hat{x}}{1.20 \times 10^{-3} \text{ s}} = (1.13 \times 10^4 \text{ N})\hat{x}$$

Note that the average force is in the positive x direction; that is, toward the pitcher, as expected. In addition, the magnitude of the average force is remarkably large. In everyday units, the force between the ball and the bat is more than 2500 pounds! This explains why the ball is observed in high-speed photographs to deform significantly during a hit—the force is so large that, for an instant, it partially flattens the ball. Finally, notice that the weight of the ball, which is only about 0.3 lb, is completely negligible compared to the forces involved during the hit.

In problems that are strictly one-dimensional, we can drop the vector notation when dealing with impulse. However, we must still be careful about the signs of the various quantities in the system. This is illustrated in the following Active Example.

ACTIVE EXAMPLE 9–1   FIND THE FINAL SPEED OF THE BALL

A 0.144-kg baseball is moving toward home plate with a speed of 43.0 m/s when it is bunted (hit softly). The bat exerts an average force of 6.50×10^3 N on the ball for 1.30 ms. The average force is directed toward the pitcher, which we take to be the positive x direction. What is the final speed of the ball?

SOLUTION *(Test your understanding by performing the calculations indicated in each step.)*

1. Relate change in momentum to impulse (Equation 9–5): $\quad \Delta p = p_f - p_i = I = F_{av} \Delta t$

2. Solve for the final momentum: $\quad p_f = F_{av} \Delta t + p_i$

3. Calculate the initial momentum: $\quad p_i = -6.19 \text{ kg} \cdot \text{m/s}$

4. Calculate the impulse: $\quad I = F_{av} \Delta t = 8.45 \text{ kg} \cdot \text{m/s}$

5. Use these results to find the final momentum: $\quad p_f = 2.26 \text{ kg} \cdot \text{m/s}$

6. Divide by the mass to find the final velocity: $\quad v_f = p_f / m = 15.7 \text{ m/s}$

INSIGHT

With our choice of coordinate system, we see that the initial momentum of the ball was in the negative x direction. The impulse applied to the ball, however, resulted in a final momentum (and velocity) in the positive x direction.

YOUR TURN

Suppose the bat is in contact with the ball for 2.60 ms rather than 1.30 ms. What is the final speed of the ball in this case?

(Answers to **Your Turn** *problems are given in the back of the book.)*

We saw in Section 9–1 that the change in momentum is different for an object that hits something and sticks compared with an object that hits and bounces off. This means that the impulse, and hence the force, is different in the two cases. We explore this in the following Conceptual Checkpoint.

CONCEPTUAL CHECKPOINT 9–1   RAIN VERSUS HAIL

A person stands under an umbrella during a rain shower. A few minutes later the raindrops turn to hail—though the number of "drops" hitting the umbrella per time and their speed remain the same. Is the force required to hold the umbrella in the hail **(a)** the same as, **(b)** more than, or **(c)** less than the force required in the rain?

Rain   Hail

▲ Most bats can take off simply by dropping from their perch on a branch or the ceiling of a cave, but vampire bats like this one must leap from the ground to become airborne. They do so by rocking forward onto their front limbs and then pushing off, using the extremely strong pectoral muscles that are also their main source of power in flight. Pushing downward on the ground, a bat experiences an upward reaction force exerted on it by the ground, with a corresponding impulse sufficient to propel it upward a considerable distance. In fact, a vampire bat can launch itself 1 m or more into the air in a mere 30 ms.

REASONING AND DISCUSSION

When raindrops strike the umbrella, they tend to splatter and run off; when hailstones hit the umbrella, they bounce back upward. As a result, the change in momentum is greater for the hail—just as the change in momentum is greater for a rubber ball bouncing off the floor than it is for a beanbag landing on the floor. Hence, the impulse and the force are greater with hail.

ANSWER

(b) The force is greater in the hail.

We conclude this section with an additional calculation involving impulse.

EXAMPLE 9–2   JUMPING FOR JOY

After winning a prize on a game show, a 72-kg contestant jumps for joy. **(a)** If the jump results in an upward speed of 2.1 m/s, what is the impulse experienced by the contestant? **(b)** Before the jump, the floor exerts an upward force of mg on the contestant. What additional average upward force does the floor exert if the contestant pushes down on it for 0.36 s during the jump?

PICTURE THE PROBLEM

Our sketch shows that the contestant's motion is purely one-dimensional, with a final speed of 2.1 m/s in the positive vertical direction. Note that we have chosen the positive y direction to be upward, therefore $\vec{\mathbf{v}}_i = 0$ and $\vec{\mathbf{v}}_f = (2.1 \text{ m/s})\hat{\mathbf{y}}$.

STRATEGY

a. From the momentum–impulse theorem, we know that impulse is equal to the change in momentum. We are given the initial and final velocities of the contestant, and his mass as well; hence the change in momentum, $\Delta\vec{\mathbf{p}}$, can be calculated using the definition of momentum, $\vec{\mathbf{p}} = m\vec{\mathbf{v}}$.

b. The average value of the additional force exerted on the contestant by the floor is $\Delta\vec{\mathbf{p}}/\Delta t$, where Δt is given as 0.36 s and $\Delta\vec{\mathbf{p}}$ is calculated in part (a).

SOLUTION

Part (a)

1. Write an expression for the impulse, noting that $\vec{\mathbf{v}}_i = 0$: $\vec{\mathbf{I}} = \Delta\vec{\mathbf{p}} = \vec{\mathbf{p}}_f - \vec{\mathbf{p}}_i = m\vec{\mathbf{v}}_f$

2. Substitute numerical values: $\vec{\mathbf{I}} = m\vec{\mathbf{v}}_f = (72 \text{ kg})(2.1 \text{ m/s})\hat{\mathbf{y}} = (150 \text{ kg} \cdot \text{m/s})\hat{\mathbf{y}}$

CONTINUED ON NEXT PAGE

CONTINUED FROM PREVIOUS PAGE

Part (b)

3. Express the average force in terms of the impulse $\vec{\mathbf{I}}$ and the time interval Δt:

$$\vec{\mathbf{F}}_{av} = \frac{\vec{\mathbf{I}}}{\Delta t} = \frac{(150 \text{ kg} \cdot \text{m/s})\hat{\mathbf{y}}}{0.36 \text{ s}} = (420 \text{ kg} \cdot \text{m/s}^2)\hat{\mathbf{y}} = (420 \text{ N})\hat{\mathbf{y}}$$

INSIGHT

The magnitude of the additional average force exerted by the floor is rather large; in fact, 420 N is approximately 95 lb, or about 60% of the contestant's weight of 160 lb. Thus, the total upward force exerted by the floor is $mg + 420 \text{ N} = 710 \text{ N} + 420 \text{ N}$, which is about 250 lb. The contestant, of course, exerts the same force downward. Fortunately, the contestant only needs to exert that force for a third of a second.

When the contestant lands, an impulse is required to bring him to rest. If he lands with stiff legs, the impulse occurs in a short time, resulting in a large force delivered to the knees—with possible harmful effects. If he bends his legs on landing, on the other hand, the time duration is significantly increased, and the force applied to the contestant is correspondingly reduced.

PRACTICE PROBLEM

Suppose the contestant lands with a speed of 2.1 m/s and comes to rest in 0.25 s. What is the magnitude of the average force exerted by the floor during landing? [**Answer:** $mg + 600 \text{ N} \sim 290 \text{ lb}$]

Some related homework problems: Problem 13, Problem 14

9–4 Conservation of Linear Momentum

In this section we turn to perhaps the most significant aspect of linear momentum—the fact that it is a conserved quantity. In this respect, it plays a fundamental role in physics similar to that of energy. We shall also see that momentum conservation leads to calculational simplifications, making it of great practical significance.

First, recall that the net force acting on an object is equal to the rate of change of its momentum

$$\sum \vec{\mathbf{F}} = \frac{\Delta \vec{\mathbf{p}}}{\Delta t}$$

Rearranging this expression, we find that the change in momentum during a time interval Δt is

$$\Delta \vec{\mathbf{p}} = \left(\sum \vec{\mathbf{F}} \right) \Delta t \qquad \qquad 9\text{–}7$$

Clearly, then, if the net force acting on an object is zero,

$$\sum \vec{\mathbf{F}} = 0$$

its change in momentum is also zero:

$$\Delta \vec{\mathbf{p}} = \left(\sum \vec{\mathbf{F}} \right) \Delta t = 0$$

Writing the change of momentum in terms of its initial and final values, we have

$$\Delta \vec{\mathbf{p}} = \vec{\mathbf{p}}_f - \vec{\mathbf{p}}_i = 0$$

or

$$\vec{\mathbf{p}}_f = \vec{\mathbf{p}}_i \qquad \qquad 9\text{–}8$$

Since the momentum does not change in this case, we say that it is **conserved.** To summarize:

Conservation of Momentum

If the net force acting on an object is zero, its momentum is conserved; that is,

$$\vec{\mathbf{p}}_f = \vec{\mathbf{p}}_i$$

Note that in some cases the force may be zero in one direction and nonzero in another. For example, an object in free fall has a nonzero y component of force, $F_y \neq 0$, but no force in the x direction, $F_x = 0$. As a result, the object's y component of momentum changes with time while its x component of momentum remains constant. Therefore, in applying momentum conservation, we must remember that both the force and the momentum are vector quantities and that the momentum conservation principle applies separately to each coordinate direction.

Thus far, our discussion has referred to the forces acting on a single object. Next, we consider a system composed of more than one object.

Internal Versus External Forces

The net force acting on a system of objects is the sum of forces applied from outside the system (external forces, $\vec{F}_{ext}$) and forces acting between objects within the system (internal forces, $\vec{F}_{int}$). Thus, we can write

$$\vec{F}_{net} = \sum \vec{F} = \sum \vec{F}_{ext} + \sum \vec{F}_{int}$$

As we shall see, internal and external forces play very *different* roles in terms of how they affect the momentum of a system.

To illustrate the distinction, consider the case of two canoes floating at rest next to one another on a lake, as described in Example 5–3 and shown in **Figure 9–4**. In this case, let's consider the "system" to be the two canoes and the people inside them. When a person in canoe 1 pushes on canoe 2, a force $\vec{F}_2$ is exerted on canoe 2. By Newton's third law, an equal and opposite force, $\vec{F}_1 = -\vec{F}_2$, is exerted on the person in canoe 1. Note that $\vec{F}_1$ and $\vec{F}_2$ are internal forces, since they act between objects in the system. In addition, note that they sum to zero:

$$\vec{F}_1 + \vec{F}_2 = (-\vec{F}_2) + \vec{F}_2 = 0$$

Internal forces always sum to zero ...

$\vec{F}_1$ $\vec{F}_2$

1   2

... and hence they have no effect on the net momentum of the system.

◀ **FIGURE 9–4 Separating two canoes**
A system comprised of two canoes and their occupants. The forces $\vec{F}_1$ and $\vec{F}_2$ are internal to the system. They sum to zero.

This is a special case, of course, but it demonstrates the following general principles:

- Internal forces, like all forces, always occur in action-reaction pairs.
- Because the forces in action-reaction pairs are equal and opposite—due to Newton's third law—internal forces must *always* sum to zero:

$$\sum \vec{F}_{int} = 0$$

The fact that internal forces always cancel means that the net force acting on a system of objects is simply the sum of the *external* forces acting on it:

$$\vec{F}_{net} = \sum \vec{F}_{ext} + \sum \vec{F}_{int} = \sum \vec{F}_{ext}$$

The external forces, on the other hand, may or may not sum to zero—it all depends on the particular situation. For example, if the system consists of the two canoes in Figure 9–4, the external forces are the weights of the people and the canoes acting downward, and the upward, normal force exerted by the water to keep the canoes afloat. These forces sum to zero, and there is no acceleration in the vertical direction. In the next few sections we consider a variety of systems in which the external forces either sum to zero, or are so small that they can be ignored. Later, in Section 9–7, we consider situations where the external forces do not sum to zero and hence must be taken into account.

▲ If the astronaut in this photo pushes on the satellite, the satellite exerts an equal but opposite force on him, in accordance with Newton's third law. If we are calculating the change in the astronaut's momentum, we must take this force into account. However, if we define the system to be the astronaut *and* the satellite, the forces between them are internal to the system. Whatever effect they may have on the astronaut or the satellite individually, they do not affect the momentum of the system as a whole. Therefore, whether a particular force counts as internal or external depends entirely on where we draw the boundaries of the system.

PROBLEM-SOLVING NOTE

Internal Versus External Forces

It is important to keep in mind that internal forces cannot change the momentum of a system—only a net external force can do that.

Finally, how do external and internal forces affect the momentum of a system? To see the connection, first note that Newton's second law gives the change in the net momentum for a given time interval Δt:

$$\Delta \vec{p}_{\text{net}} = \vec{F}_{\text{net}} \, \Delta t$$

Because the internal forces cancel, however, the change in the net momentum is directly related to the net *external* force:

$$\Delta \vec{p}_{\text{net}} = \left(\sum \vec{F}_{\text{ext}} \right) \Delta t \qquad \qquad 9\text{--}9$$

Therefore, the key distinction between internal and external forces is the following:

Conservation of Momentum for a System of Objects

- *Internal* forces have absolutely no effect on the net momentum of a system.
- If the *net external* force acting on a system is zero, its net momentum is conserved. That is,

$$\vec{p}_{1,f} + \vec{p}_{2,f} + \vec{p}_{3,f} + \cdots = \vec{p}_{1,i} + \vec{p}_{2,i} + \vec{p}_{3,i} + \cdots$$

It is important to note that these statements apply only to the *net* momentum of a system, not to the momentum of each individual object. For example, suppose a system consists of two objects, 1 and 2, and that the net external force acting on the system is zero. As a result, the net momentum must remain constant:

$$\vec{p}_{\text{net}} = \vec{p}_1 + \vec{p}_2 = \text{constant}$$

This does not mean, however, that $\vec{p}_1$ is constant or that $\vec{p}_2$ is constant. All we can say is that the *sum* of $\vec{p}_1$ and $\vec{p}_2$ does not change.

As a specific example, consider the case of the two canoes floating on a lake, as described previously. Initially the momentum of the system is zero, because the canoes are at rest. After a person pushes the canoes apart, they are both moving, and hence both have nonzero momentum. Thus, the momentum of each canoe has changed. On the other hand, because the net external force acting on the system is zero, the sum of the canoes' momenta must still vanish. We show this in the next Example.

EXAMPLE 9–3 TIPPY CANOE: COMPARING VELOCITY AND MOMENTUM

Two groups of canoeists meet in the middle of a lake. After a brief visit, a person in canoe 1 pushes on canoe 2 with a force of 46 N to separate the canoes. If the mass of canoe 1 and its occupants is 130 kg, and the mass of canoe 2 and its occupants is 250 kg, find the momentum of each canoe after 1.20 s of pushing.

PICTURE THE PROBLEM

We choose the positive x direction to point from canoe 1 to canoe 2. With this choice, the force exerted on canoe 2 is $\vec{F}_2 = (46 \, \text{N})\hat{x}$ and the force exerted on canoe 1 is $\vec{F}_1 = (-46 \, \text{N})\hat{x}$.

STRATEGY

First, we find the acceleration of each canoe using $a_x = F_x/m$. Next, we use $v_x = v_{0x} + a_x t$ to find the velocity at time t. Note that the canoes start at rest, hence $v_{0x} = 0$. Finally, the momentum can be calculated using $p_x = mv_x$.

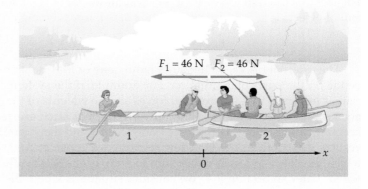

SOLUTION

1. Use Newton's second law to find the acceleration of canoe 2:

$$a_{2,x} = \frac{\sum F_{2,x}}{m_2} = \frac{46 \text{ N}}{250 \text{ kg}} = 0.18 \text{ m/s}^2$$

2. Do the same calculation for canoe 1. Note that the acceleration of canoe 1 is in the negative direction:

$$a_{1,x} = \frac{\sum F_{1,x}}{m_1} = \frac{-46 \text{ N}}{130 \text{ kg}} = -0.35 \text{ m/s}^2$$

3. Calculate the velocity of each canoe at $t = 1.20$ s:

$$v_{1,x} = a_{1,x}t = (-0.35 \text{ m/s}^2)(1.20 \text{ s}) = -0.42 \text{ m/s}$$
$$v_{2,x} = a_{2,x}t = (0.18 \text{ m/s}^2)(1.20 \text{ s}) = 0.22 \text{ m/s}$$

4. Calculate the momentum of each canoe at $t = 1.20$ s:

$$p_{1,x} = m_1 v_{1,x} = (130 \text{ kg})(-0.42 \text{ m/s}) = -55 \text{ kg} \cdot \text{m/s}$$
$$p_{2,x} = m_2 v_{2,x} = (250 \text{ kg})(0.22 \text{ m/s}) = 55 \text{ kg} \cdot \text{m/s}$$

INSIGHT

Note that the sum of the momenta of the two canoes is zero. This is just what one would expect: The canoes start at rest with zero momentum, there is zero net external force acting on the system, hence the final momentum must also be zero. The final velocities *do not* add to zero; it is momentum ($m\vec{v}$) that is conserved, not velocity ($\vec{v}$).

Finally, we solved this problem using one-dimensional kinematics so that we could clearly see the distinction between velocity and momentum. An alternative way to calculate the final momentum of each canoe is to use $\Delta\vec{p} = \vec{p}_f - \vec{p}_i = \vec{F}\Delta t$. For canoe 1 we have $\vec{p}_{1,f} = \vec{F}_1 \Delta t + \vec{p}_{1,i} = (-46 \text{ N})\hat{x}(1.20 \text{ s}) + 0 = (-55 \text{ kg} \cdot \text{m/s})\hat{x}$, in agreement with our results above. A similar calculation yields $\vec{p}_{2,f} = (55 \text{ kg} \cdot \text{m/s})\hat{x}$ for canoe 2.

PRACTICE PROBLEM

What are the final momenta if the canoes are pushed apart with a force of 56 N?   [**Answer:** $p_{1,x} = -67 \text{ kg} \cdot \text{m/s}, p_{2,x} = 67 \text{ kg} \cdot \text{m/s}$]

Some related homework problems: Problem 21, Problem 22

In a situation like that described in Example 9–3, the person in canoe 1 pushes canoe 2 away. At the same time, canoe 1 begins to move in the opposite direction. This is referred to as **recoil**. It is essentially the same as the recoil one experiences when firing a gun or when turning on a strong stream of water.

A particularly interesting example of recoil involves the human body. Perhaps you have noticed, when resting quietly in a rocking or reclining chair, that the chair wobbles back and forth slightly about once a second. The reason for this movement is that each time your heart pumps blood in one direction (from the atria to the ventricles, then to the aorta and pulmonary arteries, and so on) your body recoils in the opposite direction. Because the recoil depends on the force exerted by your heart on the blood and the volume of blood expelled from the heart with each beat, it is possible to gain valuable medical information regarding the health of your heart by analyzing the recoil it produces.

The medical instrument that employs the physical principle of recoil is called the *ballistocardiograph*. It is a completely noninvasive technology that simply requires the patient to sit comfortably in a chair fitted with sensitive force sensors under the seat and behind the back. Sophisticated bathroom scales also utilize this technology. A ballistocardiographic (BCG) scale detects the recoil vibrations of the body as a person stands on the scale. This allows the BCG scale to display not only the person's body weight but his or her heart rate as well.

A more dramatic application of heartbeat recoil is currently being used at the Riverbend Maximum Security Institution in Tennessee. The only successful breakout from this prison occurred when four inmates hid in a secret compartment in a delivery truck that was leaving the facility. The institution now uses a heartbeat recoil detector that would have foiled this escape. Vehicles leaving the prison must stop at a checkpoint where a small motion detector is attached to it with a suction cup. Any persons hidden in the vehicle will reveal their presence by the very beating of their hearts. These heartbeat detectors have proved to be 100 percent effective, even though the recoil of the heart may displace a large truck by only a few millionths of an inch. Similar systems are being used at other high-security installations and border crossings.

REAL-WORLD PHYSICS: BIO

The ballistocardiograph

REAL-WORLD PHYSICS: BIO

Heartbeat detectors

CONCEPTUAL CHECKPOINT 9-2 MOMENTUM VERSUS KINETIC ENERGY

In Example 9–3, the final momentum of the system (consisting of the two canoes and their occupants) is equal to the initial momentum of the system. Is the final kinetic energy **(a)** equal to, **(b)** less than, or **(c)** greater than the initial kinetic energy?

REASONING AND DISCUSSION
The final momentum of the two canoes is zero because one canoe has a positive momentum and the other has a negative momentum of the same magnitude. The two momenta, then, sum to zero. Kinetic energy, which is $\frac{1}{2}mv^2$, cannot be negative; hence no such cancellation is possible. Both canoes have positive kinetic energies, and therefore, the final kinetic energy is greater than the initial kinetic energy, which is zero.

Where does the increase in kinetic energy come from? It comes from the muscular work done by the person who pushes the canoes apart.

ANSWER
(c) K_f is greater than K_i.

REAL-WORLD PHYSICS
Stellar explosions

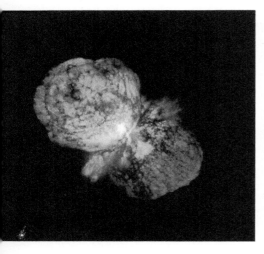

▲ This Hubble Space Telescope photograph shows the aftermath of a violent explosion of the star Eta Carinae. The explosion, which was observed on Earth in 1841 and briefly made Eta Carinae the second brightest star in the sky, produced two bright lobes of matter spewing outward in opposite directions. In this photograph, these lobes have expanded to about the size of our solar system. The momentum of the star before the explosion must be the same as the total momentum of the star and the bright lobes after the explosion. Since the lobes are roughly symmetric and move in opposite directions, their net momentum is essentially zero. Thus, we conclude that the momentum of the star itself was virtually unchanged by the explosion.

A special case of some interest is the universe. Since there is nothing external to the universe—by definition—it follows that the net external force acting on it is zero. Therefore, its net momentum is conserved. No matter what happens—a comet collides with the Earth, a star explodes and becomes a supernova, a black hole swallows part of a galaxy—the total momentum of the universe simply cannot change. A particularly vivid illustration of momentum conservation in our own galaxy is provided by the exploding star Eta Carinae. As can be seen in the Hubble Space Telescope photograph, jets of material are moving away from the star in opposite directions, just like the canoes moving apart from one another in Example 9–3.

Conservation of momentum also applies to the more everyday situation described in the next Active Example.

ACTIVE EXAMPLE 9-2 FIND THE VELOCITY OF THE BEE

A honeybee with a mass of 0.150 g lands on one end of a floating 4.75-g popsicle stick. After sitting at rest for a moment, it runs toward the other end with a velocity $\vec{v}_b$ relative to the still water. The stick moves in the opposite direction with a speed of 0.120 cm/s. What is the velocity of the bee? (Let the direction of the bee's motion be the positive x direction.)

SOLUTION *(Test your understanding by performing the calculations indicated in each step.)*

1. Set the total momentum of the system equal to zero: $\vec{p}_b + \vec{p}_s = 0$

2. Solve for the momentum of the bee: $\vec{p}_b = -\vec{p}_s = m_b v_b \hat{x}$

3. Calculate the momentum of the stick: $\vec{p}_s = -m_s v_s \hat{x} = (-0.570 \text{ g} \cdot \text{cm/s})\hat{x}$

4. Calculate the momentum of the bee: $\vec{p}_b = m_b v_b \hat{x} = -\vec{p}_s = (0.570 \text{ g} \cdot \text{cm/s})\hat{x}$

5. Divide by the bee's mass to find its velocity: $\vec{v}_b = \vec{p}_b / m_b = (3.80 \text{ cm/s})\hat{x}$

INSIGHT
Because only internal forces are at work while the bee walks on the stick, the system's total momentum must remain zero.

Suppose the mass of the popsicle stick is 9.50 g rather than 4.75 g. What is the bee's velocity in this case?

(Answers to **Your Turn** *problems are given in the back of the book.)*

9–5 Inelastic Collisions

We now turn our attention to **collisions.** By a collision we mean a situation in which two objects strike one another, and in which the net external force is either zero or negligibly small. For example, if two train cars roll along on a level track and hit one another, this is a collision. In this case, the net external force—the weight downward and the normal force exerted by the tracks upward—is zero. As a result, the momentum of the two-car system is conserved.

Another example of a collision is a baseball being struck by a bat. In this case, the external forces are not zero because the weight of the ball is not balanced by any other force. However, as we have seen in Section 9–3, the forces exerted during the hit are much larger than the weight of the ball or the bat. Hence, to a good approximation, we may neglect the external forces (the weight of the ball and bat) in this case, and say that the momentum of the ball–bat system is conserved.

Now it may seem surprising at first, but the fact that the momentum of a system is conserved during a collision does not necessarily mean that the system's kinetic energy is conserved. In fact most, or even all, of a system's kinetic energy may be converted to other forms during a collision while, at the same time, not one bit of momentum is lost. This shall be explored in detail in this section.

In general, collisions are categorized according to what happens to the kinetic energy of the system. There are two possibilities. After a collision, the final kinetic energy, K_f, is either equal to the initial kinetic energy, K_i, or it is not. If $K_f = K_i$, the collision is said to be **elastic.** We shall consider elastic collisions in the next section.

On the other hand, the kinetic energy may change during a collision. Usually it decreases due to losses associated with sound, heat, and deformation. Sometimes it increases, if the collision sets off an explosion, for instance. In any event, collisions in which the kinetic energy is not conserved are referred to as **inelastic:**

Inelastic Collisions

In an inelastic collision, the momentum of a system is conserved,

$$\vec{p}_f = \vec{p}_i$$

but its kinetic energy is not,

$$K_f \neq K_i$$

◄ In both elastic and inelastic collisions, momentum is conserved. The same is not true of kinetic energy, however. In the largely inelastic collision at left, much of the hockey players' initial kinetic energy is transformed into work: rearranging the players' anatomies and shattering the glass of the rink. In the highly elastic collision at right, the ball rebounds with very little diminution of its kinetic energy (though a little energy is lost as sound and heat).

Finally, in the special case where objects stick together after the collision, we say that the collision is **completely inelastic.**

Completely Inelastic Collisions
When objects stick together after colliding, the collision is completely inelastic.

In a completely inelastic collision, the maximum amount of kinetic energy is lost. If the total momentum of the system is zero, this means that all of the kinetic energy is lost. For systems with nonzero total momentum, however, some kinetic energy will remain after the collision—still, the amount lost is the maximum permitted by momentum conservation.

Inelastic Collisions in One Dimension

Consider a system of two identical train cars of mass m on a smooth, level track. One car is at rest initially while the other moves toward it with a speed v_0, as shown in Figure 9–5. When the cars collide, the coupling mechanism latches, causing the cars to stick together and move as a unit. What is the speed of the cars after the collision?

▶ **FIGURE 9–5 Railroad cars collide and stick together**

A moving train car collides with an identical car that is stationary. After the collision, the cars stick together and move with the same speed.

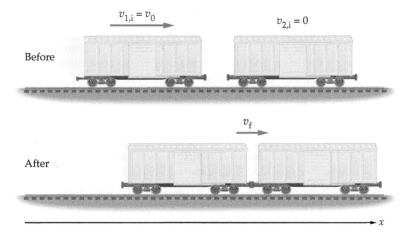

To answer this question, we begin by considering the general case that applies to any completely inelastic collision, and then we look at the specific case of the two train cars. In general, suppose that two masses, m_1 and m_2, have initial velocities $v_{1,i}$ and $v_{2,i}$ respectively. The initial momentum of the system is

$$p_i = m_1 v_{1,i} + m_2 v_{2,i}$$

After the collision, the objects move together with a common velocity v_f. Therefore, the final momentum is

$$p_f = (m_1 + m_2)v_f$$

Equating the initial and final momenta yields $m_1 v_{1,i} + m_2 v_{2,i} = (m_1 + m_2)v_f$, or

$$v_f = \frac{m_1 v_{1,i} + m_2 v_{2,i}}{m_1 + m_2} \qquad 9\text{–}10$$

We can apply this general result to the case of the two railroad cars by noting that $m_1 = m_2 = m$, $v_{1,i} = v_0$, and $v_{2,i} = 0$. Thus, the final velocity is

$$v_f = \frac{m v_0 + m \cdot 0}{m + m} = \frac{m}{2m} v_0 = \frac{1}{2} v_0 \qquad 9\text{–}11$$

As you might have guessed, the final speed is one-half the initial speed.

EXERCISE 9–2

A 1200-kg car moving at 2.5 m/s is struck in the rear by a 2600-kg truck moving at 6.2 m/s. If the vehicles stick together after the collision, what is their speed immediately after colliding? (Assume that external forces may be ignored.)

SOLUTION
Applying Equation 9–10 with $m_1 = 1200$ kg, $v_{1,i} = 2.5$ m/s, $m_2 = 2600$ kg, and $v_{2,i} = 6.2$ m/s yields $v_f = 5.0$ m/s.

During the collision of the railroad cars, some of the initial kinetic energy is converted to other forms. Some propagates away as sound, some is converted to heat, some creates permanent deformations in the metal of the latching mechanism. The precise amount of kinetic energy that is lost is addressed in the following Conceptual Checkpoint.

PROBLEM-SOLVING NOTE

Momentum Versus Energy Conservation

Be sure to distinguish between momentum conservation and energy conservation. A common error is to assume that kinetic energy is conserved just because the momentum is conserved.

CONCEPTUAL CHECKPOINT 9–3   HOW MUCH KINETIC ENERGY IS LOST?

A railroad car of mass m and speed v collides and sticks to an identical railroad car that is initially at rest. After the collision, is the kinetic energy of the system **(a)** 1/2, **(b)** 1/3, or **(c)** 1/4 of its initial kinetic energy?

REASONING AND DISCUSSION
Before the collision, the kinetic energy of the system is

$$K_i = \frac{1}{2}mv^2$$

After the collision, the mass doubles and the speed is halved. Hence, the final kinetic energy is

$$K_f = \frac{1}{2}(2m)\left(\frac{v}{2}\right)^2 = \frac{1}{2}\left(\frac{1}{2}mv^2\right) = \frac{1}{2}K_i$$

Therefore, one-half of the initial kinetic energy is converted to other forms of energy. An equivalent way to arrive at this conclusion is to express the kinetic energy in terms of the momentum, $p = mv$:

$$K = \frac{1}{2}mv^2 = \frac{1}{2}\left(\frac{m^2v^2}{m}\right) = \frac{p^2}{2m}$$

Since the momentum is the same before and after the collision, the fact that the mass doubles means the kinetic energy is halved.

ANSWER
(a) The final kinetic energy is one-half the initial kinetic energy.

Note that we know the precise amount of kinetic energy that was lost, even though we don't know just how much went into sound, how much went into heat, and so on. It is not necessary to know all of those details to determine how much kinetic energy was lost.
We also know how much momentum was lost—none.

EXAMPLE 9–4   GOAL-LINE STAND

On a touchdown attempt, a 95.0-kg running back runs toward the end zone at 3.75 m/s. A 111-kg linebacker moving at 4.10 m/s meets the runner in a head-on collision. If the two players stick together, **(a)** what is their velocity immediately after the collision? **(b)** What are the initial and final kinetic energies of the system?

PICTURE THE PROBLEM
In our sketch, we let subscript 1 refer to the red-and-gray running back, who carries the ball, and subscript 2 refer to the blue-and-gold linebacker, who will make the tackle. The direction of the running back's initial motion is taken to be in the positive x direction. Therefore, the initial velocities of the players are $\vec{v}_1 = (3.75 \text{ m/s})\hat{x}$ and $\vec{v}_2 = (-4.10 \text{ m/s})\hat{x}$.

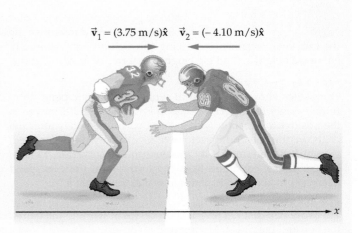

$\vec{v}_1 = (3.75 \text{ m/s})\hat{x}$ $\vec{v}_2 = (-4.10 \text{ m/s})\hat{x}$

CONTINUED ON NEXT PAGE

CONTINUED FROM PREVIOUS PAGE

STRATEGY

a. The final velocity can be found by applying momentum conservation to the system consisting of the two players. Initially, the players have momenta in opposite directions. After the collision, the players move together with a combined mass $m_1 + m_2$ and a velocity $\vec{\mathbf{v}}_f$.

b. The kinetic energies can be found by applying $\frac{1}{2}mv^2$ to the players individually to obtain the initial kinetic energy, and then to their combined motion for the final kinetic energy.

SOLUTION

Part (a)

1. Set the initial momentum equal to the final momentum:

$$m_1\vec{\mathbf{v}}_1 + m_2\vec{\mathbf{v}}_2 = (m_1 + m_2)\vec{\mathbf{v}}_f$$

2. Solve for the final velocity and substitute numerical values, being careful to use the appropriate signs:

$$\vec{\mathbf{v}}_f = \frac{m_1\vec{\mathbf{v}}_1 + m_2\vec{\mathbf{v}}_2}{m_1 + m_2}$$

$$= \frac{(95.0 \text{ kg})(3.75 \text{ m/s})\hat{\mathbf{x}} + (111 \text{ kg})(-4.10 \text{ m/s})\hat{\mathbf{x}}}{95.0 \text{ kg} + 111 \text{ kg}}$$

$$= (-0.480 \text{ m/s})\hat{\mathbf{x}}$$

Part (b)

3. Calculate the initial kinetic energy of the two players:

$$K_i = \tfrac{1}{2}m_1v_1^2 + \tfrac{1}{2}m_2v_2^2$$
$$= \tfrac{1}{2}(95.0 \text{ kg})(3.75 \text{ m/s})^2 + \tfrac{1}{2}(111 \text{ kg})(-4.10 \text{ m/s})^2$$
$$= 1600 \text{ J}$$

4. Calculate the final kinetic energy of the players, noting that they both move with the same velocity after the collision:

$$K_f = \tfrac{1}{2}(m_1 + m_2)v_f^2$$
$$= \tfrac{1}{2}(95.0 \text{ kg} + 111 \text{ kg})(-0.480 \text{ m/s})^2 = 23.7 \text{ J}$$

INSIGHT

After the collision, the two players are moving in the negative direction; that is, away from the end zone. This is because the linebacker had more negative momentum than the running back had positive momentum. As for the kinetic energy, of the original 1600 J, only 23.7 J is left after the collision. This means that over 98% of the original kinetic energy is converted to other forms. Even so, *none* of the momentum is lost.

PRACTICE PROBLEM

If the final speed of the two players is to be zero, should the speed of the running back be increased or decreased? Check your answer by calculating the required speed for the running back. [**Answer:** The running back's speed should be increased to 4.79 m/s.]

Some related homework problems: Problem 28, Problem 35

EXAMPLE 9–5 BALLISTIC PENDULUM

 **REAL-WORLD PHYSICS**   In a ballistic pendulum, an object of mass m is fired with an initial speed v_0 at the bob of a pendulum. The bob has a mass M, and is suspended by a rod of negligible mass. After the collision, the object and the bob stick together and swing through an arc, eventually gaining a height h. Find the height h in terms of m, M, v_0, and g.

PICTURE THE PROBLEM

Our sketch shows the physical setup of a ballistic pendulum. Initially, only the object of mass m is moving, and it moves in the positive x direction with a speed v_0. Immediately after the collision, the bob and object move together with a new speed, v_f, which is determined by momentum conservation. Finally, the pendulum continues to swing to the right until its speed decreases to zero and it comes to rest at the height h.

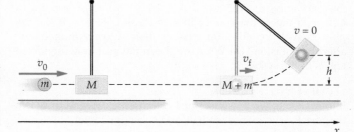

STRATEGY

There are two distinct physical processes at work in the ballistic pendulum. The first is a completely inelastic collision between the bob and the object. Momentum is conserved during this collision, but kinetic energy is not. After the collision, the remaining kinetic energy is converted into gravitational potential energy, which determines how high the bob and object will rise.

SOLUTION

1. Set the momentum just before the bob–object collision equal to the momentum just after the collision. Let v_f be the speed just after the collision:

$$mv_0 = (M + m)v_f$$

2. Solve for the speed just after the collision, v_f:

$$v_f = \left(\frac{m}{M + m}\right)v_0$$

3. Calculate the kinetic energy just after the collision:

$$K_f = \frac{1}{2}(M + m)v_f{}^2 = \frac{1}{2}(M + m)\left(\frac{m}{M + m}\right)^2 v_0{}^2$$

$$= \frac{1}{2}mv_0{}^2\left(\frac{m}{M + m}\right)$$

4. Set the kinetic energy after the collision equal to the gravitational potential energy at the height h:

$$\frac{1}{2}mv_0{}^2\left(\frac{m}{M + m}\right) = (M + m)gh$$

5. Solve for the height, h:

$$h = \left(\frac{m}{M + m}\right)^2\left(\frac{v_0{}^2}{2g}\right)$$

INSIGHT

A ballistic pendulum is often used to measure the speed of a rapidly moving object, such as a bullet. If a bullet were shot straight up, it would rise to the height $v_0{}^2/2g$, which can be thousands of feet. On the other hand, if a bullet of mass m is fired into a ballistic pendulum, in which M is much greater than m, the bullet reaches only a small fraction of this height. Thus, the ballistic pendulum makes for a more convenient and practical measurement.

PRACTICE PROBLEM

A 7.00-g bullet is fired into a ballistic pendulum whose bob has a mass of 0.950 kg. If the bob rises to a height of 0.220 m, what was the initial speed of the bullet? [**Answer:** $v_0 = 284$ m/s. If this bullet were fired straight up, it would rise 4.11 km $\approx$ 13,000 ft in the absence of air resistance.]

Some related homework problems: Problem 32, Problem 33

Inelastic Collisions in Two Dimensions

Next we consider collisions in two dimensions, where we must conserve the momentum component by component. To do this, we set up a coordinate system and resolve the initial momentum into x and y components. Next, we demand that the final momentum have precisely the same x and y components as the initial momentum. That is,

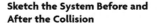

$$p_{x,i} = p_{x,f}$$

and

$$p_{y,i} = p_{y,f}$$

The following Example shows how to carry out such a calculation in a practical situation.

PROBLEM-SOLVING NOTE

Sketch the System Before and After the Collision

In problems involving collisions, it is useful to draw the system before and after the collision. Be sure to label the relevant masses, velocities, and angles.

EXAMPLE 9–6   BAD INTERSECTION: ANALYZING A TRAFFIC ACCIDENT

REAL-WORLD PHYSICS

A car with a mass of 950 kg and a speed of 16 m/s approaches an intersection, as shown on the next page. A 1300-kg minivan traveling at 21 m/s is heading for the same intersection. The car and minivan collide and stick together. Find the speed and direction of the wrecked vehicles just after the collision, assuming external forces can be ignored.

PICTURE THE PROBLEM

In our sketch, we align the x and y axes with the crossing streets. With this choice, $\vec{v}_1$ (the car's velocity) is in the positive x direction, and $\vec{v}_2$ (the minivan's velocity) is in the positive y direction. In addition, the problem statement indicates that

CONTINUED ON NEXT PAGE

CONTINUED FROM PREVIOUS PAGE

$m_1 = 950$ kg and $m_2 = 1300$ kg. After the collision, the two vehicles move together (as a unit) with a speed v_f in a direction θ with respect to the positive x axis.

STRATEGY
Because external forces can be ignored, the total momentum of the system must be conserved during the collision. This is really two conditions: (i) the x component of momentum is conserved, and (ii) the y component of momentum is conserved. These two conditions determine the two unknowns: the final speed, v_f, and the final direction, θ.

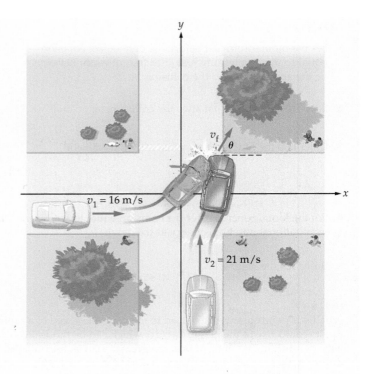

SOLUTION

1. Set the initial x component of momentum equal to the final x component of momentum:

$$m_1 v_1 = (m_1 + m_2)v_f \cos\theta$$

2. Do the same for the y component of momentum:

$$m_2 v_2 = (m_1 + m_2)v_f \sin\theta$$

3. Divide the y momentum equation by the x momentum equation. This eliminates v_f, giving an equation involving θ alone:

$$\frac{m_2 v_2}{m_1 v_1} = \frac{(m_1 + m_2)v_f \sin\theta}{(m_1 + m_2)v_f \cos\theta} = \frac{\sin\theta}{\cos\theta} = \tan\theta$$

4. Solve for θ:

$$\theta = \tan^{-1}\left(\frac{m_2 v_2}{m_1 v_1}\right) = \tan^{-1}\left[\frac{(1300 \text{ kg})(21 \text{ m/s})}{(950 \text{ kg})(16 \text{ m/s})}\right]$$
$$= \tan^{-1}(1.8) = 61°$$

5. The final speed can be found using either the x or the y momentum equation. Here we use the x equation:

$$v_f = \frac{m_1 v_1}{(m_1 + m_2)\cos\theta}$$
$$= \frac{(950 \text{ kg})(16 \text{ m/s})}{(950 \text{ kg} + 1300 \text{ kg})\cos 61°} = 14 \text{ m/s}$$

INSIGHT
As a check, you should verify that the y momentum equation gives the same value for v_f.

When a collision occurs in the real world, a traffic-accident investigation team will measure skid marks at the scene of the crash and use this information—along with some basic physics—to determine the initial speeds and directions of the vehicles. This information is often presented in court, where it can lead to a clear identification of the driver at fault.

PRACTICE PROBLEM
Suppose the speed and direction immediately after the collision are known to be $v_f = 12.5$ m/s and $\theta = 42°$, respectively. Find the initial speed of each car. [**Answer:** $v_1 = 22$ m/s, $v_2 = 14$ m/s]

Some related homework problems: Problem 29, Problem 30

9–6 Elastic Collisions

In this section we consider collisions in which both momentum and kinetic energy are conserved. As mentioned in the previous section, such collisions are referred to as elastic:

Elastic Collisions

In an elastic collision, momentum and kinetic energy are conserved. That is,

$$\vec{\mathbf{p}}_f = \vec{\mathbf{p}}_i$$

and

$$K_f = K_i$$

Most collisions in everyday life are rather poor approximations to being elastic—usually there is a significant amount of energy converted to other forms. However, the collision of objects that bounce off one another with little deformation—like billiard balls, for example—provides a reasonably good approximation to an elastic collision. In the subatomic world, on the other hand, elastic collisions are common. Elastic collisions, then, are not merely an ideal that is approached but never attained—they are constantly taking place in nature.

Elastic Collisions in One Dimension

Consider a head-on collision of two carts on an air track, as pictured in **Figure 9–6**. The carts are provided with bumpers that give an elastic bounce when the carts collide. Let's suppose that initially cart 1 is moving to the right with a speed v_0 toward cart 2, which is at rest. If the masses of the carts are m_1 and m_2, respectively, then momentum conservation can be written as follows:

$$m_1 v_0 = m_1 v_{1,f} + m_2 v_{2,f}$$

In this expression, $v_{1,f}$ and $v_{2,f}$ are the final velocities of the two carts. Note that we say velocities, not speeds, since it is possible for cart 1 to reverse direction, in which case $v_{1,f}$ would be negative.

Next, the fact that this is an elastic collision means the final velocities must also satisfy energy conservation:

$$\frac{1}{2}m_1 v_0^2 = \frac{1}{2}m_1 v_{1,f}^2 + \frac{1}{2}m_2 v_{2,f}^2$$

Thus, we now have two equations for the two unknowns, $v_{1,f}$ and $v_{2,f}$. Straightforward—though messy—algebra yields the following results:

$$v_{1,f} = \left(\frac{m_1 - m_2}{m_1 + m_2}\right)v_0$$

$$v_{2,f} = \left(\frac{2m_1}{m_1 + m_2}\right)v_0$$

9–12

Note that the final velocity of cart 1 can be positive, negative, or zero, depending on whether m_1 is greater than, less than, or equal to m_2, respectively. The final velocity of cart 2, however, is always positive.

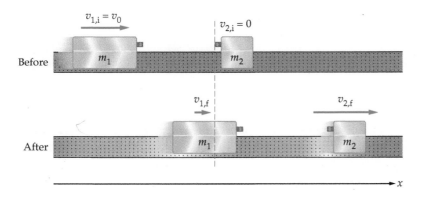

$v_{1,i} = v_0$

$v_{2,i} = 0$

Before m_1 m_2

$v_{1,f}$ $v_{2,f}$

After m_1 m_2

x

◀ **FIGURE 9–6 An elastic collision between two air carts**

In the case pictured, $v_{1,f}$ is to the right (positive), which means that m_1 is greater than m_2. In fact, we have chosen $m_1 = 2m_2$ for this plot; therefore, $v_{1,f} = v_0/3$ and $v_{2,f} = 4v_0/3$ as given by Equations 9–12. If m_1 were less than m_2, cart 1 would bounce back toward the left, meaning that $v_{1,f}$ would be negative.

EXERCISE 9–3

At an amusement park, a 96.0-kg bumper car moving with a speed of 1.24 m/s bounces elastically off a 135-kg bumper car at rest. Find the final velocities of the cars.

SOLUTION

Using Equations 9–12, we find the final velocities to be $v_{1,f} = -0.209$ m/s and $v_{2,f} = 1.03$ m/s. Note that the direction of travel of car 1 has been reversed.

Let's check a few special cases of our results. First, consider the case where the two carts have equal masses, $m_1 = m_2 = m$. Substituting into Equations 9–12, we find

$$v_{1,f} = \left(\frac{m - m}{m + m}\right)v_0 = 0$$

and

$$v_{2,f} = \left(\frac{2m}{m + m}\right)v_0 = v_0$$

Thus, after the collision, the cart that was moving with velocity v_0 is now at rest, and the cart that was at rest is now moving with velocity v_0. In effect, the carts have "exchanged" velocities. This case is illustrated in **Figure 9–7 (a)**.

Next, suppose that m_2 is much greater than m_1, or, equivalently, that m_1 approaches zero. Returning to Equations 9–12, and setting $m_1 = 0$, we find

$$v_{1,f} = \left(\frac{0 - m_2}{0 + m_2}\right)v_0 = \left(\frac{-m_2}{m_2}\right)v_0 = -v_0$$

and

$$v_{2,f} = \frac{2 \cdot 0}{0 + m_2}\, v_0 = 0$$

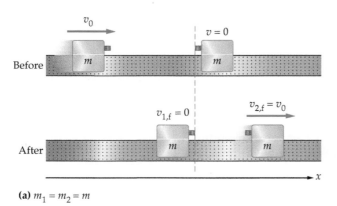

(a) $m_1 = m_2 = m$

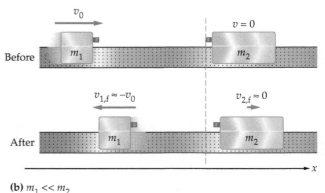

(b) $m_1 \ll m_2$

▶ **FIGURE 9–7 Elastic collisions between air carts of various masses**

(a) Carts of equal mass exchange velocities when they collide. **(b)** When a light cart collides with a stationary heavy cart, its direction of motion is reversed. Its speed is practically unchanged. **(c)** When a heavy cart collides with a stationary light cart, it continues to move in the same direction with essentially the same speed. The light cart moves off with a speed that is roughly twice the initial speed of the heavy cart.

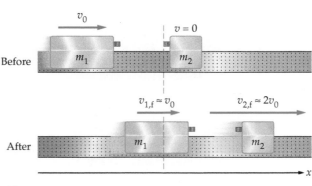

(c) $m_1 \gg m_2$

Physically, we interpret these results as follows: A very light cart collides with a heavy cart that is at rest. The heavy cart hardly budges, but the light cart is reflected, heading *backward* (remember the minus sign in $-v_0$) with the same speed it had initially. For example, if you throw a ball against a wall, the wall is the very heavy object and the ball is the light object. The ball bounces back with the same speed it had initially (assuming an ideal elastic collision). We show a case in which m_1 is much less than m_2 in **Figure 9–7 (b)**.

Finally, what happens when m_1 is much greater than m_2? To check this limit we can set m_2 equal to zero. We consider the results in the following Conceptual Checkpoint.

CONCEPTUAL CHECKPOINT 9–4 SPEED AFTER A COLLISION

A hoverfly is happily maintaining a fixed position about 10 ft above the ground when an elephant charges out of the bush and collides with it. The fly bounces elastically off the forehead of the elephant. If the initial speed of the elephant is v_0, is the speed of the fly after the collision equal to **(a)** v_0, **(b)** $1.5v_0$, or **(c)** $2v_0$?

REASONING AND DISCUSSION

We can use Equations 9–12 to find the final speeds of the fly and the elephant. First, let m_1 be the mass of the elephant, and m_2 be the mass of the fly. Clearly, m_2 is vanishingly small compared with m_1, hence we can evaluate Equations 9–12 in the limit $m_2 \rightarrow 0$. This yields

$$v_{1,f} = \left(\frac{m_1 - m_2}{m_1 + m_2} \right) v_0 \xrightarrow{m_2 \rightarrow 0} \left(\frac{m_1}{m_1} \right) v_0 = v_0$$

and

$$v_{2,f} = \left(\frac{2m_1}{m_1 + m_2} \right) v_0 \xrightarrow{m_2 \rightarrow 0} \left(\frac{2m_1}{m_1} \right) v_0 = 2v_0$$

As expected, the speed of the elephant is unaffected. The fly, however, rebounds with twice the speed of the elephant. **Figure 9–7 (c)** illustrates this case with air carts.

ANSWER

(c) The speed of the fly is $2v_0$.

▲ The apparatus shown here illustrates some of the basic features of elastic collisions between objects of equal mass. The device consists of five identical metal balls suspended by strings. When the end ball is pulled out to the side and then released so as to fall back and strike the second ball, it creates a rapid succession of elastic collisions among the balls. In each collision, one ball comes to rest while the next one begins to move with the original speed, just as with the air carts in Figure 9–7 (a). When the collisions reach the other end of the apparatus, the last ball swings out to the same height from which the first ball was released.

If two balls are pulled out and released, two balls swing out at the other side, and so on. To see why this must be so, imagine that the two balls swing in with a speed v and a single ball swings out at the other side with a speed v'. What value must v' have (a) to conserve momentum, and (b) to conserve kinetic energy? Since the required speed is $v' = 2v$ for (a) and $v' = \sqrt{2}v$ for (b), it follows that it is not possible to conserve both momentum and kinetic energy with two balls swinging in and one ball swinging out.

Note that after the collision the fly is separating from the elephant with the speed $2v_0 - v_0 = v_0$. Before the collision the elephant was approaching the fly with the same speed, v_0. This is a special case of the following general result:

> The speed of separation after a head-on elastic collision is always equal to the speed of approach before the collision.

The proof of this statement is the subject of Problem 91.

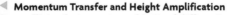
◄ **Momentum Transfer and Height Amplification**
In a collision between two objects of different mass, like the small and large balls in this photo, a significant amount of momentum can be transferred from the large object to the small object. Even though the total momentum is conserved, the small object can be given a speed that is significantly larger than any of the initial speeds. This is illustrated in the photo by the height to which the small ball bounces. A similar process occurs in the collapse of a star during a supernova explosion. The resulting collision can send jets of material racing away from the supernova at nearly the speed of light, just like the small ball that takes off with such a large speed in this collision.

Elastic Collisions in Two Dimensions

In a two-dimensional elastic collision, if we are given the final speed and direction of one of the objects, we can find the speed and direction of the other object using energy conservation and momentum conservation. For example, consider the collision of two 7.00-kg curling stones, as depicted in **Figure 9–8**. One stone is at rest initially, the other approaches with a speed $v_{1,i} = 1.50$ m/s. The collision is not head-on, and after the collision, stone 1 moves with a speed of $v_{1,f} = 0.610$ m/s in a direction 66.0° away from the initial line of motion. What are the speed and direction of stone 2?

▶ **FIGURE 9–8 Two curling stones undergo an elastic collision**

The speed of curling stone 2 after this collision can be determined using energy conservation; its direction of motion can be found using momentum conservation in either the x or the y direction.

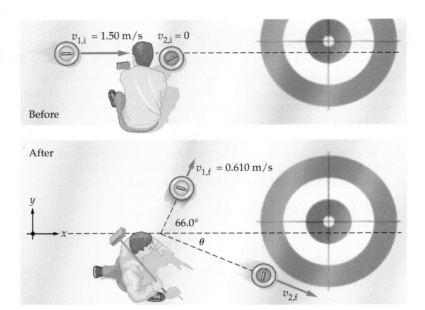

PROBLEM-SOLVING NOTE

Kinetic Energy in Elastic Collisions

Remember that in elastic collisions, by definition, the kinetic energy is conserved.

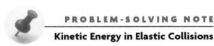

First, let's find the speed of stone 2. The easiest way to do this is to simply require that the final kinetic energy be equal to the initial kinetic energy. Initially, the kinetic energy is

$$K_i = \tfrac{1}{2}m_1v_{1,i}^2 = \tfrac{1}{2}(7.00 \text{ kg})(1.50 \text{ m/s})^2 = 7.88 \text{ J}$$

After the collision stone 1 has a speed of 0.610 m/s and stone 2 has the speed $v_{2,f}$. Hence, the final kinetic energy is

$$K_f = \tfrac{1}{2}m_1v_{1,f}^2 + \tfrac{1}{2}m_2v_{2,f}^2 = \tfrac{1}{2}(7.00 \text{ kg})(0.610 \text{ m/s})^2 + \tfrac{1}{2}m_2v_{2,f}^2$$
$$= 1.30 \text{ J} + \tfrac{1}{2}m_2v_{2,f}^2 = K_i$$

Solving for the speed of stone 2, we find

$$v_{2,f} = 1.37 \text{ m/s}$$

Next, we can find the direction of motion of stone 2 by requiring that the momentum be conserved. For example, initially there is no momentum in the y direction. This must be true after the collision as well. Hence, we have the following condition:

$$0 = m_1v_{1,f} \sin 66.0° - m_2v_{2,f} \sin \theta$$

Solving for the angle θ we find

$$\theta = 24.0°$$

As a final check, compare the initial and final x components of momentum. Initially, we have

$$p_{x,i} = m_1v_{1,i} = (7.00 \text{ kg})(1.50 \text{ m/s}) = 10.5 \text{ kg} \cdot \text{m/s}$$

Following the collision, the x component of momentum is

$$p_{x,f} = m_1 v_{1,f} \cos 66.0° + m_2 v_{2,f} \cos 24.0°$$

$$= (7.00 \text{ kg})(0.610 \text{ m/s}) \cos 66.0° + (7.00 \text{ kg})(1.37 \text{ m/s}) \cos 24.0°$$

$$= 10.5 \text{ kg} \cdot \text{m/s}$$

As expected, the momentum is unchanged.

EXAMPLE 9–7   **TWO FRUITS IN TWO DIMENSIONS: ANALYZING AN ELASTIC COLLISION**

Two astronauts on opposite ends of a spaceship are comparing lunches. One has an apple, the other has an orange. They decide to trade. Astronaut 1 tosses the 0.130-kg apple toward astronaut 2 with a speed of 1.11 m/s. The 0.160-kg orange is tossed from astronaut 2 to astronaut 1 with a speed of 1.21 m/s. Unfortunately, the fruits collide, sending the orange off with a speed of 1.16 m/s at an angle of 42.0° with respect to its original direction of motion. Find the final speed and direction of the apple, assuming an elastic collision. Give the apple's direction relative to its original direction of motion.

PICTURE THE PROBLEM
In our sketch we refer to the apple as object 1 and to the orange as object 2. We also choose the positive x direction to be in the initial direction of motion of the apple. We shall describe the "Before" and "After" sketches separately:

BEFORE
Initially, the apple moves in the positive x direction with a speed of 1.11 m/s, and the orange moves in the negative x direction with a speed of 1.21 m/s. There is no momentum in the y direction before the collision.

AFTER
After the collision, the orange moves with a speed of 1.16 m/s in a direction 42° below the negative x axis. As a result, the orange now has momentum in the negative y direction. To cancel this y momentum, the apple must move in a direction that is above the positive x axis, as indicated in the sketch.

STRATEGY
As described in the text, we first find the speed of the apple by demanding that the initial and final kinetic energies be the same. Next, we find the angle θ by conserving momentum in either the x or the y direction—the results are the same whichever direction is chosen.

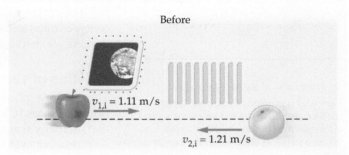

Before

$v_{1,i} = 1.11 \text{ m/s}$

$v_{2,i} = 1.21 \text{ m/s}$

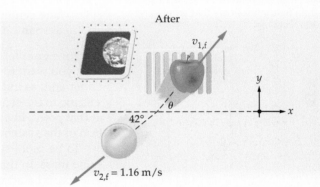

After

$v_{1,f}$

y

θ

x

42°

$v_{2,f} = 1.16 \text{ m/s}$

SOLUTION

1. Calculate the initial kinetic energy of the system:

$$K_i = \tfrac{1}{2} m_1 v_{1,i}^2 + \tfrac{1}{2} m_2 v_{2,i}^2$$
$$= \tfrac{1}{2}(0.130 \text{ kg})(1.11 \text{ m/s})^2 + \tfrac{1}{2}(0.160 \text{ kg})(1.21 \text{ m/s})^2$$
$$= 0.197 \text{ J}$$

2. Calculate the final kinetic energy of the system in terms of $v_{1,f}$:

$$K_f = \tfrac{1}{2} m_1 v_{1,f}^2 + \tfrac{1}{2} m_2 v_{2,f}^2$$
$$= \tfrac{1}{2}(0.130 \text{ kg}) v_{1,f}^2 + \tfrac{1}{2}(0.160 \text{ kg})(1.16 \text{ m/s})^2$$
$$= \tfrac{1}{2}(0.130 \text{ kg}) v_{1,f}^2 + 0.108 \text{ J}$$

3. Set $K_f = K_i$ to find $v_{1,f}$:

$$v_{1,f} = \sqrt{\frac{2(0.197 \text{ J} - 0.108 \text{ J})}{0.130 \text{ kg}}} = 1.17 \text{ m/s}$$

4. Set the final y component of momentum equal to zero to determine the angle, θ:

$$0 = m_1 v_{1,f} \sin\theta - m_2 v_{2,f} \sin 42.0°$$

Solve for $\sin\theta$:

$$\sin\theta = \frac{m_2 v_{2,f} \sin 42.0°}{m_1 v_{1,f}}$$

5. Substitute numerical values:

$$\sin\theta = \frac{(0.160 \text{ kg})(1.16 \text{ m/s}) \sin 42.0°}{(0.130 \text{ kg})(1.17 \text{ m/s})} = 0.817$$

$$\theta = \sin^{-1}(0.817) = 54.8°$$

CONTINUED ON NEXT PAGE

CONTINUED FROM PREVIOUS PAGE

INSIGHT
The x momentum equation gives the same value for θ, as expected.

PRACTICE PROBLEM
Suppose that after the collision the apple moves in the positive y direction with a speed of 1.27 m/s. What are the final speed and direction of the orange in this case? [**Answer:** The orange moves with a speed of 1.07 m/s in a direction of 74.7° below the negative x axis.]

Some related homework problems: Problem 41, Problem 94

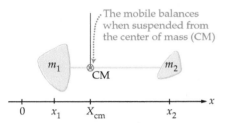

▲ **FIGURE 9–9 Balancing a mobile**
Consider a portion of a mobile with masses m_1 and m_2 at the locations x_1 and x_2, respectively. The object balances when a string is attached at the center of mass. Since the center of mass is closer to m_1 than to m_2, it follows that m_1 is greater than m_2.

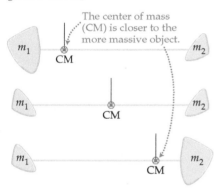

▲ **FIGURE 9–10 The center of mass of two objects**
The center of mass is closest to the larger mass, or equidistant between the masses if they are equal.

▲ Mobiles like *Myxomatose* by Alexander Calder illustrate the concept of center of mass with artistic flair. Each arm of the mobile is in balance because it is suspended at its center of mass.

9–7 Center of Mass

In this section we introduce the concept of the center of mass. We begin by defining its location for a given system of masses. Next we consider the motion of the center of mass and show how it is related to the net external force acting on the system. As we shall see, the center of mass plays a key role in the analysis of collisions.

Location of the Center of Mass

There is one point in any system of objects that has special significance—the **center of mass (CM).** One of the reasons the center of mass is so special is the fact that, in many ways, a system behaves as if all of its mass were concentrated there. As a result, a system can be balanced at its center of mass:

> The center of mass of a system of masses is the point where the system can be balanced in a uniform gravitational field.

For example, suppose you are making a mobile. At one stage in its construction, you want to balance a light rod with objects of mass m_1 and m_2 connected to either end, as indicated in **Figure 9–9**. To make the rod balance, you should attach a string to the center of mass of the system, just as if all its mass were concentrated at that point. In a sense, you can think of the center of mass as the "average" location of the system's mass.

To be more specific, suppose the two objects connected to the rod have the same mass. In this case the center of mass is at the midpoint of the rod, since this is where it balances. On the other hand, if one object has more mass than the other, the center of mass is closer to the heavier object, as indicated in **Figure 9–10**. In general, if a mass m_1 is on the x axis at the position x_1, and a mass m_2 is at the position x_2, as in Figure 9–9, the location of the center of mass, X_{cm}, is defined as the "weighted" average of the two positions:

Center of Mass for Two Objects
$$X_{cm} = \frac{m_1 x_1 + m_2 x_2}{m_1 + m_2} = \frac{m_1 x_1 + m_2 x_2}{M} \qquad 9\text{–}13$$

Note that we have used $M = m_1 + m_2$ for the total mass of the two objects, and that the two positions, x_1 and x_2, are multiplied—or weighted—by their respective masses.

To see that this definition of X_{cm} agrees with our expectations, consider first the case where the masses are equal: $m_1 = m_2 = m$. In this case, $M = m_1 + m_2 = 2m$, and $X_{cm} = (mx_1 + mx_2)/2m = \frac{1}{2}(x_1 + x_2)$. Thus, as expected, if two masses are equal, their center of mass is halfway between them. On the other hand, if m_1 is significantly greater than m_2, it follows that $M = m_1 + m_2 \sim m_1$ and $m_1 x_1 + m_2 x_2 \sim m_1 x_1$, since m_2 can be ignored in comparison to m_1. As a result, we find that $X_{cm} \sim m_1 x_1 / m_1 = x_1$; that is, the center of mass is essentially at the location of the extremely heavy mass, m_1. In general, as one mass becomes larger than the other, the center of mass moves closer to the larger mass.

EXERCISE 9–4

Suppose the masses in Figure 9–9 are separated by 0.500 m, and that $m_1 = 0.260$ kg and $m_2 = 0.170$ kg. What is the distance from m_1 to the center of mass of the system?

SOLUTION

Letting $x_1 = 0$ and $x_2 = 0.500$ m in Figure 9–9, we have

$$X_{cm} = \frac{m_1 x_1 + m_2 x_2}{m_1 + m_2} = \frac{(0.260 \text{ kg}) \cdot 0 + (0.170 \text{ kg})(0.500 \text{ m})}{0.260 \text{ kg} + 0.170 \text{ kg}} = 0.198 \text{ m}$$

Thus, the center of mass is closer to m_1 (the larger mass) than to m_2.

The center of mass is at the geometric center of a uniform object …

… even if there is no mass at that location.

▲ **FIGURE 9–11 Locating the center of mass**

In an object of continuous, uniform mass distribution, the center of mass is located at the geometric center of the object. In some cases, this means that the center of mass is not located within the object.

To extend the definition of X_{cm} to more general situations, first consider a system that contains many objects, not just two. In that case, X_{cm} is the sum of m times x for each object, divided by the total mass of the system, M. If, in addition, the objects in the system are not in a line, but are distributed in two dimensions, the center of mass will have both an x coordinate, X_{cm}, and a y coordinate, Y_{cm}. As one would expect, Y_{cm} is simply the sum of m times y for each object, divided by M. Thus, the x coordinate of the center of mass is

X Coordinate of the Center of Mass

$$X_{cm} = \frac{m_1 x_1 + m_2 x_2 + \cdots}{m_1 + m_2 + \cdots} = \frac{\sum mx}{M} \qquad \text{9–14}$$

Similarly, the y coordinate of the center of mass is

Y Coordinate of the Center of Mass

$$Y_{cm} = \frac{m_1 y_1 + m_2 y_2 + \cdots}{m_1 + m_2 + \cdots} = \frac{\sum my}{M} \qquad \text{9–15}$$

In systems with a continuous, uniform distribution of mass, the center of mass is at the geometric center of the object, as illustrated in **Figure 9–11**. Note that it is common for the center of mass to be located in a position where no mass exists, as in a life preserver, where the center of mass is precisely in the center of the hole.

EXAMPLE 9–8   CENTER OF MASS OF THE ARM

REAL-WORLD PHYSICS: BIO

A person's arm is held with the upper arm vertical, the lower arm and hand horizontal. **(a)** Find the center of mass of the arm in this configuration, given the following data: The upper arm has a mass of 2.5 kg and a center of mass 0.18 m above the elbow; the lower arm has a mass of 1.6 kg and a center of mass 0.12 m to the right of the elbow; the hand has a mass of 0.64 kg and a center of mass 0.40 m to the right of the elbow. **(b)** A 0.14-kg baseball is placed on the palm of the hand. If the diameter of the ball is 7.4 cm, find the center of mass of the arm–ball system.

PICTURE THE PROBLEM

We place the origin at the elbow, with the x and y axes pointing along the lower and upper arms, respectively. The center of mass of each of the three parts of the arm is indicated by an x; the center of mass of the entire arm is at the point labeled CM. The inset shows the baseball on the palm of the hand.

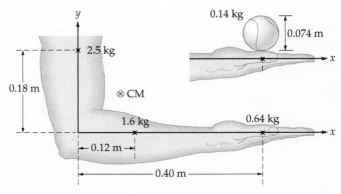

CONTINUED ON NEXT PAGE

CONTINUED FROM PREVIOUS PAGE

STRATEGY

a. Using the information given in the problem statement, we can treat the arm as a system of three point masses placed as follows: 2.5 kg at (0, 0.18 m); 1.6 kg at (0.12 m, 0); 0.64 kg at (0.40 m, 0). We substitute these masses and locations into Equations 9–14 and 9–15 to find the x and y coordinates of the center of mass, respectively.

b. Treat the center of mass found in part (a) as a point particle with a mass 2.5 kg + 1.6 kg + 0.64 kg = 4.7 kg at the location (X_{cm}, Y_{cm}). The baseball can be treated as a point particle of mass 0.14 kg at the location (0.40 m, (0.074)/2 m).

SOLUTION

Part (a)

1. Calculate the x coordinate of the center of mass:

$$X_{cm} = \frac{(2.5 \text{ kg})(0) + (1.6 \text{ kg})(0.12 \text{ m}) + (0.64 \text{ kg})(0.40 \text{ m})}{2.5 \text{ kg} + 1.6 \text{ kg} + 0.64 \text{ kg}}$$

$$= 0.095 \text{ m}$$

2. Do the same calculation for the y coordinate of the center of mass:

$$Y_{cm} = \frac{(2.5 \text{ kg})(0.18 \text{ m}) + (1.6 \text{ kg})(0) + (0.64 \text{ kg})(0)}{2.5 \text{ kg} + 1.6 \text{ kg} + 0.64 \text{ kg}}$$

$$= 0.095 \text{ m}$$

Part (b)

3. Calculate the new x coordinate of the center of mass:

$$X_{cm} = \frac{(4.7 \text{ kg})(0.095 \text{ m}) + (0.14 \text{ kg})(0.40 \text{ m})}{4.7 \text{ kg} + 0.14 \text{ kg}}$$

$$= 0.10 \text{ m}$$

4. Calculate the new y coordinate of the center of mass:

$$Y_{cm} = \frac{(4.7 \text{ kg})(0.095 \text{ m}) + (0.14 \text{ kg})(0.037 \text{ m})}{4.7 \text{ kg} + 0.14 \text{ kg}}$$

$$= 0.093 \text{ m}$$

INSIGHT

As is often the case, the center of mass of an arm held in this position is in a location where no mass exists—you might say the center of mass is having an out-of-body experience. This effect can sometimes be put to good use, as when the center of mass of a high jumper passes beneath the horizontal bar while the body passes above it. See Conceptual Question 18 for a photo of this technique in action, in the famous "Fosbury flop."

PRACTICE PROBLEM

Suppose the mass of the baseball is increased to 0.25 kg. **(a)** Does X_{cm} increase, decrease, or stay the same? **(b)** Does Y_{cm} increase, decrease, or stay the same? **(c)** Check your answers to parts (a) and (b) by finding the center of mass of the arm–ball system in this case.   [**Answer:** (a) increases; (b) decreases; (c) $X_{cm} = 0.11$ m, $Y_{cm} = 0.092$ m]

Some related homework problems: Problem 51, Problem 53

Motion of the Center of Mass

Another reason the center of mass is of such importance is that its motion often displays a remarkable simplicity when compared with the motion of other parts of a system. To analyze this motion, we consider both the velocity and the acceleration of the center of mass. Each of these quantities is defined in complete analogy with the definition of the center of mass itself.

For example, to find the velocity of the center of mass, we first multiply the mass of each object in a system, m, by its velocity, $\vec{v}$, to give $m_1\vec{v}_1, m_2\vec{v}_2$, and so on. Next, we add all these products together, $m_1\vec{v}_1 + m_2\vec{v}_2 + \cdots$, and divide by the total mass, $M = m_1 + m_2 + \cdots$. The result, by definition, is the velocity of the center of mass, $\vec{V}_{cm}$:

Velocity of the Center of Mass

$$\vec{V}_{cm} = \frac{m_1\vec{v}_1 + m_2\vec{v}_2 + \cdots}{m_1 + m_2 + \cdots} = \frac{\sum m\vec{v}}{M}$$

9–16

Comparing with Equation 9–14, we see that $\vec{V}_{cm}$ is the same as X_{cm} with each position x replaced with a velocity vector $\vec{v}$. In addition, note that the total mass of the system, M, times the velocity of the center of mass, $\vec{\mathbf{V}}_{cm}$, is simply the total momentum of the system:

$$M\vec{\mathbf{V}}_{cm} = m_1\vec{\mathbf{v}}_1 + m_2\vec{\mathbf{v}}_2 + \cdots = \vec{\mathbf{p}}_1 + \vec{\mathbf{p}}_2 + \cdots = \vec{\mathbf{p}}_{total}$$

To gain more information on how the center of mass moves, we next consider its acceleration, $\vec{\mathbf{A}}_{cm}$. As expected by analogy with $\vec{\mathbf{V}}_{cm}$, the acceleration of the center of mass is defined as follows:

Acceleration of the Center of Mass

$$\vec{\mathbf{A}}_{cm} = \frac{m_1\vec{\mathbf{a}}_1 + m_2\vec{\mathbf{a}}_2 + \cdots}{m_1 + m_2 + \cdots} = \frac{\sum m\vec{\mathbf{a}}}{M} \qquad 9\text{--}17$$

Note that the vector $\vec{\mathbf{A}}_{cm}$ contains terms like $m_1\vec{\mathbf{a}}_1$, $m_2\vec{\mathbf{a}}_2$, and so on, for each object in the system. From Newton's second law, however, we know that $m_1\vec{\mathbf{a}}_1$ is simply $\vec{\mathbf{F}}_1$, the net force acting on mass 1. The same conclusion applies to each of the masses. Therefore, we find that the total mass of the system, M, times the acceleration of the center of mass, $\vec{\mathbf{A}}_{cm}$, is simply the total force acting on the system:

$$M\vec{\mathbf{A}}_{cm} = m_1\vec{\mathbf{a}}_1 + m_2\vec{\mathbf{a}}_2 + \cdots = \vec{\mathbf{F}}_1 + \vec{\mathbf{F}}_2 + \cdots = \vec{\mathbf{F}}_{total}$$

Recall, however, that the total force acting on a system is the same as the net external force, $\vec{\mathbf{F}}_{net,ext}$, since the internal forces cancel. Therefore, $M\vec{\mathbf{A}}_{cm}$ is the net external force acting on the system:

Newton's Second Law for a System of Particles

$$M\vec{\mathbf{A}}_{cm} = \vec{\mathbf{F}}_{net,ext} \qquad 9\text{--}18$$

Zero Net External Force For systems in which $\vec{\mathbf{F}}_{net,ext}$ is zero, it follows that the acceleration of the center of mass is zero. Hence, if the center of mass is initially at rest, it remains at rest. Similarly, if the center of mass is moving initially, it continues to move with the same velocity. For example, in a collision between two air-track carts, the velocity of each cart changes as a result of the collision. The velocity of the center of mass of the two carts, however, is the same before and after the collision. We explore cases in which $\vec{\mathbf{F}}_{net,ext} = 0$ in the following Example and Active Example.

EXAMPLE 9-9 CRASH OF THE AIR CARTS

An air cart of mass m and speed v_0 moves toward a second, identical air cart that is at rest. When the carts collide they stick together and move as one. Find the velocity of the center of mass of this system **(a)** before and **(b)** after the carts collide.

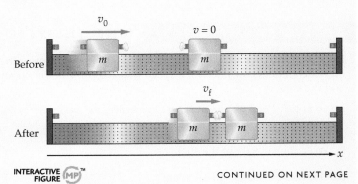

PICTURE THE PROBLEM
We choose the positive x direction to be the direction of motion of the incoming cart, whose initial speed is v_0. Note that the carts have wads of putty on their bumpers; this ensures that they stick together when they collide and thereafter move as a unit. Their final speed is v_f.

INTERACTIVE FIGURE (MP)™

CONTINUED ON NEXT PAGE

CONTINUED FROM PREVIOUS PAGE

STRATEGY

a. We can find the velocity of the center of mass by applying Equation 9–16 to the case of just two masses; $\vec{V}_{cm} = (m_1\vec{v}_1 + m_2\vec{v}_2)/M$. In this case, $\vec{v}_1 = v_0\hat{x}$, $\vec{v}_2 = 0$, and $m_1 = m_2 = m$.

b. After the collision the two masses have the same velocity, $\vec{v}_f = v_f\hat{x}$, which is given by momentum conservation (Equations 9–10 and 9–11). Hence, $\vec{V}_{cm} = (m_1\vec{v}_f + m_2\vec{v}_f)/M$.

SOLUTION

Part (a)

1. Use $\vec{V}_{cm} = (m_1\vec{v}_1 + m_2\vec{v}_2)/M$ to find the velocity of the center of mass before the collision:

$$\vec{V}_{cm} = \frac{(m_1\vec{v}_1 + m_2\vec{v}_2)}{m_1 + m_2} = \frac{(mv_0\hat{x} + m\cdot 0)}{m + m} = \tfrac{1}{2}v_0\hat{x}$$

Part (b)

2. Use momentum conservation in the x direction to find the speed of the carts after the collision:

$$mv_0 = mv_f + mv_f$$
$$v_f = \tfrac{1}{2}v_0$$

3. Calculate the velocity of the center of mass of the two carts after the collision:

$$\vec{V}_{cm} = \frac{(m_1\vec{v}_1 + m_2\vec{v}_2)}{m_1 + m_2} = \frac{(mv_f\hat{x} + mv_f\hat{x})}{m + m} = v_f\hat{x} = \tfrac{1}{2}v_0\hat{x}$$

INSIGHT

As expected, the velocity of each cart changes when they collide. On the other hand, the velocity of the center of mass is completely unaffected by the collision. This is illustrated to the right, where we show a sequence of equal-time snapshots of the system just before and just after the collision. First, we note that the incoming cart moves two distance units for every time interval until it collides with the second cart. From that point on, the two carts are locked together, and move one distance unit per time interval. In contrast, the center of mass (CM), which is centered between the two equal-mass carts, progresses uniformly throughout the sequence, advancing one unit of distance for each time interval.

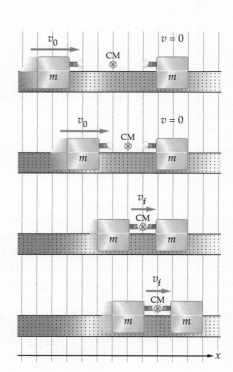

PRACTICE PROBLEM

If the mass of the cart that is moving initially is doubled to $2m$, does the velocity of the center of mass increase, decrease, or stay the same? Verify your answer by calculating the velocity of the center of mass in this case. [**Answer:** The velocity of the center of mass increases. We find that $\vec{V}_{cm} = (2v_0/3)\hat{x}$, both before and after the collision.]

Some related homework problems: Problem 54, Problem 57, Problem 81

ACTIVE EXAMPLE 9–3 FIND THE VELOCITY OF THE CENTER OF MASS

In Active Example 9–2 we found that as a 0.150-g bee runs with a speed of 3.80 cm/s in one direction, the 4.75-g popsicle stick on which it floats moves with a speed of 0.120 cm/s in the opposite direction. Find the velocity of the center of mass of the bee and the stick.

SOLUTION *(Test your understanding by performing the calculations indicated in each step.)*

1. Write the velocity of the bee:

$$\vec{v}_b = (3.80 \text{ cm/s})\hat{x}$$

2. Write the velocity of the stick:

$$\vec{v}_s = (-0.120 \text{ cm/s})\hat{x}$$

3. Use these velocities to calculate $\vec{V}_{cm}$:

$$\vec{V}_{cm} = (m_b\vec{v}_b + m_s\vec{v}_s)/(m_b + m_s) = 0$$

INSIGHT
$\vec{V}_{cm}$ is zero, and hence the center of mass stays at rest as the bee and the stick move. This is as expected, since the net external force is zero for this system, and the bee and stick started at rest initially.

YOUR TURN
If the bee increases its speed, will the velocity of the center of mass be nonzero?

(Answers to Your Turn problems are given in the back of the book.)

Nonzero Net External Force Recall that Newton's second law, as expressed in Equation 9–18, states that the acceleration of the center of mass is related to the net external force as follows:

$$M\vec{A}_{cm} = \vec{F}_{net,ext}$$

This is completely analogous to the relationship between the acceleration of an object of mass m and the net force $\vec{F}_{net}$ applied to it:

$$m\vec{a} = \vec{F}_{net}$$

Therefore, when $\vec{F}_{net,ext}$ is nonzero, we can conclude the following:

> The center of mass of a system accelerates precisely as if it were a point particle of mass M acted on by the force $\vec{F}_{net,ext}$.

For this reason, the motion of the center of mass can be quite simple compared to the motion of its constituent parts. For example, a hammer tossed into the air with a rotation is shown in **Figure 9–12**. The motion of one part of the hammer, the tip of the handle, let's say, follows a complicated path in space. On the other hand, the path of the center of mass is a simple parabola, precisely the same path that a point mass would follow.

Similarly, consider a fireworks rocket launched into the sky, as illustrated in **Figure 9–13**. The center of mass of the rocket follows a parabolic path, ignoring air resistance. At some point in its path it explodes into numerous individual pieces. The explosion is due to internal forces, however, which must therefore sum to zero. Hence, the net external force acting on the pieces of the rocket is the same before, during, and after the explosion. As a result, the center of mass has a constant downward acceleration and continues to follow the original parabolic path. It is only when an additional external force acts on the system, as when one of the pieces of the rocket hits the ground, that the path of the center of mass changes.

REAL-WORLD PHYSICS
An exploding rocket

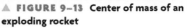
▲ **FIGURE 9–13 Center of mass of an exploding rocket**
A fireworks rocket follows a parabolic path, ignoring air resistance, until it explodes. After exploding, its center of mass continues on the same parabolic path until some of the fragments start to land.

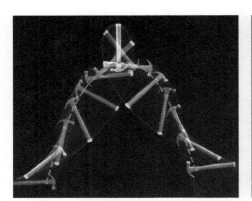 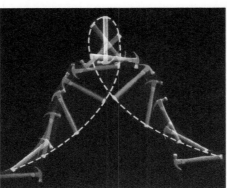

▲ **FIGURE 9–12 Simple Motion of the Center of Mass**
As this hammer flies through the air, its motion is quite complex. Some parts of the hammer follow wild trajectories with strange loops and turns. There is one point on the hammer, however, that travels on a smooth, simple parabolic path—the center of mass. The center of mass (red path on the left) travels as if all the mass of the hammer were concentrated there; other points (yellow path on the right) follow complex paths that depend on the detailed shape and rotation of the hammer.

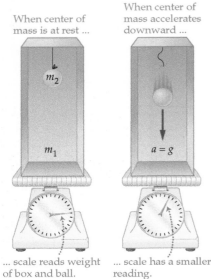

When center of mass is at rest ...

When center of mass accelerates downward ...

m_2

m_1

$a = g$

... scale reads weight of box and ball.

... scale has a smaller reading.

▲ **FIGURE 9–14 Weight and acceleration of the center of mass**

A box with a ball suspended from a string is weighed on a scale. The scale reads the weight of the box and the ball. When the string breaks and the ball falls with the acceleration of gravity, the scale reads only the weight of the box.

To see how to apply $M\vec{A}_{cm} = \vec{F}_{net,ext}$, consider the system shown in **Figure 9–14**. Here we see a box of mass m_1, inside of which is a ball of mass m_2 suspended from a light string. The entire system rests on a scale reading its weight. The scale exerts an upward force on the box of magnitude F_s. Initially, of course, $F_s = (m_1 + m_2)g$.

Now, suppose the string breaks, allowing the ball to fall with constant acceleration g toward the bottom of the box. What is the reading on the scale while the ball falls? We can guess that the answer should be simply m_1g, the weight of the box alone, but let's analyze the problem from the point of view of the center of mass.

Taking upward as the positive direction, the net external force acting on the box and the ball is

$$F_{net,ext} = F_s - m_1g - m_2g$$

The acceleration of the center of mass is

$$A_{cm} = \frac{m_1 \cdot 0 - m_2g}{M} = -\frac{m_2}{M}g$$

Setting $MA_{cm} = F_{net,ext}$ yields

$$MA_{cm} = M\left(-\frac{m_2}{M}\right)g = -m_2g = F_{net,ext} = F_s - m_1g - m_2g$$

Finally, canceling the term $-m_2g$ and solving for the weight read by the scale, F_s, we find, as expected, that

$$F_s = m_1g$$

*9–8 Systems with Changing Mass: Rocket Propulsion

We close this chapter by considering systems in which the mass can change. A rocket, for example, changes its mass as its engines operate because it ejects part of the fuel as it burns. The burning process is produced by internal forces, hence the total momentum of the rocket and its fuel remains constant.

Consider, then, a rocket in outer space, far from any large, massive objects. When the rocket's engine is fired, it expels a certain mass of fuel out the back with a speed v. If the mass of the ejected fuel is Δm, then the momentum of the ejected fuel has a magnitude equal to $(\Delta m)v$. Since the total momentum of the system must still be zero, the rocket acquires an equivalent amount of momentum in the forward direction. Hence, the momentum increase of the rocket is

$$\Delta p = (\Delta m)v$$

If the mass of fuel Δm is ejected in the time Δt, the force exerted on the rocket is the change in its momentum divided by the time interval (Equation 9–3); that is,

$$F = \frac{\Delta p}{\Delta t} = \left(\frac{\Delta m}{\Delta t}\right)v$$

The force exerted on the rocket by the ejected fuel is referred to as the **thrust**. Thus, the thrust of a rocket is

Thrust

$$\text{thrust} = \left(\frac{\Delta m}{\Delta t}\right)v$$

SI unit: newton, N

9–19

By $\Delta m / \Delta t$, we simply mean the amount of mass per time coming out of the rocket. For example, on the Saturn V rocket, the one used on the manned missions to the Moon, the main engines eject fuel at the rate of 13,800 kg/s with a speed of 2440 m/s. As a result, the thrust produced by these engines is

REAL-WORLD PHYSICS

Saturn V rocket

$$\text{thrust} = \left(\frac{\Delta m}{\Delta t} \right) v = (13{,}800 \text{ kg/s})(2440 \text{ m/s}) = 33.7 \times 10^6 \text{ N}$$

Since this is about 7.60 million pounds, and the weight of the rocket at liftoff is only 6.30 million pounds = 28.0×10^6 N, the thrust is sufficient to launch the rocket and give it an upward acceleration. In fact, the initial net force acting on the rocket is

$$F_{net} = \text{thrust} - mg = 33.7 \times 10^6 \text{ N} - 28.0 \times 10^6 \text{ N} = 5.7 \times 10^6 \text{ N}$$

The rocket's initial weight is $W = mg = 28.0 \times 10^6$ N, and hence its initial mass is $m = W/g = 2.85 \times 10^6$ kg. Therefore, the rocket lifts off with an upward acceleration of

$$a = \frac{F_{net}}{m} = \frac{5.7 \times 10^6 \text{ N}}{2.85 \times 10^6 \text{ kg}} = 2.0 \text{ m/s}^2 \approx 0.20g$$

This is a rather gentle acceleration. The gentleness lasts only a matter of seconds, however, since the decreasing mass of the rocket results in an increasing acceleration.

EXERCISE 9–5

The ascent stage of the lunar lander was designed to produce 15,500 N of thrust at liftoff. If the speed of the ejected fuel is 2500 m/s, what is the rate at which the fuel must be burned?

SOLUTION

The rate of fuel consumption is

$$\frac{\Delta m}{\Delta t} = \frac{\text{thrust}}{v} = \frac{15{,}500 \text{ N}}{2500 \text{ m/s}} = 6.2 \text{ kg/s}$$

A common question regarding rockets is: "How can a rocket accelerate in outer space when it has nothing to push against?" The answer is that rockets, in effect, push against their own fuel. The situation is similar to firing a gun. When a bullet is ejected by the internal combustion of the gunpowder, the person firing the gun feels a recoil. If the person were in space, or standing on a frictionless surface, the recoil would give him or her a speed in the direction opposite to the bullet. The burning of a rocket engine provides a continuous recoil, almost as if the rocket were firing a steady stream of bullets out the back.

▲ A rocket (top) makes use of the principle of conservation of momentum: mass (the products of explosive burning of fuel) is ejected at high speed in one direction, causing the rocket to move in the opposite direction. The same method of propulsion has evolved in octopi (bottom) and some other animals. When danger threatens and a quick escape is needed, powerful muscles contract to create a jet of water that propels the animal to safety. (A smokescreen of ink provides additional security.)

THE BIG PICTURE PUTTING PHYSICS IN CONTEXT

LOOKING BACK

We see in Section 9–1 that momentum is a vector quantity. Thus, the vector tools introduced in Chapter 3 again become important. In particular, we use vector components in our analysis of momentum conservation in Sections 9–5 and 9–6.

The connection between force (Chapter 5) and momentum is developed in Section 9–2. Newton's second law is central to impulse (Section 9–3), and Newton's third law is the key to conservation of momentum (Section 9–4).

Kinetic energy (Chapter 7) plays a key role in analyzing collisions, leading to the distinction between elastic and inelastic collisions. Potential energy (Chapter 8) enters into our analysis of the ballistic pendulum in Example 9–5.

In this chapter we see that force times the time over which it acts is related to a change in energy; in Chapters 7 and 8 we saw that force times the distance over which it acts leads to a change in energy.

LOOKING AHEAD

The concept of momentum is used again in Chapter 11, when we study the dynamics of rotational motion. In particular, we introduce angular momentum in Section 11–6 as an extension of the linear momentum introduced in this chapter.

Angular momentum is used in our analysis of planetary orbits, and especially in the discussion of Kepler's second law in Section 12–3.

The idea of angular momentum having only certain allowed values is one of the key assumptions of the Bohr model of the hydrogen atom, as we show in Section 31–3.

Linear momentum plays an important role in quantum physics. For example, the momentum of a particle is related to its de Broglie wavelength (Section 30–5) and to the uncertainty principle (Section 30–6).

CHAPTER SUMMARY

9–1 LINEAR MOMENTUM

The linear momentum of an object of mass m moving with velocity $\vec{\mathbf{v}}$ is

$$\vec{\mathbf{p}} = m\vec{\mathbf{v}} \qquad \text{9–1}$$

Momentum Is a Vector
Linear momentum is a vector, pointing in the same direction as the velocity vector, $\vec{\mathbf{v}}$.

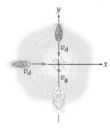

Momentum of a System of Objects
In a system of several objects, the total linear momentum is the vector sum of the individual momenta:

$$\vec{\mathbf{P}}_{\text{total}} = \vec{\mathbf{p}}_1 + \vec{\mathbf{p}}_2 + \vec{\mathbf{p}}_3 + \cdots \qquad \text{9–2}$$

9–2 MOMENTUM AND NEWTON'S SECOND LAW

In terms of momentum, Newton's second law is

$$\sum \vec{\mathbf{F}} = \frac{\Delta \vec{\mathbf{p}}}{\Delta t} \qquad \text{9–3}$$

That is, the net force acting on an object is equal to the rate of change of its momentum.

Constant Mass
For cases in which the mass is constant, Newton's second law reduces to the familiar form

$$\sum \vec{\mathbf{F}} = m\vec{\mathbf{a}} \qquad \text{9–4}$$

9–3 IMPULSE

The impulse delivered to an object by an average force $\vec{\mathbf{F}}_{\text{av}}$ acting for a time Δt is

$$\vec{\mathbf{I}} = \vec{\mathbf{F}}_{\text{av}} \Delta t \qquad \text{9–5}$$

Impulse Is a Vector
Impulse is a vector, proportional to the force vector.

Impulse and Momentum
By Newton's second law, the impulse delivered to an object is equal to the change in its momentum:

$$\vec{\mathbf{I}} = \vec{\mathbf{F}}_{\text{av}} \Delta t = \Delta \vec{\mathbf{p}} \qquad \text{9–6}$$

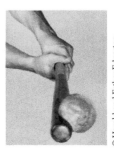

Magnitude of the Impulse and Force
Since an impulse is often delivered in a very short time interval, the average force can be large.

9–4 CONSERVATION OF LINEAR MOMENTUM

The momentum of an object is conserved (remains constant) if the net force acting on it is zero.

Internal/External Forces
In a system of objects, internal forces always sum to zero. The net force acting on a system of objects, then, is the sum of the external forces.

Conservation of Momentum in a System
In a system of objects, the net momentum is conserved if the net external force acting on the system is zero.

9–5 INELASTIC COLLISIONS

In collisions, we assume that external forces either sum to zero or are small enough to be ignored. Hence, momentum is conserved in all collisions.

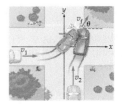

Inelastic Collision
In an inelastic collision, the final kinetic energy is different from the initial kinetic energy. The kinetic energy is usually less after a collision, but it can also be more than the initial kinetic energy.

Completely Inelastic Collision
A collision in which objects hit and stick together is referred to as completely inelastic.

Collisions in One Dimension
A one-dimensional collision occurs along a line, which we can choose to be the x axis. After the collision, the x component of momentum is equal to the x component of momentum before the collision; that is, the x component of momentum is conserved.

If two objects, of mass m_1 and m_2 and with initial velocities $v_{1,i}$ and $v_{2,i}$, collide and stick, the final velocity is

$$v_f = \frac{m_1 v_{1,i} + m_2 v_{2,i}}{m_1 + m_2}$$ 9–10

Collisions in Two Dimensions
In a two-dimensional collision, there are two separate momentum relations to be satisfied: (i) the x component of momentum is conserved, and (ii) the y component of momentum is conserved.

9–6 ELASTIC COLLISIONS

In collisions, we assume that external forces either sum to zero or are small enough to be ignored. Hence, momentum is conserved in all collisions.

Elastic Collision
In an elastic collision, the final kinetic energy is equal to the initial kinetic energy.

Collisions in One Dimension
In an elastic collision in one dimension where mass m_1 is moving with an initial velocity v_0, and mass m_2 is initially at rest, the velocities of the masses after the collision are:

$$v_{1,f} = \left(\frac{m_1 - m_2}{m_1 + m_2}\right) v_0$$

and

$$v_{2,f} = \left(\frac{2m_1}{m_1 + m_2}\right) v_0$$ 9–12

Collisions in Two Dimensions
In elastic collisions in two dimensions, three separate conditions are satisfied: (i) kinetic energy is conserved, (ii) the x component of momentum is conserved, and (iii) the y component of momentum is conserved.

9–7 CENTER OF MASS

The location of the center of mass of a two-dimensional system of objects is defined as follows:

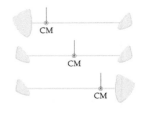

$$X_{cm} = \frac{m_1 x_1 + m_2 x_2 + \cdots}{m_1 + m_2 + \cdots} = \frac{\sum mx}{M} \qquad 9\text{–}14$$

and

$$Y_{cm} = \frac{m_1 y_1 + m_2 y_2 + \cdots}{m_1 + m_2 + \cdots} = \frac{\sum my}{M} \qquad 9\text{–}15$$

Motion of the Center of Mass

The velocity of the center of mass is

$$\vec{V}_{cm} = \frac{m_1 \vec{v}_1 + m_2 \vec{v}_2 + \cdots}{m_1 + m_2 + \cdots} = \frac{\sum m\vec{v}}{M} \qquad 9\text{–}16$$

Note that $M\vec{V}_{cm} = m_1\vec{v}_1 + m_2\vec{v}_2 + \cdots = \vec{p}_{total}$. If a system's momentum is conserved, its center of mass has constant velocity. Similarly, the acceleration of the center of mass is

$$\vec{A}_{cm} = \frac{m_1 \vec{a}_1 + m_2 \vec{a}_2 + \cdots}{m_1 + m_2 + \cdots} = \frac{\sum m\vec{a}}{M} \qquad 9\text{–}17$$

Note that $M\vec{A}_{cm} = m_1\vec{a}_1 + m_2\vec{a}_2 + \cdots = $ (net external force). That is,

$$M\vec{A}_{cm} = \vec{F}_{net,ext} \qquad 9\text{–}18$$

The center of mass accelerates as if the net external force acted on a single object of mass $M = m_1 + m_2 + \cdots$.

*9–8 SYSTEMS WITH CHANGING MASS: ROCKET PROPULSION

The mass of a rocket changes because its engines expel fuel when they are fired. If fuel is expelled with the speed v and at the rate $\Delta m / \Delta t$, the thrust experienced by the rocket is

$$\text{thrust} = \left(\frac{\Delta m}{\Delta t}\right)v \qquad 9\text{–}19$$

PROBLEM-SOLVING SUMMARY

Type of Calculation	Relevant Physical Concepts	Related Examples
Calculate the momentum of a system.	Each object in a system has a momentum of magnitude mv that points in the direction of its velocity vector. The total momentum is the vector sum of the individual momenta.	Example 9–1
Relate force and time to the impulse.	The impulse acting on a system is the average force, F_{av}, times the time interval, Δt.	Example 9–2 Active Example 9–1
Apply momentum conservation.	Momentum is conserved when the net external force acting on a system is zero.	Examples 9–3, 9–4, 9–5, 9–6, 9–7 Active Example 9–2
Find the center of mass.	The location of the center of mass is given by Equations 9–14 and 9–15.	Example 9–8
Determine the motion of the center of mass.	The center of mass moves the same as if it were a point particle of mass M (the total mass of the system) acted on by the net external force, $\vec{F}_{net,ext}$.	Example 9–9 Active Example 9–3

CONCEPTUAL QUESTIONS

For instructor-assigned homework, go to www.masteringphysics.com

(Answers to odd-numbered Conceptual Questions can be found in the back of the book.)

1. If you drop your keys, their momentum increases as they fall. Why is the momentum of the keys not conserved? Does this mean that the momentum of the universe increases as the keys fall? Explain.

2. By what factor does an object's kinetic energy change if its speed is doubled? By what factor does its momentum change?

3. A system of particles is known to have zero kinetic energy. What can you say about the momentum of the system?

4. A system of particles is known to have zero momentum. Does it follow that the kinetic energy of the system is also zero? Explain.

5. On a calm day you connect an electric fan to a battery on your sailboat and generate a breeze. Can the wind produced by the fan be used to power the sailboat? Explain.

6. In the previous question, can you use the wind generated by the fan to move a boat that has no sail? Explain why or why not.

7. Crash statistics show that it is safer to be riding in a heavy car in an accident than in a light car. Explain in terms of physical principles.

8. **(a)** As you approach a stoplight, you apply the brakes and bring your car to rest. What happened to your car's initial momentum? **(b)** When the light turns green, you accelerate until you reach cruising speed. What force was responsible for increasing your car's momentum?

9. An object at rest on a frictionless surface is struck by a second object. Is it possible for both objects to be at rest after the collision? Explain.

10. In the previous question, is it possible for one of the two objects to be at rest after the collision? Explain.

11. **(a)** Can two objects on a horizontal frictionless surface have a collision in which all the initial kinetic energy of the system is lost? Explain, and give a specific example if your answer is yes. **(b)** Can two such objects have a collision in which all the initial momentum of the system is lost? Explain, and give a specific example if your answer is yes.

12. Two cars collide at an intersection. If the cars do not stick together, can we conclude that their collision was elastic? Explain.

13. At the instant a bullet is fired from a gun, the bullet and the gun have equal and opposite momenta. Which object—the bullet or the gun—has the greater kinetic energy? Explain. How does your answer apply to the observation that it is safe to hold a gun while it is fired, whereas the bullet is deadly?

14. An hourglass is turned over, and the sand is allowed to pour from the upper half of the glass to the lower half. If the hourglass is resting on a scale, and the total mass of the hourglass and sand is M, describe the reading on the scale as the sand runs to the bottom.

15. In the classic movie *The Spirit of St. Louis*, Jimmy Stewart portrays Charles Lindbergh on his history-making transatlantic flight. Lindbergh is concerned about the weight of his fuel-laden airplane. As he flies over Newfoundland he notices a fly on the dashboard. Speaking to the fly, he wonders aloud, "Does the plane weigh less if you fly inside it as it's flying? Now that's an interesting question." What do you think?

16. A tall, slender drinking glass with a thin base is initially empty. **(a)** Where is the center of mass of the glass? **(b)** Suppose the glass is now filled slowly with water until it is completely full. Describe the position and motion of the center of mass during the filling process.

17. Lifting one foot into the air, you balance on the other foot. What can you say about the location of your center of mass?

18. In the "Fosbury flop" method of high jumping, named for the track and field star Dick Fosbury, an athlete's center of mass may pass under the bar while the athlete's body passes over the bar. Explain how this is possible.

The "Fosbury flop." (Conceptual Question 18)

PROBLEMS AND CONCEPTUAL EXERCISES

Note: Answers to odd-numbered Problems and Conceptual Exercises can be found in the back of the book. **IP** *denotes an integrated problem, with both conceptual and numerical parts;* **BIO** *identifies problems of biological or medical interest;* **CE** *indicates a conceptual exercise.* **Predict/Explain** *problems ask for two responses:* **(a)** *your prediction of a physical outcome, and* **(b)** *the best explanation among three provided. On all problems, red bullets (•, ••, •••) are used to indicate the level of difficulty.*

SECTION 9–1 LINEAR MOMENTUM

1. • Referring to Exercise 9–1, what speed must the baseball have if its momentum is to be equal in magnitude to that of the car? Give your result in miles per hour.

2. • Find the total momentum of the birds in Example 9–1 if the goose reverses direction.

3. •• A 26.2-kg dog is running northward at 2.70 m/s, while a 5.30-kg cat is running eastward at 3.04 m/s. Their 74.0-kg owner has the same momentum as the two pets taken together. Find the direction and magnitude of the owner's velocity.

4. •• **IP** Two air-track carts move toward one another on an air track. Cart 1 has a mass of 0.35 kg and a speed of 1.2 m/s. Cart 2 has a mass of 0.61 kg. **(a)** What speed must cart 2 have if the total momentum of the system is to be zero? **(b)** Since the momentum of the system is zero, does it follow that the kinetic energy of the system is also zero? **(c)** Verify your answer to part (b) by calculating the system's kinetic energy.

5. •• A 0.150-kg baseball is dropped from rest. If the magnitude of the baseball's momentum is 0.780 kg · m/s just before it lands on the ground, from what height was it dropped?

6. •• **IP** A 285-g ball falls vertically downward, hitting the floor with a speed of 2.5 m/s and rebounding upward with a speed of 2.0 m/s. **(a)** Find the magnitude of the change in the ball's momentum. **(b)** Find the change in the magnitude of the ball's momentum. **(c)** Which of the two quantities calculated in parts (a) and (b) is more directly related to the net force acting on the ball during its collision with the floor? Explain.

7. ••• Object 1 has a mass m_1 and a velocity $\vec{v}_1 = (2.80 \text{ m/s})\hat{x}$. Object 2 has a mass m_2 and a velocity $\vec{v}_2 = (3.10 \text{ m/s})\hat{y}$. The total momentum of these two objects has a magnitude of 17.6 kg·m/s and points in a direction 66.5° above the positive x axis. Find m_1 and m_2.

SECTION 9–3 IMPULSE

8. • **CE** Your car rolls slowly in a parking lot and bangs into the metal base of a light pole. In terms of safety, is it better for your collision with the light pole to be elastic, inelastic, or is the safety risk the same for either case? Explain.

9. • **CE Predict/Explain** A net force of 200 N acts on a 100-kg boulder, and a force of the same magnitude acts on a 100-g pebble. **(a)** Is the change of the boulder's momentum in one second greater than, less than, or equal to the change of the pebble's momentum in the same time period? **(b)** Choose the *best explanation* from among the following:
   I. The large mass of the boulder gives it the greater momentum.
   II. The force causes a much greater speed in the 100-g pebble, resulting in more momentum.
   III. Equal force means equal change in momentum for a given time.

10. • **CE Predict/Explain** Referring to the previous question, **(a)** is the change in the boulder's speed in one second greater than, less than, or equal to the change in speed of the pebble in the same time period? **(b)** Choose the *best explanation* from among the following:
   I. The large mass of the boulder results in a small acceleration.
   II. The same force results in the same change in speed for a given time.
   III. Once the boulder gets moving it is harder to stop than the pebble.

11. • **CE Predict/Explain** A friend tosses a ball of mass m to you with a speed v. When you catch the ball, you feel a noticeable sting in your hand, due to the force required to stop the ball. **(a)** If you now catch a second ball, with a mass $2m$ and speed $v/2$, is the sting you feel greater than, less than, or equal to the sting you felt when you caught the first ball? The time required to stop the two balls is the same. **(b)** Choose the *best explanation* from among the following:
   I. The second ball has less kinetic energy, since kinetic energy depends on v^2, and hence it produces less sting.
   II. The two balls have the same momentum, and hence they produce the same sting.
   III. The second ball has more mass, and hence it produces the greater sting.

12. • **CE** Force A has a magnitude F and acts for the time Δt, force B has a magnitude $2F$ and acts for the time $\Delta t/3$, force C has a magnitude $5F$ and acts for the time $\Delta t/10$, and force D has a magnitude $10F$ and acts for the time $\Delta t/100$. Rank these forces in order of increasing impulse. Indicate ties where appropriate.

13. • Find the magnitude of the impulse delivered to a soccer ball when a player kicks it with a force of 1250 N. Assume that the player's foot is in contact with the ball for 5.95×10^{-3} s.

14. • In a typical golf swing, the club is in contact with the ball for about 0.0010 s. If the 45-g ball acquires a speed of 67 m/s, estimate the magnitude of the force exerted by the club on the ball.

15. • A 0.50-kg croquet ball is initially at rest on the grass. When the ball is struck by a mallet, the average force exerted on it is 230 N. If the ball's speed after being struck is 3.2 m/s, how long was the mallet in contact with the ball?

16. • When spiking a volleyball, a player changes the velocity of the ball from 4.2 m/s to −24 m/s along a certain direction. If the impulse delivered to the ball by the player is −9.3 kg·m/s, what is the mass of the volleyball?

17. •• **IP** A 15.0-g marble is dropped from rest onto the floor 1.44 m below. **(a)** If the marble bounces straight upward to a height of 0.640 m, what are the magnitude and direction of the impulse delivered to the marble by the floor? **(b)** If the marble had bounced to a greater height, would the impulse delivered to it have been greater or less than the impulse found in part (a)? Explain.

18. •• To make a bounce pass, a player throws a 0.60-kg basketball toward the floor. The ball hits the floor with a speed of 5.4 m/s at an angle of 65° to the vertical. If the ball rebounds with the same speed and angle, what was the impulse delivered to it by the floor?

19. •• **IP** A 0.14-kg baseball moves toward home plate with a velocity $\vec{v}_i = (-36 \text{ m/s})\hat{x}$. After striking the bat, the ball moves vertically upward with a velocity $\vec{v}_f = (18 \text{ m/s})\hat{y}$. **(a)** Find the direction and magnitude of the impulse delivered to the ball by the bat. Assume that the ball and bat are in contact for 1.5 ms. **(b)** How would your answer to part (a) change if the mass of the ball were doubled? **(c)** How would your answer to part (a) change if the mass of the bat were doubled instead?

20. •• A player bounces a 0.43-kg soccer ball off her head, changing the velocity of the ball from $\vec{v}_i = (8.8 \text{ m/s})\hat{x} + (-2.3 \text{ m/s})\hat{y}$ to $\vec{v}_f = (5.2 \text{ m/s})\hat{x} + (3.7 \text{ m/s})\hat{y}$. If the ball is in contact with the player's head for 6.7 ms, what are **(a)** the direction and **(b)** the magnitude of the impulse delivered to the ball?

SECTION 9–4 CONSERVATION OF LINEAR MOMENTUM

21. • In a situation similar to Example 9–3, suppose the speeds of the two canoes after they are pushed apart are 0.58 m/s for canoe 1 and 0.42 m/s for canoe 2. If the mass of canoe 1 is 320 kg, what is the mass of canoe 2?

22. • Two ice skaters stand at rest in the center of an ice rink. When they push off against one another the 45-kg skater acquires a speed of 0.62 m/s. If the speed of the other skater is 0.89 m/s, what is this skater's mass?

23. • Suppose the bee in Active Example 9–2 has a mass of 0.175 g. If the bee walks with a speed of 1.41 cm/s relative to the still water, what is the speed of the 4.75-g stick relative to the water?

24. •• An object initially at rest breaks into two pieces as the result of an explosion. One piece has twice the kinetic energy of the other piece. What is the ratio of the masses of the two pieces? Which piece has the larger mass?

25. •• A 92-kg astronaut and a 1200-kg satellite are at rest relative to the space shuttle. The astronaut pushes on the satellite, giving it a speed of 0.14 m/s directly away from the shuttle. Seven and a half seconds later the astronaut comes into contact with the shuttle. What was the initial distance from the shuttle to the astronaut?

26. •• **IP** An 85-kg lumberjack stands at one end of a 380-kg floating log, as shown in **Figure 9–15**. Both the log and the lumberjack are at rest initially. **(a)** If the lumberjack now trots toward the other end of the log with a speed of 2.7 m/s relative to the log, what is the lumberjack's speed relative to the shore? Ignore friction between the log and the water. **(b)** If the mass of the log had been greater, would the lumberjack's speed relative to the shore be greater than, less than, or the same as in part (a)? Explain. **(c)** Check your answer to part (b) by calculating the lumberjack's speed relative to the shore for the case of a 450-kg log.

$v = 2.7$ m/s

▲ **FIGURE 9–15** Problem 26

27. ••• A plate drops onto a smooth floor and shatters into three pieces of equal mass. Two of the pieces go off with equal speeds v at right angles to one another. Find the speed and direction of the third piece.

SECTION 9–5 INELASTIC COLLISIONS

28. • A cart of mass m moves with a speed v on a frictionless air track and collides with an identical cart that is stationary. If the two carts stick together after the collision, what is the final kinetic energy of the system?

29. • Suppose the car in Example 9–6 has an initial speed of 20.0 m/s and that the direction of the wreckage after the collision is 40.0° above the x axis. Find the initial speed of the minivan and the final speed of the wreckage.

30. • Two 72.0-kg hockey players skating at 5.45 m/s collide and stick together. If the angle between their initial directions was 115°, what is their speed after the collision?

31. •• IP (a) Referring to Exercise 9–2, is the final kinetic energy of the car and truck together greater than, less than, or equal to the sum of the initial kinetic energies of the car and truck separately? Explain. (b) Verify your answer to part (a) by calculating the initial and final kinetic energies of the system.

32. •• IP A bullet with a mass of 4.0 g and a speed of 650 m/s is fired at a block of wood with a mass of 0.095 kg. The block rests on a frictionless surface, and is thin enough that the bullet passes completely through it. Immediately after the bullet exits the block, the speed of the block is 23 m/s. (a) What is the speed of the bullet when it exits the block? (b) Is the final kinetic energy of this system equal to, less than, or greater than the initial kinetic energy? Explain. (c) Verify your answer to part (b) by calculating the initial and final kinetic energies of the system.

33. •• IP A 0.420-kg block of wood hangs from the ceiling by a string, and a 0.0750-kg wad of putty is thrown straight upward, striking the bottom of the block with a speed of 5.74 m/s. The wad of putty sticks to the block. (a) Is the mechanical energy of this system conserved? (b) How high does the putty–block system rise above the original position of the block?

34. •• A 0.430-kg block is attached to a horizontal spring that is at its equilibrium length, and whose force constant is 20.0 N/m. The block rests on a frictionless surface. A 0.0500-kg wad of putty is thrown horizontally at the block, hitting it with a speed of 2.30 m/s and sticking. How far does the putty–block system compress the spring?

35. ••• Two objects moving with a speed v travel in opposite directions in a straight line. The objects stick together when they collide, and move with a speed of $v/4$ after the collision. (a) What is the ratio of the final kinetic energy of the system to the initial kinetic energy? (b) What is the ratio of the mass of the more massive object to the mass of the less massive object?

SECTION 9–6 ELASTIC COLLISIONS

36. • The collision between a hammer and a nail can be considered to be approximately elastic. Calculate the kinetic energy acquired by a 12-g nail when it is struck by a 550-g hammer moving with an initial speed of 4.5 m/s.

37. • A 732-kg car stopped at an intersection is rear-ended by a 1720-kg truck moving with a speed of 15.5 m/s. If the car was in neutral and its brakes were off, so that the collision is approximately elastic, find the final speed of both vehicles after the collision.

38. • CE Suppose you throw a rubber ball at an elephant that is charging directly at you (not a good idea). When the ball bounces back toward you, is its speed greater than, less than, or equal to the speed with which you threw it? Explain.

39. •• IP A charging bull elephant with a mass of 5240 kg comes directly toward you with a speed of 4.55 m/s. You toss a 0.150-kg rubber ball at the elephant with a speed of 7.81 m/s. (a) When the ball bounces back toward you, what is its speed? (b) How do you account for the fact that the ball's kinetic energy has increased?

40. •• **Moderating a Neutron** In a nuclear reactor, neutrons released by nuclear fission must be slowed down before they can trigger additional reactions in other nuclei. To see what sort of material is most effective in slowing (or moderating) a neutron, calculate the ratio of a neutron's final kinetic energy to its initial kinetic energy, K_f/K_i, for a head-on elastic collision with each of the following stationary target particles. (Note: The mass of a neutron is $m = 1.009$ u, where the atomic mass unit, u, is defined as follows: 1 u $= 1.66 \times 10^{-27}$ kg.) (a) An electron ($M = 5.49 \times 10^{-4}$ u). (b) A proton ($M = 1.007$ u). (c) The nucleus of a lead atom ($M = 207.2$ u).

41. •• In the apple-orange collision in Example 9–7, suppose the final velocity of the orange is 1.03 m/s in the negative y direction. What are the final speed and direction of the apple in this case?

42. •• The three air carts shown in **Figure 9–16** have masses, reading from left to right, of $4m$, $2m$, and m, respectively. The most massive cart has an initial speed of v_0; the other two carts are at rest initially. All carts are equipped with spring bumpers that give elastic collisions. (a) Find the final speed of each cart. (b) Verify that the final kinetic energy of the system is equal to the initial kinetic energy. (Assume the air track is long enough to accommodate all collisions.)

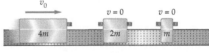

v_0

$v = 0$ $v = 0$

4m   2m   m

▲ **FIGURE 9–16** Problem 42

43. •• In this problem we show that when one ball is pulled to the left in the photo on page 275, only a single ball recoils to the right—under ideal elastic-collision conditions. To begin, suppose that each ball has a mass m, and that the ball coming in from the left strikes the other balls with a speed v_0. Now, consider the hypothetical case of two balls recoiling to the right. Determine the speed the two recoiling balls must have in order to satisfy (a) momentum conservation and (b) energy conservation. Since these speeds are not the same, it follows that momentum and energy cannot be conserved simultaneously with a recoil of two balls.

SECTION 9–7 CENTER OF MASS

44. • CE Predict/Explain A stalactite in a cave has drops of water falling from it to the cave floor below. The drops are equally

spaced in time and come in rapid succession, so that at any given moment there are many drops in midair. **(a)** Is the center of mass of the midair drops higher than, lower than, or equal to the halfway distance between the tip of the stalactite and the cave floor? **(b)** Choose the *best explanation* from among the following:
  I. The drops bunch up as they near the floor of the cave.
  II. The drops are equally spaced as they fall, since they are released at equal times.
  III. Though equally spaced in time, the drops are closer together higher up.

45. • Find the x coordinate of the center of mass of the bricks shown in **Figure 9–17**.

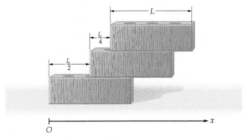

▲ **FIGURE 9–17** Problem 45

46. • You are holding a shopping basket at the grocery store with two 0.56-kg cartons of cereal at the left end of the basket. The basket is 0.71 m long. Where should you place a 1.8-kg half gallon of milk, relative to the left end of the basket, so that the center of mass of your groceries is at the center of the basket?

47. • **Earth–Moon Center of Mass** The Earth has a mass of 5.98×10^{24} kg, the Moon has a mass of 7.35×10^{22} kg, and their center-to-center distance is 3.85×10^{8} m. How far from the center of the Earth is the Earth–Moon center of mass? Is the Earth–Moon center of mass above or below the surface of the Earth? By what distance? (As the Earth and Moon orbit one another, their centers orbit about their common center of mass.)

48. •• **CE Predict/Explain** A piece of sheet metal of mass M is cut into the shape of a right triangle, as shown in **Figure 9–18**. A vertical dashed line is drawn on the sheet at the point where the mass to the left of the line ($M/2$) is equal to the mass to the right of the line (also $M/2$). The sheet is now placed on a fulcrum just under the dashed line and released from rest. **(a)** Does the metal sheet remain level, tip to the left, or tip to the right? **(b)** Choose the *best explanation* from among the following:
  I. Equal mass on either side will keep the metal sheet level.
  II. The metal sheet extends for a greater distance to the left, which shifts the center of mass to the left of the dashed line.
  III. The center of mass is to the right of the dashed line because the metal sheet is thicker there.

▲ **FIGURE 9–18** Problem 48

49. •• **CE** A pencil standing upright on its eraser end falls over and lands on a table. As the pencil falls, its eraser does not slip. The following questions refer to the contact force exerted on the pencil by the table. Let the positive x direction be in the direction the pencil falls, and the positive y direction be vertically

upward. **(a)** During the pencil's fall, is the x component of the contact force positive, negative, or zero? Explain. **(b)** Is the y component of the contact force greater than, less than, or equal to the weight of the pencil? Explain.

50. •• A cardboard box is in the shape of a cube with each side of length L. If the top of the box is missing, where is the center of mass of the open box? Give your answer relative to the geometric center of the box.

51. •• The location of the center of mass of the partially eaten, 12-inch-diameter pizza shown in **Figure 9–19** is $X_{cm} = -1.4$ in. and $Y_{cm} = -1.4$ in. Assuming each quadrant of the pizza to be the same, find the center of mass of the uneaten pizza above the x axis (that is, the portion of the pizza in the second quadrant).

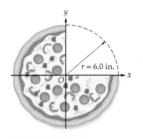

▲ **FIGURE 9–19**
Problem 51

52. •• **The Center of Mass of Sulfur Dioxide** Sulfur dioxide (SO_2) consists of two oxygen atoms (each of mass 16 u, where u is defined in Problem 40) and a single sulfur atom (of mass 32 u). The center-to-center distance between the sulfur atom and either of the oxygen atoms is 0.143 nm, and the angle formed by the three atoms is 120°, as shown in **Figure 9–20**. Find the x and y coordinates of the center of mass of this molecule.

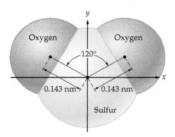

▲ **FIGURE 9–20** Problem 52

53. •• **IP** Three uniform metersticks, each of mass m, are placed on the floor as follows: stick 1 lies along the y axis from $y = 0$ to $y = 1.0$ m, stick 2 lies along the x axis from $x = 0$ to $x = 1.0$ m, stick 3 lies along the x axis from $x = 1.0$ m to $x = 2.0$ m. **(a)** Find the location of the center of mass of the metersticks. **(b)** How would the location of the center of mass be affected if the mass of the metersticks were doubled?

54. •• A 0.726-kg rope 2.00 meters long lies on a floor. You grasp one end of the rope and begin lifting it upward with a constant speed of 0.710 m/s. Find the position and velocity of the rope's center of mass from the time you begin lifting the rope to the time the last piece of rope lifts off the floor. Plot your results. (Assume the rope occupies negligible volume directly below the point where it is being lifted.)

55. •• Repeat the previous problem, this time lowering the rope onto a floor instead of lifting it.

56. •• Consider the system shown in **Figure 9–21**. Assume that after the string breaks the ball falls through the liquid with constant speed. If the mass of the bucket *and* the liquid is 1.20 kg, and the

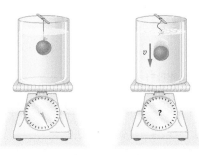

▲ **FIGURE 9–21** Problems 56 and 79

mass of the ball is 0.150 kg, what is the reading on the scale **(a)** before and **(b)** after the string breaks?

57. ••• A metal block of mass m is attached to the ceiling by a spring. Connected to the bottom of this block is a string that supports a second block of the same mass m, as shown in **Figure 9–22**. The string connecting the two blocks is now cut. **(a)** What is the net force acting on the two-block system immediately after the string is cut? **(b)** What is the acceleration of the center of mass of the two-block system immediately after the string is cut?

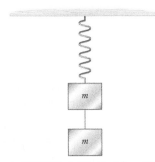

▲ **FIGURE 9–22** Problem 57

*SECTION 9–8 SYSTEMS WITH CHANGING MASS: ROCKET PROPULSION

58. • **Helicopter Thrust** During a rescue operation, a 5300-kg helicopter hovers above a fixed point. The helicopter blades send air downward with a speed of 62 m/s. What mass of air must pass through the blades every second to produce enough thrust for the helicopter to hover?

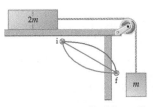

The powerful downdraft from this helicopter's blades creates a circular wave pattern in the water below. The thrust resulting from this downdraft is sufficient to support the weight of the helicopter. (Problem 58)

59. • **Rocks for a Rocket Engine** A child sits in a wagon with a pile of 0.65-kg rocks. If she can throw each rock with a speed of 11 m/s relative to the ground, causing the wagon to move, how many rocks must she throw per minute to maintain a constant average speed against a 3.4-N force of friction?

60. • A 57.8-kg person holding two 0.880-kg bricks stands on a 2.10-kg skateboard. Initially, the skateboard and the person are at rest. The person now throws the two bricks at the same time so that their speed relative to the person is 17.0 m/s. What is the recoil speed of the person and the skateboard relative to the ground, assuming the skateboard moves without friction?

61. •• In the previous problem, calculate the final speed of the person and the skateboard relative to the ground if the person throws the bricks one at a time. Assume that each brick is thrown with a speed of 17.0 m/s relative to the person.

62. •• A 0.540-kg bucket rests on a scale. Into this bucket you pour sand at the constant rate of 56.0 g/s. If the sand lands in the bucket with a speed of 3.20 m/s, **(a)** what is the reading of the scale when there is 0.750 kg of sand in the bucket? **(b)** What is the weight of the bucket and the 0.750 kg of sand?

63. •• **IP** Holding a long rope by its upper end, you lower it onto a scale. The rope has a mass of 0.13 kg per meter of length, and is lowered onto the scale at the constant rate of 1.4 m/s. **(a)** Calculate the thrust exerted by the rope as it lands on the scale. **(b)** At the instant when the amount of rope at rest on the scale has a weight of 2.5 N, does the scale read 2.5 N, more than 2.5 N, or less than 2.5 N? Explain. **(c)** Check your answer to part (b) by calculating the reading on the scale at this time.

GENERAL PROBLEMS

64. • **CE** Object A has a mass m, object B has a mass $2m$, and object C has a mass $m/2$. Rank these objects in order of increasing kinetic energy, given that they all have the same momentum. Indicate ties where appropriate.

65. • **CE** Object A has a mass m, object B has a mass $4m$, and object C has a mass $m/4$. Rank these objects in order of increasing momentum, given that they all have the same kinetic energy. Indicate ties where appropriate.

66. • **CE Predict/Explain** A block of wood is struck by a bullet. **(a)** Is the block more likely to be knocked over if the bullet is metal and embeds itself in the wood, or if the bullet is rubber and bounces off the wood? **(b)** Choose the *best explanation* from among the following:
   I. The change in momentum when a bullet rebounds is larger than when it is brought to rest.
   II. The metal bullet does more damage to the block.
   III. Since the rubber bullet bounces off, it has little effect.

67. • **CE** A juggler performs a series of tricks with three bowling balls while standing on a bathroom scale. Is the average reading of the scale greater than, less than, or equal to the weight of the juggler plus the weight of the three balls? Explain.

68. • A 72.5-kg tourist climbs the stairs to the top of the Washington Monument, which is 555 ft high. How far does the Earth move in the opposite direction as the tourist climbs?

69. •• **CE Predict/Explain** **Figure 9–23** shows a block of mass $2m$ at rest on a horizontal, frictionless table. Attached to this block by a string that passes over a pulley is a second block, with a mass m.

▲ **FIGURE 9–23** Problem 69

The initial position of the center of mass of the blocks is indicated by the point i. The blocks are now released and allowed to accelerate; a short time later their center of mass is at the point f. **(a)** Did the center of mass follow the red path, the green path, or the blue path? **(b)** Choose the *best explanation* from among the following:

I. The center of mass must always be closer to the $2m$ block than to the m block.

II. The center of mass starts at rest, and moves in a straight line in the direction of the net force.

III. The masses are accelerating, which implies parabolic motion.

70. •• A car moving with an initial speed v collides with a second stationary car that is one-half as massive. After the collision the first car moves in the same direction as before with a speed $v/3$. **(a)** Find the final speed of the second car. **(b)** Is this collision elastic or inelastic?

71. •• A 1.35-kg block of wood sits at the edge of a table, 0.782 m above the floor. A 0.0105-kg bullet moving horizontally with a speed of 715 m/s embeds itself within the block. What horizontal distance does the block cover before hitting the ground?

72. •• **IP** The carton of eggs shown in **Figure 9–24** is filled with a dozen eggs, each of mass m. Initially, the center of mass of the eggs is at the center of the carton. **(a)** Does the location of the center of mass of the eggs change more if egg 1 is removed or if egg 2 is removed? Explain. **(b)** Find the center of mass of the eggs when egg 1 is removed. **(c)** Find the center of mass of the eggs if egg 2 is removed instead.

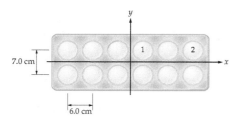

▲ **FIGURE 9–24** Problem 72

73. •• **The Force of a Storm** During a severe storm in Palm Beach, FL, on January 2, 1999, 31 inches of rain fell in a period of nine hours. Assuming that the raindrops hit the ground with a speed of 10 m/s, estimate the average upward force exerted by one square meter of ground to stop the falling raindrops during the storm. (*Note:* One cubic meter of water has a mass of 1000 kg.)

74. •• An apple that weighs 2.7 N falls vertically downward from rest for 1.4 s. **(a)** What is the change in the apple's momentum per second? **(b)** What is the total change in its momentum during the 1.4-second fall?

75. •• To balance a 35.5-kg automobile tire and wheel, a mechanic must place a 50.2-g lead weight 25.0 cm from the center of the wheel. When the wheel is balanced, its center of mass is exactly at the center of the wheel. How far from the center of the wheel was its center of mass before the lead weight was added?

76. •• A hoop of mass M and radius R rests on a smooth, level surface. The inside of the hoop has ridges on either side, so that it forms a track on which a ball can roll, as indicated in **Figure 9–25**. If a ball of mass $2M$ and radius $r = R/4$ is released as shown, the system rocks back and forth until it comes to rest with the ball at the bottom of the hoop. When the ball comes to rest, what is the x coordinate of its center?

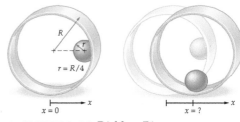

▲ **FIGURE 9–25** Problem 76

77. •• **IP** A 63-kg canoeist stands in the middle of her 22-kg canoe. The canoe is 3.0 m long, and the end that is closest to land is 2.5 m from the shore. The canoeist now walks toward the shore until she comes to the end of the canoe. **(a)** When the canoeist stops at the end of her canoe, is her distance from the shore equal to, greater than, or less than 2.5 m? Explain. **(b)** Verify your answer to part (a) by calculating the distance from the canoeist to shore.

78. •• In the previous problem, suppose the canoeist is 3.4 m from shore when she reaches the end of her canoe. What is the canoe's mass?

79. •• Referring to Problem 56, find the reading on the scale **(a)** before and **(b)** after the string breaks, assuming the ball falls through the liquid with an acceleration equal to $0.250g$.

80. •• A young hockey player stands at rest on the ice holding a 1.3-kg helmet. The player tosses the helmet with a speed of 6.5 m/s in a direction 11° above the horizontal, and recoils with a speed of 0.25 m/s. Find the mass of the hockey player.

81. •• Suppose the air carts in Example 9–9 are both moving to the right initially. The cart to the left has a mass m and an initial speed v_0; the cart to the right has an initial speed $v_0/2$. If the center of mass of this system moves to the right with a speed $2v_0/3$, what is the mass of the cart on the right?

82. •• A long, uniform rope with a mass of 0.135 kg per meter lies on the ground. You grab one end of the rope and lift it at the constant rate of 1.13 m/s. Calculate the upward force you must exert at the moment when the top end of the rope is 0.525 m above the ground.

83. •• **The Center of Mass of Water** Find the center of mass of a water molecule, referring to **Figure 9–26** for the relevant angles and distances. The mass of a hydrogen atom is 1.0 u, and the mass of an oxygen atom is 16 u, where u is the atomic mass unit (see Problem 40). Use the center of the oxygen atom as the origin of your coordinate system.

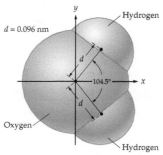

▲ **FIGURE 9–26** Problem 83

84. •• The three air carts shown in **Figure 9–27** have masses, reading from left to right, of m, $2m$, and $4m$, respectively. Initially, the cart on the right is at rest, whereas the other two carts are moving to the right with a speed v_0. All carts are equipped with putty bumpers that give completely inelastic collisions. **(a)** Find

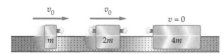

▲ **FIGURE 9–27** Problem 84

the final speed of the carts. **(b)** Calculate the ratio of the final kinetic energy of the system to the initial kinetic energy.

85. •• **IP** A fireworks rocket is launched vertically into the night sky with an initial speed of 44.2 m/s. The rocket coasts after being launched, then explodes and breaks into two pieces of equal mass 2.50 s later. **(a)** If each piece follows a trajectory that is initially at 45.0° to the vertical, what was their speed immediately after the explosion? **(b)** What is the velocity of the rocket's center of mass before and after the explosion? **(c)** What is the acceleration of the rocket's center of mass before and after the explosion?

86. •• **IP** The total momentum of two cars approaching an intersection is $\vec{p}_{total} = (15{,}000 \text{ kg} \cdot \text{m/s})\hat{x} + (2100 \text{ kg} \cdot \text{m/s})\hat{y}$. **(a)** If the momentum of car 1 is $\vec{p}_1 = (11{,}000 \text{ kg} \cdot \text{m/s})\hat{x} + (-370 \text{ kg} \cdot \text{m/s})\hat{y}$, what is the momentum of car 2? **(b)** Does your answer to part (a) depend on which car is closer to the intersection? Explain.

87. •• **Unlimited Overhang** Four identical textbooks, each of length L, are stacked near the edge of a table, as shown in Figure 9–28. The books are stacked in such a way that the distance they overhang the edge of the table, d, is maximized. Find the maximum overhang distance d in terms of L. In particular, show that $d > L$; that is, the top book is completely to the right of the table edge. (In principle, the overhang distance d can be made as large as desired simply by increasing the number of books in the stack.)

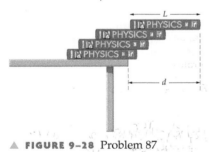

▲ **FIGURE 9–28** Problem 87

88. ••• Consider a one-dimensional, head-on elastic collision. One object has a mass m_1 and an initial velocity v_1; the other has a mass m_2 and an initial velocity v_2. Use momentum conservation and energy conservation to show that the final velocities of the two masses are

$$v_{1,f} = \left(\frac{m_1 - m_2}{m_1 + m_2}\right)v_1 + \left(\frac{2m_2}{m_1 + m_2}\right)v_2$$

$$v_{2,f} = \left(\frac{2m_1}{m_1 + m_2}\right)v_1 + \left(\frac{m_2 - m_1}{m_1 + m_2}\right)v_2$$

89. ••• Two air carts of mass $m_1 = 0.84$ kg and $m_2 = 0.42$ kg are placed on a frictionless track. Cart 1 is at rest initially, and has a spring bumper with a force constant of 690 N/m. Cart 2 has a flat metal surface for a bumper, and moves toward the bumper of the stationary cart with an initial speed $v = 0.68$ m/s. **(a)** What is the speed of the two carts at the moment when their speeds are equal? **(b)** How much energy is stored in the spring bumper when the carts have the same speed? **(c)** What is the final speed of the carts after the collision?

90. ••• **Golden Earrings and the Golden Ratio** A popular earring design features a circular piece of gold of diameter D with a circular cutout of diameter d, as shown in Figure 9–29. If this earring is to balance at the point P, show that the diameters must satisfy the condition $D = \phi d$, where $\phi = (1 + \sqrt{5})/2 = 1.61803\ldots$ is the famous "golden ratio."

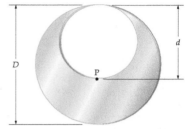

▲ **FIGURE 9–29** Problem 90

91. ••• Two objects with masses m_1 and m_2 and initial velocities $v_{1,i}$ and $v_{2,i}$ move along a straight line and collide elastically. Assuming that the objects move along the same straight line after the collision, show that their relative velocities are unchanged; that is, show that $v_{1,i} - v_{2,i} = v_{2,f} - v_{1,f}$. (You can use the results given in Problem 88.)

92. ••• **Amplified Rebound Height** Two small rubber balls are dropped from rest at a height h above a hard floor. When the balls are released, the lighter ball (with mass m) is directly above the heavier ball (with mass M). Assume the heavier ball reaches the floor first and bounces elastically; thus, when the balls collide, the ball of mass M is moving upward with a speed v and the ball of mass m is moving downward with essentially the same speed. In terms of h, find the height to which the ball of mass m rises after the collision. (Use the results given in Problem 88, and assume the balls collide at ground level.)

93. ••• On a cold winter morning, a child sits on a sled resting on smooth ice. When the 9.75-kg sled is pulled with a horizontal force of 40.0 N, it begins to move with an acceleration of 2.32 m/s². The 21.0-kg child accelerates too, but with a smaller acceleration than that of the sled. Thus, the child moves forward relative to the ice, but slides backward relative to the sled. Find the acceleration of the child relative to the ice.

94. ••• An object of mass m undergoes an elastic collision with an identical object that is at rest. The collision is not head-on. Show that the angle between the velocities of the two objects after the collision is 90°.

95. ••• **IP Weighing a Block on an Incline** A wedge of mass m_1 is firmly attached to the top of a scale, as shown in Figure 9–30. The inclined surface of the wedge makes an angle θ with the horizontal. Now, a block of mass m_2 is placed on the inclined surface of the wedge and allowed to accelerate without friction down the slope. **(a)** Show that the reading on the scale while the block slides is

$$(m_1 + m_2 \cos^2 \theta)g$$

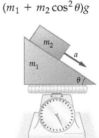

▲ **FIGURE 9–30**
Problem 95

(b) Explain why the reading on the scale is less than $(m_1 + m_2)g$. **(c)** Show that the expression in part (a) gives the expected results for $\theta = 0$ and $\theta = 90°$.

96. ••• **IP** A uniform rope of length L and mass M rests on a table. **(a)** If you lift one end of the rope upward with a constant *speed*, v, show that the rope's center of mass moves upward with constant *acceleration*. **(b)** Next, suppose you hold the rope suspended in air, with its lower end just touching the table. If you now lower the rope with a constant speed, v, onto the table, is the acceleration of the rope's center of mass upward or downward? Explain your answer. **(c)** Find the magnitude and direction of the acceleration of the rope's center of mass for the case described in part (b). Compare with part (a).

PASSAGE PROBLEMS

Navigating in Space: The Gravitational Slingshot

Many spacecraft navigate through space these days by using the "gravitational slingshot" effect, in which a close encounter with a planet results in a significant increase in magnitude and change in direction of the spacecraft's velocity. In fact, a spacecraft can attain a much greater speed with such a maneuver than it could produce with its own rockets.

The first use of this effect was on February 5, 1974, as the Mariner 10 probe—the first spacecraft to explore Mercury—made a close flyby of the planet Venus on the way to its final destination. More recently, the Cassini probe to Saturn, which was launched on October 15, 1997, and arrived at Saturn on July 1, 2004, made two close passes by Venus, followed by a flyby of Earth and a flyby of Jupiter.

A simplified version of the slingshot maneuver is illustrated in **Figure 9–31**, where we see a spacecraft moving to the left with an initial speed v_i, a planet moving to the right with a speed u, and the same spacecraft moving to the right with a final speed v_f after the encounter. The interaction can be thought of as an elastic collision in one dimension—as if the planet and spacecraft were two air carts on an air track. Both energy and momentum are conserved in this interaction, and hence the

following simple condition is satisfied (see Problem 91): The relative speed of approach is equal to the relative speed of departure. This condition, plus the fact that the speed of the massive planet is essentially unchanged, can be used to determine the final speed of the spacecraft.

97. • From the perspective of an observer on the planet, what is the spacecraft's speed of approach?

    A. $v_i + u$ **B.** $v_i - u$

    C. $u - v_i$ **D.** $v_f - u$

98. • From the perspective of an observer on the planet, what is the spacecraft's speed of departure?

    A. $v_f + u$ **B.** $v_f - u$

    C. $u - v_f$ **D.** $v_i - u$

99. •• Set the speed of departure from Problem 98 equal to the speed of approach from Problem 97. Solving this relation for the final speed, v_f, yields:

    A. $v_f = v_i + u$ **B.** $v_f = v_i - u$

    C. $v_f = v_i + 2u$ **D.** $v_f = v_i - 2u$

100. •• Consider the special case in which $v_i = u$. By what factor does the kinetic energy of the spacecraft increase as a result of the encounter?

    A. 4   **B.** 8

    C. 9   **D.** 16

INTERACTIVE PROBLEMS

101. •• **Referring to Example 9–5** Suppose a bullet of mass $m = 6.75$ g is fired into a ballistic pendulum whose bob has a mass of $M = 0.675$ kg. **(a)** If the bob rises to a height of 0.128 m, what was the initial speed of the bullet? **(b)** What was the speed of the bullet–bob combination immediately after the collision takes place?

102. •• **Referring to Example 9–5** A bullet with a mass $m = 8.10$ g and an initial speed $v_0 = 320$ m/s is fired into a ballistic pendulum. What mass must the bob have if the bullet–bob combination is to rise to a maximum height of 0.125 m after the collision?

103. •• **Referring to Example 9–9** Suppose that cart 1 has a mass of 3.00 kg and an initial speed of 0.250 m/s. Cart 2 has a mass of 1.00 kg and is at rest initially. **(a)** What is the final speed of the carts? **(b)** How much kinetic energy is lost as a result of the collision?

104. •• **Referring to Example 9–9** Suppose the two carts have equal masses and are both moving to the right before the collision. The initial speed of cart 1 (on the left) is v_0 and the initial speed of cart 2 (on the right) is $v_0/2$. **(a)** What is the speed of the center of mass of this system? **(b)** What percentage of the initial kinetic energy is lost as a result of the collision? **(c)** Suppose the collision is elastic. What are the final speeds of the two carts in this case?

▲ **FIGURE 9–31** Problems 97, 98, 99, and 100

10 Rotational Kinematics and Energy

Can you imagine life without rotating objects: vehicles without wheels, machinery without gears, carnivals without merry-go-rounds? The people on this roller coaster certainly know that rotational motion is very different from motion on a straight, linear stretch of track. In this chapter we show that the motion of rotating objects, such as a roller coaster executing a loop-the-loop, can be analyzed using many of the same methods that we applied earlier to linear motion.

It is certainly no exaggeration to say that rotation is a part of everyday life. After all, we live on a planet that rotates about its axis once a day and that revolves about the Sun once a year. The apparent motion of the Sun across the sky, for example, is actually the result of the Earth's rotational motion. In addition, engines that power cars and trucks have moving parts that rotate quite rapidly, as do CDs, CD-ROMs, and DVDs, not to mention the tumbling, rotating molecules in the air we breathe. Thus, a study of rotation yields results that apply to a great variety of natural phenomena.

In this chapter, then, we study various aspects of rotational motion. As we do, we shall make extensive use of the close analogies that exist between rotational and linear motion. In fact, many of the results derived in earlier chapters can be applied to rotation by simply replacing linear quantities with their rotational counterparts.

10–1 Angular Position, Velocity, and Acceleration

To describe the motion of an object moving in a straight line, it is useful to establish a coordinate system with a definite origin and positive direction. In terms of this coordinate system we can measure the object's position, velocity, and acceleration.

Similarly, to describe rotational motion, we define "angular" quantities that are analogous to the linear position, velocity, and acceleration. These angular quantities form the basis of our study of rotation. We begin by defining the most basic angular quantity—the angular position.

Angular Position, θ

Consider a bicycle wheel that is free to rotate about its axle, as shown in **Figure 10–1**. We say that the axle is the **axis of rotation** for the wheel. As the wheel rotates, each and every point on it moves in a circular path centered on the axis of rotation.

Now, suppose there is a small spot of red paint on the tire, and we want to describe the rotational motion of the spot. The **angular position** of the spot is defined to be the angle, θ, that a line from the axle to the spot makes with a reference line, as indicated in Figure 10–1.

Definition of Angular Position, θ

θ = angle measured from reference line   10–1

SI unit: radian (rad), which is dimensionless

The reference line simply defines $\theta = 0$; it is analogous to the origin in a linear coordinate system. The reference line begins at the axis of rotation, and may be chosen to point in any direction—just as an origin may be placed anywhere along a coordinate axis. Once chosen, however, the reference line must be used consistently.

Note that the spot of paint in Figure 10–1 is rotated counterclockwise from the reference line by the angle θ. By convention, we say that this angle is positive. Similarly, clockwise rotations correspond to negative angles.

Sign Convention for Angular Position

By convention:

$\theta > 0$ counterclockwise rotation from reference line
$\theta < 0$ clockwise rotation from reference line

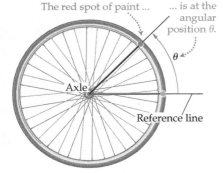

The red spot of paint ...   ... is at the angular position θ.

Axle

Reference line

▲ **FIGURE 10–1 Angular position**
The angular position, θ, of a spot of paint on a bicycle wheel. The reference line, where $\theta = 0$, is drawn horizontal here but can be chosen in any direction.

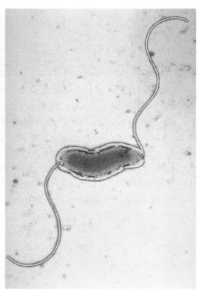

▲ Rotational motion is everywhere in our universe, on every scale of length and time. A galaxy like the one at left may take millions of years to complete a single rotation about its center, while the skater in the middle photo spins several times in a second. The bacterium at right moves in a corkscrew path by rapidly twirling its flagella (the fine projections at either end of the cell) like whips.

Now that we have established a reference line (for $\theta = 0$), and a positive direction of rotation (counterclockwise), we must choose units in which to measure angles. Common units are degrees (°) and revolutions (rev), where one revolution—that is, going completely around a circle—corresponds to 360°:

$$1 \text{ rev} = 360°$$

The most convenient units for scientific calculations, however, are radians. A **radian** (rad) is defined as follows:

> A radian is the angle for which the arc length on a circle of radius r is equal to the radius of the circle.

This definition is useful because it establishes a particularly simple relationship between an angle measured in radians and the corresponding arc length, as illustrated in **Figure 10–2**. For example, it follows from our definition that for an angle of one radian, the arc length s is equal to the radius: $s = r$. Similarly, an angle of two radians corresponds to an arc length of two radii, $s = 2r$, and so on. Thus, the arc length s for an arbitrary angle θ measured in radians is given by the following relation:

$$s = r\theta \qquad \qquad \text{10–2}$$

This simple and straightforward relation does not hold for degrees or revolutions—additional conversion factors would be needed.

In one complete revolution, the arc length is the circumference of a circle, $C = 2\pi r$. Comparing with $s = r\theta$, we see that a complete revolution corresponds to 2π radians:

$$1 \text{ rev} = 360° = 2\pi \text{ rad}$$

Equivalently,

$$1 \text{ rad} = \frac{360°}{2\pi} = 57.3°$$

One final note on the units for angles: Radians, as well as degrees and revolutions, are dimensionless. In the relation $s = r\theta$, for example, the arc length and the radius both have SI units of meters. For the equation to be dimensionally consistent, it is necessary that θ have no dimensions. Still, if an angle θ is, let's say, three radians, we will write it as $\theta = 3$ rad to remind us of the angular units being used.

Angular Velocity, ω

As the bicycle wheel in Figure 10–1 rotates, the angular position of the spot of red paint changes. This is illustrated in **Figure 10–3**. The **angular displacement** of the spot, $\Delta\theta$, is

$$\Delta\theta = \theta_f - \theta_i$$

If we divide the angular displacement by the time, Δt, during which the displacement occurs, the result is the **average angular velocity, ω_{av}**.

Definition of Average Angular Velocity, ω_{av}

$$\omega_{av} = \frac{\Delta\theta}{\Delta t} \qquad \qquad \text{10–3}$$

SI unit: radian per second $(\text{rad/s}) = \text{s}^{-1}$

This is analogous to the definition of the average linear velocity $v_{av} = \Delta x/\Delta t$. Note that the units of linear velocity are m/s, whereas the units of angular velocity are rad/s.

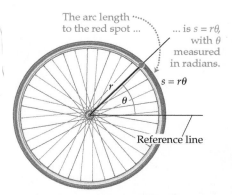

The arc length to the red spot ... ... is $s = r\theta$, with θ measured in radians.

$s = r\theta$

Reference line

▲ **FIGURE 10–2   Arc length**
The arc length, s, from the reference line to the spot of paint is given by $s = r\theta$ if the angular position θ is measured in radians.

PROBLEM-SOLVING NOTE

Radians

Remember to measure angles in radians when using the relation $s = r\theta$.

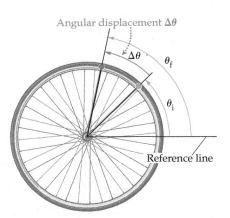

Angular displacement $\Delta\theta$

$\Delta\theta$

θ_f

θ_i

Reference line

▲ **FIGURE 10–3   Angular displacement**
As the wheel rotates, the spot of paint undergoes an angular displacement, $\Delta\theta = \theta_f - \theta_i$.

Star trails provide a clear illustration of the relationship between angle, arc, and radius in circular motion. The stars, of course, do not actually move like this, but because of the Earth's rotation they appear to follow circular paths across the sky each night, with Polaris, the North Star, very near the axis of rotation. This photo was made by opening the camera shutter for an extended period of time. Notice that each star moves through the same angle in the course of the exposure. However, the farther a star is from the axis of rotation, the longer the arc it traces out in a given period of time. (Can you estimate the length of the exposure?)

In addition to the average angular velocity, we can define an **instantaneous angular velocity** as the limit of ω_{av} as the time interval, Δt, approaches zero. The instantaneous angular velocity, then, is

Definition of Instantaneous Angular Velocity, ω

$$\omega = \lim_{\Delta t \to 0} \frac{\Delta \theta}{\Delta t}$$

10–4

SI unit: $rad/s = s^{-1}$

Generally, we shall refer to the instantaneous angular velocity simply as the angular velocity.

Note that we call ω the angular velocity, not the angular speed. The reason is that ω can be positive or negative, depending on the sense of rotation. For example, if the red paint spot rotates in the counterclockwise sense, the angular position, θ, increases. As a result, $\Delta \theta$ is positive and therefore, so is ω. Similarly, clockwise rotation corresponds to a negative $\Delta \theta$ and hence a negative ω.

Sign Convention for Angular Velocity

By convention:

$\omega > 0$ counterclockwise rotation
$\omega < 0$ clockwise rotation

The sign convention for angular velocity is illustrated in **Figure 10–4**. In analogy with linear motion, the sign of ω indicates the *direction* of the angular velocity *vector*, as we shall see in detail in Chapter 11. Similarly, the magnitude of the angular velocity is the **angular speed,** just as in the one-dimensional case.

In Exercise 10–1 we utilize the definitions and conversion factors presented so far in this section.

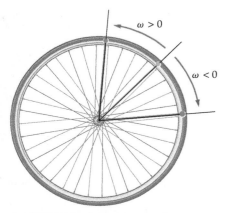

▲ **FIGURE 10–4 Angular speed and velocity**
Counterclockwise rotation is defined to correspond to a positive angular velocity, ω. Similarly, clockwise rotation corresponds to a negative angular velocity. The magnitude of the angular velocity is referred to as the angular speed.

EXERCISE 10–1

(a) An old phonograph record rotates clockwise at $33\frac{1}{3}$ rpm (revolutions per minute). What is its angular velocity in rad/s? **(b)** If a CD rotates at 22.0 rad/s, what is its angular speed in rpm?

SOLUTION

a. Convert from rpm to rad/s, and note that clockwise rotation corresponds to a negative angular velocity:

$$\omega = -33\tfrac{1}{3}\, rpm = \left(-33\tfrac{1}{3}\, \frac{rev}{min}\right)\left(\frac{2\pi\, rad}{1\, rev}\right)\left(\frac{1\, min}{60\, s}\right) = -3.49\, rad/s$$

b. Converting angular speed from rad/s to rpm gives

$$\omega = \left(22.0\, \frac{rad}{s}\right)\left(\frac{1\, rev}{2\pi\, rad}\right)\left(\frac{60\, s}{1\, min}\right) = 210\, \frac{rev}{min} = 210\, rpm$$

Note that the same symbol, ω, is used for both angular velocity and angular speed in Exercise 10–1. Which quantity is meant in a given situation will be clear from the context in which it is used.

As a simple application of angular velocity, consider the following question: An object rotates with a constant angular velocity, ω. How much time, T, is required for it to complete one full revolution?

To solve this problem, note that since ω is constant, the instantaneous angular velocity is equal to the average angular velocity. That is,

$$\omega = \omega_{av} = \frac{\Delta \theta}{\Delta t}$$

In one revolution, we know that $\Delta\theta = 2\pi$ and $\Delta t = T$. Therefore,

$$\omega = \frac{\Delta\theta}{\Delta t} = \frac{2\pi}{T}$$

Finally, solving for T we find

$$T = \frac{2\pi}{\omega}$$

The time to complete one revolution, T, is referred to as the **period.**

Definition of Period, T

$$T = \frac{2\pi}{\omega}$$ 10–5

SI unit: second, s

EXERCISE 10–2

Find the period of a record that is rotating at 45 rpm.

SOLUTION

To apply $T = 2\pi/\omega$ we must first express ω in terms of rad/s:

$$45 \text{ rpm} = \left(45\frac{\text{rev}}{\text{min}}\right)\left(\frac{2\pi \text{ rad}}{1 \text{ rev}}\right)\left(\frac{1 \text{ min}}{60 \text{ s}}\right) = 4.7 \text{ rad/s}$$

Now we can calculate the period:

$$T = \frac{2\pi}{\omega} = \frac{2\pi \text{ rad}}{4.7 \text{ rad/s}} = 1.3 \text{ s}$$

Angular Acceleration, α

If the angular velocity of the rotating bicycle wheel increases or decreases with time, we say that the wheel experiences an **angular acceleration,** α. The average angular acceleration is the change in angular velocity, $\Delta\omega$, in a given interval of time, Δt:

Definition of Average Angular Acceleration, α_{av}

$$\alpha_{av} = \frac{\Delta\omega}{\Delta t}$$ 10–6

SI unit: radian per second per second $(\text{rad/s}^2) = \text{s}^{-2}$

Note that the SI units of α are rad/s^2, which, since rad is dimensionless, is simply s^{-2}.

As expected, the instantaneous angular acceleration is the limit of α_{av} as the time interval, Δt, approaches zero:

Definition of Instantaneous Angular Acceleration, α

$$\alpha = \lim_{\Delta t \to 0} \frac{\Delta\omega}{\Delta t}$$ 10–7

SI unit: $\text{rad/s}^2 = \text{s}^{-2}$

When referring to the instantaneous angular acceleration, we will usually just say angular acceleration.

The sign of the angular acceleration is determined by whether the change in angular velocity is positive or negative. For example, if ω is becoming more positive, so that ω_f is greater than ω_i, it follows that α is positive. Similarly, if ω is becoming more negative, so that ω_f is less than ω_i, it follows that α is negative. Therefore, if ω and α have the same sign, the speed of rotation is increasing. If ω and α have opposite signs, the speed of rotation is decreasing. This is illustrated in **Figure 10–5**.

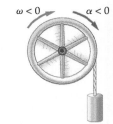

(a) Angular speed increases

(b) Angular speed increases

(c) Angular speed decreases

(d) Angular speed decreases

▲ **FIGURE 10–5 Angular acceleration and angular speed**

When angular velocity and acceleration have the same sign, as in **(a)** and **(b)**, the angular speed increases. When angular velocity and angular acceleration have opposite signs, as in **(c)** and **(d)**, the angular speed decreases.

As the wind dies, a windmill that was rotating at 2.1 rad/s begins to slow down with a constant angular acceleration of 0.45 rad/s². How long does it take for the windmill to come to a complete stop?

SOLUTION

If we choose the initial angular velocity to be positive, the angular acceleration is negative, corresponding to a deceleration. Hence, Equation 10–6 gives

$$\Delta t = \frac{\Delta \omega}{\alpha_{av}} = \frac{\omega_f - \omega_i}{\alpha} = \frac{0 - 2.1 \text{ rad/s}}{-0.45 \text{ rad/s}^2} = 4.7 \text{ s}$$

10–2 Rotational Kinematics

Just as the kinematics of Chapter 2 described linear motion, rotational kinematics describes rotational motion. In this section, as in Chapter 2, we concentrate on the important special case of constant acceleration.

As an example of a system with constant angular acceleration, consider the pulley shown in **Figure 10–6**. Wrapped around the circumference of the pulley is a string, with a mass attached to its free end. When the mass is released, the pulley begins to rotate—slowly at first, but then faster and faster. As we shall see in Chapter 11, the pulley is accelerating with constant angular acceleration.

Since α is constant, it follows that the average and instantaneous angular accelerations are equal. Hence,

$$\alpha = \alpha_{av} = \frac{\Delta \omega}{\Delta t}$$

Suppose the pulley starts with the initial angular velocity ω_0 at time $t = 0$, and that at the later time t its angular velocity is ω. Substituting these values into the preceding expression for α yields

$$\alpha = \frac{\Delta \omega}{\Delta t} = \frac{\omega - \omega_0}{t - 0} = \frac{\omega - \omega_0}{t}$$

Rearranging, we see that the angular velocity, ω, varies with time as follows:

$$\omega = \omega_0 + \alpha t$$ 10–8

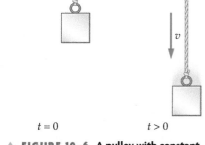

△ **FIGURE 10–6 A pulley with constant angular acceleration**
A mass is attached to a string wrapped around a pulley. As the mass falls, it causes the pulley to increase its angular speed with a constant angular acceleration.

If the angular velocity of the pulley in Figure 10–6 is −8.4 rad/s at a given time, and its angular acceleration is −2.8 rad/s², what is the angular velocity of the pulley 1.5 s later?

SOLUTION

The angular velocity, ω, is found by applying Equation 10–8:

$$\omega = \omega_0 + \alpha t = -8.4 \text{ rad/s} + (-2.8 \text{ rad/s}^2)(1.5 \text{ s}) = -12.6 \text{ rad/s}$$

Note that the angular speed has increased, as expected, since ω and α have the same sign.

Note the close analogy between Equation 10–8 for angular velocity and the corresponding relation for linear velocity, Equation 2–7:

$$v = v_0 + at$$

Clearly, the equation for angular velocity can be obtained from our previous equation for linear velocity by replacing v with ω and replacing a with α. This type of analogy between linear and angular quantities can be most useful both in deriving angular equations—by starting with linear equations and using analogies—and in obtaining a better physical understanding of angular systems. Several linear-to-angular analogs are listed in the adjacent table.

Linear Quantity	Angular Quantity
x	θ
v	ω
a	α

Using these analogies, we can rewrite all the kinematic equations in Chapter 2 in angular form. The following table gives both the linear kinematic equations and their angular counterparts.

Linear Equation (a = constant)		Angular Equation (α = constant)	
$v = v_0 + at$	2–7	$\omega = \omega_0 + \alpha t$	10–8
$x = x_0 + \frac{1}{2}(v_0 + v)t$	2–10	$\theta = \theta_0 + \frac{1}{2}(\omega_0 + \omega)t$	10–9
$x = x_0 + v_0 t + \frac{1}{2}at^2$	2–11	$\theta = \theta_0 + \omega_0 t + \frac{1}{2}\alpha t^2$	10–10
$v^2 = v_0{}^2 + 2a(x - x_0)$	2–12	$\omega^2 = \omega_0{}^2 + 2\alpha(\theta - \theta_0)$	10–11

In solving kinematic problems involving rotation, we apply these angular equations in the same way that the linear equations were applied in Chapter 2. In a sense, then, this material is a review—since the mathematics is essentially the same. The only difference comes in the physical interpretation of the results. We will emphasize the rotational interpretations throughout the chapter.

PROBLEM-SOLVING NOTE

Rotational Kinematics

Using analogies between linear and angular quantities often helps when solving problems involving rotational kinematics.

EXAMPLE 10–1   THROWN FOR A CURVE

To throw a curve ball, a pitcher gives the ball an initial angular speed of 36.0 rad/s. When the catcher gloves the ball 0.595 s later, its angular speed has decreased (due to air resistance) to 34.2 rad/s. **(a)** What is the ball's angular acceleration, assuming it to be constant? **(b)** How many revolutions does the ball make before being caught?

PICTURE THE PROBLEM
We choose the ball's initial direction of rotation to be positive. As a result, the angular acceleration will be negative. We can also identify the initial angular velocity to be $\omega_0 = 36.0$ rad/s, and the final angular velocity to be $\omega = 34.2$ rad/s.

STRATEGY
The problem states that the angular acceleration of the ball is constant. It follows that Equations 10–8 to 10–11 apply to its rotation.

a. To relate angular velocity to time, we use $\omega = \omega_0 + \alpha t$. This can be solved for α.

b. To relate angle to time we use $\theta = \theta_0 + \omega_0 t + \frac{1}{2}\alpha t^2$. The angular displacement of the ball is $\theta - \theta_0$.

SOLUTION

Part (a)

1. Solve $\omega = \omega_0 + \alpha t$ for the angular acceleration, α:

$$\omega = \omega_0 + \alpha t$$
$$\alpha = \frac{\omega - \omega_0}{t}$$

2. Substitute numerical values to find α:

$$\alpha = \frac{\omega - \omega_0}{t}$$
$$= \frac{34.2 \text{ rad/s} - 36.0 \text{ rad/s}}{0.595 \text{ s}} = -3.03 \text{ rad/s}^2$$

Part (b)

3. Use $\theta = \theta_0 + \omega_0 t + \frac{1}{2}\alpha t^2$ to calculate the angular displacement of the ball:

$$\theta - \theta_0 = \omega_0 t + \frac{1}{2}\alpha t^2$$
$$= (36.0 \text{ rad/s})(0.595 \text{ s}) + \frac{1}{2}(-3.03 \text{ rad/s}^2)(0.595 \text{ s})^2$$
$$= 20.9 \text{ rad}$$

2. Convert the angular displacement to revolutions:

$$\theta - \theta_0 = 20.9 \text{ rad} = 20.9 \text{ rad}\left(\frac{1 \text{ rev}}{2\pi \text{ rad}}\right) = 3.33 \text{ rev}$$

CONTINUED ON NEXT PAGE

CONTINUED FROM PREVIOUS PAGE

INSIGHT
The ball rotates through three-and-one-third revolutions during its time in flight.

An alternative method of solution is to use the kinematic relation given in Equation 10–9. This procedure yields $\theta - \theta_0 = \frac{1}{2}(\omega_0 + \omega)t = 20.9$ rad, in agreement with our previous result.

PRACTICE PROBLEM
(a) What is the angular velocity of the ball 0.500 s after it is thrown? (b) What is the ball's angular velocity after it completes its first full revolution? [**Answer:** (a) Use $\omega = \omega_0 + \alpha t$ to find $\omega = 34.5$ rad/s. (b) Use $\omega^2 = \omega_0^2 + 2\alpha(\theta - \theta_0)$ to find $\omega = 35.5$ rad/s.]

Some related homework problems: Problem 19, Problem 22

EXAMPLE 10–2 WHEEL OF MISFORTUNE

On a certain game show, contestants spin a wheel when it is their turn. One contestant gives the wheel an initial angular speed of 3.40 rad/s. It then rotates through one-and-one-quarter revolutions and comes to rest on the BANKRUPT space. **(a)** Find the angular acceleration of the wheel, assuming it to be constant. **(b)** How long does it take for the wheel to come to rest?

PICTURE THE PROBLEM
We choose the initial angular velocity to be positive, $\omega_0 = +3.40$ rad/s, and indicate it with a counterclockwise rotation in our sketch. Since the wheel slows to a stop, the angular acceleration must be negative; that is, in the clockwise direction. After a rotation of 1.25 rev the wheel will read BANKRUPT.

STRATEGY
As in Example 10–1, we can use the kinematic equations for constant angular acceleration, Equations 10–8 to 10–11.

a. To begin, we are given the initial angular velocity, $\omega_0 = +3.40$ rad/s, the final angular velocity, $\omega = 0$ (the wheel comes to rest), and the angular displacement, $\theta - \theta_0 = 1.25$ rev. We can find the angular acceleration using $\omega^2 = \omega_0^2 + 2\alpha(\theta - \theta_0)$.

b. Knowing the angular velocity and acceleration, we can find the time with $\omega = \omega_0 + \alpha t$.

SOLUTION

Part (a)

1. Solve $\omega^2 = \omega_0^2 + 2\alpha(\theta - \theta_0)$ for the angular acceleration, α:

$$\omega^2 = \omega_0^2 + 2\alpha(\theta - \theta_0)$$
$$\alpha = \frac{\omega^2 - \omega_0^2}{2(\theta - \theta_0)}$$

2. Convert $\theta - \theta_0 = 1.25$ rev to radians:

$$\theta - \theta_0 = 1.25 \text{ rev} = 1.25 \text{ rev}\left(\frac{2\pi \text{ rad}}{1 \text{ rev}}\right) = 7.85 \text{ rad}$$

3. Substitute numerical values to find α:

$$\alpha = \frac{\omega^2 - \omega_0^2}{2(\theta - \theta_0)} = \frac{0 - (3.40 \text{ rad/s})^2}{2(7.85 \text{ rad})} = -0.736 \text{ rad/s}^2$$

Part (b)

4. Solve $\omega = \omega_0 + \alpha t$ for the time, t:

$$\omega = \omega_0 + \alpha t$$
$$t = \frac{\omega - \omega_0}{\alpha}$$

5. Substitute numerical values to find t:

$$t = \frac{\omega - \omega_0}{\alpha} = \frac{0 - 3.40 \text{ rad/s}}{(-0.736 \text{ rad/s}^2)} = 4.62 \text{ s}$$

INSIGHT
Note that it was not necessary to define a reference line; that is, a direction for $\theta = 0$. All we need to know is the angular displacement, $\theta - \theta_0$, not the individual angles θ and θ_0. Finally, notice that we can also solve Equation 10–9 for the time in part (b), which yields $t = 2(\theta - \theta_0)/(\omega_0 + \omega) = 4.62$ s, as expected.

PRACTICE PROBLEM
What is the angular speed of the wheel after one complete revolution?   [**Answer:** $\omega = 1.52$ rad/s]

Some related homework problems: Problem 18, Problem 20

Finally, we consider a pulley that is rotating in such a way that initially it is lifting a mass with speed v. Gravity acting on the mass causes it and the pulley to slow and momentarily come to rest.

ACTIVE EXAMPLE 10–1   FIND THE TIME TO REST

A pulley rotating in the counterclockwise direction is attached to a mass suspended from a string. The mass causes the pulley's angular velocity to decrease with a constant angular acceleration $\alpha = -2.10$ rad/s². **(a)** If the pulley's initial angular velocity is $\omega_0 = 5.40$ rad/s, how long does it take for the pulley to come to rest? **(b)** Through what angle does the pulley turn during this time?

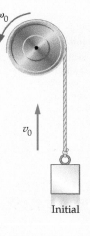

SOLUTION *(Test your understanding by performing the calculations indicated in each step.)*

1. **(a)** Relate angular velocity to time: $\omega = \omega_0 + \alpha t$

2. Solve for the time, t: $t = (\omega - \omega_0)/\alpha$

3. Substitute numerical values: $t = 2.57$ s

4. **(b)** Use $\theta = \theta_0 + \omega_0 t + \frac{1}{2}\alpha t^2$ to solve $\theta - \theta_0 = \omega_0 t + \frac{1}{2}\alpha t^2 = 6.94$ rad
   for $\theta - \theta_0$:

5. Alternatively, use $\omega^2 = \omega_0{}^2 + 2\alpha(\theta - \theta_0)$: $\theta - \theta_0 = (\omega^2 - \omega_0{}^2)/2\alpha = 6.94$ rad

INSIGHT
After the pulley comes to rest, it immediately begins to rotate in the clockwise direction as the mass falls. The pulley's angular *acceleration* is constant—it has the same value before the pulley stops, when it stops, and after it begins rotating in the opposite direction. This is analogous to a projectile thrown straight upward, where the linear velocity starts out positive, goes to zero, then changes sign, all while the linear acceleration remains constant in the negative direction.

YOUR TURN
Find the angular displacement of the pulley at the time when its angular velocity is half its initial value.

(Answers to **Your Turn** *problems are given in the back of the book.)*

10–3 Connections Between Linear and Rotational Quantities

At a local county fair a child rides on a merry-go-round. The ride completes one circuit every $T = 7.50$ s. Therefore, the angular velocity of the child, from Equation 10–5, is

$$\omega = \frac{2\pi}{T} = \frac{2\pi}{7.50 \text{ s}} = 0.838 \text{ rad/s}$$

The path followed by the child is circular, with the center of the circle at the axis of rotation of the merry-go-round. In addition, at any instant of time the child is moving in a direction that is *tangential* to the circular path, as **Figure 10–7** shows. What is the tangential speed, v_t, of the child? In other words, what is the speed of the wind in the child's face?

We can find the child's tangential speed by dividing the circumference of the circular path, $2\pi r$, by the time required to complete one circuit, T. Thus,

$$v_t = \frac{2\pi r}{T} = r\left(\frac{2\pi}{T}\right)$$

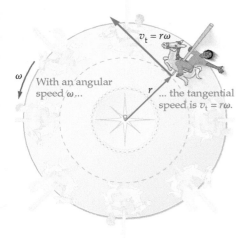

▲ **FIGURE 10–7 Angular and linear speed**
Overhead view of a child riding on a merry-go-round. The child's path is a circle centered on the merry-go-round's axis of rotation. At any given time the child is moving tangential to the circular path with a speed $v_t = r\omega$.

REAL-WORLD PHYSICS

The operation of a CD

Because $2\pi/T$ is simply ω, we can express the tangential speed as follows:

Tangential Speed of a Rotating Object

$$v_t = r\omega \qquad\qquad 10\text{–}12$$

SI unit: m/s

Note that ω must be given in rad/s for this relation to be valid.

In the case of the merry-go-round, if the radius of the child's circular path is $r = 4.25$ m, the tangential speed is $v_t = r\omega = (4.25 \text{ m})(0.838 \text{ rad/s}) = 3.56$ m/s. When it is clear that we are referring to the tangential speed, we will often drop the subscript t, and simply write $v = r\omega$.

An interesting application of the relation between linear and angular speeds is provided in the operation of a compact disk (CD). As you know, a CD is played by shining a laser beam onto the disk, and then converting the pattern of reflected light into a pattern of sound waves. For proper operation, however, the linear speed of the disk where the laser beam shines on it must be maintained at the constant value of 1.25 m/s. As the CD is played, the laser beam scans the disk in a spiral track from near the center outward to the rim. In order to maintain the required linear speed, the angular speed of the disk must decrease as the beam scans outward. The required angular speeds are determined in the following Exercise.

EXERCISE 10–5

Find the angular speed a CD must have to give a linear speed of 1.25 m/s when the laser beam shines on the disk **(a)** 2.50 cm and **(b)** 6.00 cm from its center.

SOLUTION

a. Using $v = 1.25$ m/s and $r = 0.0250$ m in Equation 10–12, we find

$$\omega = \frac{v}{r} = \frac{1.25 \text{ m/s}}{0.0250 \text{ m}} = 50.0 \text{ rad/s} = 477 \text{ rpm}$$

b. Similarly, with $r = 0.0600$ m we find

$$\omega = \frac{v}{r} = \frac{1.25 \text{ m/s}}{0.0600 \text{ m}} = 20.8 \text{ rad/s} = 199 \text{ rpm}$$

Thus, a CD slows from about 500 rpm to roughly 200 rpm as it plays.

How do the angular and tangential speeds of an object vary from one point to another? We explore this question in the following Conceptual Checkpoint.

CONCEPTUAL CHECKPOINT 10–1 COMPARE THE SPEEDS

Two children ride on a merry-go-round, with child 1 at a greater distance from the axis of rotation than child 2. Is the angular speed of child 1 **(a)** greater than, **(b)** less than, or **(c)** the same as the angular speed of child 2?

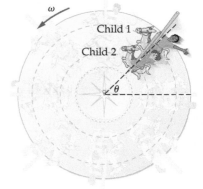

REASONING AND DISCUSSION
At any given time, the angle θ for child 1 is the same as the angle for child 2, as shown. Therefore, when the angle for child 1 has gone through 2π, for example, so has the angle for child 2. As a result, they have the same angular speed. In fact, *each and every point on the merry-go-round has exactly the same angular speed.*

The tangential speeds are different, however. Child 1 has the greater tangential speed since he travels around a larger circle in the same time that child 2 travels around a smaller circle. This is in agreement with the relation $v = r\omega$, since the radius to child 1 is greater than the radius to child 2. That is, $v_1 = r_1\omega > v_2 = r_2\omega$.

ANSWER
(c) The angular speeds are the same.

◀ In the photo at left, two identical plastic letter "E"s have been placed on a rotating turntable at different distances from the axis of rotation. The stretching and blurring of the image of the outermost letter clearly show that it is moving faster than the letter closer to the axis. Similarly, the boy near the rim of this playground merry-go-round is moving faster than the girl near the hub.

Because the children on the merry-go-round move in a circular path, they experience a centripetal acceleration, a_{cp} (Section 6–5). The centripetal acceleration is always directed toward the axis of rotation and has a magnitude given by

$$a_{cp} = \frac{v^2}{r}$$

Note that the speed v in this expression is the tangential speed, $v = v_t = r\omega$, and therefore the centripetal acceleration in terms of ω is

$$a_{cp} = \frac{(r\omega)^2}{r}$$

Canceling one power of r, we have

Centripetal Acceleration of a Rotating Object

$$a_{cp} = r\omega^2 \qquad\qquad 10\text{–}13$$

SI unit: m/s²

If the radius of a child's circular path on the merry-go-round is 4.25 m, and the angular speed of the ride is 0.838 rad/s, the centripetal acceleration of the child is $a_{cp} = r\omega^2 = (4.25 \text{ m})(0.838 \text{ rad/s})^2 = 2.98 \text{ m/s}^2$.

Though the centripetal acceleration of a merry-go-round is typically only a fraction of the acceleration of gravity, rotating devices referred to as **centrifuges** can produce centripetal accelerations many times greater than gravity. For example, the world's most powerful research centrifuge, operated by the U.S. Army Corps of Engineers, can subject 2.2-ton payloads to accelerations as high as 350g (350 times greater than the acceleration of gravity). This centrifuge is used to study earthquake engineering and dam erosion. The Air Force uses centrifuges to subject prospective jet pilots to the accelerations they will experience during rapid flight maneuvers, and in the future NASA may even use a human-powered centrifuge for gravity studies aboard the International Space Station.

REAL-WORLD PHYSICS

The centrifuge

▲ The large centrifuge shown at left, at the Gagarin Cosmonaut Training Center, is used to train Russian cosmonauts for space missions. This device, which rotates at 36 rpm, can produce a centripetal acceleration of over 290 m/s², 30 times the acceleration of gravity. The device at right is a microhematocrit centrifuge, used to separate blood cells from plasma. The volume of red blood cells in a given quantity of whole blood is a major factor in determining the oxygen-carrying capacity of the blood, an important clinical indicator.

The centrifuges most commonly encountered in everyday life are those found in virtually every medical laboratory in the world. These devices, which can produce centripetal accelerations in excess of 13,000g, are used to separate blood cells from blood plasma. They do this by speeding up the natural tendency of cells to settle out of plasma from days to minutes. The ratio of the packed cell volume to the total blood volume gives the *hematocrit value*, which is a useful clinical indicator of blood quality. In the next Example we consider the operation of a *microhematocrit centrifuge*, which measures the hematocrit value of a small (micro) sample of blood.

REAL-WORLD PHYSICS: BIO
The microhematocrit centrifuge

EXAMPLE 10-3 THE MICROHEMATOCRIT

REAL-WORLD PHYSICS: BIO

In a microhematocrit centrifuge, small samples of blood are placed in heparinized capillary tubes (heparin is an anticoagulant). The tubes are rotated at 11,500 rpm, with the bottoms of the tubes 9.07 cm from the axis of rotation. **(a)** Find the linear speed of the bottom of the tubes. **(b)** What is the centripetal acceleration at the bottom of the tubes?

PICTURE THE PROBLEM

Our sketch shows a top view of the centrifuge, with the capillary tubes rotating at 11,500 rpm. Notice that the bottoms of the tubes move in a circular path of radius 9.07 cm.

STRATEGY

a. Linear and angular speeds are related by $v = r\omega$. Once we convert the angular speed to rad/s we can use this relation to determine v.

b. The centripetal acceleration is $a_{cp} = r\omega^2$. Using ω from part (a) yields the desired result.

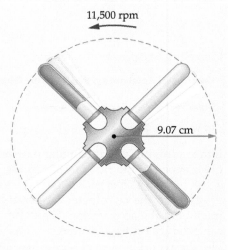

11,500 rpm

9.07 cm

SOLUTION

Part (a)

1. Convert the angular speed, ω, to radians per second:

$$\omega = (11{,}500 \text{ rev/min})\left(\frac{2\pi \text{ rad}}{1 \text{ rev}}\right)\left(\frac{1 \text{ min}}{60 \text{ s}}\right)$$
$$= 1.20 \times 10^3 \text{ rad/s}$$

2. Use $v = r\omega$ to calculate the linear speed:

$$v = r\omega = (0.0907 \text{ m})(1.20 \times 10^3 \text{ rad/s}) = 109 \text{ m/s}$$

Part (b)

3. Calculate the centripetal acceleration using $a_{cp} = r\omega^2$:

$$a_{cp} = r\omega^2 = (0.0907 \text{ m})(1.20 \times 10^3 \text{ rad/s})^2 = 131{,}000 \text{ m/s}^2$$

4. As a check, calculate the centripetal acceleration using $a_{cp} = v^2/r$:

$$a_{cp} = \frac{v^2}{r} = \frac{(109 \text{ m/s})^2}{0.0907 \text{ m}} = 131{,}000 \text{ m/s}^2$$

INSIGHT

Note that every point on a tube has the same angular speed. As a result, points near the top of a tube have smaller linear speeds and centripetal accelerations than do points near the bottom of a tube. In this case, the bottoms of the tubes experience a centripetal acceleration about 13,400 times greater than the acceleration of gravity on the surface of the Earth; that is, $a_{cp} = 131{,}000 \text{ m/s}^2 = 13{,}400g$.

PRACTICE PROBLEM

What angular speed must this centrifuge have if the centripetal acceleration at the bottom of the tubes is to be 98,100 m/s² ($\approx 10{,}000g$)? **[Answer:** $\omega = \sqrt{a_{cp}/r} = 1040 \text{ rad/s} = 9930 \text{ rpm}$**]**

Some related homework problems: Problem 34, Problem 37

If the angular speed of the merry-go-round in Conceptual Checkpoint 10–1 changes, the tangential speed of the children changes as well. It follows, then, that the children will experience a tangential acceleration, a_t. We can determine a_t by considering the relation $v_t = r\omega$. If ω changes by the amount $\Delta\omega$, with r remaining constant, the corresponding change in tangential speed is

$$\Delta v_t = r\Delta\omega$$

If this change in ω occurs in the time Δt, the tangential acceleration is

$$a_t = \frac{\Delta v_t}{\Delta t} = r\frac{\Delta\omega}{\Delta t}$$

Since $\Delta\omega/\Delta t$ is the angular acceleration, α, we find that

Tangential Acceleration of a Rotating Object

$$a_t = r\alpha \qquad\qquad 10\text{–}14$$

SI unit: m/s^2

As with the tangential speed, we will often drop the subscript t in a_t when no confusion will arise.

In general, the children on the merry-go-round may experience both tangential and centripetal accelerations at the same time. Recall that a_t is due to a changing tangential speed, and that a_{cp} is caused by a changing direction of motion, even if the tangential speed remains constant. To summarize:

Tangential Versus Centripetal Acceleration

$a_t = r\alpha$ due to changing angular speed

$a_{cp} = r\omega^2$ due to changing direction of motion

As the names suggest, the tangential acceleration is always tangential to an object's path; the centripetal acceleration is always perpendicular to its path.

In cases in which both the centripetal and tangential accelerations are present, the total acceleration is the vector sum of the two, as indicated in **Figure 10–8**. Note that $\vec{a}_t$ and $\vec{a}_{cp}$ are at right angles to one another, and hence the magnitude of the total acceleration is given by the Pythagorean theorem:

$$a = \sqrt{a_t^2 + a_{cp}^2}$$

The direction of the total acceleration, measured relative to the tangential direction, is

$$\phi = \tan^{-1}\left(\frac{a_{cp}}{a_t}\right)$$

This angle is shown in Figure 10–8.

In the next Active Example, we consider an object that is rotating with a constant angular acceleration, α. In this case, the tangential acceleration, $a_t = r\alpha$, is constant in magnitude. On the other hand, the centripetal acceleration, $a_{cp} = r\omega^2$, changes with time since the angular speed changes.

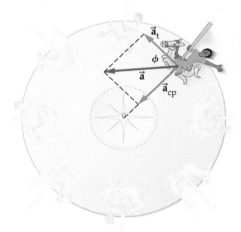

▲ **FIGURE 10–8 Centripetal and tangential acceleration**
If the angular speed of the merry-go-round is increased, the child will experience two accelerations: (i) a tangential acceleration, $\vec{a}_t$, and (ii) a centripetal acceleration, $\vec{a}_{cp}$. The child's total acceleration, $\vec{a}$, is the vector sum of $\vec{a}_t$ and $\vec{a}_{cp}$.

ACTIVE EXAMPLE 10–2   FIND THE ACCELERATION

Suppose the centrifuge in Example 10–3 is starting up with a constant angular acceleration of 95.0 rad/s^2. **(a)** What are the magnitudes of the centripetal, tangential, and total accelerations of the bottom of a tube when the angular speed is 8.00 rad/s? **(b)** What angle does the total acceleration make with the direction of motion?

CONTINUED ON NEXT PAGE

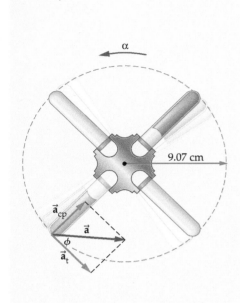

CONTINUED FROM PREVIOUS PAGE

SOLUTION *(Test your understanding by performing the calculations indicated in each step.)*

Part (a)

1. Calculate the centripetal acceleration: $a_{cp} = r\omega^2 = 5.80 \text{ m/s}^2$

2. Calculate the tangential acceleration: $a_t = r\alpha = 8.62 \text{ m/s}^2$

3. Find the magnitude of the total acceleration: $a = \sqrt{a_{cp}^2 + a_t^2} = 10.4 \text{ m/s}^2$

Part (b)

4. Find the angle ϕ for the total acceleration: $\phi = \tan^{-1}(a_{cp}/a_t) = 33.9°$

INSIGHT

Note that all points on a tube have the same angular speed. In addition, all points have the same angular acceleration. In contrast, different points have different centripetal and tangential accelerations, due to their dependence on the distance r from the axis of rotation.

YOUR TURN

Find the magnitude and direction of the total acceleration of a point *halfway* between the top and bottom of a tube.

(Answers to **Your Turn** *problems are given in the back of the book.)*

▶ **FIGURE 10–9 Rolling without slipping**
A wheel of radius r rolling without slipping. During one complete revolution, the center of the wheel moves forward through a distance $2\pi r$.

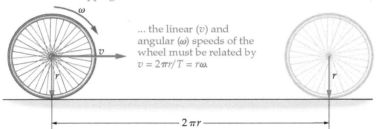

To roll without slipping ...

... the linear (v) and angular (ω) speeds of the wheel must be related by $v = 2\pi r/T = r\omega$.

10–4 Rolling Motion

We began this chapter with a bicycle wheel rotating about its axle. In that case, the axle was at rest and every point on the wheel, such as the spot of red paint, moved in a circular path about the axle. We would like to consider a different situation now. Suppose the bicycle wheel is rolling freely, as indicated in **Figure 10–9**, with no slipping between the tire and the ground. The wheel still rotates about the axle, but the axle itself is moving in a straight line. As a result, the motion of the wheel is a combination of both rotational motion and linear (or **translational**) motion.

To see the connection between the wheel's rotational and translational motions, we show one full rotation of the wheel in Figure 10–9. During this rotation, the axle translates forward through a distance equal to the circumference of the wheel, $2\pi r$. Because the time required for one rotation is the period, T, the translational speed of the axle is

$$v = \frac{2\pi r}{T}$$

Recalling that $\omega = 2\pi/T$, we find

$$v = r\omega = v_t \qquad \text{10–15}$$

Hence, the translational speed of the axle is equal to the tangential speed of a point on the rim of a wheel spinning with angular speed ω.

A rolling object, then, combines rotational motion with angular speed ω, and translational motion with linear speed $v = r\omega$, where r is the radius of the object. Let's consider these two motions one at a time. First, in **Figure 10–10 (a)** we show pure rotational motion with angular speed ω. In this case, the axle is at rest, and points at the top and bottom of the wheel have tangential velocities that are equal in magnitude, $v = r\omega$, but point in opposite directions.

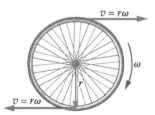

(a) Pure rotational motion

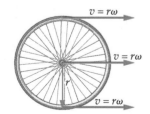

(b) Pure translational motion

▲ **FIGURE 10–10 Rotational and translational motions of a wheel**

(a) In pure rotational motion, the velocities at the top and bottom of the wheel are in opposite directions. **(b)** In pure translational motion, each point on the wheel moves with the same speed in the same direction.

Next, we consider translational motion with speed $v = r\omega$. This is illustrated in **Figure 10–10 (b)**, where we see that each point on the wheel moves in the same direction with the same speed. If this were the only motion the wheel had, it would be skidding across the ground, instead of rolling without slipping.

Finally, we combine these two motions by simply adding the velocity vectors in Figures 10–10 (a) and (b). The result is shown in **Figure 10–11**. At the top of the wheel the two velocity vectors are in the same direction, so they sum to give a speed of $2r\omega$. At the axle, the velocity vectors sum to give a speed $r\omega$. Finally, at the bottom of the wheel, the velocity vectors from rotation and translation have equal magnitude, but are in opposite directions. As a result, these velocities cancel, giving a speed of zero where the wheel is in contact with the ground.

The fact that the bottom of the wheel is instantaneously at rest, so that it is in static contact with the ground, is precisely what is meant by "rolling without slipping." Thus, a wheel that rolls without slipping is just like the situation when you are walking—even though your body as a whole moves forward, the soles of your shoes are momentarily at rest every time you place them on the ground. This point was discussed in detail in Conceptual Checkpoint 6–1.

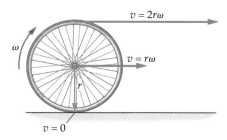

▲ **FIGURE 10–11 Velocities in rolling motion**

In a wheel that rolls without slipping, the point in contact with the ground is instantaneously at rest. The center of the wheel moves forward with the speed $v = r\omega$, and the top of the wheel moves forward with twice that speed, $v = 2r\omega$.

EXERCISE 10–6

A car with tires of radius 32 cm drives on the highway at 55 mph. **(a)** What is the angular speed of the tires? **(b)** What is the linear speed of the tops of the tires?

SOLUTION

a. Using Equation 10–15 we find

$$\omega = \frac{v}{r} = \frac{(55 \text{ mph})\left(\dfrac{0.447 \text{ m/s}}{1 \text{ mph}}\right)}{0.32 \text{ m}} = 77 \text{ rad/s}$$

This is about 12 revolutions per second.

b. The tops of the tires have a speed of $2v = 110$ mph.

▲ This photograph of a rolling wheel gives a visual indication of the speed of its various parts. The bottom of the wheel is at rest at any instant, so the image there is sharp. The top of the wheel has the greatest speed, and the image there shows the most blurring. (Compare Figure 10–11.)

10–5 Rotational Kinetic Energy and the Moment of Inertia

An object in motion has kinetic energy, whether that motion is translational, rotational, or a combination of the two. In translational motion, for example, the kinetic energy of a mass m moving with a speed v is $K = \frac{1}{2}mv^2$. We cannot use this expression for a rotating object, however, because the speed v of each particle within a rotating object varies with its distance r from the axis of rotation, as we have seen in Equation 10–12. Thus, there is no unique value of v for an entire rotating object. On the other hand, there *is* a unique value of ω, the angular speed, that applies to all particles in the object.

To see how the kinetic energy of a rotating object depends on its angular speed, we start with a particularly simple system consisting of a rod of length r and negligible mass rotating about one end with an angular speed ω. Attached to the other end of the rod is a point mass m, as **Figure 10–12** shows. To find the kinetic energy of the mass, recall that its linear speed is $v = r\omega$ (Equation 10–12). Therefore, the translational kinetic energy of the mass m is

$$K = \tfrac{1}{2}mv^2 = \tfrac{1}{2}m(r\omega)^2 = \tfrac{1}{2}(mr^2)\omega^2 \qquad \text{10–16}$$

Notice that the kinetic energy of the mass depends not only on the angular speed squared (analogous to the way the translational kinetic energy depends on the linear speed squared), but also on the radius squared—that is, the kinetic energy depends on the *distribution* of mass in the rotating object. To be specific, mass near the axis of rotation contributes little to the kinetic energy since its speed ($v = r\omega$) is small. On the other hand, the farther a mass is from the axis of rotation, the greater its speed v for a given angular velocity, and thus the greater its kinetic energy.

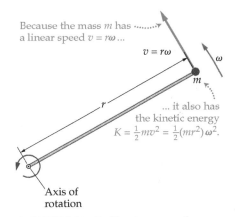

Because the mass m has a linear speed $v = r\omega$ ...

$v = r\omega$

... it also has the kinetic energy $K = \frac{1}{2}mv^2 = \frac{1}{2}(mr^2)\omega^2$.

Axis of rotation

▲ **FIGURE 10–12 Kinetic energy of a rotating object**

As this rod rotates about the axis of rotation with an angular speed ω, the mass has a speed of $v = r\omega$. It follows that the kinetic energy of the mass is $K = \frac{1}{2}mv^2 = \frac{1}{2}(mr^2)\omega^2$.

You have probably noticed that the kinetic energy in Equation 10–16 is similar in form to the translational kinetic energy. Instead of $\frac{1}{2}(m)v^2$, we now have $\frac{1}{2}(mr^2)\omega^2$. Clearly, then, the quantity mr^2 plays the role of the mass for the rotating object. This "rotational mass" is given a special name in physics: the **moment of inertia,** I. Thus, in general, the kinetic energy of an object rotating with an angular speed ω can be written as:

Rotational Kinetic Energy

$$K = \frac{1}{2}I\omega^2$$

10–17

SI unit: J

The greater the moment of inertia—which some books call the rotational inertia—the greater an object's rotational kinetic energy. As we have just seen, in the special case of a point mass m a distance r from the axis of rotation, the moment of inertia is simply $I = mr^2$.

We now show how to find the moment of inertia for an object of arbitrary, fixed shape, as in **Figure 10–13**. Suppose, for example, that this object rotates about the axis indicated in the figure with an angular speed ω. To calculate the kinetic energy of the object, we first imagine dividing it into a collection of small mass elements, m_i. We then calculate the kinetic energy of each element and sum over all elements. This extends to a large number of mass elements what we did for the single mass m.

Following this plan, the total kinetic energy of an arbitrary rotating object is

$$K = \sum \left(\tfrac{1}{2}m_i v_i^2\right)$$

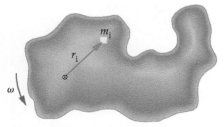

▲ **FIGURE 10–13 Kinetic energy of a rotating object of arbitrary shape**
To calculate the kinetic energy of an object of arbitrary shape as it rotates about an axis with angular speed ω, imagine dividing it into small mass elements, m_i. The total kinetic energy of the object is the sum of the kinetic energies of all the mass elements.

In this expression, m_i is the mass of one of the small mass elements and v_i is its speed. If m_i is at the radius r_i from the axis of rotation, as indicated in Figure 10–13, its speed is $v_i = r_i\omega$. Note that it is not necessary to write a separate angular speed, ω_i, for each element, because *all* mass elements of the object have exactly the same angular speed, ω. Therefore,

$$K = \sum \left(\tfrac{1}{2}m_i r_i^2 \omega^2\right) = \tfrac{1}{2}\left(\sum m_i r_i^2\right)\omega^2$$

Now, in analogy with our results for the single mass, we can define the moment of inertia, I, as follows:

Definition of Moment of Inertia, I

$$I = \sum m_i r_i^2$$

10–18

SI unit: kg $\cdot$ m²

The precise value of I for a given object depends on its distribution of mass. A simple example of this dependence is given in the following Exercise.

EXERCISE 10–7

Use the general definition of the moment of inertia, as given in Equation 10–18, to find the moment of inertia for the dumbbell-shaped object shown in **Figure 10–14**. Note that the axis of rotation goes through the center of the object and points out of the page. In addition, assume that the masses may be treated as point masses.

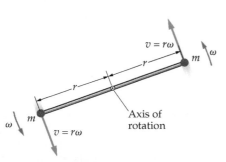

▲ **FIGURE 10–14 A dumbbell-shaped object rotating about its center**

SOLUTION
Referring to Figure 10–14, we see that $m_1 = m_2 = m$ and $r_1 = r_2 = r$. Therefore, the moment of inertia is

$$I = \sum m_i r_i^2 = m_1 r_1^2 + m_2 r_2^2 = mr^2 + mr^2 = 2mr^2$$

The connection between rotational kinetic energy and the moment of inertia is explored in more detail in the following Example.

EXAMPLE 10–4   NOSE TO THE GRINDSTONE

A grindstone with a radius of 0.610 m is being used to sharpen an ax. **(a)** If the linear speed of the stone relative to the ax is 1.50 m/s, and the stone's rotational kinetic energy is 13.0 J, what is its moment of inertia? **(b)** If the linear speed is doubled to 3.00 m/s, what is the corresponding kinetic energy of the grindstone?

PICTURE THE PROBLEM

Our sketch shows the grindstone spinning with an angular speed ω, which is not given in the problem statement. We do know, however, that the linear speed of the grindstone at its rim is $v = 1.50$ m/s and that its radius is $r = 0.610$ m. At this rate of rotation, the stone has a kinetic energy of 13.0 J.

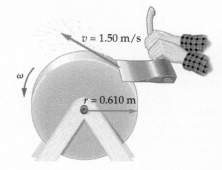

STRATEGY

a. Recall that rotational kinetic energy and moment of inertia are related by $K = \frac{1}{2}I\omega^2$; thus $I = 2K/\omega^2$. We are not given ω, but we can find it from the connection between linear and angular speed, $v = r\omega$. Thus, we begin by finding ω. We then use ω, along with the kinetic energy K, to find I.

b. Find the new angular speed with $\omega = v/r$. Use I from part (a), along with $K = \frac{1}{2}I\omega^2$, to find the new kinetic energy.

SOLUTION

Part (a)

1. Find the angular speed of the grindstone:
$$\omega = \frac{v}{r} = \frac{1.50 \text{ m/s}}{0.610 \text{ m}} = 2.46 \text{ rad/s}$$

2. Solve for the moment of inertia in terms of kinetic energy:
$$K = \tfrac{1}{2}I\omega^2 \quad \text{or} \quad I = \frac{2K}{\omega^2}$$

3. Substitute numerical values for K and ω:
$$I = \frac{2K}{\omega^2} = \frac{2(13.0 \text{ J})}{(2.46 \text{ rad/s})^2} = 4.30 \text{ J} \cdot \text{s}^2 = 4.30 \text{ kg} \cdot \text{m}^2$$

Part (b)

4. Find the angular speed of the grindstone corresponding to $v = 3.00$ m/s:
$$\omega = \frac{v}{r} = \frac{3.00 \text{ m/s}}{0.610 \text{ m}} = 4.92 \text{ rad/s}$$

5. Determine the kinetic energy, K, using the moment of inertia, I, from part (a):
$$K = \tfrac{1}{2}I\omega^2 = \tfrac{1}{2}(4.30 \text{ kg} \cdot \text{m}^2)(4.92 \text{ rad/s})^2 = 52.0 \text{ J}$$

INSIGHT

(a) We found I by relating it to the rotational kinetic energy of the grindstone. Later in this section we show how to calculate the moment of inertia of a disk directly, given its radius and mass. **(b)** Doubling the linear speed, v, results in a doubling of the angular speed, ω. The kinetic energy K depends on ω^2; therefore doubling ω increases K by a factor of 4, from 13.0 J to 4(13.0 J) = 52.0 J.

PRACTICE PROBLEM

When the ax is pressed firmly against the grindstone for sharpening, the angular speed of the grindstone decreases. If the rotational kinetic energy of the grindstone is cut in half to 6.50 J, what is its angular speed?   **[Answer:** The moment of inertia is unchanged; it depends only on the size, shape, and mass of the grindstone. Hence, $\omega = \sqrt{2K/I} = 1.74$ rad/s, which is smaller than the original $\omega = 2.46$ rad/s by a factor of $\sqrt{2}$.**]**

Some related homework problems: Problem 56, Problem 57

We return now to the dependence of the moment of inertia on the particular shape, or mass distribution, of an object. Suppose, for example, that a mass M is formed into the shape of a *hoop* of radius R. In addition, consider the case where the axis of rotation is perpendicular to the plane of the hoop and passes through its center, as shown in **Figure 10–15**. This is similar to a bicycle wheel rotating about its axle, if one ignores the spokes. In terms of small mass elements, we can write the moment of inertia as

$$I = \sum m_i r_i^2$$

Each mass element of the hoop, however, is at the same radius R from the axis of rotation; that is, $r_i = R$. Hence, the moment of inertia in this case is

$$I = \sum m_i r_i^2 = \sum m_i R^2 = \left(\sum m_i\right) R^2$$

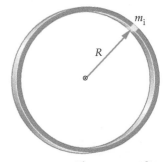

▲ **FIGURE 10–15 The moment of inertia of a hoop**

Consider a hoop of mass M and radius R. Each small mass element is at the same distance, R, from the center of the hoop. The moment of inertia in this case is $I = MR^2$.

▲ **FIGURE 10–16** **The moment of inertia of a disk**
Consider a disk of mass M and radius R. Mass elements for the disk are at distances from the center ranging from 0 to R. The moment of inertia in this case is $I = \frac{1}{2}MR^2$.

Clearly, the sum of all the elementary masses is simply the total mass of the hoop, $\Sigma m_i = M$. Therefore, the moment of inertia of a hoop of mass M and radius R is

$$I = MR^2 \text{ (hoop)}$$

In contrast, if the same mass, M, is formed into a uniform *disk* of the same radius, R, the moment of inertia is different. To see this, note that it is no longer true that $r_i = R$ for all mass elements. In fact, most of the mass elements are closer to the axis of rotation than was the case for the hoop, as indicated in **Figure 10–16**. Thus, since the r_i are generally less than R, the moment of inertia will be smaller for the disk than for the hoop. A detailed calculation, summing over all mass elements, yields the following result:

$$I = \frac{1}{2}MR^2 \text{ (disk)}$$

As expected, I is less for the disk than for the hoop.

EXERCISE 10–8

If the grindstone in Example 10–4 is a uniform disk, what is its mass?

SOLUTION
Applying the preceding equation yields

$$M = \frac{2I}{R^2} = \frac{2(4.30 \text{ kg} \cdot \text{m}^2)}{(0.610 \text{ m})^2} = 23.1 \text{ kg}$$

Thus, the grindstone has a weight of roughly 51 lb.

Table 10–1 collects moments of inertia for a variety of objects. Note that in all cases the moment of inertia is of the form $I = (\text{constant})MR^2$. It is only the constant in front of MR^2 that changes from one object to another.

Note also that objects of the same general shape but with different mass distributions—such as solid and hollow spheres—have different moments of inertia. In particular, a hollow sphere has a larger I than a solid sphere of the same mass, for the same reason that a hoop's moment of inertia is greater than a disk's—more of its mass is at a greater distance from the axis of rotation. Thus, I is a measure of both the shape *and* the mass distribution of an object.

TABLE 10–1 Moments of Inertia for Uniform, Rigid Objects of Various Shapes and Total Mass M

Hoop or cylindrical shell
$I = MR^2$

Disk or solid cylinder
$I = \frac{1}{2}MR^2$

Disk or solid cylinder (axis at rim)
$I = \frac{3}{2}MR^2$

Long thin rod (axis through midpoint)
$I = \frac{1}{12}ML^2$

Long thin rod (axis at one end)
$I = \frac{1}{3}ML^2$

Hollow sphere
$I = \frac{2}{3}MR^2$

Solid sphere
$I = \frac{2}{5}MR^2$

Solid sphere (axis at rim)
$I = \frac{7}{5}MR^2$

Solid plate (axis through center, in plane of plate)
$I = \frac{1}{12}ML^2$

Solid plate (axis perpendicular to plane of plate)
$I = \frac{1}{12}M(L^2 + W^2)$

Consider, for example, the moment of inertia of the Earth. If the Earth were a uniform sphere of mass M_E and radius R_E, its moment of inertia would be $\frac{2}{5}M_E R_E^2 = 0.4M_E R_E^2$. In fact, the Earth's moment of inertia is only $0.331M_E R_E^2$, considerably less than for a uniform sphere. This is due to the fact that the Earth is not homogeneous, but instead has a dense inner core surrounded by a less dense outer core and an even less dense mantle. The resulting concentration of mass near its axis of rotation gives the Earth a much smaller moment of inertia than it would have if its mass were uniformly distributed.

On the other hand, if the polar ice caps were to melt and release their water into the oceans, the Earth's moment of inertia would increase. This is because mass that had been near the axis of rotation (in the polar ice) would now be distributed more or less uniformly around the Earth (in the oceans). With more of the Earth's mass at greater distances from the axis of rotation, the moment of inertia would increase. If such an event were to occur, not only would the moment of inertia increase, but the length of the day would increase as well. We shall discuss the reasons for this in the next chapter.

The moment of inertia of an object also depends on the location and orientation of the axis of rotation. If the axis of rotation is moved, all of the r_i change, leading to a different result for I. This is investigated for the dumbbell system in the following Conceptual Checkpoint.

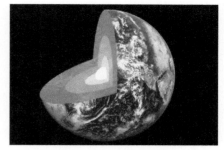

▲ The distribution of mass in the Earth is not uniform. Dense materials, like iron and nickel, have concentrated near the center, while less dense materials, like silicon and aluminum, have risen to the surface. This concentration of mass near the axis of rotation lowers the Earth's moment of inertia.

REAL-WORLD PHYSICS

Moment of inertia of the Earth

CONCEPTUAL CHECKPOINT 10-2   COMPARE THE MOMENTS OF INERTIA

If the dumbbell-shaped object in Figure 10–14 is rotated about one end, is its moment of inertia **(a)** more than, **(b)** less than, or **(c)** the same as the moment of inertia about its center? As before, assume that the masses can be treated as point masses.

REASONING AND DISCUSSION
As we saw in Exercise 10–7, the moment of inertia about the center of the dumbbell is $I = 2mR^2$. When the axis is at one end, that mass is at the radius $r = 0$, and the other mass is at $r = 2R$. Therefore, the moment of inertia is

$$I = \sum m_i r_i^2 = m \cdot 0 + m(2R)^2 = 4mR^2$$

Thus, the moment of inertia doubles when the axis of rotation is moved from the center to one end.

The reason I increases is that the moment of inertia depends on the radius squared. Hence, even small increases in r can cause significant increases in I. By moving the axis to one end, the radius to the other mass is increased to its greatest possible value. As a result, I increases.

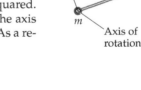

ANSWER
(a) The moment of inertia is greater about one end than about the center.

Finally, we summarize in the accompanying table the similarities between the translational kinetic energy, $K = \frac{1}{2}mv^2$, and the rotational kinetic energy, $K = \frac{1}{2}I\omega^2$. As expected, we see that the linear speed, v, has been replaced with the angular speed, ω. In addition, note that the mass m has been replaced with the moment of inertia I.

As suggested by these analogies, the moment of inertia I plays the same role in rotational motion that mass plays in translational motion. For example, the larger I the more resistant an object is to any change in its angular velocity—an object with a large I is difficult to start rotating, and once it is rotating, it is difficult to stop. We shall see further applications of this analogy in the next chapter when we consider angular momentum.

Linear Quantity	Angular Quantity
v	ω
m	I
$\frac{1}{2}mv^2$	$\frac{1}{2}I\omega^2$

10-6 Conservation of Energy

In this section, we consider the mechanical energy of objects that roll without slipping, and show how to apply energy conservation to such systems. In addition, we consider objects that rotate as a string or rope unwinds: for example, a pulley with a string wrapped around its circumference, or a yo-yo with a string wrapped around its axle. As long as the unwinding process and the rolling motion occur without slipping, the two situations are basically the same—at least as far as energy considerations are concerned.

To apply energy conservation to rolling objects, we first need to determine the kinetic energy of rolling motion. In Section 10–4 we saw that rolling motion is a combination of rotation and translation. It follows, then, that the kinetic energy of a rolling object is simply the sum of its translational kinetic energy, $\frac{1}{2}mv^2$, and its rotational kinetic energy, $\frac{1}{2}I\omega^2$:

Kinetic Energy of Rolling Motion

$$K = \tfrac{1}{2}mv^2 + \tfrac{1}{2}I\omega^2 \qquad \text{10–19}$$

Note that I in this expression is the moment of inertia about the center of the rolling object.

We can simplify the expression for the kinetic energy of a rolling object by using the fact that linear and angular speeds are related. In fact, recall that $v = r\omega$ (Equation 10–12), which can be rewritten as $\omega = v/r$. Substituting this into our expression for the rolling kinetic energy yields

Kinetic Energy of Rolling Motion: Alternative Form

$$K = \tfrac{1}{2}mv^2 + \tfrac{1}{2}I\left(\frac{v}{r}\right)^2 = \tfrac{1}{2}mv^2\left(1 + \frac{I}{mr^2}\right) \qquad \text{10–20}$$

Since $I = (\text{constant})mr^2$, the last term in Equation 10–20 is a constant that depends on the shape and mass distribution of the rolling object.

A special case of some interest is the point particle. In this case, by definition, all of the mass is at a single point. Therefore, $r = 0$, and hence $I = 0$. Substituting $I = 0$ in either Equation 10–19 or Equation 10–20 yields $K = \frac{1}{2}mv^2$, as expected. Next, we apply Equations 10–19 and 10–20 to a disk that rolls with no slipping.

EXAMPLE 10–5 LIKE A ROLLING DISK

A 1.20-kg disk with a radius of 10.0 cm rolls without slipping. If the linear speed of the disk is 1.41 m/s, find **(a)** the translational kinetic energy, **(b)** the rotational kinetic energy, and **(c)** the total kinetic energy of the disk.

PICTURE THE PROBLEM
Because the disk rolls without slipping, the angular speed and the linear speed are related by $v = r\omega$. Note that the linear speed is $v = 1.41$ m/s and the radius is $r = 10.0$ cm. Finally, we are given that the mass of the disk is 1.20 kg.

ω
$v = 1.41$ m/s
$r = 10.0$ cm

STRATEGY
We calculate each contribution to the kinetic energy separately. The linear kinetic energy, of course, is simply $\frac{1}{2}mv^2$. For the rotational kinetic energy, $\frac{1}{2}I\omega^2$, we must use the fact that the moment of inertia for a disk is $I = \frac{1}{2}mr^2$. Finally, since the disk rolls without slipping, its angular speed is $\omega = v/r$.

SOLUTION

Part (a)

1. Calculate the translational kinetic energy, $\frac{1}{2}mv^2$:

$\frac{1}{2}mv^2 = \frac{1}{2}(1.20 \text{ kg})(1.41 \text{ m/s})^2 = 1.19 \text{ J}$

Part (b)

2. Calculate the rotational kinetic energy symbolically, using $I = \frac{1}{2}mr^2$ and $\omega = v/r$:

$\frac{1}{2}I\omega^2 = \frac{1}{2}(\frac{1}{2}mr^2)\left(\frac{v}{r}\right)^2 = \frac{1}{2}(\frac{1}{2}mv^2)$

3. Substitute the numerical value for $\frac{1}{2}mv^2$ (the translational kinetic energy) obtained in Step 1:

$\frac{1}{2}I\omega^2 = \frac{1}{2}(1.19 \text{ J}) = 0.595 \text{ J}$

Part (c)

4. Sum the kinetic energies obtained in parts (a) and (b):

$K = 1.19 \text{ J} + 0.595 \text{ J} = 1.79 \text{ J}$

5. Note that the same result is obtained using Equation 10–20:

$$K = \tfrac{1}{2}mv^2\left(1 + \frac{I}{mr^2}\right) = \tfrac{1}{2}mv^2\left(1 + \frac{1}{2}\right)$$

$$= \tfrac{3}{2}(\tfrac{1}{2}mv^2) = \tfrac{3}{2}(1.19\text{ J}) = 1.79\text{ J}$$

INSIGHT

The symbolic result in Step 2 shows that the rotational kinetic energy of a uniform disk rolling without slipping is precisely one-half the disk's translational kinetic energy. Thus, 2/3 of the disk's kinetic energy is translational, 1/3 rotational. This result is independent of the disk's radius, as we can see by the cancellation of the radius r in Step 2.

To understand this cancellation, note that a larger disk has a larger moment of inertia, since it has mass farther from the axis of rotation. On the other hand, the larger disk also has a smaller angular speed, since the angular speed is inversely proportional to the radius: $\omega = v/r$. These two effects cancel, giving the same rotational kinetic energy for uniform disks of any radius—provided their linear speed is the same.

PRACTICE PROBLEM

Repeat this problem for the case of a rolling, hollow sphere.   [**Answer:** (a) 1.19 J, (b) 0.793 J, (c) 1.98 J]

Some related homework problems: Problem 58, Problem 62

CONCEPTUAL CHECKPOINT 10–3   COMPARE KINETIC ENERGIES

A solid sphere and a hollow sphere of the same mass and radius roll without slipping at the same speed. Is the kinetic energy of the solid sphere **(a)** more than, **(b)** less than, or **(c)** the same as the kinetic energy of the hollow sphere?

REASONING AND DISCUSSION

Both spheres have the same translational kinetic energy since they have the same mass and speed. The rotational kinetic energy, however, is proportional to the moment of inertia. Since the hollow sphere has the greater moment of inertia, it has the greater kinetic energy.

ANSWER

(b) The solid sphere has less kinetic energy than the hollow sphere.

Now that we can calculate the kinetic energy of rolling motion, we show how to apply it to energy conservation. For example, consider an object of mass m, radius r, and moment of inertia I at the top of a ramp, as shown in **Figure 10–17**. The object is released from rest and allowed to roll to the bottom, a vertical height h below the starting point. What is the object's speed on reaching the bottom?

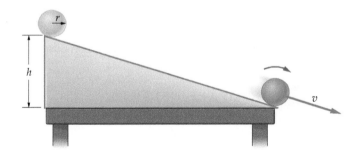

◀ **FIGURE 10–17 An object rolls down an incline**

An object starts at rest at the top of an inclined plane and rolls without slipping to the bottom. The speed of the object at the bottom depends on its moment of inertia—a larger moment of inertia results in a lower speed.

The simplest way to solve this problem is to use energy conservation. To do so, we set the initial mechanical energy at the top (i) equal to the final mechanical energy at the bottom (f). That is,

$$K_i + U_i = K_f + U_f$$

Since we are dealing with rolling motion, the kinetic energy is

$$K = \tfrac{1}{2}mv^2\left(1 + \frac{I}{mr^2}\right)$$

The potential energy is simply that due to the uniform gravitational field. Therefore,

$$U = mgy$$

With $y = h$ at the top of the ramp and the object starting at rest, we have

$$K_i + U_i = 0 + mgh = mgh$$

Similarly, with $y = 0$ at the bottom of the ramp and the object rolling with a speed v, we find

$$K_f + U_f = \tfrac{1}{2}mv^2\left(1 + \frac{I}{mr^2}\right) + 0 = \tfrac{1}{2}mv^2\left(1 + \frac{I}{mr^2}\right)$$

Setting the initial and final energies equal yields

$$mgh = \tfrac{1}{2}mv^2\left(1 + \frac{I}{mr^2}\right)$$

Solving for v, we find

$$v = \sqrt{\frac{2gh}{1 + \dfrac{I}{mr^2}}}$$

Let's quickly check one special case: namely, $I = 0$. With this substitution, we find

$$v = \sqrt{2gh}$$

This is the speed an object would have after falling straight down with no rotation through a distance h. Thus, setting $I = 0$ means there is no rotational kinetic energy, and hence the result is the same as for a point particle. As I becomes larger, the speed at the bottom of the ramp is smaller.

CONCEPTUAL CHECKPOINT 10–4 WHICH OBJECT WINS THE RACE?

A disk and a hoop of the same mass and radius are released at the same time at the top of an inclined plane. Does the disk reach the bottom of the plane **(a)** before, **(b)** after, or **(c)** at the same time as the hoop?

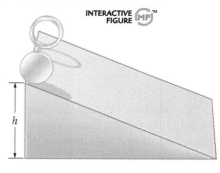

INTERACTIVE FIGURE MP

REASONING AND DISCUSSION
As we have just seen, the larger the moment of inertia, I, the smaller the speed, v. Hence the object with the larger moment of inertia (the hoop in this case) loses the race to the bottom, because its speed is less than the speed of the disk at any given height.

Another way to think about this is to recall that both objects have the same mechanical energy to begin with, namely, mgh. For the hoop, more of this initial potential energy goes into rotational kinetic energy, since the hoop has the larger moment of inertia; therefore, less energy is left for translational motion. As a result, the hoop moves more slowly and loses the race.

ANSWER
(a) The disk wins the race by reaching the bottom before the hoop.

In the next Conceptual Checkpoint, we consider the effects of a surface that changes from nonslip to frictionless.

CONCEPTUAL CHECKPOINT 10–5 COMPARE HEIGHTS

A ball is released from rest on a no-slip surface, as shown. After reaching its lowest point, the ball begins to rise again, this time on a frictionless surface. When the ball reaches its maximum height on the frictionless surface, is it **(a)** at a greater height, **(b)** at a lesser height, or **(c)** at the same height as when it was released?

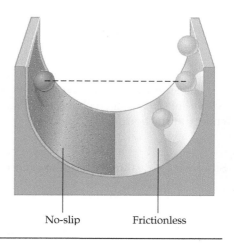

No-slip   Frictionless

REASONING AND DISCUSSION
As the ball descends on the no-slip surface, it begins to rotate, increasing its angular speed until it reaches the lowest point of the surface. When it begins to rise again, there is no friction to slow the rotational motion; thus, the ball continues to rotate with the same angular speed it had at its lowest point. Therefore, some of the ball's initial gravitational potential energy remains in the form of rotational kinetic energy. As a result, less energy is available to be converted back into gravitational potential energy, and the height is less.

ANSWER
(b) The height on the frictionless side is less.

We can also apply energy conservation to the case of a pulley, or similar object, with a string that winds or unwinds without slipping. In such cases, the relation $v = r\omega$ is valid and we can follow the same methods applied to an object that rolls without slipping.

EXAMPLE 10–6 SPINNING WHEEL

A block of mass m is attached to a string that is wrapped around the circumference of a wheel of radius R and moment of inertia I. The wheel rotates freely about its axis and the string wraps around its circumference without slipping. Initially the wheel rotates with an angular speed ω, causing the block to rise with a linear speed v. To what height does the block rise before coming to rest? Give a symbolic answer.

PICTURE THE PROBLEM

Note in our sketch that we choose the origin of the y axis to be at the initial height of the block. The positive y direction, as usual, is chosen to be upward. When the block comes to rest, then, it is at the height $y = h > 0$, where h is to be determined from the initial speed of the block and the properties of the wheel.

STRATEGY

The problem statement gives two key pieces of information. First, the string wraps onto the disk without slipping; therefore, $v = R\omega$. Second, the wheel rotates freely, which means that the mechanical energy of the system is conserved. Thus, at the height h the initial kinetic energy of the system has been converted to gravitational potential energy. This condition can be used to find h.

Before we continue, note that the mechanical energy of the system includes the following contributions: (i) linear kinetic energy for the block, (ii) rotational kinetic energy for the wheel, and (iii) gravitational potential energy for the block. We do not include the gravitational potential energy of the wheel because its height does not change.

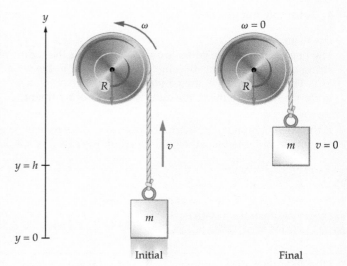

Initial   Final

SOLUTION

1. Write an expression for the initial mechanical energy of the system, E_i, including all three contributions mentioned in the Strategy:

$$E_i = \tfrac{1}{2}mv^2 + \tfrac{1}{2}I\omega^2 + mgy$$
$$= \tfrac{1}{2}mv^2 + \tfrac{1}{2}I\left(\frac{v}{R}\right)^2 + 0$$

2. Write an expression for the final mechanical energy of the system, E_f:

$$E_f = \tfrac{1}{2}mv^2 + \tfrac{1}{2}I\omega^2 + mgy$$
$$= 0 + 0 + mgh$$

3. Set the initial and final mechanical energies equal to one another, $E_i = E_f$:

$$E_i = \tfrac{1}{2}mv^2 + \tfrac{1}{2}I\left(\frac{v}{R}\right)^2 = \tfrac{1}{2}mv^2\left(1 + \frac{I}{mR^2}\right)$$
$$= E_f = mgh$$

4. Solve for the height, h:

$$h = \left(\frac{v^2}{2g}\right)\left(1 + \frac{I}{mR^2}\right)$$

INSIGHT

If the block were moving upward with speed v on its own—not attached to anything—it would rise to the height $h = v^2/2g$. We recover this result if $I = 0$, since in that case it is as if the wheel were not there. If the wheel is there, and I is nonzero, the block rises to a height that is *greater* than $v^2/2g$. The reason is that the wheel has kinetic energy, in addition to the kinetic energy of the block, and the sum of these kinetic energies must be converted to gravitational potential energy before the block and the wheel stop moving.

PRACTICE PROBLEM

Suppose the wheel is a disk with a mass equal to the mass m of the block. Find an expression for the height h in this case. [**Answer:** The moment of inertia of the wheel is $I = \tfrac{1}{2}mR^2$. Therefore, $h = (3/2)(v^2/2g)$.]

Some related homework problems: Problem 66, Problem 70, Problem 73

The situation with a yo-yo is similar, as we see in the next Active Example.

ACTIVE EXAMPLE 10–3 FIND THE YO-YO'S SPEED

Yo-Yo man releases a yo-yo from rest and allows it to drop, as he keeps the top end of the string stationary. The mass of the yo-yo is 0.056 kg, its moment of inertia is 2.9×10^{-5} kg·m^2, and the radius, r, of the axle the string wraps around is 0.0064 m. What is the linear speed, v, of the yo-yo after it has dropped through a height $h = 0.50$ m?

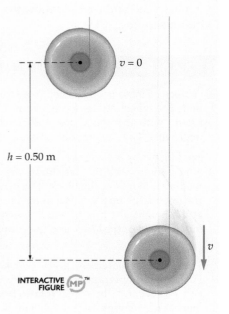

SOLUTION *(Test your understanding by performing the calculations indicated in each step.)*

1. Write the initial energy of the system:	$E_i = mgh$
2. Write the final energy of the system:	$E_f = \frac{1}{2}mv^2(1 + I/mr^2)$
3. Set $E_f = E_i$ and solve for v:	$v = \sqrt{2gh/(1 + I/mr^2)}$
4. Substitute numerical values:	$v = 0.85$ m/s

INSIGHT

The linear speed of the yo-yo is $v = r\omega$, where r is the radius of the axle from which the string unwraps without slipping. Therefore, the r in the term I/mr^2 is the radius of the axle. The outer radius of the yo-yo affects its moment of inertia, but since I is given to us in the problem statement, the outer radius is not pertinent.

YOUR TURN

If the yo-yo's moment of inertia is increased, does its final speed increase, decrease, or stay the same? Calculate the final speed for the case $I = 3.9 \times 10^{-5}$ kg·m^2.

*(Answers to **Your Turn** problems are given in the back of the book.)*

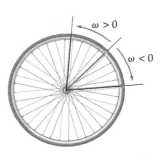

THE BIG PICTURE PUTTING PHYSICS IN CONTEXT

LOOKING BACK | LOOKING AHEAD

Our definitions of position, velocity, and acceleration from Chapter 2 are generalized in Section 10–1 to apply to rotational motion. We then use the kinematics of Chapters 2 and 4 in Section 10–2 to relate these quantities. The basic equations of motion are the same; only the names have been changed.

The kinetic energy, first defined in Chapter 7, plays a key role in defining the moment of inertia in Section 10–5.

Conservation of energy (Chapter 8) is just as important in rotational motion as it is in linear motion. We apply it to rotational motion in Section 10–6.

In Chapter 11 we relate force to angular acceleration, in much the same way that force and acceleration are related in linear motion. This results in the concept of torque in Section 11–1.

Just as linear speed is related to linear momentum (Chapter 9), angular speed is related to angular momentum. This is discussed in detail in Section 11–6.

Though a bit surprising at first, rotational motion is directly related to the motion of a pendulum swinging back and forth, and to the motion of a mass oscillating up and down on a spring. These connections are established in Section 13–3.

CHAPTER SUMMARY

10–1 ANGULAR POSITION, VELOCITY, AND ACCELERATION

To describe rotational motion, rotational analogues of position, velocity, and acceleration are defined.

Angular Position

Angular position, θ, is the angle measured from an arbitrary reference line:

$$\theta \text{ (in radians)} = \text{arc length/radius} = s/r \qquad \text{10–2}$$

Angular Velocity

Angular velocity, ω, is the rate of change of angular position. The average angular velocity is

$$\omega_{av} = \frac{\Delta\theta}{\Delta t} \qquad \text{10–3}$$

The instantaneous angular velocity is the limit of ω_{av} as Δt approaches zero:

$$\omega = \lim_{\Delta t \to 0} \frac{\Delta \theta}{\Delta t} \qquad \text{10–4}$$

Angular Acceleration

Angular acceleration, α, is the rate of change of angular velocity. The average angular acceleration is

$$\alpha_{av} = \frac{\Delta \omega}{\Delta t} \qquad \text{10–6}$$

The instantaneous angular acceleration is the limit of α_{av} as Δt approaches zero:

$$\alpha = \lim_{\Delta t \to 0} \frac{\Delta \omega}{\Delta t} \qquad \text{10–7}$$

Period of Rotation

The period, T, is the time required to complete one full rotation. If the angular velocity is constant, T is related to ω as follows:

$$T = \frac{2\pi}{\omega} \qquad \text{10–5}$$

Sign Convention

Counterclockwise rotations are positive; clockwise rotations are negative.

10–2 ROTATIONAL KINEMATICS

Rotational kinematics is the description of angular motion, in the same way that linear kinematics describes linear motion. In both cases, we assume constant acceleration.

Linear–Angular Analogues

Rotational kinematics is related to linear kinematics by the following linear–angular analogies:

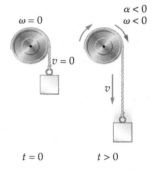

Linear Quantity	Angular Quantity
x	θ
v	ω
a	α

Kinematic Equations (Constant Acceleration)

The equations of rotational kinematics are the same as the equations of linear kinematics, with the substitutions indicated by the linear–angular analogies:

Linear Equation		Angular Equation	
$v = v_0 + at$	2–7	$\omega = \omega_0 + \alpha t$	**10–8**
$x = x_0 + \frac{1}{2}(v_0 + v)t$	2–10	$\theta = \theta_0 + \frac{1}{2}(\omega_0 + \omega)t$	**10–9**
$x = x_0 + v_0 t + \frac{1}{2}at^2$	2–11	$\theta = \theta_0 + \omega_0 t + \frac{1}{2}\alpha t^2$	**10–10**
$v^2 = v_0^2 + 2a(x - x_0)$	2–12	$\omega^2 = \omega_0^2 + 2\alpha(\theta - \theta_0)$	**10–11**

10–3 CONNECTIONS BETWEEN LINEAR AND ROTATIONAL QUANTITIES

A point on a rotating object follows a circular path. At any instant of time, the point is moving in a direction tangential to the circle, with a linear speed and acceleration. The linear speed and acceleration are related to the angular speed and acceleration.

Tangential Speed

The tangential speed, v_t, of a point on a rotating object is

$$v_t = r\omega \qquad \text{10–12}$$

Centripetal Acceleration

The centripetal acceleration, a_{cp}, of a point on a rotating object is

$$a_{cp} = r\omega^2 \qquad \text{10–13}$$

Centripetal acceleration is due to a change in direction of motion.

Tangential Acceleration

The tangential acceleration, a_t, of a point on a rotating object is

$$a_t = r\alpha \qquad \text{10–14}$$

Tangential acceleration is due to a change in speed.

Total Acceleration

The total acceleration of a rotating object is the vector sum of its tangential and centripetal accelerations.

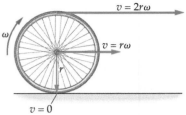

10–4 ROLLING MOTION

Rolling motion is a combination of translational and rotational motions. An object of radius r, rolling without slipping, translates with linear speed v and rotates with angular speed

$$\omega = v/r \qquad \text{10–15}$$

10–5 ROTATIONAL KINETIC ENERGY AND THE MOMENT OF INERTIA

Rotating objects have kinetic energy, just as objects in linear motion have kinetic energy.

Rotational Kinetic Energy

The kinetic energy of a rotating object is

$$K = \tfrac{1}{2}I\omega^2 \qquad \text{10–17}$$

The quantity I is the moment of inertia.

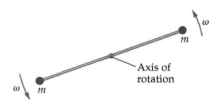

Moment of Inertia, Discrete Masses

The moment of inertia, I, of a collection of masses, m_i, at distances r_i from the axis of rotation is

$$I = \sum m_i r_i^2 \qquad \text{10–18}$$

Moment of Inertia, Continuous Distribution of Mass

In a continuous object, the moment of inertia is calculated by dividing the object into a collection of small mass elements and summing $m_i r_i^2$ for each element. Results for a variety of continuous objects are collected in Table 10–1 on p. 314.

Linear–Angular Analogue

The moment of inertia is the rotational analogue to mass in linear systems. In particular, an object with a large moment of inertia is hard to start rotating and hard to stop rotating.

10–6 CONSERVATION OF ENERGY

Energy conservation can be applied to a variety of rotational systems in the same way that it is applied to translational systems.

Kinetic Energy of Rolling Motion

The kinetic energy of an object that rolls without slipping is

$$K = \tfrac{1}{2}mv^2 + \tfrac{1}{2}I\omega^2 \qquad \text{10–19}$$

Since rolling without slipping implies that $\omega = v/r$, the kinetic energy can be written as follows:

$$K = \tfrac{1}{2}mv^2 + \tfrac{1}{2}I\left(\frac{v}{r}\right)^2 = \tfrac{1}{2}mv^2\left(1 + \frac{I}{mr^2}\right) \qquad \text{10–20}$$

Energy Conservation

Conservation of mechanical energy is a statement that the initial kinetic plus potential energy is equal to the final kinetic plus potential energy: $K_i + U_i = K_f + U_f$. By taking into account both rotational and translational kinetic energy, energy conservation can be applied in the same way as was done for linear systems.

PROBLEM-SOLVING SUMMARY

Type of Problem	Relevant Physical Concepts	Related Examples
Apply rotational kinematics with constant angular acceleration.	Rotational kinematics is completely analogous to the linear kinematics studied in Chapter 2. Angular problems are solved in the same way as the corresponding linear problems.	Example 10–1, Example 10–2 Active Example 10–1
Relate linear and angular motion.	Linear speed and angular speed are related by $v = r\omega$. Similarly, linear and angular accelerations are related by $a = r\alpha$. The centripetal acceleration of an object in circular motion is $a_{cp} = r\omega^2$.	Example 10–3 Active Example 10–2
Find the rotational kinetic energy of an object.	Rotational kinetic energy is given by $K = \frac{1}{2}I\omega^2$. The moment of inertia, I, plays the same role in rotational motion as the mass in linear motion.	Example 10–4, Example 10–5
Apply energy conservation to a rotational system.	To use energy conservation in a system with rotational motion, it is necessary to include the kinetic energy of rotation as one of the forms of energy.	Example 10–6 Active Example 10–3

CONCEPTUAL QUESTIONS

For instructor-assigned homework, go to www.masteringphysics.com

(Answers to odd-numbered Conceptual Questions can be found in the back of the book.)

1. A rigid object rotates about a fixed axis. Do all points on the object have the same angular speed? Do all points on the object have the same linear speed? Explain.

2. Can you drive your car in such a way that your tangential acceleration is zero while at the same time your centripetal acceleration is nonzero? Give an example if your answer is yes, state why not if your answer is no.

3. Can you drive your car in such a way that your tangential acceleration is nonzero while at the same time your centripetal acceleration is zero? Give an example if your answer is yes, state why not if your answer is no.

4. The fact that the Earth rotates gives people in New York a linear speed of about 750 mi/h. Where should you stand on the Earth to have the smallest possible linear speed?

5. At the local carnival you and a friend decide to take a ride on the Ferris wheel. As the wheel rotates with a constant angular speed, your friend poses the following questions: **(a)** Is my linear velocity constant? **(b)** Is my linear speed constant? **(c)** Is the magnitude of my centripetal acceleration constant? **(d)** Is the direction of my centripetal acceleration constant? What is your answer to each of these questions?

6. Why should changing the axis of rotation of an object change its moment of inertia, given that its shape and mass remain the same?

7. Give a common, everyday example for each of the following: **(a)** An object that has zero rotational kinetic energy but nonzero translational kinetic energy. **(b)** An object that has zero translational kinetic energy but nonzero rotational kinetic energy. **(c)** An object that has nonzero rotational and translational kinetic energies.

8. Two spheres have identical radii and masses. How might you tell which of these spheres is hollow and which is solid?

9. At the grocery store you pick up a can of beef broth and a can of chunky beef stew. The cans are identical in diameter and weight. Rolling both of them down the aisle with the same initial speed, you notice that the can of chunky stew rolls much farther than the can of broth. Why?

10. Suppose we change the race shown in Conceptual Checkpoint 10–4 so that a hoop of radius R and mass M races a hoop of radius R and mass $2M$. **(a)** Does the hoop with mass M finish before, after, or at the same time as the hoop with mass $2M$? Explain. **(b)** How would your answer to part (a) change if the hoops had different radii? Explain.

PROBLEMS AND CONCEPTUAL EXERCISES

Note: Answers to odd-numbered Problems and Conceptual Exercises can be found in the back of the book. **IP** *denotes an integrated problem, with both conceptual and numerical parts;* **BIO** *identifies problems of biological or medical interest;* **CE** *indicates a conceptual exercise.* **Predict/Explain** *problems ask for two responses:* **(a)** *your prediction of a physical outcome, and* **(b)** *the best explanation among three provided. On all problems, red bullets (•, ••, •••) are used to indicate the level of difficulty.*

SECTION 10–1 ANGULAR POSITION, VELOCITY, AND ACCELERATION

1. • The following angles are given in degrees. Convert them to radians: 30°, 45°, 90°, 180°.

2. • The following angles are given in radians. Convert them to degrees: $\pi/6, 0.70\pi, 1.5\pi, 5\pi$.

3. • Find the angular speed of **(a)** the minute hand and **(b)** the hour hand of the famous clock in London, England, that rings the bell known as Big Ben.

4. • Express the angular velocity of the second hand on a clock in the following units: **(a)** rev/hr, **(b)** deg/min, and **(c)** rad/s.

5. • Rank the following in order of increasing angular speed: an automobile tire rotating at 2.00×10^3 deg/s, an electric drill rotating at 400.0 rev/min, and an airplane propeller rotating at 40.0 rad/s.

6. • A spot of paint on a bicycle tire moves in a circular path of radius 0.33 m. When the spot has traveled a linear distance of 1.95 m, through what angle has the tire rotated? Give your answer in radians.

7. • What is the angular speed (in rev/min) of the Earth as it orbits about the Sun?

8. • Find the angular speed of the Earth as it spins about its axis. Give your result in rad/s.

9. • **The Crab Nebula** One of the most studied objects in the night sky is the Crab nebula, the remains of a supernova explosion observed by the Chinese in 1054. In 1968 it was discovered that a pulsar—a rapidly rotating neutron star that emits a pulse of radio waves with each revolution—lies near the center of the Crab nebula. The period of this pulsar is 33 ms. What is the angular speed (in rad/s) of the Crab nebula pulsar?

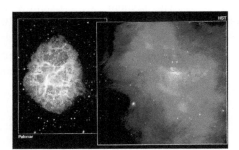

The photo at left is a true-color visible light image of the Crab nebula. In the false-color breakout, the pulsar can be seen as the left member of the pair of stars just above the center of the frame. (Problems 9 and 106)

10. •• **IP** A 3.5-inch floppy disk in a computer rotates with a period of 2.00×10^{-1} s. What are **(a)** the angular speed of the disk and **(b)** the linear speed of a point on the rim of the disk? **(c)** Does a point near the center of the disk have an angular speed that is greater than, less than, or the same as the angular speed found in part (a)? Explain. (*Note:* A 3.5-inch floppy disk is 3.5 inches in diameter.)

11. •• The angle an airplane propeller makes with the horizontal as a function of time is given by $\theta = (125 \text{ rad/s})t + (42.5 \text{ rad/s}^2)t^2$. **(a)** Estimate the instantaneous angular velocity at $t = 0.00$ s by calculating the average angular velocity from $t = 0.00$ s to $t = 0.010$ s. **(b)** Estimate the instantaneous angular velocity at $t = 1.000$ s by calculating the average angular velocity from $t = 1.000$ s to $t = 1.010$ s. **(c)** Estimate the instantaneous angular velocity at $t = 2.000$ s by calculating the average angular velocity from $t = 2.000$ s to $t = 2.010$ s. **(d)** Based on your results from parts (a), (b), and (c), is the angular acceleration of the propeller positive, negative, or zero? Explain. **(e)** Calculate the average angular acceleration from $t = 0.00$ s to $t = 1.00$ s and from $t = 1.00$ s to $t = 2.00$ s.

SECTION 10-2   ROTATIONAL KINEMATICS

12. • **CE** An object at rest begins to rotate with a constant angular acceleration. If this object rotates through an angle θ in the time t, through what angle did it rotate in the time $t/2$?

13. • **CE** An object at rest begins to rotate with a constant angular acceleration. If the angular speed of the object is ω after the time t, what was its angular speed at the time $t/2$?

14. • In Active Example 10–1, how long does it take before the angular velocity of the pulley is equal to -5.0 rad/s?

15. • In Example 10–2, through what angle has the wheel turned when its angular speed is 2.45 rad/s?

16. • The angular speed of a propeller on a boat increases with constant acceleration from 12 rad/s to 26 rad/s in 2.5 revolutions. What is the acceleration of the propeller?

17. • The angular speed of a propeller on a boat increases with constant acceleration from 11 rad/s to 28 rad/s in 2.4 seconds. Through what angle did the propeller turn during this time?

18. •• After fixing a flat tire on a bicycle you give the wheel a spin. **(a)** If its initial angular speed was 6.35 rad/s and it rotated 14.2 revolutions before coming to rest, what was its average angular acceleration? **(b)** For what length of time did the wheel rotate?

19. •• **IP** A ceiling fan is rotating at 0.96 rev/s. When turned off, it slows uniformly to a stop in 2.4 min. **(a)** How many revolutions does the fan make in this time? **(b)** Using the result from part (a), find the number of revolutions the fan must make for its speed to decrease from 0.96 rev/s to 0.48 rev/s.

20. •• A discus thrower starts from rest and begins to rotate with a constant angular acceleration of 2.2 rad/s^2. **(a)** How many revolutions does it take for the discus thrower's angular speed to reach 6.3 rad/s? **(b)** How much time does this take?

21. •• **Half Time** At 3:00 the hour hand and the minute hand of a clock point in directions that are $90.0°$ apart. What is the first time after 3:00 that the angle between the two hands has decreased by half to $45.0°$?

When the little hand is on the 3 and the big hand is on the 12 . . . . (Problem 21)

22. •• **BIO** A centrifuge is a common laboratory instrument that separates components of differing densities in solution. This is accomplished by spinning a sample around in a circle with a large angular speed. Suppose that after a centrifuge in a medical laboratory is turned off, it continues to rotate with a constant angular deceleration for 10.2 s before coming to rest. **(a)** If its initial angular speed was 3850 rpm, what is the magnitude of its angular deceleration? **(b)** How many revolutions did the centrifuge complete after being turned off?

23. •• **The Slowing Earth** The Earth's rate of rotation is constantly decreasing, causing the day to increase in duration. In the year 2006 the Earth took about 0.840 s longer to complete 365 revolutions than it did in the year 1906. What was the average angular acceleration of the Earth during this time? Give your answer in rad/s^2.

24. •• **IP** A compact disk (CD) speeds up uniformly from rest to 310 rpm in 3.3 s. **(a)** Describe a strategy that allows you to calculate the number of revolutions the CD makes in this time. **(b)** Use your strategy to find the number of revolutions.

25. •• When a carpenter shuts off his circular saw, the 10.0-inch-diameter blade slows from 4440 rpm to 0.00 rpm in 2.50 s. **(a)** What is the angular acceleration of the blade? **(b)** What is the distance traveled by a point on the rim of the blade during the deceleration? **(c)** What is the magnitude of the net displacement of a point on the rim of the blade during the deceleration?

26. •• **The World's Fastest Turbine** The drill used by most dentists today is powered by a small air turbine that can operate at angular speeds of 350,000 rpm. These drills, along with ultrasonic dental drills, are the fastest turbines in the world—far exceeding the angular speeds of jet engines. Suppose a drill starts at rest and comes up to operating speed in 2.1 s. **(a)** Find the angular acceler-

ation produced by the drill, assuming it to be constant. **(b)** How many revolutions does the drill bit make as it comes up to speed?

An air-turbine dentist drill—faster than a jet engine. (Problem 26)

SECTION 10–3 CONNECTIONS BETWEEN LINEAR AND ROTATIONAL QUANTITIES

27. • **CE Predict/Explain** Two children, Jason and Betsy, ride on the same merry-go-round. Jason is a distance R from the axis of rotation; Betsy is a distance $2R$ from the axis. Is the rotational period of Jason greater than, less than, or equal to the rotational period of Betsy? **(b)** Choose the *best explanation* from among the following:
   I. The period is greater for Jason because he moves more slowly than Betsy.
   II. The period is greater for Betsy since she must go around a circle with a larger circumference.
   III. It takes the same amount of time for the merry-go-round to complete a revolution for all points on the merry-go-round.

28. • **CE** Referring to the previous problem, what are **(a)** the ratio of Jason's angular speed to Betsy's angular speed, **(b)** the ratio of Jason's linear speed to Betsy's linear speed, and **(c)** the ratio of Jason's centripetal acceleration to Betsy's centripetal acceleration?

29. • **CE Predict/Explain A Tall Building** The world's tallest building is the Taipei 101 Tower in Taiwan, which rises to a height of 508 m (1667 ft). **(a)** When standing on the top floor of the building, is your angular speed due to the Earth's rotation greater than, less than, or equal to your angular speed when you stand on the ground floor? **(b)** Choose the *best explanation* from among the following:
   I. The angular speed is the same at all distances from the axis of rotation.
   II. At the top of the building you are farther from the axis of rotation and hence you have a greater angular speed.
   III. You are spinning faster when you are closer to the axis of rotation.

30. • The hour hand on a certain clock is 8.2 cm long. Find the tangential speed of the tip of this hand.

31. • Two children ride on the merry-go-round shown in Conceptual Checkpoint 10–1. Child 1 is 2.0 m from the axis of rotation, and child 2 is 1.5 m from the axis. If the merry-go-round completes one revolution every 4.5 s, find **(a)** the angular speed and **(b)** the linear speed of each child.

32. • The outer edge of a rotating Frisbee with a diameter of 29 cm has a linear speed of 3.7 m/s. What is the angular speed of the Frisbee?

33. • A carousel at the local carnival rotates once every 45 seconds. **(a)** What is the linear speed of an outer horse on the carousel, which is 2.75 m from the axis of rotation? **(b)** What is the linear speed of an inner horse that is 1.75 m from the axis of rotation?

34. •• **IP** Jeff of the Jungle swings on a vine that is 7.20 m long (**Figure 10–18**). At the bottom of the swing, just before hitting the tree, Jeff's linear speed is 8.50 m/s. **(a)** Find Jeff's angular speed at this time. **(b)** What centripetal acceleration does Jeff experience at the bottom of his swing? **(c)** What exerts the force that is responsible for Jeff's centripetal acceleration?

▲ **FIGURE 10–18** Problems 34 and 35

35. •• Suppose, in Problem 34, that at some point in his swing Jeff of the Jungle has an angular speed of 0.850 rad/s and an angular acceleration of 0.620 rad/s². Find the magnitude of his centripetal, tangential, and total accelerations, and the angle his total acceleration makes with respect to the tangential direction of motion.

36. •• A compact disk, which has a diameter of 12.0 cm, speeds up uniformly from 0.00 to 4.00 rev/s in 3.00 s. What is the tangential acceleration of a point on the outer rim of the disk at the moment when its angular speed is **(a)** 2.00 rev/s and **(b)** 3.00 rev/s?

37. •• **IP** When a compact disk with a 12.0-cm diameter is rotating at 5.05 rad/s, what are **(a)** the linear speed and **(b)** the centripetal acceleration of a point on its outer rim? **(c)** Consider a point on the CD that is halfway between its center and its outer rim. Without repeating all of the calculations required for parts (a) and (b), determine the linear speed and the centripetal acceleration of this point.

38. •• **IP** As Tony the fisherman reels in a "big one," he turns the spool on his fishing reel at the rate of 3.0 complete revolutions every second (**Figure 10–19**). **(a)** If the radius of the reel is 3.7 cm, what is the linear speed of the fishing line as it is reeled in? **(b)** How would your answer to part (a) change if the radius of the reel were doubled?

▲ **FIGURE 10–19** Problem 38

39. •• A Ferris wheel with a radius of 9.5 m rotates at a constant rate, completing one revolution every 36 s. Find the direction and magnitude of a passenger's acceleration when **(a)** at the top and **(b)** at the bottom of the wheel.

40. •• Suppose the Ferris wheel in the previous problem begins to decelerate at the rate of 0.22 rad/s² when the passenger is at the top of the wheel. Find the direction and magnitude of the passenger's acceleration at that time.

41. •• **IP** A person swings a 0.52-kg tether ball tied to a 4.5-m rope in an approximately horizontal circle. **(a)** If the maximum tension the rope can withstand before breaking is 11 N, what is the maximum angular speed of the ball? **(b)** If the rope is shortened, does the maximum angular speed found in part (a) increase, decrease, or stay the same? Explain.

42. •• To polish a filling, a dentist attaches a sanding disk with a radius of 3.20 mm to the drill. **(a)** When the drill is operated at 2.15×10^4 rad/s, what is the tangential speed of the rim of the disk? **(b)** What period of rotation must the disk have if the tangential speed of its rim is to be 275 m/s?

43. •• In the previous problem, suppose the disk has an angular acceleration of 232 rad/s² when its angular speed is 640 rad/s. Find both the tangential and centripetal accelerations of a point on the rim of the disk.

44. •• **The Bohr Atom** The Bohr model of the hydrogen atom pictures the electron as a tiny particle moving in a circular orbit about a stationary proton. In the lowest-energy orbit the distance from the proton to the electron is 5.29×10^{-11} m, and the linear speed of the electron is 2.18×10^6 m/s. **(a)** What is the angular speed of the electron? **(b)** How many orbits about the proton does it make each second? **(c)** What is the electron's centripetal acceleration?

45. ••• A wheel of radius R starts from rest and accelerates with a constant angular acceleration α about a fixed axis. At what time t will the centripetal and tangential accelerations of a point on the rim have the same magnitude?

SECTION 10–4   ROLLING MOTION

46. • **CE** As you drive down the highway, the top of your tires are moving with a speed v. What is the reading on your speedometer?

47. •• The tires on a car have a radius of 31 cm. What is the angular speed of these tires when the car is driven at 15 m/s?

48. • A child pedals a tricycle, giving the driving wheel an angular speed of 0.373 rev/s (**Figure 10–20**). If the radius of the wheel is 0.260 m, what is the child's linear speed?

▲ **FIGURE 10–20** Problem 48

49. • A soccer ball, which has a circumference of 70.0 cm, rolls 14.0 yards in 3.35 s. What was the average angular speed of the ball during this time?

50. •• As you drive down the road at 17 m/s, you press on the gas pedal and speed up with a uniform acceleration of 1.12 m/s² for 0.65 s. If the tires on your car have a radius of 33 cm, what is their angular displacement during this period of acceleration?

51. •• **IP** A bicycle coasts downhill and accelerates from rest to a linear speed of 8.90 m/s in 12.2 s. **(a)** If the bicycle's tires have a radius of 36.0 cm, what is their angular acceleration? **(b)** If the radius of the tires had been smaller, would their angular acceleration be greater than or less than the result found in part (a)?

SECTION 10–5   ROTATIONAL KINETIC ENERGY AND THE MOMENT OF INERTIA

52. • **CE Predict/Explain** The minute and hour hands of a clock have a common axis of rotation and equal mass. The minute hand is long, thin, and uniform; the hour hand is short, thick, and uniform. **(a)** Is the moment of inertia of the minute hand greater than, less than, or equal to the moment of inertia of the hour hand? **(b)** Choose the *best explanation* from among the following:
   I. The hands have equal mass, and hence equal moments of inertia.
   II. Having mass farther from the axis of rotation results in a greater moment of inertia.
   III. The more compact hour hand concentrates its mass and has the greater moment of inertia.

53. • **CE Predict/Explain** Tons of dust and small particles rain down onto the Earth from space every day. As a result, does the Earth's moment of inertia increase, decrease, or stay the same? **(b)** Choose the *best explanation* from among the following:
   I. The dust adds mass to the Earth and increases its radius slightly.
   II. As the dust moves closer to the axis of rotation, the moment of inertia decreases.
   III. The moment of inertia is a conserved quantity and cannot change.

54. **CE** • **Predict/Explain** Suppose a bicycle wheel is rotated about an axis through its rim and parallel to its axle. **(a)** Is its moment of inertia about this axis greater than, less than, or equal to its moment of inertia about its axle? **(b)** Choose the *best explanation* from among the following:
   I. The moment of inertia is greatest when an object is rotated about its center.
   II. The mass and shape of the wheel remain the same.
   III. Mass is farther from the axis when the wheel is rotated about the rim.

55. • The moment of inertia of a 0.98-kg bicycle wheel rotating about its center is 0.13 kg · m². What is the radius of this wheel, assuming the weight of the spokes can be ignored?

56. • What is the kinetic energy of the grindstone in Example 10–4 if it completes one revolution every 4.20 s?

57. • An electric fan spinning with an angular speed of 13 rad/s has a kinetic energy of 4.6 J. What is the moment of inertia of the fan?

58. • Repeat Example 10–5 for the case of a rolling hoop of the same mass and radius.

59. •• **CE** The L-shaped object in **Figure 10–21** can be rotated in one of the following three ways: case 1, rotation about the x axis; case 2, rotation about the y axis; and case 3, rotation about the

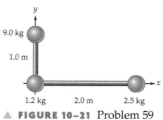

▲ **FIGURE 10–21** Problem 59

z axis (which passes through the origin perpendicular to the plane of the figure). Rank these three cases in order of increasing moment of inertia. Indicate ties where appropriate.

60. •• **IP** A 12-g CD with a radius of 6.0 cm rotates with an angular speed of 34 rad/s. **(a)** What is its kinetic energy? **(b)** What angular speed must the CD have if its kinetic energy is to be doubled?

61. •• When a pitcher throws a curve ball, the ball is given a fairly rapid spin. If a 0.15-kg baseball with a radius of 3.7 cm is thrown with a linear speed of 48 m/s and an angular speed of 42 rad/s, how much of its kinetic energy is translational and how much is rotational? Assume the ball is a uniform, solid sphere.

62. •• **IP** A basketball rolls along the floor with a constant linear speed v. **(a)** Find the fraction of its total kinetic energy that is in the form of rotational kinetic energy about the center of the ball. **(b)** If the linear speed of the ball is doubled to $2v$, does your answer to part (a) increase, decrease, or stay the same? Explain.

63. •• Find the rate at which the rotational kinetic energy of the Earth is decreasing. The Earth has a moment of inertia of $0.331 M_E R_E^2$, where $R_E = 6.38 \times 10^6$ m and $M_E = 5.97 \times 10^{24}$ kg, and its rotational period increases by 2.3 ms with each passing century. Give your answer in watts.

64. •• A lawn mower has a flat, rod-shaped steel blade that rotates about its center. The mass of the blade is 0.65 kg and its length is 0.55 m. **(a)** What is the rotational energy of the blade at its operating angular speed of 3500 rpm? **(b)** If all of the rotational kinetic energy of the blade could be converted to gravitational potential energy, to what height would the blade rise?

SECTION 10–6 CONSERVATION OF ENERGY

65. • **CE** Consider the physical situation shown in Conceptual Checkpoint 10–5. Suppose this time a ball is released from rest on the frictionless surface. When the ball comes to rest on the no-slip surface, is its height greater than, less than, or equal to the height from which it was released?

66. • Suppose the block in Example 10–6 has a mass of 2.1 kg and an initial upward speed of 0.33 m/s. Find the moment of inertia of the wheel if its radius is 8.0 cm and the block rises to a height of 7.4 cm before momentarily coming to rest.

67. • Through what height must the yo-yo in Active Example 10–3 fall for its linear speed to be 0.65 m/s?

68. •• **CE** Suppose we change the race shown in Conceptual Checkpoint 10–4 to a race between three different disks. Let disk 1 have a mass M and a radius R, disk 2 have a mass M and a radius $2R$, and disk 3 have a mass $2M$ and a radius R. Rank the three disks in the order in which they finish the race. Indicate ties where appropriate.

69. •• Calculate the speeds of **(a)** the disk and **(b)** the hoop at the bottom of the inclined plane in Conceptual Checkpoint 10–4 if the height of the incline is 0.82 m.

70. •• **IP Atwood's Machine** The two masses ($m_1 = 5.0$ kg and $m_2 = 3.0$ kg) in the Atwood's machine shown in **Figure 10–22** are released from rest, with m_1 at a height of 0.75 m above the floor. When m_1 hits the ground its speed is 1.8 m/s. Assuming that the pulley is a uniform disk with a radius of 12 cm, **(a)** outline a strategy that allows you to find the mass of the pulley. **(b)** Implement the strategy given in part (a) and determine the pulley's mass.

71. •• In Conceptual Checkpoint 10–5, assume the ball is a solid sphere of radius 2.9 cm and mass 0.14 kg. If the ball is released from rest at a height of 0.78 m above the bottom of the track on the no-slip side, **(a)** what is its angular speed when it is on the

frictionless side of the track? **(b)** How high does the ball rise on the frictionless side?

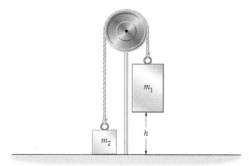

▲ **FIGURE 10–22** Problem 70

72. •• **IP** After you pick up a spare, your bowling ball rolls without slipping back toward the ball rack with a linear speed of 2.85 m/s (**Figure 10–23**). To reach the rack, the ball rolls up a ramp that rises through a vertical distance of 0.53 m. **(a)** What is the linear speed of the ball when it reaches the top of the ramp? **(b)** If the radius of the ball were increased, would the speed found in part (a) increase, decrease, or stay the same? Explain.

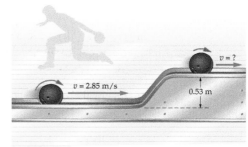

▲ **FIGURE 10–23** Problem 72

73. •• **IP** A 1.3-kg block is tied to a string that is wrapped around the rim of a pulley of radius 7.2 cm. The block is released from rest. **(a)** Assuming the pulley is a uniform disk with a mass of 0.31 kg, find the speed of the block after it has fallen through a height of 0.50 m. **(b)** If a small lead weight is attached near the rim of the pulley and this experiment is repeated, will the speed of the block increase, decrease, or stay the same? Explain.

74. •• After doing some exercises on the floor, you are lying on your back with one leg pointing straight up. If you allow your leg to fall freely until it hits the floor (**Figure 10–24**), what is the tangential speed of your foot just before it lands? Assume the leg can be treated as a uniform rod 0.95 m long that pivots freely about the hip.

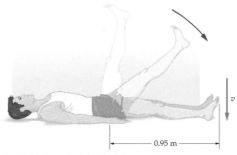

▲ **FIGURE 10–24** Problem 74

75. ••• A 2.0-kg solid cylinder (radius = 0.10 m, length = 0.50 m) is released from rest at the top of a ramp and allowed to roll without slipping. The ramp is 0.75 m high and 5.0 m long. When the cylinder reaches the bottom of the ramp, what are

(a) its total kinetic energy, (b) its rotational kinetic energy, and (c) its translational kinetic energy?

76. ••• A 2.5-kg solid sphere (radius = 0.10 m) is released from rest at the top of a ramp and allowed to roll without slipping. The ramp is 0.75 m high and 5.6 m long. When the sphere reaches the bottom of the ramp, what are (a) its total kinetic energy, (b) its rotational kinetic energy, and (c) its translational kinetic energy?

GENERAL PROBLEMS

77. • **CE** When you stand on the observation deck of the Empire State Building in New York, is your linear speed due to the Earth's rotation greater than, less than, or the same as when you were waiting for the elevators on the ground floor?

78. • **CE Hard-Boiled Versus Raw Eggs** One way to tell whether an egg is raw or hard boiled—without cracking it open—is to place it on a kitchen counter and give it a spin. If you do this to two eggs, one raw the other hard boiled, you will find that one spins considerably longer than the other. Is the raw egg the one that spins a long time, or the one that stops spinning in a short time?

79. • **CE** When the Hoover Dam was completed and the reservoir behind it filled with water, did the moment of inertia of the Earth increase, decrease, or stay the same?

80. • **Weightless on the Equator** In Quito, Ecuador, near the equator, you weigh about half a pound less than in Barrow, Alaska, near the pole. Find the rotational period of the Earth that would make you feel weightless at the equator. (With this rotational period, your centripetal acceleration would be equal to the acceleration due to gravity, g.)

81. • A diver completes $2\frac{1}{2}$ somersaults during a 2.3-s dive. What was the diver's average angular speed during the dive?

82. • What linear speed must a 0.065-kg hula hoop have if its total kinetic energy is to be 0.12 J? Assume the hoop rolls on the ground without slipping.

83. • **BIO Losing Consciousness** A pilot performing a horizontal turn will lose consciousness if she experiences a centripetal acceleration greater than 7.00 times the acceleration of gravity. What is the minimum radius turn she can make without losing consciousness if her plane is flying with a constant speed of 245 m/s?

84. •• **CE** Place two quarters on a table with their rims touching, as shown in **Figure 10–25**. While holding one quarter fixed, roll the other one—without slipping—around the circumference of the fixed quarter until it has completed one round trip. How many revolutions has the rolling quarter made about its center?

▲ **FIGURE 10–25** Problem 84

85. • **CE** The object shown in **Figure 10–26** can be rotated in three different ways: case 1, rotation about the x axis; case 2, rotation about the y axis; and case 3, rotation about the z axis. Rank these three cases in order of increasing moment of inertia. Indicate ties where appropriate.

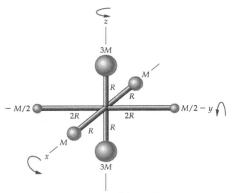

▲ **FIGURE 10–26** Problem 85

86. •• The accompanying double-exposure photograph illustrates a method for determining the speed of a BB. The circular disk in the upper part of the photo rotates with a constant angular speed of 50.4 revolutions per second. A single white radial line drawn on the disk is seen in two locations in the double exposure. Below the disk are two bright images of a BB taken during the two exposures. Use the information given here and in the photo to estimate the speed of the BB.

Speeding BB and spinning wheel. (Problems 86 and 87)

87. •• Referring to the previous problem, (a) estimate the linear speed of a point on the rim of the rotating disk. (b) By comparing the arc length between the two white lines to the distance covered by the BB, estimate the speed of the BB. (c) What radius must the disk have for the linear speed of a point on its rim to be the same as the speed of the BB? (d) Suppose a 1.0-g lump of putty is stuck to the rim of the disk. What centripetal force is required to hold the putty in place?

88. •• **IP When the Hands Align** A mathematically inclined friend e-mails you the following instructions: "Meet me in the cafeteria the first time after 2:00 P.M. today that the hands of a clock point in the same direction." (a) Is the desired meeting time before, after, or equal to 2:10 P.M.? Explain. (b) Is the desired meeting time before, after, or equal to 2:15 P.M.? Explain. (c) When should you meet your friend?

89. •• **IP** A diver runs horizontally off the end of a diving tower 3.0 m above the surface of the water with an initial speed of 2.6 m/s. During her fall she rotates with an average angular speed of 2.2 rad/s. (a) How many revolutions has she made when she hits the water? (b) How does your answer to part (a) depend on the diver's initial speed? Explain.

90. •• **IP** A potter's wheel of radius 6.8 cm rotates with a period of 0.52 s. What are (a) the linear speed and (b) the centripetal acceleration of a small lump of clay on the rim of the wheel? (c) How do your answers to parts (a) and (b) change if the period of rotation is doubled?

91. •• **IP Playing a CD** The record in an old-fashioned record player always rotates at the same angular speed. With CDs, the situation is different. For a CD to play properly, the point on the CD where the laser beam shines must have a linear speed $v_t = 1.25$ m/s, as indicated in **Figure 10–27**. **(a)** As the CD plays from the center outward, does its angular speed increase, decrease, or stay the same? Explain. **(b)** Find the angular speed of a CD when the laser beam is 2.50 cm from its center. **(c)** Repeat part (b) for the laser beam 6.00 cm from the center. **(d)** If the CD plays for 66.5 min, and the laser beam moves from 2.50 cm to 6.00 cm during this time, what is the CD's average angular acceleration?

▲ **FIGURE 10–27** Problem 91

92. •• **BIO Roller Pigeons** Pigeons are bred to display a number of interesting characteristics. One breed of pigeon, the "roller," is remarkable for the fact that it does a number of backward somersaults as it drops straight down toward the ground. Suppose a roller pigeon drops from rest and free falls downward for a distance of 14 m. If the pigeon somersaults at the rate of 12 rad/s, how many revolutions has it completed by the end of its fall?

93. •• As a marble with a diameter of 1.6 cm rolls down an incline, its center moves with a linear acceleration of 3.3 m/s². **(a)** What is the angular acceleration of the marble? **(b)** What is the angular speed of the marble after it rolls for 1.5 s from rest?

94. •• A rubber ball with a radius of 3.2 cm rolls along the horizontal surface of a table with a constant linear speed v. When the ball rolls off the edge of the table, it falls 0.66 m to the floor below. If the ball completes 0.37 revolution during its fall, what was its linear speed, v?

95. •• A college campus features a large fountain surrounded by a circular pool. Two students start at the northernmost point of the pool and walk slowly around it in opposite directions. **(a)** If the angular speed of the student walking in the clockwise direction (as viewed from above) is 0.045 rad/s and the angular speed of the other student is 0.023 rad/s, how long does it take before they meet? **(b)** At what angle, measured clockwise from due north, do the students meet? **(c)** If the difference in linear speed between the students is 0.23 m/s, what is the radius of the fountain?

96. •• **IP** A yo-yo moves downward until it reaches the end of its string, where it "sleeps." As it sleeps—that is, spins in place—its angular speed decreases from 35 rad/s to 25 rad/s. During this time it completes 120 revolutions. **(a)** How long did it take for the yo-yo to slow from 35 rad/s to 25 rad/s? **(b)** How long does it take for the yo-yo to slow from 25 rad/s to 15 rad/s? Assume a constant angular acceleration as the yo-yo sleeps.

97. •• **IP (a)** An automobile with tires of radius 32 cm accelerates from 0 to 45 mph in 9.1 s. Find the angular acceleration of the tires. **(b)** How does your answer to part (a) change if the radius of the tires is halved?

98. •• **IP** In Problems 75 and 76 we considered a cylinder and a solid sphere, respectively, rolling down a ramp. **(a)** Which object do you expect to have the greater speed at the bottom of the ramp? **(b)** Verify your answer to part (a) by calculating the speed of the cylinder and of the sphere when they reach the bottom of the ramp.

99. •• A centrifuge (Problem 22) with an angular speed of 6050 rpm produces a maximum centripetal acceleration equal to 6840g (that is, 6840 times the acceleration of gravity). **(a)** What is the diameter of this centrifuge? **(b)** What force must the bottom of the sample holder exert on a 15.0-g sample under these conditions?

100. •• **A Yo-Yo with a Brain** Yomega ("The yo-yo with a brain") is constructed with a clever clutch mechanism in its axle that allows it to rotate freely and "sleep" when its angular speed is greater than a certain critical value. When the yo-yo's angular speed falls below this value, the clutch engages, causing the yo-yo to climb the string to the user's hand. If the moment of inertia of the yo-yo is 7.4×10^{-5} kg · m², its mass is 0.11 kg, and the string is 1.0 m long, what is the smallest angular speed that will allow the yo-yo to return to the user's hand?

A brain or just a clutch?
(Problem 100)

101. •• The rotor in a centrifuge has an initial angular speed of 430 rad/s. After 8.2 s of constant angular acceleration, its angular speed has increased to 550 rad/s. During this time, what were **(a)** the angular acceleration of the rotor and **(b)** the angle through which it turned?

102. •• **BIO** A honey bee has two pairs of wings that can beat 250 times a second. Estimate **(a)** the maximum angular speed of the wings and **(b)** the maximum linear speed of a wing tip.

103. •• The Sun, with Earth in tow, orbits about the center of the Milky Way galaxy at a speed of 137 miles per second, completing one revolution every 240 million years. **(a)** Find the angular speed of the Sun relative to the center of the Milky Way. **(b)** Find the distance from the Sun to the center of the Milky Way.

104. •• A person walks into a room and switches on the ceiling fan. The fan accelerates with constant angular acceleration for 15 s until it reaches its operating angular speed of 1.9 rotations/s—after that its speed remains constant as long as the switch is "on." The person stays in the room for a short time; then, 5.5 minutes after turning the fan on, she switches it off again and leaves the room. The fan now decelerates with constant angular acceleration, taking 2.4 minutes to come to rest. What is the total number of revolutions made by the fan, from the time it was turned on until the time it stopped?

105. •• **BIO Preventing Bone Loss in Space** When astronauts return from prolonged space flights, they often suffer from bone loss, resulting in brittle bones that may take weeks for their bodies to rebuild. One solution may be to expose astronauts to periods of substantial "g forces" in a centrifuge carried aboard their spaceship. To test this approach, NASA conducted a study in which four people spent 22 hours each in a compartment attached to the end of a 28-foot arm that rotated with an angular speed of 10.0 rpm. **(a)** What centripetal acceleration did these volunteers experience? Express your answer in terms of g. **(b)** What was their linear speed?

106. ••• **Angular Acceleration of the Crab Nebula** The pulsar in the Crab nebula (Problem 9) was created by a supernova explosion that was observed on Earth in A.D. 1054. Its current period of rotation (33.0 ms) is observed to be increasing by 1.26×10^{-5} seconds per year. **(a)** What is the angular acceleration of the pulsar in rad/s²? **(b)** Assuming the angular acceleration of the pulsar to be constant, how many years will it take for the pulsar to slow to a stop? **(c)** Under the same assumption, what was the period of the pulsar when it was created?

107. ••• A thin, uniform rod of length L and mass M is pivoted about one end, as shown in **Figure 10–28**. The rod is released from rest in a horizontal position, and allowed to swing downward without friction or air resistance. When the rod is vertical, what are **(a)** its angular speed ω and **(b)** the tangential speed v_t of its free end?

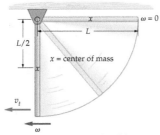

▲ **FIGURE 10–28** Problem 107

108. ••• **Center of Percussion** In the previous problem, suppose a small metal ball of mass $m = 2M$ is attached to the rod a distance d from the pivot. The rod and ball are released from rest in the horizontal position. **(a)** Show that when the rod reaches the vertical position, the speed of its tip is

$$v_t = \sqrt{3gL}\sqrt{\frac{1 + 4(d/L)}{1 + 6(d/L)^2}}$$

(b) At what finite value of d/L is the speed of the rod the same as it is for $d = 0$? (This value of d/L is the **center of percussion,** or "sweet spot," of the rod.)

109. ••• A wooden plank rests on two soup cans laid on their sides. Each can has a diameter of 6.5 cm, and the plank is 3.0 m long. Initially, one can is placed 1.0 m inward from either end of the plank, as **Figure 10–29** shows. The plank is now pulled 1.0 m to the right, and the cans roll without slipping. **(a)** How far does the center of each can move? **(b)** How many rotations does each can make?

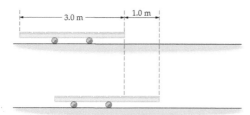

▲ **FIGURE 10–29** Problem 109

110. ••• A person rides on a 12-m-diameter Ferris wheel that rotates at the constant rate of 8.1 rpm. Calculate the magnitude and direction of the force that the seat exerts on a 65-kg person when he is **(a)** at the top of the wheel, **(b)** at the bottom of the wheel, and **(c)** halfway up the wheel.

111. ••• **IP** A solid sphere with a diameter of 0.17 m is released from rest; it then rolls without slipping down a ramp, dropping

through a vertical height of 0.61 m. The ball leaves the bottom of the ramp, which is 1.22 m above the floor, moving horizontally (**Figure 10–30**). **(a)** Through what horizontal distance d does the ball move before landing? **(b)** How many revolutions does the ball make during its fall? **(c)** If the ramp were to be made frictionless, would the distance d increase, decrease, or stay the same? Explain.

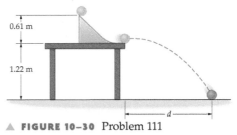

▲ **FIGURE 10–30** Problem 111

PASSAGE PROBLEMS

BIO **Human-Powered Centrifuge**

Space travel is fraught with hazards, not the least of which are the many side effects of prolonged weightlessness, including weakened muscles, bone loss, decreased coordination, and unsteady balance. If you are fortunate enough to go on a trip to Mars, which could take more than a year each way, you might be a bit "weak in the knees" by the time you arrive. This could lead to problems when you try to take your first "small step" on the surface.

To counteract these effects, NASA is looking into ways to provide astronauts with "portable gravity" on long space flights. One method under consideration is the human-powered centrifuge, which not only subjects the astronauts to artificial gravity, but also gives them aerobic exercise. The device is basically a rotating, circular platform on which two astronauts lie supine along a diameter, head-to-head at the center, with their feet at opposite rims, as shown in the accompanying photo. The radius of the platform in this test model is 6.25 ft. As one astronaut pedals to rotate the platform, the astronaut facing the other direction can exercise in the artificial gravity. Alternatively, a third astronaut on a stationary bicycle can provide the rotation for the other two.

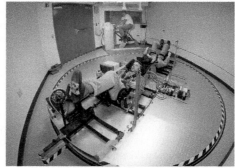

Human-powered centrifuge, designed to give astronauts exercise and artificial gravity during long space flights.

Figure 10–31 shows the centripetal acceleration (in gs) produced by a rotating platform at four different radii. Notice that the acceleration increases as the square of the angular speed. Also indicated in Figure 10–31 are acceleration levels corresponding to 1, 3, and 5 gs. It is thought that enhanced gravitational effects may be desirable since the astronauts will experience the artificial gravity for only relatively brief periods of time during the flight.

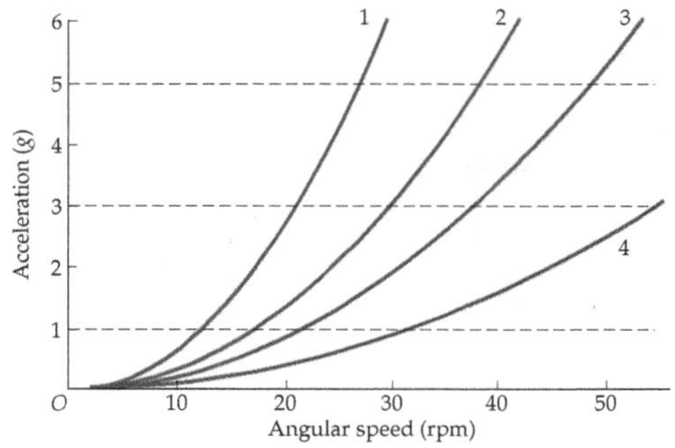

▲ **FIGURE 10–31** Problems 112, 113, 114, and 115

112. • Rank the four curves shown in Figure 10–31 in order of increasing radius. Indicate ties where appropriate.

113. • What angular speed (in rpm) must the platform in this test model have to give a centripetal acceleration of 5.00 gs at the rim?

    A. 5.07 rpm   **B.** 26.1 rpm

    C. 36.2 rpm   **D.** 48.5 rpm

114. • Which of the curves shown in Figure 10–31 corresponds to the test model?

    A. 1   **B.** 2

    C. 3   **D.** 4

115. •• Estimate the radius corresponding to curve 4 in Figure 10–31.

    A. 0.03 ft   **B.** 0.3 ft

    C. 3 ft   **D.** 6 ft

INTERACTIVE PROBLEMS

116. •• **Referring to Conceptual Checkpoint 10–4** Suppose we race a disk and a hollow spherical shell, like a basketball. The spherical shell has a mass M and a radius R; the disk has a mass $2M$ and a radius $2R$. **(a)** Which object wins the race? If the two objects are released at rest, and the height of the ramp is $h = 0.75$ m, find the speed of **(b)** the disk and **(c)** the spherical shell when they reach the bottom of the ramp.

117. •• **Referring to Conceptual Checkpoint 10–4** Consider a race between the following three objects: object 1, a disk; object 2, a solid sphere; and object 3, a hollow spherical shell. All objects have the same mass and radius. **(a)** Rank the three objects in the order in which they finish the race. Indicate a tie where appropriate. **(b)** Rank the objects in order of increasing kinetic energy at the bottom of the ramp. Indicate a tie where appropriate.

118. •• **Referring to Active Example 10–3 (a)** Suppose the radius of the axle the string wraps around is increased. Does the speed of the yo-yo after falling through a given height increase, decrease, or stay the same? **(b)** Find the speed of the yo-yo after falling from rest through a height $h = 0.50$ m if the radius of the axle is 0.0075 m. Everything else in Active Example 10–3 remains the same.

119. •• **Referring to Active Example 10–3** Suppose we use a new yo-yo that has the same mass as the original yo-yo and an axle of the same radius. The new yo-yo has a different mass distribution—most of its mass is concentrated near the rim. **(a)** Is the moment of inertia of the new yo-yo greater than, less than, or the same as that of the original yo-yo? **(b)** Find the moment of inertia of the new yo-yo if its speed after dropping from rest through a height $h = 0.50$ m is $v = 0.64$ m/s.

11 Rotational Dynamics and Static Equilibrium

Equilibrium, and the sense of serenity that comes with it, involves more than just forces that add to zero—it also depends on where the forces are applied. To keep from falling, for example, the forces exerted on this woman's hand and foot must add up to her total weight. But the total weight must be shared between her hand and foot in just the right way, or else her body will rotate and the pose will be lost. To ensure equilibrium, a new physical quantity—the torque—must also be zero. In this chapter we introduce the torque, and show that equilibrium occurs only when both the net force and the net torque are zero. We will also consider the consequences of nonzero torque.

n the previous chapter we learned how to describe uniformly accelerated rotational motion, but we did not discuss how a given angular acceleration is caused by a given force. The connection between forces and angular acceleration is the focus of this chapter.

We begin by defining a quantity that is the rotational equivalent of force. This quantity is called the *torque*. Although torque may not be as familiar a term as force, your muscles are exerting torques on your body at this very moment. In fact, every time you raise an arm, extend a finger, or stretch a leg, you exert torques to carry out these motions. Thus,

our ability to move from place to place, or to hold our body still, is intimately related to our ability to exert precisely controlled torques on our limbs.

We also introduce the notion of *angular momentum* in this chapter and show that it is related to torque in essentially the same way that linear momentum is related to force. As a result, it follows that angular momentum is conserved when the net external torque acting on a system is zero. Thus, conservation of angular momentum joins conservation of energy and conservation of linear momentum as one of the fundamental principles on which all physics is based.

11–1 Torque

Suppose you want to loosen a nut by rotating it counterclockwise with a wrench. If you have ever used a wrench in this way, you probably know that the nut is more likely to turn if you apply your force as far from the nut as possible, as indicated in Figure 11–1 (a). Applying a force near the nut would not be very effective—you could still get the nut to turn, but it would require considerably more effort! Similarly, it is much easier to open a revolving door if you push far from the axis of rotation, as indicated in Figure 11–1 (b). Clearly, then, the tendency for a force to cause a rotation increases with the distance, r, from the axis of rotation to the force. As a result, it is useful to define a quantity called the **torque**, τ, that takes into account both the magnitude of the force, F, *and* the distance from the axis of rotation, r:

▲ The long handle of this wrench enables the user to produce a large torque without having to exert a very great force.

Definition of Torque, τ, for a Tangential Force

$\tau = rF$ ~~only when F=tangential Force~~   11–1

SI unit: N · m

Note that the torque increases with both the force and the distance.

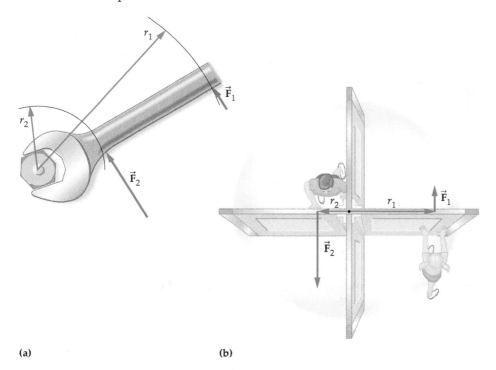

(a)   (b)

◀ **FIGURE 11–1 Applying a torque**
(a) When a wrench is used to loosen a nut, less force is required if it is applied far from the nut. **(b)** Similarly, less force is required to open a revolving door if it is applied far from the axis of rotation.

Equation 11–1 is valid only when the applied force is *tangential* to a circle of radius r centered on the axis of rotation, as indicated in Figure 11–1. The more general case is considered later in this section. First, we use Equation 11–1 to determine how much force is needed to open a swinging door, depending on where we apply the force.

EXERCISE 11–1

To open the door in Figure 11–1 (b) a tangential force F is applied at a distance r from the axis of rotation. If the minimum torque required to open the door is 3.1 N · m, what force must be applied if r is **(a)** 0.94 m or **(b)** 0.35 m?

SOLUTION

(a) Setting $\tau = r_1 F_1 = 3.1$ N · m, we find that the required force is

$$F_1 = \frac{\tau}{r_1} = \frac{3.1 \text{ N} \cdot \text{m}}{0.94 \text{ m}} = 3.3 \text{ N}$$

PROBLEM-SOLVING NOTE

The Units of Torque

Note that the units of torque are N · m, the same as the units of work. Though their units are the same, torque, τ, and work, W, represent different physical quantities and should not be confused with one another.

(b) Repeat the calculation, this time with $r_2 = 0.35$ m:

$$F_2 = \frac{\tau}{r_2} = \frac{3.1\ \text{N}\cdot\text{m}}{0.35\ \text{m}} = 8.9\ \text{N}$$

As expected, the required force is greater when it is applied closer to the hinges.

To this point we have considered tangential forces only. What happens if you exert a force in a direction that is not tangential? Suppose, for example, that you pull on a playground merry-go-round in a direction that is radial—that is, along a line that extends through the axis of rotation—as in **Figure 11–2 (a)**. In this case, your force has no tendency to cause a rotation. Instead, the axle of the merry-go-round simply exerts an equal and opposite force, and the merry-go-round remains at rest. Similarly, if you were to push or pull in a radial direction on a swinging door it would not rotate. We conclude that a *radial force produces zero torque.*

▶ **FIGURE 11–2 Only the tangential component of a force causes a torque**
(a) A radial force causes no rotation. In this case, the force $\vec{F}$ is opposed by an equal and opposite force exerted by the axle of the merry-go-round. The merry-go-round does not rotate. **(b)** A force applied at an angle θ with respect to the radial direction. The radial component of this force, $F\cos\theta$, causes no rotation; the tangential component, $F\sin\theta$, can cause a rotation.

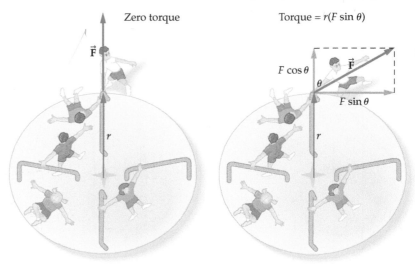

(a) A radial force produces zero torque

(b) Only the tangential component of force causes a torque

On the other hand, what if your force is at an angle θ relative to a radial line, as shown in **Figure 11–2 (b)**? To analyze this case, we first resolve the force vector $\vec{F}$ into radial and tangential components. Referring to the figure, we see that the radial component has a magnitude of $F\cos\theta$, and the tangential component has a magnitude of $F\sin\theta$. Because it is the tangential component alone that causes rotation, we define the torque to have a magnitude of $r(F\sin\theta)$. That is,

> **General Definition of Torque, τ**
>
> $$\tau = r(F\sin\theta) \qquad\qquad\qquad\text{11–2}$$
>
> SI units: $\text{N}\cdot\text{m}$

(More generally, the torque can be defined as the **cross product** between the vectors $\vec{r}$ and $\vec{F}$; that is, $\vec{\tau} = \vec{r} \times \vec{F}$. The cross product is discussed in detail in Appendix A.)

As a quick check, note that a radial force corresponds to $\theta = 0$. In this case, $\tau = r(F\sin 0) = 0$, as expected. If the force is tangential, however, it follows that $\theta = \pi/2$. This gives $\tau = r(F\sin\pi/2) = rF$, in agreement with Equation 11–1.

An equivalent way to define the torque is in terms of the **moment arm**, $r_\perp$. The idea here is to extend a line through the force vector, as in **Figure 11–3**, and then draw a second line from the axis of rotation perpendicular to the line of the force. The perpendicular distance from the axis of rotation to the line of the force is defined to be $r_\perp$. From the figure, we see that

$$r_\perp = r\sin\theta$$

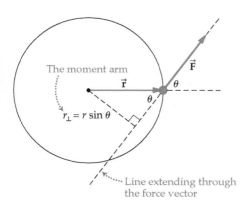

▲ **FIGURE 11–3 The moment arm**
To find the moment arm, $r_\perp$, for a given force, first extend a line through the force vector. This line is sometimes referred to as the "line of action." Next, drop a perpendicular line from the axis of rotation to the line of the force. The perpendicular distance is $r_\perp = r\sin\theta$.

In addition, we note that a simple rearrangement of the torque expression in Equation 11–2 yields

$$\tau = r(F \sin \theta) = (r \sin \theta)F$$

Thus, the torque can be written as the moment arm times the force:

$$\tau = r_\perp F \qquad\qquad 11\text{--}3$$

Just as a force applied to an object gives rise to a linear acceleration, a torque applied to an object gives rise to an angular acceleration. For example, if a torque acts on an object at rest, the object will begin to rotate; if a torque acts on a rotating object, the object's angular velocity will change. In fact, the greater the torque applied to an object, the greater its angular acceleration, as we shall see in the next section. For this reason, the sign of the torque is determined by the same convention used in Section 10–1 for angular acceleration:

Sign Convention for Torque

By convention, if a torque τ acts alone, then

$\tau > 0$ if the torque causes a counterclockwise angular acceleration
$\tau < 0$ if the torque causes a clockwise angular acceleration

In a system with more than one torque, the sign of each torque is determined by the type of angular acceleration *it alone* would produce. The net torque acting on the system, then, is the sum of each individual torque, taking into account the proper sign. This is illustrated in the following Example.

▲ The net torque on the wheel of this ship is the sum of the torques exerted by the two helmsmen. At the moment pictured, they are both exerting negative torques on the wheel, causing it to rotate in the clockwise direction. This will turn the boat to its left—or, in nautical terms, to port.

PROBLEM-SOLVING NOTE

The Sign of Torques

The sign of a torque is determined by the direction of rotation it would cause if it were the only torque acting in the system.

EXAMPLE 11–1   TORQUES TO THE LEFT AND TORQUES TO THE RIGHT

Two helmsmen, in disagreement about which way to turn a ship, exert the forces shown below on a ship's wheel. The wheel has a radius of 0.74 m, and the two forces have the magnitudes $F_1 = 72$ N and $F_2 = 58$ N. Find **(a)** the torque caused by $\vec{F}_1$ and **(b)** the torque caused by $\vec{F}_2$. **(c)** In which direction does the wheel turn as a result of these two forces?

PICTURE THE PROBLEM
Our sketch shows that both forces are applied at the distance $r = 0.74$ m from the axis of rotation. However, $F_1 = 72$ N is at an angle of 50.0° relative to the radial direction, whereas $F_2 = 58$ N is tangential, which means that its angle relative to the radial direction is 90.0°.

STRATEGY
For each force, we find the magnitude of the corresponding torque, using $\tau = rF \sin \theta$. As for the signs of the torques, we must consider the angular acceleration each force alone would cause. $\vec{F}_1$ acting alone would cause the wheel to accelerate counterclockwise, hence its torque is positive. $\vec{F}_2$ would accelerate the wheel clockwise if it acted alone, hence its torque is negative. If the sum of the two torques is positive, the wheel accelerates counterclockwise; if the sum of the two torques is negative, the wheel accelerates clockwise.

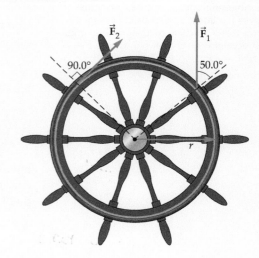

SOLUTION

Part (a)

1. Use Equation 11–2 to calculate the torque due to $\vec{F}_1$. Recall that this torque is positive:

$\tau_1 = rF_1 \sin 50.0° = (0.74\ \text{m})(72\ \text{N}) \sin 50.0° = 41\ \text{N} \cdot \text{m}$

Part (b)

2. Similarly, calculate the torque due to $\vec{F}_2$. Recall that this torque is negative:

$\tau_2 = -rF_2 \sin 90.0° = -(0.74\ \text{m})(58\ \text{N}) = -43\ \text{N} \cdot \text{m}$

Part (c)

3. Sum the torques from parts (a) and (b) to find the net torque:

$\tau_{\text{net}} = \tau_1 + \tau_2 = 41\ \text{N} \cdot \text{m} - 43\ \text{N} \cdot \text{m} = -2\ \text{N} \cdot \text{m}$

CONTINUED ON NEXT PAGE

CONTINUED FROM PREVIOUS PAGE

INSIGHT

Because the net torque is negative, the wheel accelerates clockwise. Thus, even though $\vec{F}_2$ is the smaller force, it has the greater effect in determining the wheel's direction of acceleration. This is because $\vec{F}_2$ is applied tangentially, whereas $\vec{F}_1$ is applied in a direction that is partially radial.

PRACTICE PROBLEM

What magnitude of $\vec{F}_2$ would yield zero net torque on the wheel? [**Answer:** $F_2 = 55$ N]

Some related homework problems: Problem 1, Problem 3

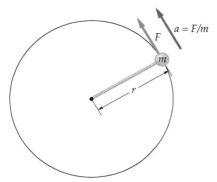

▲ **FIGURE 11–4 Torque and angular acceleration**

A tangential force F applied to a mass m gives it a linear acceleration of magnitude $a = F/m$. The corresponding angular acceleration is $\alpha = \tau/I$, where $\tau = rF$ and $I = mr^2$.

11–2 Torque and Angular Acceleration

In the previous section we indicated that a torque causes a change in the rotational motion of an object. To be more precise, a single torque, τ, acting on an object causes the object to have an angular acceleration, α. In this section we develop the specific relationship between τ and α.

Consider, for example, a small object of mass m connected to an axis of rotation by a light rod of length r, as in **Figure 11–4**. If a tangential force of magnitude F is applied to the mass, it will move with an acceleration given by Newton's second law:

$$a = \frac{F}{m}$$

From Equation 10–14, we know that the linear and angular accelerations are related by

$$\alpha = \frac{a}{r}$$

Combining these results yields the following expression for the angular acceleration:

$$\alpha = \frac{a}{r} = \frac{F}{mr}$$

Finally, multiplying both numerator and denominator by r gives

$$\alpha = \left(\frac{r}{r}\right)\frac{F}{mr} = \frac{rF}{mr^2}$$

Now this last result is rather interesting, since the numerator and denominator have simple interpretations. First, the numerator is the torque, $\tau = rF$, for the case of a tangential force (Equation 11–1). Second, the denominator is the moment of inertia of a single mass m rotating at a radius r; that is, $I = mr^2$. Therefore, we find that

$$\alpha = \frac{rF}{mr^2} = \frac{\tau}{I}$$

or, rewriting slightly,

$$\tau = I\alpha$$

Thus, once we calculate the torque, as described in the previous section, we can find the angular acceleration of a system using $\tau = I\alpha$. Notice that the angular acceleration is directly proportional to the torque, and inversely proportional to the moment of inertia—that is, a large moment of inertia means a small angular acceleration.

Now, the relationship $\tau = I\alpha$ was derived for the special case of a tangential force and a single mass rotating at a radius r. However, the result is completely general. For example, in a system with more than one torque, the relation $\tau = I\alpha$

is replaced with $\tau_{net} = \Sigma\tau = I\alpha$, where τ_{net} is the net torque acting on the system. This gives us the *rotational* version of Newton's second law:

Newton's Second Law for Rotational Motion

$$\Sigma\tau = I\alpha \qquad\qquad\qquad 11\text{–}4$$

If only a single torque acts on a system, we will simply write $\tau = I\alpha$.

EXERCISE 11–2

A light rope wrapped around a disk-shaped pulley is pulled tangentially with a force of 0.53 N. Find the angular acceleration of the pulley, given that its mass is 1.3 kg and its radius is 0.11 m.

SOLUTION
The torque applied to the disk is

$$\tau = rF = (0.11 \text{ m})(0.53 \text{ N}) = 5.8 \times 10^{-2} \text{ N}\cdot\text{m}$$

Since the pulley is a disk, its moment of inertia is given by

$$I = \tfrac{1}{2}mr^2 = \tfrac{1}{2}(1.3 \text{ kg})(0.11 \text{ m})^2 = 7.9 \times 10^{-3} \text{ kg}\cdot\text{m}^2$$

Thus, the angular acceleration of the pulley is

$$\alpha = \frac{\tau}{I} = \frac{5.8 \times 10^{-2} \text{ N}\cdot\text{m}}{7.9 \times 10^{-3} \text{ kg}\cdot\text{m}^2} = 7.3 \text{ rad/s}^2$$

It is easy to remember the rotational version of Newton's second law, $\Sigma\tau = I\alpha$, by using analogies between rotational and linear quantities. We have already seen that I is the analogue of m, and that α is the analogue of a. Similarly, τ, which causes an angular acceleration, is the analogue of F, which causes a linear acceleration. To summarize:

Linear Quantity	Angular Quantity
m	I
a	α
F	τ

Thus, just as $\Sigma F = ma$ describes linear motion, $\Sigma\tau = I\alpha$ describes rotational motion.

EXAMPLE 11–2   A FISH TAKES THE LINE

A fisherman is dozing when a fish takes the line and pulls it with a tension T. The spool of the fishing reel is at rest initially and rotates without friction (since the fisherman left the drag off) as the fish pulls for a time t. If the radius of the spool is R, and its moment of inertia is I, find **(a)** the angular displacement of the spool, **(b)** the length of line pulled from the spool, and **(c)** the final angular speed of the spool.

PICTURE THE PROBLEM
Our sketch shows the fishing line being pulled tangentially from the spool with a tension T. Because the radius of the spool is R, the torque produced by the line is $\tau = RT$. Also note that as the spool rotates through an angle $\Delta\theta$, the line moves through a linear distance $\Delta x = R\Delta\theta$. Finally, the spool starts at rest, hence $\omega_0 = 0$.

STRATEGY
This is basically an angular kinematics problem, as in Chapter 10, but in this case we must first calculate the angular acceleration using $\alpha = \tau/I$. Once α is known, we can find the angular displacement, $\Delta\theta$, using $\theta = \theta_0 + \omega_0 t + \tfrac{1}{2}\alpha t^2$. Similarly, we can find the angular speed of the spool, ω, using $\omega = \omega_0 + \alpha t$.

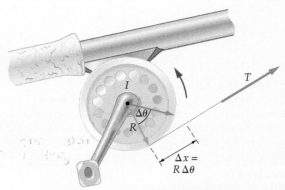

CONTINUED ON NEXT PAGE

CONTINUED FROM PREVIOUS PAGE

SOLUTION

1. Calculate the torque acting on the spool. Note that $\theta = 90°$, since the pull is tangential. The radius is $r = R$, and the force applied to the reel is the tension in the line, T:

$$\tau = rF \sin \theta = RT \sin 90° = RT$$

2. Using the result just obtained for the torque, find the angular acceleration of the reel:

$$\alpha = \frac{\tau}{I} = \frac{RT}{I}$$

Part (a)

3. Calculate the angular displacement $\Delta\theta = \theta - \theta_0$:

$$\Delta\theta = \theta - \theta_0 = \omega_0 t + \tfrac{1}{2}\alpha t^2 = \tfrac{1}{2}\alpha t^2 = \left(\frac{RT}{2I}\right)t^2$$

Part (b)

4. Calculate the length of line pulled from the spool with $\Delta x = R\,\Delta\theta$:

$$\Delta x = R\,\Delta\theta = \left(\frac{R^2 T}{2I}\right)t^2$$

Part (c)

5. Use $\omega = \omega_0 + \alpha t$ to find the final angular speed:

$$\omega = \omega_0 + \alpha t = \left(\frac{RT}{I}\right)t$$

INSIGHT
Note that the final angular speed can also be obtained from the kinematic equation relating angular speed and angular distance; $\omega^2 = \omega_0^2 + 2\alpha\,\Delta\theta = 0 + 2(RT/I)(RT/2I)t^2 = (RT/I)^2\,t^2$.

This calculation also applies to other situations in which a "line" is pulled from a "reel." Examples include telephone line or sewing thread pulled from a spool.

PRACTICE PROBLEM
How fast is the line moving at time t?   [**Answer:** $v = R\omega = (R^2 T/I)t$]

Some related homework problems: Problem 10, Problem 19

CONCEPTUAL CHECKPOINT 11–1   WHICH BLOCK LANDS FIRST?

The rotating systems shown below differ only in that the two spherical movable masses are positioned either far from the axis of rotation (left), or near the axis of rotation (right). If the hanging blocks are released simultaneously from rest, is it observed that **(a)** the block at left lands first, **(b)** the block at right lands first, or **(c)** both blocks land at the same time?

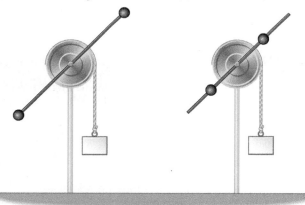

REASONING AND DISCUSSION
The net external torque, supplied by the hanging blocks, is the same for each of these systems. However, the moment of inertia of the system at right is less than that of the system at left because the movable masses are closer to the axis of rotation. Since the angular acceleration is inversely proportional to the moment of inertia ($\alpha = \tau_{net}/I$), the system at right has the greater angular acceleration, and it wins the race.

ANSWER
(b) The block at right lands first.

EXAMPLE 11–3   DROP IT

A person holds his outstretched arm at rest in a horizontal position. The mass of the arm is m and its length is 0.740 m. When the person releases his arm, allowing it to drop freely, it begins to rotate about the shoulder joint. Find **(a)** the initial angular acceleration of the arm, and **(b)** the initial linear acceleration of the man's hand. (*Hint:* In calculating the torque, assume the mass of the arm is concentrated at its midpoint. In calculating the angular acceleration, use the moment of inertia of a uniform rod of length L about one end; $I = \frac{1}{3}mL^2$.)

PICTURE THE PROBLEM
The arm is initially horizontal and at rest. When released, it rotates downward about the shoulder joint. The force of gravity, mg, acts at a distance of $(0.740 \text{ m})/2 = 0.370 \text{ m}$ from the shoulder.

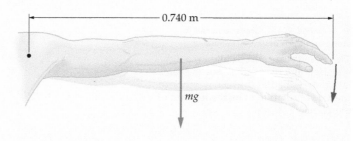

STRATEGY
The angular acceleration, α, can be found using $\tau = I\alpha$. In this case, the initial torque is $\tau = mg(L/2)$, where $L = 0.740$ m, and the moment of inertia is $I = \frac{1}{3}mL^2$.

Once the initial angular acceleration is found, the corresponding linear acceleration is obtained from $a = r\alpha$.

SOLUTION

Part (a)

1. Use $\tau = I\alpha$ to find the angular acceleration, α:

$$\alpha = \frac{\tau}{I}$$

2. Write expressions for the initial torque, τ, and the moment of inertia, I:

$$\tau = mg\frac{L}{2}$$
$$I = \frac{1}{3}mL^2$$

3. Substitute τ and I into the expression for the angular acceleration. Note that the mass of the arm cancels:

$$\alpha = \frac{\tau}{I} = \frac{mgL/2}{mL^2/3} = \frac{3g}{2L}$$

4. Substitute numerical values:

$$\alpha = \frac{3g}{2L} = \frac{3(9.81 \text{ m/s}^2)}{2(0.740 \text{ m})} = 19.9 \text{ rad/s}^2$$

Part (b)

5. Use $a = r\alpha$ to calculate the linear acceleration at the man's hand, a distance $r = L$ from the shoulder:

$$a = L\alpha = L\left(\frac{3g}{2L}\right) = \frac{3}{2}g = 14.7 \text{ m/s}^2$$

INSIGHT
Note that the linear acceleration of the hand is 1.50 times greater than the acceleration of gravity, regardless of the mass of the arm. This can be demonstrated with the following simple experiment: Hold your arm straight out with a pen resting on your hand. Now, relax your deltoid muscles, and let your arm rotate freely downward about your shoulder joint. Notice that as your arm falls downward, your hand moves more rapidly than the pen, which appears to "lift off" your hand. The pen drops with the acceleration of gravity, which is clearly less than the acceleration of the hand. This effect can be seen in the adjacent photo.

PRACTICE PROBLEM
At what distance from the shoulder is the initial linear acceleration of the arm equal to the acceleration of gravity?
[**Answer:** Set $a = r\alpha$ equal to g. This gives $r = 2L/3 = 0.493$ m.]

Some related homework problems: Problem 13, Problem 15

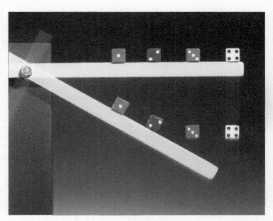

▲ As a rod of length L rotates freely about one end, points farther from the axle than $2L/3$ have an acceleration greater than g (see the Practice Problem for Example 11–3). Thus, the rod falls out from under the last two dice.

11–3 Zero Torque and Static Equilibrium

The parents of a young boy are supporting him on a long, lightweight plank, as illustrated in **Figure 11–5**. If the mass of the child is m, the upward forces exerted by the parents must sum to mg; that is,

$$F_1 + F_2 = mg$$

This condition ensures that the net force acting on the plank is zero. It *does not*, however, guarantee that the plank remains at rest.

▶ **FIGURE 11–5 Forces required for static equilibrium**

Two parents support a child on a lightweight plank of length L. For the calculation described in the text, we choose the axis of rotation to be the left end of the plank.

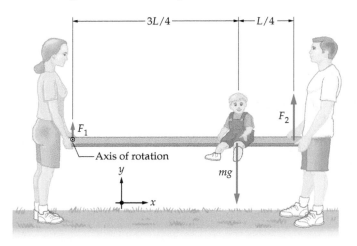

To see why, imagine for a moment that the parent on the right lets go of the plank and that the parent on the left increases her force until it is equal to the weight of the child. In this case, $F_1 = mg$ and $F_2 = 0$, which clearly satisfies the force equation we have just written. Since the right end of the plank is no longer supported, however, it drops toward the ground while the left end rises. In other words, the plank rotates in a clockwise sense. For the plank to remain completely at rest, with no translation or rotation, we must impose the following *two* conditions: First, the net force acting on the plank must be zero, so that there is no translational acceleration. Second, the net torque acting on the plank must also be zero, so that there is no rotational acceleration. If both of these conditions are met, an extended object, like the plank, will remain at rest if it starts at rest. To summarize:

Conditions for Static Equilibrium

For an extended object to be in static equilibrium, the following two conditions must be met:

(i) The net force acting on the object must be zero,

$$\sum F_x = 0, \qquad \sum F_y = 0 \qquad\qquad \text{11–5}$$

(ii) The net torque acting on the object must be zero,

$$\sum \tau = 0 \qquad\qquad \text{11–6}$$

Note that these two conditions are independent of one another; that is, satisfying one does *not* guarantee that the other is satisfied.

Let's apply these conditions to the plank that supports the child. First, we consider the forces acting on the plank, with upward chosen as the positive direction, as in Figure 11–5. Setting the net force equal to zero yields

$$F_1 + F_2 - mg = 0$$

Clearly, this agrees with the force equation we wrote down earlier.

Next, we apply the torque condition. To do so, we must first choose an axis of rotation. For example, we might take the left end of the plank to be the axis, as in Figure 11–5. With this choice, we see that the force F_1 exerts zero torque, since it acts directly through the axis of rotation. On the other hand, F_2 acts at the far end of the plank, a distance L from the axis. In addition, F_2 would cause a counter-clockwise (positive) rotation if it acted alone, as we can see in Figure 11–5. Therefore, the torque due to F_2 is

$$\tau_2 = F_2 L$$

Finally, the weight of the child, mg, acts at a distance of $3L/4$ from the axis, and would cause a clockwise (negative) rotation if it acted alone. Hence, its torque is negative:

$$\tau_{mg} = -mg\left(\tfrac{3}{4}L\right)$$

Setting the net torque equal to zero, then, yields the following condition:

$$F_2 L - mg\left(\tfrac{3}{4}L\right) = 0$$

This torque condition, along with the force condition in $F_1 + F_2 - mg = 0$, can be used to determine the two unknowns, F_1 and F_2. For example, we can begin by canceling L in the torque equation to find F_2:

$$F_2 = \tfrac{3}{4}mg$$

Substituting this result into the force condition gives

$$F_1 + \tfrac{3}{4}mg - mg = 0$$

Therefore, F_1 is

$$F_1 = \tfrac{1}{4}mg$$

These two forces support the plank, *and* keep it from rotating. As one might expect, the force nearest the child is greatest.

Our choice of the left end of the plank as the axis of rotation was completely arbitrary. In fact, if an object is in static equilibrium, the net torque acting on it is zero, regardless of the location of the axis of rotation. Hence, we are free to choose an axis of rotation that is most convenient for a given problem. In general, it is useful to pick the axis to be at the location of one of the unknown forces. This eliminates that force from the torque condition, and simplifies the remaining algebra. We consider an alternative choice for the axis of rotation in the following Active Example.

PROBLEM-SOLVING NOTE

Axis of Rotation

Any point in a system may be used as the axis of rotation when calculating torque. It is generally best, however, to choose an axis that gives zero torque for at least one of the unknown forces in the system. Such a choice simplifies the algebra needed to solve for the forces.

ACTIVE EXAMPLE 11–1 FIND THE FORCES: AXIS ON THE RIGHT

A child of mass m is supported on a light plank by his parents, who exert the forces F_1 and F_2 as indicated. Find the forces required to keep the plank in static equilibrium. Use the right end of the plank as the axis of rotation.

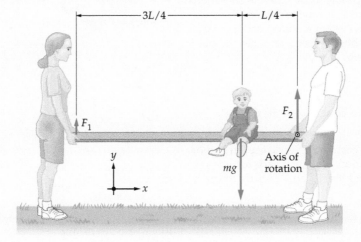

CONTINUED FROM PREVIOUS PAGE

SOLUTION *(Test your understanding by performing the calculations indicated in each step.)*

1. Set the net force acting on the plank equal to zero:

   $$F_1 + F_2 - mg = 0$$

2. Set the net torque acting on the plank equal to zero:

   $$-F_1(L) + mg\left(\tfrac{1}{4}L\right) = 0$$

3. Note that the torque condition involves only one of the two unknowns, F_1. Use this condition to solve for F_1:

   $$F_1 = \tfrac{1}{4}mg$$

4. Substitute F_1 into the force condition to solve for F_2:

   $$F_2 = mg - \tfrac{1}{4}mg = \tfrac{3}{4}mg$$

INSIGHT

As expected, the results are identical to those obtained previously. Note that in this case the torque produced by the child would cause a counterclockwise rotation, hence it is positive. Thus, the magnitude *and* sign of the torque produced by a given force depend on the location chosen for the axis of rotation.

YOUR TURN

Suppose the child moves to a new position, with the result that the force exerted by the father is reduced to $0.60mg$. Did the child move to the left or to the right? How far did the child move?

*(Answers to **Your Turn** problems are given in the back of the book.)*

A third choice for the axis of rotation is considered in Problem 24. As expected, all three choices give the same results.

In the next Example, we show that the forces supporting a person or other object sometimes act in different directions. To emphasize the direction of the forces, we solve the Example in terms of the components of the relevant forces.

EXAMPLE 11–4   TAKING THE PLUNGE

A 5.00-m-long diving board of negligible mass is supported by two pillars. One pillar is at the left end of the diving board, as shown below; the other is 1.50 m away. Find the forces exerted by the pillars when a 90.0-kg diver stands at the far end of the board.

PICTURE THE PROBLEM
We choose upward to be the positive direction for the forces. When calculating torques, we use the left end of the diving board as the axis of rotation. Note that $\vec{F}_2$ would cause a counterclockwise rotation if it acted alone, so its torque is positive. On the other hand, $m\vec{g}$ would cause a clockwise rotation, so its torque is negative. Finally, $\vec{F}_2$ acts at a distance d from the axis of rotation, and $m\vec{g}$ acts at a distance L.

STRATEGY
As usual in static equilibrium problems, we use the conditions of (i) zero net force and (ii) zero net torque to determine the unknown forces, $\vec{F}_1$ and $\vec{F}_2$. In this system all forces act in the positive or negative y direction; thus we need only set the net y component of force equal to zero.

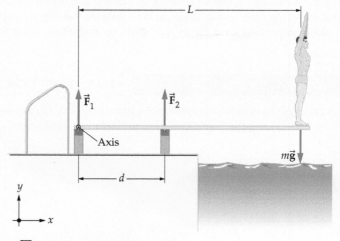

SOLUTION

1. Set the net y component of force acting on the diving board equal to zero:

   $$\sum F_y = F_{1,y} + F_{2,y} - mg = 0$$

2. Calculate the torque due to each force, using the left end of the board as the axis of rotation. Note that each force is at right angles to the radius and that $\vec{F}_1$ goes directly through the axis of rotation:

   $$\tau_1 = F_{1,y}(0) = 0$$
   $$\tau_2 = F_{2,y}(d)$$
   $$\tau_3 = -mg(L)$$

3. Set the net torque acting on the diving board equal to zero:

   $$\sum \tau = F_{1,y}(0) + F_{2,y}(d) - mg(L) = 0$$

4. Solve the torque equation for the force $F_{2,y}$:

   $$F_{2,y} = mg(L/d)$$
   $$= (90.0 \text{ kg})(9.81 \text{ m/s}^2)(5.00 \text{ m}/1.50 \text{ m}) = 2940 \text{ N}$$

5. Use the force equation to determine $F_{1,y}$:

$$F_{1,y} = mg - F_{2,y}$$
$$= (90.0 \text{ kg})(9.81 \text{ m/s}^2) - 2940 \text{ N} = -2060 \text{ N}$$

INSIGHT

The first point to notice about our solution is that $F_{1,y}$ is negative, which means that $\vec{F}_1$ is actually directed *downward*, as shown to the right. To see why, imagine for a moment that the board is no longer connected to the first pillar. In this case, the board would rotate clockwise about the second pillar, and the left end of the board would move upward. Thus, a downward force is required on the left end of the board to hold it in place.

The second point is that both pillars exert forces with magnitudes that are considerably larger than the diver's weight, $mg = 883$ N. In particular, the first pillar must pull downward with a force of $2.33mg$, while the second pillar pushes upward with a force of $2.33mg + mg = 3.33mg$. This is not unusual. In fact, it is common for the forces in a structure, such as a bridge, a building, or the human body, to be much greater than the weight it supports.

PRACTICE PROBLEM

Find the forces exerted by the pillars when the diver is 1.00 m from the right end. [**Answer:** $F_{1,y} = -1470$ N, $F_{2,y} = 2350$ N]

Some related homework problems: Problem 26, Problem 32

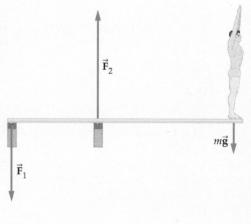

To this point we have ignored the mass of the plank holding the child and the diving board holding the swimmer, since they were described as lightweight. If we want to consider the torque exerted by an extended object of finite mass, however, we can simply treat it as if all its mass were concentrated at its center of mass, as was done in similar situations in Section 9–7. We consider such a system in the next Active Example.

REAL-WORLD PHYSICS

Applying the brakes

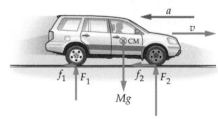

▲ As the brakes are applied on this SUV, rotational equilibrium demands that the normal forces exerted on the front tires be greater than the normal forces exerted on the rear tires—which is why braking cars are "nose down" during a rapid stop. For this reason, many cars use disk brakes for the front wheels and less powerful drum brakes for the rear wheels. As the disk brakes wear, they tend to coat the front wheels with dust from the brake pads, which give the front wheels a characteristic "dirty" look.

ACTIVE EXAMPLE 11–2   **WALKING THE PLANK: FIND THE MASS**

A cat walks along a uniform plank that is 4.00 m long and has a mass of 7.00 kg. The plank is supported by two sawhorses, one 0.440 m from the left end of the board and the other 1.50 m from its right end. When the cat reaches the right end, the plank just begins to tip. What is the mass of the cat?

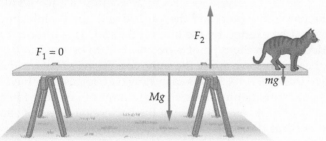

SOLUTION *(Test your understanding by performing the calculations indicated in each step.)*

1. Since the board is just beginning to tip, there is no weight on the left sawhorse:

$$F_1 = 0$$

2. Calculate the torque about the right sawhorse:

$$Mg(0.500 \text{ m}) - mg(1.50 \text{ m}) = 0$$

3. Solve the torque equation for the mass of the cat, m:

$$m = 0.333M = 2.33 \text{ kg}$$

CONTINUED ON NEXT PAGE

CONTINUED FROM PREVIOUS PAGE

INSIGHT

Note that we did not include a torque for the left sawhorse, since F_1 is zero. As an exercise, you might try repeating the calculation with the axis of rotation at the left sawhorse, or at the center of mass of the plank.

YOUR TURN

Write both the zero force and zero torque conditions for the case where the axis of rotation is at the left sawhorse.

(*Answers to* **Your Turn** *problems are given in the back of the book.*)

Forces with Both Vertical and Horizontal Components

Note that all of the previous examples have dealt with forces that point either directly upward or directly downward. We now consider a more general situation, where forces may have both vertical and horizontal components. For example, consider the wall-mounted lamp (sconce) shown in **Figure 11–6**. The sconce consists of a light curved rod that is bolted to the wall at its lower end. Suspended from the upper end of the rod, a horizontal distance H from the wall, is the lamp of mass m. The rod is also connected to the wall by a horizontal wire a vertical distance V above the bottom of the rod.

▶ **FIGURE 11–6 A lamp in static equilibrium**

A wall-mounted lamp of mass m is suspended from a light curved rod. The bottom of the rod is bolted to the wall. The rod is also connected to the wall by a horizontal wire a vertical distance V above the bottom of the rod.

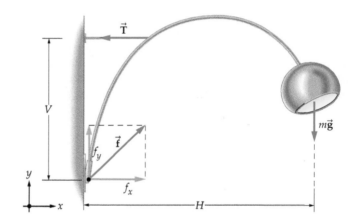

Now, suppose we are designing this sconce to be placed in the lobby of a building on campus. To ensure its structural stability, we would like to know the tension T the wire must exert and the vertical and horizontal components of the force $\vec{f}$ that must be exerted by the bolt on the rod. This information will be important in deciding on the type of wire and bolt to be used in the construction.

To find these forces, we apply the same conditions as before: the net force and the net torque must be zero. In this case, however, forces may have both horizontal and vertical components. Thus, the condition of zero net force is really two separate conditions: (i) zero net force in the horizontal direction; and (ii) zero net force in the vertical direction. These two conditions plus (iii) zero net torque, allow for a full solution of the problem.

We begin with the torque condition. A convenient choice for the axis of rotation is the bottom end of the rod, since this eliminates one of the unknown forces ($\vec{f}$). With this choice we can readily calculate the torques acting on the rod by using the moment arm expression for the torque, $\tau = r_\perp F$ (Equation 11–3). We find

$$\sum \tau = T(V) - mg(H) = 0$$

This relation can be solved immediately for the tension, giving

$$T = mg(H/V)$$

Note that the tension is increased if the wire is connected closer to the bottom of the rod; that is, if V is reduced.

Next, we apply the force conditions. First, we sum the y components of all the forces and set the sum equal to zero:

$$\sum F_y = f_y - mg = 0$$

Thus, the vertical component of the force exerted by the bolt simply supports the weight of the lamp:

$$f_y = mg$$

Finally, we sum the x components of the forces and set that sum equal to zero:

$$\sum F_x = f_x - T = 0$$

Clearly, the x component of the force exerted by the bolt is of the same magnitude as the tension, but it points in the opposite direction:

$$f_x = T = mg(H/V)$$

The bolt, then, pushes upward on the rod to support the lamp, and at the same time it pushes to the right to keep the rod from rotating.

For example, suppose the lamp in Figure 11–6 has a mass of 2.00 kg, and that $V = 12.0$ cm and $H = 15.0$ cm. In this case, we find the following forces:

$$T = mg(H/V) = (2.00 \text{ kg})(9.81 \text{ m/s}^2)(15.0 \text{ cm})/(12.0 \text{ cm}) = 24.5 \text{ N}$$

$$f_x = T = 24.5 \text{ N}$$

$$f_y = mg = (2.00 \text{ kg})(9.81 \text{ m/s}^2) = 19.6 \text{ N}$$

Note that f_x and T are greater than the weight, mg, of the lamp. Just as we found with the diving board in Example 11–4, the forces required of structural elements can be greater than the weight of the object to be supported—an important consideration when designing a structure like a bridge, an airplane, or a sconce. The same effect occurs in the human body. We find in Problem 25, for example, that the force exerted by the biceps to support a baseball in the hand is several times larger than the baseball's weight. Similar conclusions apply to muscles throughout the body.

In Example 11–5 we consider another system in which forces have both vertical and horizontal components.

▲ The chains that support this sign maintain it in a state of translational and rotational equilibrium. The forces in the chains are most easily analyzed by resolving them into vertical and horizontal components and applying the conditions for equilibrium. In particular, the net vertical force, the net horizontal force, and the net torque must all be zero.

REAL-WORLD PHYSICS

Forces required for structural stability

EXAMPLE 11–5   ARM IN A SLING

A hiker who has broken his forearm rigs a temporary sling using a cord stretching from his shoulder to his hand. The cord holds the forearm level and makes an angle of 40.0° with the horizontal where it attaches to the hand. Considering the forearm and hand to be uniform, with a total mass of 1.30 kg and a length of 0.300 m, find **(a)** the tension in the cord and **(b)** the horizontal and vertical components of the force, $\vec{f}$, exerted by the humerus (the bone of the upper arm) on the radius and ulna (the bones of the forearm).

PICTURE THE PROBLEM
In our sketch, we use the typical conventions for the positive x and y directions. In addition, since the forearm and hand are assumed to be a uniform object, we indicate the weight mg as acting at its center. The length of the forearm and hand is $L = 0.300$ m. Finally, two other forces act on the forearm: (i) the tension in the cord, $\vec{T}$, at an angle of 40.0° above the negative x axis, and (ii) the force $\vec{f}$ exerted at the elbow joint.

STRATEGY
In this system there are three unknowns: T, f_x, and f_y. These unknowns can be determined using the following three conditions: (i) net torque equals zero; (ii) net x component of force equals zero; and (iii) net y component of force equals zero.

We start with the torque condition, using the elbow joint as the axis of rotation. As we shall see, this choice of axis eliminates f, and gives a direct solution for the tension T. Next, we use T and the two force conditions to determine f_x and f_y.

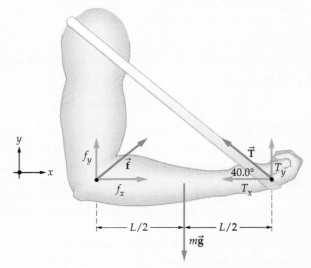

CONTINUED ON NEXT PAGE

CONTINUED FROM PREVIOUS PAGE

SOLUTION

Part (a)

1. Calculate the torque about the elbow joint. Note that f causes zero torque, mg causes a negative torque, and the vertical component of T causes a positive torque. The horizontal component of T produces no torque, since it is on a line with the axis:

$$\sum \tau = (T \sin 40.0°)L - mg(L/2) = 0$$

2. Solve the torque condition for the tension, T:

$$T = \frac{mg}{2 \sin 40.0°} = \frac{(1.30 \text{ kg})(9.81 \text{ m/s}^2)}{2 \sin 40.0°} = 9.92 \text{ N}$$

Part (b)

3. Set the sum of the x components of force equal to zero, and solve for f_x:

$$\sum F_x = f_x - T \cos 40.0° = 0$$
$$f_x = T \cos 40.0° = (9.92 \text{ N}) \cos 40.0° = 7.60 \text{ N}$$

4. Set the sum of the y components of force equal to zero, and solve for f_y:

$$\sum F_y = f_y - mg + T \sin 40.0° = 0$$
$$f_y = mg - T \sin 40.0°$$
$$= (1.30 \text{ kg})(9.81 \text{ m/s}^2) - (9.92 \text{ N}) \sin 40.0° = 6.38 \text{ N}$$

INSIGHT

It is not necessary to determine T_x and T_y separately, since we know the direction of the cord. In particular, it is clear from our sketch that the components of $\vec{T}$ are $T_x = -T \cos 40.0° = -7.60$ N and $T_y = T \sin 40.0° = 6.38$ N.

Did you notice that $\vec{f}$ is at an angle of 40.0° with respect to the positive x axis, the same angle that $\vec{T}$ makes with the negative x axis? The reason for this symmetry, of course, is that mg acts at the center of the forearm. If mg were to act closer to the elbow, for example, $\vec{f}$ would make a larger angle with the horizontal, as we see in the following Practice Problem.

PRACTICE PROBLEM

Suppose the forearm and hand are nonuniform, and that the center of mass is located at a distance of $L/4$ from the elbow joint. What are T, f_x, and f_y in this case? [**Answer:** $T = 4.96$ N, $f_x = 3.80$ N, $f_y = 9.56$ N. In this case, $\vec{f}$ makes an angle of 68.3° with the horizontal.]

Some related homework problems: Problem 33, Problem 94

ACTIVE EXAMPLE 11–3 DON'T WALK UNDER THE LADDER: FIND THE FORCES

An 85-kg person stands on a lightweight ladder, as shown. The floor is rough; hence, it exerts both a normal force, f_1, and a frictional force, f_2, on the ladder. The wall, on the other hand, is frictionless; it exerts only a normal force, f_3. Using the dimensions given in the figure, find the magnitudes of f_1, f_2, and f_3.

SOLUTION *(Test your understanding by performing the calculations indicated in each step.)*

1. Set the net torque acting on the ladder equal to zero. Use the bottom of the ladder as the axis:

$$f_3(a) - mg(b) = 0$$

2. Solve for f_3:

$$f_3 = mg(b/a) = 150 \text{ N}$$

3. Sum the x components of force and set equal to zero:

$$f_2 - f_3 = 0$$

4. Solve for f_2:

$$f_2 = f_3 = 150 \text{ N}$$

5. Sum the y components of force and set equal to zero:

$$f_1 - mg = 0$$

6. Solve for f_1:

$$f_1 = mg = 830 \text{ N}$$

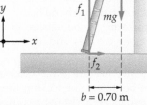

$a = 3.8$ m

$b = 0.70$ m

INSIGHT

If the floor is quite smooth, the ladder might slip—it depends on whether the coefficient of static friction is great enough to provide the needed force $f_2 = 150$ N. In this case, the normal force exerted by the floor is $N = f_1 = 830$ N. Therefore, if the coefficient of static friction is greater than 0.18 [since $0.18(830 \text{ N}) = 150$ N], the ladder will stay put. Ladders often have rubberized pads on the bottom in order to increase the static friction, and hence increase the safety of the ladder.

YOUR TURN

Write both the zero force and zero torque conditions for the case where the axis of rotation is at the top of the ladder.

*(Answers to **Your Turn** problems are given in the back of the book.)*

11-4 Center of Mass and Balance

Suppose you decide to construct a mobile. To begin, you tie a thread to a light rod, as in **Figure 11-7**. Note that the rod extends a distance x_1 to the left of the thread and a distance x_2 to the right. At the left end of the rod you attach an object of mass m_1. What mass, m_2, should be attached to the right end if the rod is to be balanced?

From the discussions in the previous sections, it is clear that if the rod is to be in static equilibrium (balanced), the net torque acting on it must be zero. Taking the point where the thread is tied to the rod as the axis of rotation, this zero-torque condition can be written as:

$$m_1 g(x_1) - m_2 g(x_2) = 0$$

Canceling g and rearranging, we find

$$m_1 x_1 = m_2 x_2 \qquad\qquad 11\text{-}7$$

This gives the following result for m_2:

$$m_2 = m_1(x_1/x_2)$$

For example, if $x_2 = 2x_1$, it follows that m_2 should be one-half of m_1.

Let's now consider a slightly different question: Where is the center of mass of m_1 and m_2? Choosing the origin of the x axis to be at the location of the thread, as indicated in Figure 11-7, we can use the definition of the center of mass, Equation 9-13, to find x_{cm}:

$$x_{cm} = \frac{m_1(-x_1) + m_2(x_2)}{m_1 + m_2} = -\left(\frac{m_1 x_1 - m_2 x_2}{m_1 + m_2}\right)$$

Referring to the zero-torque condition in Equation 11-7, we see that $m_1 x_1 - m_2 x_2 = 0$; hence the center of mass is at the origin:

$$x_{cm} = 0$$

This is precisely where the string is attached. We conclude, then, that the rod balances when the center of mass is directly below the point from which the rod is suspended. This is a general result.

Let's apply this result to the case of the mobile shown in the next Example.

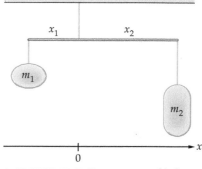

▲ **FIGURE 11-7** **Zero torque and balance**
One section of a mobile. The rod is balanced when the net torque acting on it is zero. This is equivalent to having the center of mass directly under the suspension point.

EXAMPLE 11-6   A WELL-BALANCED MEAL

As a grade-school project, students construct a mobile representing some of the major food groups. Their completed artwork is shown below. Find the masses m_1, m_2, and m_3 that are required for a perfectly balanced mobile. Assume the strings and the horizontal rods have negligible mass.

PICTURE THE PROBLEM
The dimensions of the horizontal rods, and the values of the given masses, are indicated in our sketch. Note that each rod is balanced at its suspension point.

STRATEGY
We can find all three unknown masses by repeatedly applying the condition for balance, $m_1 x_1 = m_2 x_2$.

First, we apply the balance condition to m_1 and m_2, with the distances $x_1 = 12$ cm and $x_2 = 18$ cm. This gives a relation between m_1 and m_2.

To get a second relation between m_1 and m_2, we apply the balance condition again at the next higher level of the mobile. That is, the mass $(m_1 + m_2)$ at the distance 6.0 cm must balance the mass 0.30 kg at the distance 24 cm. These two conditions determine m_1 and m_2.

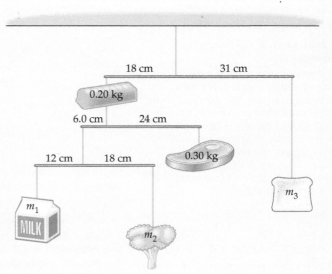

CONTINUED ON NEXT PAGE

CONTINUED FROM PREVIOUS PAGE

To find m_3 we again apply the balance condition, this time with the mass $(m_1 + m_2 + 0.30 \text{ kg} + 0.20 \text{ kg})$ at the distance 18 cm, and the mass m_3 at the distance 31 cm.

SOLUTION

1. Apply the balance condition to m_1 and m_2:

$$m_1(12 \text{ cm}) = m_2(18 \text{ cm})$$
$$m_1 = (1.5)m_2$$

2. Apply the balance condition to the next level up in the mobile. Solve for the sum, $m_1 + m_2$:

$$(m_1 + m_2)(6.0 \text{ cm}) = (0.30 \text{ kg})(24 \text{ cm})$$

$$m_1 + m_2 = \frac{(0.30 \text{ kg})(24 \text{ cm})}{6.0 \text{ cm}} = 1.2 \text{ kg}$$

3. Substitute $m_1 = (1.5)m_2$ into $m_1 + m_2 = 1.2$ kg to find m_2:

$$(1.5)m_2 + m_2 = (2.5)m_2 = 1.2 \text{ kg}$$
$$m_2 = 1.2 \text{ kg}/2.5 = 0.48 \text{ kg}$$

4. Use $m_1 = (1.5)m_2$ to find m_1:

$$m_1 = (1.5)m_2 = (1.5)0.48 \text{ kg} = 0.72 \text{ kg}$$

5. Apply the balance condition to the top level of the mobile:

$$(0.72 \text{ kg} + 0.48 \text{ kg} + 0.30 \text{ kg} + 0.20 \text{ kg})(18 \text{ cm}) = m_3(31 \text{ cm})$$

6. Solve for m_3:

$$m_3 = \frac{(1.70 \text{ kg})(18 \text{ cm})}{31 \text{ cm}} = 0.99 \text{ kg}$$

INSIGHT

With the values for m_1, m_2, and m_3 found above, the mobile balances at every level. In fact, the center of mass of the *entire* mobile is directly below the point where the uppermost string attaches to the ceiling.

PRACTICE PROBLEM

Find m_1, m_2, and m_3 if the 0.30-kg mass is replaced with a 0.40-kg mass. [**Answer:** $m_1 = 0.96$ kg, $m_2 = 0.64$ kg, $m_3 = 1.3$ kg]

Some related homework problems: Problem 43, Problem 45

(a) Zero torque (b) Nonzero torque

▲ **FIGURE 11–8 Equilibrium of a suspended object**

(a) If an object's center of mass is directly below the suspension point, its weight creates zero torque and the object is in equilibrium. (b) When an object is rotated, so that the center of mass is no longer directly below the suspension point, the object's weight creates a torque. The torque tends to rotate the object to bring the center of mass under the suspension point.

In general, if you allow an arbitrarily shaped object to hang freely, its center of mass is directly below the suspension point. To see why, note that when the center of mass is directly below the suspension point, the torque due to gravity is zero, since the force of gravity extends right through the axis of rotation. This is shown in **Figure 11–8 (a)**. If the object is rotated slightly, as in **Figure 11–8 (b)**, the force of gravity is not in line with the axis of rotation—hence gravity produces a torque. This torque tends to rotate the object, bringing the center of mass back under the suspension point.

For example, suppose you cut a piece of wood into the shape of the continental United States, as shown in **Figure 11–9**, drill a small hole in it, and hang it from the

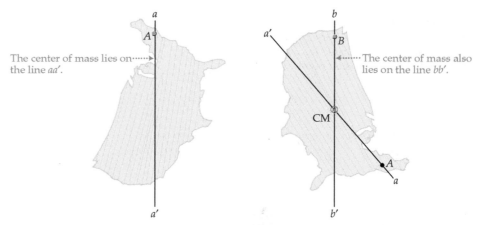

The center of mass lies on the line aa'.

The center of mass also lies on the line bb'.

▲ **FIGURE 11–9 The geometric center of the United States**

To find the center of mass of an irregularly shaped object, such as a wooden model of the continental United States, suspend it from two or more points. The center of mass lies on a vertical line extending downward from the suspension point. The intersection of these vertical lines gives the precise location of the center of mass.

point *A*. The result is that the center of mass lies somewhere on the line *aa'*. Similarly, if a second hole is drilled at point *B*, we find that the center of mass lies somewhere on the line *bb'*. The only point that is on both the line *aa'* and the line *bb'* is the point CM, near Smith Center, Kansas, which marks the location of the center of mass.

▲ In this scene from the movie *Mission Impossible*, Tom Cruise is attempting to download top-secret computer files without setting off the elaborate security system in the room. To accomplish this nearly impossible mission, he is suspended from the ceiling, since touching the floor would immediately give away his presence. To remain in equilibrium above the floor as he works, he must carefully adjust the position of his arms and legs to keep his center of mass directly below the suspension point.

CONCEPTUAL CHECKPOINT 11–2   COMPARE THE MASSES

A croquet mallet balances when suspended from its center of mass, as indicated in the drawing at left. If you cut the mallet in two at its center of mass, as in the drawing at right, how do the masses of the two pieces compare? **(a)** The masses are equal; **(b)** the piece with the head of the mallet has the greater mass; or **(c)** the piece with the head of the mallet has the smaller mass.

REASONING AND DISCUSSION
The mallet balances because the torques due to the two pieces are of equal magnitude. The piece with the head of the mallet extends a smaller distance from the point of suspension than does the other piece, hence its mass must be greater; that is, a large mass at a small distance creates the same torque as a small mass at a large distance.

ANSWER
(b) The piece with the head of the mallet has the greater mass.

Similar considerations apply to an object that is at rest on a surface, as opposed to being suspended from a point. In such a case, the object is in equilibrium as long as its center of mass is directly above the base on which it is supported. For example, when you stand upright with normal posture your feet provide a base of support, and your center of mass is above a point roughly halfway between your feet. If you lift your right foot from the floor—without changing your posture—you will begin to lose your balance and tip over. The reason is that your center of mass is no longer above the base of support, which is now your left foot. To balance on your left foot, you must lean slightly in that direction so as to position your center of mass directly above the foot. This principle applies to everything from a performer in a high-wire act to one of the "balancing rocks" that are a familiar sight in the desert Southwest. In Problem 44 we apply this condition for stability to a stack of books on the edge of a table.

◀ (Left) Although it looks precarious, this rock in Arches National Park, Utah, has probably been balancing above the desert for many thousands of years. It will remain secure on its perch as long as its center of mass lies above its base of support. (Right) Although her knowledge may be based more on practical experience than on physics, this woman knows exactly what she must do to keep from falling. By extending one leg backward as she leans forward, she keeps her center of mass safely positioned over the foot that supports her.

11–5 Dynamic Applications of Torque

In this section we focus on applications of Newton's second law for rotation. For example, consider a disk-shaped pulley of radius R and mass M with a string wrapped around its circumference, as in **Figure 11–10 (a)**. Hanging from the string is a mass m. When the mass is released, it accelerates downward and the pulley begins to rotate. If the pulley rotates without friction, and the string unwraps without slipping, what are the acceleration of the mass and the tension in the string?

▶ **FIGURE 11–10 A mass suspended from a pulley**

A mass m hangs from a string wrapped around the circumference of a disk-shaped pulley of radius R and mass M. When the mass is released, it accelerates downward. Positive directions of motion for the system are shown in parts (b) and (c). In part (c), the weight of the pulley acts downward at its center, and the axle exerts an upward force equal in magnitude to the weight of the pulley plus the tension in the string. Of the three forces acting on the pulley, only the tension in the string produces a torque about the axle.

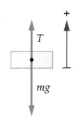

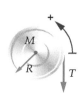

(a) Physical picture

(b) Free-body diagram for mass

(c) Torque producing force acting on pulley

At first it may seem that since the pulley rotates freely, the mass will simply fall with the acceleration of gravity. But remember, the pulley has a nonzero moment of inertia, $I > 0$, which means that it resists any change in its rotational motion. In order for the pulley to rotate, the string must pull downward on it. This means that the string also pulls upward on the mass m with a tension T. As a result, the net downward force on m is less than mg, and thus its acceleration is less than g.

To solve for the acceleration of the mass, we must apply Newton's second law to both the linear motion of the mass *and* the rotational motion of the pulley. The first step is to define a consistent choice of positive directions for the two motions. In Figure 11–10 (a) we note that when the pulley rotates counterclockwise, the mass moves upward. Thus, we choose counterclockwise to be positive for the pulley and upward to be positive for the mass.

With our positive directions established, we proceed to apply Newton's second law. Referring to the free-body diagram for the mass, shown in **Figure 11–10 (b)**, we see that

$$T - mg = ma \qquad \qquad \text{11–8}$$

Similarly, the free-body diagram for the pulley is shown in **Figure 11–10 (c)**. Note that the tension in the string, T, exerts a tangential force on the pulley at a distance R from the axis of rotation. This produces a torque of magnitude TR. Since the tension tends to cause a clockwise rotation, it follows that the torque is negative; thus, $\tau = -TR$. As a result, Newton's second law for the pulley gives

$$-TR = I\alpha \qquad \qquad \text{11–9}$$

Now, these two statements of Newton's second law are related by the fact that the string unwraps without slipping. As was discussed in Chapter 10, when a string unwraps without slipping, the angular and linear accelerations are related by

$$\alpha = \frac{a}{R}$$

Using this relation in Equation 11–9 we have

$$-TR = I\frac{a}{R}$$

or, dividing by R,

$$T = -I\frac{a}{R^2}$$

Substituting this result into Equation 11–8 yields

$$-I\frac{a}{R^2} - mg = ma$$

Finally, dividing by m and rearranging yields the acceleration, a:

$$a = -\frac{g}{\left(1 + \dfrac{I}{mR^2}\right)} \qquad\qquad \text{11–10}$$

Let's briefly check our solution for a. First, note that a is negative. This is to be expected, since the mass accelerates downward, which is the negative direction. Second, if the moment of inertia were zero, $I = 0$, or if the mass m were infinite, $m \rightarrow \infty$, the mass would fall with the acceleration of gravity, $a = -g$. When I is greater than zero and m is finite, however, the acceleration of the mass has a magnitude less than g. In fact, in the limit of an infinite moment of inertia, $I \rightarrow \infty$, the acceleration vanishes—the mass is simply unable to cause the pulley to rotate in this case.

The next Example presents another system in which Newton's laws are used to relate linear and rotational motions.

EXAMPLE 11–7 THE PULLEY MATTERS

A 0.31-kg cart on a horizontal air track is attached to a string. The string passes over a disk-shaped pulley of mass 0.080 kg and radius 0.012 m and is pulled vertically downward with a constant force of 1.1 N. Find **(a)** the tension in the string between the pulley and the cart and **(b)** the acceleration of the cart.

PICTURE THE PROBLEM
The system is shown below. We label the mass of the cart with M, the mass of the pulley with m, and the radius of the pulley with r. The applied downward force creates a tension $T_1 = 1.1$ N in the vertical portion of the string. The horizontal portion of the string, from the pulley to the cart, has a tension T_2. If the pulley had zero mass, these two tensions would be equal. In this case, however, T_2 will have a different value than T_1.

We also show the relevant forces acting on the pulley and the cart. The positive direction of rotation is counterclockwise, and the corresponding positive direction of motion for the cart is to the left.

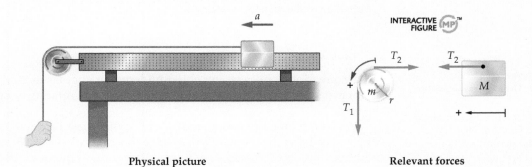

Physical picture   Relevant forces

STRATEGY
The two unknowns, T_2 and a, can be found by applying Newton's second law to both the pulley and the cart. This gives two equations for two unknowns.

In applying Newton's second law to the pulley, note that since the pulley is a disk, it follows that $I = \frac{1}{2}mr^2$. Also, since the string is not said to slip as it rotates the pulley, we can assume that the angular and linear accelerations are related by $\alpha = a/r$.

CONTINUED ON NEXT PAGE

CONTINUED FROM PREVIOUS PAGE

SOLUTION

Part (a)

1. Apply Newton's second law to the cart:

$$T_2 = Ma$$

2. Apply Newton's second law to the pulley. Note that T_1 causes a positive torque, and T_2 causes a negative torque. In addition, use the relation $\alpha = a/r$:

$$\Sigma\tau = I\alpha$$

$$rT_1 - rT_2 = \left(\tfrac{1}{2}mr^2\right)\left(\frac{a}{r}\right) = \tfrac{1}{2}mra$$

3. Use the cart equation, $T_2 = Ma$, to eliminate a in the pulley equation:

$$a = \frac{T_2}{M}$$

$$rT_1 - rT_2 = \tfrac{1}{2}mr\left(\frac{T_2}{M}\right)$$

4. Cancel r and solve for T_2:

$$T_2 = \frac{T_1}{1 + m/2M} = \frac{1.1\ \text{N}}{1 + 0.080\ \text{kg}/[2(0.31\ \text{kg})]} = 0.97\ \text{N}$$

Part (b)

5. Use $T_2 = Ma$ to find the acceleration:

$$a = \frac{T_2}{M} = \frac{0.97\ \text{N}}{0.31\ \text{kg}} = 3.1\ \text{m/s}^2$$

INSIGHT

Note that T_2 is less than T_1. As a result, the net torque acting on the pulley is in the counterclockwise direction, causing a rotation in that direction, as expected. If the mass of the pulley were zero ($m = 0$), the two tensions would be equal, and the acceleration of the cart would be $T_1/M = 3.5\ \text{m/s}^2$.

PRACTICE PROBLEM

What applied force is necessary to give the cart an acceleration of $2.2\ \text{m/s}^2$? [**Answer:** $T_1 = T_2(1 + m/2M) = (Ma)(1 + m/2M) = 0.77\ \text{N}$]

Some related homework problems: Problem 49, Problem 50

11–6 Angular Momentum

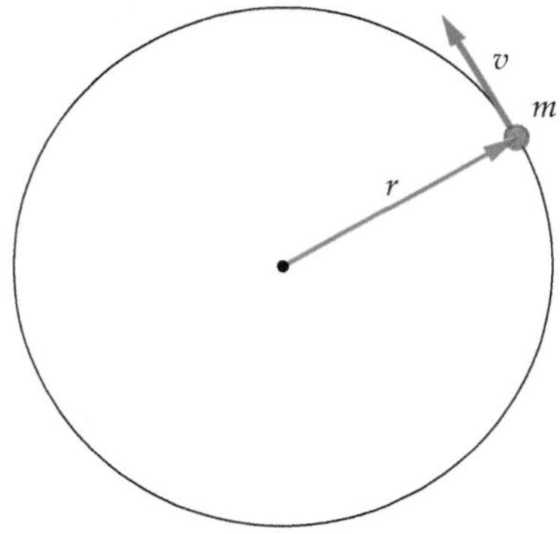

▲ **FIGURE 11–11 The angular momentum of circular motion**

A particle of mass m, moving in a circle of radius r with a speed v. This particle has an angular momentum of magnitude $L = rmv$.

When an object of mass m moves with a speed v in a straight line, we say that it has a linear momentum, $p = mv$. When the same object moves with an angular speed ω along the circumference of a circle of radius r, as in **Figure 11–11**, we say that it has an **angular momentum**, L. The magnitude of L is given by replacing m and v in the expression for p with their angular analogues I and ω (Section 10–5). Thus, we define the angular momentum as follows:

Definition of the Angular Momentum, L	
$L = I\omega$	11–11
SI unit: $\text{kg} \cdot \text{m}^2/\text{s}$	

This expression applies to any object undergoing angular motion, whether it is a point mass moving in a circle, as in Figure 11–11, or a rotating hoop, disk, or other object.

Returning for a moment to the case of a point mass m moving in a circle of radius r, recall that the moment of inertia in this case is $I = mr^2$ (Equation 10–18). In addition, the linear speed of the mass is $v = r\omega$ (Equation 10–12). Combining these results, we find

$$L = I\omega = (mr^2)(v/r) = rmv$$

Noting that mv is the linear momentum p, we find that the angular momentum of a point mass can be written in the following form:

$$L = rmv = rp \qquad \text{11–12}$$

It is important to recall that this expression applies specifically to a point particle moving along the circumference of a circle.

More generally, a point object may be moving at an angle θ with respect to a radial line, as indicated in **Figure 11–12 (a)**. In this case, it is only the tangential component of the momentum, $p \sin \theta = mv \sin \theta$, that contributes to the angular momentum, just as the tangential component of the force, $F \sin \theta$, is all that contributes to the torque. Thus, the magnitude of the angular momentum for a point particle is defined as:

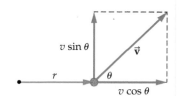

(a)

Angular Momentum, L, for a Point Particle

$$L = rp \sin \theta = rmv \sin \theta \qquad \text{11–13}$$

SI unit: $kg \cdot m^2/s$

Note that if the particle moves in a circular path the angle θ is 90° and the angular momentum is $L = rmv$, in agreement with Equation 11–12. On the other hand, if the object moves radially, so that $\theta = 0$, the angular momentum is zero; $L = rmv \sin 0 = 0$.

EXERCISE 11–3

Find the angular momentum of **(a)** a 0.13-kg Frisbee (considered to be a uniform disk of radius 7.5 cm) spinning with an angular speed of 1.15 rad/s, and **(b)** a 95-kg person running with a speed of 5.1 m/s on a circular track of radius 25 m.

SOLUTION

a. Recalling that $I = \frac{1}{2}mR^2$ for a uniform disk (Table 10–1), we have

$$L = I\omega$$

$$= \left(\tfrac{1}{2}mR^2\right)\omega = \tfrac{1}{2}(0.13\ \text{kg})(0.075\ \text{m})^2(1.15\ \text{rad/s}) = 4.2 \times 10^{-4}\ \text{kg}\cdot\text{m}^2/\text{s}$$

b. Treating the person as a particle of mass m, we find

$$L = rmv = (25\ \text{m})(95\ \text{kg})(5.1\ \text{m/s}) = 12{,}000\ \text{kg}\cdot\text{m}^2/\text{s}$$

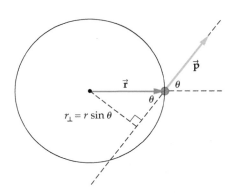

(b)

▲ **FIGURE 11–12 The angular momentum of nontangential motion**
(a) When a particle moves at an angle θ with respect to the radial direction, only the tangential component of velocity, $v \sin \theta$, contributes to the angular momentum. In the case shown here, the particle's angular momentum has a magnitude given by $L = rmv \sin \theta$. **(b)** The angular momentum of an object can also be defined in terms of the moment arm, $r_\perp$. Since $r_\perp = r \sin \theta$, it follows that $L = rmv \sin \theta = r_\perp mv$. Note the similarity between this figure and Figure 11–3.

An alternative definition of the angular momentum uses the moment arm, $r_\perp$, as was done for the torque in Equation 11–3. To apply this definition, start by extending a line through the momentum vector, $\vec{p}$, as in **Figure 11–12 (b)**. Next, draw a line from the axis of rotation perpendicular to the line through $\vec{p}$. The perpendicular distance from the axis of rotation to the line of $\vec{p}$ is the moment arm. From the figure we see that $r_\perp = r \sin \theta$. Hence, from Equation 11–13, the angular momentum is

$$L = r_\perp p = r_\perp mv$$

If an object moves in a circle of radius r, the moment arm is $r_\perp = r$ and the angular momentum reduces to our earlier result, $L = rp$.

CONCEPTUAL CHECKPOINT 11–3　ANGULAR MOMENTUM?

Does an object moving in a straight line have nonzero angular momentum **(a)** always, **(b)** sometimes, or **(c)** never?

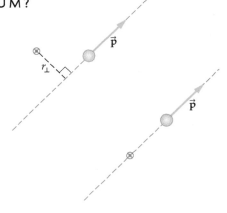

REASONING AND DISCUSSION

The answer is sometimes, because it depends on the choice of the axis of rotation. If the axis of rotation is not on the line drawn through the momentum vector, as in the left sketch at right, the moment arm is nonzero, and therefore $L = r_\perp p$ is also nonzero. If the axis of rotation is on the line of motion, as in the right sketch, the moment arm is zero; hence the linear momentum is radial and L vanishes.

ANSWER

(b) An object moving in a straight line may or may not have angular momentum, depending on the location of the axis of rotation.

▶ **FIGURE 11–13** **Angular momentum in linear and circular motion**
An object moving in **(a)** a straight line and **(b)** a circular path. In both cases, the angular position increases with time; hence, the angular momentum is positive.

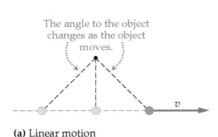

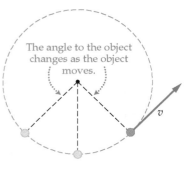

(a) Linear motion

(b) Circular motion

Note that an object moving with a momentum p in a straight line that does not go through the axis of rotation has an *angular* position that changes with time. This is illustrated in **Figure 11–13 (a)**. It is for this reason that such an object is said to have an *angular* momentum.

The sign of L is determined by whether the angle to a given object is increasing or decreasing with time. For example, the object moving counterclockwise in a circular path in **Figure 11–13 (b)** has a positive angular momentum, since θ is increasing with time. Similarly, the object in Figure 11–13 (a) also has an angle θ that increases with time, hence its angular momentum is positive as well. On the other hand, if these objects were to have their direction of motion reversed, they would have angles that decrease with time and their angular momenta would be negative.

EXAMPLE 11–8   JUMP ON

Running with a speed of 4.10 m/s, a 21.2-kg child heads toward the rim of a merry-go-round. The radius of the merry-go-round is 2.00 m, and the child moves in the direction indicated. **(a)** What is the child's angular momentum with respect to the center of the merry-go-round? Use $L = rmv \sin \theta$. **(b)** What is the moment arm, $r_\perp$, in this case? **(c)** Find the angular momentum of the child with $L = r_\perp mv$.

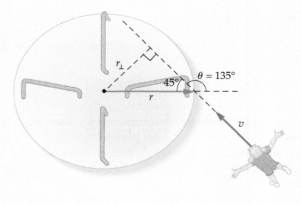

PICTURE THE PROBLEM
Our sketch shows the child approaching the rim of the merry-go-round at an angle of 135° relative to the radial direction. Note that the line of motion of the child does not go through the axis of the merry-go-round. As a result, the child has a nonzero angular momentum with respect to that axis of rotation. We also indicate the moment arm, $r_\perp$, and the 45° angle that is opposite to it.

STRATEGY
a. The child's angular momentum can be found by applying $L = rmv \sin \theta$. In this case, we see from the sketch that $\theta = 135°$ and $r = 2.00$ m. The values of m and v are given in the problem statement.
b. and c. Our sketch shows that $r_\perp$ is the side of the right triangle opposite to the angle of 45°. It follows that $r_\perp = r \sin 45°$.

SOLUTION

Part (a)

1. Evaluate $L = rmv \sin \theta$:

$$L = rmv \sin \theta = (2.00 \text{ m})(21.2 \text{ kg})(4.10 \text{ m/s}) \sin 135°$$
$$= 123 \text{ kg} \cdot \text{m}^2/\text{s}$$

Part (b)

2. Calculate the moment arm, $r_\perp$:

$$r_\perp = r \sin 45° = (2.00 \text{ m}) \sin 45° = 1.41 \text{ m}$$

Part (c)

3. Evaluate $L = r_\perp mv$:

$$L = r_\perp mv = (1.41 \text{ m})(21.2 \text{ kg})(4.10 \text{ m/s}) = 123 \text{ kg} \cdot \text{m}^2/\text{s}$$

INSIGHT
When the child lands on the merry-go-round, she will transfer angular momentum to it, causing the merry-go-round to rotate about its center. This will be discussed in more detail in the next section.

Notice that we use 45° in $r_\perp = r \sin 45°$ because we calculate the length of the opposite side of the right triangle indicated in our sketch. We could have used $r_\perp = r \sin 135°$ just as well, using the same angle as in $L = rmv \sin 135°$. The results are the same in either case, since $\sin 135° = \sin 45°$.

PRACTICE PROBLEM
For what angle relative to the radial line does the child have a maximum angular momentum? What is the angular momentum in this case?   [**Answer:** $\theta = 90°$, for which $L = rmv = 174 \text{ kg} \cdot \text{m}^2/\text{s}$]

Some related homework problems: Problem 56, Problem 57, Problem 58

Next, we consider the rate of change of angular momentum with time. Since the moment of inertia is a constant—as long as the mass and shape of the object remain unchanged—the change in L in a time interval Δt is

$$\frac{\Delta L}{\Delta t} = I\frac{\Delta \omega}{\Delta t}$$

Recall, however, that $\Delta \omega / \Delta t$ is the angular acceleration, α. Therefore, we have

$$\frac{\Delta L}{\Delta t} = I\alpha$$

Since $I\alpha$ is the torque, it follows that Newton's second law for rotational motion can be written as

Newton's Second Law for Rotational Motion

$$\sum \tau = I\alpha = \frac{\Delta L}{\Delta t} \qquad\qquad \text{11–14}$$

Clearly, this is the rotational analogue of $\Sigma F_x = ma_x = \Delta p_x / \Delta t$. Just as force can be expressed as the change in *linear* momentum in a given time interval, the torque can be expressed as the change in *angular* momentum in a time interval.

EXERCISE 11–4

In a light wind, a windmill experiences a constant torque of 255 N · m. If the windmill is initially at rest, what is its angular momentum 2.00 s later?

SOLUTION
Solve Equation 11–14 for the change in angular momentum due to a single torque τ:

$$\Delta L = L_f - L_i = \left(\sum \tau\right) \Delta t = \tau \, \Delta t$$

Since the initial angular momentum of the windmill is zero, its final angular momentum is

$$L_f = \tau \, \Delta t = (255 \text{ N} \cdot \text{m})(2.00 \text{ s}) = 510 \text{ kg} \cdot \text{m}^2/\text{s}$$

11–7 Conservation of Angular Momentum

When an ice skater goes into a spin and pulls her arms inward to speed up, she probably doesn't think about angular momentum. Neither does a diver who springs into the air and folds her body to speed her rotation. Most people, in fact, are not aware that the actions of these athletes are governed by the same basic laws of physics that cause a collapsing star to spin faster as it becomes a rapidly rotating pulsar. Yet in all these cases, as we shall see, **conservation of angular momentum** is at work.

To see the origin of angular momentum conservation, consider an object with an initial angular momentum L_i acted on by a single torque τ. After a period of time, Δt, the object's angular momentum changes in accordance with Newton's second law:

$$\tau = \frac{\Delta L}{\Delta t}$$

Solving for ΔL, we find

$$\Delta L = L_f - L_i = \tau \, \Delta t$$

Thus, the final angular momentum of the object is

$$L_f = L_i + \tau \, \Delta t$$

▲ Once she has launched herself into space, this diver is essentially a projectile. However, the principle of conservation of angular momentum allows her to control the rotational part of her motion. By curling her body up into a tight "tuck," she decreases her moment of inertia, thereby increasing the speed of her spin. To slow down for an elegant entry into the water, she will extend her body, increasing her moment of inertia.

If the torque acting on the object is zero, $\tau = 0$, it follows that the initial and final angular momenta are equal—that is, the angular momentum is conserved:

$$L_f = L_i \quad (\text{if } \tau = 0)$$

Angular momentum is also conserved in systems acted on by more than one torque, provided that the *net external torque* is zero. The reason that internal torques can be ignored is that, just as internal forces come in equal and opposite pairs that cancel, so too do internal torques. As a result, the internal torques in a system sum to zero, and the net torque acting on it is simply the net external torque. Thus, for a general system, angular momentum is conserved if $\tau_{net, ext}$ is zero:

Conservation of Angular Momentum

$L_f = L_i \quad (\text{if } \tau_{net, ext} = 0)$ 11–15

As an illustration of angular momentum conservation, we consider the case of a student rotating on a piano stool in the next Example. Notice how a change in moment of inertia results in a change in angular speed.

EXAMPLE 11–9 GOING FOR A SPIN

For a classroom demonstration, a student sits on a piano stool holding a sizable mass in each hand. Initially, the student holds his arms outstretched and spins about the axis of the stool with an angular speed of 3.72 rad/s. The moment of inertia in this case is 5.33 kg·m². While still spinning, the student pulls his arms in to his chest, reducing the moment of inertia to 1.60 kg·m². **(a)** What is the student's angular speed now? **(b)** Find the initial and final angular momenta of the student.

PICTURE THE PROBLEM
The initial and final configurations of the student are shown in our sketch. Clearly, the mass distribution in the final configuration, with the masses held closer to the axis of rotation, results in a smaller moment of inertia.

STRATEGY
Ignoring friction in the axis of the stool, since none was mentioned, we conclude that no external torques act on the system. As a result, the angular momentum is conserved. Therefore, setting the initial angular momentum, $L_i = I_i\omega_i$, equal to the final angular momentum, $L_f = I_f\omega_f$, yields the final angular speed.

SOLUTION

Part (a)

1. Apply angular momentum conservation to this system:

$$L_i = L_f$$
$$I_i\omega_i = I_f\omega_f$$

2. Solve for the final angular speed, ω_f:

$$\omega_f = \left(\frac{I_i}{I_f}\right)\omega_i$$

3. Substitute numerical values:

$$\omega_f = \left(\frac{5.33 \text{ kg·m}^2}{1.60 \text{ kg·m}^2}\right)(3.72 \text{ rad/s}) = 12.4 \text{ rad/s}$$

Part (b)

4. Use $L = I\omega$ to calculate the angular momentum.
Substitute both initial and final values as a check:

$$L_i = I_i\omega_i = (5.33 \text{ kg·m}^2)(3.72 \text{ rad/s}) = 19.8 \text{ kg·m}^2/\text{s}$$
$$L_f = I_f\omega_f = (1.60 \text{ kg·m}^2)(12.4 \text{ rad/s}) = 19.8 \text{ kg·m}^2/\text{s}$$

INSIGHT
Initially the student completes one revolution roughly every two seconds. After pulling the weights in, the student's rotation rate has increased to almost two revolutions a second—quite a dizzying pace. The same physics applies to a rotating diver or a spinning ice skater.

PRACTICE PROBLEM
What moment of inertia would be required to give a final spin rate of 10.0 rad/s?   [**Answer:** $I_f = (\omega_i/\omega_f)I_i = 1.99 \text{ kg·m}^2$]

Some related homework problems: Problem 65, Problem 67, Problem 74

▲ This 1992 satellite photo of Hurricane Andrew (left), one of the most powerful hurricanes of recent decades, clearly suggests the rotating structure of the storm. The violence of the hurricane winds can be attributed in large part to conservation of angular momentum: as air is pushed inward toward the low pressure near the eye of the storm, its rotational velocity increases. The same principle, operating on a smaller scale, explains the tremendous destructive power of tornadoes. The tornado shown at right passed through downtown Miami on May 12, 1997.

An increasing angular speed, as experienced by the student in Example 11–9, can be observed in nature as well. For example, a hurricane draws circulating air in at ground level toward its "eye," where it then rises to an altitude of 10 miles or more. As air moves inward toward the axis of rotation, its angular speed increases, just as the masses held by the student speed up when they are pulled inward. For example, if the wind has a speed of only 3.0 mph at a distance of 300 miles from the center of the hurricane, it would speed up to 150 mph when it comes to within 6.0 miles of the center. Of course, this analysis ignores friction, which would certainly decrease the wind speed. Still, the basic principle—that a decreasing distance from the axis of rotation implies an increasing speed—applies to both the student and the hurricane. Similar behavior is observed in tornadoes and waterspouts.

Another example of conservation of angular momentum occurs in stellar explosions. On occasion a star will explode, sending a portion of its material out into space. After the explosion, the star collapses to a fraction of its original size, speeding up its rotation in the process. If the mass of the star is greater than 1.44 times the mass of the Sun, the collapse can continue until a *neutron star* is formed, with a radius of only about 10 to 20 km. Neutron stars have incredibly high densities; in fact, if you could bring a teaspoonful of neutron star material to the Earth, it would weigh about 100 million tons! In addition, neutron stars produce powerful beams of X-rays and other radiation that sweep across the sky like a gigantic lighthouse beam as the star rotates. On the Earth we see pulses of radiation from these rotating beams, one for each revolution of the star. These "pulsating stars," or *pulsars*, typically have periods ranging from about 2 ms to nearly 1 s. The Crab nebula (see Problems 9 and 106 in Chapter 10) is a famous example of such a system. The dependence of angular speed on radius for a collapsing star is considered in Active Example 11–4.

REAL-WORLD PHYSICS

Hurricanes and tornadoes

▲ Among the fastest rotating objects known in nature are pulsars: stars that have collapsed to a tiny fraction of their original size. Since all the angular momentum of a star must be conserved when it collapses, the dramatic decrease in radius is accompanied by a correspondingly great increase in rotational speed. The Crab nebula pulsar, the remains of a star whose explosion was observed on Earth nearly 1000 years ago, spins at about 30 rev/s. This X-ray photograph shows rings and jets of high-energy particles flying outward from the whirling neutron star at the center.

ACTIVE EXAMPLE 11–4 A STELLAR PERFORMANCE: FIND THE ANGULAR SPEED

A star of radius $R = 2.3 \times 10^8$ m rotates with an angular speed $\omega = 2.4 \times 10^{-6}$ rad/s. If this star collapses to a radius of 20.0 km, find its final angular speed. (Treat the star as if it were a uniform sphere, and assume that no mass is lost as the star collapses.)

SOLUTION *(Test your understanding by performing the calculations indicated in each step.)*

1. Apply conservation of angular momentum: $I_i \omega_i = I_f \omega_f$

CONTINUED ON NEXT PAGE

CONTINUED FROM PREVIOUS PAGE

2. Write expressions for the initial and final moments of inertia:

$I_i = \frac{2}{5}MR_i^2$ and $I_f = \frac{2}{5}MR_f^2$

3. Solve for the final angular speed:

$\omega_f = (I_i/I_f)\omega_i = (R_i^2/R_f^2)\omega_i$

4. Substitute numerical values:

$\omega_f = 320 \text{ rad/s}$

INSIGHT

The final angular speed corresponds to a period of about 20 ms, a typical period for pulsars. Since 320 rad/s is roughly 3000 rpm, it follows that a pulsar, which has the mass of a star, rotates as fast as the engine in a racing car.

YOUR TURN

At what radius will the star's period of rotation be equal to 15 ms?

(Answers to **Your Turn** *problems are given in the back of the book.)*

Note that if the student in Example 11–9 were to stretch his arms back out again, the resulting *increase* in the moment of inertia would cause a *decrease* in his angular speed. The same effect might apply to the Earth one day. For example, a melting of the polar ice caps would lead to an increase in the Earth's moment of inertia (as we saw in Chapter 10) and thus, by angular momentum conservation, the angular speed of the Earth would decrease. This would mean that more time would be required for the Earth to complete a revolution about its axis of rotation; that is, the day would lengthen.

Since angular momentum is conserved in the systems we have studied so far, it is natural to ask whether the energy is conserved as well. We consider this question in the next Conceptual Checkpoint.

CONCEPTUAL CHECKPOINT 11–4

COMPARE KINETIC ENERGIES

A skater pulls in her arms, decreasing her moment of inertia by a factor of two, and doubling her angular speed. Is her final kinetic energy **(a)** equal to, **(b)** greater than, or **(c)** less than her initial kinetic energy?

REASONING AND DISCUSSION

Let's calculate the initial and final kinetic energies, and compare them. The initial kinetic energy is

$$K_i = \frac{1}{2}I_i\omega_i^2$$

After pulling in her arms, the skater has half the moment of inertia and twice the angular speed. Hence, her final kinetic energy is

$$K_f = \frac{1}{2}I_f\omega_f^2 = \frac{1}{2}(I_i/2)(2\omega_i)^2 = 2\left(\frac{1}{2}I_i\omega_i^2\right) = 2K_i$$

Thus, the fact that K depends on the square of ω leads to an increase in the kinetic energy. The source of this additional energy is the work done by the muscles in the skater's arms as she pulls them in to her body.

ANSWER

(b) The skater's kinetic energy increases.

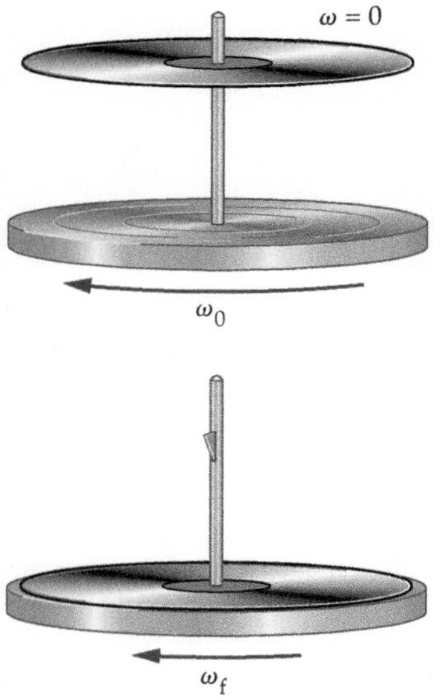

▲ FIGURE 11–14 A rotational collision
A nonrotating record dropped onto a rotating turntable is an example of a "rotational collision." Since only internal forces are involved during the collision, the final angular momentum is equal to the initial angular momentum.

Rotational Collisions

In the not-too-distant past, a person would play music by placing a record on a rotating turntable. Suppose, for example, that a turntable with a moment of inertia I_t is rotating freely with an initial angular speed ω_0. A record, with a moment of inertia I_r and initially at rest, is dropped straight down onto the rotating turntable, as in **Figure 11–14**. When the record lands, frictional forces between it and the turntable cause the record to speed up and the turntable to slow down, until they both have the same angular speed. Since only internal forces are involved during this process, it follows that the system's angular momentum is conserved. We can think of this event, then, as a "rotational collision."

Before the collision, the angular momentum of the system is

$$L_i = I_t\omega_0$$

After the collision, when both the record and the turntable are rotating with the angular speed ω_f, the system's angular momentum is

$$L_f = I_t\omega_f + I_r\omega_f$$

Setting $L_f = L_i$ yields the final angular speed:

$$\omega_f = \left(\frac{I_t}{I_t + I_r}\right)\omega_0 \qquad\qquad 11\text{--}16$$

Since this collision is completely inelastic, we expect the final kinetic energy to be less than the initial kinetic energy.

We conclude this section with a somewhat different example of a rotational collision. The physical principles involved are precisely the same, however.

ACTIVE EXAMPLE 11–5   CONSERVE ANGULAR MOMENTUM: FIND THE ANGULAR SPEED

A 34.0-kg child runs with a speed of 2.80 m/s tangential to the rim of a stationary merry-go-round. The merry-go-round has a moment of inertia of 512 kg · m² and a radius of 2.31 m. When the child jumps onto the merry-go-round, the entire system begins to rotate. What is the angular speed of the system?

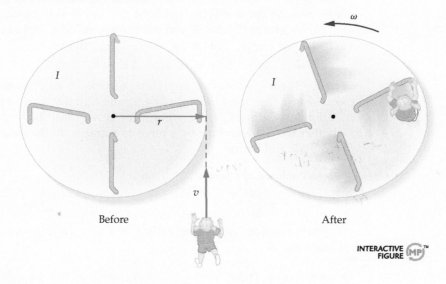

Before   After

INTERACTIVE FIGURE (MP)™

SOLUTION *(Test your understanding by performing the calculations indicated in each step.)*

1. Write the initial angular momentum of the child: $L_i = rmv$

2. Write the final angular momentum of the system: $L_f = (I + mr^2)\omega$

3. Set $L_f = L_i$ and solve for the angular speed: $\omega = rmv/(I + mr^2)$

4. Substitute numerical values: $\omega = 0.317$ rad/s

INSIGHT
If the moment of inertia of the merry-go-round had been zero, $I = 0$, the angular speed would be $\omega = v/r$. This means that the linear speed of the child, $r\omega = v$, is unchanged. If $I > 0$, however, the linear speed of the child is decreased. In this particular case, the child's linear speed after the collision is only $v = r\omega = 0.733$ m/s.

YOUR TURN
What initial speed does the child have if, after landing on the merry-go-round, it takes her 22.5 s to complete one revolution?

*(Answers to **Your Turn** problems are given in the back of the book.)*

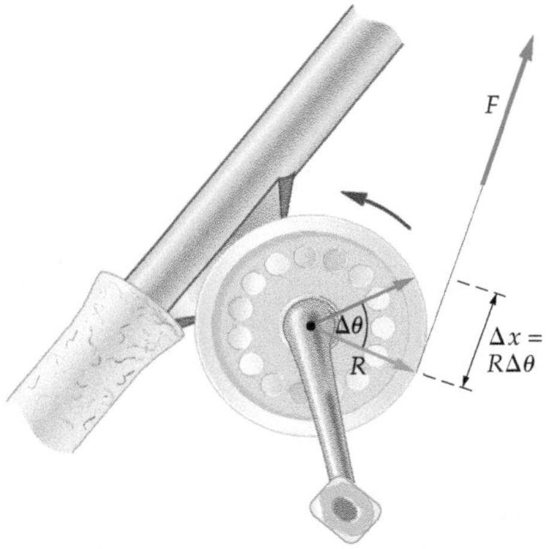

▲ **FIGURE 11-15 Rotational work**
A force F pulling a length of line Δx from a fishing reel does the work $W = F\,\Delta x$. In terms of torque and angular displacement, the work can be expressed as $W = \tau\,\Delta\theta$.

The initial and final kinetic energies of the system in Active Example 11–5 are considered in Problem 66.

11–8 Rotational Work and Power

Just as a force acting through a distance performs work on an object, so too does a torque acting through an angular displacement. To see this, consider again the fishing line pulled from a reel. If the line is pulled with a force F for a distance Δx, as in **Figure 11–15**, the work done on the reel is

$$W = F\Delta x$$

Now, since the line is unwinding without slipping, it follows that the linear displacement of the line, Δx, is related to the angular displacement of the reel, $\Delta\theta$, by the following relation:

$$\Delta x = R\Delta\theta$$

In this equation, R is the radius of the reel, and $\Delta\theta$ is measured in radians. Thus, the work can be written as

$$W = F\Delta x = FR\Delta\theta$$

Finally, the torque exerted on the reel by the line is $\tau = RF$, and hence the work done on the reel is simply torque times angular displacement:

Work Done by Torque

$$W = \tau\Delta\theta \qquad\qquad\qquad\qquad\qquad\qquad 11\text{–}17$$

Note again the analogies between angular and linear quantities in $W = F\Delta x$ and $W = \tau\Delta\theta$. As usual, τ is the analogue of F, and θ is the analogue of x.

As we saw in Chapter 7, the net work done on an object is equal to the change in its kinetic energy. This is the work–energy theorem:

$$W = \Delta K = K_\mathrm{f} - K_\mathrm{i} \qquad\qquad\qquad\qquad\qquad 11\text{–}18$$

The work-energy theorem applies regardless of whether the work is done by a force acting through a distance or a torque acting through an angle.

Similarly, power is the amount of work done in a given time, regardless whether the work is done by a force or a torque. In the case of a torque, we have $W = \tau\Delta\theta$, and hence

Power Produced by a Torque

$$P = \frac{W}{\Delta t} = \tau\frac{\Delta\theta}{\Delta t} = \tau\omega \qquad\qquad\qquad\qquad 11\text{–}19$$

Again, the analogy is clear between $P = Fv$ for the linear case, and $P = \tau\omega$ for the rotational case.

EXERCISE 11–5

It takes a good deal of effort to make homemade ice cream. **(a)** If the torque required to turn the handle on an ice cream maker is $5.7\,\mathrm{N\cdot m}$, how much work is expended on each complete revolution of the handle? **(b)** How much power is required to turn the handle if each revolution is completed in 1.5 s?

SOLUTION

a. Applying Equation 11–17 yields

$$W = \tau\Delta\theta = (5.7\,\mathrm{N\cdot m})(2\pi\,\mathrm{rad}) = 36\,\mathrm{J}$$

b. Power is the work per time; that is,

$$P = W/\Delta t = (36\,\mathrm{J})/(1.5\,\mathrm{s}) = 24\,\mathrm{W}$$

Equivalently, the angular speed of the handle is $\omega = (2\pi)/T = (2\pi)/(1.5\,\mathrm{s}) = 4.2\,\mathrm{rad/s}$, and therefore Equation 11–19 yields $P = \tau\omega = (5.7\,\mathrm{N\cdot m})(4.2\,\mathrm{rad/s}) = 24\,\mathrm{W}$.

*11–9 The Vector Nature of Rotational Motion

We have mentioned many times that the angular velocity is a vector, and that we must be careful to use the proper sign for ω. But if the angular velocity is a vector, what is its direction?

To address this question, consider the rotating wheel shown in **Figure 11–16**. Each point on the rim of this wheel has a velocity vector pointing in a different direction in the plane of rotation. Since different parts of the wheel move in different directions, how can we assign a single direction to the angular velocity vector, $\vec{\omega}$? The answer is that there is only one direction that remains fixed as the wheel rotates; the direction of the axis of rotation. By definition, then, the angular velocity vector, $\vec{\omega}$, is taken to point along the axis of rotation.

Given that $\vec{\omega}$ points along the axis of rotation, we must still decide whether it points to the left or to the right in Figure 11–16. The convention we use for assigning the direction of $\vec{\omega}$ is referred to as the right-hand rule:

Right-Hand Rule for the Angular Velocity, $\vec{\omega}$
Curl the fingers of the right hand in the direction of rotation.
The thumb now points in the direction of the angular velocity, $\vec{\omega}$.

The right-hand rule for $\vec{\omega}$ is illustrated in Figure 11–16.

The same convention for direction applies to the angular momentum vector. First, recall that the angular momentum has a magnitude given by $L = I\omega$. Hence, we choose the direction of $\vec{L}$ to be the same as the direction of $\vec{\omega}$. That is

$$\vec{L} = I\vec{\omega} \qquad\qquad 11\text{–}20$$

The angular momentum vector is also illustrated in Figure 11–16.

Similarly, torque is a vector, and it too is defined to point along the axis of rotation. The right-hand rule for torque is similar to that for angular velocity:

Right-Hand Rule for Torque, $\vec{\tau}$
Curl the fingers of the right hand in the direction of rotation that this torque would cause if it acted alone.
The thumb now points in the direction of the torque vector, $\vec{\tau}$.

Examples of torque vectors are given in **Figure 11–17**.

As an example of torque and angular momentum vectors, consider the spinning bicycle wheel shown in **Figure 11–18**. The angular momentum vector for the wheel points to the left, along the axis of rotation. If a person pushes on the rim of the wheel in the direction indicated, the resulting torque is also to the left, as shown in the figure. If this torque lasts for a time Δt, the angular momentum changes by the amount

$$\Delta\vec{L} = \vec{\tau}\,\Delta t$$

Adding $\Delta\vec{L}$ to the original angular momentum $\vec{L}_i$ yields the final angular momentum, $\vec{L}_f$, shown in Figure 11–18. Since $\vec{L}_f$ is in the same direction as $\vec{L}_i$, but with a greater magnitude, it follows that the wheel is spinning in the same direction as

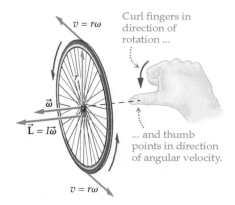

▲ **FIGURE 11–16** **The right-hand rule for angular velocity**

The angular velocity, $\vec{\omega}$, of a rotating wheel points along the axis of rotation. Its direction is given by the right-hand rule.

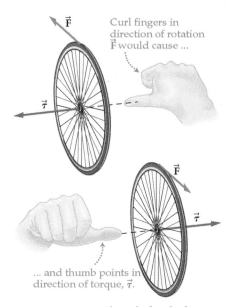

▲ **FIGURE 11–17** **The right-hand rule for torque**

Examples of torque vectors obtained using the right-hand rule.

◀ Children have always been fascinated by tops—but not only children. The physicists in the photo at right, Wolfgang Pauli and Niels Bohr, seem as delighted by a spinning top as any child. Their contributions to modern physics, discussed in Chapter 30, helped to show that subatomic particles, the ultimate constituents of matter, have a property (now referred to as "spin") that is in some ways analogous to the rotation of a top or a gyroscope.

▲ The 1.5-inch fused quartz sphere shown here is no ordinary ball. In fact, it is the most perfect sphere ever manufactured. If the Earth were this smooth, the change in elevation from the deepest ocean trench to the highest mountain peak would be only 16 feet. Such precision is required because this sphere is designed to serve as the rotor for an extremely sensitive gyroscope. The device, a million times more sensitive than those used in the best inertial navigation systems, orbits the Earth as part of an experiment to test predictions of Einstein's theory of general relativity.

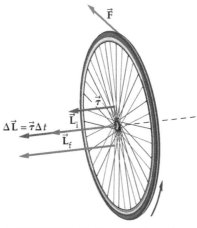

▲ **FIGURE 11–18 Torque and angular momentum vectors**
A tangential push on the spinning wheel in the direction shown causes a torque to the left. As a result, the angular momentum increases. Hence, the wheel spins faster, as expected.

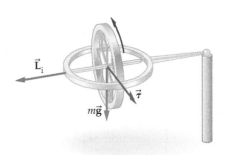

▲ **FIGURE 11–19 The torque exerted on a gyroscope**
A spinning gyroscope has an initial angular momentum to the left. The torque due to gravity is out of the page.

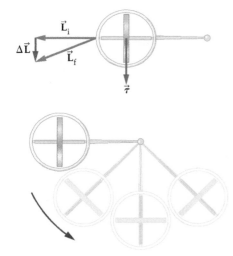

Top view

▲ **FIGURE 11–20 Precession of a gyroscope**
The gyroscope as viewed from above. In a time Δt the angular momentum changes by the amount $\Delta \vec{L} = \vec{\tau}\Delta t$. This causes the angular momentum vector, and hence the gyroscope as a whole, to rotate in a counterclockwise direction.

REAL-WORLD PHYSICS

Precession of the Earth

before, only faster. This is to be expected, considering the direction of the person's push on the wheel.

On the other hand, if a person pushes on the wheel in the opposite direction, the torque vector points to the right. As a result, $\Delta \vec{L}$ points to the right as well. When we add $\Delta \vec{L}$ and $\vec{L}_i$ to obtain the final angular momentum, $\vec{L}_f$, we find that it has the same direction as $\vec{L}_i$, but a smaller magnitude. Hence, we conclude that the wheel spins more slowly, as one would expect.

Finally, a case of considerable interest is when the torque and angular momentum vectors are at right angles to one another. The classic example of such a system is the **gyroscope**. To begin, consider a gyroscope whose axis of rotation is horizontal, as in **Figure 11–19**. If the gyroscope were to be released with no spin it would simply fall, rotating counterclockwise downward about its point of support. Curling the fingers of the right hand in the counterclockwise direction, we see that the thumb, and hence the torque due to gravity, points out of the page.

Next, imagine the gyroscope to be spinning rapidly—as would normally be the case—with its angular momentum pointing to the left in Figure 11–19. If the gyroscope is released now, it doesn't fall as before, even though the torque is the same. To see what happens instead, consider the change in angular momentum, $\Delta \vec{L}$, caused by the torque, $\vec{\tau}$, acting for a small interval of time. As shown in **Figure 11–20**, the small change, $\Delta \vec{L}$, is at right angles to $\vec{L}_i$; hence the final angular momentum, $\vec{L}_f$, is essentially the same length as $\vec{L}_i$, but pointing in a direction slightly out of the page. With each small interval of time, the angular momentum vector continues to change in direction so that, viewed from above as in Figure 11–20, the gyroscope as a whole rotates in a counterclockwise sense around its support point. This type of motion, where the axis of rotation changes direction with time, is referred to as **precession**.

Because of its spinning motion about its rotational axis, the Earth may be considered as one rather large gyroscope. Gravitational forces exerted on the Earth by the Sun and the Moon subject it to external torques that cause its rotational axis to precess. At the moment, the rotational axis of the Earth points toward Polaris, the "North Star," which remains almost fixed in position in time-lapse photographs while the other stars move in circular paths about it. In a few hundred years, however, Polaris will also move in a circular path in the sky because the Earth's axis of rotation will point in a different direction. After 26,000 years the Earth will complete one full cycle of precession, and Polaris will again be the pole star.

On a smaller scale, gyroscopes are used in the navigational systems of a variety of vehicles. In such applications, the rapidly spinning wheel of a gyroscope is mounted on nearly frictionless bearings so that it is practically free from external torques. If no torque acts on the gyroscope, its angular momentum vector remains unchanged both in magnitude and—here is the important point—in direction. With the axis of its gyroscope always pointing in the same, known direction, it is possible for a vehicle to maintain a desired direction of motion relative to the gyroscope's reference direction. On the Hubble Space Telescope, for example, six gyroscopes are used for pointing and stability, though it can operate with only three working gyroscopes if necessary.

REAL-WORLD PHYSICS

Gyroscopes in navigation and space

THE BIG PICTURE   PUTTING PHYSICS IN CONTEXT

LOOKING BACK

The concept of force (Chapters 5 and 6) is extended to torque, its rotational equivalent, in Section 11–1. We also apply Newton's laws to rotation in Section 11–6, just as for linear motion in Chapters 5 and 6.

The connection between rotational and linear quantities (Chapter 10) is used in Section 11–2 to relate torque to angular acceleration. In addition, we extend linear momentum (Chapter 9) to angular momentum in Sections 11–6 and 11–7.

Work and kinetic energy (Chapter 7) are applied to rotational systems in Section 11–8.

LOOKING AHEAD

Angular momentum and the conservation of angular momentum play important roles in the study of gravity. See, in particular, the discussion of Kepler's third law in Section 12–3.

Torque arises in the discussion of magnetic fields and the forces they exert. See Section 22–5 in particular. The torques due to magnetic fields are also the key element in the operation of electric motors, as we see in Section 23–6.

Angular momentum is quantized (given discrete values) in the Bohr model of the hydrogen atom in Section 31–4.

CHAPTER SUMMARY

11–1   TORQUE

A force applied so as to cause an angular acceleration is said to exert a torque, τ.

Tangential Force
A force is tangential if it is tangent to a circle centered on the axis of rotation.

Torque Due to a Tangential Force
A tangential force F applied at a distance r from the axis of rotation produces a torque

$$\tau = rF \qquad \qquad 11\text{–}1$$

Torque for a General Force
A force exerted at an angle θ with respect to the radial direction, and applied at a distance r from the axis of rotation, produces the torque

$$\tau = rF \sin \theta \qquad \qquad 11\text{–}2$$

11–2   TORQUE AND ANGULAR ACCELERATION

A single torque applied to an object gives it an angular acceleration.

Newton's Second Law for Rotation
The connection between torque and angular acceleration is

$$\sum \tau = I\alpha \qquad \qquad 11\text{–}4$$

In this expression, I is the moment of inertia about the axis of rotation and α is the angular acceleration about this axis.

Rotational/Translational Analogies
Torque is analogous to force, the moment of inertia is analogous to mass, and the angular acceleration is analogous to linear acceleration. Therefore, the rotational analogue of $F = ma$ is $\tau = I\alpha$.

11–3 ZERO TORQUE AND STATIC EQUILIBRIUM

The conditions for an object to be in static equilibrium are that the total force and the total torque acting on the object must be zero:

$$\sum F_x = 0, \quad \sum F_y = 0, \quad \sum \tau = 0$$

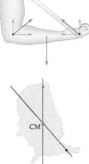

11–4 CENTER OF MASS AND BALANCE

An object balances when it is supported at its center of mass.

11–5 DYNAMIC APPLICATIONS OF TORQUE

Newton's second law can be applied to rotational systems in a way that is completely analogous to its application to linear systems.

Systems Involving Both Rotational and Linear Elements

In a system with both rotational and linear motions—such as a string passing over a pulley and attached to a mass—Newton's second law must be applied separately to the rotational and linear motions of the system. Connections between the two motions, such as $\alpha = a/r$, can be used to solve for all the accelerations in the system.

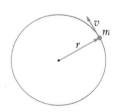

11–6 ANGULAR MOMENTUM

A moving object has angular momentum as long as its direction of motion does not extend through the axis of rotation.

Angular Momentum and Angular Speed

Angular momentum can be expressed in terms of angular speed and the moment of inertia as follows:

$$L = I\omega \qquad\qquad 11–11$$

This is the rotational analogue of $p = mv$.

Tangential Motion

An object of mass m moving tangentially with a speed v at a distance r from the axis of rotation has an angular momentum, L, given by

$$L = rmv \qquad\qquad 11–12$$

General Motion

If an object of mass m is a distance r from the axis of rotation and moves with a speed v at an angle θ with respect to the radial direction, its angular momentum is

$$L = rmv \sin \theta \qquad\qquad 11–13$$

Newton's Second Law

Newton's second law can be expressed in terms of the rate of change of the angular momentum:

$$\sum \tau = I\alpha = \frac{\Delta L}{\Delta t} \qquad\qquad 11–14$$

This is the rotational analogue of $\Sigma F = \Delta p/\Delta t$.

11–7 CONSERVATION OF ANGULAR MOMENTUM

If the net external torque acting on a system is zero, its angular momentum is conserved:

$$L_f = L_i$$

Rotational Collisions

Systems in which two rotational objects come into contact can be thought of in terms of a "rotational collision." In such a case, the total angular momentum of the system is conserved.

11–8 ROTATIONAL WORK AND POWER

A torque acting through an angle does work, just as does a force acting through a distance.

Work Done by a Torque

A torque τ acting through an angle $\Delta\theta$ does a work W given by

$$W = \tau\Delta\theta \qquad\qquad\text{11–17}$$

Work–Energy Theorem

The work–energy theorem is

$$W = \Delta K = K_f - K_i \qquad\qquad\text{11–18}$$

This theorem applies whether the work is done by a force or by a torque. In the linear case the kinetic energy is $\frac{1}{2}mv^2$; in the rotational case, the kinetic energy is $K = \frac{1}{2}I\omega^2$ (Equation 10–17).

*11–9 THE VECTOR NATURE OF ROTATIONAL MOTION

Rotational quantities have directions that point along the axis of rotation. The precise direction is given by the right-hand rule.

Right-Hand Rule

If the fingers of the *right hand* are curled in the direction of rotation, the thumb points in the direction of the rotational quantity in question. This rule applies to the angular velocity vector, $\vec{\omega}$, the angular acceleration vector, $\vec{\alpha}$, the angular momentum vector, $\vec{L}$, and the torque vector, $\vec{\tau}$.

PROBLEM-SOLVING SUMMARY

Type of Problem	Relevant Physical Concepts	Related Examples
Find the torque exerted on a system.	The torque exerted by a tangential force a distance r from the axis of rotation is $\tau = rF$. If the force is at an angle θ to the radial direction, the torque is $\tau = rF\sin\theta$.	Example 11–1
Determine the angular acceleration of a system.	First, calculate the torque exerted on the system. Next, find the angular acceleration using Newton's second law as applied to rotation, namely, $\tau = I\alpha$.	Examples 11–2, 11–3
Find the forces required for static equilibrium.	Static equilibrium requires that both the net force and the net torque acting on a system be zero.	Examples 11–4, 11–5, 11–6 Active Examples 11–1, 11–2, 11–3
Find the final angular momentum of a system.	A torque changes the angular momentum L of a system with time as follows: $\tau = \Delta L/\Delta t$. If no net torque acts on a system, its angular momentum is conserved.	Examples 11–8, 11–9 Active Examples 11–4, 11–5

CONCEPTUAL QUESTIONS

For instructor-assigned homework, go to www.masteringphysics.com

(Answers to odd-numbered Conceptual Questions can be found in the back of the book.)

1. Two forces produce the same torque. Does it follow that they have the same magnitude? Explain.

2. A car pitches down in front when the brakes are applied sharply. Explain this observation in terms of torques.

3. A tightrope walker uses a long pole to aid in balancing. Why?

4. When a motorcycle accelerates rapidly from a stop it sometimes "pops a wheelie"; that is, its front wheel may lift off the ground. Explain this behavior in terms of torques.

5. Give an example of a system in which the net torque is zero but the net force is nonzero.

6. Give an example of a system in which the net force is zero but the net torque is nonzero.

7. Is the normal force exerted by the ground the same for all four tires on your car? Explain.

8. Give two everyday examples of objects that are not in static equilibrium.

9. Give two everyday examples of objects that are in static equilibrium.

10. Can an object have zero translational acceleration and, at the same time, have nonzero angular acceleration? If your answer is no, explain why not. If your answer is yes, give a specific example.

11. Stars form when a large rotating cloud of gas collapses. What happens to the angular speed of the gas cloud as it collapses?

12. What purpose does the tail rotor on a helicopter serve?

13. Is it possible to change the angular momentum of an object without changing its linear momentum? If your answer is no, explain why not. If your answer is yes, give a specific example.

14. Suppose a diver springs into the air with no initial angular velocity. Can the diver begin to rotate by folding into a tucked position? Explain.

PROBLEMS AND CONCEPTUAL EXERCISES

Note: Answers to odd-numbered Problems and Conceptual Exercises can be found in the back of the book. **IP** *denotes an integrated problem, with both conceptual and numerical parts;* **BIO** *identifies problems of biological or medical interest;* **CE** *indicates a conceptual exercise.* **Predict/Explain** *problems ask for two responses:* **(a)** *your prediction of a physical outcome, and* **(b)** *the best explanation among three provided. On all problems, red bullets (•, ••, •••) are used to indicate the level of difficulty.*

SECTION 11–1 TORQUE

1. • To tighten a spark plug, it is recommended that a torque of 15 N · m be applied. If a mechanic tightens the spark plug with a wrench that is 25 cm long, what is the minimum force necessary to create the desired torque?

2. • **Pulling a Weed** The gardening tool shown in **Figure 11–21** is used to pull weeds. If a 1.23-N · m torque is required to pull a given weed, what force did the weed exert on the tool?

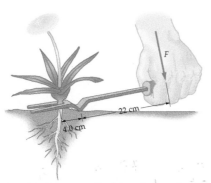

▲ **FIGURE 11–21** Problem 2

3. • A 1.61-kg bowling trophy is held at arm's length, a distance of 0.605 m from the shoulder joint. What torque does the trophy exert about the shoulder if the arm is **(a)** horizontal, or **(b)** at an angle of 22.5° below the horizontal?

4. • A person slowly lowers a 3.6-kg crab trap over the side of a dock, as shown in **Figure 11–22**. What torque does the trap exert about the person's shoulder?

▲ **FIGURE 11–22**
Problem 4

5. •• **IP BIO Force to Hold a Baseball** A person holds a 1.42-N baseball in his hand, a distance of 34.0 cm from the elbow joint, as shown in **Figure 11–23**. The biceps, attached at a distance of 2.75 cm from the elbow, exerts an upward force of 12.6 N on the

forearm. Consider the forearm and hand to be a uniform rod with a mass of 1.20 kg. **(a)** Calculate the net torque acting on the forearm and hand. Use the elbow joint as the axis of rotation. **(b)** If the net torque obtained in part (a) is nonzero, in which direction will the forearm and hand rotate? **(c)** Would the torque exerted on the forearm by the biceps increase or decrease if the biceps were attached farther from the elbow joint?

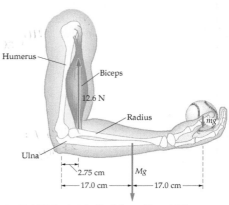

▲ **FIGURE 11–23** Problems 5 and 19

6. •• At the local playground, a 16-kg child sits on the end of a horizontal teeter-totter, 1.5 m from the pivot point. On the other side of the pivot an adult pushes straight down on the teeter-totter with a force of 95 N. In which direction does the teeter-totter rotate if the adult applies the force at a distance of **(a)** 3.0 m, **(b)** 2.5 m, or **(c)** 2.0 m from the pivot?

SECTION 11–2 TORQUE AND ANGULAR ACCELERATION

7. • **CE Predict/Explain** Consider the pulley–block systems shown in Conceptual Checkpoint 11–1. **(a)** Is the tension in the string on the left-hand rotating system greater than, less than, or equal to the weight of the mass attached to that string? **(b)** Choose the *best explanation* from among the following:
 I. The mass is in free fall once it is released.
 II. The string rotates the pulley in addition to supporting the mass.
 III. The mass accelerates downward.

8. • **CE Predict/Explain** Consider the pulley–block systems shown in Conceptual Checkpoint 11–1. **(a)** Is the tension in the string on the left-hand rotating system greater than, less than, or equal to the tension in the string on the right-hand rotating system? **(b)** Choose the *best explanation* from among the following:
 I. The mass in the right-hand system has the greater downward acceleration.
 II. The masses are equal.

III. The mass in the left-hand system has the greater downward acceleration.

9. • **CE** Suppose a torque rotates your body about one of three different axes of rotation: case A, an axis through your spine; case B, an axis through your hips; and case C, an axis through your ankles. Rank these three axes of rotation in increasing order of the angular acceleration produced by the torque. Indicate ties where appropriate.

10. • A torque of 0.97 N · m is applied to a bicycle wheel of radius 35 cm and mass 0.75 kg. Treating the wheel as a hoop, find its angular acceleration.

11. • When a ceiling fan rotating with an angular speed of 2.75 rad/s is turned off, a frictional torque of 0.120 N · m slows it to a stop in 22.5 s. What is the moment of inertia of the fan?

12. • When the play button is pressed, a CD accelerates uniformly from rest to 450 rev/min in 3.0 revolutions. If the CD has a radius of 6.0 cm and a mass of 17 g, what is the torque exerted on it?

13. •• A person holds a ladder horizontally at its center. Treating the ladder as a uniform rod of length 3.15 m and mass 8.42 kg, find the torque the person must exert on the ladder to give it an angular acceleration of 0.302 rad/s².

14. •• **IP** A wheel on a game show is given an initial angular speed of 1.22 rad/s. It comes to rest after rotating through 0.75 of a turn. **(a)** Find the average torque exerted on the wheel given that it is a disk of radius 0.71 m and mass 6.4 kg. **(b)** If the mass of the wheel is doubled and its radius is halved, will the angle through which it rotates before coming to rest increase, decrease, or stay the same? Explain. (Assume that the average torque exerted on the wheel is unchanged.)

15. •• The L-shaped object in **Figure 11–24** consists of three masses connected by light rods. What torque must be applied to this object to give it an angular acceleration of 1.20 rad/s² if it is rotated about **(a)** the x axis, **(b)** the y axis, or **(c)** the z axis (which is through the origin and perpendicular to the page)?

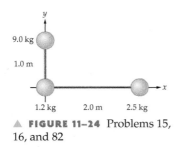

▲ **FIGURE 11–24** Problems 15, 16, and 82

16. •• **CE** The L-shaped object described in Problem 15 can be rotated in one of the following three ways: case A, about the x axis; case B, about the y axis; and case C, about the z axis (which passes through the origin perpendicular to the plane of the figure). If the same torque τ is applied in each of these cases, rank them in increasing order of the resulting angular acceleration. Indicate ties where appropriate.

17. •• **CE** A motorcycle accelerates from rest, and both the front and rear tires roll without slipping. **(a)** Is the force exerted by the ground on the rear tire in the forward or in the backward direction? Explain. **(b)** Is the force exerted by the ground on the front tire in the forward or in the backward direction? Explain. **(c)** If the moment of inertia of the front tire is increased, will the motorcycle's acceleration increase, decrease, or stay the same? Explain.

18. •• **IP** A torque of 13 N · m is applied to the rectangular object shown in **Figure 11–25**. The torque can act about the x axis, the y axis, or the z axis, which passes through the origin and points out of the page. **(a)** In which case does the object experience the greatest angular acceleration? The least angular acceleration? Explain. Find the angular acceleration when the torque acts about **(b)** the x axis, **(c)** the y axis, and **(d)** the z axis.

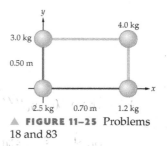

▲ **FIGURE 11–25** Problems 18 and 83

19. •• A fish takes the bait and pulls on the line with a force of 2.2 N. The fishing reel, which rotates without friction, is a cylinder of radius 0.055 m and mass 0.99 kg. **(a)** What is the angular acceleration of the fishing reel? **(b)** How much line does the fish pull from the reel in 0.25 s?

20. •• Repeat the previous problem, only now assume the reel has a friction clutch that exerts a restraining torque of 0.047 N · m.

SECTION 11–3 ZERO TORQUE AND STATIC EQUILIBRIUM

21. • **CE Predict/Explain** Suppose the person in Active Example 11–3 climbs higher on the ladder. **(a)** As a result, is the ladder more likely, less likely, or equally likely to slip? **(b)** Choose the *best explanation* from among the following:
    I. The forces are the same regardless of the person's position.
    II. The magnitude of f_2 must increase as the person moves upward.
    III. When the person is higher, the ladder presses down harder on the floor.

22. • A string that passes over a pulley has a 0.321-kg mass attached to one end and a 0.635-kg mass attached to the other end. The pulley, which is a disk of radius 9.40 cm, has friction in its axle. What is the magnitude of the frictional torque that must be exerted by the axle if the system is to be in static equilibrium?

23. • To loosen the lid on a jar of jam 8.9 cm in diameter, a torque of 8.5 N · m must be applied to the circumference of the lid. If a jar wrench whose handle extends 15 cm from the center of the jar is attached to the lid, what is the minimum force required to open the jar?

24. • Consider the system in Active Example 11–1, this time with the axis of rotation at the location of the child. Write out both the condition for zero net force and the condition for zero net torque. Solve for the two forces.

25. •• **IP BIO** Referring to the person holding a baseball in Problem 5, suppose the biceps exert just enough upward force to keep the system in static equilibrium. **(a)** Is the force exerted by the biceps more than, less than, or equal to the combined weight of the forearm, hand, and baseball? Explain. **(b)** Determine the force exerted by the biceps.

26. •• **IP BIO A Person's Center of Mass** To determine the location of her center of mass, a physics student lies on a lightweight plank supported by two scales 2.50 m apart, as

indicated in **Figure 11–26**. If the left scale reads 290 N, and the right scale reads 122 N, find **(a)** the student's mass and **(b)** the distance from the student's head to her center of mass.

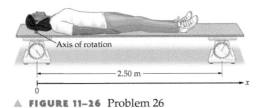

Axis of rotation

————— 2.50 m —————

▲ **FIGURE 11–26** Problem 26

27. •• **Triceratops** A set of fossilized triceratops footprints discovered in Texas show that the front and rear feet were 3.2 m apart, as shown in **Figure 11–27**. The rear footprints were observed to be twice as deep as the front footprints. Assuming that the rear feet pressed down on the ground with twice the force exerted by the front feet, find the horizontal distance from the rear feet to the triceratops's center of mass.

—3.2 m—

▲ **FIGURE 11–27** Problem 27

28. •• **IP** A schoolyard teeter-totter with a total length of 5.2 m and a mass of 38 kg is pivoted at its center. A 19-kg child sits on one end of the teeter-totter. **(a)** Where should a parent push vertically downward with a force of 210 N in order to hold the teeter-totter level? **(b)** Where should the parent push with a force of 310 N? **(c)** How would your answers to parts (a) and (b) change if the mass of the teeter-totter were doubled? Explain.

29. •• A 0.122-kg remote control 23.0 cm long rests on a table, as shown in **Figure 11–28**, with a length L overhanging its edge. To operate the power button on this remote requires a force of 0.365 N. How far can the remote control extend beyond the edge of the table and still not tip over when you press the power button? Assume the mass of the remote is distributed uniformly, and that the power button is 1.41 cm from the overhanging end of the remote.

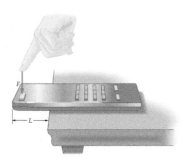

F

—L—

▲ **FIGURE 11–28** Problem 29

30. •• **IP** A 0.16-kg meterstick is held perpendicular to a vertical wall by a 2.5-m string going from the wall to the far end of the stick. **(a)** Find the tension in the string. **(b)** If a shorter string is used, will its tension be greater than, less than, or the same as that found in part (a)? **(c)** Find the tension in a 2.0-m string.

31. •• Repeat Example 11–4, this time with a uniform diving board that weighs 225 N.

32. •• Babe Ruth steps to the plate and casually points to left center field to indicate the location of his next home run. The mighty Babe holds his bat across his shoulder, with one hand holding the small end of the bat. The bat is horizontal, and the distance from the small end of the bat to the shoulder is 22.5 cm. If the bat has a mass of 1.10 kg and has a center of mass that is 67.0 cm from the small end of the bat, find the magnitude and direction of the force exerted by **(a)** the hand and **(b)** the shoulder.

33. •• A uniform metal rod, with a mass of 3.7 kg and a length of 1.2 m, is attached to a wall by a hinge at its base. A horizontal wire bolted to the wall 0.51 m above the base of the rod holds the rod at an angle of 25° above the horizontal. The wire is attached to the top of the rod. **(a)** Find the tension in the wire. Find **(b)** the horizontal and **(c)** the vertical components of the force exerted on the rod by the hinge.

34. •• **IP** In the previous problem, suppose the wire is shortened, so that the rod now makes an angle of 35° with the horizontal. The wire is horizontal, as before. **(a)** Do you expect the tension in the wire to increase, decrease, or stay the same as a result of its new length? Explain. **(b)** Calculate the tension in the wire.

35. •• Repeat Active Example 11–3, this time with a uniform 7.2-kg ladder that is 4.0 m long.

36. •• A rigid, vertical rod of negligible mass is connected to the floor by a bolt through its lower end, as shown in **Figure 11–29**. The rod also has a wire connected between its top end and the floor. If a horizontal force F is applied at the midpoint of the rod, find **(a)** the tension in the wire, and **(b)** the horizontal and **(c)** the vertical components of force exerted by the bolt on the rod.

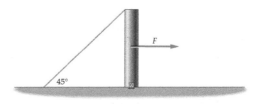

F

45°

▲ **FIGURE 11–29** Problems 36, 111, and 112

37. ••• **BIO Forces in the Foot Figure 11–30** shows the forces acting on a sprinter's foot just before she takes off at the start of the race. Find the magnitude of the force exerted on the heel by the Achilles tendon, F_H, and the magnitude of the force exerted on the foot at the ankle joint, F_J.

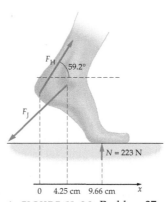

F_H
59.2°
F_J
$N = 223$ N

0   4.25 cm   9.66 cm x

▲ **FIGURE 11–30** Problem 37

38. ••• A stick with a mass of 0.214 kg and a length of 0.436 m rests in contact with a bowling ball and a rough floor, as shown in **Figure 11–31**. The bowling ball has a diameter of 21.6 cm, and the angle the stick makes with the horizontal is 30.0°. You may assume there is no friction between the stick and the bowling ball, though friction with the floor must be taken into account. **(a)** Find the magnitude of the force exerted on the stick by the bowling ball. **(b)** Find the horizontal component of the force exerted on the stick by the floor. **(c)** Repeat part (b) for the vertical component of the force.

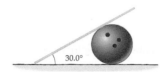

▲ **FIGURE 11–31** Problem 38

39. ••• **IP** A uniform crate with a mass of 16.2 kg rests on a floor with a coefficient of static friction equal to 0.571. The crate is a uniform cube with sides 1.21 m in length. **(a)** What horizontal force applied to the top of the crate will initiate tipping? **(b)** If the horizontal force is applied halfway to the top of the crate, it will begin to slip before it tips. Explain.

40. ••• In the previous problem, **(a)** what is the minimum height where the force *F* can be applied so that the crate begins to tip before sliding? **(b)** What is the magnitude of the force in this case?

SECTION 11–4 CENTER OF MASS AND BALANCE

41. • A hand-held shopping basket 62.0 cm long has a 1.81-kg carton of milk at one end, and a 0.722-kg box of cereal at the other end. Where should a 1.80-kg container of orange juice be placed so that the basket balances at its center?

42. • If the cat in Active Example 11–2 has a mass of 2.8 kg, how close to the right end of the two-by-four can it walk before the board begins to tip?

43. •• **IP** A 0.34-kg meterstick balances at its center. If a necklace is suspended from one end of the stick, the balance point moves 9.5 cm toward that end. **(a)** Is the mass of the necklace more than, less than, or the same as that of the meterstick? Explain. **(b)** Find the mass of the necklace.

44. •• **Maximum Overhang** Three identical, uniform books of length *L* are stacked one on top the other. Find the maximum overhang distance *d* in **Figure 11–32** such that the books do not fall over.

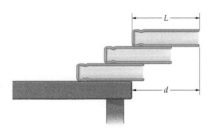

▲ **FIGURE 11–32** Problems 44 and 107

45. •• A baseball bat balances 71.1 cm from one end. If a 0.560-kg glove is attached to that end, the balance point moves 24.7 cm toward the glove. Find the mass of the bat.

SECTION 11–5 DYNAMIC APPLICATIONS OF TORQUE

46. •• A 2.85-kg bucket is attached to a disk-shaped pulley of radius 0.121 m and mass 0.742 kg. If the bucket is allowed to fall, **(a)** what is its linear acceleration? **(b)** What is the angular acceleration of the pulley? **(c)** How far does the bucket drop in 1.50 s?

47. •• **IP** In the previous problem, **(a)** is the tension in the rope greater than, less than, or equal to the weight of the bucket? Explain. **(b)** Calculate the tension in the rope.

48. •• A child exerts a tangential 42.2-N force on the rim of a disk-shaped merry-go-round with a radius of 2.40 m. If the merry-go-round starts at rest and acquires an angular speed of 0.0860 rev/s in 3.50 s, what is its mass?

49. •• **IP** You pull downward with a force of 28 N on a rope that passes over a disk-shaped pulley of mass 1.2 kg and radius 0.075 m. The other end of the rope is attached to a 0.67-kg mass. **(a)** Is the tension in the rope the same on both sides of the pulley? If not, which side has the largest tension? **(b)** Find the tension in the rope on both sides of the pulley.

50. •• Referring to the previous problem, find the linear acceleration of the 0.67-kg mass.

51. ••• A uniform meterstick of mass *M* has an empty paint can of mass *m* hanging from one end. The meterstick and the can balance at a point 20.0 cm from the end of the stick where the can is attached. When the balanced stick–can system is suspended from a scale, the reading on the scale is 2.54 N. Find the mass of **(a)** the meterstick and **(b)** the paint can.

52. ••• **Atwood's Machine** An Atwood's machine consists of two masses, m_1 and m_2, connected by a string that passes over a pulley. If the pulley is a disk of radius *R* and mass *M*, find the acceleration of the masses.

SECTION 11–6 ANGULAR MOMENTUM

53. • Calculate the angular momentum of the Earth about its own axis, due to its daily rotation. Assume that the Earth is a uniform sphere.

54. • A 0.015-kg record with a radius of 15 cm rotates with an angular speed of $33\frac{1}{3}$ rpm. Find the angular momentum of the record.

55. • In the previous problem, a 1.1-g fly lands on the rim of the record. What is the fly's angular momentum?

56. • Jogger 1 in **Figure 11–33** has a mass of 65.3 kg and runs in a straight line with a speed of 3.35 m/s. **(a)** What is the magnitude

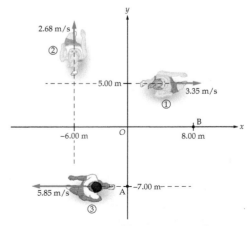

▲ **FIGURE 11–33** Problems 56, 57, and 58

of the jogger's linear momentum? **(b)** What is the magnitude of the jogger's angular momentum with respect to the origin, O?

57. • Repeat the previous problem for the case of jogger 2, whose speed is 2.68 m/s and whose mass is 58.2 kg.

58. •• **IP** Suppose jogger 3 in Figure 11–33 has a mass of 62.2 kg and a speed of 5.85 m/s. **(a)** Is the magnitude of the jogger's angular momentum greater with respect to point A or point B? Explain. **(b)** Is the magnitude of the jogger's angular momentum with respect to point B greater than, less than, or the same as it is with respect to the origin, O? Explain. **(c)** Calculate the magnitude of the jogger's angular momentum with respect to points A, B, and O.

59. • A torque of 0.12 N·m is applied to an egg beater. **(a)** If the egg beater starts at rest, what is its angular momentum after 0.65 s? **(b)** If the moment of inertia of the egg beater is 2.5×10^{-3} kg·m², what is its angular speed after 0.65 s?

60. •• A windmill has an initial angular momentum of 8500 kg·m²/s. The wind picks up, and 5.86 s later the windmill's angular momentum is 9700 kg·m²/s. What was the torque acting on the windmill, assuming it was constant during this time?

61. •• Two gerbils run in place with a linear speed of 0.55 m/s on an exercise wheel that is shaped like a hoop. Find the angular momentum of the system if each gerbil has a mass of 0.22 kg and the exercise wheel has a radius of 9.5 cm and a mass of 5.0 g.

SECTION 11–7 CONSERVATION OF ANGULAR MOMENTUM

62. • **CE Predict/Explain** A student rotates on a frictionless piano stool with his arms outstretched, a heavy weight in each hand. Suddenly he lets go of the weights, and they fall to the floor. As a result, does the student's angular speed increase, decrease, or stay the same? **(b)** Choose the *best explanation* from among the following:

   I. The loss of angular momentum when the weights are dropped causes the student to rotate more slowly.

   II. The student's moment of inertia is decreased by dropping the weights.

   III. Dropping the weights exerts no torque on the student, but the floor exerts a torque on the weights when they land.

63. • **CE** A puck on a horizontal, frictionless surface is attached to a string that passes through a hole in the surface, as shown in Figure 11–34. As the puck rotates about the hole, the string is pulled downward, bringing the puck closer to the hole. During this process, do the puck's **(a)** linear speed, **(b)** angular speed, and **(c)** angular momentum increase, decrease, or stay the same?

▲ **FIGURE 11–34** Problems 63 and 93

64. • **CE** A puck on a horizontal, frictionless surface is attached to a string that wraps around a pole of finite radius, as shown in Figure 11–35. **(a)** As the puck moves along the spiral path, does its

speed increase, decrease, or stay the same? Explain. **(b)** Does its angular momentum increase, decrease, or stay the same? Explain.

▲ **FIGURE 11–35** Problem 64

65. • As an ice skater begins a spin, his angular speed is 3.17 rad/s. After pulling in his arms, his angular speed increases to 5.46 rad/s. Find the ratio of the skater's final moment of inertia to his initial moment of inertia.

66. • Calculate both the initial and the final kinetic energies of the system described in Active Example 11–5.

67. • A diver tucks her body in midflight, decreasing her moment of inertia by a factor of two. By what factor does her angular speed change?

68. •• **IP** In the previous problem, **(a)** does the diver's kinetic energy increase, decrease, or stay the same? **(b)** Calculate the ratio of the final kinetic energy to the initial kinetic energy for the diver.

69. •• A disk-shaped merry-go-round of radius 2.63 m and mass 155 kg rotates freely with an angular speed of 0.641 rev/s. A 59.4-kg person running tangential to the rim of the merry-go-round at 3.41 m/s jumps onto its rim and holds on. Before jumping on the merry-go-round, the person was moving in the same direction as the merry-go-round's rim. What is the final angular speed of the merry-go-round?

70. •• **IP** In the previous problem, **(a)** does the kinetic energy of the system increase, decrease, or stay the same when the person jumps on the merry-go-round? **(b)** Calculate the initial and final kinetic energies for this system.

71. •• A student sits at rest on a piano stool that can rotate without friction. The moment of inertia of the student–stool system is 4.1 kg·m². A second student tosses a 1.5-kg mass with a speed of 2.7 m/s to the student on the stool, who catches it at a distance of 0.40 m from the axis of rotation. What is the resulting angular speed of the student and the stool?

72. •• **IP** Referring to the previous problem, **(a)** does the kinetic energy of the mass–student–stool system increase, decrease, or stay the same as the mass is caught? **(b)** Calculate the initial and final kinetic energies of the system.

73. •• **IP** A turntable with a moment of inertia of 5.4×10^{-3} kg·m² rotates freely with an angular speed of $33\frac{1}{3}$ rpm. Riding on the rim of the turntable, 15 cm from the center, is a cute, 32-g mouse. **(a)** If the mouse walks to the center of the turntable, will the turntable rotate faster, slower, or at the same rate? Explain. **(b)** Calculate the angular speed of the turntable when the mouse reaches the center.

74. •• A student on a piano stool rotates freely with an angular speed of 2.95 rev/s. The student holds a 1.25-kg mass in each outstretched arm, 0.759 m from the axis of rotation. The combined moment of inertia of the student and the stool, ignoring the two masses, is 5.43 kg·m², a value that remains constant. **(a)** As the student pulls his arms inward, his angular speed increases to 3.54 rev/s. How far are the masses from the axis of rotation at this time, considering the masses to be points? **(b)** Calculate the initial and final kinetic energies of the system.

75. ••• **Walking on a Merry-Go-Round** A child of mass m stands at rest near the rim of a stationary merry-go-round of radius R and moment of inertia I. The child now begins to walk around the circumference of the merry-go-round with a tangential speed v with respect to the merry-go-round's surface. **(a)** What is the child's speed with respect to the ground? Check your result in the limits **(b)** $I \rightarrow 0$ and **(c)** $I \rightarrow \infty$.

SECTION 11–8 ROTATIONAL WORK AND POWER

76. • **CE Predict/Explain** Two spheres of equal mass and radius are rolling across the floor with the same speed. Sphere 1 is a uniform solid; sphere 2 is hollow. Is the work required to stop sphere 1 greater than, less than, or equal to the work required to stop sphere 2? **(b)** Choose the *best explanation* from among the following:

    I. Sphere 2 has the greater moment of inertia and hence the greater rotational kinetic energy.

    II. The spheres have equal mass and speed; therefore, they have the same kinetic energy.

    III. The hollow sphere has less kinetic energy.

77. • How much work must be done to accelerate a baton from rest to an angular speed of 7.4 rad/s about its center? Consider the baton to be a uniform rod of length 0.53 m and mass 0.44 kg.

78. • Turning a doorknob through 0.25 of a revolution requires 0.14 J of work. What is the torque required to turn the doorknob?

79. • A person exerts a tangential force of 36.1 N on the rim of a disk-shaped merry-go-round of radius 2.74 m and mass 167 kg. If the merry-go-round starts at rest, what is its angular speed after the person has rotated it through an angle of 32.5°?

80. • To prepare homemade ice cream, a crank must be turned with a torque of 3.95 N·m. How much work is required for each complete turn of the crank?

81. • **Power of a Dental Drill** A popular make of dental drill can operate at a speed of 42,500 rpm while producing a torque of 3.68 oz·in. What is the power output of this drill? Give your answer in watts.

82. •• The L-shaped object in Figure 11–24 consists of three masses connected by light rods. Find the work that must be done on this object to accelerate it from rest to an angular speed of 2.35 rad/s about **(a)** the x axis, **(b)** the y axis, and **(c)** the z axis (which is through the origin and perpendicular to the page).

83. •• The rectangular object in Figure 11–25 consists of four masses connected by light rods. What power must be applied to this object to accelerate it from rest to an angular speed of 2.5 rad/s in 6.4 s about **(a)** the x axis, **(b)** the y axis, and **(c)** the z axis (which is through the origin and perpendicular to the page)?

84. •• **IP** A circular saw blade accelerates from rest to an angular speed of 3620 rpm in 6.30 revolutions. **(a)** Find the torque exerted on the saw blade, assuming it is a disk of radius 15.2 cm and mass 0.755 kg. **(b)** Is the angular speed of the saw blade after 3.15 revolutions greater than, less than, or equal to 1810 rpm? Explain. **(c)** Find the angular speed of the blade after 3.15 revolutions.

GENERAL PROBLEMS

85. • **CE** A uniform disk stands upright on its edge, and rests on a sheet of paper placed on a tabletop. If the paper is pulled horizontally to the right, as in Figure 11–36, **(a)** does the disk rotate clockwise or counterclockwise about its center? Explain. **(b)** Does the center of the disk move to the right, move to the left, or stay in the same location? Explain.

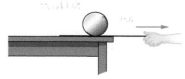

▲ **FIGURE 11–36** Problem 85

86. • **CE** Consider the two rotating systems shown in Figure 11–37, each consisting of a mass m attached to a rod of negligible mass pivoted at one end. On the left, the mass is attached at the midpoint of the rod; to the right, it is attached to the free end of the rod. The rods are released from rest in the horizontal position at the same time. When the rod to the left reaches the vertical position, is the rod to the right not yet vertical (location A), vertical (location B), or past vertical (location C)? Explain.

▲ **FIGURE 11–37** Problem 86

87. • **CE Predict/Explain** A disk and a hoop (bicycle wheel) of equal radius and mass each have a string wrapped around their circumferences. Hanging from the strings, halfway between the disk and the hoop, is a block of mass m, as shown in Figure 11–38. The disk and the hoop are free to rotate about their centers. When the block is allowed to fall, does it stay on the center line, move toward the right, or move toward the left? **(b)** Choose the *best explanation* from among the following:

    I. The disk is harder to rotate, and hence its angular acceleration is less than that of the wheel.

    II. The wheel has the greater moment of inertia and unwinds more slowly than the disk.

    III. The system is symmetric, with equal mass and radius on either side.

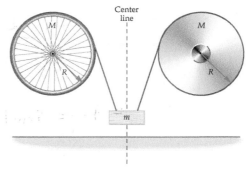

▲ **FIGURE 11–38** Problem 87

88. • **CE** A beetle sits at the rim of a turntable that is at rest but is free to rotate about a vertical axis. Suppose the beetle now begins to walk around the perimeter of the turntable. Does the beetle move forward, backward, or does it remain in the same location relative to the ground? Answer for two different cases, **(a)** the turntable is much more massive than the beetle and **(b)** the turntable is massless.

89. • **CE** A beetle sits near the rim of a turntable that is rotating without friction about a vertical axis. The beetle now begins to walk toward the center of the turntable. As a result, does the angular speed of the turntable increase, decrease, or stay the same? Explain.

90. • **CE** Suppose the Earth were to magically expand, doubling its radius while keeping its mass the same. Would the length of the day increase, decrease, or stay the same? Explain.

91. • After getting a drink of water, a hamster jumps onto an exercise wheel for a run. A few seconds later the hamster is running in place with a speed of 1.3 m/s. Find the work done by the hamster to get the exercise wheel moving, assuming it is a hoop of radius 0.13 m and mass 6.5 g.

92. •• A 47.0-kg uniform rod 4.25 m long is attached to a wall with a hinge at one end. The rod is held in a horizontal position by a wire attached to its other end. The wire makes an angle of 30.0° with the horizontal, and is bolted to the wall directly above the hinge. If the wire can withstand a maximum tension of 1450 N before breaking, how far from the wall can a 68.0-kg person sit without breaking the wire?

93. •• **IP** A puck attached to a string moves in a circular path on a frictionless surface, as shown in Figure 11–34. Initially, the speed of the puck is v and the radius of the circle is r. If the string passes through a hole in the surface, and is pulled downward until the radius of the circular path is $r/2$, **(a)** does the speed of the puck increase, decrease, or stay the same? **(b)** Calculate the final speed of the puck.

94. •• **BIO The Masseter Muscle** The masseter muscle, the principal muscle for chewing, is one of the strongest muscles for its size in the human body. It originates on the lower edge of the zygomatic arch (cheekbone) and inserts in the angle of the mandible. Referring to the lower diagram in **Figure 11–39**, where $d = 7.60$ cm and $D = 10.85$ cm, **(a)** find the torque produced about the axis of rotation by the masseter muscle. The force exerted by the masseter muscle is $F_M = 455$ N. **(b)** Find the biting force, F_B, exerted on the mandible by the upper teeth. Find **(c)** the horizontal and **(d)** the vertical component of the force F_J exerted on the mandible at the joint where it attaches to the skull. Assume that the mandible is in static equilibrium, and that upward is the positive vertical direction.

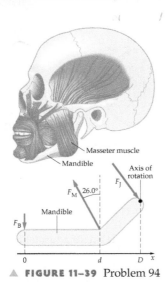

▲ **FIGURE 11–39** Problem 94

95. •• **Exercising the Biceps** You are designing exercise equipment to operate as shown in **Figure 11–40**, where a person pulls upward on an elastic cord. The cord behaves like an ideal spring and has an unstretched length of 31 cm. If you would like the torque about the elbow joint to be 81 N · m in the position shown, what force constant, k, is required for the cord?

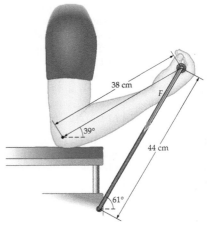

▲ **FIGURE 11–40** Problem 95

96. •• **Horsepower of a Car** Auto mechanics use the following formula to calculate the horsepower (HP) of a car engine:

$$HP = \text{Torque} \cdot \text{RPM}/C$$

In this expression, Torque is the torque produced by the engine in ft · lb, RPM is the angular speed of the engine in revolutions per minute, and C is a dimensionless constant. **(a)** Find the numerical value of C. **(b)** The Shelby Series 1 engine is advertised to generate 320 hp at 6500 rpm. What is the corresponding torque produced by this engine? Give your answer in ft · lb.

97. •• **Balancing a *T. rex*** Paleontologists believe that *Tyrannosaurus rex* stood and walked with its spine almost horizontal, as indicated in **Figure 11–41**, and that its tail was held off the ground to balance its upper torso about the hip joint. Given that the total mass of *T. rex* was 5400 kg, and that the placement of the center of mass of the tail and the upper torso was as shown in Figure 11–41, find the mass of the tail required for balance.

▲ **FIGURE 11–41** Problem 97

98. •• **IP** You hold a uniform, 28-g pen horizontal with your thumb pushing down on one end and your index finger pushing upward 3.5 cm from your thumb. The pen is 14 cm long. **(a)** Which of these two forces is greater in magnitude? **(b)** Find the two forces.

99. •• In Active Example 11–3, suppose the ladder is uniform, 4.0 m long, and weighs 60.0 N. Find the forces exerted on the ladder when the person is **(a)** halfway up the ladder and **(b)** three-fourths of the way up the ladder.

100. •• When you arrive at Duke's Dude Ranch, you are greeted by the large wooden sign shown in **Figure 11–42**. The left end of the sign is held in place by a bolt, the right end is tied to a

rope that makes an angle of 20.0° with the horizontal. If the sign is uniform, 3.20 m long, and has a mass of 16.0 kg, what are **(a)** the tension in the rope, and **(b)** the horizontal and vertical components of the force, $\vec{\mathbf{F}}$, exerted by the bolt?

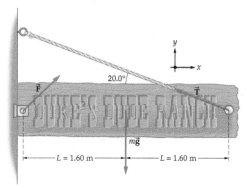

▲ **FIGURE 11–42** Problem 100

101. •• A 67.0-kg person stands on a lightweight diving board supported by two pillars, one at the end of the board, the other 1.10 m away. The pillar at the end of the board exerts a downward force of 828 N. **(a)** How far from that pillar is the person standing? **(b)** Find the force exerted by the second pillar.

102. •• In Example 11–4, find $\vec{\mathbf{F}}_1$ and $\vec{\mathbf{F}}_2$ as a function of the distance, x, of the swimmer from the left end of the diving board. Assume that the diving board is uniform and has a mass of 85.0 kg.

103. •• **Flats Versus Heels** A woman might wear a pair of flat shoes to work during the day, as in **Figure 11–43 (a)**, but a pair of high heels, **Figure 11–43 (b)**, when going out for the evening. Assume that each foot supports half her weight, $w = W/2 = 279$ N, and that the forces exerted by the floor on her feet occur at the points A and B in both figures. Find the forces F_A (point A) and F_B (point B) for **(a)** flat shoes and **(b)** high heels. **(c)** How have the high heels changed the weight distribution between the woman's heels and toes?

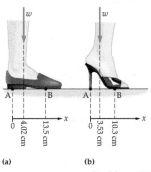

▲ **FIGURE 11–43** Problem 103

104. •• **BIO** A young girl sits at the edge of a dock by the bay, dipping her feet in the water. At the instant shown in **Figure 11–44**, she holds her lower leg stationary with her quadriceps muscle at an angle of 39° with respect to the horizontal. Use the information given in the figure, plus the fact that her lower leg has a mass of 3.4 kg, to determine the magnitude of the force, F_Q, exerted on the lower leg by the quadriceps.

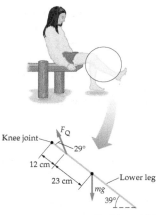

▲ **FIGURE 11–44** Problem 104

105. •• **BIO Deltoid Muscle** A crossing guard holds a STOP sign at arm's length, as shown in **Figure 11–45**. Her arm is horizontal, and we assume that the deltoid muscle is the only muscle supporting her arm. The weight of her upper arm is $W_u = 18$ N, the weight of her lower arm is $W_l = 11$ N, the weight of her hand is $W_h = 4.0$ N, and the weight of the sign is $W_s = 8.9$ N. The location where each of these forces acts on the arm is indicated in the figure. A force of magnitude f_d is exerted on the humerus by the deltoid, and the shoulder joint exerts a force on the humerus with horizontal and vertical components given by f_x, and f_y, respectively. **(a)** Is the magnitude of f_d greater than, less than, or equal to the magnitude of f_x? Explain. Find **(b)** f_d, **(c)** f_x, and **(d)** f_y. (The weights in Figure 11–45 are drawn to scale; the unknown forces are to be determined. If a force is found to be negative, its direction is opposite to that shown.)

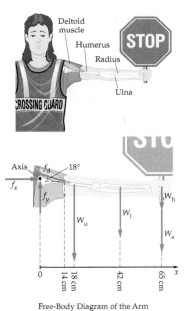

Free-Body Diagram of the Arm

▲ **FIGURE 11–45** Problem 105

106. •• **BIO Triceps** To determine the force a person's triceps muscle can exert, a doctor uses the procedure shown in **Figure 11–46**, where the patient pushes down with the palm of his hand on a force meter. Given that the weight of the lower arm is $Mg = 15.6$ N, and that the force meter reads $F = 89.0$ N, what is the force F_T exerted vertically upward by the triceps?

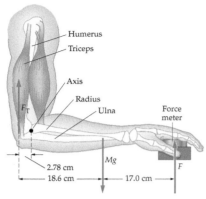

▲ **FIGURE 11–46** Problem 106

107. •• **IP** Suppose a fourth book, the same as the other three, is added to the stack of books shown in Figure 11–32. **(a)** What is the maximum overhang distance, d, in this case? **(b)** If the mass of each book is increased by the same amount, does your answer to part (a) increase, decrease, or stay the same? Explain.

108. •• **IP** Suppose partial melting of the polar ice caps increases the moment of inertia of the Earth from $0.331 \, M_E R_E^2$ to $0.332 \, M_E R_E^2$. **(a)** Would the length of a day (the time required for the Earth to complete one revolution about its axis) increase or decrease? Explain. **(b)** Calculate the change in the length of a day. Give your answer in seconds.

109. ••• A bicycle wheel of radius R and mass M is at rest against a step of height $3R/4$, as illustrated in **Figure 11–47**. Find the minimum horizontal force F that must be applied to the axle to make the wheel start to rise up over the step.

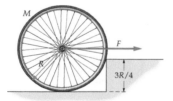

▲ **FIGURE 11–47** Problem 109

110. ••• A 0.101-kg yo-yo has an outer radius R that is 5.60 times greater than the radius r of its axle. The yo-yo is in equilibrium if a mass m is suspended from its outer edge, as shown in **Figure 11–48**. Find the tension in the two strings, T_1 and T_2, and the mass m.

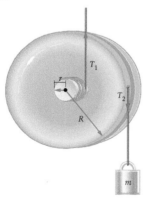

▲ **FIGURE 11–48** Problem 110

111. ••• In Problem 36, assume that the rod has a mass of M and that its bottom end simply rests on the floor, held in place by static friction. If the coefficient of static friction is μ_s, find the maximum force F that can be applied to the rod at its midpoint before it slips.

112. ••• In the previous problem, suppose the rod has a mass of 2.3 kg and the coefficient of static friction is $1/7$. **(a)** Find the greatest force F that can be applied at the midpoint of the rod without causing it to slip. **(b)** Show that if F is applied $1/8$ of the way down from the top of the rod, it will never slip at all, no matter how large the force F.

113. ••• A cylinder of mass m and radius r has a string wrapped around its circumference. The upper end of the string is held fixed, and the cylinder is allowed to fall. Show that its linear acceleration is $(2/3)g$.

114. ••• Repeat the previous problem, replacing the cylinder with a solid sphere. Show that its linear acceleration is $(5/7)g$.

115. ••• A mass M is attached to a rope that passes over a disk-shaped pulley of mass m and radius r. The mass hangs to the left side of the pulley. On the right side of the pulley, the rope is pulled downward with a force F. Find **(a)** the acceleration of the mass, **(b)** the tension in the rope on the left side of the pulley, and **(c)** the tension in the rope on the right side of the pulley. **(d)** Check your results in the limits $m \to 0$ and $m \to \infty$.

116. ••• **Bricks in Equilibrium** Consider a system of four uniform bricks of length L stacked as shown in **Figure 11–49**. What is the maximum distance, x, that the middle bricks can be displaced outward before they begin to tip?

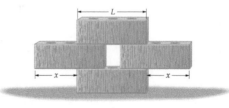

▲ **FIGURE 11–49** Problem 116

PASSAGE PROBLEMS

BIO Correcting Torsiversion

Torsiversion is a medical condition in which a tooth is rotated away from its normal position about the long axis of the root. Studies show that about 2 percent of the population suffer from this condition to some degree. For those who do, the improper alignment of the tooth can lead to tooth-to-tooth collisions during eating, as well as other problems. Typical patients display a rotation ranging from 20° to 60°, with an average around 30°.

An example is shown in **Figure 11–50 (a)**, where the first premolar is not only displaced slightly from its proper location in the negative y direction, but also rotated clockwise from its normal orientation. To correct this condition, an orthodontist might use an archwire and a bracket to apply both a force and a torque to the tooth. In the simplest case, two forces are applied to the tooth in different locations, as indicated by F_1 and F_2 in Figure 11–50 (a). These two forces, if chosen properly, can reposition the tooth by exerting a net force in the positive y direction, and also reorient it by applying a torque in the counterclockwise direction.

In a typical case, it may be desired to have a net force in the positive y direction of 1.8 N. In addition, the distances in Figure 11–50 (a) can be taken to be $d = 3.2$ mm and $D = 4.5$ mm. Given these conditions, a range of torques is possible for various values of the y components of the forces, F_{1y} and F_{2y}. For example, **Figure 11–50 (b)** shows the values of F_{1y} and F_{2y} necessary to produce a given torque, where the torque is measured about the center of the tooth (which is also the origin of the coordinate system). Notice that the two forces always add to 1.8 N in the positive y direction, though one of the forces changes sign as the torque is increased.

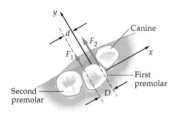

(a)

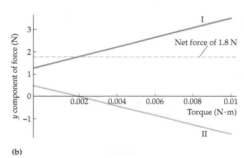

(b)

▲ **FIGURE 11–50** Problems 117, 118, 119, and 120

117. • The two, solid straight lines in Figure 11–50 (b) represent the two forces applied to the tooth. Which line corresponds to which force?

    A. I = F_{1y}, II = F_{2y} **B.** I = F_{2y}, II = F_{1y}

118. • What is the value of the torque that corresponds to one of the forces being equal to zero?

    A. 0.0023 N·m   **B.** 0.0058 N·m

    C. 0.0081 N·m   **D.** 0.017 N·m

119. •• Find the values of F_{1y} and F_{2y} required to give zero net torque.

    A. $F_{1y} = -1.2$ N, $F_{2y} = 3.0$ N   **B.** $F_{1y} = 1.1$ N, $F_{2y} = 0.75$ N

    C. $F_{1y} = -0.73$ N, $F_{2y} = 2.5$ N   **D.** $F_{1y} = 0.52$ N, $F_{2y} = 1.3$ N

120. •• Find the values of F_{1y} and F_{2y} required to give a net torque of 0.0099 N·m. This is a torque that would be effective at rotating the tooth.

    A. $F_{1y} = -1.7$ N, $F_{2y} = 3.5$ N   **B.** $F_{1y} = -3.8$ N, $F_{2y} = 5.6$ N

    C. $F_{1y} = -0.23$ N, $F_{2y} = 2.0$ N   **D.** $F_{1y} = 4.0$ N, $F_{2y} = -2.2$ N

INTERACTIVE PROBLEMS

121. •• **Referring to Example 11–7** Suppose the mass of the pulley is doubled, to 0.160 kg, and that everything else in the system remains the same. **(a)** Do you expect the value of T_2 to increase, decrease, or stay the same? Explain. **(b)** Calculate the value of T_2 for this case.

122. •• **Referring to Example 11–7** Suppose the mass of the cart is doubled, to 0.62 kg, and that everything else in the system remains the same. **(a)** Do you expect the value of T_2 to increase, decrease, or stay the same? Explain. **(b)** Calculate the value of T_2 for this case.

123. •• **Referring to Active Example 11–5** Suppose the child runs with a different initial speed, but that everything else in the system remains the same. What initial speed does the child have if the angular speed of the system after the collision is 0.425 rad/s?

124. •• **Referring to Active Example 11–5** Suppose everything in the system is as described in Active Example 11–5 except that the child approaches the merry-go-round in a direction that is not tangential. Find the angle θ between the direction of motion and the outward radial direction (as in Example 11–8) that is required if the final angular speed of the system is to be 0.272 rad/s.

Momentum: A Conserved Quantity

When objects interact, momentum may be conserved while mechanical energy is dissipated. Why? These pages explore momentum conservation and point out key differences between momentum and mechanical energy.

❶ How do linear and angular momentum relate?

The equations of linear and angular momentum are analogous, and all the principles presented on these pages apply to angular as well as linear momentum.

	Definition	Newton's 2nd law
Linear momentum:	$\vec{p} = m\vec{v}$	$\Sigma\vec{F} = m\vec{a} = \dfrac{\Delta\vec{p}}{\Delta t}$
Angular momentum:	$\vec{L} = I\vec{\omega}$	$\Sigma\vec{\tau} = I\vec{\alpha} = \dfrac{\Delta\vec{L}}{\Delta t}$

Analogous quantities	
Linear	Angular
Acceleration $\vec{a}$	Angular acceleration $\vec{\alpha}$
Force $\vec{F}$	Torque $\vec{\tau}$
Velocity $\vec{v}$	Angular velocity $\vec{\omega}$
Mass m	Moment of inertia I

❷ Why is momentum conserved?

Momentum conservation follows from Newton's laws.
Recall that the general form of Newton's second law relates force to momentum:

An object's change in momentum … … equals the net force acting on the object …

$$\Sigma\vec{F} = \Delta\vec{p}/\Delta t \quad \text{or} \quad \Delta\vec{p} = (\Sigma\vec{F})\Delta t$$

… multiplied by the time over which the force acts.

For an individual object, momentum is conserved (does not change) when the net force acting on the object is zero (that is, $\Delta\vec{p} = 0$ when $\Sigma\vec{F} = 0$).

For a system of objects, momentum conservation follows from Newton's third law:
- The momentum of a system of objects is the vector sum of the momenta of the individual objects.
- The forces between objects in the system (**internal forces**) cannot change the system's momentum because, by Newton's third law, the objects exert *equal but opposite forces* on each other, which cause *equal and opposite momentum changes*.
- **Thus, only external forces can change the momentum of a system.**

In the following interaction, the two skaters undergo equal and opposite momentum changes, whereas the system's momentum $\vec{p}_{sys}$ is conserved.

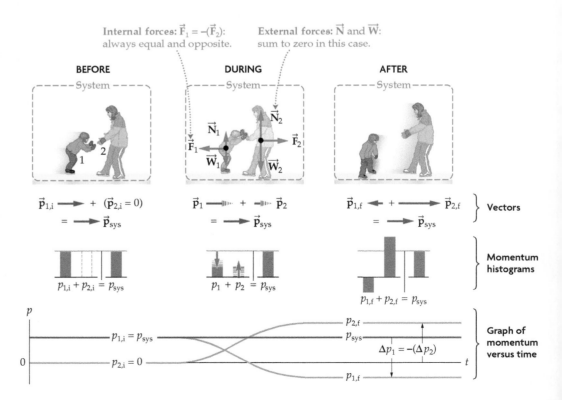

❸ How can momentum be conserved when mechanical energy is not?

Force times time versus force times distance: Momentum change is due to *a force acting over a time* Δt, whereas changes in mechanical energy result from *a force acting over a distance D* (i.e., from work):

$$\Delta \vec{p} = \vec{F}(\Delta t) \qquad \Delta E = W = F(D)$$

How do these relationships apply to the inelastic collision shown below?

Arrow shot into styrofoam block attached to air-track cart

START: Collision begins

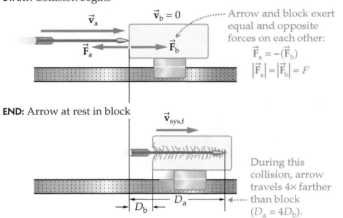

Arrow and block exert equal and opposite forces on each other:
$$\vec{F}_a = -(\vec{F}_b)$$
$$|\vec{F}_a| = |\vec{F}_b| = F$$

END: Arrow at rest in block

During this collision, arrow travels 4× farther than block ($D_a = 4D_b$).

Momentum: The collision lasts the same time Δt for the arrow and block, so their mometum changes are equal and opposite:

$$\Delta \vec{p}_a = \vec{F}_a \Delta t = -(\vec{F}_b)\Delta t = -\Delta \vec{p}_b$$

Mechanical energy: The objects exert the same force magnitude F on each other, but the arrow travels farther during the collision because it penetrates the block: $D_a > D_b$. Thus, the arrow loses more mechanical energy than the block gains:

$$\Delta E_a = F_a(D_a) = -40\,\text{J} \qquad \Delta E_b = F_b(D_b) = +10\,\text{J}$$

Conclusion: The collision dissipates mechanical energy while conserving momentum, as the following graphs show:

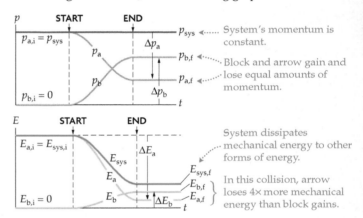

System's momentum is constant.

Block and arrow gain and lose equal amounts of momentum.

System dissipates mechanical energy to other forms of energy.

In this collision, arrow loses 4× more mechanical energy than block gains.

❹ How does momentum conservation help us solve problems?

- You can use momentum conservation to analyze any interaction between objects for which the net external force acting on the system during the collision is zero (or is negligible compared to the internal forces).
- If the net external force is not negligible, you cannot use momentum conservation! This applies to the players at right, who push on the ground while colliding.
- For elastic collisions, you must use conservation of mechanical energy as well as conservation of momentum. (Section 9.6 solves these simultaneous equations for special cases.)

Collisions in which momentum is conserved can be categorized as follows, according to how kinetic energy changes or is conserved.

The external reaction forces of the earth on these players' feet cannot be ignored.

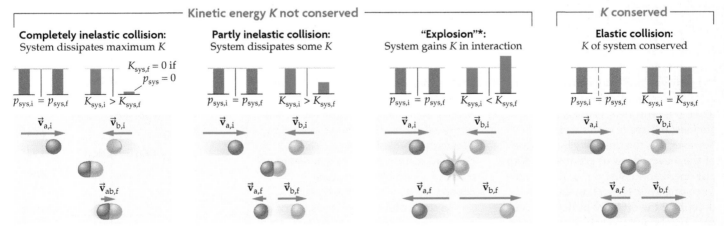

*Physicists use the term "explosion" to mean any interaction that adds kinetic energy to the system. Thus, the collision in Step 2 on the facing page is an explosion.

12 Gravity

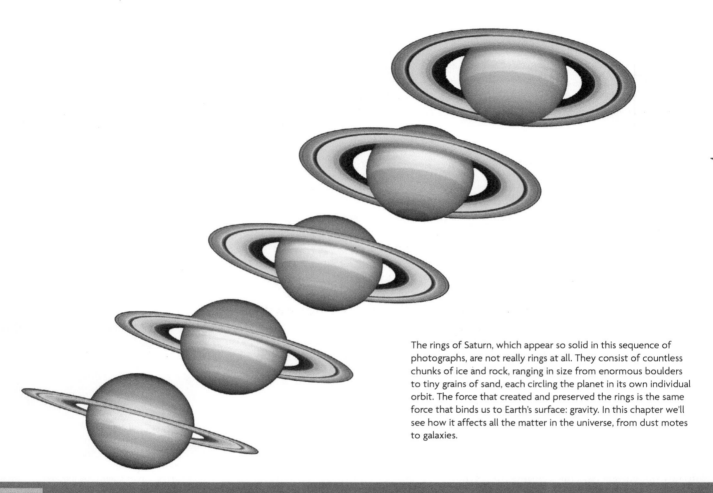

The rings of Saturn, which appear so solid in this sequence of photographs, are not really rings at all. They consist of countless chunks of ice and rock, ranging in size from enormous boulders to tiny grains of sand, each circling the planet in its own individual orbit. The force that created and preserved the rings is the same force that binds us to Earth's surface: gravity. In this chapter we'll see how it affects all the matter in the universe, from dust motes to galaxies.

The study of gravity has always been a central theme in physics, from Galileo's early experiments on free fall in the seventeenth century, to Einstein's general theory of relativity in the early years of the twentieth century, and Stephen Hawking's work on black holes in recent years. Perhaps the grandest milestone in this endeavor, however, was the discovery by Newton of the **universal law of gravitation**. With just one simple equation to describe the force of gravity, Newton was able to determine the orbits of planets, moons, and comets, and to explain such earthly

phenomena as the tides and the fall of an apple.

Before Newton's work, it was generally thought that the heavens were quite separate from the Earth, and that they obeyed their own "heavenly" laws. Newton showed, on the contrary, that the same law of gravity that operates on the surface of the Earth applies to the Moon and to other astronomical objects. As a result of Newton's efforts, physics expanded its realm of applicability to natural phenomena throughout the universe.

So successful was Newton's law of gravitation that Edmond Halley (1656–1742) was able to use it to predict the return of the comet that today bears his name. Though he did not live to see its return in 1758, the fact that the comet did reappear when predicted was an event unprecedented in human history. Roughly a hundred years later, Newton's theory of gravity scored an even more impressive success. Astronomers observing the planet Uranus noticed small deviations in its orbit, which they thought might be due to the gravitational tug of a previously unknown planet. Using Newton's law to calculate the predicted position of the new planet—now called Neptune—it was found on the very first night of observations, September 23, 1846. The fact that Neptune was precisely where the law of gravitation said it should be still stands as one of the most astounding triumphs in the history of science.

Today, Newton's law of gravitation is used to determine the orbits that take spacecraft from the Earth to various destinations within our solar system and beyond. Appropriately enough, spacecraft were even sent to view Halley's comet at close range in 1986. In addition, the law allows us to calculate with pinpoint accuracy the time of solar eclipses and other astronomical events in the distant past and remote future. This incredibly powerful and precise law of nature is the subject of this chapter.

12-1 Newton's Law of Universal Gravitation

It's ironic, but the first fundamental force of nature to be recognized as such, **gravity**, is also the weakest of the fundamental forces. Still, it is the force most apparent to us in our everyday lives, and is the force responsible for the motion of the Moon, the Earth, and the planets. Yet the connection between falling objects on Earth and planets moving in their orbits was not known before Newton.

The flash of insight that came to Newton—whether it was due to seeing an apple fall to the ground or not—is simply this: The force causing an apple to accelerate downward is the same force causing the Moon to move in a circular path around the Earth. To put it another way, Newton was the first to realize that the Moon is *constantly falling* toward the Earth, though without ever getting closer to it, and that it falls for the same reason that an apple falls. This is illustrated in a classic drawing due to Newton, shown to the right.

To be specific, in the case of the apple the motion is linear as it accelerates downward toward the center of the Earth. In the case of the Moon the motion is circular with constant speed. As discussed in Section 6–5, an object in uniform circular motion accelerates toward the center of the circle. It follows, therefore, that the Moon *also* accelerates toward the center of the Earth. In fact, the force responsible for the Moon's centripetal acceleration is the Earth's gravitational attraction, the same force responsible for the fall of the apple.

To describe the force of gravity, Newton proposed the following simple law:

Newton's Law of Universal Gravitation
The force of gravity between any two point objects of mass m_1 and m_2 is attractive and of magnitude

$$F = G\frac{m_1 m_2}{r^2}$$ 12–1

In this expression, r is the distance between the masses, and G is a constant referred to as the **universal gravitation constant**. Its value is

$$G = 6.67 \times 10^{-11} \, \text{N} \cdot \text{m}^2/\text{kg}^2$$ 12–2

The force is directed along the line connecting the masses, as indicated in **Figure 12–1**.

Note that each mass experiences a force of the same magnitude, $F = Gm_1m_2/r^2$, but acting in opposite directions. That is, the force of gravity between two objects forms an action-reaction pair.

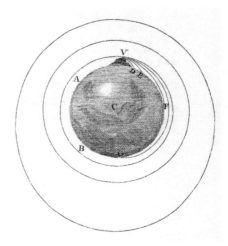

▲ In this illustration from his great work, the *Principia*, published in 1687, Newton presents a "thought experiment" to show the connection between free fall and orbital motion. Imagine throwing a projectile horizontally from the top of a mountain. The greater the initial speed of the projectile, the farther it travels in free fall before striking the ground. In the absence of air resistance, a great enough initial speed could result in the projectile circling the Earth and returning to its starting point. Thus, an object orbiting the Earth is actually in free fall—it simply has a large horizontal speed.

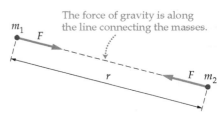

▲ **FIGURE 12–1 Gravitational force between point masses**
Two point masses, m_1 and m_2, separated by a distance r exert equal and opposite attractive forces on one another. The magnitude of the forces, F, is given by Equation 12–1.

According to Newton's law, all objects in the universe attract all other objects in the universe by way of the gravitational interaction. It is in this sense that the force law is termed "universal." Thus, the net gravitational force acting on you is due not only to the planet on which you stand, which is certainly responsible for the majority of the net force, but also to people nearby, planets, and even stars in far-off galaxies. In short, everything in the universe "feels" everything else, thanks to gravity.

The fact that G is such a small number means that the force of gravity between objects of human proportions is imperceptibly small. This is shown in the following Exercise.

EXERCISE 12–1

A man takes his dog for a walk on a deserted beach. Treating people and dogs as point objects for the moment, find the force of gravity between the 105-kg man and his 11.2-kg dog when they are separated by a distance of **(a)** 1.00 m and **(b)** 10.0 m.

SOLUTION

a. Substituting numerical values into Equation 12–1 yields

$$F = G\frac{m_1 m_2}{r^2} = (6.67 \times 10^{-11}\,\mathrm{N \cdot m^2/kg^2})\frac{(105\,\mathrm{kg})(11.2\,\mathrm{kg})}{(1.00\,\mathrm{m})^2} = 7.84 \times 10^{-8}\,\mathrm{N}$$

b. Repeating the calculation for $r = 10.0$ m gives

$$F = G\frac{m_1 m_2}{r^2} = (6.67 \times 10^{-11}\,\mathrm{N \cdot m^2/kg^2})\frac{(105\,\mathrm{kg})(11.2\,\mathrm{kg})}{(1.00\,\mathrm{m})^2} = 7.84 \times 10^{-10}\,\mathrm{N}$$

The forces found in Exercise 12–1 are imperceptibly small. In comparison, the force exerted by the Earth on the man is 1030 N and the force exerted on the dog is 110 N—these forces are several orders of magnitude greater than the force between the man and the dog. In general, gravitational forces are significant only when large masses, such as the Earth or the Moon, are involved.

Exercise 12–1 also illustrates how rapidly the force of gravity decreases with distance. In particular, since F varies as $1/r^2$, it is said to have an **inverse square dependence** on distance. Thus, for example, an increase in distance by a factor of 10 results in a decrease in the force by a factor of $10^2 = 100$. A plot of the force of gravity versus distance is given in **Figure 12–2**. Note that even though the force diminishes rapidly with distance, it never completely vanishes; thus, we say that gravity is a force of infinite range.

Note also that the force of gravity between two masses depends on the product of the masses, m_1 times m_2. With this type of dependence, it follows that if either mass is doubled, the force of gravity is doubled as well. This would not be the case, for example, if the force of gravity depended on the *sum* of the masses, $m_1 + m_2$.

Finally, if a given mass is acted on by gravitational interactions with a number of other masses, the net force acting on it is simply the vector sum of each of the forces individually. This property of gravity is referred to as **superposition**. As an example, superposition implies that the net gravitational force exerted on you at this moment is the vector sum of the force exerted by the Earth, plus the force exerted by the Moon, plus the force exerted by the Sun, and so on. The following Example illustrates superposition.

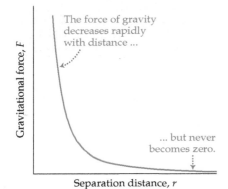

▲ **FIGURE 12–2 Dependence of the gravitational force on separation distance, r**
The $1/r^2$ dependence of the gravitational force means that it decreases rapidly with distance. Still, it never completely vanishes. For this reason, we say that gravity is a force of infinite range; that is, every mass in the universe experiences a nonzero force from every other mass in the universe, no matter how far away.

PROBLEM-SOLVING NOTE

Net Gravitational Force

To find the net gravitational force acting on an object, you should (i) resolve each of the forces acting on the object into components and (ii) add the forces component by component.

EXAMPLE 12–1 HOW MUCH FORCE IS WITH YOU?

As part of a daring rescue attempt, the *Millennium Eagle* passes between a pair of twin asteroids, as shown. If the mass of the spaceship is 2.50×10^7 kg and the mass of each asteroid is 3.50×10^{11} kg, find the net gravitational force exerted on the *Millennium Eagle* **(a)** when it is at location A and **(b)** when it is at location B. Treat the spaceship and the asteroids as if they were point objects.

PICTURE THE PROBLEM

Our sketch shows the spaceship as it follows a path between the twin asteroids. The relevant distances and masses are indicated, as are the two points of interest, A and B. Note that at location A the force $\vec{F}_1$ points above the x axis at the angle θ_1 (to be determined); the force $\vec{F}_2$ points below the x axis at the angle $\theta_2 = -\theta_1$, as can be seen by symmetry. At location B, the two forces act in opposite directions.

STRATEGY

To find the net gravitational force exerted on the spaceship, we first determine the magnitude of the force exerted on it by each asteroid. This is done by using Equation 12–1 and the distances given in our sketch. Next, we resolve these forces into x and y components. Finally, we sum the force components to find the net force.

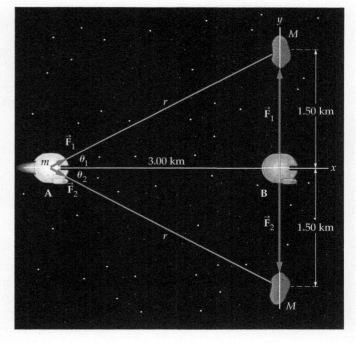

SOLUTION

Part (a)

1. Use the Pythagorean theorem to find the distance r from point A to each asteroid. Also, refer to the sketch to find the angle between $\vec{F}_1$ and the x axis. The angle between $\vec{F}_2$ and the x axis has the same magnitude but the opposite sign:

$$r = \sqrt{(3.00 \times 10^3 \text{ m})^2 + (1.50 \times 10^3 \text{ m})^2} = 3350 \text{ m}$$

$$\theta_1 = \tan^{-1}\left(\frac{1.50 \times 10^3 \text{ m}}{3.00 \times 10^3 \text{ m}}\right) = \tan^{-1}(0.500) = 26.6°$$

$$\theta_2 = -\theta_1 = -26.6°$$

2. Use r and Equation 12–1 to calculate the magnitude of the forces $\vec{F}_1$ and $\vec{F}_2$ at point A:

$$F_1 = F_2 = G\frac{mM}{r^2}$$

$$= (6.67 \times 10^{-11} \text{ N} \cdot \text{m}^2/\text{kg}^2)\frac{(2.50 \times 10^7 \text{ kg})(3.50 \times 10^{11} \text{ kg})}{(3350 \text{ m})^2}$$

$$= 52.0 \text{ N}$$

3. Use the values of θ_1 and θ_2 found in Step 1 to calculate the x and y components of $\vec{F}_1$ and $\vec{F}_2$:

$$F_{1,x} = F_1 \cos \theta_1 = (52.0 \text{ N}) \cos 26.6° = 46.5 \text{ N}$$
$$F_{1,y} = F_1 \sin \theta_1 = (52.0 \text{ N}) \sin 26.6° = 23.3 \text{ N}$$
$$F_{2,x} = F_2 \cos \theta_2 = (52.0 \text{ N}) \cos(-26.6°) = 46.5 \text{ N}$$
$$F_{2,y} = F_2 \sin \theta_2 = (52.0 \text{ N}) \sin(-26.6°) = -23.3 \text{ N}$$

4. Add the components of $\vec{F}_1$ and $\vec{F}_2$ to find the components of the net force, $\vec{F}$:

$$F_x = F_{1,x} + F_{2,x} = 93.0 \text{ N}$$
$$F_y = F_{1,y} + F_{2,y} = 0$$

Part (b)

5. Use Equation 12–1 to find the magnitude of the forces exerted on the spaceship by the asteroids at location B:

$$F_1 = F_2 = G\frac{mM}{r^2}$$

$$= (6.67 \times 10^{-11} \text{ N} \cdot \text{m}^2/\text{kg}^2)\frac{(2.50 \times 10^7 \text{ kg})(3.50 \times 10^{11} \text{ kg})}{(1.50 \times 10^3 \text{ m})^2}$$

$$= 259 \text{ N}$$

6. Use the fact that $\vec{F}_1$ and $\vec{F}_2$ have equal magnitudes and point in opposite directions to determine the net force, $\vec{F}$, acting on the spaceship:

$$\vec{F} = \vec{F}_1 + \vec{F}_2 = 0$$

CONTINUED ON NEXT PAGE

CONTINUED FROM PREVIOUS PAGE

INSIGHT

We find that the net force at location A is in the positive x direction, as one would expect by symmetry. At location B, where the force exerted by each asteroid is about 5 times greater than it is at location A, the *net* force is zero since the attractive forces exerted by the two asteroids are equal and opposite, and thus cancel. Note that the forces in our sketch have been drawn in correct proportion.

Rocket scientists often use the gravitational force between astronomical objects and spacecraft to accelerate the spacecraft and send them off to distant parts of the solar system. In fact, this gravitational attraction makes possible the "slingshot" effect illustrated in Figure 9–31.

PRACTICE PROBLEM

Find the net gravitational force acting on the spaceship when it is at the location $x = 5.00 \times 10^3$ m, $y = 0$.   [**Answer:** 41.0 N in the negative x direction]

Some related homework problems: Problem 9, Problem 11, Problem 12

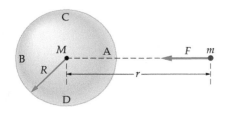

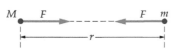

▲ **FIGURE 12–3 Gravitational force between a point mass and a sphere**

The force is the same as if all the mass of the sphere were concentrated at its center.

12–2 Gravitational Attraction of Spherical Bodies

Newton's law of gravity applies to point objects. How, then, do we calculate the force of gravity for an object of finite size? In general, the approach is to divide the finite object into a collection of small mass elements, then use superposition and the methods of calculus to determine the net gravitational force. For an arbitrary shape, this calculation can be quite difficult. For objects with a uniform spherical shape, however, the final result is remarkably simple, as was shown by Newton.

Uniform Sphere

Consider a uniform sphere of radius R and mass M, as in **Figure 12–3**. A point object of mass m is brought near the sphere, though still outside it at a distance r from its center. The object experiences a relatively strong attraction from mass near the point A, and a weaker attraction from mass near point B. In both cases the force is along the line connecting the mass m and the center of the sphere; that is, along the x axis. In addition, mass at the points C and D exert a net force that is also along the x axis—just as in the case of the twin asteroids in Example 12–1. Thus, the symmetry of the sphere guarantees that the net force it exerts on m is directed toward the sphere's center. The magnitude of the force exerted by the sphere must be calculated with the methods of calculus—which Newton invented and then applied to this problem. As a result of his calculations, Newton was able to show that **the net force exerted by the sphere on the mass m is the same as if all the mass of the sphere were concentrated at its center.** That is, the force between the mass m and the sphere of mass M has a magnitude that is simply

$$F = G\frac{mM}{r^2} \qquad \text{12–3}$$

Let's apply this result to the case of a mass m on the surface of the Earth. If the mass of the Earth is M_E, and its radius is R_E, it follows that the force exerted on m by the Earth is

$$F = G\frac{mM_E}{R_E^2} = m\left(\frac{GM_E}{R_E^2}\right)$$

We also know, however, that the gravitational force experienced by a mass m on the Earth's surface is simply $F = mg$, where g is the acceleration due to gravity. Therefore, we see that

$$m\left(\frac{GM_E}{R_E^2}\right) = mg$$

or

$$g = \frac{GM_E}{R_E^2} = \frac{(6.67 \times 10^{-11}\ \text{N} \cdot \text{m}^2/\text{kg}^2)(5.97 \times 10^{24}\ \text{kg})}{(6.37 \times 10^6\ \text{m})^2} = 9.81\ \text{m/s}^2 \qquad \text{12–4}$$

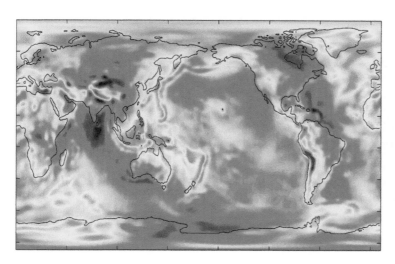

◀ This global model of the Earth's gravitational strength was constructed from a combination of surface gravity measurements and satellite tracking data. It shows how the acceleration of gravity varies from the value at an idealized "sea level" that takes into account the Earth's nonspherical shape. (The Earth is somewhat flattened at the poles—its radius is greatest at the equator.) Gravity is strongest in the red areas and weakest in the dark blue areas.

This result can be extended to objects above the Earth's surface, and hence farther from the center of the Earth, as we show in the next Example.

EXAMPLE 12–2 THE DEPENDENCE OF GRAVITY ON ALTITUDE

 REAL-WORLD PHYSICS If you climb to the top of Mt. Everest, you will be about 5.50 mi above sea level. What is the acceleration due to gravity at this altitude?

PICTURE THE PROBLEM
At the top of the mountain, your distance from the center of the Earth is $r = R_E + h$, where $h = 5.50$ mi is the altitude.

STRATEGY
First, use $F = GmM_E/r^2$ to find the force due to gravity on the mountaintop. Then, set $F = mg_h$ to find the acceleration g_h at the height h.

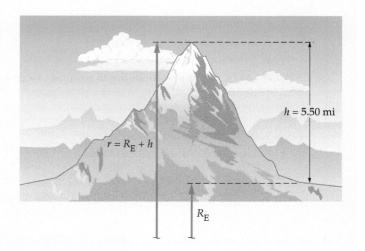

$h = 5.50$ mi

$r = R_E + h$

R_E

SOLUTION

1. Calculate the force F due to gravity at a height h above the Earth's surface:

$$F = G\frac{mM_E}{(R_E + h)^2}$$

2. Set F equal to mg_h and solve for g_h:

$$F = G\frac{mM_E}{(R_E + h)^2} = mg_h$$

$$g_h = G\frac{M_E}{(R_E + h)^2}$$

3. Factor out R_E^2 from the denominator, and use the fact that $GM_E/R_E^2 = g$:

$$g_h = \left(\frac{GM_E}{R_E^2}\right)\frac{1}{\left(1 + \dfrac{h}{R_E}\right)^2} = \frac{g}{\left(1 + \dfrac{h}{R_E}\right)^2}$$

4. Substitute numerical values, with $h = 5.50$ mi = $(5.50 \text{ mi})(1609 \text{ m/mi}) = 8850$ m, and $R_E = 6.37 \times 10^6$ m:

$$g_h = \frac{g}{\left(1 + \dfrac{h}{R_E}\right)^2} = \frac{9.81 \text{ m/s}^2}{\left(1 + \dfrac{8850 \text{ m}}{6.37 \times 10^6 \text{ m}}\right)^2} = 9.78 \text{ m/s}^2$$

CONTINUED ON NEXT PAGE

CONTINUED FROM PREVIOUS PAGE

INSIGHT

As expected, the acceleration due to gravity is less as one moves farther from the center of the Earth. Thus, if you were to climb to the top of Mt. Everest, you would lose weight—not only because of the physical exertion required for the climb, but also because of the reduced gravity. In particular, a person with a mass of 60 kg (about 130 lb) would lose about half a pound of weight just by standing on the summit of the mountain.

A plot of g_h as a function of h is shown in **Figure 12–4 (a)**. The plot indicates the altitude of Mt. Everest and the orbit of the space shuttle. **Figure 12–4 (b)** shows g_h out to the orbit of communications and weather satellites, which orbit at an altitude of roughly 22,300 mi.

PRACTICE PROBLEM

Find the acceleration due to gravity at the altitude of the space shuttle's orbit, 250 km above the Earth's surface. [**Answer:** $g_h = 9.08$ m/s², a reduction of only 7.44% compared to the acceleration of gravity on the surface of the Earth.]

Some related homework problems: Problem 15, Problem 17

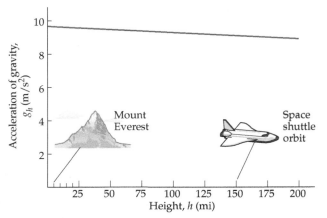

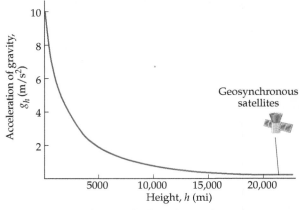

(a) Acceleration of gravity near the Earth's surface

(b) Acceleration of gravity far from the Earth

FIGURE 12–4 ▲ **The acceleration due to gravity at a height h above the Earth's surface**

(a) In this plot, the peak of Mt. Everest is at about $h = 5.50$ mi, and the space shuttle orbit is at roughly $h = 150$ mi. **(b)** This shows the decrease in the acceleration of gravity from the surface of the Earth to an altitude of about 25,000 mi. The orbit of geosynchronous satellites—ones that orbit above a fixed point on the Earth—is at roughly $h = 22,300$ mi.

Equation 12–4 can be used to calculate the acceleration due to gravity on other objects in the solar system besides the Earth. For example, to calculate the acceleration due to gravity on the Moon, g_m, we simply use the mass and radius of the Moon in Equation 12–4. Once g_m is known, the weight of an object of mass m on the Moon is found by using $W_m = mg_m$.

▶ (Left) The weak lunar gravity permits astronauts, even encumbered by their massive space suits, to bound over the Moon's surface. The low gravitational pull, only about one-sixth that of Earth, is a consequence not only of the Moon's smaller size, but also of its lower average density. (Right) The force of gravity on the surface of Mars is only about 38% of its strength on Earth. This was an important factor in designing NASA's Phoenix Mars Lander, shown here lifting a scoop of dirt on its 16th Martian day after landing in May 2008.

EXERCISE 12–2

a. Find the acceleration due to gravity on the surface of the Moon.

b. The lunar rover had a mass of 225 kg. What was its weight on the Earth and on the Moon? (*Note:* The mass of the Moon is $M_m = 7.35 \times 10^{22}$ kg and its radius is $R_m = 1.74 \times 10^6$ m.)

SOLUTION

a. For the Moon, the acceleration due to gravity is

$$g_m = \frac{GM_m}{R_m^2} = \frac{(6.67 \times 10^{-11}\,\text{N}\cdot\text{m}^2/\text{kg}^2)(7.35 \times 10^{22}\,\text{kg})}{(1.74 \times 10^6\,\text{m})^2} = 1.62\,\text{m/s}^2$$

This is about one-sixth the acceleration due to gravity on the Earth.

b. On the Earth, the rover's weight was

$$W = mg = (225\,\text{kg})(9.81\,\text{m/s}^2) = 2210\,\text{N}$$

On the Moon, its weight was

$$W_m = mg_m = (225\,\text{kg})(1.62\,\text{m/s}^2) = 365\,\text{N}$$

As expected, this is roughly one-sixth its Earth weight.

The replacement of a sphere with a point mass at its center can be applied to many physical systems. For example, the force of gravity between two spheres of finite size is the same as if *both* were replaced by point masses. Thus, the gravitational force between the Earth, with mass M_E, and the Moon, with mass M_m, is

$$F = G\frac{M_E M_m}{r^2}$$

The distance r in this expression is the center-to-center distance between the Earth and the Moon, as shown in **Figure 12–5**. It follows, then, that in many calculations involving the solar system, moons and planets can be treated as point objects.

Weighing the Earth

The British physicist Henry Cavendish performed an experiment in 1798 that is often referred to as "weighing the Earth." What he did, in fact, was measure the value of the universal gravitation constant, G, that appears in Newton's law of gravity. As we have pointed out before, G is a very small number; hence a sensitive experiment is needed for its measurement. It is because of this experimental difficulty that G was not measured until more than 100 years after Newton published the law of gravitation.

In the Cavendish experiment, illustrated in **Figure 12–6**, two masses m are suspended from a thin thread. Near each suspended mass is a large stationary mass M, as shown. Each suspended mass is attracted by the force of gravity toward the large mass near it; hence the rod holding the suspended masses tends to rotate and twist the thread. The angle through which the thread twists can be measured by bouncing a beam of light from a mirror attached to the thread. If the force required to twist the thread through a given angle is known (from previous experiments), a measurement of the twist angle gives the magnitude of the force of gravity. Finally, knowing the masses m and M, and the distance between their centers, r, we can use Equation 12–1 to solve for G. Cavendish found $6.754 \times 10^{-11}\,\text{N}\cdot\text{m}^2/\text{kg}^2$, in good agreement with the currently accepted value given in Equation 12–2.

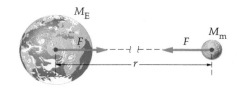

▲ **FIGURE 12–5 Gravitational force between the Earth and the Moon**

The force is the same as if both the Earth and the Moon were point masses. (The sizes of the Earth and Moon are in correct proportion in this figure, but the separation between the two should be much greater than that shown here. In reality, it is about 30 times the diameter of the Earth, and so would be about 2 ft on this scale.)

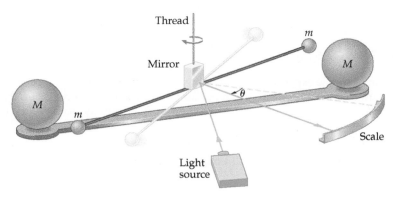

◀ **FIGURE 12–6 The Cavendish experiment**

The gravitational attraction between the masses m and M causes the rod and the suspending thread to twist. Measurement of the twist angle allows for a direct measurement of the gravitational force.

To see why Cavendish is said to have weighed the Earth, recall that the force of gravity on the surface of the Earth, mg, can be written as follows:

$$mg = G\frac{mM_E}{R_E^2}$$

Canceling m and solving for M_E yields

$$M_E = \frac{gR_E^2}{G} \qquad\qquad\qquad\qquad \text{12–5}$$

Before the Cavendish experiment, the quantities g and R_E were known from direct measurement, but G had yet to be determined. When Cavendish measured G, he didn't actually "weigh" the Earth, of course. Instead, he calculated its mass, M_E.

EXERCISE 12–3

Use $M_E = gR_E^2/G$ to calculate the mass of the Earth.

SOLUTION

Substituting numerical values, we find

$$M_E = \frac{gR_E^2}{G} = \frac{(9.81 \text{ m/s}^2)(6.37 \times 10^6 \text{ m})^2}{6.67 \times 10^{-11} \text{ N} \cdot \text{m}^2/\text{kg}^2} = 5.97 \times 10^{24} \text{ kg}$$

As soon as Cavendish determined the mass of the Earth, geologists were able to use the result to calculate its average density; that is, its average mass per volume. Assuming a spherical Earth of radius R_E, its total volume is

$$V_E = \tfrac{4}{3}\pi R_E^3 = \tfrac{4}{3}\pi(6.37 \times 10^6 \text{ m})^3 = 1.08 \times 10^{21} \text{ m}^3$$

Dividing this into the total mass yields the average density, ρ:

$$\rho = \frac{M_E}{V_E} = \frac{5.97 \times 10^{24} \text{ kg}}{1.08 \times 10^{21} \text{ m}^3} = 5530 \text{ kg/m}^3 = 5.53 \text{ g/cm}^3$$

This is an interesting result because typical rocks found near the surface of the Earth, such as granite, have a density of only about 3.00 g/cm^3. We conclude, then, that the interior of the Earth must have a greater density than its surface. In fact, by analyzing the propagation of seismic waves around the world, we now know that the Earth has a rather complex interior structure, including a solid inner core with a density of about 15.0 g/cm^3 (see Section 10–5).

REAL-WORLD PHYSICS

The internal structure of the Earth and the Moon

A similar calculation for the Moon yields an average density of about 3.33 g/cm^3, essentially the same as the density of the lunar rocks brought back during the Apollo program. Hence, it is likely that the Moon does not have an internal structure similar to that of the Earth.

Since G is a universal constant—with the same value everywhere in the universe—it can be used to calculate the mass of other bodies in the solar system as well. This is illustrated in the following Example.

EXAMPLE 12–3   MARS ATTRACTS!

After landing on Mars, an astronaut performs a simple experiment by dropping a rock. A quick calculation using the drop height and the time of fall yields a value of 3.73 m/s^2 for the rock's acceleration. **(a)** Find the mass of Mars, given that its radius is $R_M = 3.39 \times 10^6$ m. **(b)** What is the acceleration of gravity due to Mars at a distance $2R_M$ from the center of the planet?

PICTURE THE PROBLEM

Our sketch shows an astronaut dropping a rock to the ground on the surface of Mars. If the acceleration of the rock is measured, we find $g_M = 3.73 \text{ m/s}^2$, where the subscript M refers to Mars. In addition, we indicate the radius of Mars in our sketch, where $R_M = 3.39 \times 10^6$ m.

STRATEGY

a. Since the acceleration of gravity is g_M on the surface of Mars, it follows that the force of gravity on an object of mass m is $F = mg_M$. This force is also given by Newton's law of gravity—that is, $F = GmM_M/R_M^2$. Setting these expressions for the force equal to one another yields the mass of Mars, M_M.

b. Set $F = ma$ equal to $F = GmM_M/(2R_M)^2$ and solve for the acceleration, a.

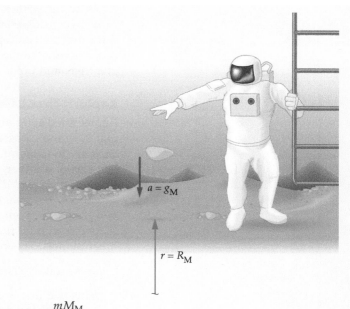

$a = g_M$

$r = R_M$

SOLUTION

Part (a)

1. Set mg_M equal to GmM_M/R_M^2:

$$mg_M = G\frac{mM_M}{R_M^2}$$

2. Cancel m and solve for the mass of Mars:

$$M_M = \frac{g_M R_M^2}{G}$$

3. Substitute numerical values:

$$M_M = \frac{(3.73 \text{ m/s}^2)(3.39 \times 10^6 \text{ m})^2}{6.67 \times 10^{-11} \text{ N} \cdot \text{m}^2/\text{kg}^2} = 6.43 \times 10^{23} \text{ kg}$$

Part (b)

4. Apply Newton's law of gravity with $r = 2R_M$. Use the fact that $g_M = GM_M/R_M^2$ from Step 1 to simplify the calculation:

$$ma = G\frac{mM_M}{(2R_M)^2} \quad \text{or}$$

$$a = G\frac{M_M}{(2R_M)^2} = \tfrac{1}{4}\left(G\frac{M_M}{R_M^2}\right) = \tfrac{1}{4}(g_M) = \tfrac{1}{4}(3.73 \text{ m/s}^2) = 0.933 \text{ m/s}^2$$

INSIGHT

The important point here is that the universal gravitation constant, G, applies as well on Mars as on Earth, or any other object. Therefore, knowledge of the size and acceleration of gravity of an astronomical body is sufficient to determine its mass.

PRACTICE PROBLEM

If the radius of Mars were reduced to 3.00×10^6 m, with its mass remaining the same, would the acceleration of gravity on Mars increase, decrease, or stay the same? Check your answer by calculating the acceleration of gravity for this case.   [**Answer:** The acceleration of gravity increases to 4.77 m/s^2.]

Some related homework problems: Problem 20, Problem 21

12–3 Kepler's Laws of Orbital Motion

If you go outside each clear night and observe the position of Mars with respect to the stars, you will find that its apparent motion across the sky is rather complex. Instead of moving on a simple curved path, it occasionally reverses direction (this is known as *retrograde motion*). A few months later it reverses direction yet again and resumes its original direction of motion. Other planets exhibit similar odd behavior.

The Danish astronomer Tycho Brahe (1546–1601) followed the paths of the planets, and Mars in particular, for many years, even though the telescope had not yet been invented. He used, instead, an elaborate sighting device to plot the precise position of the planets. Brahe was joined in his work by Johannes Kepler (1571–1630) in 1600, and after Brahe's death, Kepler inherited his astronomical observations.

Kepler made good use of Brahe's life work, extracting from his carefully collected data the three laws of orbital motion we know today as Kepler's laws. These laws make it clear that the Sun and the planets do not orbit the Earth, as Ptolemy—the ancient Greek astronomer—claimed, but rather that the Earth, along with the other planets, orbit the Sun, as proposed by Copernicus (1473–1543).

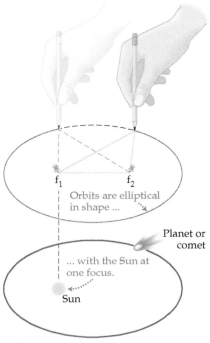

▲ **FIGURE 12–7 Drawing an ellipse**
To draw an ellipse, put two tacks in a piece of cardboard. The tacks define the "foci" of the ellipse. Now connect a length of string to the two tacks, and use a pencil and the string to sketch out a smooth closed curve, as shown. This closed curve is an ellipse. In a planetary orbit a planet follows an elliptical path, with the Sun at one focus. Nothing is at the other focus.

Why the planets obey Kepler's laws no one knew—not even Kepler—until Newton considered the problem decades after Kepler's death. Newton was able to show that each of Kepler's laws follows as a direct consequence of the universal law of gravitation. In the remainder of this section we consider Kepler's three laws one at a time, and point out the connection between them and the law of gravitation.

Kepler's First Law

Kepler tried long and hard to find a circular orbit around the Sun that would match Brahe's observations of Mars. After all, up to that time everyone from Ptolemy to Copernicus believed that celestial objects moved in circular paths of one sort or another. Though the orbit of Mars was exasperatingly close to being circular, the small differences between a circular path and the experimental observations just could not be ignored. Eventually, after a great deal of hard work and disappointment over the loss of circular orbits, Kepler discovered that Mars followed an orbit that was elliptical rather than circular. The same applied to the other planets. This observation became Kepler's first law:

| Planets follow elliptical orbits, with the Sun at one focus of the ellipse. |

This is a fine example of the scientific method in action. Though Kepler expected and wanted to find circular orbits, he would not allow himself to ignore the data. If Brahe's observations had not been so accurate, Kepler probably would have chalked up the small differences between the data and a circular orbit to error. As it was, he had to discard a treasured—but incorrect—theory, and move on to an unexpected, but ultimately correct, view of nature.

Kepler's first law is illustrated in **Figure 12–7**, along with a definition of an ellipse in terms of its two foci. In the case where the two foci merge, as in **Figure 12–8**, the ellipse reduces to a circle. Thus, a circular orbit *is* allowed by Kepler's first law, but only as a special case.

Newton was able to show that, because the force of gravity decreases with distance as $1/r^2$, closed orbits must have the form of ellipses or circles, as stated in Kepler's first law. He also showed that orbits that are not closed—say the orbit of a comet that passes by the Sun once and then leaves the solar system—are either parabolic or hyperbolic.

Kepler's Second Law

When Kepler plotted the position of a planet on its elliptical orbit, indicating at each position the time the planet was there, he made an interesting observation. First, draw a line from the Sun to a planet at a given time. Then a certain time later—perhaps a month—draw a line again from the Sun to the new position of the planet. The result is that the planet has "swept out" a wedge-shaped area, as indicated in **Figure 12–9 (a)**. If this procedure is repeated when the planet is on a different part of its orbit, another wedge-shaped area is generated. Kepler's observation was that the areas of these two wedges are equal:

| As a planet moves in its orbit, it sweeps out an equal amount of area in an equal amount of time. |

Kepler's second law follows from the fact that the force of gravity on a planet is directly toward the Sun. As a result, gravity exerts zero torque about the Sun,

▶ **FIGURE 12–8 The circle as a special case of the ellipse**
As the two foci of an ellipse approach one another, the ellipse becomes more circular. In the limit that the foci merge, the ellipse becomes a circle.

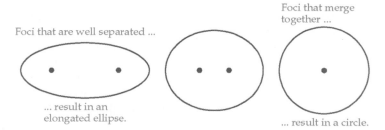

Foci that are well separated ...

... result in an elongated ellipse.

Foci that merge together ...

... result in a circle.

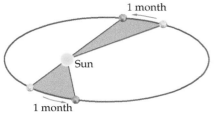

1 month

Sun

1 month

(a) Equal areas in equal times

Sun

(b) Equal areas in equal times for highly elliptical orbit

◀ **FIGURE 12–9 Kepler's second law**
(a) The second law states that a planet sweeps out equal areas in equal times.
(b) In a highly elliptical orbit, the long, thin area is equal to the broad, fan-shaped area.

which means that the angular momentum of a planet in its orbit must be conserved. As Newton showed, conservation of angular momentum is equivalent to the equal-area law stated by Kepler.

CONCEPTUAL CHECKPOINT 12–1 COMPARE SPEEDS

The Earth's orbit is slightly elliptical. In fact, the Earth is closer to the Sun during the northern hemisphere winter than it is during the summer. Is the speed of the Earth during winter **(a)** greater than, **(b)** less than, or **(c)** the same as its speed during summer?

REASONING AND DISCUSSION
According to Kepler's second law, the area swept out by the Earth per month is the same in winter as it is in summer. In winter, however, the radius from the Sun to the Earth is less than it is in summer. Therefore, if this smaller radius is to sweep out the same area, the Earth must move more rapidly.

ANSWER
(a) The speed of the Earth is greater during the winter.

Though we have stated the first two laws in terms of planets, they apply equally well to any object orbiting the Sun. For example, a comet might follow a highly elliptical orbit, as in **Figure 12–9 (b)**. When it is near the Sun, it moves very quickly, for the reason discussed in Conceptual Checkpoint 12–1, sweeping out a broad wedge-shaped area in a month's time. Later in its orbit, the comet is far from the Sun and moving slowly. In this case, the area it sweeps out in a month is a long, thin wedge. Still, the two wedges have equal areas.

Kepler's Third Law

Finally, Kepler studied the relation between the mean distance of a planet from the Sun, r, and its period—that is, the time, T, it takes for the planet to complete one orbit. **Figure 12–10** shows a plot of period versus distance for the planets of the solar system. Kepler tried to "fit" these results to a simple dependence between T and r. If he tried a linear fit—that is, T proportional to r (the bottom curve in Figure 12–10)—he found that the period did not increase rapidly enough with distance. On the other hand, if he tried T proportional to r^2 (the top curve in Figure 12–10), the period increased too rapidly. Splitting the difference, and trying T proportional to $r^{3/2}$, yields a good fit (the middle curve in Figure 12–10). This is Kepler's third law:

> The period, T, of a planet increases as its mean distance from the Sun, r, raised to the 3/2 power. That is,
>
> $T = (\text{constant})r^{3/2}$ 12–6

It is straightforward to derive this result for the special case of a circular orbit. Consider, then, a planet orbiting the Sun at a distance r, as in **Figure 12–11**. Since the planet moves in a circular path, a centripetal force must act on it, as we saw in Section 6–5. In addition, this force must be directed toward the center of the circle; that is, toward the Sun. It is as if you were to swing a ball on the end of a string in a circle above your head, as in Figure 6–12 (p. 169). In order for the ball to move in a circular path, you have to exert a force on the ball toward the center of the circular path. This force is exerted through the string. In the case of a planet orbiting the Sun, the centripetal force is provided by the force of gravity between the Sun and the planet.

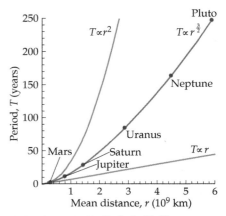

Pluto

$T \propto r^2$ $T \propto r^{\frac{3}{2}}$

Neptune

Uranus

Mars   Saturn $T \propto r$
Jupiter

Mean distance, r (10^9 km)

Period, T (years)

▲ **FIGURE 12–10 Kepler's third law and some near misses**

These plots represent three possible mathematical relationships between period of revolution, T (in years), and mean distance from the Sun, r (in kilometers). The lower curve shows $T = (\text{constant})r$; the upper curve is $T = (\text{constant})r^2$. The middle curve, which fits the data, is $T = (\text{constant})r^{3/2}$. This is Kepler's third law.

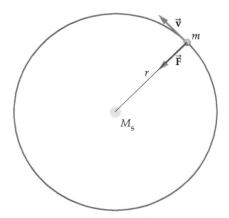

$\vec{v}$

m

$\vec{F}$

r

M_s

▲ **FIGURE 12–11 Centripetal force on a planet in orbit**

As a planet revolves about the Sun in a circular orbit of radius r, the force of gravity between it and the Sun, $F = GmM_s/r^2$, provides the required centripetal force.

If the planet has a mass m, and the Sun has a mass M_s, the force of gravity between them is

$$F = G\frac{mM_s}{r^2}$$

Now, this force creates the centripetal acceleration of the planet, a_{cp}, which, according to Equation 6–15, is

$$a_{cp} = \frac{v^2}{r}$$

Thus, the centripetal force necessary for the planet to orbit is ma_{cp}:

$$F = ma_{cp} = m\frac{v^2}{r}$$

Since the speed of the planet, v, is the circumference of the orbit, $2\pi r$, divided by the time to complete an orbit, T, we have

$$F = m\frac{v^2}{r} = m\frac{(2\pi r/T)^2}{r} = \frac{4\pi^2 rm}{T^2}$$

Setting the centripetal force equal to the force of gravity yields

$$\frac{4\pi^2 rm}{T^2} = G\frac{mM_s}{r^2}$$

Eliminating m and rearranging, we find

$$T^2 = \frac{4\pi^2}{GM_s}r^3$$

or

$$T = \left(\frac{2\pi}{\sqrt{GM_s}}\right)r^{3/2} = (\text{constant})r^{3/2} \qquad \text{12–7}$$

As predicted by Kepler, T is proportional to $r^{3/2}$.

Deriving Kepler's third law by using Newton's law of gravitation has allowed us to calculate the constant that multiplies $r^{3/2}$. Note that the constant depends on the mass of the Sun; that is, *T depends on the mass being orbited*. It does not depend on the mass of the planet orbiting the Sun, however, as long as the planet's mass is much less than the mass of the Sun. As a result, Equation 12–7 applies equally to all the planets.

This result can also be applied to the case of a moon or a satellite (an artificial moon) orbiting a planet. To do so, we simply note that it is the planet that is being orbited, not the Sun. Hence, to apply Equation 12–7, we just replace the mass of the Sun, M_s, with the mass of the appropriate planet.

As an example, let's calculate the mass of Jupiter. One of the four moons of Jupiter discovered by Galileo is Io, which completes one orbit every 42 h 27 min =

PROBLEM-SOLVING NOTE

The Mass in Kepler's Third Law

When applying Kepler's third law, recall that the mass in Equation 12–7, M_s, refers to the mass of the object being orbited. Thus, the third law can be applied to satellites of any object, as long as M_s is replaced by the orbited mass.

▶ Kepler's laws of orbital motion apply to planetary satellites as well as planets. Jupiter, the largest planet in the solar system, has at least 16 moons, all of which travel in elliptical orbits that obey Kepler's laws. (The moons in the photo at left, passing in front of Jupiter, are Io and Europa, two of the four largest Jovian satellites discovered by Galileo in 1609.) Even some asteroids have been found to have their own satellites. The large cratered object in the photo at right is 243 Ida, an asteroid some 56 km long; its miniature companion at the top of the photo is Dactyl, about 1.5 km in diameter. Like all gravitationally bound bodies, Ida and Dactyl orbit their common center of mass.

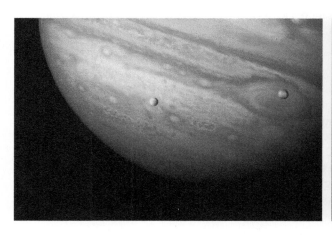
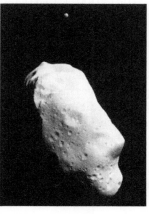

1.53×10^5 s. Given that the average distance from the center of Jupiter to Io is 4.22×10^8 m, we can find the mass of Jupiter as follows:

$$T = \left(\frac{2\pi}{\sqrt{GM_J}}\right)r^{3/2}$$

$$M_J = \frac{4\pi^2 r^3}{GT^2} = \frac{4\pi^2(4.22 \times 10^8 \text{ m})^3}{(6.67 \times 10^{-11} \text{ N} \cdot \text{m}^2/\text{kg}^2)(1.53 \times 10^5 \text{ s})^2} = 1.90 \times 10^{27} \text{ kg}$$

EXAMPLE 12–4 THE SUN AND MERCURY

The Earth revolves around the Sun once a year at an average distance of 1.50×10^{11} m. **(a)** Use this information to calculate the mass of the Sun. **(b)** Find the period of revolution for the planet Mercury, whose average distance from the Sun is 5.79×10^{10} m.

PICTURE THE PROBLEM
Our sketch shows the orbits of Mercury, Venus, and the Earth in correct proportion. In addition, each of these orbits is slightly ellip- tical, though the deviation from circularity is too small for the eye to see. Finally, we indicate that the orbital radius for Mercury is 5.79×10^{10} m and the orbital radius for Earth is 1.50×10^{11} m.

STRATEGY

a. To find the mass of the Sun, we solve Equation 12–7 for M_s. Note that the period $T = 1$ yr must be converted to seconds before we evaluate the formula.

b. The period of Mercury is found by substituting $r = 5.79 \times 10^{10}$ m in Equation 12–7.

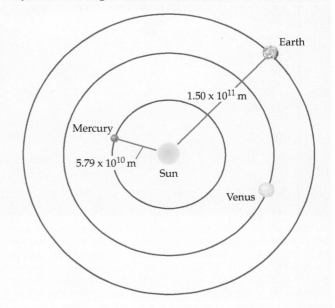

SOLUTION

Part (a)

1. Solve Equation 12–7 for the mass of the Sun:

$$T = \left(\frac{2\pi}{\sqrt{GM_s}}\right)r^{3/2}$$

$$M_s = \frac{4\pi^2 r^3}{GT^2}$$

2. Calculate the period of the Earth in seconds:

$$T = 1 \text{ y}\left(\frac{365.24 \text{ days}}{1 \text{ y}}\right)\left(\frac{24 \text{ hr}}{1 \text{ day}}\right)\left(\frac{3600 \text{ s}}{1 \text{ hr}}\right) = 3.16 \times 10^7 \text{ s}$$

3. Substitute numerical values in the expression for the mass of the Sun obtained in Step 1:

$$M_s = \frac{4\pi^2 r^3}{GT^2}$$

$$= \frac{4\pi^2(1.50 \times 10^{11} \text{ m})^3}{(6.67 \times 10^{-11} \text{ N} \cdot \text{m}^2/\text{kg}^2)(3.16 \times 10^7 \text{ s})^2}$$

$$= 2.00 \times 10^{30} \text{ kg}$$

Part (b)

4. Substitute $r = 5.79 \times 10^{10}$ m into Equation 12–7. In addition, use the mass of the Sun obtained in part (a):

$$T = \left(\frac{2\pi}{\sqrt{GM_s}}\right)r^{3/2}$$

$$= \left(\frac{2\pi}{\sqrt{(6.67 \times 10^{-11} \text{ N} \cdot \text{m}^2/\text{kg}^2)(2.00 \times 10^{30} \text{ kg})}}\right) \times (5.79 \times 10^{10} \text{ m})^{3/2}$$

$$= 7.58 \times 10^6 \text{ s} = 0.240 \text{ y} = 87.7 \text{ days}$$

CONTINUED ON NEXT PAGE

CONTINUED FROM PREVIOUS PAGE

INSIGHT

In part (a), notice that the mass of the Sun is almost a million times more than the mass of the Earth, as determined in Exercise 12–3. In fact, the Sun accounts for 99.9% of all the mass in the solar system.

In part (b) we see that Mercury, with its smaller orbital radius, has a shorter year than the Earth.

PRACTICE PROBLEM

Venus orbits the Sun with a period of 1.94×10^7 s. What is its average distance from the Sun? **[Answer:** $r = 1.08 \times 10^{11}$ m]

Some related homework problems: Problem 28, Problem 32

 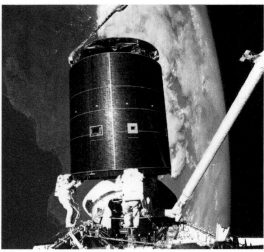

▲ Many weather and communications satellites are placed in geosynchronous orbits that allow them to remain "stationary" in the sky— that is, fixed over one point on the Earth's equator. Because the Earth rotates, the period of such a satellite must exactly match that of the Earth. The altitude needed for such an orbit is about 36,000 km (see Active Example 12–1). Other satellites, such as those used in the Global Positioning System (GPS), the Hubble Space Telescope, and the American space shuttles, operate at much lower altitudes—typically just a few hundred miles. The photo at left shows the communications satellite Intelsat VI just prior to its capture by astronauts of the space shuttle *Endeavour*. A launch failure had left the satellite stranded in low orbit. The astronauts snared the satellite (right) and fitted it with a new engine that boosted it to its geosynchronous orbit, where it is still in operation today.

REAL-WORLD PHYSICS

Geosynchronous satellites

A *geosynchronous satellite* is one that orbits above the equator with a period equal to one day. From the Earth, such a satellite appears to be in the same location in the sky at all times, making it particularly useful for applications such as communications and weather forecasting. From Kepler's third law, we know that a satellite has a period of one day only if its orbital radius has a particular value. We determine this value in the following Active Example.

ACTIVE EXAMPLE 12–1 FIND THE ALTITUDE OF A GEOSYNCHRONOUS SATELLITE

Find the altitude above the Earth's surface where a satellite orbits with a period of one day ($R_E = 6.37 \times 10^6$ m, $M_E = 5.97 \times 10^{24}$ kg, $T = 1$ day $= 8.64 \times 10^4$ s).

SOLUTION *(Test your understanding by performing the calculations indicated in each step.)*

1. Rewrite Equation 12–7, using the mass of the Earth in place of the mass of the Sun: $\qquad T = \left(2\pi / \sqrt{GM_E}\right) r^{3/2}$

2. Solve for the radius, r: $\qquad r = (T/2\pi)^{2/3} (GM_E)^{1/3}$

3. Substitute numerical values: $\qquad r = 4.22 \times 10^7$ m

4. Subtract the radius of the Earth to find the altitude: $\qquad r - R_E = 3.58 \times 10^7$ m

INSIGHT

Thus, *all* geosynchronous satellites orbit 3.58×10^7 m $\approx$ 22,300 mi above our heads.

YOUR TURN

Find the altitude above the surface of the Moon where a "lunasynchronous" satellite would orbit. [*Note:* The length of a lunar day is one month (27.332 days), which is why we see only one side of the Moon.]

(Answers to **Your Turn** *problems are given in the back of the book.)*

Not all spacecraft are placed in geosynchronous orbits, however. The U.S. space shuttle, for example, orbits at an altitude of about 150 mi. At that altitude, it takes less than an hour and a half to complete one orbit. The International Space Station, operational although still under construction, orbits at a similar altitude.

The 24 satellites of the Global Positioning System (GPS) are also in relatively low orbits. These satellites, which have an average altitude of 12,550 mi and orbit the Earth every 12 hours, are used to provide a precise determination of an observer's position anywhere on Earth. The operating principle of the GPS is illustrated in **Figure 12–12**. Imagine, for example, that satellite 2 emits a radio signal at a particular time (all GPS satellites carry atomic clocks on board). This signal travels away from the satellite with the speed of light (see Chapter 25) and is detected a short time later by an observer's GPS receiver. Multiplying the time delay by the speed of light gives the distance of the receiver from satellite 2. Thus, in our example, the observer must lie somewhere on the red circle in Figure 12–12. Similar time delay measurements for signals from satellite 11 show that the observer is also somewhere on the green circle; hence the observer is either at the point shown in Figure 12–12, or at the second intersection of the red and green circles on the other side of the planet. Measurements from satellite 6 can resolve the ambiguity and place the observer at the point shown in the figure. Measurements from additional satellites can even determine the observer's altitude. GPS receivers, which are used by hikers, boaters, and others who need to know their precise location, typically use signals from as many as 12 satellites. As currently operated, the GPS gives positions with a typical accuracy of 2 m to 10 m.

Orbital Maneuvers

We now show how Kepler's laws can give insight into maneuvering a satellite in orbit. Suppose, for example, that you are piloting a spacecraft in a circular orbit, and you would like to move to a lower circular orbit. As you might expect, you should begin by using your rockets to decrease your speed—that is, fire the rockets that point in the forward direction so that their thrust (Section 9–8) is opposite to your direction of motion. The result of firing the decelerating rockets at a given point A in your original orbit is shown in **Figure 12–13 (a)**. Note that your new orbit is not a circle, as desired, but rather an ellipse. To produce a circular orbit you can simply fire the decelerating rockets once again at point B, on the opposite side of the Earth from point A. The net result of these two firings is that you now move in a circular orbit of smaller radius.

Similarly, to move to a larger orbit, you must fire your accelerating rockets twice. The first firing puts you into an elliptical orbit that moves farther from the Earth, as **Figure 12–13 (b)** shows. After the second firing you are again in a circular orbit. This simplest type of orbital transfer, requiring just two rocket burns, is referred to as a *Hohmann transfer*. The Hohmann transfer is the basic maneuver used to send spacecraft such as the Mars lander from Earth's orbit about the Sun to the orbit of Mars.

The Global Positioning System (GPS)

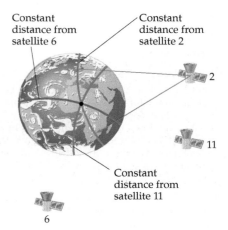

▲ **FIGURE 12–12 The Global Positioning System**

A system of 24 satellites in orbit about the Earth makes it possible to determine a person's location with great accuracy. Measuring the distance of a person from satellite 2 places the person somewhere on the red circle. Similar measurements using satellite 11 place the person's position somewhere on the green circle, and further measurements can pinpoint the person's location.

Maneuvering spacecraft

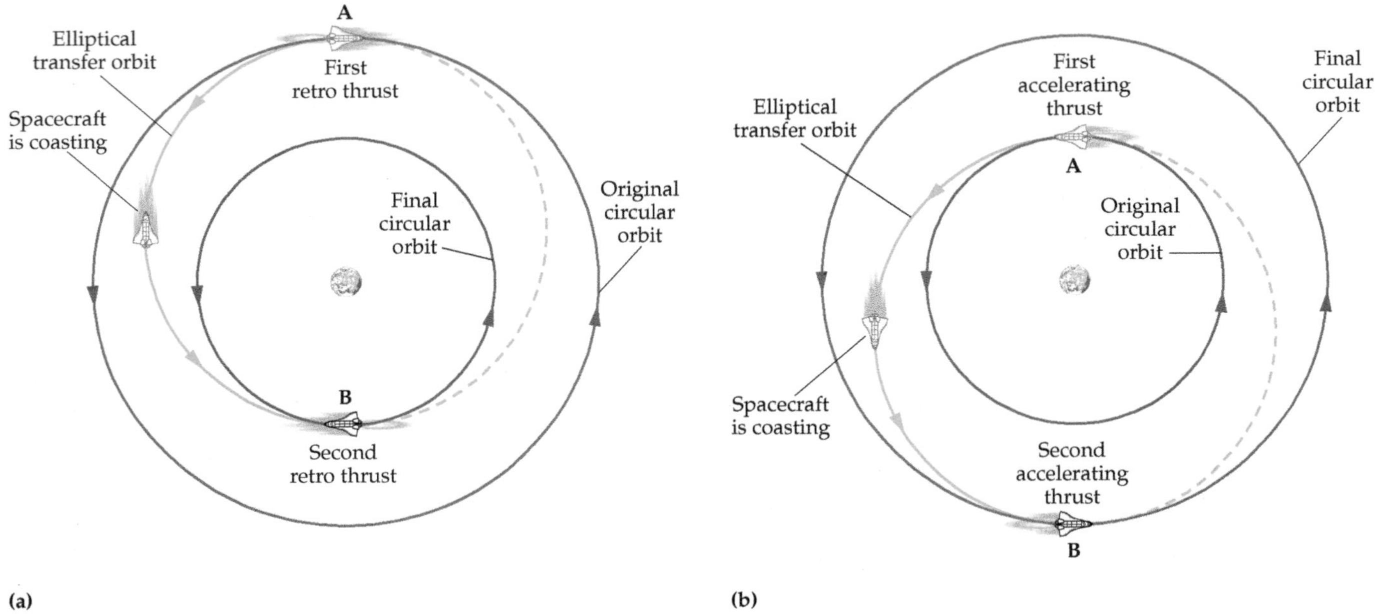

(a)   (b)

▲ **FIGURE 12–13** **Orbital maneuvers**
(a) The radius of a satellite's orbit can be decreased by firing the decelerating rockets once at point A and again at point B. Between firings the satellite follows an elliptical orbit. The satellite speeds up as it falls inward toward the Earth during this maneuver. For this reason its final speed in the new circular orbit is greater than its speed in the original orbit, even though the decelerating rockets have slowed it down twice. **(b)** The radius of a satellite's orbit can be increased by firing the accelerating rockets once at point A and again at point B. Between firings the satellite follows an elliptical orbit. The satellite slows down as it moves farther from the Earth during this maneuver. For this reason its final speed in the new circular orbit is less than its speed in the original orbit, even though the accelerating rockets have sped it up twice.

CONCEPTUAL CHECKPOINT 12–2 WHICH ROCKETS TO USE?

As you pilot your spacecraft in a circular orbit about the Earth, you notice the space station you want to dock with several miles ahead in the same orbit. To catch up with the space station, should you **(a)** fire your accelerating rockets or **(b)** fire your decelerating rockets?

REASONING AND DISCUSSION
Since you want to catch up with something miles ahead, you must accelerate, right? Well, not in this case. Accelerating moves you into an elliptical orbit, as in Figure 12–13 (b), and with a second acceleration you can make your new orbit circular with a greater radius. Recall from Kepler's third law, however, that the larger the radius of an orbit the larger the period, as Equation 12–7 shows. Thus, on your new higher path you take longer to complete an orbit, so you fall farther behind the space station. The same is true even if you fire your rockets only once and stay on the elliptical orbit—it also has a longer period than the original orbit.

On the other hand, two decelerating burns will put you into a circular orbit of smaller radius, and thus smaller period. As a result, you complete an orbit in less time than before and catch up with the space station. After catching up, you can perform two accelerating burns to move you back into the original orbit to dock.

ANSWER
(b) You should fire your decelerating rockets.

12–4 Gravitational Potential Energy

In Chapter 8 we saw that the principle of conservation of energy can be used to solve a number of problems that would be difficult to handle with a straightforward application of Newton's laws of mechanics. Before we can apply energy conservation to astronomical situations, however, we must know the gravitational potential energy for a spherical object such as the Earth. Now you may be wondering, "Don't we already know the potential energy of gravity?" Well, in fact, in Chapter 8 we said that the gravitational potential energy a distance h above the Earth's surface is $U = mgh$. As was mentioned at the time, however, this result is valid only near the Earth's surface, where we can say that the acceleration of gravity, g, is approximately constant.

As the distance from the Earth increases we know that g decreases, as was shown in Example 12–2. It follows that mgh cannot be valid for arbitrary h. Indeed, it can be shown that the gravitational potential energy of a system consisting of a mass m a distance r from the center of the Earth is

$$U = -G\frac{mM_E}{r} \qquad\qquad \text{12–8}$$

A plot of $U = -GmM_E/r$ is presented in **Figure 12–14**. Note that U approaches zero as r approaches infinity. This is a common convention in astronomical systems. In fact, since only *differences* in potential energy matter, as was mentioned in Chapter 8, the choice of the reference point ($U = 0$) is completely arbitrary. When we considered systems that were near the Earth's surface, it was natural to let $U = 0$ at ground level. When we consider, instead, distances of astronomical scale, it is generally more convenient to choose the potential energy to be zero when objects are separated by an infinite distance.

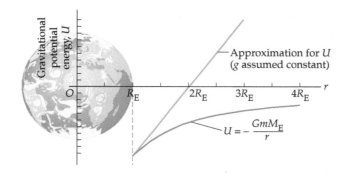

◀ **FIGURE 12–14 Gravitational potential energy as a function of the distance r from the center of the Earth**

The lower curve in this plot shows the gravitational potential energy, $U = -GmM_E/r$, for r greater than R_E. Near the Earth's surface, U is approximately linear, corresponding to the result $U = mgh$ given in Chapter 8.

EXERCISE 12–4

Use Equation 12–8 to find the gravitational potential energy of a 12.0-kg meteorite when it is **(a)** one Earth radius above the surface of the Earth, and **(b)** on the surface of the Earth.

SOLUTION

a. In this case, the distance from the center of the Earth is $2R_E$, thus

$$U = -G\frac{mM_E}{2R_E}$$

$$= -(6.67 \times 10^{-11}\,\text{N}\cdot\text{m}^2/\text{kg}^2)\frac{(12.0\,\text{kg})(5.97 \times 10^{24}\,\text{kg})}{2(6.37 \times 10^6\,\text{m})} = -3.75 \times 10^8\,\text{J}$$

b. Now, the distance from the center of the Earth is R_E, therefore

$$U = -\frac{GmM_E}{R_E}$$

$$= -(6.67 \times 10^{-11}\,\text{N}\cdot\text{m}^2/\text{kg}^2)\frac{(12.0\,\text{kg})(5.97 \times 10^{24}\,\text{kg})}{6.37 \times 10^6\,\text{m}} = -7.50 \times 10^8\,\text{J}$$

Note that the potential energy in part (b) is twice what it was in part (a), since the distance from the center of the Earth to the meteorite has been halved.

At first glance, Equation 12–8 doesn't seem to bear any similarity to mgh, which we know to be valid near the surface of the Earth. Even so, there is a direct connection between these two expressions. Recall that when we say that the potential energy at a height h is mgh, what we mean is that when a mass m is raised from the ground to a height h, the potential energy of the system increases by the amount mgh. Let's calculate the corresponding difference in potential energy using Equation 12–8.

First, at a height h above the surface of the Earth we have $r = R_E + h$; hence the potential energy there is

$$U = -G\frac{mM_E}{R_E + h}$$

On the surface of the Earth, where $r = R_E$, we have

$$U = -G\frac{mM_E}{R_E}$$

The corresponding difference in potential energy is

$$\Delta U = \left(-G\frac{mM_E}{R_E + h}\right) - \left(-G\frac{mM_E}{R_E}\right)$$

$$= \left(-G\frac{mM_E}{R_E}\right)\left(\frac{1}{1 + h/R_E}\right) - \left(-G\frac{mM_E}{R_E}\right)$$

If h is much smaller than the radius of the Earth, it follows that h/R_E is a small number. In this case, we can apply the useful approximation $1/(1 + x) \approx 1 - x$ [see Figure A–5 (b) in Appendix A] to write $1/(1 + h/R_E) \approx 1 - h/R_E$. As a result, we have

$$\Delta U = \left(-G\frac{mM_E}{R_E}\right)(1 - h/R_E) - \left(-G\frac{mM_E}{R_E}\right) = m\left[\frac{GM_E}{R_E^2}\right]h$$

The term in square brackets should look familiar—according to Equation 12–4 it is simply g. Hence, the increase in potential energy at the height h is

$$\Delta U = mgh$$

as expected.

The straight line in Figure 12–14 corresponds to the potential energy mgh. Near the Earth's surface, it is clear that mgh and $-GmM_E/r$ are in close agreement. For larger r, however, the fact that gravity is getting weaker means that the potential energy does not continue rising as rapidly as it would if gravity were of constant strength.

An important distinction between the potential energy, U, and the gravitational force, $\vec{F}$, is that the force is a vector, whereas the potential energy is a scalar—that is, U is simply a number. As a result:

> The total gravitational potential energy of a system of objects is the sum of the gravitational potential energies of each pair of objects separately.

Since U is not a vector, there are no x or y components to consider, as would be the case with a vector. Finally, the potential energy given in Equation 12–8 applies to a mass m and the Earth, with mass M_E. More generally, if two point masses, m_1 and m_2, are separated by a distance r, their gravitational potential energy is

Gravitational Potential Energy, U

$$U = -G\frac{m_1m_2}{r} \qquad\qquad 12\text{–}9$$

SI unit: joule, J

In the next Example we use this result, and the fact that U is a scalar, to find the total gravitational potential energy for a system of three point masses.

EXAMPLE 12–5   SIMPLE ADDITION

Three masses are positioned as follows: $m_1 = 2.5$ kg is at the origin; $m_2 = 0.75$ kg is at $x = 0$, $y = 1.25$ m; and $m_3 = 0.75$ kg is at $x = 1.25$ m and $y = 1.25$ m. Find the total gravitational potential energy of this system.

PICTURE THE PROBLEM
The masses and their positions are shown in our sketch. The horizontal and vertical distances are $r = 1.25$ m; the diagonal distance is $\sqrt{2}r$.

STRATEGY
The potential energy associated with each pair of masses is given by Equation 12–9. The total potential energy of the system is the sum of the potential energy for each of the three pairs of masses.

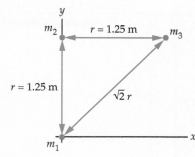

SOLUTION

1. Use Equation 12–9 to calculate the potential energy for masses 1 and 2:

$$U_{12} = -G\frac{m_1 m_2}{r_{12}}$$

$$= -(6.67 \times 10^{-11}\,\text{N} \cdot \text{m}^2/\text{kg}^2)\frac{(2.5\,\text{kg})(0.75\,\text{kg})}{(1.25\,\text{m})}$$

$$= -1.0 \times 10^{-10}\,\text{J}$$

2. Similarly, calculate the potential energy for masses 2 and 3:

$$U_{23} = -G\frac{m_2 m_3}{r_{23}}$$

$$= -(6.67 \times 10^{-11}\,\text{N} \cdot \text{m}^2/\text{kg}^2)\frac{(0.75\,\text{kg})(0.75\,\text{kg})}{(1.25\,\text{m})}$$

$$= -3.0 \times 10^{-11}\,\text{J}$$

3. Do the same calculation for masses 1 and 3:

$$U_{13} = -G\frac{m_1 m_3}{r_{13}}$$

$$= -(6.67 \times 10^{-11}\,\text{N} \cdot \text{m}^2/\text{kg}^2)\frac{(2.5\,\text{kg})(0.75\,\text{kg})}{\sqrt{2}(1.25\,\text{m})}$$

$$= -7.1 \times 10^{-11}\,\text{J}$$

4. The total potential energy is the sum of the three contributions calculated above:

$$U_{\text{total}} = U_{12} + U_{23} + U_{13}$$

$$= -1.0 \times 10^{-10}\,\text{J} - 3.0 \times 10^{-11}\,\text{J} - 7.1 \times 10^{-11}\,\text{J}$$

$$= -2.0 \times 10^{-10}\,\text{J}$$

INSIGHT
Note that the total gravitational potential energy of this system, $U_{\text{total}} = -2.0 \times 10^{-10}$ J, is less than it would be if the separation of the masses were to approach infinity, in which case $U_{\text{total}} = 0$. The implications of this change in potential energy, in terms of energy conservation, are considered in the next section.

PRACTICE PROBLEM
If the distance $r = 1.25$ m is reduced by a factor of two to $r = 0.625$ m, does the potential energy of the system increase, decrease, or stay the same? Verify your answer by calculating the potential energy in this case.   [**Answer:** The potential energy decreases; that is, it becomes more negative. We find $U = 2(-2.0 \times 10^{-10}$ J).]

Some related homework problems: Problem 42, Problem 43

12–5 Energy Conservation

Now that we know the gravitational potential energy, U, at an arbitrary distance from a spherical object, we can apply energy conservation to astronomical situations in the same way we applied it to systems near the Earth's surface in Chapter 8. To be specific, the mechanical energy, E, of an object of mass m a distance r from the Earth is

$$E = K + U = \tfrac{1}{2}mv^2 - G\frac{mM_E}{r} \qquad\qquad \text{12–10}$$

REAL-WORLD PHYSICS

The impact of meteorites

PROBLEM-SOLVING NOTE

Energy Conservation in Astronomical Systems

To apply conservation of energy to an object that moves far from the surface of a planet, one must use $U = -GmM/r$, where r is the distance from the center of the planet.

Using energy conservation—that is, setting the initial mechanical energy equal to the final mechanical energy—we can answer questions such as the following: Suppose that an asteroid has zero speed infinitely far from the Earth. If this asteroid were to fall directly toward the Earth, what speed would it have when it strikes the Earth's surface?

As you probably know, this is not an entirely academic question. Asteroids and comets, both large and small, have struck the Earth innumerable times during its history. In fact, a particularly large object appears to have struck the Earth on the Yucatan Peninsula in Mexico, near the town of Chicxulub, some 65 million years ago. Evidence suggests that this impact may have led to the mass extinctions of the Cretaceous period, during which the dinosaurs disappeared from the Earth. Unfortunately, such events are not limited to the distant past. For example, as recently as 50,000 years ago, an iron asteroid tens of meters in diameter and shining 10,000 times brighter than the Sun (from atmospheric heating) slammed into the ground near Winslow, Arizona, forming the 1.2-km-wide Barringer Meteor Crater. More recently yet, at sunrise on June 30, 1908, a relatively small stony asteroid streaked through the atmosphere and exploded at an altitude of several kilometers near the Tunguska River in Siberia. The energy released by the explosion was comparable to that of an H-bomb, and it flattened the forest for kilometers in all directions. One can only imagine the consequences if an event like this were to occur near a populated area. Finally, an uncomfortably close call occurred in the early evening of December 9, 1994, when an asteroid the size of a mountain passed the Earth at a distance only one-third the distance from the Earth to the Moon. Thus, though extremely unlikely, the scenarios depicted in movies such as *Armageddon* and *Deep Impact* are not completely unrealistic.

Returning to our original question, we can use energy conservation to determine the speed such an asteroid or comet might have when it hits the Earth. To begin, we assume the asteroid starts at rest, and hence its initial kinetic energy is zero, $K_i = 0$. In addition, the initial potential energy of the system, U_i, is also zero, since $U = -GmM_E/r$ approaches zero as r approaches infinity. As a result, the total initial mechanical energy of the asteroid–Earth system is zero: $E_i = K_i + U_i = 0$. Because gravity is a conservative force (as discussed in Section 8–1), the total mechanical energy remains constant as the asteroid falls toward the Earth. Thus, as the

 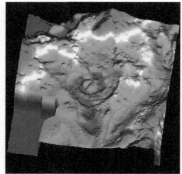

▲ Bodies from space have struck the Earth countless times in the past and continue to do so on a regular basis. Most such objects are relatively small, ranging in size from grains of dust to fist-sized rocks, and burn up from friction as they pass through the atmosphere, creating the bright streaks that we know as meteors. But larger objects, including the occasional comet or asteroid, also cross our path from time to time, and some of these make it to the surface—often with very dramatic results. The crater at left, in Rotorua, New Zealand, must be of relatively recent origin (thousands rather than millions of years old), since erosion has not yet erased this scar on the Earth's surface.

The image at right is a false-color gravity anomaly map of the Chicxulub impact crater in Mexico. The object that struck here some 65 million years ago may have produced such far-reaching climatic disruption that the dinosaurs and many other species became extinct as a result. At the center of the crater the strength of gravity is lower than normal (blue) because of the presence of low-density rock: debris from the impact and sediments that have accumulated in the crater.

asteroid moves closer to the Earth and U becomes increasingly negative, the kinetic energy K must become increasingly positive so that their sum, $U + K$, is always zero.

We now set the initial energy equal to the final energy to determine the final speed, v_f. Recalling that the final distance r is the radius of the Earth, R_E, we have

$$E_i = E_f$$
$$0 = \tfrac{1}{2}mv_f^2 - G\frac{mM_E}{R_E}$$

Solving for the final speed yields

$$v_f = \sqrt{\frac{2GM_E}{R_E}} \qquad\qquad 12\text{–}11$$

Substituting numerical values into this expression gives

$$v_f = \sqrt{\frac{2GM_E}{R_E}} = \sqrt{\frac{2(6.67 \times 10^{-11}\,\text{N}\cdot\text{m}^2/\text{kg}^2)(5.97 \times 10^{24}\,\text{kg})}{6.37 \times 10^6\,\text{m}}}$$
$$= 11{,}200\,\text{m/s} \ (25{,}000\,\text{mi/h}) \qquad\qquad 12\text{–}12$$

Thus, a typical asteroid hits the Earth moving at about 7.0 mi/s—about 16 times faster than a rifle bullet! Note that this result is independent of the asteroid's mass.

To help visualize energy conservation in this system, we plot the gravitational potential energy U in **Figure 12–15**. Also indicated in the plot is the total energy, $E = 0$. Since $U + K$ must always equal zero, the value of K goes up as the value of U goes down. This is illustrated graphically in the figure with the help of several histogram bars.

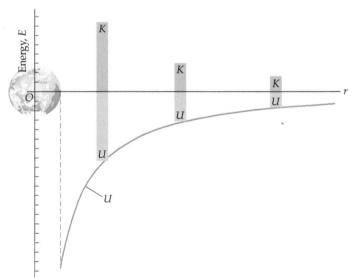

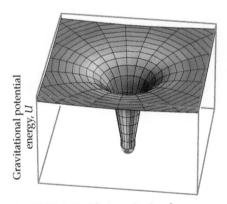

◀ **FIGURE 12–15 Potential and kinetic energies of an object falling toward Earth**

As an object with zero total energy moves closer to the Earth, its gravitational potential energy, U, becomes increasingly negative. In order for the total energy to remain zero, $E = U + K = 0$, it is necessary for the kinetic energy to become increasingly positive.

▲ **FIGURE 12–16 A gravitational potential "well"**

The illustration is a three-dimensional plot of the gravitational potential energy near an object such as the Earth. An object approaching the Earth speeds up as it "falls" into the gravitational potential well.

Another way to think about this is to imagine a smooth wooden or plastic surface constructed to have the same shape as the plot of U shown in Figure 12–15. An object placed on this surface has a gravitational potential energy proportional to the height of the surface above a given reference level. Thus, if a small block is allowed to slide without friction on the surface, it will move downhill and speed up as it drops lower in elevation. That is, its kinetic energy will increase as the potential energy of the system decreases. This is completely analogous to the behavior of an asteroid as it "falls" toward the Earth.

A somewhat more elaborate plot showing the same physics is presented in **Figure 12–16**. The two-dimensional surface in this case represents the potential energy function U as one moves away from the Earth in any direction. In particular, the dependence of U on distance r along any radial line in Figure 12–16 is the same as the shape of U versus r in Figure 12–15. Because the potential energy drops downward in such a plot, this type of situation is often referred to as a "potential well." If a marble is allowed to roll on such a surface, its motion is similar in many ways to the motion of an object near the Earth. In fact, if the marble is started with the right initial velocity, it will roll in a circular or elliptical "orbit" for a long time before falling into the center of the well. (Eventually, of course, the well does swallow up the marble. Though the retarding force of rolling friction is quite small, it still causes the marble to descend into a lower and lower orbit—just as air resistance causes a satellite to descend lower and lower into the Earth's atmosphere until it finally burns up.)

EXAMPLE 12–6 ARMAGEDDON RENDEZVOUS

In the movie *Armageddon*, a crew of hard-boiled oil drillers rendezvous with a menacing asteroid just as it passes the orbit of the Moon on its way toward Earth. Assuming the asteroid starts at rest infinitely far from the Earth, as in the previous discussion, find its speed when it passes the Moon's orbit. Assume the Moon orbits at a distance of $60R_E$ from the center of the Earth and that its gravitational influence may be neglected.

PICTURE THE PROBLEM
Our sketch shows the Earth, the Moon, and the asteroid. The initial position of the asteroid is at infinity, where its speed is zero. For the purposes of this problem, its final position is at the Moon's orbit, where its speed is v_f. At this point, the asteroid is heading directly for the Earth.

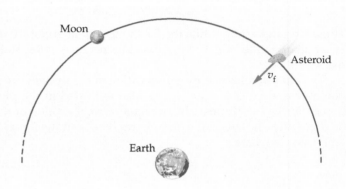

STRATEGY
The basic strategy is the same as that used to obtain the speed of an asteroid in Equation 12–12; namely, we set the initial energy equal to the final energy and solve for the final speed v_f. In this case, the final radius is $r = 60R_E$. As before, the initial energy is zero.

SOLUTION

1. Set the initial energy of the system equal to its final energy:

$$E_i = E_f$$

$$0 = \tfrac{1}{2}mv_f^2 - G\frac{mM_E}{60R_E}$$

2. Solve for the final speed, v_f:

$$v_f = \sqrt{\frac{2GM_E}{60R_E}} = \frac{1}{\sqrt{60}}\left(\sqrt{\frac{2GM_E}{R_E}}\right)$$

3. Substitute the numerical value given in Equation 12–12 for the quantity in parentheses:

$$v_f = \frac{1}{\sqrt{60}}(11{,}200 \text{ m/s}) = 1450 \text{ m/s} \sim 3200 \text{ mi/h}$$

INSIGHT
Note that the majority of the asteroid's increase in speed occurs after it passes the Moon. The reason for this can be seen in the accompanying plot of the gravitational potential energy, U.

Note that U drops downward more and more rapidly as the Earth is approached. Thus, while there is relatively little increase in K from infinite distance to $r = 60R_E$, there is a substantially larger increase in K from $r = 60R_E$ to $r = R_E$.

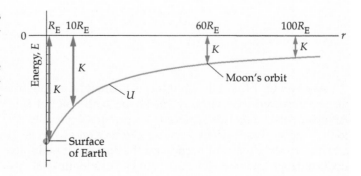

PRACTICE PROBLEM
At what distance from the center of the Earth is the asteroid's speed equal to 3535 m/s? **[Answer:** $r = 6.37 \times 10^7$ m = $10R_E$**]**

Some related homework problems: Problem 50, Problem 52

ACTIVE EXAMPLE 12-2 FIND THE DISTANCE TO A SATELLITE

A satellite in an elliptical orbit has a speed of 9.00 km/s when it is at its closest approach to the Earth (perigee). The satellite is 7.00×10^6 m from the center of the Earth at this time. When the satellite is at its greatest distance from the center of the Earth (apogee), its speed is 3.66 km/s. How far is the satellite from the center of the Earth at apogee? ($R_E = 6.37 \times 10^6$ m, $M_E = 5.97 \times 10^{24}$ kg)

SOLUTION *(Test your understanding by performing the calculations indicated in each step.)*

1. Set the energy at perigee, E_1, equal to the energy at apogee, E_2:

$$\tfrac{1}{2}mv_1{}^2 - GmM_E/r_1 = \tfrac{1}{2}mv_2{}^2 - GmM_E/r_2$$

2. Solve for $1/r_2$:

$$1/r_2 = 1/r_1 + \left(v_2{}^2 - v_1{}^2\right)/(2GM_E)$$

3. Substitute numerical values:

$$1/r_2 = 5.80 \times 10^{-8}\ \text{m}^{-1}$$

4. Invert to obtain r_2:

$$r_2 = 1.72 \times 10^7\ \text{m}$$

INSIGHT

In this case, apogee is about 2.5 times farther from the center of the Earth than perigee.

YOUR TURN

What is the speed of the satellite when it is 8.75×10^6 m from the center of the Earth?

*(Answers to **Your Turn** problems are given in the back of the book.)*

▲ Comet Hale-Bopp, one of the largest and brightest comets to visit our celestial neighborhood in recent decades, photographed in April 1997. While most of the planets and planetary satellites in the solar system have roughly circular orbits, the orbits of many comets are highly elliptical. In accordance with Kepler's second law, these objects spend most of their time moving slowly through cold, distant regions of the solar system (often far beyond the orbit of Pluto). Their visits to the inner solar system are infrequent and relatively brief.

Escape Speed

Resisting the pull of Earth's gravity has always held a fascination for the human species, from Daedalus and Icarus with their wings of feathers and wax, to Leonardo da Vinci and his flying machine, to the Montgolfier brothers and their hot-air balloons. In his 1865 novel, *From the Earth to the Moon*, Jules Verne imagined launching a spacecraft to the Moon by firing it straight upward from a cannon. Not a bad idea—if you could survive the initial blast. Today, rockets are fired into space using the same basic idea, though they smooth out the initial blast by burning their engines over a period of several minutes.

Suppose, then, that you would like to launch a rocket of mass m with an initial speed sufficient not only to reach the Moon, but to allow it to escape the Earth altogether. If we refer to this speed as the **escape speed** for the Earth, v_e, the initial energy of the rocket is

$$E_i = K_i + U_i = \tfrac{1}{2}mv_e{}^2 - G\frac{mM_E}{R_E}$$

If the rocket just barely escapes the Earth, its speed will decrease to zero as its distance from the Earth approaches infinity. Therefore, the rocket's final kinetic energy is zero, as is the potential energy of the system, since $U = -GmM_E/r$ goes to zero as $r \to \infty$. It follows that

$$E_f = K_f + U_f = 0 - 0 = 0$$

Equating these energies yields

$$\tfrac{1}{2}mv_e{}^2 - G\frac{mM_E}{R_E} = 0$$

Therefore, the escape speed from the Earth is

$$v_e = \sqrt{\frac{2GM_E}{R_E}} = 11{,}200\ \text{m/s} \approx 25{,}000\ \text{mi/h} \qquad \text{12–13}$$

Note that the escape speed is precisely the same as the speed of the asteroid calculated in Equation 12–12. This is not surprising when you consider that an object launched from the Earth to infinity is just the reverse of an object falling from infinity to the Earth.

The result given in Equation 12–13 can be applied to other astronomical objects as well by simply replacing M_E and R_E with the appropriate mass and radius for that object.

EXERCISE 12–5

Calculate the escape speed for an object launched from the Moon.

SOLUTION

For the Moon we use $M_m = 7.35 \times 10^{22}$ kg and $R_m = 1.74 \times 10^6$ m. With these values, the escape speed is

$$v_e = \sqrt{\frac{2GM_m}{R_m}} = \sqrt{\frac{2(6.67 \times 10^{-11}\,\text{N} \cdot \text{m}^2/\text{kg}^2)(7.35 \times 10^{22}\,\text{kg})}{1.74 \times 10^6\,\text{m}}}$$

$$= 2370 \text{ m/s } (5320 \text{ mi/h})$$

The relatively low escape speed of the Moon means that it is much easier to launch a rocket into space from the Moon than from the Earth. For example, the tiny lunar module that blasted off from the Moon to return the astronauts to Earth could not have come close to escaping from the Earth.

REAL-WORLD PHYSICS

Planetary atmospheres

Similarly, the Moon's low escape speed is the reason it has no atmosphere. Even if you could magically supply the Moon with an atmosphere, it would soon evaporate into space because the individual molecules in the air move with speeds great enough to escape. On the Earth, however, where the escape speed is much higher, gravity can prevent the rapidly moving molecules from moving off into space. Even so, light molecules, like hydrogen and helium, move faster for a given temperature than the heavier molecules like nitrogen and oxygen, as we shall see in Chapter 17. For this reason, the Earth's atmosphere contains virtually no hydrogen or helium. (In fact, helium was first discovered on the Sun, as we point out in Chapter 31; hence its name, which derives from the Greek word for the Sun, "helios.") Since a stable atmosphere is a likely requirement for the development of life, it follows that the escape speed is an important quantity when considering the possibility of life on other planets.

CONCEPTUAL CHECKPOINT 12–3   COMPARE ESCAPE SPEEDS

Is the escape speed for a 10-N rocket **(a)** equal to, **(b)** less than, or **(c)** greater than the escape speed for a 10,000-N rocket?

REASONING AND DISCUSSION

The derivation of the escape speed in Equation 12–13 shows that the mass of the rocket, m, cancels. Hence, the escape speed is the same for all objects, regardless of their mass. On the other hand, the kinetic energy required to give the 10,000-N rocket the escape speed is 1000 times greater than the kinetic energy required for the 10-N rocket.

ANSWER

(a) Equal. The escape speed is independent of the mass that is escaping.

EXAMPLE 12–7   HALF ESCAPE

Suppose Jules Verne's cannon launches a rocket straight upward with an initial speed equal to one-half the escape speed. How far from the center of the Earth does this rocket travel before momentarily coming to rest? (Ignore air resistance in the Earth's atmosphere.)

PICTURE THE PROBLEM

Our sketch shows the rocket launched vertically from the Earth's surface with an initial speed equal to half the escape speed, $v_0 = \frac{1}{2}v_e$. The rocket moves radially away from the Earth until it comes to rest, $v = 0$, at a distance r from the center of the Earth.

STRATEGY

Since we ignore air resistance, the final energy of the rocket, E_f, must be equal to its initial energy, E_0. Setting these energies equal determines the point where the rocket comes to rest.

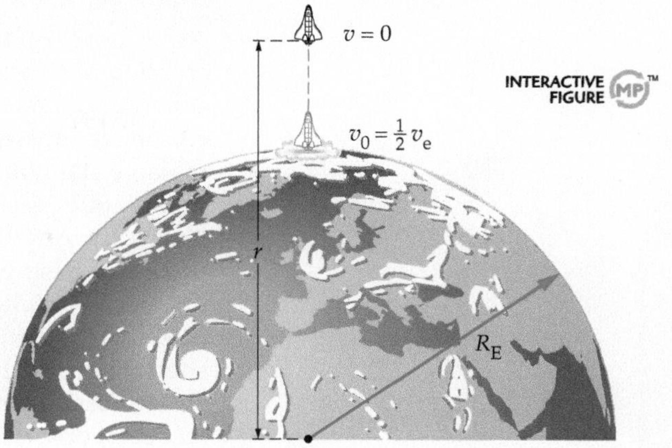

$v = 0$
INTERACTIVE FIGURE
$v_0 = \frac{1}{2}v_e$
r
R_E

SOLUTION

1. The initial speed, v_0, is one-half the escape speed. Use Equation 12–13 to write an expression for v_0:

$$v_0 = \tfrac{1}{2}v_e = \tfrac{1}{2}\sqrt{\frac{2GM_E}{R_E}} = \sqrt{\frac{GM_E}{2R_E}}$$

2. Write out the initial energy of the rocket, E_0:

$$E_0 = K_0 + U_0 = \tfrac{1}{2}mv_0^2 - \frac{GmM_E}{R_E}$$

$$= \tfrac{1}{2}m\left(\sqrt{\frac{GM_E}{2R_E}}\right)^2 - \frac{GmM_E}{R_E} = -\frac{3}{4}\frac{GmM_E}{R_E}$$

3. Write out the final energy of the rocket. Note that the rocket is a distance r from the center of the Earth when it comes to rest:

$$E_f = K_f + U_f = 0 - \frac{GmM_E}{r} = -\frac{GmM_E}{r}$$

4. Equate the initial and final energies:

$$-\frac{3}{4}\frac{GmM_E}{R_E} = -\frac{GmM_E}{r}$$

5. Solve the relation for r:

$$r = \tfrac{4}{3}R_E$$

INSIGHT

An initial speed of v_e allows the rocket to go to infinity before stopping. If the rocket is launched with half that initial speed, however, it can only rise to a height of $4R_E/3 - R_E = R_E/3$ above the Earth's surface. Quite a dramatic difference.

PRACTICE PROBLEM

Find the rocket's maximum distance from the center of the Earth, r, if its launch speed is $3v_e/4$. **[Answer:** $r = 16R_E/7 = 2.29R_E$**]**

Some related homework problems: Problem 49, Problem 56

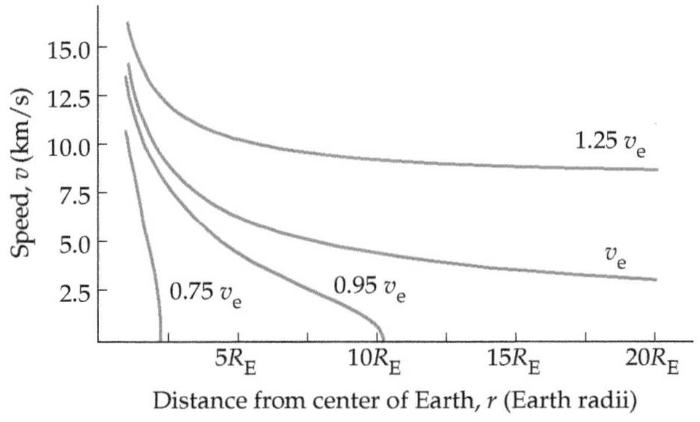

Speed, v (km/s)
15.0
12.5
10.0
7.5
5.0
2.5
1.25 v_e
v_e
0.75 v_e
0.95 v_e
$5R_E$
$10R_E$
$15R_E$
$20R_E$
Distance from center of Earth, r (Earth radii)

◀ **FIGURE 12–17 Speed of a rocket as a function of distance from the center of the Earth, *r*, for various vertical launch speeds**
The lower two curves show launch speeds that are less than the escape speed, v_e. In these cases the rocket comes to rest momentarily at a finite height above the Earth. The next higher curve shows the speed of a rocket launched with the escape speed, v_e. In this case, the rocket slows to zero speed as the distance approaches infinity. The top curve corresponds to a launch speed greater than the escape speed—this rocket has a finite speed even at infinite distance.

A plot of the speed of a rocket as a function of its distance from the center of the Earth is presented in **Figure 12–17** for a variety of initial speeds. Note that when the initial speed is less than the escape speed, the rocket comes to rest momentarily at a finite distance, r. In particular, if the launch speed is $0.75v_e$, as in the Practice Problem of Example 12–7, the rocket's maximum distance from the center of the Earth is $2.29R_E$.

Black Holes

As we can see from Equation 12–13, the escape speed of an object increases with increasing mass and decreasing radius. Thus, for example, if a massive star were to collapse to a relatively small size, its escape speed would become very large. According to Einstein's theory of general relativity, the escape speed of a compressed, massive star could even exceed the speed of light. In this case nothing—not even light—could escape from the star. For this reason, such objects are referred to as *black holes*. Anything entering a black hole would be making a one-way trip to an unknown destiny.

Since black holes cannot be seen directly, our evidence for their existence is indirect. However, we can predict that as matter is drawn toward a black hole it should become heated to the point where it would emit strong beams of X-rays before disappearing from view. X-ray beams matching these predictions have in fact been observed. These observations, coupled with a variety of others, give astronomers confidence that massive black holes reside at the core of many galaxies—including our own!

Finally, just as a black hole can bend a beam of light back on itself and prevent it from escaping, any massive object can bend light—at least a little. For example, light from distant stars is deflected as it passes by the Sun by 1.75 seconds of an arc (the size of a quarter at a distance of 1.8 miles). Light passing by an entire galaxy of stars or cluster of galaxies can be bent by significant amounts, however, as Figure 12–18 indicates. This effect is referred to as *gravitational lensing*, since the galaxies act much like the lenses we will study in Chapter 26. Because of gravitational lensing, the images of very distant galaxies or quasars in deep-space astronomical photographs sometimes appear in duplicate, in quadruplicate, or even spread out into circular arcs.

*12–6 Tides

The reason for the ocean tides that rise and fall twice a day was a perplexing and enduring mystery until Newton introduced his law of universal gravitation. Even Galileo, who made so many advances in physics and astronomy, could not explain the tides. However, with the understanding that a force is required to cause an object to move in a circular path, and that the force of gravity becomes weaker with distance, it is possible to describe the tides in detail. In this section we show how it can be done. In addition, we extend the basic idea of tides to several related phenomena.

To begin, consider the idealized situation shown in Figure 12–19 (a). Here we see an object of finite size (a moon or a planet, for example) orbiting a point mass. If all the mass of the object were concentrated at its center, the gravitational force exerted on it by the central mass would be precisely the amount needed to cause it to move in its circular path. Since the object is of finite size, however, the force exerted on various parts of it has different magnitudes. For example, points closer to the central mass experience a greater force than points farther away.

To see the effect of this variation in force, we use a dark red vector in Figure 12–19 (a) to indicate the force exerted by the central mass at three different points on the object. In addition, we use a light red vector to show the force that is required at each of these three points to cause a mass at that distance to orbit the central mass. Comparing these vectors, we see that the forces are identical at the center of the object—as expected. On the near side of the object, however, the force exerted by the central mass is larger than the force needed to hold the object in orbit, and on the far side the force due to the central mass is less than the force needed to hold the object in orbit. The result is that the near side of the object is pulled closer to the central mass and the far side tends to move farther from the central mass. This causes an egg-shaped deformation of the object, as indicated in Figure 12–19 (a).

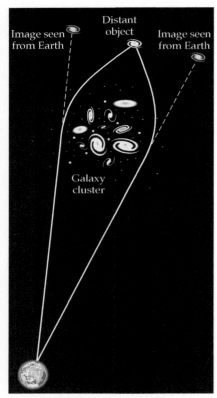

REAL-WORLD PHYSICS

Black holes and gravitational lensing

▲ **FIGURE 12–18 Gravitational lensing**
Astronomers often find that very distant objects seem to produce multiple images in their photographs. The cause is the gravitational attraction of intervening galaxies or clusters of galaxies, which are so massive that they can significantly bend the light from remote objects as it passes by them on its way to Earth.

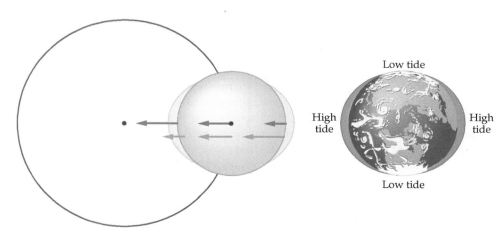

(a) The mechanism responsible for tides

(b) Tidal deformations on Earth

▲ **FIGURE 12–19 The reason for two tides a day**
(a) Tides are caused by a disparity between the gravitational force exerted at various points on a finite-sized object (dark red arrows) and the centripetal force needed for circular motion (light red arrows). Note that the gravitational force decreases with distance, as expected. On the other hand, the centripetal force required to keep an object moving in a circular path *increases* with distance. On the near side, therefore, the gravitational force is stronger than required, and the object is stretched inward. On the far side, the gravitational force is weaker than required, and the object stretches outward. **(b)** On the Earth, the water in the oceans responds more to the deforming effects of tides than do the solid rocks of the land. The result is two high tides and two low tides daily on opposite sides of the Earth.

Any two objects orbiting one another cause deformations of this type. For example, the Earth causes a deformation in the Moon, and the Moon causes a similar deformation in the Earth. In **Figure 12–19 (b)** we show the Earth and the waters of its ocean deformed into an egg shape. Since the waters in the oceans can flow, they deform much more than the underlying rocky surface of the Earth. As a result, the water level relative to the surface of the Earth is greater at the *tidal bulges* shown in the figure. As the Earth rotates about its axis, a person at a given location will observe two high tides and two low tides each day. This is the basic mechanism of the tides on Earth, but the actual situation is complicated by the shape of the coastline at different locations and by the additional tidal effects due to the Sun.

The Moon has no oceans, of course, but the tidal bulges produced in it by the Earth are the reason we see only one side of the Moon. Specifically, the Earth exerts gravitational forces on the tidal bulges of the Moon, causing them to point directly toward the Earth. If the Moon were to rotate slightly away from this alignment, the forces exerted by the Earth would cause a torque that would return the Moon to the original alignment. The net result is that the Moon's period of rotation about its axis is equal to its period of revolution about the Earth. This effect, known as **tidal locking**, is common among the various moons in the solar system.

A particularly interesting example of tidal locking is provided by Jupiter's moon Io, a site of intense volcanism (see the photo on p. 107). Io follows an elliptical orbit around Jupiter, and its tidal deformation is larger when it is closer to Jupiter than when it is farther away. As a result, each time Io orbits Jupiter it is squeezed into a greater deformation and then released. This continual flexing of

REAL-WORLD PHYSICS
Tides

REAL-WORLD PHYSICS
Tidal locking

◀ Tides on Earth are caused chiefly by the Moon's gravitational pull, though at full and new moon, when the Moon and Sun are aligned, the Sun's gravity can enhance the effect. In some places on Earth, such as the Bay of Fundy between Maine and Nova Scotia, local topographic conditions produce abnormally large tides.

Io causes its internal temperature to rise, just as a rubber ball gets warmer if you squeeze and release it in your hand over and over. It is this mechanism that is largely responsible for Io's ongoing volcanic activity.

REAL-WORLD PHYSICS
Roche limit and Saturn's rings

In extreme cases, tidal deformation can become so large that an object is literally torn apart. Since tidal deformation increases as a moon moves closer to the planet it orbits, there is a limiting orbital radius—known as the **Roche limit**—inside of which this breakup occurs. A most spectacular example of this effect can be seen in the rings of Saturn, all of which exist well within the Roche limit. The small chunks of ice and other materials that make up the rings may be the remains of a moon that moved too close to Saturn and was destroyed by tidal forces. On the other hand, they may represent material that tidal forces prevented from aggregating to form a moon in the first place. In either case, this dramatic debris field will now never coalesce to form a moon—tidal effects will not allow such a process to occur. Similar remarks apply to the smaller, much fainter rings that spacecraft have observed around Jupiter, Uranus, and Neptune.

THE BIG PICTURE PUTTING PHYSICS IN CONTEXT

LOOKING BACK

The general force of gravity, as presented in Equation 12–1, is a vector quantity. Therefore, vector calculations (Chapter 3) are important here. See, in particular, Example 12–1. We also use the connection between force and acceleration, $F = ma$ (Chapter 5), in Section 12–2.

The conservation of angular momentum (Chapter 11) plays a key role in gravity, leading to Kepler's second law in Section 12–3.

Just as the force of gravity is generalized in this chapter, so too is the gravitational potential energy. Thus, the expression $U = mgh$ (Chapter 8) is generalized to $U = -Gm_1m_2/r$ in Section 12–4. We then use this new form of the potential energy in situations involving energy conservation in Section 12–5.

LOOKING AHEAD

In Chapter 19 we shall see that the force between two electric charges, denoted q_1 and q_2, has exactly the same form as the general force of gravity between two masses, Equation 12–1. The electric force is referred to as Coulomb's law, and is presented in Equation 19–5.

The force between electric charges is conservative, and hence it leads to an electric potential energy that has the same form as the gravitational potential energy in Section 12–4. See Sections 20–1 and 20–2.

The analysis used to derive Kepler's third law in Section 12–3 is used again when we explore the Bohr model of the hydrogen atom in Chapter 31. The calculation is the same, but in hydrogen the Coulomb force between electric charges (Equation 19–5) is responsible for the orbital motion.

CHAPTER SUMMARY

12–1 NEWTON'S LAW OF UNIVERSAL GRAVITATION

The force of gravity between two point masses, m_1 and m_2, separated by a distance r is attractive and of magnitude

$$F = G\frac{m_1m_2}{r^2} \qquad \text{12–1}$$

G is the universal gravitation constant:

$$G = 6.67 \times 10^{-11}\,\text{N}\cdot\text{m}^2/\text{kg}^2 \qquad \text{12–2}$$

Gravity exerts an action-reaction pair of forces on m_1 and m_2; that is, the force exerted by gravity on m_1 is equal in magnitude but opposite in direction to the force exerted on m_2.

Inverse Square Dependence
The force of gravity decreases with distance, r, as $1/r^2$. This is referred to as an inverse square dependence.

Superposition
If more than one mass exerts a gravitational force on a given object, the net force is simply the vector sum of each force individually.

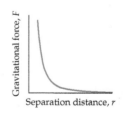

Gravitational force, F

Separation distance, r

12–2 GRAVITATIONAL ATTRACTION OF SPHERICAL BODIES

In calculating gravitational forces, spherical objects can be replaced by point masses.

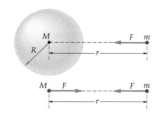

Uniform Sphere
If a mass m is outside a uniform sphere of mass M, the gravitational force between m and the sphere is equivalent to the force exerted by a point mass M located at the center of the sphere.

Acceleration of Gravity
Replacing the Earth with a point mass at its center, we find that the acceleration of gravity on the surface of the Earth is

$$g = \frac{GM_E}{R_E^2} \qquad \text{12–4}$$

Weighing the Earth
Cavendish was the first to determine the value of the universal gravitation constant G by direct experiment. Knowing G allows one to calculate the mass of the Earth:

$$M_E = \frac{gR_E^2}{G} \qquad \text{12–5}$$

12–3 KEPLER'S LAWS OF ORBITAL MOTION

Kepler determined three laws that describe the motion of the planets in our solar system. Newton showed that Kepler's laws are a direct consequence of his law of universal gravitation.

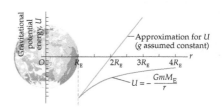

Kepler's First Law
The orbits of the planets are ellipses, with the Sun at one focus.

Kepler's Second Law
Planets sweep out equal area in equal time.

Kepler's Third Law
The period of a planet's orbit, T, is proportional to the 3/2 power of its average distance from the Sun, r:

$$T = \left(\frac{2\pi}{\sqrt{GM_s}}\right)r^{3/2} = (\text{constant})r^{3/2} \qquad \text{12–7}$$

12–4 GRAVITATIONAL POTENTIAL ENERGY

The gravitational potential energy, U, between two point masses m_1 and m_2 separated by a distance r is

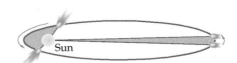

$$U = -G\frac{m_1 m_2}{r} \qquad \text{12–9}$$

Zero Level
The zero level of the gravitational potential energy between two point masses is chosen to be at infinite separation of the two masses.

U Is a Scalar
The gravitational potential energy, U, is a scalar. Therefore, the total potential energy for a group of objects is simply the numerical sum of the potential energy associated with each pair of masses.

12–5 ENERGY CONSERVATION

With the gravitational potential energy given in Section 12–4, energy conservation can be applied to astronomical situations.

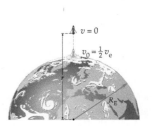

Total Mechanical Energy
An object with mass m, speed v, and at a distance r from the center of the Earth has a total energy given by

$$E = K + U = \frac{1}{2}mv^2 - \frac{GmM_E}{r} \qquad \text{12–10}$$

Escape Speed

An object launched from the surface of the Earth with the escape speed v_e can move infinitely far from the Earth. In the limit of infinite separation, the object slows to zero speed.

The escape speed for the Earth is given by

$$v_e = \sqrt{\frac{2GM_E}{R_E}} \qquad\qquad 12\text{–}13$$

Its numerical value is 11,200 m/s = 25,000 mi/h. A similar expression can be applied to other astronomical bodies.

*12–6   TIDES

Tides result from the variation of the gravitational force from one side of an astronomical object to the other side.

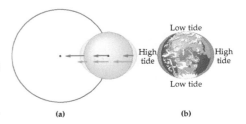

Tidal Locking

Tidal locking occurs when one astronomical object always points its tidal bulge at the object it orbits.

Roche Limit

Tidal deformation increases as an astronomical object moves closer to the body it orbits. At the Roche limit, the tidal deformation is so great that it breaks the object into small pieces.

PROBLEM-SOLVING SUMMARY

Type of Problem	Relevant Physical Concepts	Related Examples
Find the force due to gravity.	The magnitude of the force is given by Newton's law of universal gravitation, $F = Gm_1m_2/r^2$. The direction of the force is attractive and along the line connecting m_1 and m_2. If more than one force is involved, the net force is the vector sum of the individual forces.	Examples 12–1, 12–2, 12–3
Relate the period of a planet to the radius of its orbit and the mass of the body it orbits.	Use Kepler's third law, $T = \left(2\pi/\sqrt{GM}\right)r^{3/2}$.	Example 12–4 Active Example 12–1
Determine the speed of an object at a particular location, given its initial speed and location.	Use energy conservation, with the gravitational potential energy given by $U = -Gm_1m_2/r$.	Examples 12–6, 12–7 Active Example 12–2

CONCEPTUAL QUESTIONS

For instructor-assigned homework, go to www.masteringphysics.com

(Answers to odd-numbered Conceptual Questions can be found in the back of the book.)

1. It is often said that astronauts in orbit experience weightlessness because they are beyond the pull of Earth's gravity. Is this statement correct? Explain.

2. When a person passes you on the street, you do not feel a gravitational tug. Explain.

3. Two objects experience a gravitational attraction. Give a reason why the gravitational force between them does not depend on the sum of their masses.

4. Imagine bringing the tips of your index fingers together. Each finger contains a certain finite mass, and the distance between them goes to zero as they come into contact. From the force law $F = Gm_1m_2/r^2$ one might conclude that the attractive force between the fingers is infinite, and, therefore, that your fingers must remain forever stuck together. What is wrong with this argument?

5. Does the radius vector of Mars sweep out the same amount of area per time as that of the Earth? Why or why not?

6. When a communications satellite is placed in a geosynchronous orbit above the equator, it remains fixed over a given point on the ground. Is it possible to put a satellite into an orbit so that it remains fixed above the North Pole? Explain.

7. **The Mass of Pluto** On June 22, 1978, James Christy made the first observation of a moon orbiting Pluto. Until that time the mass of Pluto was not known, but with the discovery of its moon, Charon, its mass could be calculated with some accuracy. Explain.

8. Rockets are launched into space from Cape Canaveral in an easterly direction. Is there an advantage to launching to the east versus launching to the west? Explain.

9. One day in the future you may take a pleasure cruise to the Moon. While there you might climb a lunar mountain and throw a rock horizontally from its summit. If, in principle, you could throw the rock fast enough, it might end up hitting you in the back. Explain.

10. Apollo astronauts orbiting the Moon at low altitude noticed occasional changes in their orbit that they attributed to localized concentrations of mass below the lunar surface. Just what effect would such "mascons" have on their orbit?

11. If you light a candle on the space shuttle—which would not be a good idea—would it burn the same as on the Earth? Explain.

12. The force exerted by the Sun on the Moon is more than twice the force exerted by the Earth on the Moon. Should the Moon be thought of as orbiting the Earth or the Sun? Explain.

13. **The Path of the Moon** The Earth and Moon exert gravitational forces on one another as they orbit the Sun. As a result, the path they follow is not the simple circular orbit you would expect if either one orbited the Sun alone. Occasionally you will see a suggestion that the Moon follows a path like a sine wave centered on a circular path, as in the upper part of **Figure 12–20**. This is *incorrect*. The Moon's path is qualitatively like that shown in the lower part of Figure 12–20. Explain. (Refer to Conceptual Question 12.)

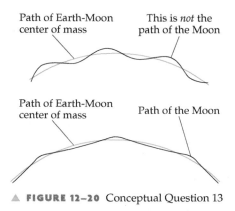

▲ **FIGURE 12–20** Conceptual Question 13

PROBLEMS AND CONCEPTUAL EXERCISES

Note: Answers to odd-numbered Problems and Conceptual Exercises can be found in the back of the book. **IP** *denotes an integrated problem, with both conceptual and numerical parts;* **BIO** *identifies problems of biological or medical interest;* **CE** *indicates a conceptual exercise.* **Predict/Explain** *problems ask for two responses:* **(a)** *your prediction of a physical outcome, and* **(b)** *the best explanation among three provided. On all problems, red bullets (•, ••, •••) are used to indicate the level of difficulty.*

SECTION 12–1 NEWTON'S LAW OF UNIVERSAL GRAVITATION

1. • **CE** System A has masses m and m separated by a distance r; system B has masses m and $2m$ separated by a distance $2r$; system C has masses $2m$ and $3m$ separated by a distance $2r$; and system D has masses $4m$ and $5m$ separated by a distance $3r$. Rank these systems in order of increasing gravitational force. Indicate ties where appropriate.

2. • In each hand you hold a 0.16-kg apple. What is the gravitational force exerted by each apple on the other when their separation is **(a)** 0.25 m and **(b)** 0.50 m?

3. • A 6.1-kg bowling ball and a 7.2-kg bowling ball rest on a rack 0.75 m apart. **(a)** What is the force of gravity exerted on each of the balls by the other ball? **(b)** At what separation is the force of gravity between the balls equal to 2.0×10^{-9} N?

4. • A communications satellite with a mass of 480 kg is in a circular orbit about the Earth. The radius of the orbit is 35,000 km as measured from the center of the Earth. Calculate **(a)** the weight of the satellite on the surface of the Earth and **(b)** the gravitational force exerted on the satellite by the Earth when it is in orbit.

5. • **The Attraction of Ceres** Ceres, the largest asteroid known, has a mass of roughly 8.7×10^{20} kg. If Ceres passes within 14,000 km of the spaceship in which you are traveling, what force does it exert on you? (Use an approximate value for your mass, and treat yourself and the asteroid as point objects.)

6. • In one hand you hold a 0.11-kg apple, in the other hand a 0.24-kg orange. The apple and orange are separated by 0.85 m. What is the magnitude of the force of gravity that **(a)** the orange exerts on the apple and **(b)** the apple exerts on the orange?

7. •• **IP** A spaceship of mass m travels from the Earth to the Moon along a line that passes through the center of the Earth and the center of the Moon. **(a)** At what distance from the center of the Earth is the force due to the Earth twice the magnitude of the force due to the Moon? **(b)** How does your answer to part (a) depend on the mass of the spaceship? Explain.

8. •• At new moon, the Earth, Moon, and Sun are in a line, as indicated in **Figure 12–21**. Find the direction and magnitude of the net gravitational force exerted on **(a)** the Earth, **(b)** the Moon, and **(c)** the Sun.

▲ **FIGURE 12–21** Problem 8

9. •• When the Earth, Moon, and Sun form a right triangle, with the Moon located at the right angle, as shown in **Figure 12–22**, the Moon is in its third-quarter phase. (The Earth is viewed here from above its North Pole.) Find the magnitude and direction of the net force exerted on the Moon. Give the direction relative to the line connecting the Moon and the Sun.

▲ **FIGURE 12–22** Problems 9, 10, and 73

10. •• Repeat the previous problem, this time finding the magnitude and direction of the net force acting on the Sun. Give the direction relative to the line connecting the Sun and the Moon.

11. •• **IP** Three 6.75-kg masses are at the corners of an equilateral triangle and located in space far from any other masses. **(a)** If the sides of the triangle are 1.25 m long, find the magnitude of the net force exerted on each of the three masses. **(b)** How does your answer to part (a) change if the sides of the triangle are doubled in length?

12. •• **IP** Four masses are positioned at the corners of a rectangle, as indicated in **Figure 12–23**. **(a)** Find the magnitude and direction of the net force acting on the 2.0-kg mass. **(b)** How do your answers to part (a) change (if at all) if all sides of the rectangle are doubled in length?

▲ **FIGURE 12–23** Problems 12 and 42

13. ••• Suppose that three astronomical objects (1, 2, and 3) are observed to lie on a line, and that the distance from object 1 to object 3 is D. Given that object 1 has four times the mass of object 3 and seven times the mass of object 2, find the distance between objects 1 and 2 for which the net force on object 2 is zero.

SECTION 12–2 GRAVITATIONAL ATTRACTION OF SPHERICAL BODIES

14. • Find the acceleration due to gravity on the surface of (a) Mercury and (b) Venus.

15. • At what altitude above the Earth's surface is the acceleration due to gravity equal to $g/2$?

16. • Two 6.7-kg bowling balls, each with a radius of 0.11 m, are in contact with one another. What is the gravitational attraction between the bowling balls?

17. • What is the acceleration due to Earth's gravity at a distance from the center of the Earth equal to the orbital radius of the Moon?

18. • **Gravity on Titan** Titan is the largest moon of Saturn and the only moon in the solar system known to have a substantial atmosphere. Find the acceleration due to gravity on Titan's surface, given that its mass is 1.35×10^{23} kg and its radius is 2570 km.

19. •• **IP** At a certain distance from the center of the Earth, a 4.6-kg object has a weight of 2.2 N. (a) Find this distance. (b) If the object is released at this location and allowed to fall toward the Earth, what is its initial acceleration? (c) If the object is now moved twice as far from the Earth, by what factor does its weight change? Explain. (d) By what factor does its initial acceleration change? Explain.

20. •• The acceleration due to gravity on the Moon's surface is known to be about one-sixth the acceleration due to gravity on the Earth. Given that the radius of the Moon is roughly one-quarter that of the Earth, find the mass of the Moon in terms of the mass of the Earth.

21. •• **IP An Extraterrestrial Volcano** Several volcanoes have been observed erupting on the surface of Jupiter's closest Galilean moon, Io. Suppose that material ejected from one of these volcanoes reaches a height of 5.00 km after being projected straight upward with an initial speed of 134 m/s. Given that the radius of Io is 1820 km, (a) outline a strategy that allows you to calculate the mass of Io. (b) Use your strategy to calculate Io's mass.

22. •• **IP Verne's Trip to the Moon** In his novel *From the Earth to the Moon*, Jules Verne imagined that astronauts inside a spaceship would walk on the floor of the cabin when the force exerted on the ship by the Earth was greater than the force exerted by the Moon. When the force exerted by the Moon was greater, he thought the astronauts would walk on the ceiling of the cabin. (a) At what distance from the center of the Earth would the forces exerted on the spaceship by the Earth and the Moon be equal? (b) Explain why Verne's description of gravitational effects is incorrect.

23. ••• Consider an asteroid with a radius of 19 km and a mass of 3.35×10^{15} kg. Assume the asteroid is roughly spherical. (a) What is the acceleration due to gravity on the surface of the asteroid? (b) Suppose the asteroid spins about an axis through its center, like the Earth, with a rotational period T. What is the smallest value T can have before loose rocks on the asteroid's equator begin to fly off the surface?

SECTION 12–3 KEPLER'S LAWS OF ORBITAL MOTION

24. • **CE Predict/Explain The Speed of the Earth** The orbital speed of the Earth is greatest around January 4 and least around July 4. (a) Is the distance from the Earth to the Sun on January 4 greater than, less than, or equal to its distance from the Sun on July 4? (b) Choose the *best explanation* from among the following:
    I. The Earth's orbit is circular, with equal distance from the Sun at all times.
    II. The Earth sweeps out equal area in equal time, thus it must be closer to the Sun when it is moving faster.
    III. The greater the speed of the Earth, the greater its distance from the Sun.

25. • **CE** A satellite orbits the Earth in a circular orbit of radius r. At some point its rocket engine is fired in such a way that its speed increases rapidly by a small amount. As a result, do the (a) apogee distance and (b) perigee distance increase, decrease, or stay the same?

26. • **CE** Repeat the previous problem, only this time with the rocket engine of the satellite fired in such a way as to slow the satellite.

27. • **CE Predict/Explain The Earth–Moon Distance Is Increasing** Laser reflectors left on the surface of the Moon by the Apollo astronauts show that the average distance from the Earth to the Moon is increasing at the rate of 3.8 cm per year. (a) As a result, will the length of the month increase, decrease, or remain the same? (b) Choose the *best explanation* from among the following:
    I. The greater the radius of an orbit, the greater the period, which implies a longer month.
    II. The length of the month will remain the same due to conservation of angular momentum.
    III. The speed of the Moon is greater with increasing radius; therefore, the length of the month will be less.

28. • **Apollo Missions** On Apollo missions to the Moon, the command module orbited at an altitude of 110 km above the lunar surface. How long did it take for the command module to complete one orbit?

29. • Find the orbital speed of a satellite in a geosynchronous circular orbit 3.58×10^7 m above the surface of the Earth.

30. • **An Extrasolar Planet** In July of 1999 a planet was reported to be orbiting the Sun-like star Iota Horologii with a period of 320 days. Find the radius of the planet's orbit, assuming that Iota Horologii has the same mass as the Sun. (This planet is presumably similar to Jupiter, but it may have large, rocky moons that enjoy a relatively pleasant climate.)

31. • Phobos, one of the moons of Mars, orbits at a distance of 9378 km from the center of the red planet. What is the orbital period of Phobos?

32. • The largest moon in the solar system is Ganymede, a moon of Jupiter. Ganymede orbits at a distance of 1.07×10^9 m from the center of Jupiter with an orbital period of about 6.18×10^5 s. Using this information, find the mass of Jupiter.

33. •• **IP An Asteroid with Its Own Moon** The asteroid 243 Ida has its own small moon, Dactyl. (See the photo on p. 390) (a) Outline a strategy to find the mass of 243 Ida, given that the orbital radius of Dactyl is 89 km and its period is 19 hr. (b) Use your strategy to calculate the mass of 243 Ida.

34. •• **GPS Satellites** GPS (Global Positioning System) satellites orbit at an altitude of 2.0×10^7 m. Find **(a)** the orbital period, and **(b)** the orbital speed of such a satellite.

35. •• **IP** Two satellites orbit the Earth, with satellite 1 at a greater altitude than satellite 2. **(a)** Which satellite has the greater orbital speed? Explain. **(b)** Calculate the orbital speed of a satellite that orbits at an altitude of one Earth radius above the surface of the Earth. **(c)** Calculate the orbital speed of a satellite that orbits at an altitude of two Earth radii above the surface of the Earth.

36. •• **IP** Calculate the orbital periods of satellites that orbit **(a)** one Earth radius above the surface of the Earth and **(b)** two Earth radii above the surface of the Earth. **(c)** How do your answers to parts (a) and (b) depend on the mass of the satellites? Explain. **(d)** How do your answers to parts (a) and (b) depend on the mass of the Earth? Explain.

37. •• **IP** The Martian moon Deimos has an orbital period that is greater than the other Martian moon, Phobos. Both moons have approximately circular orbits. **(a)** Is Deimos closer to or farther from Mars than Phobos? Explain. **(b)** Calculate the distance from the center of Mars to Deimos given that its orbital period is 1.10×10^5 s.

38. ••• **Binary Stars** Centauri A and Centauri B are binary stars with a separation of 3.45×10^{12} m and an orbital period of 2.52×10^9 s. Assuming the two stars are equally massive (which is approximately the case), determine their mass.

39. ••• Find the speed of Centauri A and Centauri B, using the information given in the previous problem.

SECTION 12–4   GRAVITATIONAL POTENTIAL ENERGY

40. • **Sputnik** The first artificial satellite to orbit the Earth was Sputnik I, launched October 4, 1957. The mass of Sputnik I was 83.5 kg, and its distances from the center of the Earth at apogee and perigee were 7330 km and 6610 km, respectively. Find the difference in gravitational potential energy for Sputnik I as it moved from apogee to perigee.

41. •• **CE Predict/Explain** **(a)** Is the amount of energy required to get a spacecraft from the Earth to the Moon greater than, less than, or equal to the energy required to get the same spacecraft from the Moon to the Earth? **(b)** Choose the *best explanation* from among the following:
    I. The escape speed of the Moon is less than that of the Earth; therefore, less energy is required to leave the Moon.
    II. The situation is symmetric, and hence the same amount of energy is required to travel in either direction.
    III. It takes more energy to go from the Moon to the Earth because the Moon is orbiting the Earth.

42. •• **IP** Consider the four masses shown in Figure 12–23. **(a)** Find the total gravitational potential energy of this system. **(b)** How does your answer to part (a) change if all the masses in the system are doubled? **(c)** How does your answer to part (a) change if, instead, all the sides of the rectangle are halved in length?

43. •• Calculate the gravitational potential energy of a 8.8-kg mass **(a)** on the surface of the Earth and **(b)** at an altitude of 350 km. **(c)** Take the difference between the results for parts (b) and (a), and compare with mgh, where $h = 350$ km.

44. •• Two 0.59-kg basketballs, each with a radius of 12 cm, are just touching. How much energy is required to change the separation between the centers of the basketballs to **(a)** 1.0 m and **(b)** 10.0 m? (Ignore any other gravitational interactions.)

45. •• Find the minimum kinetic energy needed for a 39,000-kg rocket to escape **(a)** the Moon or **(b)** the Earth.

SECTION 12–5   ENERGY CONSERVATION

46. • **CE Predict/Explain** Suppose the Earth were to suddenly shrink to half its current diameter, with its mass remaining constant. **(a)** Would the escape speed of the Earth increase, decrease, or stay the same? **(b)** Choose the *best explanation* from among the following:
    I. Since the radius of the Earth would be smaller, the escape speed would also be smaller.
    II. The Earth would have the same amount of mass, and hence its escape speed would be unchanged.
    III. The force of gravity would be much stronger on the surface of the compressed Earth, leading to a greater escape speed.

47. • **CE** Is the energy required to launch a rocket vertically to a height h greater than, less than, or equal to the energy required to put the same rocket into orbit at the height h? Explain.

48. • Suppose one of the Global Positioning System satellites has a speed of 4.46 km/s at perigee and a speed of 3.64 km/s at apogee. If the distance from the center of the Earth to the satellite at perigee is 2.00×10^4 km, what is the corresponding distance at apogee?

49. • **Meteorites from Mars** Several meteorites found in Antarctica are believed to have come from Mars, including the famous ALH84001 meteorite that some believe contains fossils of ancient life on Mars. Meteorites from Mars are thought to get to Earth by being blasted off the Martian surface when a large object (such as an asteroid or a comet) crashes into the planet. What speed must a rock have to escape Mars?

The meteorite ALH84001 (left), dislodged from the Martian surface by a tremendous impact, drifted through space for millions of years before falling to Earth in Antarctica about 13,000 years ago. The electron micrograph at right shows tubular structures within the meteorite; some scientists think they are traces of primitive, bacteria-like organisms that may have lived on Mars billions of years ago. (Problem 49)

50. • Referring to Example 12–1, if the *Millennium Eagle* is at rest at point A, what is its speed at point B?

51. • What is the launch speed of a projectile that rises vertically above the Earth to an altitude equal to one Earth radius before coming to rest momentarily?

52. • A projectile launched vertically from the surface of the Moon rises to an altitude of 365 km. What was the projectile's initial speed?

53. • Find the escape velocity for **(a)** Mercury and **(b)** Venus.

54. •• **IP Halley's Comet** Halley's comet, which passes around the Sun every 76 years, has an elliptical orbit. When closest to the Sun (perihelion) it is at a distance of 8.823×10^{10} m and moves with a speed of 54.6 km/s. The greatest distance between Halley's comet and the Sun (aphelion) is 6.152×10^{12} m. **(a)** Is the speed of Halley's comet greater than or less than 54.6 km/s

when it is at aphelion? Explain. **(b)** Calculate its speed at aphelion.

55. •• **The End of the Lunar Module** On Apollo Moon missions, the lunar module would blast off from the Moon's surface and dock with the command module in lunar orbit. After docking, the lunar module would be jettisoned and allowed to crash back onto the lunar surface. Seismometers placed on the Moon's surface by the astronauts would then pick up the resulting seismic waves. Find the impact speed of the lunar module, given that it is jettisoned from an orbit 110 km above the lunar surface moving with a speed of 1630 m/s.

56. •• If a projectile is launched vertically from the Earth with a speed equal to the escape speed, how high above the Earth's surface is it when its speed is half the escape speed?

57. •• Suppose a planet is discovered orbiting a distant star. If the mass of the planet is 10 times the mass of the Earth, and its radius is one-tenth the Earth's radius, how does the escape speed of this planet compare with that of the Earth?

58. •• A projectile is launched vertically from the surface of the Moon with an initial speed of 1050 m/s. At what altitude is the projectile's speed one-half its initial value?

59. •• To what radius would the Sun have to be contracted for its escape speed to equal the speed of light? (Black holes have escape speeds greater than the speed of light; hence we see no light from them.)

60. •• **IP** Two baseballs, each with a mass of 0.148 kg, are separated by a distance of 395 m in outer space, far from any other objects. **(a)** If the balls are released from rest, what speed do they have when their separation has decreased to 145 m? **(b)** Suppose the mass of the balls is doubled. Would the speed found in part (a) increase, decrease, or stay the same? Explain.

61. ••• On Earth, a person can jump vertically and rise to a height *h*. What is the radius of the largest spherical asteroid from which this person could escape by jumping straight upward? Assume that each cubic meter of the asteroid has a mass of 3500 kg.

*SECTION 12–6 TIDES

62. •• As will be shown in Problem 63, the magnitude of the tidal force exerted on an object of mass *m* and length *a* is approximately $4GmMa/r^3$. In this expression, *M* is the mass of the body causing the tidal force and *r* is the distance from the center of *m* to the center of *M*. Suppose you are 1 million miles away from a black hole whose mass is a million times that of the Sun. **(a)** Estimate the tidal force exerted on your body by the black hole. **(b)** At what distance will the tidal force be approximately 10 times greater than your weight?

63. ••• A dumbbell has a mass *m* on either end of a rod of length 2*a*. The center of the dumbbell is a distance *r* from the center of the Earth, and the dumbbell is aligned radially. If $r \gg a$, show that the difference in the gravitational force exerted on the two masses by the Earth is approximately $4GmM_Ea/r^3$. (*Note:* The difference in force causes a tension in the rod connecting the masses. We refer to this as a *tidal force.*) [*Hint:* Use the fact that $1/(r-a)^2 - 1/(r+a)^2 \sim 4a/r^3$ for $r \gg a$.]

64. ••• Referring to the previous problem, suppose the rod connecting the two masses *m* is removed. In this case, the only force between the two masses is their mutual gravitational attraction. In addition, suppose the masses are spheres of radius *a* and mass $m = \frac{4}{3}\pi a^3 \rho$ that touch each other. (The Greek letter ρ stands for the density of the masses.) **(a)** Write an expression for the gravitational force between the masses *m*. **(b)** Find the distance from the center of the Earth, *r*, for which the gravitational force found in part (a) is equal to the tidal force found in Problem 63.

This distance is known as the *Roche limit*. **(c)** Calculate the Roche limit for Saturn, assuming $\rho = 3330$ kg/m³. (The famous rings of Saturn are within the Roche limit for that planet. Thus, the innumerable small objects, composed mostly of ice, that make up the rings will never coalesce to form a moon.)

GENERAL PROBLEMS

65. • **CE** You weigh yourself on a scale inside an airplane flying due east above the equator. If the airplane now turns around and heads due west with the same speed, will the reading on the scale increase, decrease, or stay the same? Explain.

66. • **CE** Rank objects A, B, and C in **Figure 12–24** in order of increasing net gravitational force experienced by the object. Indicate ties where appropriate.

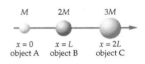

$x = 0$ $x = L$ $x = 2L$
object A   object B   object C

▲ **FIGURE 12–24**
Problems 66 and 67

67. • **CE** Referring to Figure 12–24, rank objects A, B, and C in order of increasing initial acceleration each would experience if it alone were allowed to move. Indicate ties where appropriate.

68. • **CE** When the Moon is in its new-moon position (directly between the Earth and the Sun), does the net force exerted on it by the Sun and the Earth point toward the Sun, or point toward the Earth? Explain. (Refer to Conceptual Questions 12 and 13 as well as Figure 12–20.)

69. • **CE** A satellite goes through one complete orbit of the Earth. **(a)** Is the net work done on it by the Earth's gravitational force positive, negative, or zero? Explain. **(b)** Does your answer to part (a) depend on whether the orbit is circular or elliptical?

70. • **CE The Crash of Skylab** Skylab, the largest spacecraft ever to fall back to the Earth, met its fiery end on July 11, 1979, after flying directly over Everett, WA, on its last orbit. On the *CBS Evening News* the night before the crash, anchorman Walter Cronkite, in his rich baritone voice, made the following statement: "NASA says there is a little chance that Skylab will land in a populated area." After the commercial, he immediately corrected himself by saying, "I meant to say '*there is little chance*' Skylab will hit a populated area." In fact, it landed primarily in the Indian Ocean off the west coast of Australia, though several pieces were recovered near the town of Esperance, Australia, which later sent the U.S. State Department a $400 bill for littering. The cause of Skylab's crash was the friction it experienced in the upper reaches of the Earth's atmosphere. As the radius of Skylab's orbit decreased, did its speed increase, decrease, or stay the same? Explain.

71. • Consider a system consisting of three masses on the *x* axis. Mass $m_1 = 1.00$ kg is at $x = 1.00$ m; mass $m_2 = 2.00$ kg is at $x = 2.00$ m; and mass $m_3 = 3.00$ kg is at $x = 3.00$ m. What is the total gravitational potential energy of this system?

72. •• An astronaut exploring a distant solar system lands on an unnamed planet with a radius of 3860 km. When the astronaut jumps upward with an initial speed of 3.10 m/s, she rises to a height of 0.580 m. What is the mass of the planet?

73. •• **IP** When the Moon is in its third-quarter phase, the Earth, Moon, and Sun form a right triangle, as shown in Figure 12–22. Calculate the magnitude of the force exerted on the Moon by **(a)** the Earth and **(b)** the Sun. **(c)** Does it make more sense to think of the Moon as orbiting the Sun, with a small effect due to the Earth, or as orbiting the Earth, with a small effect due to the Sun?

74. •• An equilateral triangle 10.0 m on a side has a 1.00-kg mass at one corner, a 2.00-kg mass at another corner, and a 3.00-kg mass at the third corner (**Figure 12–25**). Find the magnitude and direction of the net force acting on the 1.00-kg mass.

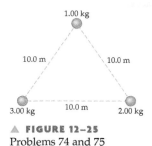

▲ FIGURE 12–25
Problems 74 and 75

75. •• Suppose that each of the three masses in Figure 12–25 is replaced by a mass of 5.95 kg and radius 0.0714 m. If the balls are released from rest, what speed will they have when they collide at the center of the triangle? Ignore gravitational effects from any other objects.

76. •• **A Near Miss!** In the early morning hours of June 14, 2002, the Earth had a remarkably close encounter with an asteroid the size of a small city. The previously unknown asteroid, now designated 2002 MN, remained undetected until three days after it had passed the Earth. At its closest approach, the asteroid was 73,600 miles from the center of the Earth—about a third of the distance to the Moon. **(a)** Find the speed of the asteroid at closest approach, assuming its speed at infinite distance to be zero and considering only its interaction with the Earth. **(b)** Observations indicate the asteroid to have a diameter of about 2.0 km. Estimate the kinetic energy of the asteroid at closest approach, assuming it has an average density of 3.33 g/cm^3. (For comparison, a 1-megaton nuclear weapon releases about 5.6×10^{15} J of energy.)

77. •• **IP** Suppose a planet is discovered that has the same amount of mass in a given volume as the Earth, but has half its radius. **(a)** Is the acceleration due to gravity on this planet more than, less than, or the same as the acceleration due to gravity on the Earth? Explain. **(b)** Calculate the acceleration due to gravity on this planet.

78. •• **IP** Suppose a planet is discovered that has the same total mass as the Earth, but half its radius. **(a)** Is the acceleration due to gravity on this planet more than, less than, or the same as the acceleration due to gravity on the Earth? Explain. **(b)** Calculate the acceleration due to gravity on this planet.

79. •• Show that the speed of a satellite in a circular orbit a height h above the surface of the Earth is

$$v = \sqrt{\frac{GM_E}{R_E + h}}$$

80. •• In a binary star system, two stars orbit about their common center of mass, as shown in **Figure 12–26**. If $r_2 = 2r_1$, what is the ratio of the masses m_2/m_1 of the two stars?

81. •• Find the orbital period of the binary star system described in the previous problem.

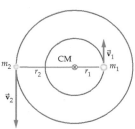

▲ FIGURE 12–26
Problems 80 and 81

82. •• Using the results from Problem 54, find the angular momentum of Halley's comet **(a)** at perihelion and **(b)** at aphelion. (Take the mass of Halley's comet to be 9.8×10^{14} kg.)

83. •• **Exploring Mars** In the not-too-distant future astronauts will travel to Mars to carry out scientific explorations. As part of their mission, it is likely that a "geosynchronous" satellite will be placed above a given point on the Martian equator to facilitate communications. At what altitude above the surface of Mars should such a satellite orbit? (*Note:* The Martian "day" is 24.6229 hours. Other relevant information can be found in Appendix C.)

84. •• **IP** A satellite is placed in Earth orbit 1000 miles higher than the altitude of a geosynchronous satellite. Referring to Active Example 12–1, we see that the altitude of the satellite is 23,300 mi. **(a)** Is the period of this satellite greater than or less than 24 hours? **(b)** As viewed from the surface of the Earth, does the satellite move eastward or westward? Explain. **(c)** Find the orbital period of this satellite.

85. •• Find the speed of the *Millennium Eagle* at point A in Example 12–1 if its speed at point B is 0.905 m/s.

86. •• Show that the force of gravity between the Moon and the Sun is always greater than the force of gravity between the Moon and the Earth.

87. •• The astronomical unit AU is defined as the mean distance from the Sun to the Earth (1 AU = 1.50×10^{11} m). Apply Kepler's third law (Equation 12–7) to the solar system, and show that it can be written as

$$T = Cr^{3/2}$$

In this expression, the period T is measured in years, the distance r is measured in astronomical units, and the constant C has a magnitude that you must determine.

88. •• **(a)** Find the kinetic energy of a 1720-kg satellite in a circular orbit about the Earth, given that the radius of the orbit is 12,600 miles. **(b)** How much energy is required to move this satellite to a circular orbit with a radius of 25,200 miles?

89. •• **IP Space Shuttle Orbit** On a typical mission, the space shuttle ($m = 2.00 \times 10^6$ kg) orbits at an altitude of 250 km above the Earth's surface. **(a)** Does the orbital speed of the shuttle depend on its mass? Explain. **(b)** Find the speed of the shuttle in its orbit. **(c)** How long does it take for the shuttle to complete one orbit of the Earth?

90. ••• **IP** Consider an object of mass m orbiting the Earth at a radius r. **(a)** Find the speed of the object. **(b)** Show that the total mechanical energy of this object is equal to (-1) times its kinetic energy. **(c)** Does the result of part (b) apply to an object orbiting the Sun? Explain.

91. ••• In a binary star system two stars orbit about their common center of mass. Find the orbital period of such a system, given that the stars are separated by a distance d and have masses m and $2m$.

92. ••• Three identical stars, at the vertices of an equilateral triangle, orbit about their common center of mass (**Figure 12–27**). Find

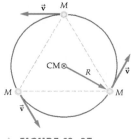

▲ FIGURE 12–27
Problem 92

the period of this orbital motion in terms of the orbital radius, R, and the mass of each star, M.

93. ••• Find an expression for the kinetic energy of a satellite of mass m in an orbit of radius r about a planet of mass M.

94. ••• Referring to Example 12–1, find the x component of the net force acting on the *Millennium Eagle* as a function of x. Plot your result, showing both negative and positive values of x.

95. ••• A satellite orbits the Earth in an elliptical orbit. At perigee its distance from the center of the Earth is 22,500 km and its speed is 4280 m/s. At apogee its distance from the center of the Earth is 24,100 km and its speed is 3990 m/s. Using this information, calculate the mass of the Earth.

PASSAGE PROBLEMS

Exploring Comets with the *Stardust* Spacecraft

On February 7, 1999, NASA launched a spacecraft with the ambitious mission of making a close encounter with a comet, collecting samples from its tail, and returning the samples to Earth for analysis. This spacecraft, appropriately named *Stardust*, took almost five years to rendezvous with its objective—comet Wild 2 (pronounced "Vilt 2")—and another two years to return its samples. The reason for the long round trip is that the spacecraft had to make three orbits around the Sun, and also an Earth Gravity Assist (EGA) flyby, to increase its speed enough to put it in an orbit appropriate for the encounter.

When *Stardust* finally reached comet Wild 2 on January 2, 2004, it flew within 147 miles of the comet's nucleus, snapping pictures and collecting tiny specks of dust in the glistening coma. The approach speed between the spacecraft and the comet at the encounter was a relatively "slow" 6200 m/s, so that dust particles could be collected safely without destroying the vehicle. Note that "slow" is put in quotation marks; after all, 6200 m/s is still about six times the speed of a rifle bullet!

 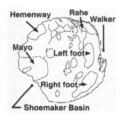

Comet Wild 2 and some of its surface features, including the Walker basin, the site of unusual jets of outward-flowing dust and rocks.

The roughly spherical comet Wild 2 has a radius of 2.7 km, and the acceleration due to gravity on its surface is $0.00010g$. The two curves in **Figure 12–28** show the surface acceleration as a function of radius for a spherical comet with two different masses, one of which corresponds to comet Wild 2. Also indicated are radii at which these two hypothetical comets have densities equal to that of ice and granite.

The *Stardust* spacecraft is still in space; only its small return capsule came back to Earth. It has now been given a new assignment—to visit and photograph comet Tempel 1, the object of the Deep Impact collision on July 4, 2005. This mission, called *New Exploration of Tempel 1* (NExT), is scheduled to make its close encounter with comet Tempel 1 on February 14, 2011.

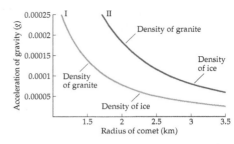

▲ **FIGURE 12–28** Problems 96, 97, 98, and 99

96. • Which of the two curves in Figure 12–28 corresponds to comet Wild 2?

    A. Curve I   **B.** Curve II

97. • What is the mass of comet Wild 2?

    A. 1.1×10^8 kg   **B.** 1.1×10^{12} kg

    C. 1.1×10^{14} kg   **D.** 1.1×10^{18} kg

98. • Find the speed needed to escape from the surface of comet Wild 2. (*Note:* It is easy for a person to jump upward with a speed of 3 m/s.)

    A. 1.6 m/s   **B.** 2.3 m/s

    C. 72 m/s   **D.** 230 m/s

99. •• Suppose comet Wild 2 had a small satellite in orbit around it, just as Dactyl orbits asteroid 243 Ida (see page 390). If this satellite were to orbit at twice the radius of the comet, what would be its period of revolution?

    A. 0.93 h   **B.** 2.9 h

    C. 5.8 h   **D.** 8.2 h

INTERACTIVE PROBLEMS

100. •• Find the orbital radius that corresponds to a "year" of 150 days.

101. •• **IP** Suppose the mass of the Sun is suddenly doubled, but the Earth's orbital radius remains the same. (a) Would the length of an Earth year increase, decrease, or stay the same? (b) Find the length of a year for the case of a Sun with twice the mass. (c) Suppose the Sun retains its present mass, but the mass of the Earth is doubled instead. Would the length of the year increase, decrease, or stay the same?

102. •• **IP Referring to Example 12–7** (a) If the mass of the Earth were doubled, would the escape speed of a rocket increase, decrease, or stay the same? (b) Calculate the escape speed of a rocket for the case of an Earth with twice its present mass. (c) If the mass of the Earth retains its present value, but the mass of the rocket is doubled, does the escape speed increase, decrease, or stay the same?

103. •• **IP Referring to Example 12–7** Suppose the Earth is suddenly shrunk to half its present radius without losing any of its mass. (a) Would the escape speed of a rocket increase, decrease, or stay the same? (b) Find the escape speed for an Earth with half its present radius.

13 Oscillations About Equilibrium

In this era of atomic timekeepers and electronic digital read-outs, a pendulum seems little more than a quaint reminder of the age of grandfather clocks. But pendulums played an important role in the development of physics, and analyzing the motion of a pendulum still provides insight into key physical principles. In this chapter we will explore the behavior of objects that swing, vibrate, or oscillate—and lay the foundations for understanding many natural phenomena, including sound.

In Chapter 11 we considered systems in static equilibrium. Such systems are seldom left undisturbed for very long, it seems, before they are displaced from equilibrium by a bump, a kick, or a nudge. When this happens to a system, it often results in **oscillations** back and forth from one side of the equilibrium position to the other.

The basic cause of oscillations is the fact that when an object is displaced from a position of stable equilibrium it experiences a *restoring force* that is directed back toward the equilibrium position. Thus, the restoring force accelerates the object in the direction of

its initial, equilibrium position. When it reaches equilibrium the force acting on it is zero, but it doesn't come to rest. In moving back to equilibrium, it has gained speed and momentum, and hence its inertia carries it through the equilibrium position to the other side, where the restoring force is now in the opposite direction. The process repeats itself, leading to a series of oscillations.

Perhaps the most familiar oscillating system is the simple pendulum, like the ones that keep time in grandfather clocks. Modern digital wristwatches also use oscillators to keep time, but theirs are tiny quartz crystals. In fact, oscillating systems are found in nature over virtually all length scales, from water molecules that oscillate in a microwave oven, to planets that oscillate when struck by an asteroid, to the universe itself, which some think may oscillate in a series of "big bangs" followed by equally momentous "big crunches."

13–1 Periodic Motion

A motion that repeats itself over and over is referred to as **periodic motion.** The beating of your heart, the ticking of a clock, and the movement of a child on a swing are familiar examples. One of the key characteristics of a periodic system is the time required for the completion of one cycle of its repetitive motion. For example, the pendulum in a grandfather clock might take one second to swing from maximum displacement in one direction to maximum displacement in the opposite direction, or two seconds for a complete cycle of oscillation. In this case, we say that the **period**, T, of the pendulum is 2 s.

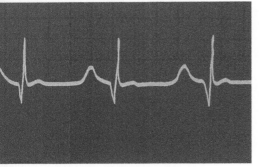

▲ Periodic phenomena are found everywhere in nature, from the movements of the heavenly bodies to the vibration of individual atoms. The trace of an electrocardiogram (ECG or EKG), as shown here, records the rhythmic electrical activity that accompanies the beating of our hearts.

Definition of Period, T

T = time required for one cycle of a periodic motion

SI unit: seconds/cycle = s

Note that a cycle (that is, an oscillation) is dimensionless.

Closely related to the period is another common measure of periodic motion, the **frequency,** f. The frequency of an oscillation is simply the number of oscillations per unit of time. Thus, f tells us how frequently, or rapidly, an oscillation takes place—the higher the frequency, the more rapid the oscillations. By definition, the frequency is simply the inverse of the period, T:

Definition of Frequency, f

$$f = \frac{1}{T}$$

13–1

SI unit: cycle/second = 1/s = s^{-1}

Note that if the period of an oscillation, T, is very small, corresponding to rapid oscillations, the corresponding frequency, $f = 1/T$, will be large, as expected.

A special unit has been introduced for the measurement of frequency. It is the **hertz** (Hz), named for the German physicist Heinrich Hertz (1857–1894), in honor of his pioneering studies of radio waves. By definition, one Hz is one cycle per second:

$$1\,\text{Hz} = 1\,\text{cycle/second}$$

High frequencies are often measured in kilohertz (kHz), where $1\,\text{kHz} = 10^3\,\text{Hz}$, or megahertz (MHz), where $1\,\text{MHz} = 10^6\,\text{Hz}$.

EXERCISE 13–1

The processing "speed" of a computer refers to the number of binary operations it can perform in one second, so it is really a frequency. If the processor of a personal computer operates at 1.80 GHz, how much time is required for one processing cycle?

SOLUTION

The frequency of the computer's processor is f = 1.80 GHz. Therefore, we can use Equation 13–1 to solve for the processing period:

$$T = \frac{1}{f} = \frac{1}{1.80\,\text{GHz}} = \frac{1}{1.80 \times 10^9\,\text{cycles/s}} = 5.56 \times 10^{-10}\,\text{s}$$

The high frequency of the computer corresponds to a very small period—less than a billionth of a second to complete one operation. We next consider a situation in which the frequency is considerably smaller.

EXERCISE 13–2

A tennis ball is hit back and forth between two players warming up for a match. If it takes 2.31 s for the ball to go from one player to the other, what are the period and frequency of the ball's motion?

SOLUTION

The period of this motion is the time for the ball to complete one round trip from one player to the other and back. Therefore,

$$T = 2(2.31 \text{ s}) = 4.62 \text{ s}$$

$$f = \frac{1}{T} = \frac{1}{4.62 \text{ s}} = 0.216 \text{ Hz}$$

Notice that the period and frequency of periodic motion can vary over a remarkably large range. Table 13–1 gives a sampling of typical values of T and f.

TABLE 13–1 Typical Periods and Frequencies

System	Period (s)	Frequency (Hz)
Precession of the Earth	8.2×10^{11} (26,000 y)	1.2×10^{-12}
Hour hand of a clock	43,200 (12 h)	2.3×10^{-5}
Minute hand of a clock	3600	2.8×10^{-4}
Second hand of clock	60	0.017
Pendulum in grandfather clock	2.0	0.50
Human heartbeat	1.0	1.0
Lower range of human hearing	5.0×10^{-2}	20
Wing beat of housefly	5.0×10^{-3}	200
Upper range of human hearing	5.0×10^{-5}	20,000
Computer processor	5.6×10^{-10}	1.8×10^{9}

13–2 Simple Harmonic Motion

Periodic motion can take many forms, as illustrated by the tennis ball going back and forth between players in Exercise 13–2, or an expectant father pacing up and down in a hospital hallway. There is one type of periodic motion, however, that is of particular importance. It is referred to as **simple harmonic motion.**

A classic example of simple harmonic motion is provided by the oscillations of a mass attached to a spring. (See Section 6–2 for a discussion of ideal springs and the forces they exert.) To be specific, consider an air-track cart of mass m attached to a spring of force constant k, as in **Figure 13–1**. When the spring is at its equilibrium length—neither stretched nor compressed—the cart is at the position $x = 0$, where it will remain at rest if left undisturbed. If the cart is displaced from equilibrium by a distance x, however, the spring exerts a restoring force given by Hooke's law, $F = -kx$. In words:

> A spring exerts a restoring force whose magnitude is proportional to the distance it is displaced from equilibrium.

This direct proportionality between distance from equilibrium and force is the key feature of a mass–spring system that leads to simple harmonic motion. As for the direction of the spring force:

> The force exerted by a spring is opposite in direction to its displacement from equilibrium; this accounts for the minus sign in $F = -kx$.
> In general, a restoring force is one that *always* points toward the equilibrium position.

Now, suppose the cart is released from rest at the location $x = A$. As indicated in Figure 13–1, the spring exerts a force on the cart to the left, causing the cart to accelerate toward the equilibrium position. When the cart reaches $x = 0$, the net

▶ **FIGURE 13–1 A mass attached to a spring undergoes simple harmonic motion about $x = 0$**

(a) The mass is at its maximum positive value of x. Its velocity is zero, and the force on it points to the left with maximum magnitude. **(b)** The mass is at the equilibrium position of the spring. Here the speed has its maximum value, and the force exerted by the spring is zero. **(c)** The mass is at its maximum displacement in the negative x direction. The velocity is zero here, and the force points to the right with maximum magnitude. **(d)** The mass is at the equilibrium position of the spring, with zero force acting on it and maximum speed. **(e)** The mass has completed one cycle of its oscillation about $x = 0$.

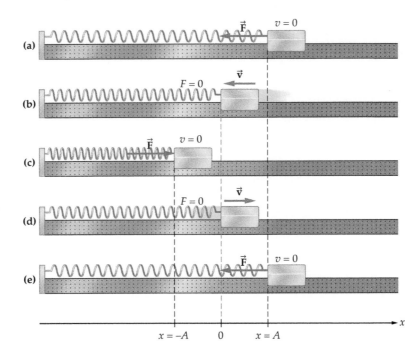

force acting on it is zero. Its speed is not zero at this point, however, and so it continues to move to the left. As the cart compresses the spring, it experiences a force to the right, causing it to decelerate and finally come to rest at $x = -A$. The spring continues to exert a force to the right; thus, the cart immediately begins to move to the right until it comes to rest again at $x = A$, completing one oscillation in the time T.

If a pen is attached to the cart, it can trace its motion on a strip of paper moving with constant speed, as indicated in **Figure 13–2**. On this "strip chart" we obtain a record of the cart's motion as a function of time. As we see in Figure 13–2, the motion of the cart looks like a sine or a cosine function.

Mathematical analysis, using the methods of calculus, shows that this is indeed the case; that is, the position of the cart as a function of time can be represented by a sine or a cosine function. The reason that either function works can be seen by considering **Figure 13–3**. If we take $t = 0$ to be at point 1, for example, the position as a function of time starts at zero, just like a sine function; if we choose $t = 0$ to be at point 2, however, the position versus time starts at its maximum value, just like a cosine function. It is really the same mathematical function, differing only in the choice of starting point.

Returning to Figure 13–1, note that the position of the mass oscillates between $x = +A$ and $x = -A$. Since A represents the extreme displacement of the cart on

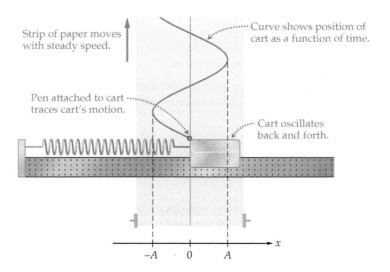

▶ **FIGURE 13–2 Displaying position versus time for simple harmonic motion**

As an air-track cart oscillates about its equilibrium position, a pen attached to it traces its motion onto a moving sheet of paper. This produces a "strip chart," showing that the cart's motion has the shape of a sine or a cosine.

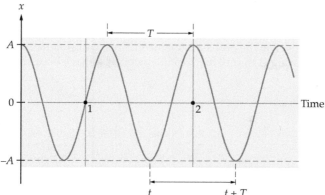

◀ FIGURE 13–3 **Simple harmonic motion as a sine or a cosine**
The strip chart from Figure 13–2. The cart oscillates back and forth from $x = +A$ to $x = -A$, completing one cycle in the time T. The function traced by the pen can be represented as a sine function if $t = 0$ is taken to be at point 1, where the function is equal to zero. The function can be represented by a cosine if $t = 0$ is taken to be at point 2, where the function has its maximum value.

either side of equilibrium, we refer to it as the **amplitude** of the motion. It follows that the amplitude is one-half the total range of motion. In addition, recall that the cart's motion repeats with a period T. As a result, the position of the cart is the same at the time $t + T$ as it is at the time t, as shown in Figure 13–3. Combining all these observations results in the following mathematical description of position versus time:

Position Versus Time in Simple Harmonic Motion

$$x = A \cos\left(\frac{2\pi}{T}t\right)$$

13–2

SI unit: m

This type of dependence on time—as a sine or a cosine—is characteristic of simple harmonic motion. With this particular choice, the position at $t = 0$ is $x = A \cos(0) = A$; thus, Equation 13–2 describes an object that has its maximum displacement at $t = 0$, as in Figure 13–3.

To see how Equation 13–2 works, recall that the cosine oscillates between $+1$ and -1. Therefore, $x = A \cos(2\pi t/T)$ will oscillate between $+A$ and $-A$, just as in the strip chart. Next, consider what happens if we replace the time t with the time $t + T$. This gives

$$x = A \cos\left(\frac{2\pi}{T}(t + T)\right)$$

$$= A \cos\left(\frac{2\pi}{T}t + \frac{2\pi}{T}T\right) = A \cos\left(\frac{2\pi}{T}t + 2\pi\right)$$

Finally, using the fact that $\cos(\theta + 2\pi) = \cos\theta$ for any angle θ, we can rewrite the last expression as follows:

$$x = A \cos\left(\frac{2\pi}{T}t\right)$$

Therefore, as expected, the position at time $t + T$ is precisely the same as the position at time t.

PROBLEM-SOLVING NOTE

Using Radians

When evaluating Equation 13–2, be sure you have your calculator set to "radians" mode.

EXAMPLE 13–1 SPRING TIME

An air-track cart attached to a spring completes one oscillation every 2.4 s. At $t = 0$ the cart is released from rest at a distance of 0.10 m from its equilibrium position. What is the position of the cart at **(a)** 0.30 s, **(b)** 0.60 s, **(c)** 2.7 s, and **(d)** 3.0 s?

PICTURE THE PROBLEM

In our sketch, we place the origin of the x-axis at the equilibrium position of the cart and the positive direction to point to the right. The cart is released from rest at $x = 0.10$ m, which means that its amplitude is $A = 0.10$ m. After it is released, the cart oscillates back and forth between $x = 0.10$ m and $x = -0.10$ m.

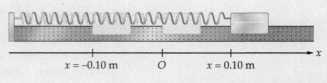

$x = -0.10$ m O $x = 0.10$ m

CONTINUED ON NEXT PAGE

CONTINUED FROM PREVIOUS PAGE

STRATEGY

Note that the period of oscillation, $T = 2.4$ s, is given in the problem statement. Thus, we can find the position of the cart by evaluating $x = A \cos(2\pi t/T)$ at the desired times, using $A = 0.10$ m. (*Note*: Remember to have your calculator set to radian mode when evaluating these cosine functions.)

SOLUTION

Part (a)

1. Calculate x at the time $t = 0.30$ s:

$$x = A \cos\left(\frac{2\pi}{T}t\right) = (0.10 \text{ m}) \cos\left[\left(\frac{2\pi}{2.4 \text{ s}}\right)(0.30 \text{ s})\right]$$

$$= (0.10 \text{ m}) \cos(\pi/4) = 7.1 \text{ cm}$$

Part (b)

2. Now, substitute $t = 0.60$ s:

$$x = A \cos\left(\frac{2\pi}{T}t\right) = (0.10 \text{ m}) \cos\left[\left(\frac{2\pi}{2.4 \text{ s}}\right)(0.60 \text{ s})\right]$$

$$= (0.10 \text{ m}) \cos(\pi/2) = 0$$

Part (c)

3. Repeat with $t = 2.7$ s:

$$x = A \cos\left(\frac{2\pi}{T}t\right) = (0.10 \text{ m}) \cos\left[\left(\frac{2\pi}{2.4 \text{ s}}\right)(2.7 \text{ s})\right]$$

$$= (0.10 \text{ m}) \cos(9\pi/4) = 7.1 \text{ cm}$$

Part (d)

4. Repeat with $t = 3.0$ s:

$$x = A \cos\left(\frac{2\pi}{T}t\right) = (0.10 \text{ m}) \cos\left[\left(\frac{2\pi}{2.4 \text{ s}}\right)(3.0 \text{ s})\right]$$

$$= (0.10 \text{ m}) \cos(5\pi/2) = 0$$

INSIGHT

Note that the results for parts (c) and (d) are the same as for parts (a) and (b), respectively. This is because the times in (c) and (d) are greater than the corresponding times in (a) and (b) by one period; that is, 2.7 s = 0.30 s + 2.4 s and 3.0 s = 0.60 s + 2.4 s.

PRACTICE PROBLEM

What is the first time the cart is at the position $x = -5.0$ cm?   [**Answer:** $t = T/3 = 0.80$ s]

Some related homework problems: Problem 10, Problem 17, Problem 18

Though the motion of the air-track cart is strictly one-dimensional, it bears a close relationship to uniform circular motion. In the next section we explore this connection between simple harmonic motion and uniform circular motion in detail.

13–3 Connections Between Uniform Circular Motion and Simple Harmonic Motion

Imagine a turntable that rotates with a constant angular speed $\omega = 2\pi/T$, taking the time T to complete a revolution. At the rim of the turntable we place a small peg, as indicated in **Figure 13–4**. If we view the turntable from above, we see the peg undergoing uniform circular motion.

On the other hand, suppose we view the turntable from the side, so that the peg appears to move back and forth. Perhaps the easiest way to view this motion is to shine a light that casts a shadow of the peg on a screen, as shown in Figure 13–4. While the peg itself moves on a circular path, its shadow moves back and forth in a straight line.

To be specific, let the radius of the turntable be $r = A$, so that the shadow moves from $x = +A$ to $x = -A$. When the shadow is at $x = +A$, release a mass on a spring that is also at $x = +A$, so that the mass and the shadow start together. If we adjust the period of the mass so that it completes one oscillation in the same time T that the turntable completes one revolution, we find that the mass and the shadow move as one for all times. This is also illustrated in Figure 13–4. Since the mass undergoes simple harmonic motion, it follows that the shadow does so as well.

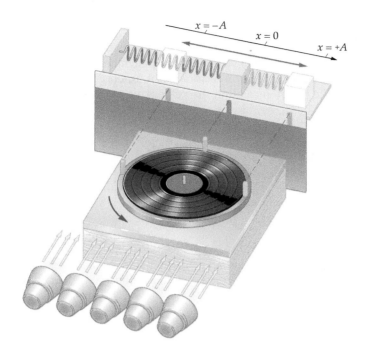

◀ **FIGURE 13-4   The relationship between uniform circular motion and simple harmonic motion**

A peg is placed at the rim of a turntable that rotates with constant angular velocity. Viewed from above, the peg exhibits uniform circular motion. If the peg is viewed from the side, however, it appears to move back and forth in a straight line, as we can see by shining a light to cast a shadow of the peg onto a screen. The shadow moves with simple harmonic motion. If we compare this motion with the behavior of a mass on a spring, moving with the same period as the turntable and an amplitude of motion equal to the radius of the turntable, we find that the mass and the shadow of the peg move together in simple harmonic motion.

We now use this connection, plus our knowledge of circular motion, to obtain detailed results for the position, velocity, and acceleration of a particle undergoing simple harmonic motion.

Position

In **Figure 13-5** we show the peg at the angular position θ, where θ is measured relative to the x axis. If the peg starts at $\theta = 0$ at $t = 0$, and the turntable rotates with a constant angular speed ω, we know from Equation 10–10 that the angular position of the peg is simply

$$\theta = \omega t \qquad \text{13-3}$$

That is, the angular position increases linearly with time.

Now, imagine drawing a radius vector of length A to the position of the peg, as indicated in Figure 13–5. When we project the shadow of the peg onto the screen, the shadow is at the location $x = A \cos \theta$, which is the x component of the radius vector. Therefore, the position of the shadow as a function of time is

Position of the Shadow as a Function of Time

$$x = A \cos \theta = A \cos(\omega t) = A \cos\left(\frac{2\pi}{T} t\right) \qquad \text{13-4}$$

SI unit: m

Note that we have used Equation 13–3 to express θ in terms of the time, t. Clearly, Equations 13–4 and 13–2 are identical, so the shadow does indeed exhibit simple harmonic motion, just like a mass on a spring.

For notational simplicity, we will often write the position of a mass on a spring in the form $x = A \cos(\omega t)$, which is more compact than $x = A \cos(2\pi t/T)$. When referring to a rotating turntable, ω is called the angular speed; when referring to simple harmonic motion, or other periodic motion, we have a slightly different name for ω. In these situations, ω is called the **angular frequency**:

Definition of Angular Frequency, ω

$$\omega = 2\pi f = \frac{2\pi}{T} \qquad \text{13-5}$$

SI unit: rad/s = s^{-1}

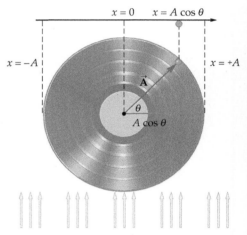

▲ **FIGURE 13-5   Position versus time in simple harmonic motion**

A peg rotates on the rim of a turntable of radius A. When the peg is at the angular position θ, its shadow is at $x = A \cos \theta$. Note that $A \cos \theta$ is also the x component of the radius vector $\vec{A}$ from the center of the turntable to the peg.

Velocity

We can find the velocity of the shadow in the same way that we determined its position; first find the velocity of the peg, then take its x component. The result of this calculation will be the velocity as a function of time for simple harmonic motion.

To begin, recall that the velocity of an object in uniform circular motion of radius r has a magnitude equal to

$$v = r\omega$$

In addition, the velocity is tangential to the object's circular path, as indicated in Figure 13–6 (a). Therefore, referring to the figure, we see that when the peg is at the angular position θ, the velocity vector makes an angle θ with the vertical. As a result, the x component of the velocity is $-v \sin \theta$. Combining these results, we find that the velocity of the peg, along the x axis, is

$$v_x = -v \sin \theta = -r\omega \sin \theta$$

In what follows we shall drop the x subscript, since we know that the shadow and a mass on a spring move only along the x axis. Recalling that $r = A$ and $\theta = \omega t$, we have

Velocity in Simple Harmonic Motion

$$v = -A\omega \sin(\omega t) \qquad\qquad 13\text{–}6$$

SI unit: m/s

We plot x and v for simple harmonic motion in Figure 13–6 (b). Note that when the displacement from equilibrium is a maximum, the velocity is zero. This is to be expected, since at $x = +A$ and $x = -A$ the object is momentarily at rest as it turns around. Not surprisingly, these points are referred to as **turning points** of the motion.

On the other hand, the speed is a maximum when the displacement from equilibrium is zero. Similarly, a mass on a spring is moving with its greatest speed as it goes through $x = 0$. From the expression $v = -A\omega \sin(\omega t)$, and the fact that the largest value of $\sin \theta$ is 1, we see that the maximum speed of the mass is

$$v_{\text{max}} = A\omega \qquad\qquad 13\text{–}7$$

After the mass passes $x = 0$ it begins either to compress or to stretch the spring, and hence it slows down.

Acceleration

The acceleration of an object in uniform circular motion has a magnitude given by

$$a_{\text{cp}} = r\omega^2$$

▶ **FIGURE 13–6 Velocity versus time in simple harmonic motion**

(a) The velocity of a peg rotating on the rim of a turntable is tangential to its circular path. As a result, when the peg is at the angle θ, its velocity makes an angle of θ with the vertical. The x component of the velocity, then, is $-v \sin \theta$. **(b)** Position, x, and velocity, v, as a function of time for simple harmonic motion. The speed is greatest when the object passes through equilibrium, $x = 0$. On the other hand, the speed is zero when the position is greatest—that is, at the turning points. Finally, note that as x moves in the negative direction, the velocity is negative. Similar remarks apply to the positive direction.

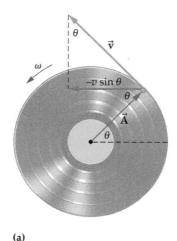

(a)

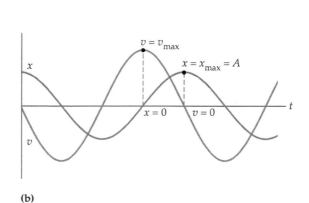

(b)

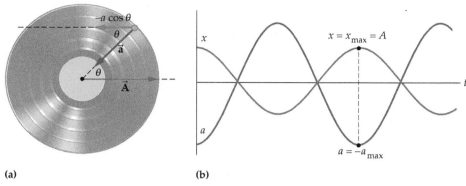

(a)   (b)

◀ **FIGURE 13–7 Acceleration versus time in simple harmonic motion**

(a) The acceleration of a peg on the rim of a uniformly rotating turntable is directed toward the center of the turntable. Hence, when the peg is at the angle θ, the acceleration makes an angle θ with the horizontal. The x component of the acceleration is $-a \cos \theta$. (b) Position, x, and acceleration, a, as a function of time for simple harmonic motion. Note that when the position has its greatest positive value, the acceleration has its greatest negative value.

In addition, the direction of the acceleration is toward the center of the circular path, as indicated in **Figure 13–7 (a)**. Thus, when the angular position of the peg is θ, the acceleration vector is at an angle θ below the x axis, and its x component is $-a_{cp} \cos \theta$. Again setting $r = A$ and $\theta = \omega t$, we find

Acceleration in Simple Harmonic Motion

$$a = -A\omega^2 \cos(\omega t) \qquad \qquad 13\text{–}8$$

SI unit: m/s^2

The position and acceleration for simple harmonic motion are plotted in **Figure 13–7 (b)**. Note that the acceleration and position vary with time in the same way but with opposite signs. That is, when the position has its maximum *positive* value, the acceleration has its maximum *negative* value, and so on. After all, the restoring force of the spring is opposite to the position, hence the acceleration, $a = F/m$, must also be opposite to the position. In fact, comparing Equations 13–4 and 13–8 we see that the acceleration can be written as

$$a = -\omega^2 x$$

Finally, since the largest value of x is the amplitude A, we see that the maximum acceleration is of magnitude

$$a_{max} = A\omega^2 \qquad \qquad 13\text{–}9$$

We conclude this section with a few examples using position, velocity, and acceleration in simple harmonic motion.

PROBLEM-SOLVING NOTE

Be Sure to Use Radians

Note that Equations 13–4, 13–6, and 13–8 must all be evaluated in terms of radians.

EXAMPLE 13–2   VELOCITY AND ACCELERATION

As in Example 13–1, an air-track cart attached to a spring completes one oscillation every 2.4 s. At $t = 0$ the cart is released from rest with the spring stretched 0.10 m from its equilibrium position. What are the velocity and acceleration of the cart at **(a)** 0.30 s and **(b)** 0.60 s?

PICTURE THE PROBLEM
Once again, we place the origin of the x axis at the equilibrium position of the cart, with the positive direction pointing to the right. In addition, the cart is released from rest at $x = 0.10$ m, which means that it will have zero speed at $x = 0.10$ m and $x = -0.10$ m. Its speed will be a maximum at $x = 0$, however, which is also the point where the acceleration is zero.

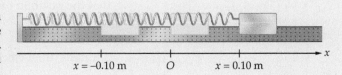

$x = -0.10$ m O $x = 0.10$ m

STRATEGY
After calculating the angular frequency, $\omega = 2\pi/T$, we simply substitute $t = 0.30$ s and $t = 0.60$ s into $v = -A\omega \sin(\omega t)$ and $a = -A\omega^2 \cos(\omega t)$. Remember to set your calculators to radian mode.

CONTINUED ON NEXT PAGE

CONTINUED FROM PREVIOUS PAGE

SOLUTION

1. Calculate the angular frequency for this motion:

$$\omega = \frac{2\pi}{T} = \frac{2\pi}{(2.4\text{ s})} = 2.6\text{ rad/s}$$

Part (a)

2. Calculate v at the time $t = 0.30$ s. Express ω in terms of π—that is, $\omega = 2\pi/(2.4\text{ s})$. This isn't necessary, but it makes it easier to evaluate the sine and cosine functions. (See the discussion following the Example for additional details):

$$v = -A\omega \sin(\omega t)$$
$$= -(0.10\text{ m})(2.6\text{ rad/s}) \sin\left[\left(\frac{2\pi}{2.4\text{ s}}\right)(0.30\text{ s})\right]$$
$$= -(26\text{ cm/s}) \sin(\pi/4) = -18\text{ cm/s}$$

3. Similarly, calculate a at $t = 0.30$ s:

$$a = -A\omega^2 \cos(\omega t)$$
$$= -(0.10\text{ m})(2.6\text{ rad/s})^2 \cos\left[\left(\frac{2\pi}{2.4\text{ s}}\right)(0.30\text{ s})\right]$$
$$= -(68\text{ cm/s}^2) \cos(\pi/4) = -48\text{ cm/s}^2$$

Part (b)

4. Calculate v at the time $t = 0.60$ s:

$$v = -A\omega \sin(\omega t)$$
$$= -(0.10\text{ m})(2.6\text{ rad/s}) \sin\left[\left(\frac{2\pi}{2.4\text{ s}}\right)(0.60\text{ s})\right]$$
$$= -(26\text{ cm/s}) \sin(\pi/2) = -26\text{ cm/s}$$

5. Similarly, calculate a at $t = 0.60$ s:

$$a = -A\omega^2 \cos(\omega t)$$
$$= -(0.10\text{ m})(2.6\text{ rad/s})^2 \cos\left[\left(\frac{2\pi}{2.4\text{ s}}\right)(0.60\text{ s})\right]$$
$$= -(68\text{ cm/s}^2) \cos(\pi/2) = 0$$

INSIGHT

Note that the cart speeds up from $t = 0.30$ s to $t = 0.60$ s; in fact, the maximum speed of the cart, $v_{max} = A\omega = 26$ cm/s, occurs at $t = 0.60$ s $= T/4$. Referring to Example 13–1, we see that this is precisely the time when the cart is at the equilibrium position, $x = 0$. As expected, the acceleration is zero at this time.

PRACTICE PROBLEM

What is the first time the velocity of the cart is +26 cm/s? [**Answer:** $v = +26$ cm/s at $t = 3T/4 = 1.8$ s]

Some related homework problems: Problem 23, Problem 24

PROBLEM-SOLVING NOTE

Expressing Time in Terms of the Period

When evaluating the expression $x = A\cos(2\pi t/T)$ at the time t, it is often helpful to express t in terms of the period T.

In problems like the preceding Example, it is often useful to express the time t in terms of the period, T. For example, if the period is $T = 2.4$ s it follows that $t = 0.60$ s is $T/4$. Thus, the angular frequency times the time is

$$\omega t = \left(\frac{2\pi}{T}\right)\left(\frac{T}{4}\right) = \pi/2$$

This result was used in Steps 4 and 5 in Example 13–2. Using $\omega t = \pi/2$ we find that the position of the cart is

$$x = A\cos(\omega t) = A\cos(\pi/2) = 0$$

Similarly, the velocity of the cart is

$$v = -A\omega \sin(\omega t) = -A\omega \sin(\pi/2) = -A\omega$$

and its acceleration is

$$a = -A\omega^2 \cos(\omega t) = -A\omega^2 \cos(\pi/2) = 0$$

When expressed in this way, it is clear why x and a are zero and why v has its maximum negative value.

EXAMPLE 13–3   TURBULENCE!

On December 29, 1997, a United Airlines flight from Tokyo to Honolulu was hit with severe turbulence 31 minutes after takeoff. Data from the airplane's "black box" indicated the 747 moved up and down with an amplitude of 30.0 m and a maximum acceleration of 1.8g. Treating the up-and-down motion of the plane as simple harmonic, find (a) the time required for one complete oscillation and (b) the plane's maximum vertical speed.

PICTURE THE PROBLEM
Our sketch shows the 747 airliner moving up and down with an amplitude of $A = 30.0$ m relative to its normal horizontal flight path. The period of motion, T, is the time required for one complete cycle of this up-and-down motion.

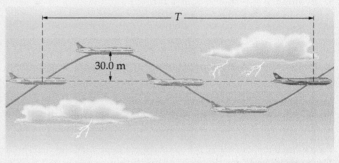

STRATEGY
We are given the maximum acceleration and the amplitude of motion. With these quantities, and the basic equations of simple harmonic motion, we can determine the other characteristics of the motion.

a. We know that the maximum acceleration of simple harmonic motion is $a_{max} = A\omega^2$ (Equation 13–9). This relation can be solved for ω in terms of the known quantities a_{max} and A. We rearrange $\omega = 2\pi/T$ to solve for the period of motion, T.

b. The maximum vertical speed is found using $v_{max} = A\omega$ (Equation 13–7).

INTERACTIVE FIGURE (MP)™

SOLUTION

Part (a)

1. Relate a_{max} to the angular frequency, ω:

$$a_{max} = A\omega^2$$

2. Solve for ω, and express in terms of T:

$$\omega = \sqrt{a_{max}/A} = 2\pi/T$$

3. Solve for T and substitute numerical values for g and A:

$$T = \frac{2\pi}{\sqrt{a_{max}/A}}$$

$$= \frac{2\pi}{\sqrt{1.8g/A}} = \frac{2\pi}{\sqrt{1.8(9.81 \text{ m/s}^2)/(30.0 \text{ m})}} = 8.2 \text{ s}$$

Part (b)

4. Calculate the maximum vertical speed using $v_{max} = A\omega = 2\pi A/T$:

$$v_{max} = A\omega = \frac{2\pi A}{T} = \frac{2\pi(30.0 \text{ m})}{8.2 \text{ s}} = 23 \text{ m/s}$$

INSIGHT
We don't expect the up-and-down motion of the plane to be exactly simple harmonic—after all, it's unlikely the plane's path has precisely the shape of a cosine function. Still, the approximation is reasonable. In fact, many systems are well approximated by simple harmonic motion, and hence the equations derived in this section are used widely in physics.

Notice that the maximum vertical speed of the passengers (23 m/s) is roughly 50 mi/h, and that this speed is first in the upward direction, and then 4.1 s later in the downward direction.

PRACTICE PROBLEM
What amplitude of motion would result in a maximum acceleration of 0.50g, everything else remaining the same?
[**Answer:** $A = 0.50g/\omega^2 = 0.50gT^2/4\pi^2 = 8.4$ m]

Some related homework problems: Problem 23, Problem 25

ACTIVE EXAMPLE 13–1   BOBBING FOR APPLES: FIND THE POSITION, VELOCITY, AND ACCELERATION

A Red Delicious apple floats in a barrel of water. If you lift the apple 2.00 cm above its floating level and release it, it bobs up and down with a period of $T = 0.750$ s. Assuming the motion is simple harmonic, find the position, velocity, and acceleration of the apple at the times (a) $T/4$ and (b) $T/2$.

SOLUTION *(Test your understanding by performing the calculations indicated in each step.)*

1. Identify the amplitude of motion: $A = 2.00$ cm

2. Calculate the angular frequency: $\omega = 2\pi/T = 8.38$ rad/s

CONTINUED ON NEXT PAGE

CONTINUED FROM PREVIOUS PAGE

Part (a)

3. Evaluate $x = A \cos(\omega t)$ at $t = T/4$:

$x = A \cos(\pi/2) = 0$

4. Evaluate $v = -A\omega \sin(\omega t)$ at $t = T/4$:

$v = -A\omega \sin(\pi/2) = -A\omega$
$\quad = -16.8\,\text{cm/s}$

5. Evaluate $a = -A\omega^2 \cos(\omega t)$ at $t = T/4$:

$a = -A\omega^2 \cos(\pi/2) = 0$

Part (b)

6. Evaluate $x = A \cos(\omega t)$ at $t = T/2$:

$x = A \cos(\pi) = -A = -2.00\,\text{cm}$

7. Evaluate $v = -A\omega \sin(\omega t)$ at $t = T/2$:

$v = -A\omega \sin(\pi) = 0$

8. Evaluate $a = -A\omega^2 \cos(\omega t)$ at $t = T/2$:

$a = -A\omega^2 \cos(\pi) = A\omega^2 = 140\,\text{cm/s}^2$

INSIGHT
The acceleration in part (b) may seem rather large, but remember that $140\,\text{cm/s}^2 = 1.40\,\text{m/s}^2$, so the acceleration is only a fraction of the acceleration of gravity.

YOUR TURN
The maximum kinetic energy of this bobbing apple is 0.00388 J. What is its mass?

*(Answers to **Your Turn** problems are given in the back of the book.)*

13–4 The Period of a Mass on a Spring

In this section we show how the period of a mass on a spring is related to the mass, m, the force constant of the spring, k, and the amplitude of motion, A. As a first step, note that the net force acting on the mass at the position x is

$$F = -kx$$

Now, since $F = ma$, it follows that

$$ma = -kx$$

Substituting the time dependence of x and a, as given in Equations 13–4 and 13–8 in the previous section, we find

$$m[-A\omega^2 \cos(\omega t)] = -k[A \cos(\omega t)]$$

Canceling $-A \cos(\omega t)$ from each side of the equation yields

$$\omega^2 = k/m$$

or

$$\omega = \sqrt{\frac{k}{m}} \qquad\qquad 13\text{–}10$$

Finally, noting that $\omega = 2\pi/T$, it follows that the period of a mass on a spring is

Period of a Mass on a Spring

$$T = 2\pi\sqrt{\frac{m}{k}} \qquad\qquad 13\text{–}11$$

SI unit: s

EXERCISE 13–3

When a 0.22-kg air-track cart is attached to a spring, it oscillates with a period of 0.84 s. What is the force constant for this spring?

SOLUTION
From Equation 13–11 we find

$$k = 4\pi^2 m/T^2 = 12\,\text{N/m}$$

As one might expect, the period increases with the mass and decreases with the spring's force constant. For example, a larger mass has greater inertia, and hence it takes longer for the mass to move back and forth through an oscillation. On the other hand, a larger value of the force constant, k, indicates a stiffer spring. Clearly, a mass on a stiff spring completes an oscillation in less time than one on a soft, squishy spring.

The relationship between mass and period given in Equation 13–11 is used by NASA to measure the mass of astronauts in orbit. Recall that astronauts are in free fall as they orbit, as was discussed in Chapter 12, and therefore they are "weightless." As a result, they cannot simply step onto a bathroom scale to determine their mass. Thus, NASA has developed a device, known as the Body Mass Measurement Device (BMMD), to get around this problem. The BMMD is basically a spring attached to a chair, into which an astronaut is strapped. As the astronaut oscillates back and forth, the period of oscillation is measured. Knowing the force constant k and the period of oscillation T, the astronaut's mass can be determined from Equation 13–11. The result is simply $m = kT^2/4\pi^2$. See Problem 76 for an application of this result.

Note that the period given in Equation 13–11 is independent of the amplitude, A, which canceled in the derivation of this equation. This might seem counterintuitive at first: Shouldn't it take more time for a mass to cover the greater distance implied by a larger amplitude? While it is true that a mass will cover a greater distance when the amplitude is increased, it is also true that a larger amplitude implies a larger force exerted by the spring. With a greater force acting on it, the mass moves more rapidly; in fact, the speed of the mass is increased just enough that it covers the greater distance in precisely the same time.

These relationships between the motion of a mass on a spring and the mass, the force constant, and the amplitude are summarized in Figure 13–8.

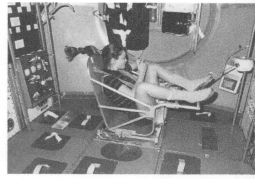

▲ Because astronauts are in free fall when orbiting the Earth, they behave as if they were "weightless." It is nevertheless possible to determine the mass of an astronaut by exploiting the properties of oscillatory motion. The chair into which astronaut Tamara Jernigan is strapped is attached to a spring. If the force constant of the spring is known, her mass can be determined simply by measuring the period with which she rocks back and forth. This instrument is known as a Body Mass Measurement Device (BMMD).

REAL-WORLD PHYSICS

Measuring the mass of a "weightless" astronaut

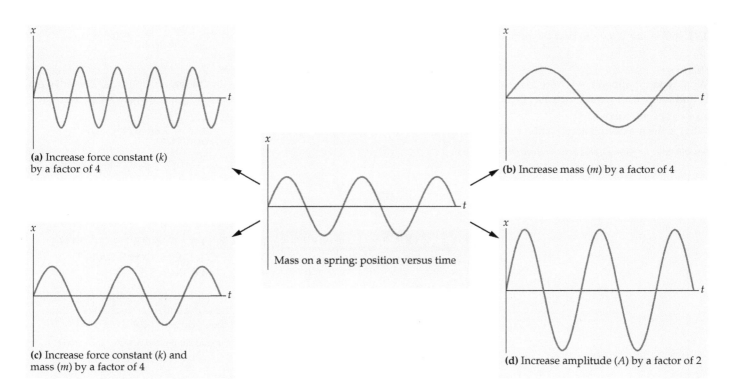

▲ **FIGURE 13–8 Factors affecting the motion of a mass on a spring**
The motion of a mass on a spring is determined by the force constant of the spring, k, the mass, m, and the amplitude, A. **(a)** Increasing the force constant causes the mass to oscillate with a greater frequency. **(b)** Increasing the mass lowers the frequency of oscillation. **(c)** If the force constant and the mass are both increased by the same factor, the effects described in parts (a) and (b) cancel, resulting in no change in the motion. **(d)** An increase in amplitude has no effect on the oscillation frequency. However, it will increase the maximum speed and maximum acceleration of the mass.

EXAMPLE 13–4 SPRING INTO MOTION

A 0.120-kg mass attached to a spring oscillates with an amplitude of 0.0750 m and a maximum speed of 0.524 m/s. Find **(a)** the force constant and **(b)** the period of motion.

PICTURE THE PROBLEM

Our sketch shows a mass oscillating about the equilibrium position of a spring, which we place at $x = 0$. The amplitude of the oscillations is 0.0750 m, and therefore the mass moves back and forth between $x = 0.0750$ m and $x = -0.0750$ m. The maximum speed of the mass, which occurs at $x = 0$, is $v_{max} = 0.524$ m/s.

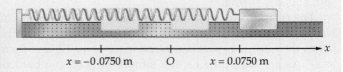

$x = -0.0750$ m O $x = 0.0750$ m

STRATEGY

a. To find the force constant, we first use the maximum speed, $v_{max} = A\omega$ (Equation 13–7), to determine the angular frequency ω. Once we know ω, we can obtain the force constant with $\omega = \sqrt{k/m}$ (Equation 13–10).

b. We can find the period from the angular frequency, using $\omega = 2\pi/T$. Alternatively, we can use the force constant and the mass in $T = 2\pi\sqrt{m/k}$ (Equation 13–11).

SOLUTION

Part (a)

1. Calculate the angular frequency in terms of the maximum speed:

$$v_{max} = A\omega$$
$$\omega = \frac{v_{max}}{A} = \frac{0.524 \text{ m/s}}{0.0750 \text{ m}} = 6.99 \text{ rad/s}$$

2. Solve $\omega = \sqrt{k/m}$ for the force constant:

$$\omega = \sqrt{k/m}$$
$$k = m\omega^2 = (0.120 \text{ kg})(6.99 \text{ rad/s})^2 = 5.86 \text{ N/m}$$

Part (b)

3. Use $\omega = 2\pi/T$ to find the period:

$$\omega = 2\pi/T$$
$$T = \frac{2\pi}{\omega} = \frac{2\pi}{6.99 \text{ rad/s}} = 0.899 \text{ s}$$

4. Use $T = 2\pi\sqrt{m/k}$ to find the period:

$$T = 2\pi\sqrt{m/k} = 2\pi\sqrt{\frac{0.120 \text{ kg}}{5.86 \text{ N/m}}} = 0.899 \text{ s}$$

INSIGHT

What would happen if we were to attach a larger mass to this same spring and release it with the same amplitude? The answer is that the period would increase, the angular frequency would decrease, and hence the maximum speed would also decrease.

PRACTICE PROBLEM

What is the maximum acceleration of the mass described in this Example?   [**Answer:** $a_{max} = A\omega^2 = 3.66$ m/s^2]

Some related homework problems: Problem 36, Problem 38

ACTIVE EXAMPLE 13–2 MASS ON A SPRING: FIND THE FORCE CONSTANT AND THE MASS

When a 0.420-kg mass is attached to a spring, it oscillates with a period of 0.350 s. If, instead, a different mass, m_2, is attached to the same spring, it oscillates with a period of 0.700 s. Find **(a)** the force constant of the spring and **(b)** the mass m_2.

SOLUTION *(Test your understanding by performing the calculations indicated in each step.)*

Part (a)

1. Let the initial mass and period be m_1 and T_1, respectively:

$m_1 = 0.420$ kg
$T_1 = 0.350$ s

2. Use Equation 13–11 to write an expression for T_1:

$T_1 = 2\pi\sqrt{m_1/k}$

3. Solve this expression for the force constant, k:

$k = 4\pi^2 m_1/T_1^2 = 135$ N/m

Part (b)

4. Write an expression for T_2:

$$T_2 = 2\pi\sqrt{m_2/k}$$

5. Solve for m_2:

$$m_2 = kT_2^2/4\pi^2 = 1.68 \text{ kg}$$

INSIGHT

In general, to double the period of a mass on a given spring—as in this case where it went from 0.350 s to 0.700 s—the mass must be increased by a factor of 4, in accordance with Equation 13–11. Therefore, an alternative way to find the second mass is $m_2 = 4(0.420 \text{ kg}) = 1.68 \text{ kg}$, in agreement with our result in Step 5.

YOUR TURN

The maximum speed of the second mass is 0.787 m/s. What is its amplitude of motion?

*(Answers to **Your Turn** problems are given in the back of the book.)*

A Vertical Spring

To this point we have considered only springs that are horizontal, and that are therefore unstretched at their equilibrium position. In many cases, however, we may wish to consider a vertical spring, as in **Figure 13–9**.

Now, when a mass m is attached to a vertical spring, it causes the spring to stretch. In fact, the vertical spring is in equilibrium when it exerts an upward force equal to the weight of the mass. That is, the spring stretches by an amount y_0 given by

$$ky_0 = mg$$

or

$$y_0 = mg/k \qquad \text{13–12}$$

Thus, a mass on a vertical spring oscillates about the equilibrium point $y = -y_0$. In all other respects the oscillations are the same as for a horizontal spring. In particular, the motion is simple harmonic, and the period is given by Equation 13–11.

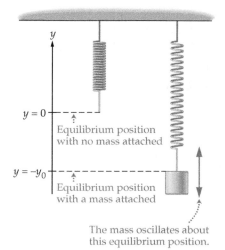

▲ FIGURE 13–9 A mass on a vertical spring
A mass stretches a vertical spring from its initial equilibrium at $y = 0$ to a new equilibrium at $y = -y_0 = -mg/k$. The mass executes simple harmonic motion about this new equilibrium.

▲ A ball attached to a vertical spring oscillates up and down with simple harmonic motion. If successive images taken at equal time intervals are displaced laterally, as in the sequence of photos at left, the ball appears to trace out a sinusoidal pattern (compare with Figure 13–2). The bungee jumper at right will oscillate in a similar fashion, though friction and air resistance will reduce the amplitude of his bounces.

EXAMPLE 13–5   **IT'S A STRETCH**

A 0.260-kg mass is attached to a vertical spring. When the mass is put into motion, its period is 1.12 s. **(a)** How much does the mass stretch the spring when it is at rest in its equilibrium position? **(b)** Suppose this experiment is repeated on a planet where the acceleration due to gravity is twice what it is on Earth. By what multiplicative factors do the period and equilibrium stretch change?

CONTINUED ON NEXT PAGE

CONTINUED FROM PREVIOUS PAGE

PICTURE THE PROBLEM
We choose the vertical axis to have its origin at the unstretched position of the spring. Once the mass is attached, the spring stretches to the position $y = -y_0$. The mass oscillates about this point with a period of 1.12 s.

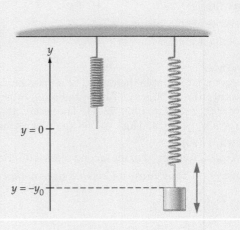

STRATEGY
a. In order to find the stretch of the spring, $y_0 = mg/k$, we need to know the force constant, k. We can find k from the period of oscillation—that is, from $T = 2\pi\sqrt{m/k}$.
b. Replace g with $2g$ in both $T = 2\pi\sqrt{m/k}$ and $y_0 = mg/k$. Note that g does not occur in the expression for the period T.

SOLUTION

Part (a)

1. Use the period $T = 2\pi\sqrt{m/k}$ to solve for the force constant:

$$T = 2\pi\sqrt{m/k}$$
$$k = \frac{4\pi^2 m}{T^2} = \frac{4\pi^2(0.260 \text{ kg})}{(1.12 \text{ s})^2} = 8.18 \text{ kg/s}^2 = 8.18 \text{ N/m}$$

2. Set the magnitude of the spring force, ky_0, equal to mg to solve for y_0:

$$ky_0 = mg$$
$$y_0 = \frac{mg}{k} = \frac{(0.260 \text{ kg})(9.81 \text{ m/s}^2)}{8.18 \text{ N/m}} = 0.312 \text{ m}$$

Part (b)

3. Use $2g$ in place of g in the expressions for the period T and the magnitude of the equilibrium stretch, y_0:

$$T = 2\pi\sqrt{m/k} \xrightarrow[g \to 2g]{} T$$
$$y_0 = mg/k \xrightarrow[g \to 2g]{} 2y_0$$

INSIGHT
We see that doubling the force of gravity has no effect on the period (changes it by a factor of 1), but doubles the equilibrium stretch. Therefore, one would observe the same period of oscillation on the Moon or Mars—or even in orbit, as in the case of the Body Mass Measurement Device mentioned earlier in this section.

PRACTICE PROBLEM
A 0.170-kg mass stretches a vertical spring 0.250 m when at rest. What is its period when set into vertical motion? [**Answer:** $T = 1.00$ s]

Some related homework problems: Problem 39, Problem 42

CONCEPTUAL CHECKPOINT 13–1 **COMPARE PERIODS**

When a mass m is attached to a vertical spring with a force constant k, it oscillates with a period T. If the spring is cut in half and the same mass is attached to it, is the period of oscillation **(a)** greater than, **(b)** less than, or **(c)** equal to T?

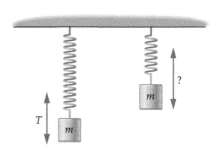

REASONING AND DISCUSSION
The downward force exerted by the mass is of magnitude mg, as is the upward force exerted by the spring. Note that *each coil* of the spring experiences the *same force*, just as each point in a string experiences the same tension. Therefore, each coil elongates by the same amount, regardless of how many coils there are in a given spring. It follows, then, that the total elongation of the spring with half the number of coils is half the total elongation of the longer spring. Since half the elongation for the same applied force means a greater force constant, the half-spring has a larger value of k—it is stiffer. As a result, its period of oscillation is less than the period of the full spring.

ANSWER
(b) The period for the half-spring is less than for the full spring.

13–5 Energy Conservation in Oscillatory Motion

In an ideal system with no friction or other nonconservative forces, the total energy is conserved. For example, the total energy E of a mass on a horizontal spring is the sum of its kinetic energy, $K = \frac{1}{2}mv^2$, and its potential energy, $U = \frac{1}{2}kx^2$. Therefore,

$$E = K + U = \tfrac{1}{2}mv^2 + \tfrac{1}{2}kx^2 \qquad \text{13–13}$$

Since E remains the same throughout the motion, it follows that there is a continual tradeoff between kinetic and potential energy.

This energy tradeoff is illustrated in **Figure 13–10**, where the horizontal line represents the total energy of the system, E, and the parabolic curve is the spring's potential energy, U. At any given value of x, the sum of U and K must equal E; therefore, since U is the amount of energy from the axis to the parabola, K is the amount of energy from the parabola to the horizontal line. We can see, then, that the kinetic energy vanishes at the turning points, $x = +A$ and $x = -A$, as expected. On the other hand, the kinetic energy is greatest at $x = 0$ where the potential energy vanishes.

Since the mass oscillates back and forth with time, the kinetic and potential energies also change with time. For example, the potential energy is

$$U = \tfrac{1}{2}kx^2$$

Letting $x = A\cos(\omega t)$, we have

$$U = \tfrac{1}{2}kA^2\cos^2(\omega t) \qquad \text{13–14}$$

Clearly, the maximum value of U is

$$U_{max} = \tfrac{1}{2}kA^2$$

From Figure 13–10, we see that the maximum value of U is simply the total energy of the system, E. Therefore

$$E = U_{max} = \tfrac{1}{2}kA^2 \qquad \text{13–15}$$

This result leads to the following conclusion:

> In simple harmonic motion, the total energy is proportional to the square of the amplitude of motion.

Similarly, the kinetic energy of the mass is

$$K = \tfrac{1}{2}mv^2$$

Letting $v = -A\omega\sin(\omega t)$ yields

$$K = \tfrac{1}{2}mA^2\omega^2\sin^2(\omega t)$$

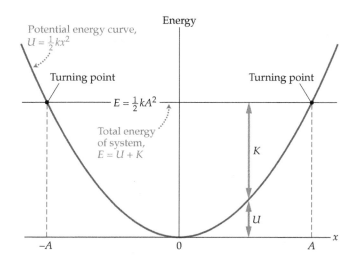

Potential energy curve,
$U = \frac{1}{2}kx^2$

Turning point

Turning point

Energy

$E = \frac{1}{2}kA^2$

Total energy
of system,
$E = U + K$

K

U

$-A$

0

A

x

◀ **FIGURE 13–10 Energy as a function of position in simple harmonic motion**

The parabola represents the potential energy of the spring, $U = \frac{1}{2}kx^2$. The horizontal line shows the total energy of the system, $E = U + K$, which is constant. It follows that the distance from the parabola to the total-energy line is the kinetic energy, K. Note that the kinetic energy vanishes at the turning points, $x = A$ and $x = -A$. At these points the energy is purely potential, and thus the total energy of the system is $E = \frac{1}{2}kA^2$.

FIGURE 13–11 Energy as a function of time in simple harmonic motion
The sum of the potential energy, U, and the kinetic energy, K, is equal to the (constant) total energy E at all times. Note that when one energy (U or K) has its maximum value, the other energy is zero.

REAL-WORLD PHYSICS
Maximum Potential and Kinetic Energy

The maximum potential energy of a mass–spring system is the same as the maximum kinetic energy of the mass. When the system has its maximum potential energy, the kinetic energy of the mass is zero; when the mass has its maximum kinetic energy, the potential energy of the system is zero.

It follows that the maximum kinetic energy is

$$K_{max} = \tfrac{1}{2}mA^2\omega^2 \qquad \text{13–16}$$

As noted, the maximum kinetic energy occurs when the potential energy is zero; hence the maximum kinetic energy must equal the total energy, E. That is,

$$E = U + K = U_{max} + 0 = 0 + K_{max}$$

At first glance, Equation 13–16 doesn't seem to be the same as Equation 13–15. However, if we recall that $\omega^2 = k/m$ (Equation 13–10), we see that

$$K_{max} = \tfrac{1}{2}mA^2\omega^2 = \tfrac{1}{2}mA^2(k/m) = \tfrac{1}{2}kA^2$$

Therefore, $K_{max} = U_{max} = E$, as expected, and the kinetic energy as a function of time is

$$K = \tfrac{1}{2}kA^2 \sin^2(\omega t) \qquad \text{13–17}$$

K and U are plotted as functions of time in **Figure 13–11**. The horizontal line at the top is E, the sum of U and K at all times. This shows quite graphically the back-and-forth tradeoff of energy between kinetic and potential. Mathematically, we can see that the total energy E is constant as follows:

$$E = U + K = \tfrac{1}{2}kA^2 \cos^2(\omega t) + \tfrac{1}{2}kA^2 \sin^2(\omega t)$$
$$= \tfrac{1}{2}kA^2[\cos^2(\omega t) + \sin^2(\omega t)] = \tfrac{1}{2}kA^2$$

The last step follows from the fact that $\cos^2\theta + \sin^2\theta = 1$ for all θ.

EXAMPLE 13–6 STOP THE BLOCK

A 0.980-kg block slides on a frictionless, horizontal surface with a speed of 1.32 m/s. The block encounters an unstretched spring with a force constant of 245 N/m, as shown in the sketch. **(a)** How far is the spring compressed before the block comes to rest? **(b)** How long is the block in contact with the spring before it comes to rest?

PICTURE THE PROBLEM
As our sketch shows, the initial energy of the system is entirely kinetic; namely, the kinetic energy of the block with mass $m = 0.980$ kg and speed $v_0 = 1.32$ m/s. When the block momentarily comes to rest after compressing the spring by the amount A, its kinetic energy has been converted into the potential energy of the spring.

STRATEGY

a. We can find the compression, A, by using energy conservation. We set the initial kinetic energy of the block, $\tfrac{1}{2}mv_0^2$, equal to the spring potential energy, $\tfrac{1}{2}kA^2$, and solve for A.

b. If the mass were attached to the spring, it would complete one oscillation in the time $T = 2\pi\sqrt{m/k}$. In moving from the equilibrium position of the spring to maximum compression, the mass has undergone one-quarter of a cycle; thus the time is $T/4$.

SOLUTION

Part (a)

1. Set the initial kinetic energy of the block equal to the spring potential energy:

$$\tfrac{1}{2}mv_0^2 = \tfrac{1}{2}kA^2$$

2. Solve for A, the maximum compression:

$$A = v_0\sqrt{m/k} = (1.32 \text{ m/s})\sqrt{\frac{0.980 \text{ kg}}{245 \text{ N/m}}} = 0.0835 \text{ m}$$

Part (b)

3. Calculate the period of one oscillation:

$$T = 2\pi\sqrt{m/k} = 2\pi\sqrt{\frac{0.980 \text{ kg}}{245 \text{ N/m}}} = 0.397 \text{ s}$$

4. Divide T by four, since the block has been in contact with the spring for one-quarter of an oscillation:

$$t = \tfrac{1}{4}T = \tfrac{1}{4}(0.397 \text{ s}) = 0.0993 \text{ s}$$

INSIGHT

If the horizontal surface had been rough, some of the block's initial kinetic energy would have been converted to thermal energy. In this case, the maximum compression of the spring would be less than that just calculated.

PRACTICE PROBLEM

If the initial speed of the mass in this Example is increased, does the time required to bring it to rest increase, decrease, or stay the same? Check your answer by calculating the time for an initial speed of 1.50 m/s.   [**Answer:** Increasing v increases the amplitude, A. The period is independent of amplitude, however. Thus, the time is the same, $t = 0.0993$ s.]

Some related homework problems: Problem 54, Problem 89

In the following Active Example, we consider a bullet striking a block that is attached to a spring. As the bullet embeds itself in the block, the completely inelastic bullet–block collision dissipates some of the initial kinetic energy into thermal energy. Only the kinetic energy remaining after the collision is available for compressing the spring.

ACTIVE EXAMPLE 13–3 BULLET-BLOCK COLLISION: FIND THE COMPRESSION AND COMPRESSION TIME

A bullet of mass m embeds itself in a block of mass M, which is attached to a spring of force constant k. If the initial speed of the bullet is v_0, find **(a)** the maximum compression of the spring and **(b)** the time for the bullet–block system to come to rest. (See Example 9–5 for a similar system involving a pendulum.)

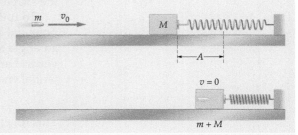

SOLUTION (Test your understanding by performing the calculations indicated in each step.)

Part (a)

1. Use momentum conservation to find the final speed, v, of the bullet–block system:

$$mv_0 = (m + M)v$$
$$v = mv_0/(m + M)$$

2. Find the kinetic energy of the bullet–block system after the collision:

$$\tfrac{1}{2}(m + M)v^2 = \tfrac{1}{2}m^2v_0^2/(m + M)$$

3. Set this kinetic energy equal to $\tfrac{1}{2}kA^2$ to find the maximum compression of the spring:

$$A = mv_0/\sqrt{k(m + M)}$$

Part (b)

4. As in the previous Example, the time to come to rest is one-quarter of a period:

$$t = T/4 = \tfrac{1}{2}\pi\sqrt{(m + M)/k}$$

INSIGHT

Note that the maximum compression depends directly on the initial speed of the bullet. Thus, a measurement of the compression could be used to determine the bullet's speed. On the other hand, the time for the bullet–block system to come to rest is independent of the bullet's speed.

YOUR TURN

Suppose the force constant of the spring is quadrupled. By what factor does the amplitude of compression, A, change? By what factor does the time to come to rest, t, change?

*(Answers to **Your Turn** problems are given in the back of the book.)*

13–6 The Pendulum

One Sunday in 1583, as Galileo Galilei attended services in a cathedral in Pisa, Italy, he suddenly realized something interesting about the chandeliers hanging from the ceiling. Air currents circulating through the cathedral had set them in motion with small oscillations, and Galileo noticed that chandeliers of equal length oscillated with equal periods, even if their amplitudes were different. Indeed, as any given chandelier oscillated with decreasing amplitude its period remained constant. He verified this observation by timing the oscillations with his pulse!

Galileo was much struck by this observation, and after rushing home, he experimented with pendula constructed from different lengths of string and different weights. Continuing to use his pulse as a stopwatch, he observed that the period of a pendulum varies with its length, but is independent of the weight attached to the string. Thus, in one exhilarating afternoon, the young medical student discovered the key characteristics of a pendulum and launched himself on a new career in science. Later, he would go on to construct the first crude pendulum clock and a medical device, known as the pulsilogium, to measure a patient's pulse rate.

In modern terms, we would say that the chandeliers observed by Galileo were undergoing simple harmonic motion, as expected for small oscillations. As we know, the period of simple harmonic motion is independent of amplitude. The fact that the period is also independent of the mass is a special property of the pendulum, as we shall see next.

REAL-WORLD PHYSICS

The pendulum clock and pulsilogium

The Simple Pendulum

A simple pendulum consists of a mass m suspended by a light string or rod of length L. The pendulum has a stable equilibrium when the mass is directly below the suspension point, and oscillates about this position if displaced from it.

To understand the behavior of the pendulum, let's begin by considering the potential energy of the system. As shown in **Figure 13–12**, when the pendulum is at an angle θ with respect to the vertical, the mass m is above its lowest point by a vertical height $L(1 - \cos \theta)$. If we let the potential energy be zero at $\theta = 0$, the potential energy for general θ is

$$U = mgL(1 - \cos \theta)$$ 13–18

This function is plotted in **Figure 13–13**.

▶ **FIGURE 13–12 Motion of a pendulum**
(a) As a pendulum swings away from its equilibrium position, it rises a vertical distance $L - L \cos \theta = L(1 - \cos \theta)$.
(b) As a pendulum bob swings back and forth, it leaks a trail of sand onto a moving sheet of paper, creating a "strip chart" similar to that produced by a mass on a spring in Figure 13–2. In particular, the angle of the pendulum with the vertical varies with time like a sine or a cosine.

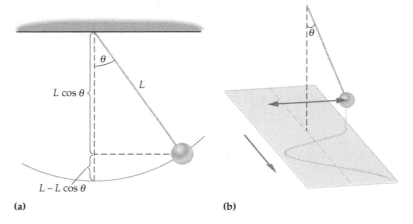

$L \cos \theta$

θ

L

θ

$L - L \cos \theta$

(a)

(b)

▶ **FIGURE 13–13 The potential energy of a simple pendulum**

As a simple pendulum swings away from the vertical by an angle θ, its potential energy increases, as indicated by the solid curve. Near $\theta = 0$ the potential energy of the pendulum is essentially the same as that of a mass on a spring (dashed curve). Therefore, when a pendulum oscillates with small displacements from the vertical, it exhibits simple harmonic motion—the same as a mass on a spring.

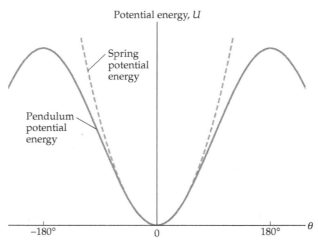

Potential energy, U

Spring potential energy

Pendulum potential energy

$-180°$ 0 $180°$ θ

Note that the stable equilibrium of the pendulum corresponds to a minimum of the potential energy, as expected. Near this minimum, the shape of the potential energy curve is approximately the same as for a mass on a spring, as indicated in Figure 13–13. As a result, when a pendulum oscillates with small displacements from the vertical, its motion is virtually the same as the motion of a mass on a spring; that is, the pendulum exhibits simple harmonic motion.

Next, we consider the forces acting on the mass m. In **Figure 13–14** we show the force of gravity, $m\vec{\mathbf{g}}$, and the tension force in the supporting string, $\vec{\mathbf{T}}$. The tension acts in the radial direction and supplies the force needed to keep the mass moving along its circular path. The net tangential force acting on m, then, is simply the tangential component of its weight:

$$F = mg \sin \theta$$

The direction of the net tangential force is always toward the equilibrium point. Thus F is a restoring force, as expected.

Now, for small angles θ (measured in *radians*), the sine of θ is approximately equal to the angle itself. That is,

$$\sin \theta \approx \theta$$

This is illustrated in **Figure 13–15**. Notice that there is little difference between $\sin \theta$ and θ for angles smaller than about $\pi/8$ rad = 22.5 degrees. In addition, we see from Figure 13–14 that the arc length displacement of the mass from equilibrium is

$$s = L\theta$$

Equivalently,

$$\theta = s/L$$

Therefore, if the mass m is displaced from equilibrium by a small arc length s, the force it experiences is restoring and of magnitude

$$F = mg \sin \theta \approx mg\theta = (mg/L)s \qquad \text{13–19}$$

Note that the restoring force is proportional to the displacement, just as expected for simple harmonic motion.

Let's compare the pendulum to a mass on a spring. In the latter case, the restoring force has a magnitude given by

$$F = kx$$

The restoring force acting on the pendulum has precisely the same form, if we let $x = s$ and

$$k = mg/L$$

Therefore, the period of a pendulum is simply the period of a mass on a spring, $T = 2\pi\sqrt{m/k}$, with k replaced by mg/L:

$$T = 2\pi\sqrt{\frac{m}{k}} = 2\pi\sqrt{\frac{m}{(mg/L)}}$$

Canceling the mass m, we find

Period of a Pendulum (small amplitude)

$$T = 2\pi\sqrt{\frac{L}{g}} \qquad \text{13–20}$$

SI unit: s

This is the classic formula for the period of a pendulum. Note that T depends on the length of the pendulum, L, and on the acceleration of gravity, g. It is independent, however, of the mass m and the amplitude A, as noted by Galileo.

The mass does not appear in the expression for the period of a pendulum, for the same reason that different masses free fall with the same acceleration. In particular, a large mass tends to move more slowly because of its large inertia; on the

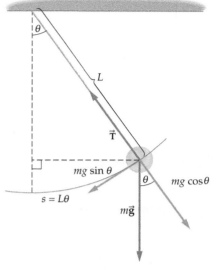

▲ **FIGURE 13–14 Forces acting on a pendulum bob**
When the bob is displaced by an angle θ from the vertical, the restoring force is the tangential component of the weight, $mg \sin \theta$.

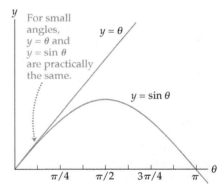

▲ **FIGURE 13–15 Relationship between sin θ and θ**
For small angles measured in radians, $\sin \theta$ is approximately equal to θ. Thus, when considering small oscillations of a pendulum, we can replace $\sin \theta$ with θ. (See also Appendix A.)

other hand, the larger a mass the greater the gravitational force acting on it. These two effects cancel in free fall, as well as in a pendulum.

EXERCISE 13–4

The pendulum in a grandfather clock is designed to take one second to swing in each direction; that is, 2.00 seconds for a complete period. Find the length of a pendulum with a period of 2.00 seconds.

SOLUTION

Solve Equation 13–20 for L and substitute numerical values:

REAL-WORLD PHYSICS

Adjusting a grandfather clock

$$L = \frac{gT^2}{4\pi^2} = \frac{(9.81 \text{ m/s}^2)(2.00 \text{ s})^2}{4\pi^2} = 0.994 \text{ m}$$

CONCEPTUAL CHECKPOINT 13–2   RAISE OR LOWER THE WEIGHT?

If you look carefully at a grandfather clock, you will notice that the weight at the bottom of the pendulum can be moved up or down by turning a small screw. Suppose you have a grandfather clock at home that runs slow. Should you turn the adjusting screw so as to **(a)** raise the weight or **(b)** lower the weight?

REASONING AND DISCUSSION

To make the clock run faster, we want it to go from *tick* to *tick* more rapidly; in other words, we want the period of the pendulum to be decreased. From Equation 13–20 we can see that shortening the pendulum—that is, decreasing L—decreases the period. Hence, the weight should be raised, which effectively shortens the pendulum.

ANSWER

(a) The weight should be raised. This shortens the period and makes the clock run faster.

EXAMPLE 13–7   DROP TIME

A pendulum is constructed from a string 0.627 m long attached to a mass of 0.250 kg. When set in motion, the pendulum completes one oscillation every 1.59 s. If the pendulum is held at rest and the string is cut, how long will it take for the mass to fall through a distance of 1.00 m?

PICTURE THE PROBLEM

Note that the pendulum has a length $L = 0.627$ m and a period of oscillation $T = 1.59$ s. When the pendulum is held at rest in a vertical position, a pair of scissors is used to cut the string. The mass then falls straight downward with an acceleration g through a distance $y = 1.00$ m.

STRATEGY

At first it might seem that the period of oscillation and the time of fall are unrelated. Recall, however, that the period of a pendulum depends on both its length *and* the acceleration of gravity g *at the location of the pendulum.*

To solve this problem, then, we first use the period T to find the acceleration of gravity g. Once g is known, the time of fall is a straightforward kinematics problem (see Example 2–10).

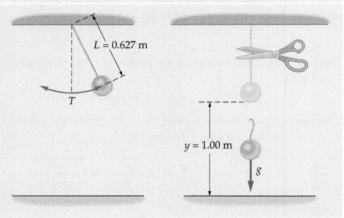

SOLUTION

1. Use the formula for the period of a pendulum to solve for the acceleration of gravity:

$$T = 2\pi\sqrt{L/g} \quad \text{or} \quad g = \frac{4\pi^2 L}{T^2}$$

2. Substitute numerical values to find g:

$$g = \frac{4\pi^2 L}{T^2} = \frac{4\pi^2(0.627 \text{ m})}{(1.59 \text{ s})^2} = 9.79 \text{ m/s}^2$$

3. Use kinematics to solve for the time to drop from rest through a distance y:

$$y = \tfrac{1}{2}gt^2 \quad \text{or} \quad t = \sqrt{2y/g}$$

4. Substitute $y = 1.00$ m and the value of g just found to find the time:

$$t = \sqrt{2y/g} = \sqrt{\frac{2(1.00 \text{ m})}{9.79 \text{ m/s}^2}} = 0.452 \text{ s}$$

INSIGHT

The fact that the acceleration of gravity g varies from place to place on the Earth was mentioned in Chapter 2. In fact, "gravity maps," such as the one shown in the photo at the right, are valuable tools for geologists attempting to understand the underground properties of a given region. One instrument geologists use to make gravity maps is basically a very precise pendulum whose period can be accurately measured. Slight changes in the period from one location to another, or from one elevation to another, correspond to slight changes in g. More common in recent decades is an electronic "gravimeter" that uses a mass on a spring and relates the force of gravity to the stretch of the spring. These gravimeters can measure g with an accuracy of one part in 1000 million.

PRACTICE PROBLEM

If a mass falls 1.00 m in a time of 0.451 s, what are **(a)** the acceleration of gravity and **(b)** the period of a pendulum of length 0.500 m at that location?   [**Answer:** (a) 9.83 m/s², (b) 1.42 s]

Some related homework problems: Problem 60, Problem 62

▲ A map of gravitational strength for the state of Ohio. The purple areas are those where the gravitational field is weakest. Areas where the field is strongest (red) represent regions where denser rocks lie near the surface.

*The Physical Pendulum

In the ideal version of a simple pendulum, a bob of mass m swings back and forth a distance L from the suspension point. All of the pendulum's mass is assumed to be concentrated in the bob, which is treated as a point mass. On the other hand, a **physical pendulum** is one in which the mass is not concentrated at a point, but instead is distributed over a finite volume. Examples are shown in **Figure 13–16**. Detailed mathematical analysis shows that if the moment of inertia (Chapter 10) of a physical pendulum about its axis of rotation is I, and the distance from the axis to the center of mass is ℓ, the period of the pendulum is given by the following:

Period of a Physical Pendulum

$$T = 2\pi\sqrt{\frac{\ell}{g}}\left(\sqrt{\frac{I}{m\ell^2}}\right)$$

13–21

SI unit: s

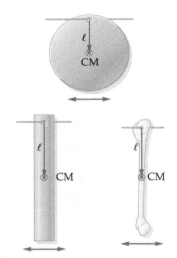

▲ **FIGURE 13–16 Examples of physical pendula**

In each case, an object of definite size and shape oscillates about a given pivot point. The period of oscillation depends in detail on the location of the pivot point as well as on the distance ℓ from it to the center of mass, CM.

Note that the first part of the expression, $2\pi\sqrt{\ell/g}$, is the period of a simple pendulum with all its mass concentrated at the center of mass. The second factor, $\sqrt{I/m\ell^2}$, is a correction that takes into account the size and shape of the physical pendulum. Thus, writing the period in this form, rather than canceling one power of ℓ, makes for a convenient comparison with the simple pendulum.

To see how Equation 13–21 works in practice, we first apply it to a simple pendulum of mass m and length L. In this case, the moment of inertia is $I = mL^2$, and the distance to the center of mass is $\ell = L$. As a result, the period is

$$T = 2\pi\sqrt{\frac{\ell}{g}}\left(\sqrt{\frac{I}{m\ell^2}}\right) = 2\pi\sqrt{\frac{L}{g}}\left(\sqrt{\frac{mL^2}{mL^2}}\right) = 2\pi\sqrt{\frac{L}{g}}$$

Thus, as expected, Equation 13–21 also applies to a simple pendulum.

Next, we apply Equation 13–21 to a nontrivial physical pendulum; namely, your leg. When you walk, your leg rotates about the hip joint much like a uniform rod pivoted about one end, as indicated in **Figure 13–17**. Thus, if we approximate your leg as a uniform rod of length L, its period can be found using

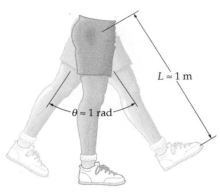

▲ **FIGURE 13–17 The leg as a physical pendulum**
As a person walks, each leg swings much like a physical pendulum. A reasonable approximation is to treat the leg as a uniform rod about 1 m in length.

REAL-WORLD PHYSICS: BIO

Walking speed

Equation 13–21. Recall from Chapter 10 (see Table 10–1) that the moment of inertia of a rod of length L about one end is

$$I = \tfrac{1}{3}mL^2$$

Similarly, the center of mass of your leg is essentially at the center of your leg; thus,

$$\ell = \tfrac{1}{2}L$$

Combining these results, we find that the period of your leg is roughly

$$T = 2\pi\sqrt{\frac{\ell}{g}}\left(\sqrt{\frac{I}{m\ell^2}}\right) = 2\pi\sqrt{\frac{\tfrac{1}{2}L}{g}}\left(\sqrt{\frac{\tfrac{1}{3}mL^2}{m\left(\tfrac{1}{2}L\right)^2}}\right) = 2\pi\sqrt{\frac{L}{g}}\left(\sqrt{\frac{2}{3}}\right)$$

Given that a typical human leg is about a meter long ($L = 1.0$ m), we find that its period of oscillation about the hip is approximately $T = 1.6$ s.

The significance of this result is that the natural walking pace of humans and other animals is largely controlled by the swinging motion of their legs as physical pendula. In fact, a great deal of research in animal locomotion has focused on precisely this type of analysis. In the case just considered, suppose that the leg in Figure 13–17 swings through an angle of roughly 1.0 radian, as the foot moves from behind the hip to in front of the hip for the next step. The arc length through which the foot moves is $s = r\theta \approx (1.0\text{ m})(1.0\text{ rad}) = 1.0$ m. Since it takes half a period ($T/2 = 0.80$ s) for the foot to move from behind the hip to in front of it, the average speed of the foot is roughly

$$v = \frac{d}{t} \approx \frac{1.0\text{ m}}{0.80\text{ s}} \approx 1.3\text{ m/s}$$

This is the typical speed of a person taking a brisk walk.

▼ When animals walk, the swinging movement of their legs can be approximated fairly well by treating the legs as physical pendula. Such analysis has proved useful in analyzing the gaits of various creatures, from Beatles to elephants.

PROBLEM-SOLVING NOTE

The Period of a Physical Pendulum

When finding the period of a physical pendulum, recall that I is the moment of inertia about the pivot point and ℓ is the distance from the pivot point to the center of mass.

Returning to Equation 13–21, we can see that the smaller the moment of inertia I, the smaller the period. After all, an object with a small moment of inertia rotates quickly and easily. It therefore completes an oscillation in less time than an object with a larger moment of inertia. In the case of the human leg, the fact that its mass is distributed uniformly along its length—rather than concentrated at the far end—means that its moment of inertia and period are less than for a simple pendulum 1 m long.

ACTIVE EXAMPLE 13–4   FIND THE PERIOD OF OSCILLATION

A Christmas ornament is made from a hollow glass sphere of mass M and radius R. The ornament is suspended from a small hook near its surface. If the ornament is nudged slightly, what is its period of oscillation? (*Note:* The moment of inertia about the pivot point is $I = \frac{5}{3}MR^2$.)

SOLUTION *(Test your understanding by performing the calculations indicated in each step.)*

1. Identify the distance from the axis to the $\ell = R$
   center of mass:

2. Substitute I and ℓ into Equation 13–21: $T = 2\pi\sqrt{\dfrac{R}{g}}\left(\sqrt{\dfrac{5}{3}}\right)$

INSIGHT

The period is greater than that of a simple pendulum of length R.

YOUR TURN

Would you expect the period for a solid spherical ornament to be greater than, less than, or the same as for a hollow spherical ornament? Verify your conclusion by calculating T for a solid spherical ornament. Refer to Table 10–1 for the appropriate moment of inertia.

(Answers to **Your Turn** *problems are given in the back of the book.)*

13–7 Damped Oscillations

To this point we have restricted our considerations to oscillating systems in which no mechanical energy is gained or lost. In most physical systems, however, there is some loss of mechanical energy to friction, air resistance, or other nonconservative forces. As the mechanical energy of a system decreases, its amplitude of oscillation decreases as well, as expected from Equation 13–15. This type of motion is referred to as a **damped oscillation.**

In a typical situation, an oscillating mass may lose its mechanical energy to a force such as air resistance that is proportional to the speed of the mass and opposite in direction. The force in such a case can be written as

$$\vec{\mathbf{F}} = -b\vec{\mathbf{v}}$$

The constant b is referred to as the **damping constant**; it is a measure of the strength of the damping force, and its SI units are kg/s.

If the damping constant is small, the system will continue to oscillate, but with a continuously decreasing amplitude. This type of motion, referred to as **underdamped,** is illustrated in **Figure 13–18 (a)**. In such cases, the amplitude decreases exponentially with time. Thus, if A_0 is the initial amplitude of an oscillating mass m, the amplitude at the time t is

$$A = A_0 e^{-bt/2m}$$

The exponential dependence of the amplitude is indicated by the dashed curve in the figure.

As the damping is increased, a point is reached where the system no longer oscillates, but instead simply relaxes back to the equilibrium position, as shown in **Figure 13–18 (b)**. A system with this type of behavior is said to be **critically damped.** If the damping is increased beyond this point, the system is said to be **overdamped.** In this case, the system still returns to equilibrium without oscillating, but the time required is greater. This is also illustrated in the figure.

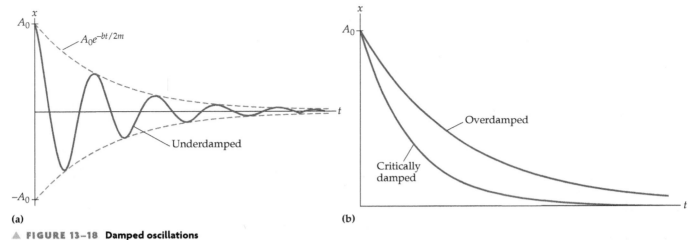

(a)

(b)

▲ **FIGURE 13–18 Damped oscillations**
(a) In underdamped oscillations, the position continues to oscillate as a function of time, but the amplitude of oscillation decreases exponentially. **(b)** In critically damped and overdamped motion, no oscillations occur. Instead, an object simply settles back to its equilibrium position without overshooting. Equilibrium is reached most rapidly in the critically damped case.

Some mechanical systems are designed to be near the condition for critical damping. If such a system is displaced from equilibrium, it will return to equilibrium, without oscillating, in the shortest possible time. For example, shock absorbers are designed so that a car that has just hit a bump will return to equilibrium quickly, without a lot of up-and-down oscillations.

13–8 Driven Oscillations and Resonance

In the previous section we considered the effects of removing energy from an oscillating system. It is also possible, however, to increase the energy of a system, or to replace the energy lost to various forms of friction. This can be done by applying an external force that does positive work.

Suppose, for example, that you hold the end of a string from which a small weight is suspended, as in **Figure 13–19**. If the weight is set in motion and you hold your hand still, it will soon stop oscillating. If you move your hand back and forth in a horizontal direction, however, you can keep the weight oscillating indefinitely. The motion of your hand is said to be "driving" the weight, leading to **driven oscillations.**

The response of the weight in this example depends on the frequency of your hand's back-and-forth motion, as you can readily verify for yourself. For instance, if you move your hand very slowly, the weight will simply track the motion of your hand. Similarly, if you oscillate your hand very rapidly, the weight will exhibit only small oscillations. Oscillating your hand at an intermediate frequency, however, can result in large amplitude oscillations for the weight.

Just what is an appropriate intermediate frequency? Well, to achieve a large response, your hand should drive the weight at the frequency at which it oscillates when not being driven. This is referred to as the **natural frequency,** f_0, of the system. For example, the natural frequency of a pendulum of length L is simply the inverse of its period:

$$f_0 = \frac{1}{T} = \frac{1}{2\pi}\sqrt{\frac{g}{L}}$$

Similarly, the natural frequency of a mass on a spring is

$$f_0 = \frac{1}{T} = \frac{1}{2\pi}\sqrt{\frac{k}{m}}$$

In general, driving any system at a frequency near its natural frequency results in large oscillations.

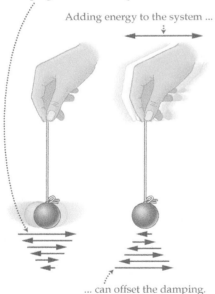

Damping reduces the amplitude of motion.

Adding energy to the system ...

... can offset the damping.

▲ **FIGURE 13–19 Driven oscillations**
If the support point of a pendulum is held still, its oscillations quickly die away due to damping. If the support point is oscillated back and forth, however, the pendulum will continue swinging. This is called "driving" the pendulum. If the driving frequency is close to the natural frequency of the pendulum—the frequency at which it oscillates when the support point is held still—its amplitude of motion can become quite large.

As an example, **Figure 13–20** shows a plot of amplitude, A, versus driving frequency, f, for a mass on a spring. Note the large amplitude for frequencies near f_0. This type of large response, due to frequency matching, is known as **resonance,** and the curves shown in Figure 13–20 are referred to as **resonance curves.** The five curves shown in Figure 13–20 correspond to different amounts of damping, as indicated. As we can see, systems with small damping have a high, narrow peak on their resonance curve. This means that resonance is a large effect in these systems, and that it is very sensitive to frequency. On the other hand, systems with large damping have resonance peaks that are broad and low.

Resonance plays an important role in a variety of physical systems, from a pendulum to atoms in a laser to a tuner in a radio or TV. As we shall see in Chapter 24, for example, adjusting the tuning knob in a radio changes the resonance frequency of the electric circuit in the tuner. When its resonance frequency matches the frequency being broadcast by a station (101 MHz, perhaps), that station is picked up. To change stations, we simply change the resonance frequency of the tuner to the frequency of another station. A good tuner will have little damping, so stations that are even slightly "off resonance" will have small response, and hence will not be heard.

Mechanical examples of resonance are all around us as well. In fact, you might want to try the following experiment the next time you notice a spider in its web. Move close to the web and hum, starting with a low pitch. Slowly increase the pitch of your humming, and soon you will notice the spider react excitedly. You have hit the resonance frequency of its web, causing it to vibrate and making the spider think he has snagged a lunch. If you continue to increase your humming frequency, the spider quiets down again, because you have gone past the resonance. Each individual spider web you encounter will resonate at a specific, and different, frequency.

Man-made structures can show resonance effects as well. One of the most dramatic and famous examples is the collapse of Washington's Tacoma Narrows bridge in 1940. High winds through the narrows had often set the bridge into a gentle swaying motion, resulting in its being known by the affectionate nickname "Galloping Girdie." During one particular wind storm, however, the bridge experienced a resonance-like effect, and the amplitude of its swaying motion began to increase. Alarmed officials closed the bridge to traffic, and a short time later the swaying motion became so great that the bridge broke apart and fell into the waters below. Needless to say, bridges built since that time have been designed to prevent such catastrophic oscillations.

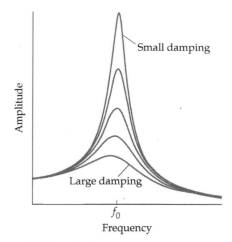

▲ **FIGURE 13–20 Resonance curves for various amounts of damping**
When the damping is small, the amplitude of oscillation can become very large for frequencies close to the natural frequency, f_0. When the damping is large, the amplitude has only a low, broad peak near the natural frequency.

▲ Anyone who has ever pushed a child on a swing (left) knows that the timing of the pushes is critical. If they are synchronized with the natural frequency of the swing, the amplitude can increase rapidly. This phenomenon of resonance can have dangerous consequences. In 1940, the Tacoma Narrows bridge (right), completed only four months earlier, collapsed when high winds set the bridge swaying at one of its resonant frequencies.

THE BIG PICTURE PUTTING PHYSICS IN CONTEXT

LOOKING BACK | LOOKING AHEAD

Uniform circular motion (Chapter 10) is used to better understand simple harmonic motion in Section 13–3.

Newton's second law, $F = ma$ (Chapter 5), is used in the discussion of a mass on a spring in Section 13–4. We also use the force law for a spring, $F = kx$ (Chapter 6), in that section.

The concepts of kinetic energy (Chapter 7) and potential energy (Chapter 8) play key roles in understanding oscillatory motion. In particular, we apply energy conservation to oscillations in Section 13–5.

Frequency, f, and period, T, play key roles in the study of mechanical waves and sound in Chapter 14. They reappear when we study electromagnetic waves in Chapter 25.

Though a mass on a spring may seem far removed from an electric circuit, we show in Chapter 24 that there is in fact a deep connection. In particular, the motion of a mass on a spring is directly analogous to the current in a specific type of circuit referred to as an *RLC* circuit.

In Chapter 30 we study the beginnings of modern physics, and blackbody radiation in particular. As we shall see, the frequency f of light is directly related to the energy of a "particle of light," referred to as a photon.

CHAPTER SUMMARY

13–1 PERIODIC MOTION

Periodic motion repeats after a definite length of time.

Period

The period, T, is the time required for a motion to repeat:

T = time required for one cycle of a periodic motion

Frequency

Frequency, f, is the number of oscillations per unit time.

Equivalently, f is the inverse of the period:

$$f = \frac{1}{T}$$

13–1

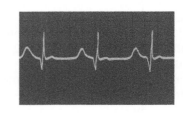

Angular Frequency

Angular frequency, ω, is 2π times the frequency:

$$\omega = 2\pi f = \frac{2\pi}{T}$$

13–5

Rapid motion corresponds to a short period and a large frequency.

13–2 SIMPLE HARMONIC MOTION

A particular type of periodic motion is simple harmonic motion. A classic example of simple harmonic motion is the oscillation of a mass attached to a spring.

Restoring Force

Simple harmonic motion occurs when the restoring force is proportional to the displacement from equilibrium.

Amplitude

The maximum displacement from equilibrium is referred to as the amplitude, A.

Position Versus Time

The position, x, of an object undergoing simple harmonic motion varies with time as $A \cos(\omega t)$:

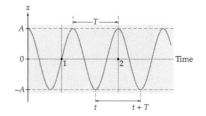

$$x = A \cos\left(\frac{2\pi}{T}t\right) = A \cos(\omega t)$$

13–2, 13–4

13–3 CONNECTIONS BETWEEN UNIFORM CIRCULAR MOTION AND SIMPLE HARMONIC MOTION

A close relationship exists between uniform circular motion and simple harmonic motion. In particular, circular motion viewed from the side—by projecting a shadow on a screen, for example—is simple harmonic.

Velocity

The velocity as a function of time in simple harmonic motion is

$$v = -A\omega \sin(\omega t)$$
13–6

Acceleration

The acceleration as a function of time in simple harmonic motion is

$$a = -A\omega^2 \cos(\omega t)$$
13–8

Maximum Speed and Acceleration

The maximum speed of an object in simple harmonic motion is

$$v_{max} = A\omega$$
13–7

Its maximum acceleration has a magnitude of

$$a_{max} = A\omega^2$$
13–9

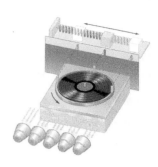

13–4 THE PERIOD OF A MASS ON A SPRING

An important special case of simple harmonic motion is a mass on a spring.

Period

The period of a mass m attached to a spring of force constant k is

$$T = 2\pi \sqrt{\frac{m}{k}}$$
13–11

Vertical Spring

A mass attached to a vertical spring causes it to stretch to a new equilibrium position. Oscillations about this new equilibrium are simple harmonic, with a period given by Equation 13–11.

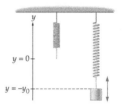

13–5 ENERGY CONSERVATION IN OSCILLATORY MOTION

In an ideal oscillatory system, the total energy remains constant. This means that the kinetic and potential energies of the system vary with time in such a way that their sum remains fixed.

Total Energy

The total energy in simple harmonic motion is proportional to the amplitude, A, squared. For a mass on a spring, the total energy, E, is

$$E = \tfrac{1}{2}kA^2$$
13–15

Potential Energy as a Function of Time

For a mass on a spring, the potential energy varies with time as follows:

$$U = \tfrac{1}{2}kA^2 \cos^2(\omega t)$$
13–14

Kinetic Energy as a Function of Time

Similarly, the kinetic energy as a function of time is

$$K = \tfrac{1}{2}kA^2 \sin^2(\omega t)$$
13–17

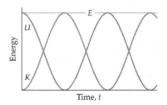

13–6 THE PENDULUM

A pendulum oscillating with small amplitude also exhibits simple harmonic motion.

Simple Pendulum

A simple, or ideal, pendulum is one in which all the mass is concentrated at a single point a distance L from the suspension point.

Period of a Simple Pendulum

The period of a simple pendulum of length L is

$$T = 2\pi \sqrt{\frac{L}{g}}$$
13–20

*Physical Pendulum

In a physical pendulum, the mass is distributed throughout a finite volume. Thus, a physical pendulum has a definite shape, whereas a simple pendulum is characterized by a point mass.

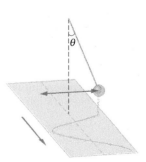

*Period of a Physical Pendulum

The period of a physical pendulum is

$$T = 2\pi\sqrt{\frac{\ell}{g}}\left(\sqrt{\frac{I}{m\ell^2}}\right) \qquad 13\text{–}21$$

In this expression, I is the moment of inertia about the pivot point, and ℓ is the distance from the pivot point to the center of mass.

13–7 DAMPED OSCILLATIONS

Systems in which mechanical energy is lost to other forms, such as heat or sound, eventually come to rest at the equilibrium position. How they move as they come to rest depends on the amount of damping.

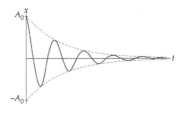

Underdamping

In an underdamped case, a system of mass m and damping constant b continues to oscillate as its amplitude steadily decreases with time. The decrease in amplitude is exponential:

$$A = A_0 e^{-bt/2m}$$

Critical Damping

In a system with critical damping, no oscillations occur. The system simply relaxes back to equilibrium in the least possible time.

Overdamping

An overdamped system also relaxes back to equilibrium with no oscillations. The relaxation occurs more slowly in this case than in critical damping.

13–8 DRIVEN OSCILLATIONS AND RESONANCE

If an oscillating system is driven by an external force, it is possible for energy to be added to the system. This added energy may simply replace energy lost to friction, or, in the case of resonance, it may result in oscillations of large amplitude and energy.

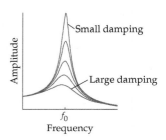

Natural Frequency

The natural frequency of an oscillating system is the frequency at which it oscillates when free from external disturbances.

Resonance

Resonance is the response of an oscillating system to a driving force of the appropriate frequency.

PROBLEM-SOLVING SUMMARY

Type of Problem	Relevant Physical Concepts	Related Examples
Find the position, velocity, and acceleration as a function of time for an object undergoing simple harmonic motion.	In simple harmonic motion, the position, velocity, and acceleration are all sinusoidal functions of time. In particular, $x = A\cos(\omega t)$, $v = -A\omega\sin(\omega t)$, and $a = -A\omega^2\cos(\omega t)$, where $\omega = 2\pi/T$.	Examples 13–1, 13–2 Active Example 13–1
Calculate the maximum speed and acceleration for simple harmonic motion.	The maximum speed is $v_{max} = A\omega$, and the maximum acceleration is $a_{max} = A\omega^2$.	Examples 13–3, 13–4
Relate the period of a mass on a spring to the mass and the force constant.	The period of a mass m attached to a spring of force constant k is $T = 2\pi\sqrt{m/k}$.	Examples 13–4, 13–5, 13–6 Active Examples 13–2, 13–3
Relate the period of a pendulum to its length and to the acceleration of gravity.	The period of a simple pendulum of length L is $T = 2\pi\sqrt{L/g}$. Note that the period is independent of the mass, but does depend on the acceleration of gravity.	Example 13–7
Find the period of a physical pendulum.	Identify the moment of inertia, I, about the pivot point and the distance from the pivot point to the center of mass, ℓ. Then use $T = 2\pi\sqrt{\ell/g}\left(\sqrt{I/m\ell^2}\right)$.	Active Example 13–4

CONCEPTUAL QUESTIONS

For instructor-assigned homework, go to www.masteringphysics.com

(Answers to odd-numbered Conceptual Questions can be found in the back of the book.)

1. A basketball player dribbles a ball with a steady period of T seconds. Is the motion of the ball periodic? Is it simple harmonic? Explain.

2. A person rides on a Ferris wheel that rotates with constant angular speed. If the Sun is directly overhead, does the person's shadow on the ground undergo periodic motion? Does it undergo simple harmonic motion? Explain.

3. An air-track cart bounces back and forth between the two ends of an air track. Is this motion periodic? Is it simple harmonic? Explain.

4. If a mass m and a mass $2m$ oscillate on identical springs with identical amplitudes, they both have the same maximum kinetic energy. How can this be? Shouldn't the larger mass have more kinetic energy? Explain.

5. An object oscillating with simple harmonic motion completes a cycle in a time T. If the object's amplitude is doubled, the time

required for one cycle is still T, even though the object covers twice the distance. How can this be? Explain.

6. The position of an object undergoing simple harmonic motion is given by $x = A \cos(Bt)$. Explain the physical significance of the constants A and B. What is the frequency of this object's motion?

7. The velocity of an object undergoing simple harmonic motion is given by $v = -C \sin(Dt)$. Explain the physical significance of the constants C and D. What are the amplitude and period of this object's motion?

8. The pendulum bob in Figure 13–12 leaks sand onto the strip chart. What effect does this loss of sand have on the period of the pendulum? Explain.

9. Soldiers on the march are often ordered to break cadence in their step when crossing a bridge. Why is this a good idea?

PROBLEMS AND CONCEPTUAL EXERCISES

Note: Answers to odd-numbered Problems and Conceptual Exercises can be found in the back of the book. **IP** *denotes an integrated conceptual/quantitative problem, with both conceptual and numerical parts;* **BIO** *identifies problems of biological or medical interest;* **CE** *indicates a conceptual exercise.* **Predict/Explain** *problems ask for two responses:* **(a)** *your prediction of a physical outcome, and* **(b)** *the best explanation among three provided. On all problems, red bullets (•, ••, •••) are used to indicate the level of difficulty.*

SECTION 13–1   PERIODIC MOTION

1. • A small cart on a 5.0-m-long air track moves with a speed of 0.85 m/s. Bumpers at either end of the track cause the cart to reverse direction and maintain the same speed. Find the period and frequency of this motion.

2. • A person in a rocking chair completes 12 cycles in 21 s. What are the period and frequency of the rocking?

3. • While fishing for catfish, a fisherman suddenly notices that the bobber (a floating device) attached to his line is bobbing up and down with a frequency of 2.6 Hz. What is the period of the bobber's motion?

4. • If you dribble a basketball with a frequency of 1.77 Hz, how long does it take for you to complete 12 dribbles?

5. • You take your pulse and observe 74 heartbeats in a minute. What are the period and frequency of your heartbeat?

6. •• **IP** **(a)** Your heart beats with a frequency of 1.45 Hz. How many beats occur in a minute? **(b)** If the frequency of your heartbeat increases, will the number of beats in a minute increase, decrease, or stay the same? **(c)** How many beats occur in a minute if the frequency increases to 1.55 Hz?

7. •• You rev your car's engine to 2700 rpm (rev/min). **(a)** What are the period and frequency of the engine? **(b)** If you change the period of the engine to 0.044 s, how many rpms is it doing?

SECTION 13–2   SIMPLE HARMONIC MOTION

8. • **CE** A mass moves back and forth in simple harmonic motion with amplitude A and period T. **(a)** In terms of A, through what distance does the mass move in the time T? **(b)** Through what distance does it move in the time $5T/2$?

9. • **CE** A mass moves back and forth in simple harmonic motion with amplitude A and period T. **(a)** In terms of T, how long does it take for the mass to move through a total distance of $2A$? **(b)** How long does it take for the mass to move through a total distance of $3A$?

10. • The position of a mass oscillating on a spring is given by $x = (3.2 \text{ cm}) \cos[2\pi t/(0.58 \text{ s})]$. **(a)** What is the period of this motion? **(b)** What is the first time the mass is at the position $x = 0$?

11. • The position of a mass oscillating on a spring is given by $x = (7.8 \text{ cm}) \cos[2\pi t/(0.68 \text{ s})]$. **(a)** What is the frequency of this motion? **(b)** When is the mass first at the position $x = -7.8$ cm?

12. •• **CE** A position-versus-time plot for an object undergoing simple harmonic motion is given in **Figure 13–21**. Rank the six points indicated in the figure in order of increasing **(a)** speed, **(b)** velocity, and **(c)** acceleration. Indicate ties where necessary.

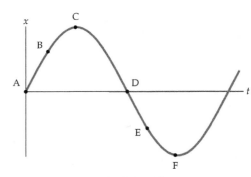

▲ **FIGURE 13–21** Problem 12

13. •• **CE** A mass on a spring oscillates with simple harmonic motion of amplitude A about the equilibrium position $x = 0$. Its maximum speed is v_{max} and its maximum acceleration is a_{max}. **(a)** What is the speed of the mass at $x = 0$? **(b)** What is the acceleration of the mass at $x = 0$? **(c)** What is the speed of the mass at $x = A$? **(d)** What is the acceleration of the mass at $x = A$?

14. •• A mass oscillates on a spring with a period of 0.73 s and an amplitude of 5.4 cm. Write an equation giving x as a function of time, assuming the mass starts at $x = A$ at time $t = 0$.

15. •• **IP Molecular Oscillations** An atom in a molecule oscillates about its equilibrium position with a frequency of 2.00×10^{14} Hz and a maximum displacement of 3.50 nm. **(a)** Write an expression giving x as a function of time for this atom, assuming that $x = A$ at $t = 0$. **(b)** If, instead, we assume that $x = 0$ at $t = 0$, would your expression for position versus time use a sine function or a cosine function? Explain.

16. •• A mass oscillates on a spring with a period T and an amplitude 0.48 cm. The mass is at the equilibrium position $x = 0$ at $t = 0$, and is moving in the positive direction. Where is the mass at the times **(a)** $t = T/8$, **(b)** $t = T/4$, **(c)** $t = T/2$ and **(d)** $t = 3T/4$? **(e)** Plot your results for parts (a) through (d) with the vertical axis representing position and the horizontal axis representing time.

17. •• The position of a mass on a spring is given by $x = (6.5 \text{ cm}) \cos[2\pi t/(0.88 \text{ s})]$. **(a)** What is the period, T, of this motion? **(b)** Where is the mass at $t = 0.25$ s? **(c)** Show that the mass is at the same location at 0.25 s $+ T$ seconds as it is at 0.25 s.

18. •• **IP** A mass attached to a spring oscillates with a period of 3.35 s. **(a)** If the mass starts from rest at $x = 0.0440$ m and time $t = 0$, where is it at time $t = 6.37$ s? **(b)** Is the mass moving in the positive or negative x direction at $t = 6.37$ s? Explain.

19. ••• An object moves with simple harmonic motion of period T and amplitude A. During one complete cycle, for what length of time is the position of the object greater than $A/2$?

20. ••• An object moves with simple harmonic motion of period T and amplitude A. During one complete cycle, for what length of time is the speed of the object greater than $v_{max}/2$?

21. ••• An object executing simple harmonic motion has a maximum speed v_{max} and a maximum acceleration a_{max}. Find (a) the amplitude and (b) the period of this motion. Express your answers in terms of v_{max} and a_{max}.

SECTION 13–3 CONNECTIONS BETWEEN UNIFORM CIRCULAR MOTION AND SIMPLE HARMONIC MOTION

22. • A ball rolls on a circular track of radius 0.62 m with a constant angular speed of 1.3 rad/s in the counterclockwise direction. If the angular position of the ball at $t = 0$ is $\theta = 0$, find the x component of the ball's position at the times 2.5 s, 5.0 s, and 7.5 s. Let $\theta = 0$ correspond to the positive x direction.

23. •• An object executing simple harmonic motion has a maximum speed of 4.3 m/s and a maximum acceleration of 0.65 m/s². Find **(a)** the amplitude and **(b)** the period of this motion.

24. • A child rocks back and forth on a porch swing with an amplitude of 0.204 m and a period of 2.80 s. Assuming the motion is approximately simple harmonic, find the child's maximum speed.

25. •• **IP** A 30.0-g goldfinch lands on a slender branch, where it oscillates up and down with simple harmonic motion of amplitude 0.0335 m and period 1.65 s. **(a)** What is the maximum acceleration of the finch? Express your answer as a fraction of the acceleration of gravity, g. **(b)** What is the maximum speed of the goldfinch? **(c)** At the time when the goldfinch experiences its maximum acceleration, is its speed a maximum or a minimum? Explain.

26. •• **BIO Tuning Forks in Neurology** Tuning forks are used in the diagnosis of nervous afflictions known as large-fiber polyneuropathies, which are often manifested in the form of reduced sensitivity to vibrations. Disorders that can result in this type of pathology include diabetes and nerve damage from exposure to heavy metals. The tuning fork in **Figure 13–22** has a frequency of 128 Hz. If the tips of the fork move with an amplitude of 1.25 mm, find **(a)** their maximum speed and **(b)** their maximum acceleration. Give your answer to part (b) as a multiple of g.

▲ **FIGURE 13–22** A Buck neurological hammer with tuning fork and Wartenburg pinwheel. (Problem 26)

27. •• A vibrating structural beam in a spacecraft can cause problems if the frequency of vibration is fairly high. Even if the amplitude of vibration is only a fraction of a millimeter, the acceleration of the beam can be several times greater than the acceleration due to gravity. As an example, find the maximum acceleration of a beam that vibrates with an amplitude of 0.25 mm at the rate of 110 vibrations per second. Give your answer as a multiple of g.

28. •• A peg on a turntable moves with a constant tangential speed of 0.77 m/s in a circle of radius 0.23 m. The peg casts a shadow on a wall. Find the following quantities related to the motion of the shadow: **(a)** the period, **(b)** the amplitude, **(c)** the maximum speed, and **(d)** the maximum magnitude of the acceleration.

29. •• The pistons in an internal combustion engine undergo a motion that is approximately simple harmonic. If the amplitude of motion is 3.5 cm, and the engine runs at 1700 rev/min, find **(a)** the maximum acceleration of the pistons and **(b)** their maximum speed.

30. •• A 0.84-kg air cart is attached to a spring and allowed to oscillate. If the displacement of the air cart from equilibrium is $x = (10.0 \text{ cm}) \cos[(2.00 \text{ s}^{-1})t + \pi]$, find **(a)** the maximum kinetic energy of the cart and **(b)** the maximum force exerted on it by the spring.

31. •• **IP** A person rides on a mechanical bucking horse (see **Figure 13–23**) that oscillates up and down with simple harmonic motion. The period of the bucking is 0.74 s and the amplitude is slowly increasing. At a certain amplitude the rider must hang on to prevent separating from the mechanical horse. **(a)** Give a strategy that will allow you to calculate this amplitude. **(b)** Carry out your strategy and find the desired amplitude.

▲ **FIGURE 13-23** Problem 31

SECTION 13-4 THE PERIOD OF A MASS ON A SPRING

32. • **CE Predict/Explain** If a mass m is attached to a given spring, its period of oscillation is T. If two such springs are connected end to end and the same mass m is attached, **(a)** is the resulting period of oscillation greater than, less than, or equal to T? **(b)** Choose the *best explanation* from among the following:
    I. Connecting two springs together makes the spring stiffer, which means that less time is required for an oscillation.
    II. The period of oscillation does not depend on the length of a spring, only on its force constant and the mass attached to it.
    III. The longer spring stretches more easily, and hence takes longer to complete an oscillation.

33. • **CE Predict/Explain** An old car with worn-out shock absorbers oscillates with a given frequency when it hits a speed bump. If the driver adds a couple of passengers to the car and hits another speed bump, **(a)** is the car's frequency of oscillation greater than, less than, or equal to what it was before? **(b)** Choose the *best explanation* from among the following:
    I. Increasing the mass on a spring increases its period, and hence decreases its frequency.
    II. The frequency depends on the force constant of the spring but is independent of the mass.
    III. Adding mass makes the spring oscillate more rapidly, which increases the frequency.

34. • **CE Predict/Explain** The two blocks in **Figure 13-24** have the same mass, m. All the springs have the same force constant, k, and are at their equilibrium length. When the blocks are set into oscillation, **(a)** is the period of block 1 greater than, less than, or equal to the period of block 2? **(b)** Choose the *best explanation* from among the following:
    I. Springs in parallel are stiffer than springs in series; therefore the period of block 1 is smaller than the period of block 2.

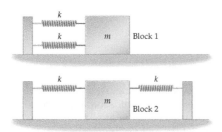

▲ **FIGURE 13-24** Problems 34 and 38

II. The two blocks experience the same restoring force for a given displacement from equilibrium, and hence they have equal periods of oscillation.
III. The force of the two springs on block 2 partially cancel one another, leading to a longer period of oscillation.

35. • Show that the units of the quantity $\sqrt{k/m}$ are s^{-1}.

36. • A 0.46-kg mass attached to a spring undergoes simple harmonic motion with a period of 0.77 s. What is the force constant of the spring?

37. •• **CE** System A consists of a mass m attached to a spring with a force constant k; system B has a mass $2m$ attached to a spring with a force constant k; system C has a mass $3m$ attached to a spring with a force constant $6k$; and system D has a mass m attached to a spring with a force constant $4k$. Rank these systems in order of increasing period of oscillation.

38. •• Find the periods of block 1 and block 2 in Figure 13-24, given that $k = 49.2 \, \text{N/m}$ and $m = 1.25 \, \text{kg}$.

39. •• When a 0.50-kg mass is attached to a vertical spring, the spring stretches by 15 cm. How much mass must be attached to the spring to result in a 0.75-s period of oscillation?

40. •• A spring with a force constant of 69 N/m is attached to a 0.57-kg mass. Assuming that the amplitude of motion is 3.1 cm, determine the following quantities for this system: **(a)** ω, **(b)** v_{max}, **(c)** T.

41. •• Two people with a combined mass of 125 kg hop into an old car with worn-out shock absorbers. This causes the springs to compress by 8.00 cm. When the car hits a bump in the road, it oscillates up and down with a period of 1.65 s. Find **(a)** the total load supported by the springs and **(b)** the mass of the car.

42. •• A 0.85-kg mass attached to a vertical spring of force constant 150 N/m oscillates with a maximum speed of 0.35 m/s. Find the following quantities related to the motion of the mass: **(a)** the period, **(b)** the amplitude, **(c)** the maximum magnitude of the acceleration.

43. •• When a 0.213-kg mass is attached to a vertical spring, it causes the spring to stretch a distance d. If the mass is now displaced slightly from equilibrium, it is found to make 102 oscillations in 56.7 s. Find the stretch distance, d.

44. •• **IP** The springs of a 511-kg motorcycle have an effective force constant of 9130 N/m. **(a)** If a person sits on the motorcycle, does its period of oscillation increase, decrease, or stay the same? **(b)** By what percent and in what direction does the period of oscillation change when a 112-kg person rides the motorcycle?

45. ••• **IP** If a mass m is attached to a given spring, its period of oscillation is T. If two such springs are connected end to end, and the same mass m is attached, **(a)** is its period greater than, less than, or the same as with a single spring? **(b)** Verify your answer to part (a) by calculating the new period, T', in terms of the old period T.

SECTION 13-5 ENERGY CONSERVATION IN OSCILLATORY MOTION

46. • How much work is required to stretch a spring 0.133 m if its force constant is 9.17 N/m?

47. • A 0.321-kg mass is attached to a spring with a force constant of 13.3 N/m. If the mass is displaced 0.256 m from equilibrium and released, what is its speed when it is 0.128 m from equilibrium?

48. • Find the total mechanical energy of the system described in the previous problem.

49. •• A 1.8-kg mass attached to a spring oscillates with an amplitude of 7.1 cm and a frequency of 2.6 Hz. What is its energy of motion?

50. •• **IP** A 0.40-kg mass is attached to a spring with a force constant of 26 N/m and released from rest a distance of 3.2 cm from the equilibrium position of the spring. **(a)** Give a strategy that allows you to find the speed of the mass when it is halfway to the equilibrium position. **(b)** Use your strategy to find this speed.

51. •• **(a)** What is the maximum speed of the mass in the previous problem? **(b)** How far is the mass from the equilibrium position when its speed is half the maximum speed?

52. •• A bunch of grapes is placed in a spring scale at a supermarket. The grapes oscillate up and down with a period of 0.48 s, and the spring in the scale has a force constant of 650 N/m. What are **(a)** the mass and **(b)** the weight of the grapes?

53. •• What is the maximum speed of the grapes in the previous problem if their amplitude of oscillation is 2.3 cm?

54. •• **IP** A 0.505-kg block slides on a frictionless horizontal surface with a speed of 1.18 m/s. The block encounters an unstretched spring and compresses it 23.2 cm before coming to rest. **(a)** What is the force constant of this spring? **(b)** For what length of time is the block in contact with the spring before it comes to rest? **(c)** If the force constant of the spring is increased, does the time required to stop the block increase, decrease, or stay the same? Explain.

55. •• A 2.25-g bullet embeds itself in a 1.50-kg block, which is attached to a spring of force constant 785 N/m. If the maximum compression of the spring is 5.88 cm, find **(a)** the initial speed of the bullet and **(b)** the time for the bullet–block system to come to rest.

SECTION 13–6 THE PENDULUM

56. • **CE** Metronomes, such as the penguin shown in the photo, are useful devices for music students. If it is desired to have the metronome tick with a greater frequency, should the penguin's bow tie be moved upward or downward?

How do you like my tie? (Problem 56)

57. • **CE Predict/Explain** A grandfather clock keeps correct time at sea level. If the clock is taken to the top of a nearby mountain, **(a)** would you expect it to keep correct time, run slow, or run fast? **(b)** Choose the *best explanation* from among the following:
  I.   Gravity is weaker at the top of the mountain, leading to a greater period of oscillation.
  II. The length of the pendulum is unchanged, and therefore its period remains the same.
  III. The extra gravity from the mountain causes the period to decrease.

58. • **CE** A pendulum of length L has a period T. How long must the pendulum be if its period is to be $2T$?

59. • An observant fan at a baseball game notices that the radio commentators have lowered a microphone from their booth to just a few inches above the ground, as shown in **Figure 13–25**. The microphone is used to pick up sound from the field and from the fans. The fan also notices that the microphone is slowly swinging back and forth like a simple pendulum. Using her digital watch, she finds that 10 complete oscillations take 60.0 s. How high above the field is the radio booth? (Assume the microphone and its cord can be treated as a simple pendulum.)

▲ **FIGURE 13–25** Problem 59

60. • A simple pendulum of length 2.5 m makes 5.0 complete swings in 16 s. What is the acceleration of gravity at the location of the pendulum?

61. • **United Nations Pendulum** A large pendulum with a 200-lb gold-plated bob 12 inches in diameter is on display in the lobby of the United Nations building. The pendulum has a length of 75 ft. It is used to show the rotation of the Earth—for this reason it is referred to as a Foucault pendulum. What is the least amount of time it takes for the bob to swing from a position of maximum displacement to the equilibrium position of the pendulum? (Assume that the acceleration due to gravity is $g = 9.81 \text{ m/s}^2$ at the UN building.)

62. • Find the length of a simple pendulum that has a period of 1.00 s. Assume that the acceleration of gravity is $g = 9.81 \text{ m/s}^2$.

63. •• **IP** If the pendulum in the previous problem were to be taken to the Moon, where the acceleration of gravity is $g/6$, **(a)** would its period increase, decrease, or stay the same? **(b)** Check your result in part (a) by calculating the period of the pendulum on the Moon.

*64. •• A hula hoop hangs from a peg. Find the period of the hoop as it gently rocks back and forth on the peg. (For a hoop with axis at the rim $I = 2mR^2$, where R is the radius of the hoop.)

*65. •• A fireman tosses his 0.98-kg hat onto a peg, where it oscillates as a physical pendulum (**Figure 13–26**). If the center of mass of the hat is 8.4 cm from the pivot point, and its period of oscillation is 0.73 s, what is the moment of inertia of the hat about the pivot point?

▲ **FIGURE 13–26** Problem 65

*66. •• **IP** Consider a meterstick that oscillates back and forth about a pivot point at one of its ends. **(a)** Is the period of a simple pendulum of length $L = 1.00$ m greater than, less than, or the same as the period of the meterstick? Explain. **(b)** Find the length L of a simple pendulum that has a period equal to the period of the meterstick.

*67. •• On the construction site for a new skyscraper, a uniform beam of steel is suspended from one end. If the beam swings back and forth with a period of 2.00 s, what is its length?

*68. •• **BIO** (a) Find the period of a child's leg as it swings about the hip joint. Assume the leg is 0.55 m long and can be treated as a uniform rod. (b) Estimate the child's walking speed.

69. ••• Suspended from the ceiling of an elevator is a simple pendulum of length L. What is the period of this pendulum if the elevator (a) accelerates upward with an acceleration a, or (b) accelerates downward with an acceleration whose magnitude is greater than zero but less than g? Give your answer in terms of L, g, and a.

GENERAL PROBLEMS

70. • **CE** An object undergoes simple harmonic motion with a period T. In the time $3T/2$ the object moves through a total distance of $12D$. In terms of D, what is the object's amplitude of motion?

71. • **CE** A mass on a string moves with simple harmonic motion. If the period of motion is doubled, with the force constant and the amplitude remaining the same, by what multiplicative factor do the following quantities change: (a) angular frequency, (b) frequency, (c) maximum speed, (d) maximum acceleration, (e) total mechanical energy?

72. • **CE** If the amplitude of a simple harmonic oscillator is doubled, by what multiplicative factor do the following quantities change: (a) angular frequency, (b) frequency, (c) period, (d) maximum speed, (e) maximum acceleration, (f) total mechanical energy?

73. • **CE** A mass m is suspended from the ceiling of an elevator by a spring of force constant k. When the elevator is at rest, the period of the mass is T. Does the period increase, decrease, or remain the same when the elevator (a) moves upward with constant speed or (b) moves upward with constant acceleration?

74. • **CE** A pendulum of length L is suspended from the ceiling of an elevator. When the elevator is at rest, the period of the pendulum is T. Does the period increase, decrease, or remain the same when the elevator (a) moves upward with constant speed or (b) moves upward with constant acceleration?

75. • A 1.8-kg mass is attached to a spring with a force constant of 59 N/m. If the mass is released with a speed of 0.25 m/s at a distance of 8.4 cm from the equilibrium position of the spring, what is its speed when it is halfway to the equilibrium position?

76. • **BIO Measuring an Astronaut's Mass** An astronaut uses a Body Mass Measurement Device (BMMD) to determine her mass. What is the astronaut's mass, given that the force constant of the BMMD is 2600 N/m and the period of oscillation is 0.85 s? (See the discussion on page 427 for more details on the BMMD.)

77. • A typical atom in a solid might oscillate with a frequency of 10^{12} Hz and an amplitude of 0.10 angstrom (10^{-11} m). Find the maximum acceleration of the atom and compare it with the acceleration of gravity.

78. • **Sunspot Observations** Sunspots vary in number as a function of time, exhibiting an approximately 11-year cycle. Galileo made the first European observations of sunspots in 1610, and daily observations were begun in Zurich in 1749. At the present time we are well into the 23rd observed cycle. What is the frequency of the sunspot cycle? Give your answer in Hz.

79. • **BIO Weighing a Bacterium** Scientists are using tiny, nanoscale cantilevers 4 micrometers long and 500 nanometers wide—essentially miniature diving boards—as a sensitive way to measure mass. The cantilevers oscillate up and down with a frequency that depends on the mass placed near the tip, and a laser beam is used to measure the frequency. A single *E. coli* bacterium was measured to have a mass of 665 femtograms =

6.65×10^{-16} kg with this device, as the cantilever oscillated with a frequency of 14.5 MHz. Treating the cantilever as an ideal, massless spring, find its effective force constant.

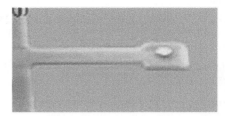

A silicon and silicon nitride cantilever with a 50-nanometer gold dot near its tip.
(Problem 79)

80. •• **CE** An object undergoing simple harmonic motion with a period T is at the position $x = 0$ at the time $t = 0$. At the time $t = 0.25T$ the position of the object is positive. State whether x is positive, negative, or zero at the following times: (a) $t = 1.5T$, (b) $t = 2T$, (c) $t = 2.25T$, and (d) $t = 6.75T$.

81. •• The maximum speed of a 3.1-kg mass attached to a spring is 0.68 m/s, and the maximum force exerted on the mass is 11 N. (a) What is the amplitude of motion for this mass? (b) What is the force constant of the spring? (c) What is the frequency of this system?

82. •• The acceleration of a block attached to a spring is given by $a = -(0.302 \text{ m/s}^2) \cos([2.41 \text{ rad/s}]t)$. (a) What is the frequency of the block's motion? (b) What is the maximum speed of the block? (c) What is the amplitude of the block's motion?

83. •• **Helioseismology** In 1962, physicists at Cal Tech discovered that the surface of the Sun vibrates due to the violent nuclear reactions that roil within its core. This has led to a new field of solar science known as helioseismology. A typical vibration of the Sun is shown in **Figure 13–27**; it has a period of 5.7 minutes. The blue patches in Figure 13–27 are moving outward; the red patches are moving inward. (a) Find the angular frequency of this vibration. (b) The maximum speed at which a patch of the surface moves during a vibration is 4.5 m/s. What is the amplitude of the vibration, assuming it to be simple harmonic motion?

▲ **FIGURE 13–27** A typical vibration pattern of the Sun. (Problem 83)

84. •• **IP** A 9.50-g bullet, moving horizontally with an initial speed v_0, embeds itself in a 1.45-kg pendulum bob that is initially at rest. The length of the pendulum is $L = 0.745$ m. After the collision, the pendulum swings to one side and comes to rest when it has gained a vertical height of 12.4 cm. (a) Is the kinetic energy of the bullet–bob system immediately after the collision greater than, less than, or the same as the kinetic energy of the system just before the collision? Explain. (b) Find the initial speed of the bullet. (c) How long does it take for the bullet–bob system to come to rest for the first time?

85. •• **BIO Spiderweb Oscillations** A 1.44-g spider oscillates on its web, which has a damping constant of 3.30×10^{-5} kg/s. How long does it take for the spider's amplitude of oscillation to decrease by 10.0 percent?

86. •• An object undergoes simple harmonic motion with a period T and amplitude A. In terms of T, how long does it take the object to travel from $x = A$ to $x = A/2$?

87. •• Find the period of oscillation of a disk of mass 0.32 kg and radius 0.15 m if it is pivoted about a small hole drilled near its rim.

88. •• Calculate the ratio of the kinetic energy to the potential energy of a simple harmonic oscillator when its displacement is half its amplitude.

89. •• A 0.363-kg mass slides on a frictionless floor with a speed of 1.24 m/s. The mass strikes and compresses a spring with a force constant of 44.5 N/m. **(a)** How far does the mass travel after contacting the spring before it comes to rest? **(b)** How long does it take for the spring to stop the mass?

90. •• A large rectangular barge floating on a lake oscillates up and down with a period of 4.5 s. Find the damping constant for the barge, given that its mass is 2.44×10^5 kg and that its amplitude of oscillation decreases by a factor of 2.0 in 5.0 minutes.

91. •• **IP** Figure 13–28 shows a displacement-versus-time graph of the periodic motion of a 3.8-kg mass on a spring. **(a)** Referring to the figure, do you expect the maximum speed of the mass to be greater than, less than, or equal to 0.50 m/s? Explain. **(b)** Calculate the maximum speed of the mass. **(c)** How much energy is stored in this system?

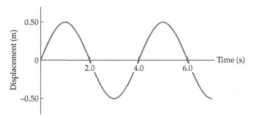

▲ FIGURE 13–28 Problems 91 and 92

92. •• **IP** A 3.8-kg mass on a spring oscillates as shown in the displacement-versus-time graph in Figure 13–28. **(a)** Referring to the graph, at what times between $t = 0$ and $t = 6.0$ s does the mass experience a force of maximum magnitude? Explain. **(b)** Calculate the magnitude of the maximum force exerted on the mass. **(c)** At what times shown in the graph does the mass experience zero force? Explain. **(d)** How much force is exerted on the mass at the time $t = 0.50$ s?

93. •• A 0.45-kg crow lands on a slender branch and bobs up and down with a period of 1.5 s. An eagle flies up to the same branch, scaring the crow away, and lands. The eagle now bobs up and down with a period of 4.8 s. Treating the branch as an ideal spring, find **(a)** the effective force constant of the branch and **(b)** the mass of the eagle.

94. ••• A mass m is connected to the bottom of a vertical spring whose force constant is k. Attached to the bottom of the mass is a string that is connected to a second mass m, as shown in Figure 13–29. Both masses are undergoing simple harmonic vertical motion of amplitude A. At the instant when the acceleration of the masses is a maximum in the upward direction the string breaks, allowing the lower mass to drop to the floor. Find the resulting amplitude of motion of the remaining mass.

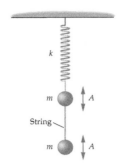

▲ FIGURE 13–29 Problem 94

95. ••• **IP** Consider the pendulum shown in Figure 13–30. Note that the pendulum's string is stopped by a peg when the bob swings to the left, but moves freely when the bob swings to the right. **(a)** Is the period of this pendulum greater than, less than, or the same as the period of the same pendulum without the peg? **(b)** Calculate the period of this pendulum in terms of L and ℓ. **(c)** Evaluate your result for $L = 1.0$ m and $\ell = 0.25$ m.

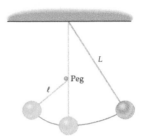

▲ FIGURE 13–30 Problem 95

96. ••• When a mass m is attached to a vertical spring with a force constant k, it stretches the spring by the amount L. Calculate **(a)** the period of this mass and **(b)** the period of a simple pendulum of length L.

97. ••• An object undergoes simple harmonic motion of amplitude A and angular frequency ω about the equilibrium point $x = 0$. Use energy conservation to show that the speed of the object at the general position x is given by the following expression:

$$v = \omega \sqrt{A^2 - x^2}$$

*98. ••• A physical pendulum consists of a light rod of length L suspended in the middle. A large mass m_1 is attached to one end of the rod, and a lighter mass m_2 is attached to the other end, as illustrated in Figure 13–31. Find the period of oscillation for this pendulum.

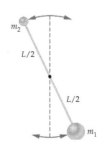

▲ FIGURE 13–31 Problem 98

99. ••• **IP** A vertical hollow tube is connected to a speaker, which vibrates vertically with simple harmonic motion (Figure 13–32). The speaker operates with constant amplitude, A, but variable

frequency, f. A slender pencil is placed inside the tube. **(a)** At low frequencies the pencil stays in contact with the speaker at all times; at higher frequencies the pencil begins to rattle. Explain the reason for this behavior. **(b)** Find an expression for the frequency at which rattling begins.

▲ **FIGURE 13–32** Problem 99

PASSAGE PROBLEMS

BIO A Cricket Thermometer, by Jiminy

Insects are ectothermic, which means their body temperature is largely determined by the temperature of their surroundings. This can have a number of interesting consequences. For example, the wing coloration in some butterfly species is determined by the ambient temperature, as is the body color of several species of dragonfly. In addition, the wing beat frequency of beetles taking flight varies with temperature due to changes in the resonant frequency of their thorax.

The origin of such temperature effects can be traced back to the fact that molecules have higher speeds and greater energy as temperature is increased (see Chapters 16 and 17). Thus, for example, molecules that collide and react as part of the metabolic process will do so more rapidly when the reactions are occurring at a higher temperature. As a result, development rates, heart rates, wing beats, and other processes all occur more rapidly.

One of the most interesting thermal effects is the temperature dependence of chirp rate in certain insects. This behavior has been observed in cone-headed grasshoppers, as well as several types of cricket. A particularly accurate connection between chirp rate and temperature is found in the snowy tree cricket (*Oecanthus fultoni* Walker), which chirps at a rate that follows the expression $N = T - 39$, where N is the number of chirps in 13 seconds, and T is the numerical value of the temperature in degrees Fahrenheit. This formula, which is known as Dolbear's law, is plotted in **Figure 13–33** (green line) along with data points (blue dots) for the snowy tree cricket.

The snowy tree cricket.

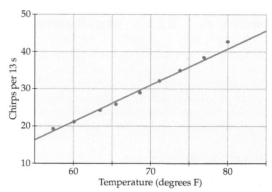

▲ **FIGURE 13–33** Problems 100, 101, 102, and 103

100. • If the temperature is increased by 10 degrees Fahrenheit, how many additional chirps are heard in a 13-s interval?

   A. 5   **B.** 10

   C. 13   **D.** 39

101. • What is the temperature in degrees Fahrenheit if a cricket is observed to give 35 chirps in 13 s?

   A. 13 °F   **B.** 35 °F

   C. 74 °F   **D.** 90 °F

102. • What is the frequency of the cricket's chirping (in Hz) when the temperature is 68 °F?

   A. 0.45 Hz   **B.** 2.2 Hz

   C. 5.2 Hz   **D.** 29 Hz

103. •• Suppose the temperature decreases uniformly from 75 °F to 63 °F in 12 minutes. How many chirps does the cricket produce during this time?

   A. 28   **B.** 1700

   C. 3800   **D.** 22,000

INTERACTIVE PROBLEMS

104. •• **IP Referring to Example 13–3** Suppose we can change the plane's period of oscillation, while keeping its amplitude of motion equal to 30.0 m. **(a)** If we want to reduce the maximum acceleration of the plane, should we increase or decrease the period? Explain. **(b)** Find the period that results in a maximum acceleration of $1.0g$.

105. •• **IP Referring to Example 13–6** Suppose the force constant of the spring is doubled, but the mass and speed of the block are still 0.980 kg and 1.32 m/s, respectively. **(a)** By what multiplicative factor do you expect the maximum compression of the spring to change? Explain. **(b)** Find the new maximum compression of the spring. **(c)** Find the time required for the mass to come to rest after contacting the spring.

106. •• **IP Referring to Example 13–6 (a)** If the block's initial speed is increased, does the total time the block is in contact with the spring increase, decrease, or stay the same? **(b)** Find the total time of contact for $v_0 = 1.65$ m/s, $m = 0.980$ kg, and $k = 245$ N/m.

Appendix A   Basic mathematical tools

This text is designed for students with a working knowledge of basic algebra and trigonometry. Even so, it is useful to review some of the mathematical tools that are of particular importance in the study of physics. In this Appendix we cover a number of topics related to mathematical notation, trigonometry, algebra, mathematical expansions, and vector multiplication.

MATHEMATICAL NOTATION

Common mathematical symbols

In Table A–1 we present some of the more common mathematical symbols, along with a translation into English. Though these symbols are probably completely familiar, it is worthwhile to be sure we all interpret them in the same way.

TABLE A–1   Mathematical Symbols

$=$	is equal to
$\neq$	is not equal to
$\approx$	is approximately equal to
$\propto$	is proportional to
$>$	is greater than
$\geq$	is greater than or equal to
$\gg$	is much greater than
$<$	is less than
$\leq$	is less than or equal to
$\ll$	is much less than
$\pm$	plus or minus
$\mp$	minus or plus
x_{av} or $\bar{x}$	average value of x
Δx	change in x $(x_f - x_i)$
$\lvert x \rvert$	absolute value of x
Σ	sum of
$\rightarrow 0$	approaches 0
∞	infinity

A couple of the symbols in Table A–1 warrant further discussion. First, Δx, which means "change in x," is used frequently, and in many different contexts. Pronounced "delta x," it is defined as the final value of x, x_f, minus the initial value of x, x_i:

$$\Delta x = x_f - x_i \qquad \text{A–1}$$

Thus, Δx is not Δ times x; it is a shorthand way of writing $x_f - x_i$. The same delta notation can be applied to any quantity—it does not have to be x. In general, we can say that

$$\Delta(anything) = (anything)_f - (anything)_i$$

For example, $\Delta t = t_f - t_i$ is the change in time, $\Delta \vec{v} = \vec{v}_f - \vec{v}_i$ is the change in velocity, and so on. Throughout this text, we use the delta notation whenever we want to indicate the change in a given quantity.

Second, the Greek letter Σ (capital sigma) is also encountered frequently. In general, Σ is shorthand for "sum." For example, suppose we have a system comprised of nine masses, m_1 through m_9. The total mass of the system, M, is simply

$$M = m_1 + m_2 + m_3 + m_4 + m_5 + m_6 + m_7 + m_8 + m_9$$

This is a rather tedious way to write M, however, and would be even more so if the number of masses were larger. To simplify our equation, we use the Σ notation:

$$M = \sum_{i=1}^{9} m_i \qquad \text{A–2}$$

With this notation we could sum over any number of masses, simply by changing the upper limit of the sum.

In addition, Σ is often used to designate a general summation, where the number of terms in the sum may not be known, or may vary from one system to another. In a case like this we would simply write Σ without specific upper and lower limits. Thus, a general way of writing the total mass of a system is as follows:

$$M = \sum m \qquad \text{A–3}$$

Vector notation

When we draw a vector to represent a physical quantity, we typically use an arrow whose length is proportional to the magnitude of the quantity, and whose direction is the direction of the quantity. (This and other aspects of vector notation are discussed in Chapter 3.) A slight problem arises, however, when a physical quantity points into or out of the page. In such a case, we use the conventions illustrated in Figure A–1.

Figure A–1 (a) shows a vector pointing out of the page. Note that we see only the tip. Below, we show the corresponding convention, which is a dot set off by a circle. The dot represents the point of the vector's arrow coming out of the page toward you.

A similar convention is employed in Figure A–1 (b) for a vector pointing into the page. In this case, the arrow moves directly away from you, giving a view of its "tail feathers." The feathers are placed in an X-shaped pattern, so we represent the vector as an X set off by a circle.

These conventions are used in Chapter 22 to represent the magnetic field vector, $\vec{B}$, and in other locations in the text as well.

(a) **(b)**

▲ **FIGURE A–1   Vectors pointing out of and into the page**
(a) A vector pointing out of the page is represented by a dot in a circle. The dot indicates the tip of the vector's arrow. **(b)** A vector pointing into the page is represented by an X in a circle. The X indicates the "tail feathers" of the vector's arrow.

Scientific notation

In physics, the numerical value of a physical quantity can cover an enormous range, from the astronomically large to the microscopically small. For example, the mass of the Earth is roughly

$$M_E = 5970000000000000000000000 \text{ kg}$$

In contrast, the mass of a hydrogen atom is approximately

$$M_{hydrogen} = 0.00000000000000000000000000167 \text{ kg}$$

Clearly, representing such large and small numbers with a long string of zeros is clumsy and prone to error.

The preferred method for handling such numbers is to replace the zeros with the appropriate power of ten. For example, the mass of the Earth can be written as follows:

$$M_E = 5.97 \times 10^{24} \text{ kg}$$

The factor of 10^{24} simply means that the decimal point for the mass of the Earth is 24 places to the right of its location in 5.97. Similarly, the mass of a hydrogen atom is

$$M_{hydrogen} = 1.67 \times 10^{-27} \text{ kg}$$

In this case, the correct location of the decimal point is 27 places to the left of its location in 1.67. This type of representation, using powers of ten, is referred to as **scientific notation.**

Scientific notation also simplifies various mathematical operations, such as multiplication and division. For example, the product of the mass of the Earth and the mass of a hydrogen atom is

$$
\begin{aligned}
M_E M_{hydrogen} &= (5.97 \times 10^{24} \text{ kg})(1.67 \times 10^{-27} \text{ kg}) \\
&= (5.97 \times 1.67)(10^{24} \times 10^{-27}) \text{ kg}^2 \\
&= 9.99 \times 10^{24-27} \text{ kg}^2 \\
&= 9.99 \times 10^{-3} \text{ kg}^2
\end{aligned}
$$

Similarly, the mass of a hydrogen atom divided by the mass of the Earth is

$$
\begin{aligned}
\frac{M_{hydrogen}}{M_E} &= \frac{1.67 \times 10^{-27} \text{ kg}}{5.97 \times 10^{24} \text{ kg}} = \frac{1.67}{5.97} \times \frac{10^{-27}}{10^{24}} \\
&= 0.280 \times 10^{-27-24} \\
&= 0.280 \times 10^{-51} = 2.80 \times 10^{-52}
\end{aligned}
$$

Note the change in location of the decimal point in the last two expressions, and the corresponding change in the power of ten.

Exponents and their manipulation are discussed in greater detail later in this Appendix.

TRIGONOMETRY

Degrees and radians

We all know the definition of a degree; there are 360 degrees in a circle. The definition of a radian is somewhat less well known; there are 2π radians in a circle. An equivalent definition of the radian is the following:

A radian is the angle for which the corresponding arc length is equal to the radius.

To visualize this definition, consider a pie with a piece cut out, as shown in Figure A–2 (a). Note that a piece of pie has three sides—two radial lines from the center, and an arc of crust. If a piece of pie is cut with an angle of one radian, all three sides are

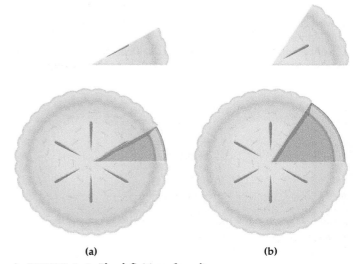

(a)   (b)

▲ **FIGURE A–2 The definition of a radian**
(a) This piece of pie is cut with an angle less than a radian. Thus, the two radial sides (coming out from the center) are longer than the arc of crust. **(b)** The angle for this piece of pie is equal to one radian (about 57.3°). Thus, all three sides of the piece are of equal length.

equal in length, as shown in Figure A–2 (b). Since a radian is about 57.3°, this amounts to a fairly good-sized piece of pie. Thus, if you want a healthy helping of pie, just tell the server, "One radian, please."

Now, radians are particularly convenient when we are interested in the length of an arc. In Figure A–3 we show a circular arc corresponding to the radius r and the angle θ. *If the angle θ is measured in radians*, the length of the arc, s, is given by

$$s = r\theta \qquad\qquad \text{A–4}$$

Note that this simple relation is *not valid* when θ is measured in degrees. For a full circle, in which case $\theta = 2\pi$, the length of the arc (which is the circumference of the circle) is $2\pi r$, as expected.

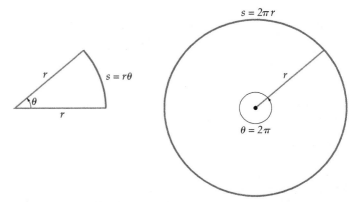

▲ **FIGURE A–3 The Length of an arc**
The arc created by a radius r rotated through an angle θ has a length $s = r\theta$. If the radius is rotated through a full circle, the angle is $\theta = 2\pi$, and the arc length is the circumference of a circle, $s = 2\pi r$.

Trigonometric functions and the Pythagorean theorem

Next, we consider some of the more important and frequently used results from trigonometry. We start with the right triangle, shown in Figure A–4, and the basic **trigonometric functions,**

$\sin \theta$ (sine theta), $\cos \theta$ (cosine theta), and $\tan \theta$ (tangent theta). The cosine of an angle θ is defined to be the side adjacent to the angle divided by the hypotenuse; $\cos \theta = x/r$. Similarly, the sine is defined to be the opposite side divided by the hypotenuse, $\sin \theta = y/r$, and the tangent is the opposite side divided by the adjacent side, $\tan \theta = y/x$. These relations are summarized in the following equations:

$$\cos \theta = \frac{x}{r}$$

$$\sin \theta = \frac{y}{r} \qquad \text{A–5}$$

$$\tan \theta = \frac{y}{x} = \frac{\sin \theta}{\cos \theta}$$

Note that each of the trigonometric functions is the ratio of two lengths, and hence is dimensionless.

According to the **Pythagorean theorem,** the sides of the right triangle in Figure A–4 are related as follows:

$$x^2 + y^2 = r^2 \qquad \text{A–6}$$

Dividing by r^2 yields

$$\frac{x^2}{r^2} + \frac{y^2}{r^2} = 1$$

This can be re-written in terms of sine and cosine to give

$$\sin^2 \theta + \cos^2 \theta = 1$$

Figure A–4 also shows how sine and cosine are used in a typical calculation. In many cases, the hypotenuse of a triangle, r, and one of its angles, θ, are given. To find the short sides of the triangle we rearrange the relations given in Equation A–5. For example, in Figure A–4 we see that $x = r \cos \theta$ is the length of the short side adjacent to the angle, θ, and $y = r \sin \theta$ is the length of the short side opposite the angle. The following Example applies this type of calculation to the case of an inclined roadway.

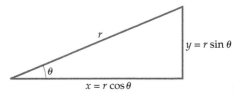

▲ **FIGURE A–4 Relating the short sides of a right triangle to its hypotenuse**

The trigonometric functions $\sin \theta$ and $\cos \theta$ and the Pythagorean theorem are useful in relating the lengths of the short sides of a right triangle to the length of its hypotenuse.

EXAMPLE A–1 HIGHWAY TO HEAVEN

You are driving on a long straight road that slopes uphill at an angle of 6.4° above the horizontal. At one point you notice a sign that reads, "Elevation 1500 feet." What is your elevation after you have driven another 1.0 mi?

PICTURE THE PROBLEM
From our sketch, we see that the car is moving along the hypotenuse of a right triangle. The length of the hypotenuse is one mile.

STRATEGY
The elevation gain is the vertical side of the triangle, y. We find y by multiplying the hypotenuse, r, by the sine of theta. That is, since $\sin \theta = y/r$ it follows that $y = r \sin \theta$.

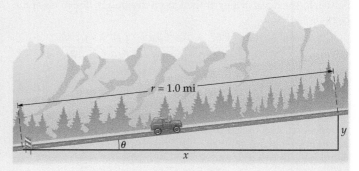

SOLUTION

1. Calculate the elevation gain, y:

$$y = r \sin \theta$$
$$= (1.0 \text{ mi}) \sin 6.4° = (1.0 \text{ mi})(0.11) = 0.11 \text{ mi}$$

2. Convert y from miles to feet:

$$y = (0.11 \text{ mi})\left(\frac{5280 \text{ ft}}{1 \text{ mi}}\right) = 580 \text{ ft}$$

3. Add the elevation gain to the original elevation to obtain the new elevation:

$$\text{elevation} = 1500 \text{ ft} + 580 \text{ ft} = 2100 \text{ ft}$$

INSIGHT
As surprising as it may seem, the horizontal distance covered by the car is $r \cos \theta = (5280 \text{ ft}) \cos 6.4° = 5200 \text{ ft}$, only about 80 ft less than the total distance driven by the car. At the same time, the car rises a distance of 580 ft.

PRACTICE PROBLEM
How far up the road from the first sign should the road crew put another sign reading "Elevation 3500 ft"?
[**Answer:** 18,000 ft = 3.4 mi]

In some problems, the sides of a triangle (x and y) are given and it is desired to find the corresponding hypotenuse, r, and angle, θ. For example, suppose that $x = 5.0$ m and $y = 2.0$ m. Using the Pythagorean theorem, we find $r = \sqrt{x^2 + y^2} = \sqrt{(5.0 \text{ m})^2 + (2.0 \text{ m})^2} = 5.4$ m. Similarly, to find the angle we use the definition of tangent: $\tan \theta = y/x$. The inverse of this relation is $\theta = \tan^{-1}(y/x) = \tan^{-1}(2.0 \text{ m}/5.0 \text{ m}) = \tan^{-1}(0.40)$. Note that the expression $\tan^{-1}$ is the *inverse tangent function*—it does not mean 1 divided by tangent, but rather "the angle whose tangent is——." Your calculator should have a button on it labeled $\tan^{-1}$. If you enter 0.40 and then press $\tan^{-1}$, you should get 22° (to two significant figures), which means that $\tan 22° = 0.40$. Inverse sine and cosine functions work in the same way.

Trigonometric identities

In addition to the basic definitions of sine, cosine, and tangent just given, there are a number of useful relationships involving these functions referred to as **trigonometric identities.** First, consider changing the sign of an angle. This corresponds to flipping the triangle in Figure A–4 upside-down, which changes the sign of y but leaves x unaffected. The result is that sine changes its sign, but cosine does not. Specifically, for a general angle A we find the following:

$$\sin(-A) = -\sin A$$
$$\cos(-A) = \cos A \qquad \text{A–7}$$

Next, we consider trigonometric identities relating to the sum or difference of two angles. For example, consider two general angles A and B. The sine and cosine of the sum of these angles, $A + B$, are given below:

$$\sin(A + B) = \sin A \cos B + \sin B \cos A$$
$$\cos(A + B) = \cos A \cos B - \sin A \sin B \qquad \text{A–8}$$

By changing the sign of B, and using the results given in Equation A–7, we obtain the corresponding results for the difference between two angles:

$$\sin(A - B) = \sin A \cos B - \sin B \cos A$$
$$\cos(A - B) = \cos A \cos B + \sin A \sin B \qquad \text{A–9}$$

Applications of these relations can be found in Chapters 4, 14, 23, and 24.

To see how one might use a relation like $\sin(A + B) = \sin A \cos B + \sin B \cos A$, consider the case where $A = B = \theta$. With this substitution we find

$$\sin(\theta + \theta) = \sin \theta \cos \theta + \sin \theta \cos \theta$$

Simplifying somewhat yields the commonly used double-angle formula

$$\sin 2\theta = 2 \sin \theta \cos \theta \qquad \text{A–10}$$

This expression is used in deriving Equation 4–16.

As a final example of using trigonometric identities, let $A = 90°$ and $B = \theta$. Making these substitutions in Equations A–9 yields

$$\sin(90° - \theta) = \sin 90° \cos \theta - \sin \theta \cos 90° = \cos \theta$$
$$\cos(90° - \theta) = \cos 90° \cos \theta + \sin 90° \sin \theta = \sin \theta \qquad \text{A–11}$$

ALGEBRA

The quadratic equation

A well-known result that finds many uses in physics is the solution to the **quadratic equation**

$$ax^2 + bx + c = 0 \qquad \text{A–12}$$

In this equation, a, b, and c are constants and x is a variable. When we refer to the solution of the quadratic equation, we mean the values of x that satisfy Equation A–12. These values are given by the following expression:

Solutions to the Quadratic Equation

$$x = \frac{-b \pm \sqrt{b^2 - 4ac}}{2a} \qquad \text{A–13}$$

Note that there are two solutions to the quadratic equation, in general, corresponding to the plus and minus sign in front of the square root. In the special case that the quantity under the square root vanishes, there will be only a single solution. If the quantity under the square root is negative the result for x is not physical, which means a mistake has probably been made in the calculation.

To illustrate the use of the quadratic equation and its solution, we consider a standard one-dimensional kinematics problem, such as one might encounter in Chapter 2:

> A ball is thrown straight upward with an initial speed of 11 m/s. How long does it take for the ball to first reach a height of 4.5 m above its launch point?

The first step in solving this problem is to write the equation giving the height of the ball, y, as a function of time. Referring to Equation 2–11, we have

$$y = y_0 + v_0 t - \tfrac{1}{2}g t^2$$

To make this look more like a quadratic equation, we move all the terms onto the left-hand side, which yields

$$\tfrac{1}{2}g t^2 - v_0 t + y - y_0 = 0$$

This is the same as Equation A–12 if we make the following identifications: $x = t$; $a = \tfrac{1}{2}g$; $b = -v_0$; $c = y - y_0$. The desired solution, then, is given by making these substitutions in Equation A–13:

$$t = \frac{v_0 \pm \sqrt{v_0^2 - 2g(y - y_0)}}{g}$$

The final step is to use the appropriate numerical values; $g = 9.81$ m/s², $v_0 = 11$ m/s, $y - y_0 = 4.5$ m. Straightforward calculation gives $t = 0.54$ s and $t = 1.7$ s. Therefore, the time it takes to first reach a height of 4.5 m is 0.54 s; the second solution is the time when the ball is again at a height of 4.5 m, this time on its way down.

Two equations in two unknowns

In some problems, two unknown quantities are determined by two interlinked equations. In such cases it often seems at first that you have not been given enough information to obtain a solution. By patiently writing out what is known, however, you can generally use straightforward algebra to solve the problem.

As an example, consider the following problem: A father and daughter share the same birthday. On one birthday the father announces to his daughter, "Today I am four times older than you, but in 5 years I will be only three times older." How old are the father and daughter now?

You might be able to solve this problem by guessing, but here's how to approach it systematically. First, write what is given in the form of equations. Letting F be the father's age in years, and D the daughter's age in years, we know that on this birthday

$$F = 4D \qquad\qquad \text{A–14}$$

In 5 years, the father's age will be $F + 5$, the daughter's age will be $D + 5$, and the following will be true:

$$F + 5 = 3(D + 5)$$

Multiplying through the parenthesis gives

$$F + 5 = 3D + 15 \qquad\qquad \text{A–15}$$

Now if we subtract Equation A–15 from Equation A–14 we can eliminate one of the unknowns, F:

$$
\begin{aligned}
F &= 4D \\
-F + 5 &= 3D + 15 \\
\hline
-5 &= D - 15
\end{aligned}
$$

The solution to this new equation is clearly $D = 10$, and thus the father's age is $F = 4D = 40$.

The following Example investigates a similar problem. In this case, we use the fact that if you drive with a speed v for a time t the distance covered is $d = vt$.

EXAMPLE A–2   HIT THE ROAD

It takes 1.50 h to drive with a speed v from home to a nearby town, a distance d away. Later, on the way back, the traffic is lighter, and you are able to increase your speed by 15 mi/h. With this higher speed, you get home in just 1.00 h. Find your initial speed v, and the distance to the town, d.

PICTURE THE PROBLEM
Our sketch shows home and the town, separated by a distance d. Going to town the speed is v, returning home the speed is $v + 15$ mi/h.

STRATEGY
To determine the two unknowns, v and d, we need two separate equations. One equation corresponds to what we know about the trip to the town, the second equation corresponds to what we know about the return trip.

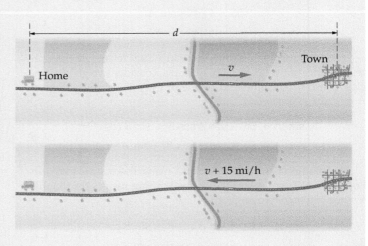

SOLUTION

1. Write an equation for the trip to the town. Recall that this trip takes one and a half hours:

   $$d = vt = v(1.50\text{ h})$$

2. Write an equation for the trip home. This trip takes one hour, and covers the same distance d:

   $$d = (v + 15\text{ mi/h})t = (v + 15\text{ mi/h})(1.00\text{ h})$$

3. Subtract these two equations to eliminate d:

   $$
   \begin{aligned}
   d &= v(1.50\text{ h}) \\
   - \quad d &= (v + 15\text{ mi/h})(1.00\text{ h}) \\
   \hline
   0 &= v(1.50\text{ h}) - v(1.00\text{ h}) - (15\text{ mi/h})(1.00\text{ h})
   \end{aligned}
   $$

4. Solve this new equation for v:

   $$0 = v(1.50\text{ h}) - v(1.00\text{ h}) - (15\text{ mi/h})(1.00\text{ h})$$
   $$0 = v(0.50\text{ h}) - (15\text{ mi/h})(1.00\text{ h})$$
   $$v = \frac{(15\text{ mi/h})(1.00\text{ h})}{(0.50\text{ h})} = 30\text{ mi/h}$$

5. Use the first equation to solve for d:

   $$d = vt = (30\text{ mi/h})(1.50\text{ h}) = 45\text{ mi}$$

Exponents and logarithms

An **exponent** is the power to which a number is raised. For example, in the expression 10^3, we say that the exponent of 10 is 3. To evaluate 10^3 we simply multiply 10 by itself three times:

$$10^3 = 10 \times 10 \times 10 = 1000$$

Similarly, a negative exponent implies an inverse, as in the relation $10^{-1} = 1/10$. Thus, to evaluate a number like 10^{-4}, for example, we multiply $1/10$ by itself four times:

$$10^{-4} = \frac{1}{10} \times \frac{1}{10} \times \frac{1}{10} \times \frac{1}{10} = \frac{1}{10{,}000} = 0.0001$$

The relations just given apply not just to powers of 10, of course, but to any number at all. Thus, x^4 is

$$x^4 = x \times x \times x \times x$$

and x^{-3} is

$$x^{-3} = \frac{1}{x} \times \frac{1}{x} \times \frac{1}{x} = \frac{1}{x^3}$$

Using these basic rules, it follows that exponents add when two or more numbers are multiplied together:

$$x^2 x^3 = (x \times x)(x \times x \times x)$$
$$= x \times x \times x \times x \times x = x^5 = x^{2+3}$$

On the other hand, exponents multiply when a number is raised to a power:

$$(x^2)^3 = (x \times x) \times (x \times x) \times (x \times x)$$
$$= x \times x \times x \times x \times x \times x = x^6 = x^{2\times3}$$

In general, the rules obeyed by exponents can be summarized as follows:

$$x^n x^m = x^{n+m}$$

$$x^{-n} = \frac{1}{x^n}$$

$$\frac{x^n}{x^m} = x^{n-m} \qquad \text{A–16}$$

$$(xy)^n = x^n y^n$$

$$(x^n)^m = x^{nm}$$

Fractional exponents, such as $1/n$, indicate the nth root of a number. Specifically, the square root of x is written as

$$\sqrt{x} = x^{1/2}$$

For n greater than 2 we write the nth root in the following form:

$$\sqrt[n]{x} = x^{1/n} \qquad \text{A–17}$$

Thus, the nth root of a number, x, is the value that gives x when multiplied by itself n times: $(x^{1/n})^n = x^{n/n} = x^1 = x$.

A general method for calculating the exponent of a number is provided by the **logarithm.** For example, suppose x is equal to 10 raised to the power n:

$$x = 10^n$$

In this expression, 10 is referred to as the *base*. The exponent, n, is equal to the logarithm (log) of x:

$$n = \log x$$

The notation "log" is known as the *common logarithm*, and it refers specifically to base 10.

As an example, suppose that $x = 1000 = 10^n$. Clearly, we can write x as 10^3, which means that the exponent of x is 3:

$$\log x = \log 1000 = \log 10^3 = 3$$

When dealing with a number this simple, the exponent can be determined without a calculator. Suppose, however, that $x = 1205 = 10^n$. To find the exponent for this value of x we use the "log" button on a calculator. The result is

$$n = \log 1205 = 3.081$$

Thus, 10 raised to the 3.081 power gives 1205.

Another base that is frequently used for calculating exponents is $e = 2.718\ldots$. To represent $x = 1205$ in this base we write

$$x = 1205 = e^m$$

The logarithm to base e is known as the *natural logarithm*, and it is represented by the notation "ln." Using the "ln" button on a calculator, we find

$$m = \ln 1205 = 7.094$$

Thus, e raised to the 7.094 power gives 1205. The connection between the common and natural logarithms is as follows:

$$\ln x = 2.3026 \log x \qquad \text{A–18}$$

In the example just given, we have $\ln 1205 = 7.094 = 2.3026 \log 1205 = 2.3026(3.081)$.

The basic rules obeyed by logarithms follow directly from the rules given for exponents in Equation A–16. In particular,

$$\ln(xy) = \ln x + \ln y$$

$$\ln\left(\frac{x}{y}\right) = \ln x - \ln y \qquad \text{A–19}$$

$$\ln x^n = n \ln x$$

Though these rules are stated in terms of natural logarithms, they are satisfied by logarithms with any base.

MATHEMATICAL EXPANSIONS

We conclude with a brief consideration of small quantities in mathematics. Consider the following equation:

$$(1 + x)^3 = 1 + 3x + 3x^2 + x^3$$

This expression is valid for all values of x. However, if x is much smaller than one, $x \ll 1$, we can say to a good approximation that

$$(1 + x)^3 \approx 1 + 3x$$

Now, just how good is this approximation? After all, it ignores two terms that would need to be included to produce an equality. In the case $x = 0.001$, for example, the two terms that are neglected, $3x^2$ and x^3, have a combined contribution of only about 3 ten-thousandths of a percent! Clearly, then, little error is made in the approximation $(1 + 0.001)^3 \sim 1 + 3(0.001) = 1.003$. This can be seen visually in **Figure A–5 (a)**, where we plot $(1 + x)^3$ and $1 + 3x$ for x ranging from 0 to 1. Note that there is little difference in the two expressions for x less than about 0.1.

This is just one example of a general result in mathematics that can be derived from the **binomial expansion.** In general, we can say that the following approximation is valid for $x \ll 1$:

$$(1 + x)^n \approx 1 + nx \qquad \text{A–20}$$

This result holds for arbitrary n, not just for the case of $n = 3$. For example, if $n = -1$ we have

$$(1 + x)^{-1} = \frac{1}{1 + x} \approx 1 - x$$

We plot $(1 + x)^{-1}$ and $1 - x$ in **Figure A–5 (b)**, and again we see that the results are in good agreement for x less than about 0.1.

An example of an expansion that arises in the study of relativity concerns the following quotient:

$$\frac{1}{\sqrt{1 - \dfrac{v^2}{c^2}}}$$

In this expression v is the speed of an object and c is the speed of light. Since objects we encounter generally have speeds much less than the speed of light, the ratio v/c is much less than one, and v^2/c^2 is even smaller than v/c. Thus, if we let $x = v^2/c^2$ we have

$$\frac{1}{\sqrt{1 - x}}$$

We can apply the binomial expansion to this result if we replace n with $-1/2$ and x with $-x$ in Equation A–20. This yields

$$\frac{1}{\sqrt{1 - \dfrac{v^2}{c^2}}} \approx 1 + \frac{1}{2}\frac{v^2}{c^2}$$

The two sides of this approximate equality are plotted in **Figure A–5 (c)**, showing the accuracy of the approximation for small v/c.

Another type of mathematical expansion leads to the following useful results:

$$\sin \theta \approx \theta$$
$$\cos \theta \approx 1 - \frac{1}{2}\theta^2 \qquad \text{A–21}$$

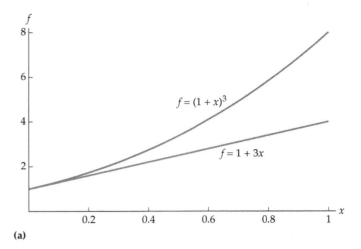

(a)

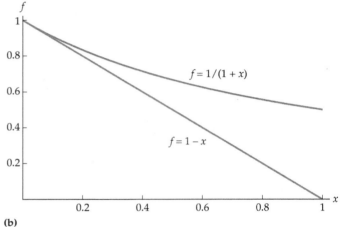

(b)

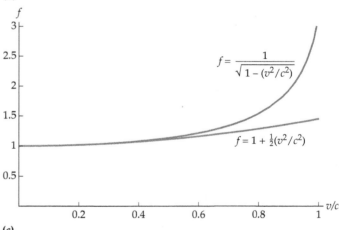

(c)

▲ **FIGURE A–5 Examples of mathematical expansions**
(a) A comparison between $(1 + x)^3$ and the result obtained from the binomial expansion, $1 + 3x$. (b) A comparison between $1/(1 + x)$ and the result obtained from the binomial expansion, $1 - x$. (c) A comparison between $1/\sqrt{1 - (v^2/c^2)}$ and the result obtained from the binomial expansion, $1 + \frac{1}{2}(v^2/c^2)$.

These expansions are valid for small angles θ measured in radians. Note that the result $\sin \theta \approx \theta$ is used to derive Equations 6–13 and 13–19. (See Table 6–2, p. 170, and Figure 13–15, p. 435, for more details on this expansion.)

VECTOR MULTIPLICATION

There are two distinct ways to multiply vectors, referred to as the **dot product** and the **cross product.** The difference between these two types of multiplication is that the dot product yields a scalar (a number) as its result, whereas the cross product results in a vector. Both types of product have important applications in physics. In what follows, we present the basic techniques associated with dot and cross products, and point out places in the text where they are used.

The dot product

Consider two vectors, $\vec{A}$ and $\vec{B}$, as shown in **Figure A–6 (a)**. The magnitudes of these vectors are A and B, respectively, and the angle between them is θ. We define the dot product of $\vec{A}$ and $\vec{B}$ as follows:

$$\vec{A} \cdot \vec{B} = AB \cos \theta \qquad \text{A–22}$$

In words, the dot product of two vectors is a scalar equal to the magnitude of one vector times the magnitude of the second vector times the cosine of the angle between them.

A geometric interpretation of the dot product is presented in **Figure A–6 (b)**. We begin by projecting the vector $\vec{A}$ onto the direction of vector $\vec{B}$. This is done by dropping a perpendicular from the tip of $\vec{A}$ onto the line that passes through $\vec{B}$, as shown in **Figure A–6 (b)**. Note that the projection of $\vec{A}$ on the direction of $\vec{B}$ has a length given by $A \cos \theta$. It follows that the dot product is simply the projection of $\vec{A}$ onto $\vec{B}$ times the magnitude of $\vec{B}$; that is, $(A \cos \theta)B = AB \cos \theta = \vec{A} \cdot \vec{B}$. Equivalently, the dot product can be thought of as the projection of $\vec{B}$ onto $\vec{A}$ times the magnitude of $\vec{A}$.

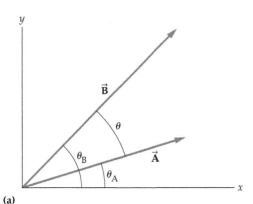

(a)

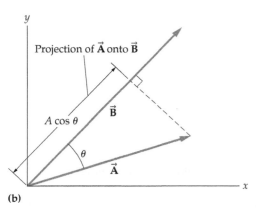

(b)

▲ **FIGURE A–6 The dot product between vectors $\vec{A}$ and $\vec{B}$.**

A few special cases will help to clarify the dot product. Suppose, for example, that $\vec{A}$ and $\vec{B}$ are parallel. In this case, $\theta = 0$ and $\vec{A} \cdot \vec{B} = AB$. Therefore, when vectors are parallel, the dot product is simply the product of their magnitudes. On the other hand, suppose $\vec{A}$ and $\vec{B}$ point in opposite directions. Now we have $\theta = 180$, and therefore $\vec{A} \cdot \vec{B} = -AB$. In general, the sign of $\vec{A} \cdot \vec{B}$ is positive if the angle between $\vec{A}$ and $\vec{B}$ is less than $90°$, and is negative if the angle between them is greater than $90°$. Finally, if $\vec{A}$ and $\vec{B}$ are perpendicular to one another—that is, if $\theta = 90°$—we see that $\vec{A} \cdot \vec{B} = AB \cos 90° = 0$. In this case, neither vector has a nonzero projection onto the other vector.

Dot products have a particularly simple form when applied to unit vectors. Recall, for example, that $\hat{x}$ and $\hat{y}$ have unit magnitude and are perpendicular to one another. It follows that

$$\hat{x} \cdot \hat{x} = 1, \quad \hat{x} \cdot \hat{y} = \hat{y} \cdot \hat{x} = 0, \quad \hat{y} \cdot \hat{y} = 1 \qquad \text{A–23}$$

These results can be applied to the general two-dimensional vectors $\vec{A} = A_x\hat{x} + A_y\hat{y}$ and $\vec{B} = B_x\hat{x} + B_y\hat{y}$ to give

$$\begin{aligned} \vec{A} \cdot \vec{B} &= (A_x\hat{x} + A_y\hat{y}) \cdot (B_x\hat{x} + B_y\hat{y}) \\ &= A_xB_x\hat{x} \cdot \hat{x} + A_xB_y\hat{x} \cdot \hat{y} + A_yB_x\hat{y} \cdot \hat{x} + A_yB_y\hat{y} \cdot \hat{y} \quad \text{A–24} \\ &= A_xB_x + A_yB_y \end{aligned}$$

Thus, the dot product of two-dimensional vectors is simply the product of their x components plus the product of their y components.

At first glance the result $\vec{A} \cdot \vec{B} = AB \cos \theta$ looks quite different from the result $\vec{A} \cdot \vec{B} = A_xB_x + A_yB_y$. They are identical, however, as we now show. Suppose that $\vec{A}$ is at an angle θ_A to the positive x axis, and that $\vec{B}$ is at an angle $\theta_B > \theta_A$ to the x axis, from which it follows that the angle between $\vec{A}$ and $\vec{B}$ is $\theta = \theta_B - \theta_A$. Noting that $A_x = A \cos \theta_A$ and $A_y = A \sin \theta_A$, and similarly for B_x and B_y, we have

$$\vec{A} \cdot \vec{B} = AB(\cos \theta_A \cos \theta_B + \sin \theta_A \sin \theta_B)$$

The second trigonometric identity in Equation A–9 can be applied to the quantity in brackets, with the result that $\vec{A} \cdot \vec{B} = A_xB_x + A_yB_y = AB \cos(\theta_B - \theta_A) = AB \cos \theta$, as desired.

The most prominent application of dot products in this text is in Chapter 7, where in Equation 7–3 we define the work to be $W = Fd \cos \theta$, with θ the angle between $\vec{F}$ and $\vec{d}$. Clearly, this is simply a statement that work is the dot product of force and displacement:

$$W = \vec{F} \cdot \vec{d} = Fd \cos \theta$$

Later in the text, in Equation 19–11, we define the electric flux to be $\Phi = EA \cos \theta$. If we let $\vec{A}$ represent a vector that has a magnitude equal to the area, A, and points in the direction of the normal to the area, we can write the electric flux as a dot product:

$$\Phi = \vec{E} \cdot \vec{A} = EA \cos \theta$$

Similar remarks apply to the magnetic flux, defined in Equation 23–1.

The cross product

When two vectors are multiplied with the cross product, the result is a third vector that is perpendicular to both original vectors. An example is shown in **Figure A–7**, where we see a vector $\vec{A}$, a vector $\vec{B}$, and their cross product, $\vec{C}$:

$$\vec{C} = \vec{A} \times \vec{B} \qquad \text{A–25}$$

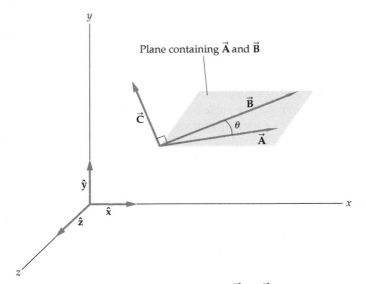

▲ **FIGURE A–7 The vector cross product of $\vec{\mathbf{A}}$ and $\vec{\mathbf{B}}$.**

Notice that $\vec{\mathbf{C}}$ is perpendicular to the plane formed by the vectors $\vec{\mathbf{A}}$ and $\vec{\mathbf{B}}$. In addition, the direction of $\vec{\mathbf{C}}$ is given by the following right-hand rule:

> To find the direction of $\vec{\mathbf{C}} = \vec{\mathbf{A}} \times \vec{\mathbf{B}}$, point the fingers of your right hand in the direction of $\vec{\mathbf{A}}$ and curl them toward $\vec{\mathbf{B}}$. Your thumb is now pointing in the direction of $\vec{\mathbf{C}}$.

It is clear from this rule that if $\vec{\mathbf{A}} \times \vec{\mathbf{B}} = \vec{\mathbf{C}}$, then $\vec{\mathbf{B}} \times \vec{\mathbf{A}} = -\vec{\mathbf{C}}$.

The magnitude of $\vec{\mathbf{C}} = \vec{\mathbf{A}} \times \vec{\mathbf{B}}$ depends on the magnitudes of the vectors $\vec{\mathbf{A}}$ and $\vec{\mathbf{B}}$, and on the angle θ between them. In particular,

$$C = AB \sin \theta \qquad \text{A–26}$$

Comparing with Equation A–22, we see that the cross product involves a $\sin \theta$, whereas the dot product depends on $\cos \theta$. As a result, it follows that the cross product has zero magnitude when $\vec{\mathbf{A}}$ and $\vec{\mathbf{B}}$ point in the same direction ($\theta = 0°$) or in opposite directions ($\theta = 180°$). On the other hand, the cross product has its greatest magnitude, $C = AB$, when $\vec{\mathbf{A}}$ and $\vec{\mathbf{B}}$ are perpendicular to one another ($\theta = 90°$).

When we apply these rules to unit vectors, which are at right angles to one another and of unit magnitude, the results are particularly simple. For example, consider the cross product $\hat{\mathbf{x}} \times \hat{\mathbf{y}}$. Referring to Figure A–7, we see that this cross product points in the positive z direction. In addition, the magnitude of $\hat{\mathbf{x}} \times \hat{\mathbf{y}}$ is $(1)(1) \sin 90° = 1$. It follows, therefore, that $\hat{\mathbf{x}} \times \hat{\mathbf{y}} = \hat{\mathbf{z}}$. On the

other hand, $\hat{\mathbf{x}} \times \hat{\mathbf{x}} = \hat{\mathbf{y}} \times \hat{\mathbf{y}} = \hat{\mathbf{z}} \times \hat{\mathbf{z}} = 0$ because $\theta = 0°$ in each of these cases. To summarize:

$$\begin{aligned}
\hat{\mathbf{x}} \times \hat{\mathbf{y}} &= \hat{\mathbf{z}}, & \hat{\mathbf{y}} \times \hat{\mathbf{z}} &= \hat{\mathbf{x}}, & \hat{\mathbf{z}} \times \hat{\mathbf{x}} &= \hat{\mathbf{y}} \\
\hat{\mathbf{y}} \times \hat{\mathbf{x}} &= -\hat{\mathbf{z}}, & \hat{\mathbf{z}} \times \hat{\mathbf{y}} &= -\hat{\mathbf{x}}, & \hat{\mathbf{x}} \times \hat{\mathbf{z}} &= -\hat{\mathbf{y}} \qquad \text{A–27} \\
\hat{\mathbf{x}} \times \hat{\mathbf{x}} &= 0, & \hat{\mathbf{y}} \times \hat{\mathbf{y}} &= 0, & \hat{\mathbf{z}} \times \hat{\mathbf{z}} &= 0
\end{aligned}$$

As an example of how to use these unit-vector results, consider the cross product of the two-dimensional vectors shown in Figure A–6, $\vec{\mathbf{A}} = A_x\hat{\mathbf{x}} + A_y\hat{\mathbf{y}}$ and $\vec{\mathbf{B}} = B_x\hat{\mathbf{x}} + B_y\hat{\mathbf{y}}$. Straightforward application of Equation A–27 yields

$$\begin{aligned}
\vec{\mathbf{C}} = \vec{\mathbf{A}} \times \vec{\mathbf{B}} &= (A_x\hat{\mathbf{x}} + A_y\hat{\mathbf{y}}) \times (B_x\hat{\mathbf{x}} + B_y\hat{\mathbf{y}}) \\
&= A_xB_x(\hat{\mathbf{x}} \times \hat{\mathbf{x}}) + A_xB_y(\hat{\mathbf{x}} \times \hat{\mathbf{y}}) \\
&\quad + A_yB_x(\hat{\mathbf{y}} \times \hat{\mathbf{x}}) + A_yB_y(\hat{\mathbf{y}} \times \hat{\mathbf{y}}) \\
&= (A_xB_y - A_yB_x)\hat{\mathbf{z}} \qquad \text{A–28}
\end{aligned}$$

Notice that $\vec{\mathbf{C}}$ is perpendicular to both $\vec{\mathbf{A}}$ and $\vec{\mathbf{B}}$, as required for a cross product. In addition, the magnitude of $\vec{\mathbf{C}}$ is

$$A_xB_y - A_yB_x = AB(\cos \theta_A \sin \theta_B - \sin \theta_A \cos \theta_B)$$

If we now apply the first trigonometric identity in Equation A–9, we recover the result given in Equation A–26:

$$\begin{aligned}
C &= AB(\cos \theta_A \sin \theta_B - \sin \theta_A \cos \theta_B) \\
&= AB \sin(\theta_B - \theta_A) = AB \sin \theta
\end{aligned}$$

The first application of cross products in this text is torque, which is discussed in Chapter 11. In fact, Equation 11–2 defines the magnitude of the torque, τ, as follows: $\tau = r(F \sin \theta)$. As one might expect by referring to Equations A–25 and A–26, the torque vector, $\vec{\boldsymbol{\tau}}$, can be written as the following cross product:

$$\vec{\boldsymbol{\tau}} = \vec{\mathbf{r}} \times \vec{\mathbf{F}}$$

Similarly, the angular momentum vector, $\vec{\mathbf{L}}$, whose magnitude is given in Equation 11–13, is simply

$$\vec{\mathbf{L}} = \vec{\mathbf{r}} \times \vec{\mathbf{p}}$$

Finally, the cross product appears again in magnetism. In fact, the magnitude of the magnetic force on a charge q with a velocity $\vec{\mathbf{v}}$ in a magnetic field $\vec{\mathbf{B}}$ is $F = qvB \sin \theta$, as given in Equation 22–1. As one might guess, the vector form of this force is

$$\vec{\mathbf{F}} = q\vec{\mathbf{v}} \times \vec{\mathbf{B}}$$

The advantage of a cross product expression like this is that it contains both the direction and magnitude of a vector in one compact equation. In fact, we can now see the origin of the right-hand rule for magnetic forces given in Section 22–2.

Appendix B   Typical values

Mass

Sun	2.00×10^{30} kg
Earth	5.97×10^{24} kg
Moon	7.35×10^{22} kg
747 airliner (maximum takeoff weight)	3.5×10^5 kg
blue whale	178,000 kg = 197 tons
elephant	5400 kg
mountain gorilla	180 kg
human	70 kg
bowling ball	7 kg
half gallon of milk	1.81 kg = 4 lbs
baseball	0.141–0.148 kg
golf ball	0.045 kg
female calliope hummingbird (smallest bird in North America)	3.5×10^{-3} kg $= \frac{1}{8}$ oz
raindrop	3×10^{-5} kg
antibody molecule (IgG)	2.5×10^{-22} kg
hydrogen atom	1.67×10^{-27} kg

Length

orbital radius of Earth (around Sun)	1.5×10^8 km
orbital radius of Moon (around Earth)	3.8×10^5 km
altitude of geosynchronous satellite	35,800 km = 22,300 mi
radius of Earth	6370 km
altitude of Earth's ozone layer	50 km
height of Mt. Everest	8848 m
height of Washington Monument	169 m = 555 ft
pitcher's mound to home plate	18.44 m
baseball bat	1.067 m
CD (diameter)	120 mm
aorta (diameter)	18 mm
period in sentence (diameter)	0.5 mm
red blood cell	7.8 μm $= \frac{1}{3300}$ in.
typical bacterium (E. coli)	2 μm
wavelength of green light	550 nm
virus	20–300 nm
large protein molecule	25 nm
diameter of DNA molecule	2.0 nm
radius of hydrogen atom	5.29×10^{-11} m

Time

estimated age of Earth	approx. 4.6 billion y $\approx 10^{17}$ s
estimated age of human species	approx. 150,000 y $\approx 5 \times 10^{12}$ s
half life of carbon-14	5730 y = 1.81×10^{11} s
period of Halley's comet	76 y = 2.40×10^9 s
half life of technetium-99	6 h = 2.16×10^4 s
time for driver of car to apply brakes	0.46 s
human reaction time	60–180 ms
air bag deployment time	10 ms

period of middle C sound wave	3.9 ms
collision time for batted ball	2 ms
decay of excited atomic state	10^{-8} s
period of green light wave	1.8×10^{-15} s

Speed

light	3×10^8 m/s
meteor	35–95 km/s
space shuttle (orbital velocity)	8.5 km/s = 19,000 mi/h
rifle bullet	700–750 m/s
sound in air (STP)	340 m/s
fastest human nerve impulses	140 m/s
747 at takeoff	80.5 m/s
kangaroo	18.1 m/s = 40.5 mi/h
200-m dash (Olympic record)	10.1 m/s
butterfly	1 m/s
blood speed in aorta	0.35 m/s
giant tortoise	0.076 m/s = 0.170 mi/h
Mer de Glace glacier (French Alps)	4×10^{-6} m/s

Acceleration

protons in particle accelerator	9×10^{13} m/s^2
ultracentrifuge	3×10^6 m/s^2
meteor impact	10^5 m/s^2
baseball struck by bat	3×10^4 m/s^2
loss of consciousness	$7.14g = 70$ m/s^2
acceleration of gravity on Earth (g)	9.81 m/s^2
braking auto	8 m/s^2
acceleration of gravity on the moon	1.62 m/s^2
rotation of Earth at equator	3.4×10^{-2} m/s^2

Appendix C   Planetary data

Name	Equatorial Radius (km)	Mass (Relative to Earth's)*	Mean Density (kg/m³)	Surface Gravity (Relative to Earth's)	Orbital Semimajor Axis × 10⁶ km	A. U.	Escape Speed (km/s)	Orbital Period (Years)	Orbital Eccentricity
Mercury	2440	0.0553	5430	0.38	57.9	0.387	4.2	0.240	0.206
Venus	6052	0.816	5240	0.91	108.2	0.723	10.4	0.615	0.007
Earth	6370	1	5510	1	149.6	1	11.2	1.000	0.017
Mars	3394	0.108	3930	0.38	227.9	1.523	5.0	1.881	0.093
Jupiter	71,492	318	1360	2.53	778.4	5.203	60	11.86	0.048
Saturn	60,268	95.1	690	1.07	1427.0	9.539	36	29.42	0.054
Uranus	25,559	14.5	1270	0.91	2871.0	19.19	21	83.75	0.047
Neptune	24,776	17.1	1640	1.14	4497.1	30.06	24	163.7	0.009
Pluto	1137	0.0021	2060	0.07	5906	39.84	1.2	248.0	0.249

*Mass of Earth = 5.97×10^{24} kg

Appendix D   Elements of electrical circuits

Circuit Element	Symbol	Physical Characteristics
resistor		Resists the flow of electric current. Converts electrical energy to thermal energy.
capacitor		Stores electrical energy in the form of an electric field.
inductor		Stores electrical energy in the form of a magnetic field.
incandescent lightbulb		A device containing a resistor that gets hot enough to give off visible light.
battery		A device that produces a constant difference in electrical potential between its terminals.
ac generator		A device that produces a potential difference between its terminals that oscillates with time.
switches (open and closed)		Devices to control whether electric current is allowed to flow through a portion of a circuit.
ground		Sets the electric potential at a point in a circuit equal to a constant value usually taken to be $V = 0$.

Appendix E Periodic table of the elements

Legend:
- Atomic number — 26
- Symbol — Fe
- Atomic mass — 55.85
- Outer electron configuration — $3d^6 4s^2$

Transition elements (d-block)

PERIODS (rows 1–7)

Period	GROUP I	GROUP II												GROUP III	GROUP IV	GROUP V	GROUP VI	GROUP VII	GROUP VIII
1	1 H 1.01 $1s^1$																		2 He 4.00 $1s^2$
2	3 Li 6.94 $2s^1$	4 Be 9.01 $2s^2$												5 B 10.81 $2p^1$	6 C 12.01 $2p^2$	7 N 14.01 $2p^3$	8 O 16.00 $2p^4$	9 F 19.00 $2p^5$	10 Ne 20.18 $2p^6$
3	11 Na 22.99 $3s^1$	12 Mg 24.31 $3s^2$												13 Al 26.98 $3p^1$	14 Si 28.09 $3p^2$	15 P 30.97 $3p^3$	16 S 32.07 $3p^4$	17 Cl 35.45 $3p^5$	18 Ar 39.95 $3p^6$

Period 4:

Group	Element	Mass	Config
I	19 K	39.10	$4s^1$
II	20 Ca	40.08	$4s^2$
	21 Sc	44.96	$3d^1 4s^2$
	22 Ti	47.88	$3d^2 4s^2$
	23 V	50.94	$3d^3 4s^2$
	24 Cr	52.00	$3d^5 4s^1$
	25 Mn	54.94	$3d^5 4s^2$
	26 Fe	55.85	$3d^6 4s^2$
	27 Co	58.93	$3d^7 4s^2$
	28 Ni	58.69	$3d^8 4s^2$
	29 Cu	63.55	$3d^{10} 4s^1$
	30 Zn	65.39	$3d^{10} 4s^2$
III	31 Ga	69.72	$4p^1$
IV	32 Ge	72.61	$4p^2$
V	33 As	74.92	$4p^3$
VI	34 Se	78.96	$4p^4$
VII	35 Br	79.90	$4p^5$
VIII	36 Kr	83.80	$4p^6$

Period 5:

Group	Element	Mass	Config
I	37 Rb	85.47	$5s^1$
II	38 Sr	87.62	$5s^2$
	39 Y	88.96	$4d^1 5s^2$
	40 Zr	91.22	$4d^2 5s^2$
	41 Nb	92.91	$4d^4 5s^1$
	42 Mo	95.94	$4d^5 5s^1$
	43 Tc	(98)	$4d^5 5s^2$
	44 Ru	101.07	$4d^7 5s^1$
	45 Rh	102.91	$4d^8 5s^1$
	46 Pd	106.42	$4d^{10} 5s^6$
	47 Ag	107.87	$4d^{10} 5s^1$
	48 Cd	112.41	$4d^{10} 5s^2$
III	49 In	114.82	$5p^1$
IV	50 Sn	118.71	$5p^2$
V	51 Sb	121.76	$5p^3$
VI	52 Te	127.60	$5p^4$
VII	53 I	126.90	$5p^5$
VIII	54 Xe	131.29	$5p^6$

Period 6:

Group	Element	Mass	Config
I	55 Cs	132.91	$6s^1$
II	56 Ba	137.33	$6s^2$
	57 La	138.91	$5d^1 6s^2$
	72 Hf	178.49	$5d^2 6s^2$
	73 Ta	180.95	$5d^3 6s^2$
	74 W	183.85	$5d^4 6s^2$
	75 Re	186.21	$5d^5 6s^2$
	76 Os	190.2	$5d^6 6s^2$
	77 Ir	192.22	$5d^7 6s^2$
	78 Pt	195.08	$5d^9 6s^1$
	79 Au	196.97	$5d^{10} 6s^1$
	80 Hg	200.59	$5d^{10} 6s^2$
III	81 Tl	204.36	$6p^1$
IV	82 Pb	207.2	$6p^2$
V	83 Bi	208.98	$6p^3$
VI	84 Po	(209)	$6p^4$
VII	85 At	(210)	$6p^5$
VIII	86 Rn	(222)	$6p^6$

Period 7:

Group	Element	Mass	Config
I	87 Fr	(223)	$7s^1$
II	88 Ra	226.03	$7s^2$
	89 Ac	227.03	$6d^1 7s^2$
	104 Rf	(261)	$6d^2 7s^2$
	105 Db	(262)	$6d^3 7s^2$
	106 Sg	(266)	$6d^4 7s^2$
	107 Bh	(264)	$6d^5 7s^2$
	108 Hs	(269)	$6d^6 7s^2$
	109 Mt	(268)	$6d^7 7s^2$
	110	(271)	
	111	(272)	
	112	(277)	
IV	114	(289)	
VI	116	(289)	
VIII	118	(293)	

Lanthanides (f-block):

Element	Mass	Config
58 Ce	140.12	$5d^1 4f^1 6s^2$
59 Pr	140.91	$4f^3 6s^2$
60 Nd	144.24	$4f^4 6s^2$
61 Pm	(145)	$4f^6 6s^2$
62 Sm	150.36	$4f^6 6s^2$
63 Eu	151.96	$4f^7 6s^2$
64 Gd	157.25	$5d^1 4f^7 6s^2$
65 Tb	158.93	$4f^9 6s^2$
66 Dy	162.50	$4f^{10} 6s^2$
67 Ho	164.93	$4f^{11} 6s^2$
68 Er	167.26	$4f^{12} 6s^2$
69 Tm	168.93	$4f^{13} 6s^2$
70 Yb	173.04	$4f^{14} 6s^2$
71 Lu	174.97	$5d^1 4f^{14} 6s^2$

Actinides (f-block):

Element	Mass	Config
90 Th	232.04	$6d^2 7s^2$
91 Pa	231.04	$5f^2 6d^1 7s^2$
92 U	238.03	$5f^3 6d^1 7s^2$
93 Np	237.05	$5f^4 6d^1 7s^2$
94 Pu	(244)	$5f^6 6d^0 7s^2$
95 Am	(243)	$5f^7 6d^0 7s^2$
96 Cm	(247)	$5f^7 6d^1 7s^2$
97 Bk	(247)	$5f^8 6d^1 7s^2$
98 Cf	(251)	$5f^{10} 6d^0 7s^2$
99 Es	(252)	$5s^{11} 6d^0 7s^2$
100 Fm	(257)	$5f^{12} 6d^0 7s^2$
101 Md	(258)	$5f^{13} 6d^0 7s^2$
102 No	(259)	$5f^{14} 6d^0 7s^2$
103 Lr	(262)	$5f^{14} 6d^1 7s^2$

* Lanthanides
† Actinides

Appendix F   Properties of selected isotopes

Atomic Number (Z)	Element	Symbol	Mass Number (A)	Atomic Mass*	Abundance (%) or Decay Mode† (if radioactive)	Half-Life (if radioactive)
0	(Neutron)	n	1	1.008665	β^-	10.6 min
1	Hydrogen	H	1	1.007825	99.985	
	Deuterium	D	2	2.014102	0.015	
	Tritium	T	3	3.016049	β^-	12.33 y
2	Helium	He	3	3.016029	0.00014	
			4	4.002603	≈ 100	
3	Lithium	Li	6	6.015123	7.5	
			7	7.016003	92.5	
4	Beryllium	Be	7	7.016930	EC, γ	53.3 d
			8	8.005305	2α	6.7×10^{-17} s
			9	9.012183	100	
5	Boron	B	10	10.012938	19.9	
			11	11.009305	80.1	
			12	12.014353	β^-	20.2 ms
6	Carbon	C	11	11.011433	β^+, EC	20.3 min
			12	12.000000	98.89	
			13	13.003355	1.11	
			14	14.003242	β^-	5730 y
7	Nitrogen	N	13	13.005739	β^-	9.96 min
			14	14.003074	99.63	
			15	15.000109	0.37	
8	Oxygen	O	15	15.003065	β^+, EC	122 s
			16	15.994915	99.76	
			18	17.999159	0.204	
9	Fluorine	F	19	18.998403	100	
			18	18.000938	EC	109.77 min
10	Neon	Ne	20	19.992439	90.51	
			22	21.991384	9.22	
11	Sodium	Na	22	21.994435	β^+, EC, γ	2.602 y
			23	22.989770	100	
			24	23.990964	β^-, γ	15.0 h
12	Magnesium	Mg	24	23.985045	78.99	
13	Aluminum	Al	27	26.981541	100	
14	Silicon	Si	28	27.976928	92.23	
			31	30.975364	β^-, γ	2.62 h
15	Phosphorus	P	31	30.973763	100	
			32	31.973908	β^-	14.28 d
16	Sulfur	S	32	31.972072	95.0	
			35	34.969033	β^-	87.4 d
17	Chlorine	Cl	35	34.968853	75.77	
			37	36.965903	24.23	
18	Argon	Ar	40	39.962383	99.60	
19	Potassium	K	39	38.963708	93.26	
			40	39.964000	β^-, EC, γ, β^+	1.28×10^9 y

Atomic Number (Z)	Element	Symbol	Mass Number (A)	Atomic Mass*	Abundance (%) or Decay Mode† (if radioactive)	Half-Life (if radioactive)
20	Calcium	Ca	30	39.962591	96.94	
24	Chromium	Cr	52	51.940510	83.79	
25	Manganese	Mn	55	54.938046	100	
26	Iron	Fe	56	55.934939	91.8	
27	Cobalt	Co	59	58.933198	100	
			60	59.933820	β^-, γ	5.271 y
28	Nickel	Ni	58	57.935347	68.3	
			60	59.930789	26.1	
			64	63.927968	0.91	
29	Copper	Cu	63	62.929599	69.2	
			64	63.929766	β^-, β^+	12.7 h
			65	64.927792	30.8	
30	Zinc	Zn	64	63.929145	48.6	
			66	65.926035	27.9	
33	Arsenic	As	75	74.921596	100	
35	Bromine	Br	79	78.918336	50.69	
36	Krypton	Kr	84	83.911506	57.0	
			89	88.917563	β^-	3.2 min
			92	91.926153	β^-	1.84 s
38	Strontium	Sr	86	85.909273	9.8	
			88	87.905625	82.6	
			90	89.907746	β^-	28.8 y
39	Yttrium	Y	89	89.905856	100	
41	Niobium	Nb	98	97.910331	β^-	2.86 s
43	Technetium	Tc	98	97.907210	β^-, γ	4.2×10^6 y
47	Silver	Ag	107	106.905095	51.83	
			109	108.904754	48.17	
48	Cadmium	Cd	114	113.903361	28.7	
49	Indium	In	115	114.90388	95.7; β^-	5.1×10^{14} y
50	Tin	Sn	120	119.902199	32.4	
51	Antimony	Sb	133	132.915237	β^-	2.5 min
53	Iodine	I	127	126.904477	100	
			131	130.906118	β^-, γ	8.04 d
54	Xenon	Xe	132	131.90415	26.9	
			136	135.90722	8.9	
55	Cesium	Cs	133	132.90543	100	
56	Barium	Ba	137	136.90582	11.2	
			138	137.90524	71.7	
			141	140.914406	β^-	18.27 min
			144	143.92273	β^-	11.9 s
61	Promethium	Pm	145	144.91275	EC, α, γ	17.7 y
74	Tungsten (Wolfram)	W	184	183.95095	30.7	
76	Osmium	Os	191	190.96094	β^-, γ	15.4 d
			192	191.96149	41.0	
78	Platinum	Pt	195	194.96479	33.8	
79	Gold	Au	197	196.96656	100	

Atomic Number (Z)	Element	Symbol	Mass Number (A)	Atomic Mass*	Abundance (%) or Decay Mode† (if radioactive)	Half-Life (if radioactive)
81	Thallium	Tl	205	204.97441	70.5	
			210	209.990069	β^-	1.3 min
82	Lead	Pb	204	203.973044	β^-, 1.48	1.4×10^{17} y
			206	205.97446	24.1	
			207	206.97589	22.1	
			208	207.97664	52.3	
			210	209.98418	α, β^-, γ	22.3 y
			211	210.98874	β^-, γ	36.1 min
			212	211.99188	β^-, γ	10.64 h
			214	213.99980	β^-, γ	26.8 min
83	Bismuth	Bi	209	208.98039	100	
			211	210.98726	α, β^-, γ	2.15 min
			212	211.991272	α	60.55 min
84	Polonium	Po	210	209.98286	α, γ	138.38 d
			212	211.988852	α	0.299 μs
			214	213.99519	α, γ	164 μs
86	Radon	Rn	222	222.017574	α, β	3.8235 d
87	Francium	Fr	223	223.019734	α, β^-, γ	21.8 min
88	Radium	Ra	226	226.025406	α, γ	1.60×10^3 y
			228	228.031069	β^-	5.76 y
89	Actinium	Ac	227	227.027751	α, β^-, γ	21.773 y
90	Thorium	Th	228	228.02873	α, γ	1.9131 y
			231	231.036297	α, β^-	25.52 h
			232	232.038054	100; α, γ	1.41×10^{10} y
			234	234.043596	β^-	24.10 d
91	Protactium	Pa	234	234.043302	β^-	6.70 h
92	Uranium	U	232	232.03714	α, γ	72 y
			233	233.039629	α, γ	1.592×10^5 y
			235	235.043925	0.72; α, γ	7.038×10^8 y
			236	236.045563	α, γ	2.342×10^7 y
			238	238.050786	99.275; α, γ	4.468×10^9 y
			239	239.054291	β^-, γ	23.5 min
93	Neptunium	Np	239	239.052932	β^-, γ	2.35 d
94	Plutonium	Pu	239	239.052158	α, γ	2.41×10^4 y
95	Americium	Am	243	243.061374	α, γ	7.37×10^3 y
96	Curium	Cm	245	245.065487	α, γ	8.5×10^3 y
97	Berkelium	Bk	247	247.07003	α, γ	1.4×10^3 y
98	Californium	Cf	249	249.074849	α, γ	351 y
99	Einsteinium	Es	254	254.08802	α, γ, β^-	276 d
100	Fermium	Fm	253	253.08518	EC, α, γ	3.0 d
101	Mendelevium	Md	255	255.0911	EC, α	27 min
102	Nobelium	No	255	255.0933	EC, α	3.1 min
103	Lawrencium	Lr	257	257.0998	α	$\approx$35 s

*The masses given throughout this table are those for the neutral atom, including the Z electrons.
†EC stands for electron capture.

Answers to Your Turn Problems

CHAPTER 1
Active Example 1–1 1.26 km/h

CHAPTER 2
Active Example 2–1 (a) 10.7 mi.
(b) $\Delta\vec{x} = (2.1 \text{ mi})\hat{x}$. Note that these results are independent of the location of the origin.

CHAPTER 3
Active Example 3–1 D will decrease by a factor of two, but θ is unchanged. Numerical calculation gives $D = 2.33$ m and $\theta = 20.5°$.
Active Example 3–2 Reducing the time interval by a factor of two increases the magnitude of the acceleration by a factor of two, but does not change the direction. We find $a_{av} = 2.68 \text{ m/s}^2$, and $\theta = 53.6°$ north of east.

CHAPTER 4
Active Example 4–1 4.89 s. As expected, more time is required in this case.
Active Example 4–2 With $v_0 = 22$ m/s we find $R = 49$ m, for an increase of 20 percent (to two significant figures). In general, the fact that R depends on the *second* power of v_0 means that an increase of p percent in v_0 will result in roughly a $2p$ percent increase in R.

CHAPTER 5
Active Example 5–1 Doubling the force doubles the acceleration. This, in turn, reduces the stopping distance by a factor of two. We find $\Delta x = 61.0$ m.
Active Example 5–2 (a) In this case, the horizontal component of force will be greater than before. Therefore, the final speed will be greater as well. **(b)** $v_x = 1.40$ m/s.

CHAPTER 6
Active Example 6–1 Referring to Active Example 6–1, we see that the angle must be less than 20.0°. Numerical calculation yields $\theta = 14.0°$.
Active Example 6–2 For a tension greater than that found in Active Example 6–2, the sag angle must be less than 3.50°. We find $\theta = 2.96°$.
Active Example 6–3 Referring to Active Example 6–3, we see that the speed must be greater than 17.0 m/s. In fact, we find $v = 19.4$ m/s.

CHAPTER 7
Active Example 7–1 Doubling the mass doubles the initial kinetic energy of the block. Because the potential energy of the spring depends on the compression squared, the compression will be increased by a factor of the square root of 2. Therefore, the new compression is 0.17 m.
Active Example 7–2 Recalling that $P = Fv$, it follows that increasing the speed from 29.1 m/s to 32.0 m/s requires an increase in power by

the factor (32.0/29.1). Thus, the needed power is 4.10×10^4 W.

CHAPTER 8
Active Example 8–1 If we set the energy at the halfway position equal to $-mg(d/2) + \frac{1}{2}k(d/2)^2 + \frac{1}{2}mv^2$, we find $v = 0.664$ m/s. Notice that this is *greater* than the speed when the block reaches the position $y = 0$. The reason is that when the block is between $y = -mg/k$ and $y = 0$ the net force acting on it is downward, and hence it decelerates before it reaches $y = 0$.
Active Example 8–2 Using $d = 3.50$ m in step 3, we find $W_{nc} = -6060$ J.
Active Example 8–3 In this case, we find $h = 14.8$ m. Note that the height is less for an increased mass.

CHAPTER 9
Active Example 9–1 This time of contact would result in a final speed of 74.4 m/s.
Active Example 9–2 Doubling the mass of the stick means that the bee's velocity will be doubled in magnitude. Therefore, $\vec{v}_b = \vec{p}_b/m_b = (7.60 \text{ cm/s})\hat{x}$.
Active Example 9–3 No. The stick will move in the opposite direction with a greater speed, but the center of mass will remain at rest.

CHAPTER 10
Active Example 10–1 The time required is one-half the time for the pulley to come to rest. During this time, the pulley rotates through three-quarters of its total angular displacement; that is, $\theta - \theta_0 = \frac{3}{4}(6.94 \text{ rad}) = 5.21$ rad.
Active Example 10–2 Notice that both a_{cp} and a_t depend linearly on the radius, r. Therefore, at half the radius to the bottom of the tubes, the total acceleration has half the magnitude given in Active Example 10–2. The direction of the acceleration is unchanged, however. Thus, $a = 5.20 \text{ m/s}^2$ and $\phi = 33.9°$.
Active Example 10–3 The final speed decreases if the moment of inertia is increased. This is because with a larger moment of inertia, there is more kinetic energy of rotation for given speed. In this case, we find $v = 0.74$ m/s.

CHAPTER 11
Active Example 11–1 The child moved to the left (away from the father). The distance from the child to the father is now $0.40\ L$; therefore, the child moved to the left a distance of $0.15\ L$.
Active Example 11–2 Zero force condition: $F_2 - Mg - mg = 0$. Zero torque condition: $-Mg(1.56 \text{ m}) + F_2(2.06 \text{ m}) - mg(3.56 \text{ m}) = 0$.
Active Example 11–3 Zero force condition, horizontal: $f_2 - f_3 = 0$. Zero force condition, vertical: $f_1 - mg = 0$. Zero torque condition, with L = distance from base of ladder to wall: $mg(L - b) + f_2(a) - f_1(L) = 0$.

Active Example 11–4 This period corresponds to an angular speed of 420 rad/s; therefore, the radius of the star must be less than 20.0 km. Straightforward substitution yields $R_f = 17$ km.
Active Example 11–5 If it takes 22.5 s to complete one revolution, the angular speed of the merry-go-round is 0.279 rad/s. Noting that the angular speed of the merry-go-round is proportional to the initial speed of the child, we find that $v = 2.46$ m/s. As expected, this result is less than 2.80 m/s.

CHAPTER 12
Active Example 12–1 8.67×10^7 m
Active Example 12–2 7.63 km/s

CHAPTER 13
Active Example 13–1 A direct application of $K_{max} = \frac{1}{2}mv_{max}^2$ yields $m = 0.275$ kg.
Active Example 13–2 We know that $v_{max} = A\omega$ and $\omega = 2\pi/T$, with $T = 0.700$ s. Therefore, $A = 0.0877$ m.
Active Example 13–3 The amplitude is directly proportional to the initial speed; therefore, doubling the initial speed doubles the amplitude. The period, however, is independent of the amplitude. As a result, the time required to come to rest does not change.
Active Example 13–4 The moment of inertia of a solid sphere is less than that for a hollow sphere. Therefore, the solid sphere has the smaller period. Substituting $I = \frac{7}{5}MR^2$ in Equation 13–21 yields $T = 2\pi\sqrt{\frac{R}{g}}\left(\sqrt{\frac{7}{5}}\right)$.

CHAPTER 14
Active Example 14–1 Comparing to a whisper at 1 m, we find $r = 8.63$ km. Of course, other intervening sounds over such a large distance would surely drown out the "whisper."
Active Example 14–2 The next higher frequency resulting in constructive interference corresponds to a path length difference of 1.5λ. This means that $\lambda = 1.10$ m, and hence $f = 312$ Hz.

CHAPTER 15
Active Example 15–1 0.0140 N
Active Example 15–2 The volume of the water must be 0.955 times the volume of the wood, or $V_{water} = 3.22 \times 10^{-3} \text{ m}^3$. The volume of the wood is $(0.150 \text{ m})^3$; that is, $V_{wood} = 3.38 \times 10^{-3} \text{ m}^3$.
Active Example 15–3 4.06 m

CHAPTER 16
Active Example 16–1 Referring to the figure in Example 16–1, we see that the correct temperature should be somewhere between 70 °F and 90 °F. In fact, if we solve the equation $3t = 9t/5 + 32$, we find $t = T_C = (80/3)$ °C and $3t = T_F = 80$ °F.

Active Example 16–2 The iron has a lower specific heat than aluminum; therefore less heat is required for a given change in temperature. This implies that the final temperature of the system with an iron can will be greater than with an aluminum can. Numerical calculation yields $T = 31$ °C to two significant figures. If three significant figures are used, we find $T = 30.7$ °C for the aluminum can and $T = 31.3$ °C for the iron can.

CHAPTER 17

Active Example 17–1 Recall that $n = PV/RT$. Halving the temperature, by itself, doubles the number of moles. On the other hand, halving the diameter reduces the volume—and the number of moles—by a factor of eight. Combining the two effects, we find that the number of moles is reduced by a factor of 4.

Active Example 17–2 The height is proportional to the temperature. Therefore, changing the final height by a factor of $(19/28)$ changes the final temperature by the same factor. The final temperature, then, is 330 K $(19/28) = 220$ K. Note that this is less than the initial temperature, as expected.

Active Example 17–3 The shear deformation, Δx, is proportional to the height of the pancakes, L_0. Therefore, the shear deformation doubles to 5.0 cm.

Active Example 17–4 Brass has a smaller bulk modulus than gold, and hence its volume changes more for a given change in pressure. The change in volume of a brass doubloon is $\Delta V = -7.2 \times 10^{-10}$ m^3.

CHAPTER 18

Active Example 18–1 There are an infinite number of ways in which this can be done. Perhaps the simplest is to move straight up from point A to a pressure of 200 kPa, then expand at constant pressure from 0.25 m^3 to 0.54 m^3. Finally, drop straight down in pressure back to the value of 120 kPa and point B.

Active Example 18–2 Increasing T_h by 20 K gives $e = 0.277$; decreasing T_c by 20 K gives $e = 0.291$. Clearly, it is more effective to decrease the temperature of the cold reservoir.

Active Example 18–3 In this case, we find that the heat released to the cold reservoir is 595 J. This increases the entropy of the cold reservoir by 1.95 J/K. Therefore, the total entropy increase of the universe is 1.95 J/K − 1.82 J/K = 0.13 J/K. Note that this is a positive value, as expected.

CHAPTER 19

Active Example 19–1 The point of zero force remains in the same place. This can be seen most clearly in step 3, where we see that doubling each charge simply yields an additional factor of two on each side of the equation. Since the factor of two appears on both sides of the equation, it cancels.

Active Example 19–2 The new sphere exerts less force than the original sphere. Specifically, the new sphere has half the radius of the original sphere, and one quarter its surface area.

Therefore, it has one quarter the total charge, and exerts one quarter as much force.

Active Example 19–3 The new Gaussian surface has zero electric flux—there is no flux through either end cap, nor through the curved sides of the cylindrical surface. This means that the net charge contained within the Gaussian surface is zero, which is evident when we note that the two plates of the capacitor have opposite charge densities of equal magnitude.

CHAPTER 20

Active Example 20–1 We are given that the electric potential at point A is *higher* than at point B; therefore, the electric potential energy of an electron (with its negative charge) is *less* at point A than at point B. As an electron moves from point A to point B its electric potential energy increases by 7.2×10^{-19} J.

Active Example 20–2 The initial speed must be considerably greater than 5.00 m/s. In fact, it must be 14.6 m/s.

Active Example 20–3 There is no change in the electric potential energy. The reason is that moving the charge as described does not change the *separation* between any pair of charges in the system. Therefore, the total electric potential energy is as given in step 4.

CHAPTER 21

Active Example 21–1 The required time is 230 s.

Active Example 21–2 In this case, we find $I_1 = 0.13$ A, $I_2 = 0.11$ A, and $I_3 = 0.020$ A. Notice that each current flows in the direction indicated in the sketch of the circuit.

Active Example 21–3 The 5.00-μF capacitor stores more energy than the 10.0-μF capacitor because more work is required to force a given amount of charge onto its plates. In fact, we find that the 5.00-μF capacitor stores 1.60×10^{-4} J of energy, twice as much (to three significant figures) as the 7.98×10^{-5} J stored in the 10.0-μF capacitor.

CHAPTER 22

Active Example 22–1 The reason is that the orbital speed is directly proportional to the radius, as we see in Equation 22–3. Therefore, reducing the radius (or circumference) by a given factor reduces the speed by the same factor. It follows that the time required to travel a distance equal to one circumference is independent of the radius.

Active Example 22–2 In this case, the fields produced by the two wires are in the same direction; namely, into the page. The net field is 9.1×10^{-6} T, into the page.

CHAPTER 23

Active Example 23–1 One way to calculate the current is to note that the light bulb consumes a power of 5.0 W and has a resistance of 12 Ω. We can solve $P = I^2R$ to find $I = 0.65$ A. A second way is to note from Example 23–3 that the external force acting on the rod has a magnitude of 1.6 N. The rod moves with constant speed, however, and hence the magnetic force

acting on it, $F = ILB$, must have the same magnitude. If we equate these magnitudes, we find $I = 0.64$ A. The slight discrepancy between these answers is due to round-off error, as can be verified by repeating the calculations with more significant figures.

Active Example 23–2 The value of the inductance changes by a greater factor if we double the number of turns. This is because the inductance depends on the square of the number of turns, but depends only linearly on the cross-sectional area. Specifically, we find the following: (a) doubling N quadruples the inductance; (b) tripling A triples the inductance.

Active Example 23–3 From Equation 23–22 we see that the voltage in the secondary circuit is $V_s = V_p(N_s/N_p)$. Therefore, if $V_p \rightarrow 2V_p$ and $N_p \rightarrow 4N_p$, it is clear that we must double N_s to keep V_s the same.

CHAPTER 24

Active Example 24–1 The capacitive reactance is equal to 64 Ω when the frequency is reduced to 9.2 Hz. At this frequency, the current is 1.2 A.

Active Example 24–2 (a) 40 V. **(b)** 58 V.

Active Example 24–3 Setting the impedance of the circuit equal to 2.50 V/1.50 A = 1.67 Ω, we find $f = 68.0$ Hz and $f = 108$ Hz, to three significant figures.

CHAPTER 25

Active Example 25–1 If the beam spreads out to twice its initial diameter, its area quadruples. This means, in turn, that the intensity of the beam decreases by a factor of four. The intensity, however, depends on the fields squared. Therefore, it follows that both E_{max} and B_{max} decrease by a factor of two.

Active Example 25–2 With three equally rotated polarizers, we find a transmitted intensity of $0.689I_0$. This is considerably greater than the intensity found with two polarizers. In general, the more smoothly and continuously the plane of polarization is rotated, the greater the transmitted intensity.

CHAPTER 26

Active Example 26–1 The magnification of the tooth will decrease. After all, as the object moves closer to the mirror, the mirror behaves more and more like a plane mirror, in which case the magnification is 1. With $f = 1.38$ cm and $d_o = 1.00$ cm we find $d_i = -3.63$ cm and $m = 3.63$.

Active Example 26–2 Referring to Figure 26–34, it is clear that to obtain a larger magnification we must move the object closer to the lens. To obtain $m = 0.75$, we find that the object distance must be reduced from 12 cm to $d_o = 2.633$ cm, to four significant figures. The corresponding image distance is −1.975 cm.

CHAPTER 27

Active Example 27–1 The camera is now focussed at a distance of 1.72 m.

Active Example 27–2 The only change from the analysis given in the text for Figure 27–5 is that the concave mirror has a positive focal length (+12.5 cm) rather than a negative focal length. Therefore, the image distance for the mirror is 21.4 cm. This image is then an object for the lens, producing the final image of the system 15.4 cm to the left of the lens. The final magnification is −0.384, indicating an inverted image 38.4% of its original height.

Active Example 27–3 In this case, the far point is 202 cm from the person's eyes. Note that this far point is closer to the eye than the far point in Example 27–2; therefore, the required refractive power has a magnitude that is greater than 0.312.

Active Example 27–4 The second person's vision needs more correction, since the near point is farther from the eyes. Therefore, the refractive power of the second person's contacts must be greater, which, in turn, means that the focal length must be smaller. In fact, we find $f = 28.6$ cm.

CHAPTER 28

Active Example 28–1 The desired minimum thickness is one-quarter the wavelength in the material. Recall, however, that the wavelength in a material with an index of refraction n is $\lambda_n = \lambda/n$ (Equation 28–4). Therefore, if the index of refraction is increased, the minimum thickness will be decreased. In this case, we find a minimum thickness of 97.4 nm.

Active Example 28–2 The second dark fringe corresponds to $m = 2$ in Equation 28–12. With this substitution, we find that the linear distance is $y = 6.96$ cm.

Active Example 28–3 As the aperture of a telescope increases, the minimum angular

separation that can be resolved decreases, as can be seen from Equation 28–15. If a telescope can resolve smaller angular separations, it follows that its maximum resolution distance is greater. For the case $D = 3.0$ m, we find $L = 1.1 \times 10^{10}$ m.

Active Example 28–4 First, convert the wavelength 486.2 nm to the frequency $f = 6.170 \times 10^{14}$ Hz and the wavelength 563.0 nm to the frequency $f' = 5.329 \times 10^{14}$ Hz. With these results, we can now apply Equation 25–3 to find $u = 4.089 \times 10^7$ m/s. Since this is only 13.6% of the speed of light, the approximations used to derive Equation 25–3 should be valid.

CHAPTER 29

Active Example 29–1 The speed in this case is $v = 0.953c$.

Active Example 29–2 In this case, the velocity of the probe relative to the planet is $v = 0.306c$. The corresponding length is $L = 9.52$ m.

CHAPTER 30

Active Example 30–1 Increasing the wavelength by a factor of 1.25 results in a reduction in the frequency by a factor of 1.25. Similarly, the energy of a photon (which is proportional to frequency) is reduced by a factor of 1.25. Since each photon carries less energy, it follows that more photons will be required per second at this new wavelength. In fact, the minimum number of photons per second will be increased by the factor 1.25.

Active Example 30–2 The de Broglie wavelength is inversely proportional to speed;

therefore, doubling the speed results in a wavelength that is reduced by a factor of two.

CHAPTER 31

Active Example 31–1 In this case, the final state is $n_f = 2$.

Active Example 31–2 In singly ionized helium, the charge of the nucleus is $+Ze = +2e$; therefore, $Z = 2$. Referring to Equation 31–9, we see that the energy of any given energy level depends on Z^2. It follows that the energy—and frequency—of the absorbed photon increases by a factor of $2^2 = 4$.

Active Example 31–3 Direct substitution in Equation 31–14 shows that $Z = 51$ is the largest value of Z that requires an acceleration voltage less than 35 kV.

CHAPTER 32

Active Example 32–1 Doubling the wavelength reduces the frequency of the gamma ray (and its energy) by a factor of two. Since the mass difference is proportional to the energy of the gamma ray, it too will be reduced by a factor of two.

Active Example 32–2 Direct substitution in Equation 32–9 shows that the number of radon atoms has decreased by a factor of two when $t = 3.83$ d. Note that this result is in agreement with Equation 32–10.

Active Example 32–3 Using Equation 32–12, we see that the activity of the radon decreases to 10.0 Bq after 12.7 d.

Active Example 32–4 This reaction releases 12.9 MeV.

Answers to Odd-Numbered Conceptual Questions

CHAPTER 1

1. No. The factor of 2 is dimensionless.
3. **(a)** Not possible, since units have dimensions. For example, seconds can only have the dimension of time. **(b)** Possible, since different units can be used to measure the same dimensions. For example, time can be measured in seconds, minutes, or hours.
5. To the nearest power of ten: **(a)** 1 m; **(b)** 10^{-2} m; **(c)** 10 m; **(d)** 100 m; **(e)** 10^7 m.

CHAPTER 2

1. The displacement is the same for you and your dog; the distance covered by the dog is greater.
3. **(a)** Yes. If you drive in a complete circle your distance is the circumference of the circle, but your displacement is zero. **(b)** Yes. The distance and the magnitude of the displacement are equal if you drive in a straight line. **(c)** No. Any deviation from a straight line results in a distance that is greater than the magnitude of the displacement.
5. Their velocities are different because they travel in different directions.

7. Since the car circles the track its direction of motion must be changing. Therefore, its velocity changes as well. Its speed, however, can be constant.
9. Constant-velocity motion; that is, straight-line motion with constant speed.
11. **(a)** The time required to stop is doubled. **(b)** The distance required to stop increases by a factor of four.
13. Yes, if it moves with constant velocity.
15. **(a)** No. If air resistance can be ignored, the acceleration of the ball is the same at each point on its flight. **(b)** Same answer as part (a).
17. Ignoring air resistance, the two gloves have the same acceleration.

CHAPTER 3

1. **(a)** scalar; **(b)** vector; **(c)** vector; **(d)** scalar.
3. **(a)** $\vec{A}$ and $\vec{B}$ have the same magnitude. **(b)** $\vec{A}$ and $\vec{B}$ have opposite directions.
5. Yes, if they have the same magnitude and point in opposite directions.
7. Note that the magnitudes A, B, and C satisfy the Pythagorean theorem. It follows that $\vec{A}$, $\vec{B}$, and $\vec{C}$ form a right triangle,

with $\vec{C}$ as the hypotenuse. Thus, $\vec{A}$ and $\vec{B}$ are perpendicular to one another.
9. $\vec{A}$ and $\vec{B}$ must be collinear and point in opposite directions. In addition, the magnitude of $\vec{A}$ must be greater than the magnitude of $\vec{B}$; that is, $|A| > |B|$.
11. The vector $\vec{A}$ points in one of two directions: (1) 135° counterclockwise from the x axis; (2) 45° clockwise from the x axis. Case (1) corresponds to $A_x < 0$ and case (2) corresponds to $A_x > 0$.
13. Tilt the umbrella forward so that it points in the opposite direction of the rain's velocity relative to you.

CHAPTER 4

1. Ignoring air resistance, the acceleration of a projectile is vertically downward at all times.
3. The projectile was launched at an angle of 30° above the positive x axis; when it landed its direction of motion was 30° below the positive x axis. Hence, its change in direction was 60° clockwise.
5. At its highest point, the projectile is moving horizontally. This means that gravity

has reduced its y component of velocity to zero. The x component of velocity is unchanged by gravity, however. Therefore, the projectile has a velocity equal to $\vec{\mathbf{v}} = (4 \text{ m/s})\hat{\mathbf{x}}$ at the highest point in its trajectory.

7. Less than 45°. See Figure 4–9.

9. **(a)** From the child's point of view the scoop of ice cream falls straight downward. **(b)** From the point of view of the parents the scoop of ice cream follows a parabolic trajectory.

11. **(a)** At its highest point the projectile moves horizontally. Therefore, its launch angle was 50°. **(b)** In this case, the launch angle was 150°, or, equivalently, 30° above the negative x axis.

CHAPTER 5

1. The force exerted on the car by the brakes causes it to slow down, but your body continues to move forward with the same velocity (due to inertia) until the seat belt exerts a force on it to decrease its speed.

3. No. You are at rest relative to your immediate surroundings, but you are in motion relative to other objects in the universe.

5. When the magnitude of the force exerted on the girl by the rope equals the magnitude of her weight, the net force acting on her is zero. As a result, she moves with constant velocity.

7. **(a)** The upper string breaks, because the tension in it is equal to the applied force on the lower string plus the weight of the block. When the tension in the upper string reaches the breaking point, the tension in the lower string is below this value. **(b)** The lower string breaks in this case, because of the inertia of the block. As you move your hand downward rapidly the lower string stretches and breaks before the block can move a significant distance and stretch the upper string.

9. Each time the astronauts throw or catch the ball they exert a force on it, and it exerts an equal and opposite force on them. This causes the astronauts to move farther apart from one another with increasing speed as the game progresses.

11. Mr. Ed's reasoning is incorrect because he is adding two action-reaction forces that act on *different* objects. Wilbur should point out that the net force exerted on the cart is simply the force exerted on it by Mr. Ed. Thus the cart will accelerate. The equal and opposite reaction force acts on Mr. Ed, and does not cancel the force acting on the cart.

13. The whole brick has twice the force acting on it, but it also has twice the mass. Since the acceleration of an object is proportional to the force exerted on it and inversely proportional to its mass, the whole brick has the same acceleration as the half brick.

15. Yes. An object with zero net force acting on it has a constant velocity. This velocity may or may not have zero magnitude.

17. The acceleration of an object is inversely proportional to its mass. The diver and the Earth experience the same force, but the Earth—with its much larger mass—has a much smaller acceleration.

19. An astronaut can tell which of two objects is more massive by pushing on both with the same force. Since acceleration is inversely proportional to mass, the more massive object can be recognized by its smaller acceleration.

21. On solid ground you come to rest in a much smaller distance than when you plunge into water. The smaller the distance over which you come to rest the greater the acceleration, and the greater the acceleration the greater the force exerted on you. Thus, when you land on solid ground the large force it exerts on you may be enough to cause injury.

23. Yes, in fact it happens all the time. Whenever you throw a ball upward it moves in the opposite direction to the net force acting on it, until it reaches the top of its trajectory.

25. This is an example of bad physics. Though the rocket-powered backpack may well produce enough force to give the truck a large acceleration, that force must be transmitted to the truck through the boy's arms. A force large enough to rapidly accelerate a truck would crush a person's arms.

CHAPTER 6

1. The clothesline has a finite mass, and so the tension in the line must have an upward component to oppose the downward force of gravity. Thus, the line sags much the same as if a weight were hanging from it.

3. The braking distance of a skidding car depends on its initial speed and the coefficient of kinetic friction. Thus, if the coefficient of friction is known reasonably well, the initial speed can be determined from the length of the skid marks.

5. The force that ultimately is responsible for stopping a train is the frictional force between its metal wheels and the metal track. These are fairly smooth surfaces. In contrast, the frictional force that stops a car is between the rubber tires and the concrete roadway. These are rougher surfaces with a greater coefficient of friction.

7. As you brake harder your car has a greater acceleration. The greater the acceleration of the car, the greater the force required to give the flat of strawberries the same acceleration. When the required force exceeds the maximum force of static friction the strawberries begin to slide.

9. For a drop of water to stay on a rotating wheel an inward force is required to give the drop the necessary centripetal acceleration. Since the force between a drop of water and the wheel is small, the drop will separate from the wheel rather than follow its circular path.

11. A centripetal force is required to make the motorcycle follow a circular path, and this force increases rapidly with the speed of the cycle. If the necessary centripetal force exceeds the weight of the motorcycle, because its speed is high enough, then the track must exert a downward force on the cycle at the top of the circle. This keeps the cycle in firm contact with the track.

13. Since the passengers are moving in a circular path a centripetal force must be exerted on them. This force, which is radially inward, is supplied by the wall of the cylinder.

15. This helps because the students sitting on the trunk increase the normal force between your tires and the road. Since the force of friction is proportional to the normal force, this increases the frictional force enough (one hopes) to allow your car to move.

17. The normal force exerted on a gecko by a vertical wall is zero. If the gecko is to stay in place, however, the force of static friction must exert an upward force equal to the gecko's weight. For this to happen when the normal force is zero would require an infinite coefficient of static friction. Thus, we conclude that the physics of gecko feet is more complex than our simple models of friction.

19. Yes. The steering wheel can accelerate a car—even if its speed remains the same—by changing its direction of motion.

21. When a bicycle rider leans inward on a turn, the force applied to the wheels of the bicycle by the ground is both upward and inward. It is this inward force that produces the centripetal acceleration of the rider.

CHAPTER 7

1. No. Work requires that a force acts through a distance.

3. True. To do work on an object a force must have a nonzero component along its direction of motion.

5. Yes, you must do work against the force of gravity to raise your body upward out of bed.

7. The frictional force between your shoes and the ground does positive work on you whenever you begin to walk.

9. Gravity exerts an equal and opposite force on the package, and hence the net work done on it is zero. The result is no change in kinetic energy.

11. No, we must also know how much time it takes for engine 1 to do the work. For example, if engine 1 takes twice as much time to do twice the work of engine 2, it has the same power output as engine 2. If it takes more than twice as much time, then engine 1 actually produces less power than engine 2.

CHAPTER 8

1. The kinetic energy cannot be negative, since m and v^2 are always positive or zero. The gravitational potential energy can be negative since any level can be chosen to be zero.

3. Since both distance and average force are doubled, the work done in stretching the spring is quadrupled. Equivalently, the potential energy of the spring is proportional to $(\Delta x)^2$, and hence doubling the stretch distance quadruples the spring's potential energy.

5. If the spring is permanently deformed, it will not return to its original length. As a result, the work that was done to stretch the spring is not fully recovered—some of it goes into the energy of deformation. For this reason, the spring force is not conservative during the deformation. If the spring is now stretched or compressed by a small amount about its new equilibrium position, its force is again conservative—though the force constant will be different.

7. When the term "energy conservation" is used in everyday language, it doesn't refer to the total amount of energy in the universe. Instead, it refers to using energy wisely, especially when a particular source of energy—like oil or natural gas—is finite and nonrenewable.

9. A variety of conservative and nonconservative forces are involved in the situation shown in the photo. First, the engine of the earth mover does positive nonconservative work as it digs out and lifts a load of rocks. At the same time, gravity does negative conservative work on the rocks as the gravitational potential energy of the system increases. Next, the earth mover does positive nonconservative work to transport the rocks to the dump truck. When the rocks are released, gravity does positive conservative work as the gravitational potential energy of the system is converted to kinetic energy. Nonconservative frictional forces do negative work to convert the kinetic energy of the rocks into sound and heat when they land in the truck. Finally, the increased load in the truck does conservative work as it compresses the springs, storing part of the system's energy in the form of spring potential energy.

11. Zero force implies that the rate of change in the potential energy with distance is zero—that is, the potential energy is constant—but the value of the potential energy can be anything at all. Similarly, if the potential energy is zero, it does not mean that the force is zero. Again, what matters is the rate of change of the potential energy with distance.

13. The dive begins with the diver climbing the ladder to the diving board, which converts chemical energy in the muscles into an increased gravitational potential energy. Next, by jumping on the board the diver causes the board to flex and to store potential energy. As the board rebounds, the diver springs into the air, using the kinetic energy derived from the leg muscles and the potential energy released by the board. The diver's kinetic energy is then converted into an increased gravitational potential energy until the highest point of the dive is reached. After that, gravitational potential energy is converted back to kinetic energy as the diver moves downward. Finally, the kinetic energy of the diver is converted into heat, sound, and flowing water as splashdown occurs.

CHAPTER 9

1. The momentum of the keys increases as they fall because a net force acts on them. The momentum of the universe is unchanged because an equal and opposite force acts on the Earth.

3. If the kinetic energy is zero the speeds must be zero as well. This means that the momentum is zero.

5. Yes, in much the same way that a propeller in water can power a speedboat.

7. When a heavy object and a light object collide they exert equal and opposite forces on one another. Since the light object has less mass, its acceleration is greater. This can result in more severe injuries for the light vehicle.

9. No. The fact that the initial momentum of the system is nonzero means that the final momentum must also be nonzero. Thus, it is not possible for both objects to be at rest after the collision.

11. (a) Yes. Suppose two objects have momenta of equal magnitude. If these objects collide in a head-on, completely inelastic collision, they will be at rest after the collision. In this case, all of the initial kinetic energy is converted to other forms of energy. (b) No. In order for its momentum to change, an external force must act on the system. We are given, however, that the system is isolated. Therefore, the only forces acting on it are internal forces.

13. The kinetic energy of the bullet is much greater than that of the gun. Thus, less energy is dissipated in stopping the gun.

15. The plane weighs the same whether the fly lands on the dashboard or flies about the cockpit. The reason is that the fly must exert a downward force on the air in the cockpit equal in magnitude to its own weight in order to stay aloft. This force ultimately acts downward on the plane, just as if the fly had landed.

17. Your center of mass is somewhere directly above the area of contact between your foot and the ground.

CHAPTER 10

1. All points on the rigid object have the same angular speed. Not all points have the same linear speed, however. The farther a given point is from the axis of rotation the greater its linear speed.

3. No. As long as you are driving in a circular path you will have a nonzero centripetal acceleration.

5. (a) No, because your direction of motion is constantly changing. (b) Yes, your linear speed is simply the radius of the wheel times your angular speed. (c) Yes. It is equal to your linear speed squared divided by the radius of the wheel. (d) No. Your centripetal acceleration is always toward the center of the wheel, but this is in a different direction as you rotate to different locations.

7. (a) A basketball thrown with no spin. (b) A spinning airplane propeller on a plane that is at rest. (c) A bicycle wheel on a moving bicycle.

9. When the chunky stew is rolled down the aisle, all of the contents of the can roll together with approximately the same angular speed. This is because the chunky stew is thick and almost solid. The beef broth, however, is little more than water. Therefore, when the broth is rolled down the aisle, almost all that is actually rolling is the metal can itself. It follows that the stew has the greater initial kinetic energy, and hence it rolls a greater distance.

CHAPTER 11

1. No. Torque depends both on the magnitude of the force and on the distance from the axis of rotation, or moment arm, at which it is applied. A small force can produce the same torque as a large force if it is applied farther from the axis of rotation.

3. The long pole has a large moment of inertia, which means that for a given applied torque the walker and pole have a small angular acceleration. This allows more time for the walker to "correct" his balance.

5. A force applied radially to a wheel produces zero torque, though the net force is nonzero.

7. No. In most cars the massive engine is located in the front, thus the car's center of mass is not in the middle of the car, but is closer to the front end. This means that the force exerted on the front tires is greater than the force exerted on the rear tires. (This situation is analogous to Active Example 11–1.)

9. You are in static equilibrium as you sit in your chair; so is the building where you have your physics class.

11. The angular speed of the dust cloud increases, just like a skater pulling in her arms, due to conservation of angular momentum.

13. Yes. Imagine turning on a ceiling fan. This increases the fan's angular momentum, without changing its linear momentum.

CHAPTER 12

1. No. The force of Earth's gravity is practically as strong in orbit as it is on the surface of the Earth. The astronauts experience weightlessness because they are in constant free fall.

3. If the gravitational force depended on the sum of the two masses, it would predict a

nonzero force even when one of the masses is zero. That is, there would be a gravitational force between a mass and a point in empty space, which is certainly not what is observed.

5. No. The amount of area swept out per time varies from planet to planet; what is constant is the amount of area swept out by a *given* planet per time.

7. Once the period of Charon is determined, the mass of the body it orbits (Pluto) can be calculated using Equation 12–7.

9. On the Moon, where there is no atmosphere, a rock can orbit at any altitude where it clears the mountains—as long as it has sufficient speed. Thus, if you could give the rock enough speed, it would orbit the Moon and come up to you from behind.

11. No. In the weightless environment of the Shuttle there would be no convection, which is needed to bring fresh oxygen to the flame. Without convection a flame usually goes out very quickly. In carefully controlled experiments on the Shuttle, however, small flames have been maintained for considerable times. These "weightless" flames are spherical in shape, as opposed to the tear-shaped flames here on Earth.

13. The net force acting on the Moon is always directed toward the Sun, never away from the Sun. Therefore, the Moon's orbit must always curve toward the Sun. The path shown in the upper part of Figure 12–20, though it seems "intuitive," sometimes curves toward the Sun, sometimes away from the Sun. The correct path, shown in the lower part of Figure 12–20, curves sharply toward the Sun when both the Sun and the Earth pull inward on the Moon, and curves only slightly toward the Sun when the Moon is pulled in opposite directions by the Sun and the Earth.

CHAPTER 13

1. The motion is periodic. It is not simple harmonic, however, because the position and velocity of the ball do not vary sinusoidally with time.

3. The motion of the air cart is periodic; it repeats after a fixed length of time. It is not simple harmonic motion, however, because the position and velocity of the cart do not vary sinusoidally with time.

5. The period remains the same because, even though the distance traveled by the object is doubled, its speed at any given time is also doubled.

7. Referring to Equation 13–6, we see that the constant C represents the maximum speed of the object, $C = v_{max} = A\omega$; similarly, the constant D is the angular frequency, $D = \omega = 2\pi/T$. It follows that the amplitude is $A = C/D$ and the period is $T = 2\pi/D$.

9. If soldiers march in synchrony, the bridge will oscillate with the frequency of their step. If this frequency is near a resonance frequency of the bridge, the amplitude of oscillation could increase to dangerous levels.

CHAPTER 14

1. To generate a longitudinal wave, hit the nail on the head in a direction parallel to its length. To generate a transverse wave, hit the nail in a direction that is perpendicular to its length.

3. Typical waves at stadiums are transverse, since people move vertically up and down while the wave moves horizontally. To produce a longitudinal wave people could move back-and-forth to their left or right.

5. If the speed of sound depended on frequency, the sound in the first row—where the travel time is small—would not be affected significantly. Farther back from the stage, however, sounds with different frequencies would arrive at different times—the bass would be "out of sync" with the treble.

7. The part of the nail that vibrates most freely is the portion not yet in the wood. As you drive the nail farther into the wood, therefore, the part that vibrates becomes shorter and shorter. The vibrating portion of the nail is similar to the vibrating air column in an organ pipe, and hence the frequency goes up as the length decreases.

9. When you tune a violin you change the tension in the string. This causes the speed of waves in the string to change. The wavelength of a given mode of oscillation is unchanged, however, due to the fixed length of string. Thus, changing the speed while keeping the wavelength constant results in a change in frequency, according to the relation $v = f\lambda$.

11. No, the energy of oscillation is the same at all times. When the string is flat, the energy of oscillation is purely kinetic.

13. You hear no beats because the difference in frequency between these notes is too great to produce detectable beats.

CHAPTER 15

1. To draw a liquid up a straw you expand your lungs, which reduces the air pressure inside your mouth to less than atmospheric pressure. The resulting difference in pressure produces a net upward force on the liquid in the straw.

3. The pressure in a tank of water increases with depth, hence the pressure is greatest near the bottom. To provide sufficient support there, the metal bands must be spaced more closely together.

5. This experiment shows that a certain pressure is needed at the bottom of the water column and not just a certain weight of water. To blow the top off the barrel it is necessary to increase the pressure in the barrel enough so that the increase in pressure times the surface area of the top exceeds 400 N. Thus, the required height of water is the height that gives the necessary increase in pressure. But the increase in pressure, ρgh, depends only on the height of the water in the tube, not on its weight.

7. Two quantities are unknown; the object's density and its volume. The two weight measurements provide two independent conditions that can be solved for the two unknowns.

9. The Great Salt Lake has water with a higher salinity, and hence a higher density, than ocean water. In fact, the density of its water is somewhat greater than the density of a typical human body. This means that a person can float in the Great Salt Lake much like a block of wood floats in fresh water.

11. The problem is that as you go deeper into the water, the pressure pushing against your chest and lungs increases rapidly. Even if you had a long tube on your snorkel, you would find it difficult to expand your lungs to take a breath. The air coming through the snorkel is at atmospheric pressure, but the water pushing against your chest might have twice that pressure or more. Thus, scuba gear not only holds air for you to breathe in a tank, it also feeds this air to you under pressure.

13. As the water falls it speeds up. Still, the amount of water that passes a given point in a given time is the same at any height. If the thickness of the water stayed the same, and its speed increased, the amount of water per time would increase. Hence, the thickness of the water must decrease to offset the increase in speed.

15. If you takeoff into the wind the air speed over the wings is greater than if you takeoff with the wind. This means that more lift is produced when taking off into the wind, which is clearly the preferable situation.

17. The ball should spin so that the side facing the batter is moving upward and the side facing the pitcher is moving downward.

CHAPTER 16

1. The coffee is not in equilibrium because its temperature is different from that of its surroundings. Over time the temperature of the coffee will decrease, until finally it is the same as room temperature. At this point it will be in equilibrium—as long as the room stays at the same temperature.

3. The discrepancy is not serious. After all, a temperature of 15,000,000 °C is equivalent to a temperature of 15,000,273.15 K. A difference of 273.15 out of 15 million is generally insignificant.

5. If the glass and the mercury had the same coefficient of volume expansion, the level of mercury in the glass would not change

with temperature. This is because the volume of the cavity in the glass would expand by the same amount as the volume of mercury.

7. The mercury level drops at the beginning because the glass is the first to increase its temperature when it comes into contact with the hot liquid. Therefore, the glass expands before the mercury, leading to a drop in level. As the mercury attains the same temperature few moments later, its level will increase.

9. As the temperature of the house decreases, the length of the various pieces of wood from which it is constructed will decrease as well. As the house adjusts to these changing lengths, it will often creak or groan.

11. If the objects have different masses, the less massive object will have a greater temperature change, since it has the smaller heat capacity. On the other hand, the objects may have the same mass but differ in the material from which they are made. In this case, the object with the smaller specific heat will have the greater temperature change.

13. As the ground warms up on a sunny day, the ground of the surrounding suburbs warms up faster, since it has a smaller specific heat. This would lead to a wind blowing from the city to the suburbs.

15. Even though the flame at the far end of the match is very hot, the wood from which it is made is a poor conductor of heat. The air between the flame and your finger is an even poorer conductor of heat.

17. Two important factors work in favor of the water-filled balloon. First, the water has a large heat capacity, hence it can take on a large amount of heat with little change in temperature. Second, water is a better conductor of heat than air, hence the heat from the flame is conducted into a large volume of water—which gives it a larger effective heat capacity.

19. When penguins (or people) huddle together their rate of heat production is the same, but the surface area over which this heat is radiated to the surroundings is decreased. This results in the penguins being warmer.

21. Object 1 must have the higher temperature, to compensate for object 2's greater emissivity. Since radiated power depends on temperature raised to the fourth power, the temperature of object 1 must be greater by a factor of 2 to the one fourth power.

CHAPTER 17

1. The volume of an ideal gas is given by $V = nRT/P$. Thus, we expect the volume of the oxygen bags to vary inversely with pressure—the lower the pressure in the cabin, the larger the bags.

3. Recall that velocity takes into account both the speed of an object and its direc-

tion of motion. Therefore, the average *velocity* of air molecules in a room is zero, since they move randomly in all directions.

5. Airplanes can have a difficult time taking off from high-altitude airports because the air is thin and provides less lift than air at sea level. When the air is cool, however, its density is greater than when it is warm. Therefore, taking off in the morning or evening will provide the airplane with more lift—which can be a very important advantage at high altitude.

7. The boiling temperature of water depends on the pressure at which the boiling occurs—the higher the pressure, the higher the boiling temperature. Thus, in the autoclave, where the pressure is greater than atmospheric pressure, the temperature of boiling water is greater than 100 °C.

9. The alcohol, besides having antiseptic qualities, evaporates readily. As it evaporates, it draws heat from the body.

11. As high-speed molecules leave the drop, it draws heat from its surroundings to keep its temperature constant. As long as the temperature of the drop is constant, it will continue to have the same fraction of molecules moving quickly enough to escape.

CHAPTER 18

1. No. If the engine has friction it is not reversible.

3. The answer, in both cases, is yes.
(a) Compress a gas in a thermally insulated cylinder. This will cause its temperature to rise. (b) If you expand a gas in a thermally insulated cylinder, its temperature will decrease.

5. One cannot conclude that heat was added to the system. For example, if a gas in a thermally insulated cylinder is compressed, its temperature will rise with no heat transfer.

7. Yes. You can convert mechanical work completely into heat by rubbing your hands together.

9. (a) No; (b) yes; (c) no; (d) no; (e) yes; (f) no.

11. Yes, this is possible. The problem is that you would need low-temperature reservoirs of ever lower temperature to keep the process going.

13. No. As you do work to put things in order you give off heat to the atmosphere. This increases the entropy of the air by more than the decrease in entropy of the room, for a net increase in entropy.

15. (a) Popped popcorn; (b) an omelet; (c) a pile of bricks; (d) a burned piece of paper.

CHAPTER 19

1. No. When an object becomes charged it is because of a transfer of charge between it and another object.

3. The charged comb causes the paper to become polarized, with the side nearest the

comb acquiring a charge opposite to the charge of the comb. The result is an attractive interaction between the comb and the paper.

5. Yes. If the suspended object were neutral, it would be attracted to the charged rod by polarization effects. The fact that the suspended object is repelled indicates it has a charge of the same sign as that of the rod.

7. Both force laws depend on the product of specific properties of the objects involved; in the case of gravity it is the mass that is relevant, in the case of electrostatics it is the electric charge. In addition, both forces decrease with increasing distance as $1/r^2$. The extremely important difference between the forces, however, is that gravity is always attractive, whereas electrostatic forces can be attractive or repulsive.

9. No. Only for very special displacements will the electrostatic force act in a direction that points back toward the equilibrium point. For a general displacement the electrostatic force does not point toward the equilibrium point, and the fifth charge would move farther from equilibrium, making the system unstable.

11. One difference is that when an object is charged by induction, there is no physical contact between the object being charged and the object used to do the charging. In contrast, charging by contact—as the name implies—involves direct physical contact to transfer charge from one object to another. The main difference is that when an object is charged by induction, the sign of the charge the object acquires is opposite to that of the object used to do the charging. Charging by contact gives the object being charged the same sign of charge as the original charged object.

13. No. The direction of the forces might be different simply because the sign of the charges are different. The magnitude of the forces might be different simply because the magnitudes of the charges are different.

15. By definition, electric field lines point in the direction of the electric force on a positive charge at any given location in space. This force can point in only one direction at any one location, however. Therefore, electric field lines cannot cross, because if they did, it would imply two different directions for the electric force at the same location.

17. The electric field depends on both charges. The total electric field at any point is simply the superposition of the electric field produced by each charge separately.

19. Gauss's law is useful as a calculational tool only in cases of high symmetry, where one can produce a gaussian surface on which the electric field is either constant or has no perpendicular component. It is not possible to do this in any simple way for the case of a charged disk.

Gauss's law still applies—it's just not particularly useful.

CHAPTER 20

1. The electric field is a measure of how much the electric potential changes from one position to another. Therefore, the electric field in each of these regions is zero.

3. Not necessarily. The electric field is related to the rate of change of electric potential, not to the value of the electric potential. Therefore, if the electric field is zero in some region of space, it follows that the electric potential is constant in that region. The constant value of the electric potential may be zero, but it may also be positive or negative.

5. Zero. The electric field is perpendicular to an equipotential, therefore the work done in moving along an equipotential is zero.

7. If the electric field is not perpendicular to an equipotential, the field would do work on a charge that moves along the equipotential. In this case, the potential energy of the charge would change, and the surface would not in fact be an equipotential.

9. When the capacitor is disconnected from the battery, the charge on the capacitor plates simply remains where it is—there is no way for it to go anywhere else. When the terminals are connected to one another the charges flow from plate to plate until both plates have zero charge.

11. The capacitance of a capacitor depends on **(b)** the separation of the plates and **(e)** the area of the plates. The capacitance does not depend on **(a)** the charge on the plates, **(c)** the voltage difference between the plates, or **(d)** the electric field between the plates.

13. No. As an example, note that the volume of a milk container is not zero just because the container happens to be empty of milk. The same can be said about the capacitance of a capacitor that happens to be uncharged.

CHAPTER 21

1. Electric current is in the opposite direction to the motion of negative charge, therefore the electric current of the falling electron is upward.

3. No. By rubbing the comb through your hair you have transferred charge from your hair to the comb, but the net charge of you and the comb together is still zero. Therefore, no current is produced when you walk.

5. No. An electron may have a fairly large velocity at any given time, but because its direction of motion keeps changing—due to its collisions with atoms in the wire—its average velocity is almost zero.

7. Connect the four resistors in a parallel arrangement with two branches, each branch containing two resistors connected in series. In this way, the equivalent resistance of each branch is 2R, and the equivalent resistance of two resistors of 2R in parallel is simply R, as desired.

9. Resistors connected in series have the same current flowing through them.

11. Each electron in the wire affects its neighbors by exerting a force on them, causing them to move. Thus, when electrons begin to move out of a battery their motion sets up a propagating influence that moves through the wire at nearly the speed of light, causing electrons everywhere in the wire to begin moving.

13. A number of factors come into play here. First, the bottom of a bird's foot is tough, and definitely not a good conductor of electricity. Second, and more important, is the fact that a potential difference is required for there to be a flow of current. Just being in contact with a high-voltage wire isn't enough to cause a problem; somewhere else there must be contact with a lower voltage. But the bird is in contact with essentially the same high voltage in two different places (where its feet touch the wire), which doesn't lead to a potential difference. The only potential difference the bird experiences is due to the very small voltage drop along the segment of wire between the bird's two feet.

15. The junction rule is based on conservation of electric charge; the loop rule is based on the conservation of energy.

17. Capacitors in parallel have the same potential difference between their plates.

CHAPTER 22

1. No. The particles may have charge of the same sign but move in opposite directions along the same line. In this way, they would both move perpendicular to the field, but would deflect in opposite directions.

3. No. If the electron moves in the same direction as the magnetic field, or opposite to the direction of the field, the magnetic force exerted on it will be zero. As a result, its velocity will remain constant.

5. The radius of curvature is proportional to the speed of the particle. It follows that the particle moving in a circle of large radius (and large circumference) has a proportionally larger speed than the particle moving in a circle of small radius (and small circumference). Therefore, the time required for an orbit ($t = d/v$) is the same for both particles.

CHAPTER 23

1. The magnetic field indicates the strength and direction of the magnetic force that a charged particle moving with a certain velocity would experience at a given point in space. The magnetic flux, on the other hand, can be thought of as a measure of the "amount" of magnetic field that passes through a given area.

3. As the magnet falls, it induces eddy currents in the copper tube. These induced currents produce a magnetic field opposite in direction to that of the magnet. This results in a magnetic repulsion that slows the fall of the magnet. In fact, the motion of the magnet is much the same as if it had been dropped into a tube filled with honey.

5. When the switch is closed, a magnetic field is produced in the wire coil and in the iron rod. This results in an increasing magnetic flux through the metal ring, and a corresponding induced emf. The current produced by the induced emf generates a magnetic field opposite in direction to the field in the iron rod. The resulting magnetic repulsion propels the ring into the air.

7. Initially, the rod accelerates to the left, due to the downward current it carries. As it speeds up, however, the motional emf it generates will begin to counteract the emf of the battery. Eventually the two emfs balance one another, and current stops flowing in the rod. From this point on, the rod continues to move with constant speed.

9. As the shuttle orbits, it moves through the Earth's magnetic field at high speed. A long conducting wire moving through the field can generate an induced emf. In fact, the emf is given by the product of the length of the wire, the speed of the shuttle, and the perpendicular component of the magnetic field. With such large values for the speed and length, the induced emf can be great enough to provide substantial electrical power.

11. The final current in an *RL* circuit is determined only by the resistor *R* and the emf of the battery. The reason is that when the current stops changing, the back emf in an inductor vanishes. Thus, the inductor behaves like an ideal wire of zero resistance when the current reaches its final value.

CHAPTER 24

1. The average voltage in an ac circuit is zero because it oscillates symmetrically between positive and negative values. To calculate the rms voltage, however, one first squares the voltage. This gives values that are always greater than or equal to zero. Therefore, the rms voltage will be nonzero unless the voltage in the circuit is zero at all times.

3. An *LC* circuit consumes zero power because ideal inductors and capacitors have no resistance. From a different point of view, the phase angle in an *LC* circuit is either $\phi = +90°$ or $\phi = -90°$, depending on whether the frequency is less than or greater than the resonance frequency, respectively. In either case, the power factor, cos ϕ, is zero; hence the power consumed by the circuit is zero.

5. In the phasor diagram for an *LC* circuit, the impedance is always perpendicular to the current—the only question, therefore, is whether ϕ is $+90°$ or $-90°$. At a frequency less than the resonance frequency the capacitive reactance ($X_C = 1/\omega C$) is greater than the inductive reactance ($X_L = \omega L$). Therefore, the situation is similar to that of a circuit with only a capacitor, in which case the phase angle is $\phi = -90°$.

7. As frequency is increased there is no change in resistance, *R*. On the other hand, the capacitive reactance ($X_C = 1/\omega C$) decreases and the inductive reactance ($X_L = \omega L$) increases.

9. Mass resists changes in its motion due to its inertia. Similarly, an inductor resists changes in the current flowing through it due to its inductance. Therefore, mass and inductance are analogous. As for the spring constant, a stiff spring (large spring constant) gives little stretch for a given force. Similarly, a capacitor with a small capacitance stores little charge for a given voltage. Since charge is what moves in a circuit, it follows that displacement and charge are analogous. Therefore, the spring constant and the inverse of the capacitance are analogous.

11. Yes. Recall that the impedance of an *RLC* circuit is $Z = \sqrt{R^2 + (X_L - X_C)^2}$. Because the quantity in parentheses is squared, we get the same impedance when X_L is greater than X_C by a certain amount as when X_C is greater than X_L by the same amount.

CHAPTER 25

1. Presumably, an "invisible man" would be invisible because light passes through his body unimpeded, just as if it were passing through thin air. If some light were deflected or absorbed, we would see this effect and the person would no longer be invisible. For a person to see, however, some light must be absorbed by the retina. This absorption would cause the invisible man to be visible.

3. As a grain of dust becomes smaller, its volume—and therefore its mass—decreases more rapidly than does its area. It follows that radiation pressure, which acts on the surface of the grain, becomes increasingly important as the size of the grain is decreased. Gravity, which acts on the mass of the grain, becomes less important in this limit.

5. Your watch must have an LCD display. In such watches, the light coming from the display is linearly polarized. If the polarization direction of the display and the sunglasses align, you can read the time. If these directions are at 90° to one another no light will pass through the sunglasses, and the display will appear black.

7. Radio stations generate their electromagnetic waves with large vertical antennas.

As a result, their waves are polarized in the vertical direction, as in Figure 25–1. On the other hand, the light we see from the sun and from light bulbs is unpolarized because the atoms emitting the light can have any orientation relative to one another. Hence, even if individual atoms emit polarized light, the net result from a group of atoms is light with no preferred direction of polarization.

9. Sound waves cannot be polarized. This is because sound is a longitudinal wave, and the molecules can move in only a single direction—back and forth along the direction of propagation. In contrast, the electric field in an electromagnetic wave, which is transverse, can point in any direction within the plane that is transverse to the direction of propagation. This means that the electromagnetic wave can have different polarizations.

11. The two projected images give a view of a scene from slightly different angles, just as your eyes view a three-dimensional object from different angles. Without the headsets, the screen is a confusing superposition of the two images; with the headsets, your right eye sees one view of the scene and your left eye sees the other view. As these views are combined in your brain, you experience a realistic three-dimensional effect.

CHAPTER 26

1. Three images are formed of object A. One extends from $(-2\,\mathrm{m}, 2\,\mathrm{m})$ to $(-1\,\mathrm{m}, 2\,\mathrm{m})$ to $(-1\,\mathrm{m}, 3\,\mathrm{m})$. Another image forms an "L" from $(1\,\mathrm{m}, -3\,\mathrm{m})$ to $(1\,\mathrm{m}, -2\,\mathrm{m})$ to $(2\,\mathrm{m}, -2\,\mathrm{m})$. Finally, the third image extends from $(-1\,\mathrm{m}, -3\,\mathrm{m})$ to $(-1\,\mathrm{m}, -2\,\mathrm{m})$ to $(-2\,\mathrm{m}, -2\,\mathrm{m})$.

3. A plane mirror is flat, which means that its radius of curvature is infinite. This means that the focal length of the mirror is also infinite. Whether you consider the focal length to be positive infinity (the limit of a concave mirror) or negative infinity (the limit of a convex mirror) doesn't matter, because in either case the term $1/f$ in the mirror equation will be zero.

5. We can consider the Sun to be infinitely far from the mirror. As a result, its parallel rays will be focused at the focal point of the mirror. Therefore, the distance from the mirror to the paper should be $f = \frac{1}{2}R$.

7. The key to this system is the fact that the lifeguards can run much faster on the sand than they can swim in the water. Therefore, the path ACB—even though it is longer—has a shorter travel time because more time is spent on the sand and less time is spent in the water.

9. In a real image, light passes through the location of the image before reaching the eye. In a virtual image, light propagates *as if* it were coming from the image—though the reflected or refracted light never actually passes through the image location.

11. When the mug is filled with water, light coming upward from the bottom of the mug is bent toward the horizontal when it passes from water to air. If the light had not been bent, it would have passed over your head—placing the bottom of the mug out of sight. With the bending, however, the light can now propagate to your eyes—making the bottom of the mug visible.

13. No. In order to see, a person's eyes must first bring light to a focus, and then must absorb the light to convert it to nervous impulses that can travel to the brain. Both the bending of the light and its absorption would give away the presence of the invisible man. Therefore, if the man were truly invisible, he would be unable to see.

CHAPTER 27

1. When you focus on an object at infinity your ciliary muscles are relaxed. It takes muscular effort to focus your eyes on nearby objects.

3. If you are a distance *D* in front of a mirror your image is a distance *D* behind the mirror. Therefore, you can see your image clearly if the distance from you to your image, 2*D*, is equal to *N*. In other words, the minimum distance to the mirror is $D = N/2$.

5. The person with the smaller near-point distance can examine an object at closer range than the person with the larger near-point distance. Therefore, the person with the larger near-point distance benefits more from the magnifier.

7. The image you see when looking through a telescope is virtual. First, the objective forms a real image of a distant object, as shown in Figure 27–16. Next, the eyepiece forms an upright and enlarged image of the objective's image. The situation with the eyepiece is essentially the same as that shown in Figure 26–35 (b). Therefore, it is clear that the final image is virtual in this case.

CHAPTER 28

1. At a point where destructive interference is complete, there is no energy. The total energy in the system is unchanged, however, because those regions with constructive interference have increased amounts of energy. One can simply think of the energy as being redistributed.

3. No. The net signal could be near zero if the waves from the two antennas interfere destructively.

5. In this case, the interference pattern would be reversed. That is, bright fringes in the ordinary pattern would now be the location of dark fringes, and dark fringes would be replaced with bright fringes. For example, in the usual case there is a bright fringe halfway between the slits because the paths lengths are equal. Changing the phase of the light from one slit by 180°, however, results in destructive interference (a dark fringe) at the center of the pattern.

7. A ray of light reflected from the lower surface of the curved piece of glass has no phase change. On the other hand, a ray of light reflected from the top surface of the flat piece of glass undergoes a phase change of half a wavelength. Near the center of the pattern the path difference for these two rays goes to zero. As a result, they are half a wavelength out of phase there, and undergo destructive interference.

9. In general, the larger the aperture in an optical instrument, the greater the resolution. This follows directly from Equation 28–14, where we see that a large aperture diameter D implies a small angle θ. The angular separation that can be resolved is decreased—by making θ smaller—and the resolution is increased.

11. The soap film in the photograph is thinnest near the top (as one might expect) because in that region the film appears black. Specifically, the light reflected from the front surface of the film has its phase changed by 180°; light that reflects from the back surface of the film has no change in phase. Therefore, light from the front and back surfaces of the film will undergo destructive interference as the path length between the surfaces goes to zero. This is why the top of the film, where the film is thinnest, appears black in the photo.

CHAPTER 29

1. The light received from these galaxies moves with the speed c, as is true for all light in a vacuum.

3. Velocities add by simple addition in the limit $c \to \infty$. This is evident from Equation 29–4 when one notices that the second term in the denominator vanishes in this limit, making the denominator equal to 1.

5. Yes. All light, regardless of its wavelength, has the same speed in a vacuum. The *frequency* of this "red shifted" light will be affected, however. Recalling that $v = \lambda f$, we see that a longer wavelength also implies a smaller frequency.

7. Since the total energy of an object of finite mass goes to infinity in the limit that $v \to c$, an infinite amount of energy is required to accelerate an object to the speed c.

CHAPTER 30

1. The "ultraviolet catastrophe" refers to the classical prediction that the intensity of light emitted by a blackbody increases without limit as the frequency is increased.

3. No, all objects with finite temperature give off blackbody radiation. Only an object at absolute zero—which is unattainable—gives off no blackbody radiation.

5. If you look at a painting, photo, decal, or similar object, you are viewing light that

it reflects to you. Therefore, when an area appears red, it is because the pigments there absorb blue photons and reflect red photons. Similarly, a blue area absorbs red photons. Blue photons carry considerably more energy than red photons, however, and hence blue photons are more likely to cause damage to the pigment molecules, or to alter their structure. It follows that red pigments (which absorb blue photons) are more likely to become faded when exposed to intense light.

7. If two blackbody curves intersected, there would be a range of frequencies where the low-temperature blackbody gives off more energy than the high-temperature blackbody. In this frequency range, then, it would be possible for energy to be spontaneously transferred from the low-temperature body to the high-temperature body, in violation of the second law of thermodynamics.

9. The likely explanation is that the second metal has a greater work function than the first metal. In this case, a shorter-wavelength photon—that is, a photon with higher frequency and higher energy—would be required to supply the additional energy needed to eject an electron.

11. The resolution of a microscope is determined by the wavelength of the imaging radiation—the smaller the wavelength the greater the resolution. Since the typical wavelength of an electron in an electron microscope is much smaller than the wavelength of visible light, the electron microscope has the greater resolution.

CHAPTER 31

1. Rutherford's alpha particle scattering experiments indicate that the positive charge in an atom is concentrated in a small volume, rather than spread throughout the atom, as in Thomson's model.

3. In the Bohr model, the electron orbits at a well-defined radius; in the quantum mechanical model, the electron can be found at virtually any distance from the nucleus.

5. (a) The glass tube of a neon sign contains a low-pressure gas. Therefore, we expect the light from the sign to be in the form of a line spectrum. (b) The light from an incandescent lightbulb is basically blackbody radiation from a hot object; therefore, its radiation is distributed continuously as a function of frequency.

7. No, there is no upper limit to the radius of a Bohr orbit. In fact, the radius increases as n^2 for $n = 1, 2, 3, \ldots$.

9. No, the energy does not increase without limit. The energy of a given level in hydrogen ranges from a low of -13.6 eV to a maximum of 0.

11. (a) The angular momentum in the quantum mechanical model of the hydrogen atom is zero if the quantum number ℓ is zero. In the $n = 1$ state, the only allowed value for ℓ is 0, and hence the angular momentum must be zero for $n = 1$. (b) Yes. For $n > 1$, there are n allowed values for ℓ. One of these values is always zero, therefore the angular momentum can be zero for any value of n.

13. These elements all have similar configurations of their outermost electrons. In fact, the outermost electrons in fluorine, chlorine, and bromine are $2p^5$, $3p^5$, and $4p^5$, respectively. Therefore, each of these atoms is one electron shy of completing the p subshell. This accounts for their similar chemical behavior.

CHAPTER 32

1. The radius of a nucleus is given by the following expression: $r = (1.2 \times 10^{-15}$ m$)A^{1/3}$. Therefore, the radius depends only on the total number of nucleons in the nucleus, A, and not on the number of protons and neutrons separately. If the number of protons plus the number of neutrons is the same for two nuclei, their radii will be equal as well.

3. No. An alpha particle contains two protons, whereas any form of hydrogen contains only a single proton. Therefore, hydrogen cannot give off an alpha particle.

5. A nucleus that contained more than one proton and no neutrons would be unstable because the electrostatic repulsion between the protons would blow the nucleus apart. Neutrons tend to push the protons farther apart, reducing their mutual repulsion, and at the same time add more to the attractive strong nuclear force that holds nuclei together.

7. Carbon-14 dating is useful for objects that are of biological origin and—at most—are on the order of thousands of years old. (a) It is useful for dating such things as human or animal remains, plant tissue, clothing, and charcoal from a fire. (b) It is not useful for dating inorganic materials, like rocks and minerals, or biological materials that are millions of years old, like dinosaur fossils.

9. The obsidian arrowhead cannot be dated with carbon-14, because it is not of biological origin.

11. Yes. The two samples may contain different quantities of the radioactive isotope, and hence their activities may be different.

13. No. The RBE is related to the amount of biological effect produced by a given type of radiation, not to the amount of energy it delivers.

Answer to Odd-Numbered Problems and Conceptual Exercises

Note: In cases where an ambiguity might arise, numbers in this text are assumed to have the smallest possible number of significant figures. For example, a number like 150 is assumed to have just two significant figures—the zero simply indicates the location of the decimal point. To represent this number with three significant figures, we would use the form 1.50×10^2.

CHAPTER 1

1. (a) 0.114 gigadollar
   (b) 1.14×10^{-4} teradollar
3. 3×10^8 m/s
5. (a) consistent (b) consistent (c) consistent
7. (a) No (b) Yes (c) No (d) Yes
9. $p = -2$
11. $[M]\frac{[L]}{[T]^2}$
13. (a) 3.14 (b) 3.1416 (c) 3.141593
15. 383.9 m
17. (a) two (b) four
19. (a) 75 ft/s (b) 51 mi/h
21. 18 ft^3
23. 0.9788 km
25. 32.9 m
27. (a) greater than (b) 88 km/h
29. 322 ft/s^2
31. (a) 67 mutchkins (b) 0.031 gal
33. (a) 0.060 m^2 (b) $\frac{1}{4} A_{old}$
35. 32.2 ft/s
37. (a) 10^{10} gal/y (b) 10^9 lb/y
39. (a) 10^6 lb (b) 10^4 lb
41. (a) No (b) Yes (c) Yes (d) Yes
43. 7.41×10^{-4} m/s
45. (a) 3.05 m and 5.14 m/s
47. (a) 310 mi/h (b) 0.70 m
49. (a) 51 revolutions (b) 8.7 ft/rev
51. $q = -\frac{1}{2}; p = \frac{1}{2}$
53. plot C
55. C. 64.3 °F

CHAPTER 2

1. (a) 1.95 mi (b) 0.75 mi
3. (a) 15 m (b) 10 m
5. (a) 130 m; 100 m (b) 260 m; 0
7. (a) less than (b) I
9. 10.13 m/s; 22.66 mi/h
11. (a) 3.5 km (b) 14 s
13. 2.57 s
15. 0.010 s
17. 6.0 m/s
19. 11 m
21. (a)

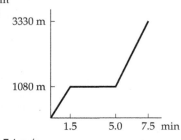

   (b) 7.4 m/s

23.

	A	B	C	D
(a)–(d)	positive	zero	positive	negative
(e)–(h)	2.0 m/s	0 m/s	1.0 m/s	−1.5 m/s

25. (a)

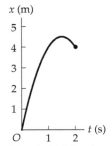

   (b) 4.0 m/s (c) 4.0 m/s
27. 35 mi/h
29. (a)

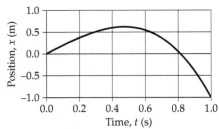

   (b) 0.55 m/s (c) 0.56 m/s
   (d) closer to 0.56 m/s
31. (a) less than (b) III
33. (a) 3.8 m/s (b) 9.9 m/s
35. (a) 27.9 m/s north (b) 9.48 m/s north
37. (a) 10 m (b) 20 m (c) 40 m
39. (a) a factor of two (b) 3.8 s (c) 7.6 s
41. 10.3 m/s
43. 3.53 m/s^2 to the north
45. (a) cases 3 and 4 (b) case 2 (c) cases 2 and 3
47. (a) 2.06 m/s (b) 9.83 m
49. (a) 0.90 m (b) 3.6 m (c) 8.1 m
51. 600g
53. (a) 0.077 s (b) 0.46 μm
55. 3.8×10^4 m/s^2
57. (a) 21 m (b) greater than 6.0 m/s; 8.49 m
59. (a) 32 m/s^2 (b) less than 8.0 cm; 4.0 cm
61. 180g
63. (a) 0.25 s (b) 110 m/s^2 (c) 0.55 m; 11 m/s
65. (a) 6.3 s (b) 22 m (c) 10 m/s
67. 11.3 m
69. B. The speed of ball 1 is equal to the speed of ball 2.
71. The statement is accurate.
73. 4.9 m/s
75. (a) 8.4 m/s upward
   (b) 1.4 m/s downward
77. 0.10 s
79. (a) equal to (b) II
81. $x_{Bill} = (3.0 \text{ m}) - (4.9 \text{ m/s}^2)t^2$
   $x_{Ted} = (1.0 \text{ m}) + (4.2 \text{ m/s})t - (4.9 \text{ m/s}^2)t^2$
83. (a) 11 m (b) 15 m/s (c) 2.1 s
85. 9.6 m
87. (a) the first (dropped) ball
   (b) ball 1: 25.3 m/s; ball 2: 16.5 m/s

89. (a) 0.49 s (b) 4.8 m/s
91. (a) more than 2.0 m (b) 8 m
93. (a) 6.7 m/s (b) −5.9 m/s (c) 9.6 m/s
95. 5.8 m/s
97. −29 m/s^2
99. more for ball A
101. (a) 3.8 m/s^2 (b) 15 m/s
103. (a) 2 (b) 4
   (c) 0.41 s and 0.82 s; 0.20 m and 0.82 m
105. (a) 2.64 s (b) more than
   (c) 1.87 s > 0.77 s
107. (a) 9.81 m/s^2 downward
   (b) 13.9 m (c) 2.21 s (d) 16.5 m/s
109. 3.0 m
111. (a) $\frac{1}{2}gt^2$ (d) gt (c) 13.4 m (d) 16.2 m/s
113. 6.67 cm
115. (a) 3.0 m; 4.4 m/s (b) 130 drops/min
117. 5.5 m; 11 m/s
119. (a) 10.0 ms (b) 4.50 m/s (c) 10.0 cm
123. B. 6.78 ft/s
125. plot C
127. 4.3 m/s^2
129. (a) 2.3 s (b) 20 m/s

CHAPTER 3

1. (a) factor of 2
   (b) factor of 1
3. $D < C < B < A$
5. 119 ft
7. 3°
9. (a) (90 ft)$\hat{x}$ + (90 ft)$\hat{y}$
   (b) (90 ft)$\hat{y}$ (c) (0 ft)$\hat{x}$ + (0 ft)$\hat{y}$
11. 1.5 Å
13. (a) 3.5 cm (b) less than (c) 1.7 cm
15. (a) $\vec{A}$ (b) $\vec{B}$
17. (a) 51 m deep (b) 140 m
19. (a) less than (b) equal to
21. (a)

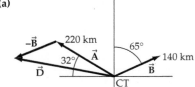

   (b) 320 km, 10° north of west
23. (a)

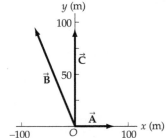

   (b) about 120 m; about 130°
   (c) 121 m; 128°

25. (a) $-27°$; 11 units (b) $207°$; 11 units
 (c) $27°$; 11 units
27. $(40 \text{ m})\hat{x} + (-36 \text{ m})\hat{y}$
29. (a) 23 m (b) 23 m
31. (a) $-22°$; 5.4 m (b) $110°$; 5.4 m (c) $45°$; 4.2 m
33. (a) $(23 \text{ m})\hat{x} + (-27 \text{ m})\hat{y}$
 (b) $(-23 \text{ m})\hat{x} + (27 \text{ m})\hat{y}$
35. $(2.1 \text{ m})\hat{x} + (0.74 \text{ m})\hat{y}$
37. (a) equal to
 (b) 7.8 cm at $153°$; 7.8 cm at $63°$
39. 0.037 m/s; $31°$ west of north
41. $59°$ north of east; 4.9 m/s
43. $(-9.8 \text{ m/s}^2)\hat{y}$
45. 9.59 m/s
47. (a) $(-0.00233 \text{ m/s}^2)\hat{x}$
 (b) $(-0.00233 \text{ m/s}^2)\hat{x}$
49. 15.3 m/s
51. 25 s
53. (a) $11°$ west of north
 (b)

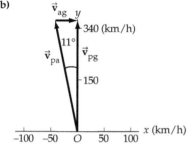

 (c) increased
55. 11 m/s
57. (a) Jet Ski A (b) $\frac{\Delta t_A}{\Delta t_B} = 0.82$
59. (a) equal to (b) II
61. $-53.1°$; 40.3 m
63. between $270°$ and $360°$
65. (a) toward the rear (b) 19.8 m/s
 (c) 17.9 m/s
67. $A_x = 44$ m, $A_y = 31$ m, $A_z = 37$ m
69. (a) $(-9.81 \text{ m/s}^2)\hat{y}$ (b) $(-9.81 \text{ m/s}^2)\hat{y}$
 (c) $(-9.81 \text{ m/s}^2)\hat{y}$
71. (a) ≈ 38 ft
 (b) 39 ft; $15°$ clockwise from $\vec{A}$
73. (a) 3.7 (b) 67 m/s
75. (a) $10°$ (b) $(7.1 \text{ m/s})\hat{x}$ (c) decrease
77. 28 m; 19 m
79. C. 1.00 m/s
81. C. 0.806 m/s
83. (a) $12°$ upstream (b) decrease

CHAPTER 4
1. (a) straight upward (b) III
3. (a) 12.0 s (b) 55.5 s
5. (a) $x = -55$ m; $y = 31$ m
 (b) $v_x = -22$ m/s; $v_y = 6.2$ m/s
 (c) increase with time
7. (a) $27°$ (b) 1.1 m/s
9. (a) greater than (b) II
11. 46.2 m/s
13. 1.77 m/s^2
15. (a) 9.9 m (b) 0.99 m
17. (a) 3.1 m (b) 3.4 m beyond the far edge
19. 2.6 m/s
21. (a) 0.982 m/s (b) 1.52 m
23. (a) 29.4 m
 (b) 57.8 m/s; $85.0°$ below horizontal
25. (a) 9.81 m/s^2 downward
 (b) 1.1 m/s (c) 3.2 m/s

27. (a) A < B < C (b) C < B < A
29. (a) 14.3 m/s (b) 2.24 s
31. 1.27 m/s
33. 1.3 m
35. (a) the same as (b) 18 m/s; 18 m/s
37. (a) 121 m (b) 24.3 m/s
39. 24.8 m/s
41. (a) 17 m/s; $25°$ (b) No; the y-component
 of the velocity is still positive.
43. 1.07 m
45. 111 m/s
47. (a) $32°$ (b) 0.76 s
49. (a) 29.8 m/s (b) 4.29 s
51. (a) plot B (b) III
53. (a) 9.43 m/s; $11.4°$ above horizontal
 (b) 9.26 m/s; $3.68°$ below horizontal
55. (a) 213 m (b) $52.5°$
57. equal to
59. (a) equal to (b) II
61. (a) $64°$ west of north (b) 350 m
63. 0.786 m
65. (a) $(5.00 \text{ m/s})\hat{x} + (-2.00 \text{ m/s})\hat{y}$
 (b) 5.39 m/s; $21.8°$ below horizontal
 (c) 6.00 m (d) 0.92 s
67. (a) 1.52 m (b) $(4.03 \text{ m/s})\hat{y}$
69. (a) 0.199 s (b) 0.452 m
71. (a) 9.29 m/s (b) $56.4°$ below horizontal
73. (a) 12.1 m/s; top (b) 12.9 m/s; $19.9°$
 (c) 0.978 m (d) 0.978 m
75. 14.5 m/s
77. (a) To find the initial speed
 of the puck, eliminate t from the
 equations $x = (v_0 \cos \theta)t$ and
 $y = (v_0 \sin \theta)t - (12)gt^2$, then solve for v_0.
 (b) 25.1 m/s
79. (a) $64.9°$ (b) 21 m/s (c) 1.8 s
81. (a) 2.48 cm (b) 0.0187 s
83. $76.0°$
85. $v = \sqrt{v_0^2 + 2gh}$ independent of angle θ
89. (a) 9.9 m/s; top (b) 11 m/s; $24°$
 (c) 0.98 m (d) 0.98 m
91. C. 12.3 m
93. A. 13.2 m
95. (a) $60.5°$ (b) 15.9 m (c) $41.6°$ (d) 18.4 m
97. (a) $42.3°$ (b) 3.12 m (c) 7.36 m/s

CHAPTER 5
1. $\frac{1}{2}T$
3. 2.57 m
5. 1.6 kN
7. (a) less than (b) III
9. (a) $(85 \text{ N})\hat{x}$ (b) increased
11. (a) 5.1 kN opposite to the direction of
 motion (b) 15.3 m
13. (a) 18.7 kN opposite to the direction of
 motion (b) Determine the acceleration
 from the speeds and displacement and
 the force from the acceleration and mass.
15. (a) greater than (b) II
17. (a) two forces (b) gravity and your hand
 (c) No (d) No
19. (a) the same as (b) more than (c) 0.70 m/s^2
21. (a) 1.04 N (b) 3.59 N
23. (a) sometimes true (b) never true
 (c) always true (d) sometimes true
25. 11 kN
27. 28 N
29. A < D < B < C
31. (a) 0.42 kN (b) less than

33. $146°$; 7.8 N
35. (a) $24.5°$ (b) 4.77×10^{20} N
 (c) 0.00649 m/s^2
37. (a) 0.023 N (b) 6.6 days
39. (a) 2.3 m/s^2 (b) -2.4 m/s^2
41. 1.5 m/s^2 downward
43. (a) 72 N (b) 1.4 m/s^2
45. (a)

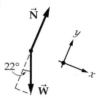

 (b) 0.59 kN
47. (a) $\frac{1}{2}mg$ (b) mg (c) $2mg$
49. (a) 23 N (b) increase
51. $60°$
53. (a) higher than (b) I
55. (a) greater than (b) III
57. $(-18.3 \text{ N})\hat{x}$
59. (a) 5.5×10^{-3} m/s^2 (b) 8.3×10^9 m (c) 1/3
61. 9.1 kg
63. (a) 99 m/s^2 (b) 0.22 N
 (c) stay the same (d) increase
65. (a) 0.42 kN opposite the direction of
 motion (b) 2
67. (a) 2.2 N (b) 1.4 s
69. 290 kg
71. (a) 4.2×10^5 N (b) Determine the acceleration during takeoff using the given data
 (x, t). Then calculate the force using
 $F = ma$.
73. (a) 2.06 kg (b) 5.00 kg
75. 74 kg
77. $F_1 = \frac{1}{2}m(a_1 + a_2)$; $F_2 = \frac{1}{2}m(a_1 - a_2)$
79. C. 1.05×10^4 N
81. D. 4.21×10^4 N
83. (a) decreased (b) 3.33 kg (c) 1.50 m/s^2
85. (a) greater than (b) $36°$ (c) 0.079 m/s^2

CHAPTER 6
1. (a) equal to (b) II
3. 1.8 m
5. 1.2
7. 0.75 N opposite the direction of the push
9. (a) As the hanging fraction of the tie is
 increased, the gravitational force is increased and the mass of the tie still lying
 on the table is reduced, so that the maximum static friction force is decreased.
 When the gravitational force exceeds the
 force of static friction, the tie begins
 sliding off the table.
 (b) $\mu_s = 1/3$
11. 3.5 m/s^2
13. (a) 0.39
 (b) First, determine the runner's acceleration from $v^2 = v_0^2 + 2a\Delta x$. Next, equate
 the force associated with this acceleration
 to the force of static friction between the
 runner's shoes and the track. Solve for μ_s.
15. (a) 13 m (b) increase (c) stay the same
17. (a) 2.55 m/s^2 opposite the direction of
 motion (b) 4.26 m/s
19. (a) greater than (b) less than
21. 2.13 kN/m

23. 948 N
25. 0.072
27. (a) 2.64 s (b) A shorter time would require a larger acceleration, which in turn would require greater tension in the rope because $T = ma + mg = m(a + g)$. Thus the tension would become greater than 755 N and the rope would break.
29. (a) When the car accelerates from the stoplight, the string must exert a forward force on the tassel in order to accelerate it in the horizontal direction at the same rate as the car's acceleration. The string must also continue to exert an upward force on the tassel to balance the force of gravity. As a result the tassel hangs at an angle, deflected toward the back of the car. (b) 1.11 m/s²
31. (a) less than (b) 0.85 N (c) 2.0 N
33. (a) 0.31 kN downward (b) 0.63 kN (c) 0.63 kN
35. (a) 5.1 N (b) 15 N
37. 4.5 kg
39. 0.85 N
41. (a) 60.0° (b) 106 N
43. (a) decrease (b) I
45. (a) upward (b) 0.076 m/s²
47. (a) 4.9 N (b) 15 N
49. (a) 3.2 m/s² (b) 2.6 N (c) decrease
51. more
53. (a) No (b) Yes (c) Yes (d) No
55. 5.6 kN
57. 36 m/s
59. 0.67 kN
61. (a) Your apparent weight is greater at the bottom of the Ferris wheel, where the normal force must both support your weight and provide the upward centripetal acceleration. (b) 0.52 kN at top; 0.56 kN at bottom
63. 19 m/s
65. less than
67. A < C < B
69. 2.2 kg
71. 0.140
73. 5.62 kg
75. (a) 0.76 m/s² (b) 6.0 N
77. (a) 0.030 N down the incline (b) 0.042 N up the incline
79.

Applied Force	Friction Force Magnitude	Motion
0 N	0 N	at rest
5.0 N	5.0 N	at rest
11 N	11 N	at rest
15 N	8.8 N	accelerating
11 N	8.8 N	accelerating
8.0 N	8.8 N → 8.0 N	decelerating → at rest
5.0 N	5.0 N	at rest

81. (a) 23 N (b) stay the same

83. (a) greater than (b) 3.4 N (c) 0.41 kg
85. (a) 19° (b) 0.78 N
87. (a) 32 N (b) increase
89. (a) greater than (b) 1.88 kN
91. (a) static (b) 0.50
93. 26 m/s²
95. 8.6°; The mass of the dice drops out of the equations.
97. 28°
99. $T = mg \sin \theta$
101. 5.4 cm
103. left string: $T_1 = \left(\dfrac{m_1 m_3}{m_1 + m_2 + m_3}\right)g$; right string: $T_2 = \left[\dfrac{m_3(m_1 + m_2)}{m_1 + m_2 + m_3}\right]g$
105. $v = \sqrt{\dfrac{Mrg}{m}}$
107. (a) 10 m/s² (b) 47° (c) Because the weight and centripetal acceleration both depend linearly on the mass, the mass cancels out of the expression for the angle θ.
109. (a) 24 kg (b) 0.27
111. D. 25 N/m
113. C. 2.5 N/m
115. (a) less than (b) 22.5° (c) 4.34 s
117. (a) 1.00 kg (b) 6.98 N (c) 0.712

CHAPTER 7

1. zero
3. (a) negative (b) zero
5. 4.36 kg
7. 3.37 m
9. (a) positive (b) 7.8 kJ
11. 0.15 kJ
13. (a) 14 J (b) decrease
15. (a) 1700 J (b) −1700 J
17. 21°
19. 2.2 kJ
21. (a) 8.03 kJ (b) 2.01 kJ (c) 32.1 kJ
23. D < A = D < B
25. (a) −10 J (b) 0.63 N upward
27. (a) −587 J (b) 0.284
29. (a) less than 3.5 m/s (b) −3.1 m/s
31. $\frac{1}{2}\Delta x$
33. 14 m/s
35. (a) 0.45 J (b) 0.24 J
37. $\sqrt{2(\Delta x)}$
39. (a) 16 kN/m (b) more than 180 J; 540 J
41. (a) 0.82 kJ (b) 1.1 kJ
43. 380 W = 0.51 hp
45. 0.32 mW
47. 2.20 m/s
49. (a) 33.3 N (b) double the speed
51. (a) 1.15×10^{-4} W (b) decreased
53. (a) 3T (b) $v\sqrt{2}$
55. positive
57. 2v
59. (a) 630 N (b) 76 W
61. 386 W
63. (a) 1.15×10^5 J (b) 170 m
65. (a) $W_0/4$ (b) $3W_0/4$
67. 74 m/s
69. (a) 10 kJ (b) −10 kJ
71. (a) increase (b) 8.2 W (c) 12 W
73. (a) 0.96 J (b) 1.3 J (c) −1.2 J
75. 86 N

77. (a) 130 J (b) 2200 W (c) more than
79. (a) 15 h (b) 0.62 m/s (c) 1.6 s
81. -8.4×10^6 N
83. $\dfrac{\frac{1}{2}x^2}{1/k_1 + 1/k_2}$
85. (a) 42.2° (b) 14.8 kg
87. C. 2.5−25 m/s
89. A. 0.65 N
91. (a) 1.6 kg (b) greater than (c) 0.63 m/s

CHAPTER 8

1. (a) −3 J (b) −4 J
3. path 1: −100 J; path 2: −47 J; path 3: −66 J
5. (a) 51 J; 51 J (b) increase
7. (a) equal to (b) II
9. 0.54 kN
11. 6.5 mJ
13. (a) a factor of 4 (b) 3.85 J
15. (a) 1.2 cm (b) 2.3 cm
17. −0.70 J
19. (a) greater than (b) equal to 3 m/s
21. (a) $v/2$ (b) II
23. B = D = F < E < C
25. 6.78 m/s
27. Only statement (C) is correct.
29.

y (m)	4.0	3.0	2.0	1.0	0
U (J)	8.2	6.2	4.1	2.1	0
K (J)	0	2.1	4.1	6.2	8.2
E (J)	8.2	8.2	8.2	8.2	8.2

31. (a) 15 m/s (b) 43 m
33. (a) 0; 113 J; 113 J (b) 113 J; 226 J; 113 J
35. (a) 0.95 J (b) 0.95 J (c) 41°
37. 4 cm
39. (a) less than (b) III
41. 2.7 m/s
43. −57 MJ
45. (a) decrease (b) stay the same (c) decrease
47. (a) −314 J (b) 0.305
49. 134 kJ
51. (a) 0.937 m (b) 16.5 J (c) −7.72 J
53. 415 N/m
55. (a) 3.8 m/s (b) 2.7 m/s (c) 3.0 m/s (d) points A and E
57.

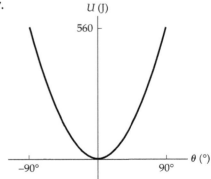

59. (a) 8.6 J (b) 0.2 m (c) 4.8 m

61. (a)

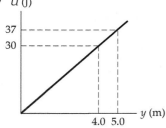

(b) 4.0 m
63. (a) disagree **(b)** agree **(c)** agree
65. greater than
67. (a) less than **(b)** equal to
69. 2.87 m
71. (a) 1.5 mm **(b)** 0.46 J
73. (a) −0.86 J **(b)** greater than **(c)** −1.2 J
75. (a) 53.0 MJ **(b)** 218 m/s
77. 1.04 m
79. (a) 634 N **(b)** decrease
81. 7.20 m/s
83. 0.121 m
85. 1.1 kN
87. 0.85 m
89. 5.3 cm
91. (b) Tension depends on a_{cp}, which is directly proportional to v^2 and inversely proportional to the radius r. Therefore, l cancels out because both v_B^2 and r are proportional to l.
93. 48.2°
95. (a) 0.79 m/s **(b)** positive **(c)** 0.36 J
97. 0.688 m
99. (a) negative **(b)** −46 J **(c)** 38 N
101. C. 290 N/m
103. A. 0.766 mJ
105. (a) 0.948 m/s **(b)** 1.29 kg

CHAPTER 9
1. 2.49×10^5 mi/h
3. 77.1° north of east; 0.980 m/s
5. 1.38 m
7. 2.51 kg; 5.21 kg
9. (a) equal to **(b)** III
11. (a) equal to **(b)** II
13. 7.44 kg · m/s
15. 7.0 ms
17. (a) 0.133 kg · m/s **(b)** greater than
19. (a) 5.6 kg · m/s; 27° above horizontal
(b) The magnitude would double but the direction would stay the same.
(c) Neither the magnitude nor the direction would change.
21. 440 kg
23. −0.519 mm/s
25. 14 m
27. $\sqrt{2}v$ at 225° from the direction of the first piece
29. minivan: $v_i = 12$ m/s; wreckage: $v_f = 11$ m/s
31. (a) less than **(b)** initial: 54 kJ; final: 48 kJ
33. (a) No **(b)** 3.86 cm
35. (a) 1/16 **(b)** 5/3
37. $v_{truck} = 6.25$ m/s; $v_{car} = 21.7$ m/s
39. (a) 16.9 m/s **(b)** Kinetic energy has been transferred from the elephant to the ball.
41. 1.32 m/s; 107° counterclockwise from the +x axis

43. (a) $\dfrac{v_0}{2}$ **(b)** $\dfrac{v_0}{\sqrt{2}}$
45. $\frac{11}{12}L$
47. 4.67×10^6 m; 1.70×10^6 m below the surface of the Earth
49. (a) positive **(b)** less than
51. $x_{cm} = -4.2$ in.; $y_{cm} = 4.2$ in.
53. (a) $X_{cm} = 0.67$ m; $Y_{cm} = 0.17$ m
(b) The location of the center of mass would not be affected.
55. $Y_{cm} = [1.00 - (0.355 \text{ s}^{-1})t]^2$ m, $0 < t < 2.82$ s;
$V_{cm} = (0.252 \text{ m/s}^2)t - 0.710$ m/s

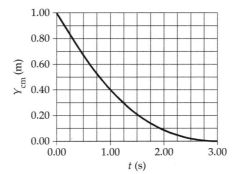

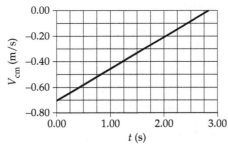

57. (a) zero **(b)** zero
59. 29 rocks/min
61. 0.489 m/s
63. (a) 0.25 N **(b)** more than 2.5 N **(c)** 2.8 N
65. C < A < B
67. equal to
69. (a) green path **(b)** II
71. 2.20 m
73. 0.24 N
75. 0.354 mm
77. (a) greater than **(b)** 3.6 m
79. (a) 13.2 N **(b)** 12.9 N
81. $2m$
83. $X_{cm} = 6.5 \times 10^{-12}$ m; $Y_{cm} = 0$
85. (a) 27.8 m/s **(b)** $(19.7 \text{ m/s})\hat{y}$ both before and after **(c)** $(-9.81 \text{ m/s}^2)\hat{y}$ both before and after
87. $\frac{25}{24}L$
89. (a) 0.23 m/s **(b)** 0.065 J **(c)** 0.45 m/s; −0.23 m/s
93. 0.828 m/s²
95. (b) The net force on the two masses must point downward, so that the scale force upward must be less than the weight of the masses; $(m_1 + m_2)g$.
97. A. $v_i + u$
99. C. $v_f = v_i + 2u$
101. (a) 0.160 km/s **(b)** 1.58 m/s
103. (a) 0.19 m/s **(b)** −0.022 J

CHAPTER 10
1. $\frac{\pi}{6}, \frac{\pi}{4}, \frac{\pi}{2}, \pi$
3. (a) 1 rev/h **(b)** 2 rev/day
5. tire, propeller, drill
7. 1.90×10^{-6} rev/min
9. 190 rad/s
11. (a) 1.3×10^2 rad/s **(b)** 2.1×10^2 rad/s
(c) 3.0×10^2 rad/s **(d)** positive
(e) 85 rad/s²; 85 rad/s²
13. $\omega/2$
15. 3.78 rad
17. 47 rad
19. (a) 69 rev **(b)** 52 rev
21. 3:08:11
23. -6.14×10^{-22} rad/s²
25. (a) −29.6 rev/s² **(b)** 242 ft **(c)** 10.0 in.
27. (a) equal to **(b)** III
29. (a) equal to **(b)** I
31. (a) 1.4 rad/s for each child
(b) child 1: 2.8 m/s; child 2: 2.1 m/s
33. (a) 0.38 m/s **(b)** 0.24 m/s
35. $a_{cp} = 5.20$ m/s²; $a_t = 4.46$ m/s²; $a = 6.85$ m/s²; 49.4°
37. (a) 0.303 m/s **(b)** 1.53 m/s²
(c) 0.152 m/s; 0.765 m/s²
39. (a) 0.29 m/s² downward
(b) 0.29 m/s² upward
41. (a) 2.2 rad/s **(b)** increase
43. $a_t = 0.742$ m/s²; $a_{cp} = 1.3$ km/s²
45. $\sqrt{1/\alpha}$
47. 48 rad/s
49. 34.3 rad/s
51. (a) 2.03 rad/s² **(b)** greater than
53. (a) increase **(b)** I
55. 0.36 m
57. 0.054 kg · m²
59. $I_1 < I_2 < I_3$
61. $K_t = 170$ J; $K_t = 0.072$ J
63. -3.5×10^{12} W
65. less than
67. 0.29 m
69. (a) 3.3 m/s **(b)** 2.8 m/s
71. (a) 1.1×10^2 rad/s **(b)** 0.56 m
73. (a) 3.0 m/s **(b)** decrease
75. (a) 15 J **(b)** 4.9 J **(c)** 9.8 J
77. greater than
79. increase
81. 6.8 rad/s
83. 874 m
85. $I_3 < I_2 < I_1$
87. (a) 22.1 m/s **(b)** 190 m/s
(c) 60 cm **(d)** 7.0 N
89. (a) 0.27 rev
(b) It does not depend on her initial speed.
91. (a) decrease **(b)** 50.0 rad/s **(c)** 20.8 rad/s
(d) -7.31×10^{-3} rad/s²
93. (a) 4.1×10^2 rad/s² **(b)** 6.2×10^2 rad/s²
95. (a) 92 s **(b)** 240° cw from north **(c)** 10 m
97. (a) 6.9 rad/s² **(b)** It doubles.
99. (a) 0.334 m **(b)** 1.01 kN
101. (a) 15 rad/s² **(b)** 4.0×10^3 rad
103. (a) 8.3×10^{-16} rad/s **(b)** 1.7×10^{17} mi
105. (a) 0.95g **(b)** 8.9 m/s
107. (a) $\sqrt{3g/L}$ **(b)** $\sqrt{3gL}$
109. (a) 0.50 m **(b)** 2.4 rotations
111. (a) 1.5 m **(b)** 2.7 rev **(c)** increase
113. D. 48.5 rpm
115. C. 3 ft

117. (a) Solid sphere wins, then disk, then hollow sphere. (b) All kinetic energies are equal.

119. (a) greater than (b) 5.3×10^{-5} kg·m^2

CHAPTER 11

1. 60 N
3. (a) 9.56 N·m (b) 8.83 N·m
5. (a) -2.14 N·m (b) clockwise (c) increase
7. (a) less than (b) III
9. C < B < A
11. 0.982 kg·m^2
13. 2.10 N·m
15. (a) 11 N·m (b) 12 N·m (c) 23 N·m
17. (a) forward (b) backward (c) decrease
19. (a) 81 rad/s^2 (b) 0.14 m
21. (a) more likely (b) II
23. 57 N
25. (a) more than (b) 90.3 N
27. 1.1 m
29. 9.14 cm
31. 3.32 kN; -2.21 kN
33. (a) 39 N (b) 39 N (c) 36 N
35. $f_1 = 0.90$ kN; $f_2 = f_3 = 0.17$ kN
37. $F_H = 330$ N; $F_J = 534$ N
39. (a) 79.5 N (b) 159 N
41. 18.7 cm
43. (a) less than (b) 0.080 kg
45. 1.05 kg
47. (a) less than (b) 3.22 N
49. (a) No; your side of the pulley (b) your side: 28 N; other side: 18 N
51. (a) 0.104 kg (b) 0.156 kg
53. 7.05×10^{33} kg·m^2/s
55. 8.6×10^{-5} kg·m^2/s
57. (a) 156 kg·m/s (b) 936 kg·m^2/s
59. (a) 0.078 kg·m^2/s (b) 31 rad/s
61. 2.6×10^{-4} kg·m^2/s
63. (a) increase (b) increase (c) stay the same
65. 0.581
67. a factor of 2
69. 2.84 rad/s
71. 0.37 rad/s
73. (a) faster (b) 38 rev/min
75. (a) $\dfrac{Iv}{I + mR^2}$ (b) As $I \to 0$, $v_{c,g} \to 0$. (c) As $I \to \infty$, $v_{c,g} \to v$.
77. 0.28 J
79. 0.423 rad/s
81. 116 W
83. (a) 0.88 W (b) 1.2 W (c) 2.1 W
85. (a) counterclockwise (b) move to the right
87. (a) move toward the left (b) II
89. increase
91. 5.5 mJ
93. (a) increase (b) $2v$
95. 4.4 kN/m
97. 2.0×10^3 kg
99. (a) $f_1 = 0.89$ kN; $f_2 = f_3 = 0.15$ kN (b) $f_1 = 0.89$ kN; $f_2 = f_3 = 0.22$ kN
101. (a) 2.49 m (b) 1.49 kN
103. (a) $F_A = 196$ N; $F_B = 83.1$ N (b) $F_A = 183$ N; $F_B = 95.6$ N
105. (a) greater than (b) 0.38 kN (c) 0.36 kN (d) -0.08 kN
107. (a) $\frac{25}{24}L$ (b) stay the same
109. $\sqrt{15Mg}$
111. $\dfrac{2\mu_s Mg}{1 - \mu_s}$

115. (a) $\dfrac{F - Mg}{M + \frac{1}{2}m}$ (b) F (c) $\dfrac{2MF + mMg}{2M + m}$ (d) As $m \to 0$, $a \to F/M - g$ and $T_2 \to F$. As $m \to \infty$, $a \to 0$ and $T_2 \to Mg$.
117. B. I = F_{2y}, II = F_{1y}
119. D. $F_{1y} = 0.52$ N, $F_{2y} = 1.3$ N
121. (a) decrease (b) 0.87 N
123. 3.75 m/s

CHAPTER 12

1. B < A < C < D
3. (a) 5.2×10^{-9} N (b) 1.2 m
5. 0.021 N
7. (a) 3.32×10^8 m (b) The answer to part (a) is independent of the mass of the spaceship.
9. 4.79×10^{22} N at 24.4° toward Earth off the line from the Moon to the Sun
11. (a) 3.37×10^{-9} N (b) reduced by a factor of four
13. $\frac{2}{3}D$
15. 2.46×10^6 m
17. 0.00270 m/s^2
19. 2.9×10^7 m (b) 0.48 m/s^2 (c) 1/4 (d) 1/4
21. (a) Use $\frac{1}{2}mv_f^2 = mgh_f$ to find g, and use $g = GM/R^2$ to find M. (b) 8.94×10^{22} kg
23. (a) 6.2×10^{-4} m/s^2 (b) 9.7 h
25. (a) increase (b) stay the same
27. (a) increase (b) I
29. 3.07 km/s
31. 7.64 h
33. (a) Solve Kepler's third law (Equation 12–7) for the mass of 243 Ida, using the orbit distance and period given in the problem. (b) 8.9×10^{16} kg
35. (a) satellite 2 (b) 4.56 km/s
37. (a) farther (b) 2.36×10^7 m
39. 4.30 km/s
41. (a) greater than (b) I
43. (a) -5.5×10^8 J (b) -5.2×10^8 J (c) 2.9×10^7 J; $mgh = 3.0 \times 10^7$ J
45. (a) 1.1×10^{11} J (b) 2.4×10^{12} J
47. less than
49. 5.03 km/s
51. 7.91 km/s
53. (a) 4.25 km/s (b) 10.4 km/s
55. 1.73 km/s
57. It is 10 times that of the Earth.
59. 2.96 km
61. $\sqrt{(1.00 \times 10^7 \text{ m})h}$
65. increase
67. B < C < A
69. (a) zero (b) No
71. -6.34×10^{-10} J
73. (a) 1.98×10^{20} N (b) 4.36×10^{20} N (c) orbiting the Sun, with a small effect due to the Earth
75. 7.39×10^{-5} m/s
77. (a) less than (b) 4.91 m/s^2
81. $\sqrt{\dfrac{72\pi^2 r_1^3}{Gm_1}}$
83. 1.71×10^7 m
85. 0.886 m/s
87. C = 1.00
89. (a) No (b) 7.76 km/s (c) 1.49 h
91. $\sqrt{\dfrac{4\pi^2 d^3}{3Gm}}$
93. $\dfrac{GMm}{2r}$

95. 6.09×10^{24} kg
97. C. 1.1×10^{14} kg
99. D. 8.2 h
101. (a) decrease (b) 258 d (c) stay the same
103. (a) increase (b) 15.8 km/s

CHAPTER 13

1. 12 s; 0.085 Hz
3. 0.38 s
5. 0.81 s; 1.2 Hz
7. (a) 0.022 s; 45 Hz (b) 1400 rpm
9. (a) $\frac{1}{2}T$ (b) $\frac{3}{4}T$
11. (a) 1.5 Hz (b) 0.34 s
13. (a) v_{max} (b) zero (c) zero (d) $-a_{max}$
15. (a) $x = (3.50 \text{ nm})\cos(\omega t)$ where $\omega = 4.00\pi \times 10^{14}$ rad/s (b) sine
17. (a) 0.88 s (b) -1.4 cm
19. $T/3$
21. (a) v_{max}^2/a_{max} (b) $2\pi v_{max}/a_{max}$
23. (a) 28 m (b) 42 s
25. (a) $0.0495g$ (b) 0.128 m/s (c) minimum
27. $12g$
29. (a) 1.1 km/s^2 (b) 6.2 m/s
31. (a) The rider must begin hanging on when a_{max} (at the top of the cycle) equals g. (b) 0.14 m
33. (a) less than (b) I
37. D < C < A < B
39. 0.47 kg
41. (a) 1.06×10^3 kg (b) 932 kg
43. 7.68 cm
45. (a) greater than (b) $\sqrt{2}T$
47. 1.43 m/s
49. 1.2 J
51. (a) 0.26 m/s (b) 2.8 cm
53. 0.30 m/s
55. (a) 897 m/s (b) 0.0687 s
57. (a) run slow (b) I
59. 8.95 m
61. 2.4 s
63. (a) increase (b) 2.45 s
65. 0.011 kg·m^2
67. 1.49 m
69. (a) $2\pi\sqrt{\dfrac{L}{g + a}}$ (b) $2\pi\sqrt{\dfrac{L}{g - a}}$
71. (a) 1/2 (b) 1/2 (c) 1/2 (d) 1/4 (e) 1.00
73. (a) remain the same (b) remain the same
75. 0.49 m/s
77. 4×10^{14} m/s^2; $(4 \times 10^{13})g$
79. 5.52 N/m
81. (a) 0.13 m (b) 84 N/m (c) 0.83 Hz
83. (a) 0.018 rad/s (b) 250 m
85. 9.20 s
87. 0.95 s
89. (a) 0.112 m (b) 0.142 s
91. (a) greater than 0.50 m/s (b) 0.79 m/s (c) 1.2 J
93. (a) 7.9 N/m (b) 4.6 kg
95. (a) less than (b) $\pi\sqrt{\ell/g} + \pi\sqrt{L/g}$ (c) 1.5 s
99. (a) The pencil begins to rattle when the maximum acceleration of the speaker exceeds the acceleration due to gravity. (b) $\frac{1}{2}\sqrt{g/A}$
101. C. 74 °F
103. B. 1700
105. (a) $1/\sqrt{2}$ (b) 5.90 cm (c) 0.0702 s

CHAPTER 14

1. (a) 56 cm (b) 6.5 cm
3. 1.2 m
5. (a) 0.61 m (b) 1.1 m (c) The answer in part (a) is unchanged; the answer in part (b) is halved.
7. 0.51 m/s; 67 Hz
9. 4.00
11. (a) greater than (b) I
13. 4.00
15. (a) less time (b) 0.18 s (c) 0.17 s
17. 1.4
19. $y = (0.16 \text{ m})\cos\left(\frac{2\pi}{2.1 \text{ m}}x - \frac{\pi}{0.90 \text{ s}}t\right)$
21. (a) positive (b) $\lambda = 2\pi/B$ (c) $f = C/2\pi$ (d) $x = \pi/B$
23. (a) 15 cm (b) 10 cm (c) 24 s (d) 0.42 cm/s (e) to the right
25. (a) A and C (b) B and D (c) C (d) A (e) C
27. (a) 0.098 s (b) 28 mm
29. (a) 0.807 m (b) decrease (c) 0.722 m
31. 1.78 m/s
33. 1.6 mW/m^2
35. 67.6 W/m^2
37. (a) 104 dB (b) 99.6 dB (c) 2.0×10^6 m
39. (a) 69.5 dB (b) less than
41. 21.7 m
43. $\lambda_3 < \lambda_2 < \lambda_1$
45. 1.50×10^2 Hz
47. (a) 35.3 kHz (b) higher (c) 35.4 kHz
49. 524 Hz
51. 51 m/s
53. (a) 0.33 kHz (b) (i) bicyclist A speeds up
55. 11.2 m/s
57.

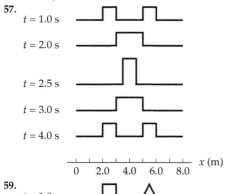

59.

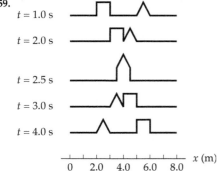

61. 1.2 kHz
63. 0.322 m
65. 0.31 kHz
67. (a) a lower frequency (b) III
69. 77 Hz
71. (a) 3.6 kHz; 9.6 kHz (b) 11 kHz; 3.2 cm (c) greater than
73. (a) 7.60 Hz (b) 15.2 Hz (c) increase

75. (a) 93.5 Hz (b) 31.2 Hz
77. (a) 55 Hz (b) 3.1 m
79. (a) equal to (b) I
81. 264 Hz and 258 Hz
83. (a) 13.8 Hz (b) increase (c) 18.3 Hz
85. 1.21 m
87. (a) minimum (b) maximum
89. A, III; B, I; C, I; D, III; E, II; F, II
91. 2.9 km
93. 6.72×10^6 m
95. four
97. 9.0 km
99. (a) increase (b) 618 Hz
101. 36 m/s
103. 6.73 m/s if approaching, 7.00 m/s if receding
105. (a) 2.00 (b) 1/3 (c) 2.00
107. (a) 0.0032 J (b) 0.0081 J (c) No
109. 0.83 m
111. 3.9×10^7 years
113. (a) increase
115. $\sqrt{\frac{2\pi\lambda}{g}}$
117. C. 64 Hz
119. B. 2.3 m
121. (a) greater than (b) 30.1 m/s
123. (a) increase (b) 464 Hz

CHAPTER 15

1. 10^3 N
3. No
5. 1.05×10^4 kg/m; silver
7. (a) 10^{-1} Pa (b) 10^{-6} atm
9. 4.3
11. 615 N
13. (a) greater than (b) equal to
15. 2.17×10^6 Pa
17. (a) 98.2 kPa (b) 10.0 m
19. 0.11 N
21. (a) 995 m (b) greater than
23. (a) greater than (b) 52 Pa
25. 0.16 cm
27. (a) 0.770 m (b) increased
29. (a) equal to (b) I
31. fall
33. 41 cm
35. 1.12 kg/m^3
37. (a) decrease (b) III
39. less than
41. at the same level as
43. (a) 2.34×10^{-4} m^3 (b) 8.70×10^3 kg/m^3
45. (a) 1.04×10^3 kg/m^3 (b) 0.0745 m^3 (c) 26 N
47. (a) 0.008 m^3 (b) 18 N
49. 2.1 cm
51. 39 m/s
53. 16 min
55. (a) 0.78 cm/s (b) 0.13 cm/s
57. 7.9 m/s
59. (a) 32 cm/s (b) 43 Pa
61. (a) 53 m/s (b) 19 cm
63. 1.08×10^5 Pa
65. (a) 1.42 kPa (b) 45 kN
67. (a) 980 kN (b) upward
69. (a) less than (b) $\Delta P = -\frac{15}{2}\rho v^2$
71. (a) 25 cm^3 (b) 2.2
73. (a) 1.0 m/s (b) 0.79 kPa (c) 1/2 (d) 1/4
75. lean forward
77. (a) higher (b) stay the same
79. tilted inward toward the axis of rotation

81. greater than
83. 904 m/s; $v/v_s = 2.64$
85. 95.3 kPa
87. 2.4×10^5 N
89. (a) compressed 0.15 m (b) stretched 0.063 m
91. 16 m/s
93. (a) 11 N
95. (a) 1.050×10^5 Pa (b) increase (c) 1.052×10^5 Pa
97. 41 km
99. (a) $v = \sqrt{2gd}$ (b) the same as
101. (a) 9.58×10^{-3} m^3 (b) 10.1 kg
103. 4.4×10^5 Pa
105. (a) 17 μm (b) Yes (c) 21 kg
107. $2\pi\sqrt{\dfrac{p_1 H}{p_2 g}}$
109. 0.28
113. 16 kg
115. C. 0.28H
117. B. 0.40H
119. 0.60 cm
121. 2.00

CHAPTER 16

1. -128.6 °F
3. (a) 37.0 °C (b) 310.2 K
5. (a) 5.7×10^3 °C (b) 1.0×10^4 °F
7. (a) 79.9 kPa (b) 192 °C
9. 0.23 K/s
11. -6.85 °C
13. steel
15. (a) B = C < D = E < A (b) A = C = E < B < D
17. 1.6 m
19. (a) heated (b) 430 °C
21. 0.93 L
23. (a) aluminum (b) 2.5×10^{-5} m^3
25. (a) Water will overflow. (b) 24 cm^3
27. 0.12 kW or 0.16 hp
29. (a) 1.4×10^{-3} C° (b) greater than (c) 2.6×10^{-3} F°
31. (a) greater than (b) III
33. 23.3 °C
35. 15 kJ
37. (a) 7.2×10^2 pellets (b) decrease (c) 4.4×10^2 pellets
39. (a) 0.18 kJ/K (b) 0.96 kJ/(kg·K)
41. 385 J/(kg·K); copper
43. 70.5 °C
45. $\Delta T_B < \Delta T_A < \Delta T_C$
47. twin 1
49. 65 kJ/min
51. 3.29 h
53. (a) 19.4 J/s (b) 0.16 C°
55. 2.64 cm
57. (a) The heat flow rate through both rods must be the same. (b) 89 cm
59. 56
61. too long
63. (a) No (b) Yes (c) No
65. (a) greater than (b) II
67. 25.1 cm × 2.01 m × 9.9 m
69. (a) 2700 °F (b) 1800 K
71. 250 °F
73. (a) 1.30×10^3 J, 1.29 times more than the specific heat (b) 4.19×10^6 J, 1000 times more than the specific heat
75. 77.9 °F

77. (a) increase (b) 1.710 mm
 (c) 1.955 s before; 1.957 s after
79. 3.5×10^2 C°
81. 0.17 C°
83. (a) 1.54×10^6 m (b) 5.51 km/s
85. (a) 0.21 kW (b) 0.42 kW
89. (a) decreased (b) -83 C°
93. greater than
95. **A.** 107 ft 7.8 in.
97. 82 °C
99. (a) greater than (b) 139 °C

CHAPTER 17

1. (a) equal to (b) less than
3. (a) decrease (b) I
5. 0.0224 m^3
7. 316 K
9. 1.33×10^3kg
11. 10^{-15} Pa
13. 13 L
15. (a) 0.032 m^3 (b) 1.9×10^{-4}
 (c) The molecules occupy less than 0.02% of the total volume of the gas, so the assumption is valid.
17. (a) 3.0×10^{23} molecules/m^3
 (b) greater than
 (c) 2.68×10^{25} molecules/m^3
19. 348 K
21.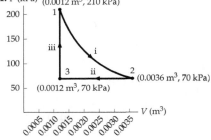
23. increase by a factor of 4.00
25. (a) unknowable (b) false
 (c) unknowable (d) false (e) true
27. 632 m/s
29. (a) greater than (b) 2.07 km/s
31. 191 K
33. $v_{238}/v_{235} = 0.996$
35. face 2
37. 67 kg
39. 1.1×10^6 N/m^2
41. $Y_3 < Y_1 = Y_2 < Y_4$
43. (a) 1.8×10^{-3} (b) 0.60 cm
45. 233 N
47. about 4.2 kPa
49. (a) about 3.5 MPa (b) increase
51. (a) 0 °C (b) 100 °C (c) increase (d) increase
53. (a) First the water ice changes from solid to liquid, then the liquid changes to a gas.
 (b) The solid water sublimates to a gas.
55. (a) First the solid carbon dioxide changes to liquid, then the liquid changes to a gas.
 (b) First the solid carbon dioxide changes to liquid, then the liquid changes to a gas.
57. 3.2×10^5 J
59. 362 kJ
61. (a) No (b) 0 °C; 0.4 kg
63. (a) 27.3 s (b) 61.5 s (c) 246 s
 (d) The water is boiling.

65. (a) 2.62 kJ (b) 30.9 kJ (c) 0.058 kg; 0.68 kg
67. 19.1 °C
69. 123 °C (All of the water has vaporized.)
71. (a) 3.6 °C (b) No ice is present.
73. 50.3 h
75. room 2
77. (a) less than (b) III
79. 2.0×10^{22} molecules
81. (a) 0.39 ft^3 (b) 2.0×10^2 atm (c) 3.0 kg
83. 1.1×10^{24} molecules
85. (a) 7.3 kN (b) reduced by a factor of 2
87. (a) 4.2×10^{-7} m (b) 2.7×10^{-6} m
89. (a) 4.6 MJ (b) 2.5 km/s
91. (a) 0.469 kg (b) 0.320 kg (c) 0.171 kg
93. 1.4×10^{-4} kg
95. **C.** 91.9 atm
97. **B.** 9.2×10^{-5} m^3
99. (a) 18 °C (b) five ice cubes

CHAPTER 18

1. (a) zero (b) zero (c) -100 J
3. $\Delta U = -10.8 \times 10^5$ J; $W = 6.7 \times 10^5$ J; $Q = -4.1 \times 10^5$ J
5. (a) 119 J (b) 35 J (c) 0
7. (a) -492 kJ (b) 117 Cal
9. (a) 4.24 MJ/mi (b) decrease
11. (a) zero (b) -53 J (c) -150 J
 (d) 200 J (e) 350 J
13. (a) zero (b) 5.1×10^{-3} m^3
15. 60 Pa
17. (a) on the system (b) -670 J
19. (a) 1200 kJ (b) No
21. (a) 332 K (b) 555 kJ
23. (a) added to the system (b) 55 kJ
25. (a) 150 kJ (b) zero (c) 150 kJ
27. (a) $T_A = 267$ K; $T_B = 357$ K; $T_C = 89.1$ K
 (b) A → B: heat enters; B → C: heat leaves; C → A: heat enters
 (c) A → B: 376 kJ; B → C: -375 kJ; C → A: 150 kJ
29. (a) 94 kJ into the gas (b) 92 kJ into the gas
31. (a) $3P_iV_i$ (b) $\frac{15}{2}P_iV_i$ (c) $\frac{21}{2}P_iV_i$
33. (a) greater than (b) II
35. (a) 0.95 K (b) 0.57 K
37. (a) 2.9 K (b) 4.9 K
39. (a) 0.315 (b) 0.630 (c) 100 kPa; 222 K
41. (a) process 1: 159 kJ; process 2: 1060 kJ
 (b) 424 kJ (c) 795 kJ
43. (a) stay the same (b) decrease
45. 0.28
47. (a) 8.5 kJ (b) 6.0 kJ
49. (a) 1.16 GW (b) 1.71 GW
51. (a) 382 K (b) decreased (c) 327 K
53. 4.5×10^2 K, 5.0×10^2 K
55. (a) less than (b) I
57. (a) 19.7 kJ (b) 54.2 kJ
59. 0.41 kW
61. 1.5×10^5 J
63. (a) increase (b) III
65. (a) stay the same (b) I
67. -3.8 kJ/K
69. 9.6 W/K
71. (a) increase (b) 1.3 W/K
73. equal to
75. less than
77. 0.071 kg

79. (a) 365 K (b) increase (c) 1.52 kJ/K
 (d) 555 kJ; 555 kJ
81. (a) 318 kJ (b) 795 kJ (c) 1113 kJ
83. (a) 751 kJ (b) 194 kJ (c) 945 kJ
85. (a) 1.1×10^{31} J/K (b) 3.28×10^{31} J
87. (a) 0.0557 m^3 (b) -1.22 kJ (c) -1.22 kJ
89. (a) 0.47 J/K (b) 0.40 kJ
91. (a) -38 J (b) zero (c) -171 J (d) 212 J
 (e) 120 J
93. (a)

	Q	W	ΔU
A → B	806 J	806 J	0
B → C	-938 J	-375 J	-563 J
C → A	563 J	0	563 J

 (b) 0.31
97. (a) 6.10%
99. (a) 6.78%
101. (a) less than (b) 0.46 (c) -1.8 J/K
 (d) 1.8 J/K

CHAPTER 19

1. (a) decrease
 (b) I
3. (a) negative
 (b) toward
5. -7.8×10^{-12} C
7. -1×10^6 C
9. 0.178 C
11. D < A < C < B
13. the center
15. C < A < B
17. 1.37 m
19. 4.7×10^{-10} m
21. 3.0 electrons
23. $(63$ N$)\hat{x}$
25. (a) $F_1 = F_3 < F_2$
 (b) 0°
 (c) 150°
 (d) 300°
27. 0.12 m
29. 5.5 km
31. 174.6°; 4.2 N
33. (a) 35 cm (b) No. The forces would reverse direction but would still balance.
35. (a) 248°; 58 N (b) The direction would not change but the magnitude would be cut to a fourth.
37. (a) greater than (b) 3.09×10^6 m/s
39. (a) 3.7×10^{-7} C (b) no
 (c) The tension will be zero.
41. $q_1 = 9q_2$
43. (a) 6.74×10^4 N/C (b) 1.69×10^4 N/C
45. (a) $(-3.0 \times 10^7$ N/C$)\hat{x}$
 (b) $(5.9 \times 10^7$ N/C$)\hat{x}$
47. (a) $(-3.3 \times 10^4$ N/C$)\hat{y}$
 (b) $(9.81$ m/s$^2)\hat{y}$
49. 3.5 pC
51. (a) configuration (2)
 (b) case 1: $\vec{E}_{1,\,net} = 0$;
 case 2:
$$\vec{E}_{2,net} = \left(-\frac{4\sqrt{2}\,k\,q}{a^2}\right)\hat{y}$$
53. (a) positive (b) 5.00 μC (c) 5.00 μC
55.

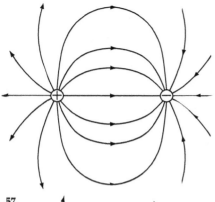

57.

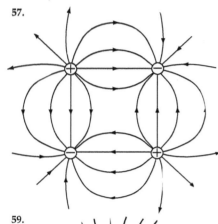

59.

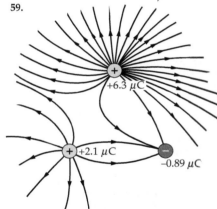

61. **(a)** the same as **(b)** II
63. $D < C < B < A$
65. $6.8 \times 10^5 \, \text{N} \cdot \text{m}^2/\text{C}$
67. $6.2 \times 10^{-6} \, \text{C/m}^2$
69. **(a)** $-1.14 \times 10^5 \, \text{N} \cdot \text{m}^2/\text{C}$
    (b) $1.46 \times 10^5 \, \text{N} \cdot \text{m}^2/\text{C}$
    (c) $3.28 \times 10^5 \, \text{N} \cdot \text{m}^2/\text{C}$
    (d) $-2.90 \, \mu\text{C}$
71. **(a)** greater than **(b)** II
73. the same as
75. negative
77. $+2q$ and $+q$
79. 8.4×10^8 electrons
81. **(a)** $-Q$ **(b)** $+Q$ **(c)** zero
83. $1.2 \times 10^{25} \, \text{N}$; 10^{22} times stronger
85. **(a)** (ii) to the left of $x = 0.30$ m
    (b) 0.297 m
87. **(a)** $9.39 \times 10^{-7} \, \text{C/m}$ **(b)** 0.954 m

89. **(a)** 0.55 N; $-\hat{\mathbf{y}}$ direction
    (b) greater than
    (c) $(-4.4 \, \text{N})\hat{\mathbf{y}}$
91. **(a)** $6.7 \times 10^5 \, \text{N/C}$ **(b)** stay the same
93. **(a)** 5.71×10^{13} C **(b)** no change
95. 0.254 m
97. $8.85 \times 10^{-6} \, \text{C/m}^2$
99. **(a)** $1.3 \times 10^3 \, \text{N/C}$ **(b)** 5.3×10^{-2} N
101. **(a)** $4.13 \times 10^3 \, \text{N/C}$ **(b)** $6.22 \times 10^6 \, \text{m/s}$
103. **B.** 5.81×10^8 electrons
105. **C.** 4.4 cm
107. **(a)** greater than **(b)** less than
    (c) $1.83 \times 10^5 \, \text{N/C}$ **(d)** 11.8°
109. **(a)** greater than **(b)** $-4.50 \, \mu\text{C}$

CHAPTER 20

1. increasing
3. **(a)** 0 **(b)** -4.1×10^6 V
    (c) -4.1×10^6 V
5. $2.43 \times 10^6 \, \text{V/m}$
7. **(a)** 90 V **(b)** 18 V
9. 2×10^4 V
11. **(a)** 1.9 kV **(b)** increase **(c)** 3.8 kV
13. 110 m/s
15. **(a)** region 4, region 4
    (b) 1, 13 V/m; 2, 0; 3, -5.1 V/m;
    4, 68 V/m
17. **(a)** decrease **(b)** II
19. $9.4 \times 10^7 \, \text{m/s}$
21. **(a)** negative x direction **(b)** 3.8 cm/s
    (c) less than
23. **(a)** $-\sqrt{2} \, Q$ **(b)** negative
25. **(a)** $-Q$ **(b)** positive **(c)** negative
27. **(a)** -2.2×10^4 V **(b)** -2.2×10^4 V
    (c) -1.5×10^4 V
29. 1.34 cm
31. **(a)**

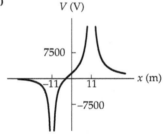

(b) closer to the negative charge
(c) -3.3 m
33. **(a)**

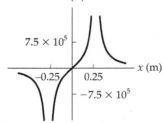

(b) 0.21 m and 0.29 m
35. **(a)** 20.0 m/s **(b)** greater than **(c)** 28.3 m/s
37. **(a)** 0.86 J **(b)** less than **(c)** -0.54 J
39. **(a)** 76.7 kV **(b)** 14.1 m/s
41. $-(4 - \sqrt{2})(kQ^2/a)$
43. **(a)** greater than **(b)** III

45. **(a)**

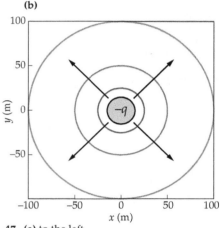

(b)

47. **(a)** to the left
    (b) A, positive; B, positive; C, positive;
    D, negative; E, negative
    (c) $E < D < A < C < B$
    (d) less than
49. **(a)** 559 V/m; 243° **(b)** 8.95 mm
51. 1.8 V
53. $0.18 \, \mu\text{F}$
55. **(a)** 19 kV **(b)** decrease **(c)** 9.7 kV
57. **(a)** $1.87 \, \mu\text{m}$ **(b)** $6.9 \, \mu\text{m}$
59. 15 kV
61. **(a)** 4.0 nF **(b)** 6.6 C
63. $35 \, \mu\text{J}$
65. **(a)** 5.8×10^{-14} J **(b)** decrease
67. $10.6 \, \text{J/m}^3$
69. **(a)** 0.29 C **(b)** 48 J
71. decreasing
73. **(a)** increase **(b)** increase
75. **(a)** decrease **(b)** decrease
    (c) decrease **(d)** decrease
77. **(a)** remain the same **(b)** increase
    (c) increase **(d)** increase
79. The capacitance is cut to a fourth.
81. **(a)** $x = -0.5$ m **(b)** region 3 **(c)** $x = -4.5$ m
83. 13.6 eV
85. **(a)** smallest at C, greatest at A
    (b) A, 43 kV; B, 31 kV; C, 29 kV; D, 31 kV
87. **(a)** -6.96 J **(b)** 20.1 m/s
89. -5.9×10^{-14} J
91. **(a)** positive **(b)** -1.7×10^{-16} C
93. **(a)** from one end of its body to the other
    (b) 5.3×10^{-9} C

95. **(a)** increase **(b)** 0.071 mm
97. **(a)** directed into the cell; 1.2×10^7 N/C
  (b) 97 mV; outer wall
99. 3.58×10^{-14} m
101. **(a)**

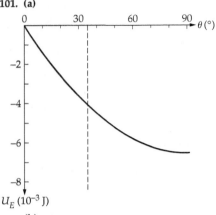

U_E (10^{-3} J)

  (b)

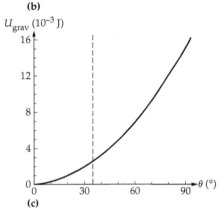

U_{grav} (10^{-3} J)

  (c)

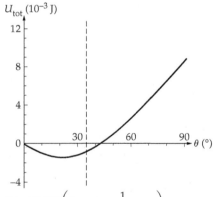

U_{tot} (10^{-3} J)

103. $(22 \text{ kV})\left(1 - \dfrac{1}{\sqrt{5 + 4\cos\theta}}\right)$
105. 6.92 cm; 1.19 nC
107. **B.** 7.6×10^{-12} F
109. **C.** 1.6×10^{-6} J
111. **(a)** 1.50 m **(b)** -1.50 m

CHAPTER 21
1. 3600 C
3. 9.4×10^{19} electrons/s
5. 6.25×10^4 electrons/s
7. **(a)** 1.5 kC **(b)** 8.5 y
9. material A
11. 1/3
13. 51 Ω
15. 0.68 kΩ
17. **(a)** 2.5 mV **(b)** increase

19. **(a)** 7.2×10^{-13} A
  (b) decrease by a factor of 2
21. **(a)** 0.11 Ω/m **(b)** decrease
  (c) 0.074 Ω/m
23. $\left(\dfrac{C}{A}\right)^2 I_{AB}$
25. **(a)** bulb A **(b)** 4
27. 51 A
29. 0.58 kW
31. \$0.072/kWh
33. 155-minute reserve capacity
35. **(a)** in series **(b)** III
37. **(a)** decrease **(b)** III
39. 6 resistors
41. **(a)** 3.1 W **(b)** 1.5 kW
43. **(a)** 71 mA
  (b) $V_{42\,\Omega} = 3.0$ V; $V_{17\,\Omega} = 1.2$ V;
  $V_{110\,\Omega} = 7.8$ V
45. **(a)** 29 V **(b)** $I_{65\,\Omega} = 0.45$ A;
  $I_{25\,\Omega} = 1.2$ A; $I_{170\,\Omega} = 0.17$ A
47. 0.16 kV
49. 0.84 V
51. **(a)** $I_{7.1\,\Omega} = 0.29$ A, $I_{3.2\,\Omega} = 1.1$ A
  (b) 1.4 A **(c)** 11.3 V
53. **(a)**

R (Ω)	1.5	2.5	4.8	3.3	8.1	6.3
I (A)	6.0	3.6	0.38	0.55	0.22	1.1

  (b) less than
55. **(a)** 129 V **(b)** decrease
57. **(a)** stay the same **(b)** I_0
59. **(a)** decrease **(b)** 0.12 A ; clockwise
61. **(a)** $I_{11\,\Omega} = 0.92$ A, $I_{6.2\,\Omega} = I_{12\,\Omega} = 0.27$ A,
  $I_{7.5\,\Omega} = 0.65$ A **(b)** same as (a)
63. **(a)** $I_{9.8\,\Omega} = I_{3.9\,\Omega} = 0.72$ A, $I_{1.2\,\Omega} = 1.8$ A,
  $I_{6.7\,\Omega} = 1.0$ A
  (b) greater than **(c)** 2.2 V
65. **(a)** C_1 **(b)** C_2
67. **(a)** increase **(b)** II
69. 1.1 V
71. **(a)** $B < A < C$ **(b)** $B < A = C$
73. **(a)** 23 μF **(b)** the 15-μF capacitor
  (c) $Q_{7.5\,\mu F} = 110$ μC, $Q_{15\,\mu F} = 230$ μC
75. 2.56 μF
77. 6.47 V
79. **(a)** 2.6×10^{-4} C **(b)** 28 mA
81. **(a)** 9.75 ms **(b)** 668 μC **(c)** 68.6 mA
83. 6.1 kΩ
85. **(a)** 6.7×10^{-4} s **(b)** 1.4 A **(c)** increased
87. charge
89. **(a)** increased **(b)** $\sqrt{2}$
91. **(a)** R_2 **(b)** R_1
93. **(a)** increase **(b)** III
95. **(a)** increase **(b)** stay the same
97. **(a)** increase **(b)** II
99. Connect the 146-Ω and 521-Ω resistors in
  series. Then connect this pair in parallel
  with the 413-Ω resistor.
101. 3.1×10^{-8} A
103. **(a)** $A = B = C$ **(b)** $A < C < B$
105. 0.53 V
107. **(a)** 0.91 J **(b)** 4.0 min
109. **(a)** greater than **(b)** 0.82 A **(c)** 0.54 A
111. **(a)** $R_1 = 18$ Ω, $R_2 = 62$ Ω
113. $R/9$
115. **(a)** greater
  (b) $I_{45\,\Omega} = 0.27$ A, $I_{35\,\Omega} = I_{82\,\Omega} = 0.103$ A
117. **(a)** 2.4 W/m **(b)** 2.0 W/m

119. **(a)** $P_{13\,\Omega} = 7.7$ W, $P_{6.5\,\Omega} = 3.8$ W,
  $P_{24\,\Omega} = 9.4$ W; all zero as $t \to \infty$
  (b) 0.38 mC **(c)** 7.0 mJ **(d)** It quadruples.
121. 44 V, 43 Ω
123. 7.50 Ω
125. **A.** 1.25×10^7 Ω
127. increase
129. **(a)** 329 Ω **(b)** 794 Ω
131. **(a)** 273 μC **(b)** decrease **(c)** 58.7 ms

CHAPTER 22
1. **(a)** less than **(b)** II
3. positive z direction
5. A, negative; B, negative; C, positive
7. 9.9×10^8 m/s^2
9. 0
11. **(a)** 81° **(b)** 38° **(c)** 1.2°
13. 4.4×10^{-16} N
15. **(a)** particle 2 **(b)** 1/4
17. **(a)** $(5.0 \times 10^6$ N/C$)\hat{x}$
  (b) $(-0.2$ T$)\hat{z}$
19. 5.4 μm
21. 2.5 km/s
23. **(a)** 1.1 m/s **(b)** bottom electrode; no
25. **(a)** 9.83 m/s
  (b) 13.9 s
27. 3.1 cm
29. **(a)** 1.00 **(b)** 0.0233
31. 3.3 N
33. $(-0.34$ T$)\hat{z}$
35. 2.4 A
37. $\tan^{-1}\dfrac{ILB}{mg}$
39. 3.5 A
41. 60°
43. **(a)** less than **(b)** $\pi/4$
45. 2.50×10^{-5} T
49. 1.3 kA
51. **(a)** point B
  (b) point A, 2.1 μT; point B, 13 μT
53. **(a)** 2.57×10^{-5} N/m **(b)** the same as
55. terminal A
57. 35 mA
59. 17.2 T
61. east
63. out of the page
65. greater than $\theta = 45°$ and
  less than $\theta = 90°$
67. toward wire 3
69. 0
71. 0.946
73. 7.0 μm
75. **(a)** $F_3 < F_2 = F_4 < F_1$ **(b)** $\vec{v}_3$
77. **(a)** $B_3 < B_1 < B_2$
  (b) B_1, out of the page; B_2, into the page;
  B_3, out of the page
79. **(a)** stay the same **(b)** III
81. **(a)** toward the wire **(b)** 3×10^{-5} N
83. $(-2.0 \times 10^3$ N/C$)\hat{x} + (3.2 \times 10^3$ N/C$)\hat{y}$
85. 2.3 mN; 65° measured from the positive z
  axis toward the negative y axis in the yz
  plane
87. **(a)** 4.52×10^7 C/kg **(b)** less than
89. $(-4$ μT$)\hat{z}$, $(12$ μT$)\hat{z}$, $(-4$ μT$)\hat{z}$
91. **(a)** less than **(b)** 1.2 A; to the left
93. **(a)** 1.6×10^{11} N **(b)** The force from the
  magnetar is 280,000 times greater than
  the electron-proton force within a hydrogen atom.

95. (a) negative y axis (b) 43.0 cm
97. (a) 4.3 mT (b) 230 A
99. (a) 2.6 kT/s (b) increase by a factor of $\sqrt{2}$
101. $\frac{1}{2}\mu_0\lambda\omega$

103. (a) clockwise (b) $\dfrac{2I}{3\pi}$
105. 64 mT
107. C. 2.5×10^{-10} A
109. A. 22 cm
111. (a) increase (b) 2 cm
113. 5.9 A to the right

CHAPTER 23
1. 1.6×10^{-4} Wb
3. 0.020 T
5. 1.9 Wb
7. (a) 11.7 A
(b) The current would be cut to a fourth.
9. 14 V
11. (a) -0.1 kV (b) 0 (c) 0.04 kV
13. 1, counterclockwise; 2, zero; 3, zero;
4, clockwise
15. (a) near $t = 0.5$ s (b) 0.1 s, 0.3 s, 0.5 s, . . .
(c) -0.06 kV, 0, 0.06 kV
17. 7.1 V
19. 3.8×10^3
21. (a) location 1, upward; location 2, zero;
location 3, upward (b) III
23. minimum
25. counterclockwise
27. (a) less than (b) less than
29. (a) zero (b) clockwise
31. (a) zero (b) zero (c) no
33. bottom
35. no
37. 47 mV
39. (a) 52.3 mN (b) 0.300 W (c) 0.300 W
41. (a) 0.86 A (b) 4.1 m/s
43. 33 mT
45. (a) horizontal (b) 29.3 mV
47. -1.40 V
49. (a) 6.9×10^{-3} m^2 (b) 0.42 V
51. -15.5 mV
53. 3.6×10^{-4} s
55. (a) 4.0×10^{-4} s (b) 57 mA (c) 65 mA
57. (a) 3.8 H (b) 0.25 s (c) 1.6 A
59. 8.2 mJ
61. (a) 9.95×10^8 J/m^3 (b) 1.50×10^{10} V/m
63. (a) 0.075 J (b) 0.14 J (c) decrease
65. (a) 57 A (b) 0.15 T (c) 8.7 kJ/m^3
67. $6\,I_s$
69. (a) less than (b) 9.4 turns
71. 92
73. 0.36 A; 0.16 kV
75. less than
77. either increasing and to the right or
decreasing and to the left
79. 4.7×10^{-10} Wb
81. 4.0 mWb
83. 0.29 V
85. 0.15 kV
87. 339 V
89. 0.990 km
91. (a) 66 μs (b) 43 μJ
93. 1.1 μV
95. (a) zero (b) $-vWB$ (c) zero
(d) parts (a) and (c), zero; part (b),
counterclockwise

97. (a) $\dfrac{1}{\sqrt{\varepsilon_0\mu_0}}$ (b) 3.00×10^8 m/s
99. C. 2.1×10^{-4} V
101. B. 0.11 s
103. (a) zero (b) zero (c) counterclockwise
(d) to the left
105. (a) to the right (b) clockwise (c) 2.2 T

CHAPTER 24
1. 39 V
3. 81 Ω
5. (a) 2.99 W (b) 5.97 W
7. $V_{\text{rms}} = V_{\text{avg}}$
9. 86.9 Hz
11. (a) 5.9 μA (b) 8.3 μA
13. (a) 9.0 V (b) -6.7 V (c) 6.7 V
15. (a) 1.16 kΩ (b) 0.137 μF
(c) 0.860 mA (d) 4.3 mA
17. $0 \le f < 60$ Hz
19. 53.4 Ω
21. 0.10 $k\Omega$
23. (a) 74.6 Hz (b) 4.61 W
25. 0.967
27.

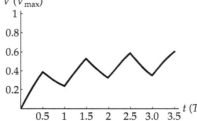

$V\,(V_{\text{max}})$

29. 45.2 Ω
31. 22 V
33. (a) 79 Ω (b) 21 V (c) 14 V
35. (a) 12.2 A (b) 0.500 (c) 6.09 A
37. 29 mH
39. (a)

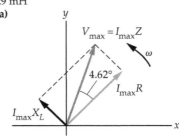

(b) 136 W
41. (a) 17 Ω (b) 14 A (c) 1.5 kW
43. parallel
45. (a) the same as (b) I
47. (a) greater than (b) III
49. 1.51 kΩ
51. (a) 10 A (b) 5.0 A
53. (a) 0.962 (b) increase (c) 0.998
55. (a) 0.173 V (b) 7.84 V (c) 1.84 V
(d) greater than
57. 7.9 kΩ or 5.3 kΩ
59. (a) $T/4$ (b) $T/2$
61. decrease
63. 43 Ω
65. (a) decreased (b) decreased
67. increased
69. (a) 494 Hz (b) 180 Ω (c) 0.58
71. (a) 9.7 pH (b) 10 Ω
73. 27 mJ

75. (a) the same as (b) I
77. (a) increase (b) II
79. 572 mA
81. 66.3 Ω
83. (a) greater than (b) 137 Hz (c) 175 Ω
85. 26 ms
87. 4.16 W
89. (a) 606 Ω (b) increase
91. (a) 29 Ω (b) 71 μF (c) decrease
93. (a) 535.6 Hz
(b) decreased
95. (a) 0.10 kW (b) 0.55 H
97. (a) 1.3 pF (b) increase (c) 5.0 Ω (d) 15 Ω
99. $R = 76$ Ω, $C = 99$ nF
101. (a) 0.24 kHz (b) 93 V (c) 76 V
103. decrease
105. C. 8.06 A
107. (a) increase (b) 87.2 Hz (c) 0.634 A

CHAPTER 25
1. increasing
3. (a) x direction (b) z direction
(c) positive y direction
5. (a) up (b) down (c) east (d) west
7. (a) zero
(b) $(-9.57 \times 10^{-9}$ T$)\hat{\mathbf{x}} + (2.07 \times 10^{-8}$ T$)\hat{\mathbf{y}}$
9. case 1, positive x direction;
case 2, positive z direction;
case 3, negative x direction
11. 4.1×10^{16} m
13. 1.14
15. (a) away from (b) $0.12c$
17. 3.00×10^8 ms
19. the father
21. 4.945×10^{14} Hz
23. 2.82 kHz
25. (a) 8.238×10^{14} Hz
(b) 8.203×10^{14} Hz
27. 1.0×10^{18} Hz
29. 1.7×10^3 waves
31. 1.71 m
33. (a) 9.38×10^{14} Hz to 1.07×10^{15} Hz
(b) UV-A

35. (a) decrease (b) $\dfrac{3}{4}$

37. 97 s
39. 93 m
41. (a) 0.2 km (b) 2 m
43. (a) factor of 2 (b) factor of 4
45. 1.33×10^{-10} T
47. (a) 1.1 kV/m (b) 3.3 kW/m^2
(c) 1.6 kW/m^2
49. 61.4 V/m
51. (a) 83 mW/m^2 (b) 0.83 mW/m^2
53. 6.6×10^{-4}
55. 1.7×10^{-11} J
57. 2.3 mN
59. (a) NIF (b) NIF (c) NIF
61. (a) 0.2 mJ (b) 3.8 kW/cm^2 (c) 3.8×10^5
63. (a) 0.28 kW/m^2 (b) 4.6 cm
65. (a) 34 mJ (b) 2.1 μPa
67. (a) 1.56×10^{12} W (b) 4.95×10^{17} W/m^2
(c) 1.37×10^{10} V/m
69. (a) greater than (b) III
71. (a) green (b) red (c) blue
73. 0.134

75. $\cos^{-1}\dfrac{1}{\sqrt{5}}$

77. (a) C < A = B
    (b) case A, 9.25 W/m^2; case B, 9.25 W/m^2; case C, zero
79. (a) d-glutamic acid
    (b) l-leucine, 0.576 mW/m^2; d-glutamic acid, 0.732 mW/m^2
81. (a) $0.375I_0 \cos^2(\theta - 30.0°)$
    (b) $I_{max} = 0.375I_0$
    (c) 30.0° or 210.0°
83. reflecting
85. 2.00×10^{-11} m
87. 0.40 km
89. (a) 6 MW/m^2 (b) less than (c) 1 MW/m^2
91. 1.2×10^7 m/s away from Earth
93. (a) Both arms show a red shift.
    (b) 8.149×10^{14} Hz
    (c) 8.114×10^{14} Hz
95. (a) 58.0° (b) 593 W/m^2
97. 6.6
99. (a) 1.0 mW/m^2 (b) 0.71 kN/C
101. (a) 1.08 W/m^2 (b) 543 W/m^2
103. (a) less than
    (b) $I_u = 9.4$ W/m^2; $I_p = 12.1$ W/m^2
105. 40 m^2
107. (a) 0.95 kW/m^2 (b) 1.9 kW/m^2
    (c) 3.2 μJ/m^3 (d) 1.0×10^{-11} N
    (e) The laser beam must be normal to the plane of the mirror.
109. (a) 50% (b) 0% (c) 63.4° (d) $0.138 I_0$
111. C. 6.45×10^{14} Hz
113. A. 3.25×10^{-5} N/m^2
115. 40°

CHAPTER 26
1. 38°
3. 2θ
5. 55 cm
7. (a) 36 cm below (b) 8.9°
    (c) You will still see the buckle.
9. counterclockwise
11. (a) 5.2 m/s (b) 4.1 m/s
13. 33 cm wide and 7.5 cm high
15. 23 cm
17. concave
19. −7.98 cm
21. (a) upright (b) reduced (c) virtual
23. $R/2$
25. toward the right
27. increases
29. 0.67 m; −0.33
31. −0.40 m; 0.20
33. (a) concave (b) 7.34 m (c) 16.4 m
35. (a) −1.9 (b) inverted (c) 1.2 m
37. (a) −84 cm (b) 42 cm
39. (a) −9.0 cm (b) −12 cm
41. 12 m
43. $d_o = 1.4$ m; $d_i = 0.48$ m
45. (a) point 1 (b) point 4
47. (a) equal to (b) greater than
49. medium A
51. 1.82
53. 1.5
55. (a) greater than (b) 55°
57. 14.4 ns
59. 21.6°
61. 4.7 ft
63. $1.71 \le n_{prism} < 2.02$
65. (a) 72° (b) No
67. 1.4

69. 30.5°
71. (a) $d_i \approx \frac{2}{3}|f|$ (b) upright (c) virtual
73. (a) $d_i \approx 2f$ (b) inverted (c) real
75. (a) The final image is located to the right of lens 2, just beyond F_2.
    (b) inverted (c) real
77. $d_i = -15$ cm, $m = 0.52$
79. (a) 0.98 m (b) 68 cm
81. (a) farther away (b) 2.8 cm
83. (a) 34 cm (b) −1.2
85. (a) farther away (b) 34 cm
87. 2.8 cm
89. (a) virtual (b) 69 cm (c) convex
91. 0.33°
93. 46.2 cm from the lens
95. $R/2$
97. (a) decrease (b) II
99. liquid B
101. (a) converge (b) diverge
103. 0.25 m
105. (a) 29 cm and 9.8 cm
    (b) 29 cm, real and inverted; 9.8 cm, virtual and upright
107. (a) 1.8 (b) No
109. (a) 40.6°
    (b) The answer to part (a) does not depend on the thickness of the oil film.
111. (a) 48.8° (b) No
113. (a) 1.69 m (b) 80.3 m
115. (a) 0.286 (b) 0.082
117. $\dfrac{f_1 f_2}{f_1 + f_2}$
119. $(t \sin\theta)\left(1 - \dfrac{\cos\theta}{\sqrt{n^2 - \sin^2\theta}}\right)$
121. (a) 506 ns (b) 510 ns
123. (a) 13.3° (b) No (c) 2.24
125. B. 105 cm
127. B. 134 cm
129. (a) 3.0 cm (b) −0.49 (c) increase
131. (a) 5.0 cm (b) −2.5 cm (c) increase

CHAPTER 27
1. (a) farther from (b) II
3. flower
5. (a) 2.58 cm (b) 2.38 cm
7. (a) 8.5 (b) 2.4
9. 3.0 m
11. 87 mm
13. (a) 1/25 s (b) 5.6
15. (a) 3.33 (b) 30.6
17. farsighted
19.

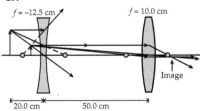

21. 0.80 m
23. 60.7 cm
25. (a) 5 mm in front of the lens closest to the object
    (b) 0.15
27. (a) increase (b) 3.5 mm
29. (a) 12 cm to the left of the converging lens
    (b) −0.12
31. −135 cm

33. 8.4 cm
35. 45 cm; 2.2 diopters
37. (a) nearsighted (b) diverging
    (c) −3.34 diopters
39. (a) 45.8 diopters (b) decrease
41. 24.2 cm
43. (a) diverging (b) converging
    (c) distant objects: −0.20 diopters; near objects: +2.3 diopters
45. far: 2.27 m; near: 42.0 cm
47. (a) 47 cm to the right of lens 2; 0.38
    (b) 3.0 cm to the right of lens 2; −0.61
    (c) 15.8 cm to the right of lens 2; 0.316
49. (a) 9.042×10^{-3} rad (b) 2.1 m
51. (a) f_1 (b) $M_1 = 6.0$; $M_2 = 2.9$
53. (a) 6.47 cm (b) 3.96
55. 3.72
57. lens 1
59. 3.3×10^{-3} rad
61. 0.324 mm
63. 9.1 mm
65. (a) 7.85 mm (b) 10 cm (c) 5.1 cm
67. (a) 1600 mm should be the objective
    (b) 50×
69. 2.8 m
71. 24 cm
73. 0.040
75. (a) −57 cm (b) 1.1 m
77. 1.8 cm
79. (a) decrease (b) II
81. microscope
83. (a) positive (b) I
85. (a) 41.7 diopters (b) increase
87. (a)

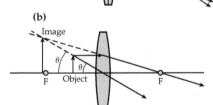

(b)

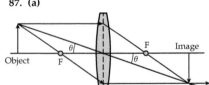

(c)

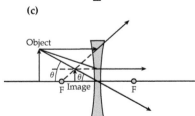

(d) A simple magnifier helps the eye view an object that is closer than the near point, thus making it appear larger.
89. (a) 2.42 cm (b) 2.42 cm
91. 4.6 cm
93. (a) 9.7 cm (b) increase
95. (a) 8.3 cm from the lens on the same side as the virtual object
    (b) real
97. 9.24 cm
99. 16 cm

101. **(a)** 12.2 cm to the right of the lens **(b)** virtual **(c)** 0.174 **(d)** upright

103. $\dfrac{f_1}{f_2}$

105. 19.8 cm; −63.0 cm

107. positive

109. **A.** 1.9 mm

111. **(a)** greater than **(b)** −351 cm

113. **(a)** greater than **(b)** 2.81 diopters

CHAPTER 28

1. destructively

3. 134 m

5. 0.18 kHz

7. 406 Hz; 812 Hz

9. 0.68 kHz; 2.0 kHz

11. **(a)** 600 m **(b)** maximum **(c)** 200 m

13. **(a)** increase **(b)** $\Delta \ell = m\lambda$

15. **(a)** increase **(b)** decrease

17. 623 nm

19. **(a)** 415 nm **(b)** increase **(c)** 587 nm

21. 154 μm

23. 658 nm

25. 86.9 cm

27. **(a)** 2.24 cm **(b)** increased

29. greater than

31. 488 nm and 627 nm

33. 493 nm and 658 nm

35. **(a)** destructive interference **(b)** 3.5 m

37. **(a)** destructive interference **(b)** constructive interference **(c)** constructive interference

39. **(a)** 102 nm **(b)** thinner

41. **(a)** 503.2 nm **(b)** 670.9 nm and 402.6 nm

43. **(a)** 2.00 **(b)** 0.500 **(c)** 2.00

45. 36°

47. 24.8 cm

49. **(a)** 12 μm **(b)** decrease

51. **(a)** 25.0 μm **(b)** less than

53. **(a)** dark cloudy day **(b)** I

55. **(a)** 0.78 m **(b)** 1.3 m

57. 5.5 cm

59. 17 cm

61. **(a)** 0.91 arc sec **(b)** 1.7 km

63. 2.95°, 5.92°, 8.90°

65. 3.4°

67. 371.3 cm^{-1}

69. one

71. 660 nm

73. **(a)** The $m = 3$ maximum of the 420-nm light overlaps the $m = 2$ maximum of the 630-nm light. **(b)** 35°

75. 3.94 m

77. **(a)** outward **(b)** $W = \lambda$

79. decrease

81.

$\theta(°)$	θ(rad)	$\sin\theta$	$\tan\theta$	$\sin\theta/\tan\theta$
0.0100°	0.000175	0.000175	0.000175	1.00
1.00°	0.0175	0.0175	0.0175	1.00
5.00°	0.0873	0.0872	0.0875	0.996
10.0°	0.175	0.174	0.176	0.985
20.0°	0.349	0.342	0.364	0.940
30.0°	0.524	0.500	0.577	0.866
40.0°	0.698	0.643	0.839	0.766

83. 24.4 km

85. **(a)** The bubble is thick enough for constructive interference but not destructive interference at visible wavelengths. **(b)** 108 nm

87. 76 μm

89. 491 nm

91. **(a)** 496 nm **(b)** greater than

93. 401 nm and 515 nm

95. $\dfrac{2d}{\lambda} - \dfrac{1}{2} = m$ where $m = 0, 1, 2, \ldots$

97. 5.9 μm

99. **C.** 0.369 mm

101. **C.** 11.5 ft

103. **(a)** longer than **(b)** 0.63 μm

105. **(a)** increase **(b)** 15.1°

CHAPTER 29

1. **(a)** greater than **(b)** I

3. **(a)** proper time **(b)** proper time **(c)** proper time **(d)** dilated time

5. **(a)** according to the clock on Earth **(b)** I

7. 0.87c

9. 0.99986c

11. 748 m

13. 0.80c

15. 0.17 rad/s

17. **(a)** less than **(b)** 55 beats/min

19. 1.01 ms

21. 4:32 P.M.

23. less than

25. 1.13 m

27. 49 m

29. **(a)** 0.60c **(b)** 3.2 m

31. **(a)** less than **(b)** 0.583c **(c)** 2.84 cm

33. 72°

35. **(a)** (i) the *Picard* is longer **(b)** 2.3

37. 0.879c

39. 31 mi/h

41. 0.98c

43. 0.64c

45. **(a)** No **(b)** 0.98c

47. 2.86 × 10^8 m/s

49. 1.6 m/s

51. 9.4 × 10^7 kg

53. 0.999c

55. 0.19 nJ

57. 4.9 × 10^{-16} kg

59. 1.02 MeV

61. 0.88c

63. 0.35 kg

65. **(a)** 0.75% **(b)** 69%

67. **(a)** 43.5 J **(b)** greater than **(c)** 7.00 × 10^8 J

69. 2.4 kg

71. **(a)** 7.7 × 10^6 km **(b)** 5.8 × 10^6 m/s^2 **(c)** decreases by a factor of 2

73. **(a)** the pilot **(b)** you **(c)** the pilot **(d)** you

75. greater than

77. greater than

79. 1.00c **(b)** $K_{ant} = 3.6 × 10^9$ eV $\ll 1.0 × 10^{20}$ eV

81. 1.20 × 10^{-18} kg·m/s

83. **(a)** 0.643c **(b)** 2.29 × 10^{-22} kg·m/s **(c)** −2.29 × 10^{-22} kg·m/s **(d)** 9.85 km/s

85. 0.33c

87. **(a)** 11 m **(b)** less than **(c)** 6.1 m

89. **(a)** 3.11 × 10^8 m/s **(b)** 2.28 × 10^8 m/s

91. **(a)** $\dfrac{1}{2}c$ **(b)** $\dfrac{1}{\sqrt{2}}c$

99. **C.** 0.312c

101. **A.** 0.301c

103. **(a)** 0.371c **(b)** 0.454c **(c)** 0.922c

CHAPTER 30

1. **(a)** lower than **(b)** II

3. 1.81 × 10^{13} Hz; 16.6 μm

5. 3.4 × 10^{14} Hz

7. **(a)** star B **(b)** 0.36

9. **(a)** 1.68 × 10^{14} Hz **(b)** infrared

11. **(a)** blue < green < red **(b)** red < green < blue **(c)** blue < green < red

13. **(a)** greater than **(b)** I

15. No, because each photon has too little energy to eject an electron.

17. 4.6 × 10^{32} photons/s

19. 7.3 × 10^{18} photons/s

21. 2.08 × 10^{15} Hz

23. **(a)** 1.5 × 10^{20} photons/s **(b)** 1.0 × 10^{12} photons/s

25. **(a)** 1.09 × 10^{15} Hz; 275 nm **(b)** ultraviolet

27. **(a)** red **(b)** blue **(c)** red: 4.9 × 10^{20} photons/s; blue: 5.8 × 10^{19} photons/s

29. **(a)** aluminum **(b)** Al: 1.03 × 10^{15} Hz; Ca: 6.93 × 10^{14} Hz

31. **(a)** cadmium **(b)** Zn: 0.19 eV; Cd: 0.30 eV

33. **(a)** 369 eV **(b)** 4.00 × 10^{14} Hz ≤ f < 1.03 × 10^{15} Hz

35. 6.377 × 10^{-34} J·s

37. 2

39. 2.9 × 10^6 m/s

41. 1.1 × 10^{18} Hz

43. 0.815 m/s

45. **(a)** photon B **(b)** 666 nm

47. **(a)** 2.39 × 10^{16} photons/s **(b)** 2.10 × 10^{-27} kg·m/s **(c)** 5.00 × 10^{-11} N

49. 4.5 keV

51. 107°

53. **(a)** The change in wavelength is the same for both photons. **(b)** X-ray **(c)** visible: 9.3 × 10^{-4} %; X-ray: 16%

55. **(a)** 0.315 nm **(b)** incident: 3.94 keV; scattered: 3.88 keV **(c)** 60 eV

57. 41.4 pm; 4.80 fJ

59. **(a)** decrease **(b)** II

61. 13.7 km/s

63. 2.0 × 10^{-36} m

65. **(a)** 1.58 km/s **(b)** 62.4°

67. **(a)** electron **(b)** 1836

69. $\dfrac{h}{\sqrt{2mqV}}$

71. 1.4 × 10^{-20} kg·m/s

73. 1.1 × 10^{-26} J

75. 1.8 × 10^{-25} J

77. **(a)** 7.0 × 10^{-25} kg·m/s **(b)** 1.7 eV

79. 62 nm

81. **(a)** increase **(b)** decrease **(c)** decrease **(d)** decrease

83. **(a)** decrease **(b)** decrease

85. 3.65×10^{-17} W
87. (a) 1.6×10^{15} photons/s
(b) 3.3×10^{-19} N
89. 1×10^{19} photons
91. 0.58 nm
93. 9200 K; No
95. (a) decreased (b) -10.2 eV
97. (a) decrease
99. (a) 1.32 fm (b) 1.51×10^{-10} J
101. D. 2.29 eV
103. B. 1.08 eV
105. (a) less than (b) $54°$

CHAPTER 31

1. 8.4×10^{-16}
3. 5.6 pJ
5. 369.7 nm
7. 121.5 nm; 102.6 nm; 97.23 nm
9. (a) 121.5 nm (b) 820.4 nm
11. (a) increase (b) I
13. $C < B < A$
15. 2.42×10^{-3}
17. 0.544 eV
19. $\left(\dfrac{n}{n+1}\right)^2 U$
21. (a) 1.51 eV (b) -3.02 eV (c) -1.51 eV
23. $n_i = 3$ to $n_f = 2$
25. (a) (iii) $n_i = 7$ to $n_f = 8$; 19.06 μm
(b) (ii) $n_i = 2$ to $n_f = 8$; 388.9 nm
(c) only (iv), $n_i = 6$ to $n_f = 2$
27. (a) 2.83×10^{-10} m
(b) greater than
(c) Li^{2+}, 2.75 eV; H, 0.306 eV
29. (a) 1.22×10^{-15} s (b) 8×10^6 orbits
31. (a) 6 (b) increase (c) -0.555 eV
33. (a) $f_{photon} = \dfrac{2\pi^2 mk^2 e^4}{h^3}\left[\dfrac{1}{(n-1)^2} - \dfrac{1}{n^2}\right]$
(b) $f_{electron} = \dfrac{4\pi^2 mk^2 e^4}{n^3 h^3}$
(c) They are the same.
35. 0.332 nm
37. 1.32 nm
39. 0, 1, 2, 3, 4
41. (a) 2 (b) none (c) 5 (d) none
43. (a) 75 (b) 76 (c) -2.35 meV
45. (a) greater than (b) $\sqrt{2}$
47. (a) 10 (b) 8
49. $1s^2 2s^2 2p^2$
51. $1s^2 2s^2 2p^3$

53.

n	ℓ	m_ℓ	m_s
3	1	-1	$-\frac{1}{2}$
3	1	-1	$\frac{1}{2}$
3	1	0	$-\frac{1}{2}$
3	1	0	$\frac{1}{2}$
3	1	1	$-\frac{1}{2}$
3	1	1	$\frac{1}{2}$

55. $1s^2 2s^2 2p^6 3s^2 3p^6 3d^8 4s^2$
59. (a) stay the same (b) III
61. 0.167 nm
63. 0.195 nm
65. (a) 80.6 keV (b) 80.6 kV
67. (a) $B < A < C$ (b) $C < A < B$
69. excited state
71. less than
73. 78,700 K
75. (a) 2.55 eV (b) 5.55×10^{-28} J
(c) the same as
77. (a) 1.52×10^{-16} s (b) 0.00105 A
79. (a) 22.8 nm (b) $n_i = 16$ and $n_f = 4$
81. 0.0585 nm
83. (a) greater than
(b) 4.38×10^7 m^{-1}
85. (b) $v_n = \dfrac{1}{m}\sqrt{nqB\hbar}$
89. greater than
91. B. 2.42 eV
93. (a) $n = 12$ (b) 7.62 nm

CHAPTER 32

1. (a) $Z = 92$; $N = 146$; $A = 238$
(b) $Z = 94$; $N = 145$; $A = 239$
(c) $Z = 60$; $N = 84$; $A = 144$
3. (a) 7.0 fm (b) 4.7 fm
5. (a) 2.3×10^{17} kg/m^3
(b) the same as
(c) 2.3×10^{17} kg/m^3
7. (a) 6.4×10^6 m/s (b) 0.27 pm
(c) less than
9. (a) 3.7 fm (b) 240
11. (a) more than (b) 7.4 fm (c) 5.9 fm
13. (a) the same as (b) III
15. alpha (α) and beta (β)
17. $^4_2$He

19. α decay; β decay; β decay; α decay; α decay; α decay; α decay; α decay; β decay; α decay; α decay; β decay; α decay; β decay
21. (a) $^{212}_{84}$Po $\longrightarrow$ $^{208}_{82}$Pb + $^4_2$He; 8.95 MeV
(b) $^{239}_{94}$Pu $\longrightarrow$ $^{235}_{92}$U + $^4_2$He; 5.244 MeV
23. (a) $^{18}_{9}$F $\longrightarrow$ $^{18}_{8}$O + e^+ + v; 0.634 MeV
(b) $^{22}_{11}$Na $\longrightarrow$ $^{22}_{10}$Ne + e^+ + v; 1.819 MeV
25. (a) $^{66}_{29}$Cu (b) 0.2 MeV
27. less than
29. 0.181 d^{-1}
31. 4.5 d
33. (a) 0.115 h^{-1} (b) 1.7×10^9 nuclei
35. 1.97×10^4 y
37. 1.44×10^4 y
39. 3.90×10^3 y
41. 1559 MeV
43. (a) 8.790 MeV/nucleon
(b) 7.570 MeV/nucleon
45. 15.66 MeV
47. 3 neutrons
49. $^1_0$n + $^{235}_{92}$U $\longrightarrow$ $^{88}_{38}$Sr + $^{136}_{54}$Xe + 12 $^1_0$n; 126.5 MeV
51. 1.2×10^6 kg
53. 4.033 MeV
55. 5.494 MeV
57. (a) 4.33×10^9 kg/s (b) 0.0307%
59. 1.0×10^3 rad
61. (a) 0.38 J (b) 0.54 mK
63. (a) 6.9×10^{11} electrons (b) 0.078 J
(c) 93 rem
65. 2
67. greater than
69. (a) $^{206}_{80}$Hg (b) $^{239}_{93}$Np (c) $^{11}_5$B
71. 260 rem
73. (a) 2.83×10^9 y (b) 1.16×10^9 y
75. $^{210}_{81}$T1
77. 1.7 Ci
79. (a) 1.2×10^{-15} m $\leq r \leq 7.1 \times 10^{-15}$ m
(b) 35.2 (c) 209
81. 2220 y
83. (a) less than (b) 7.274 MeV
85. (a) 4.2×10^5 rad (b) stay the same
87. 264 m/s
89. 1.9 mK
91. B. 1.2 Ci

Index

MULTIPLES AND PREFIXES FOR METRIC UNITS

Multiple	Prefix (Abbreviation)	Pronunciation
10^{24}	yotta- (Y)	yot'ta (*a* as in *a*bout)
10^{21}	zetta- (Z)	zet'ta (*a* as in *a*bout)
10^{18}	exa- (E)	ex'a (*a* as in *a*bout)
10^{15}	peta- (P)	pet'a (as in *peta*l)
10^{12}	tera- (T)	ter'a (as in *terra*ce)
10^{9}	giga- (G)	ji'ga (*ji* as in *ji*ggle, *a* as in *a*bout)
10^{6}	mega- (M)	meg'a (as in *mega*phone)
10^{3}	kilo- (k)	kil'o (as in *kilo*watt)
10^{2}	hecto- (h)	hek'to (*heck-toe*)
10	deka- (da)	dek'a (*deck* plus *a* as in *a*bout)
10^{-1}	deci- (d)	des'i (as in *deci*mal)
10^{-2}	centi- (c)	sen'ti (as in *senti*mental)
10^{-3}	milli- (m)	mil'li (as in *mili*tary)
10^{-6}	micro- (μ)	mi'kro (as in *micro*phone)
10^{-9}	nano- (n)	nan'oh (*an* as in *ann*ual)
10^{-12}	pico- (p)	pe'ko (*peek-oh*)
10^{-15}	femto- (f)	fem'toe (*fem* as in *fem*inine)
10^{-18}	atto- (a)	at'toe (as in *an*atomy)
10^{-21}	zepto- (z)	zep'toe (as in *zep*pelin)
10^{-24}	yocto- (y)	yock'toe (as in *sock*)

THE GREEK ALPHABET

Alpha	A	α
Beta	B	β
Gamma	Γ	γ
Delta	Δ	δ
Epsilon	E	ε
Zeta	Z	ζ
Eta	H	η
Theta	Θ	θ
Iota	I	ι
Kappa	K	κ
Lambda	Λ	λ
Mu	M	μ
Nu	N	ν
Xi	Ξ	ξ
Omicron	O	o
Pi	Π	π
Rho	P	ρ
Sigma	Σ	σ
Tau	T	τ
Upsilon	Υ	υ
Phi	Φ	ϕ
Chi	X	χ
Psi	Ψ	ψ
Omega	Ω	ω

SI BASE UNITS

Physical Quantity	Name of Unit	Symbol
Length	meter	m
Mass	kilogram	kg
Time	second	s
Electric current	ampere	A
Temperature	kelvin	K
Amount of substance	mole	mol
Luminous intensity	candela	cd

SOME SI DERIVED UNITS

Physical Quantity	Name of Unit	Symbol	SI Unit
Frequency	hertz	Hz	s^{-1}
Energy	joule	J	$kg \cdot m^2/s^2$
Force	newton	N	$kg \cdot m/s^2$
Pressure	pascal	Pa	$kg/(m \cdot s^2)$
Power	watt	W	$kg \cdot m^2/s^3$
Electric charge	coulomb	C	$A \cdot s$
Electric potential	volt	V	$kg \cdot m^2/(A \cdot s^3)$
Electric resistance	ohm	Ω	$kg \cdot m^2/(A^2 \cdot s^3)$
Capacitance	farad	F	$A^2 \cdot s^4/(kg \cdot m^2)$
Inductance	henry	H	$kg \cdot m^2/(A^2 \cdot s^2)$
Magnetic field	tesla	T	$kg/(A \cdot s^2)$
Magnetic flux	weber	Wb	$kg \cdot m^2/(A \cdot s^2)$

SI UNITS OF SOME OTHER PHYSICAL QUANTITIES

Physical Quantity	SI Unit
Density (ρ)	kg/m^3
Speed (v)	m/s
Acceleration (a)	m/s^2
Momentum, impulse (p)	$kg \cdot m/s$
Angular speed (ω)	rad/s
Angular acceleration (α)	rad/s^2
Torque (τ)	$kg \cdot m^2/s^2$ *or* $N \cdot m$
Specific heat (c)	$J/(kg \cdot K)$
Thermal conductivity (k)	$W/(m \cdot K)$ *or* $J/(s \cdot m \cdot K)$
Entropy (S)	J/K *or* $kg \cdot m^2/(K \cdot s^2)$ *or* $N \cdot m/K$
Electric field (E)	N/C *or* V/m

APPENDICES IN THE TEXT

FUNDAMENTAL CONSTANTS

Quantity	Symbol	Approximate Value
Speed of light	c	3.00×10^8 m/s $= 3.00 \times 10^{10}$ cm/s $= 186,000$ mi/s
Universal gravitational constant	G	6.67×10^{-11} N·m^2/kg^2
Stefan-Boltzmann constant	σ	5.67×10^{-8} W/(m^2·K^4)
Boltzmann's constant	k	1.38×10^{-23} J/K
Avogadro's number	N_A	6.022×10^{23} mol^{-1}
Gas constant	$R = N_A k$	8.31 J/(mol·K) $= 1.99$ cal/(mol·K)
Coulomb's law constant	$k = 1/4\pi\varepsilon_o$	8.99×10^9 N·m^2/C^2
Electron charge	e	1.60×10^{-19} C
Permittivity of free space	ε_o	8.85×10^{-12} C^2/(N·m^2)
Permeability of free space	μ_o	$4\pi \times 10^{-7}$ T·m/A $= 1.26 \times 10^{-6}$ T·m/A
Planck's constant	h	6.63×10^{-34} J·s
	$\hbar = h/2\pi$	1.05×10^{-34} J·s
Atomic mass unit	u	1.6605×10^{-27} kg $\leftrightarrow 931.5$ MeV
Electron mass	m_e	9.10939×10^{-31} kg $= 5.49 \times 10^{-4}$ u $\leftrightarrow 0.511$ MeV
Neutron mass	m_n	$1.675\ 00 \times 10^{-27}$ kg $= 1.008\ 665$ u $\leftrightarrow 939.57$ MeV
Proton mass	m_p	$1.672\ 65 \times 10^{-27}$ kg $= 1.007\ 267$ u $\leftrightarrow 938.28$ MeV

USEFUL PHYSICAL DATA

Acceleration due to gravity (surface of Earth)	9.81 m/s^2 $= 32.2$ ft/s^2
Absolute zero	0 K $= -273.15$ °C $= -459.67$ °F
Standard temperature & pressure (STP)	0 °C $= 273.15$ K
	1 atm $= 101.325$ kPa
Density of air (STP)	1.29 kg/m^3
Speed of sound in air (20 °C)	343 m/s
Density of water (4 °C)	1.000×10^3 kg/m^3
Latent heat of fusion of water	3.35×10^5 J/kg
Latent heat of vaporization of water	2.26×10^6 J/kg
Specific heat of water	4186 J/(kg·K)

SOLAR SYSTEM DATA*

Equatorial radius of Earth	6.37×10^3 km $= 3950$ mi
Mass of Earth	5.97×10^{24} kg
Radius of Moon	1740 km $= 1080$ mi
Mass of Moon	7.35×10^{22} kg $\approx \frac{1}{81}$ mass of Earth
Average distance of Moon from Earth	3.84×10^5 km $= 2.39 \times 10^5$ mi
Radius of Sun	6.95×10^5 km $= 432,000$ mi
Mass of Sun	2.00×10^{30} kg
Average distance of Earth from Sun	1.50×10^8 km $= 93.0 \times 10^6$ mi

*See Appendix C for additional planetary data.